HEAT CONDUCTION

HEAT CONDUCTION

M. Necati Özışık
Department of Mechanical and Aerospace Engineering
North Carolina State University, Raleigh

A WILEY-INTERSCIENCE PUBLICATION

JOHN WILEY AND SONS, New York · Chichester · Brisbane · Toronto

Library of Congress Cataloging in Publication Data

Özışık, M. Necati.
  Heat conduction.

  "A Wiley-Interscience publication."
  Includes bibliographies and index.
  1. Heat-Conduction. I. Title.

QC321.034   536'.23   79-990
ISBN 0-471-05481-X

Photoset by Thomson Press (India) Limited, New Delhi
Printed in the United States of America

10 9 8 7 6 5 4 3 2 1

PREFACE

The conduction of heat in solids has numerous applications in various branches of science and engineering. There is considerable interest in the solution of heat conduction problems with the ultimate objective of obtaining useful and practical information.

A variety of methods, exact, approximate, and purely numerical, are available for the solution of these problems. Analytical approaches, when applicable, are advantageous because they provide an understanding of the role of various system parameters affecting heat transfer and because they establish the dominant features of the problem. On the other hand, purely numerical computations can provide answers to more realistic system response. Both the analytical and the purely numerical approaches are useful; the choice of a particular method should depend on the nature of the problem considered.

If advantage is to be taken of the best salient features of the variety of techniques available for the solution of a given problem, the engineer and scientist must be familiar with the use of such methods. To provide engineering students with the necessary background for the solution of heat conduction problems, many engineering schools have adopted a graduate level course in heat conduction. This book provides comprehensive and systematic coverage of the basic theory and applications of various methods for solving heat conduction problems. The level can readily be followed by graduate students of engineering and science.

This book is significantly different from my previous book, *Boundary Value Problems of Heat Conduction*. There the emphasis was on the systematic use of integral transform techniques for the solution of heat conduction problems. In this book, I have used a more conventional approach to develop the fundamental analysis leading to the solution of general heat conduction problems. Various methods of solving heat diffusion problems are presented and the interrelation among them is illustrated. Numerous problems, with solutions, are included in each chapter to demonstrate the application of the theory to different types of questions. The integral transform technique is included in later chapters after presentation, by the conventional methods of analysis, of the material needed for the application of this technique.

To follow the material in this book, all the reader needs is an understanding of the methods of advanced calculus and of the solution of elementary partial differential equations. This book is intended to contribute to effective teaching at a graduate level and to serve as a reference volume for scientists, engineering graduates, and industry.

Chapter 1 reviews the pertinent background on the derivation of heat conduction equation, boundary conditions, and important system parameters. Chapters 2, 3, and 4 are devoted to the solution of time dependent heat conduction problems in the rectangular, cylindrical, and spherical coordinates, respectively, by the application of the classical method of separation of variables and orthogonal expansion technique. In the process of developing solutions for simple heat conduction problems, the resulting eigenfunctions, normalization integrals, and eigenconditions are systematically tabulated for all possible combinations of boundary conditions. Such tabulations are intended to serve as ready reference in the solution of the more general multidimensional time dependent problems as well as in the application of the integral transform technique to the solution of heat conduction problems in later chapters.

Chapter 5 describes the use of Duhamel's method and generalizes the solutions developed in Chapters 2, 3, and 4 for the solution of heat conduction problem involving time dependent boundary conditions and heat generation. Chapter 6 is devoted to the generalization and compact representation of the solutions developed in Chapters 2 to 5 using Green's functions. The determination of the Green's functions is directly related to the solutions developed in Chapters 2 to 4. Chapter 7 presents the use of Laplace transformation in the solution of time dependent heat conduction problems. The utility of the Laplace transform technique is illustrated in order to obtain solutions which converge rapidly for very short times.

Chapter 8 is devoted to the solution of one-dimensional, time dependent heat conduction problems in parallel layers of slabs and concentric cylinders and spheres. A generalized orthogonal expansion technique is used to solve the homogeneous problems; therefore, no additional mathematical techniques are needed to follow the material in this chapter. Green's function approach is used to generalize the analysis to the solution of problems involving heat generation.

Chapter 9 presents approximate analytical methods of solving heat conduction problems by a variety of techniques, including the integral method, the variational method, the Galerkin method, and the use of partial integration. The accuracy of these various approximate methods is illustrated by comparing the approximate results with the exact solutions. Chapter 10 is devoted to the solution of phase change problems involving melting and solidification by a variety of analytical approaches, including exact methods of solutions, the approximate method by the integral technique, and the use of the moving heat source approach. Chapter 11 deals with the solution of some nonlinear heat conduction problems with a variety of techniques, including the uses of Kirchhoff transformation, the linearization, the Boltzmann transformation, and the similarity transformation via one-parameter group theory. Chapter 12 presents the numerical methods of solving the steady and time dependent heat conduction problems by finite difference methods. Chapter 13 introduces the use of integral transform technique in the solution of general time-dependent heat conduction equation in finite regions. The application of this technique for the solution of heat conduction problems in rectangular, cylindrical, and spherical coordinates requires no additional background, since all the basic relationships needed for the development of the integral transform pairs have already been developed and systematically tabulated in Chapters 2 to 4. Chapter 14 generalizes the integral transform technique to the solution of time dependent heat conduction problems in parallel layers of slabs, coaxial cylinders, and concentric spheres. Chapter 15 presents the analysis of heat conduction problems in an anisotropic medium. A host of useful information, such as the roots of transcendental equations, some properties of Bessel functions, and the numerical values of Bessel functions and Legendre polynomials are included in the Appendix for ready reference.

All pertinent relations, whenever possible, are developed from the fundamentals at a level consistent with the mathematical background needed to follow this book; otherwise the results are stated and the original references are cited. In order to preserve the continuity of the material presented, additional details for the derivations are presented as notes at the end of each chapter.

Finally, I would like to acknowledge that without the understanding and patience of my wife, Gül, this project would not have been realized.

M. Necati Özışık

Raleigh, North Carolina
June 1979

CONTENTS

Chapter 1

HEAT-CONDUCTION FUNDAMENTALS   1

1-1 The Heat Flux, 1
1-2 The Differential Equation of Heat Conduction, 4
1-3 Heat-Conduction Equation in Different
     Orthogonal Coordinate Systems, 7
1-4 Boundary Conditions, 12
1-5 Dimensionless Heat-Conduction Parameters, 15
1-6 Homogeneous and Nonhomogeneous Problems, 17
1-7 Methods of Solution of Heat-Conduction Problems, 18
     References, 21
     Problems, 22

Chapter 2

**THE SEPARATION OF VARIABLES IN THE
RECTANGULAR COORDINATE SYSTEM**   25

2-1 Method of Separation of Variables, 25
2-2 Separation of The Heat-Conduction Equation
     in the Rectangular Coordinate System, 30
2-3 One-Dimensional Homogeneous Problems
     in a Finite Medium, 32
2-4 One-Dimensional Homogeneous Problems
     in a Semi-Infinite Medium, 39
2-5 One-Dimensional Homogeneous Problems
     in an Infinite Medium, 43
2-6 Multidimensional Homogeneous Problems, 46
2-7 Product Solution, 54

2-8   Multidimensional Steady-State Problems with
       No Heat Generation, 57
2-9   Multidimensional Steady-State Problems with
       Heat Generation, 66
2-10   Splitting Up of Nonhomogeneous Problems
       into Simpler Problems, 69
2-11   Useful Transformations, 74
       References, 76
       Problems, 77
       Notes, 79

Chapter 3

THE SEPARATION OF VARIABLES IN THE CYLINDRICAL COORDINATE SYSTEM

83

3-1   Separation of Heat-Conduction Equation in the
       Cylindrical Coordinate System, 83
3-2   Representation of an Arbitrary Function in Terms
       of Bessel Functions, 88
3-3   Homogeneous Problems in (r, t) Variables, 100
3-4   Homogeneous Problems in (r, z, t) Variables, 110
3-5   Homogeneous Problems in (r, ϕ, t) Variables, 114
3-6   Homogeneous Problems in (r, ϕ, z, t) Variables, 123
3-7   Product Solution, 127
3-8   Multidimensional Steady-State Problems with
       No Heat Generation, 129
3-9   Multidimensional Steady-State Problems with
       Heat Generation, 133
3-10   Splitting Up of Nonhomogeneous Problems into
       Simpler Problems, 136
       References, 138
       Problems, 139
       Notes, 141

Chapter 4

THE SEPARATION OF VARIABLES IN THE SPHERICAL COORDINATE SYSTEM

144

4-1   Separation of The Heat-Conduction Equation in the
       Spherical Coordinate System, 144

4-2 Legendre Functions and Legendre's
     Associated Functions, 148
4-3 Representation of an Arbitrary Function in
     Terms of Legendre Functions, 154
4-4 Homogeneous Problems in (r, t) Variables, 162
4-5 Homogeneous Problems in (r, μ, t) Variables, 168
4-6 Homogeneous Problems in (r, μ, ϕ, t) Variables, 175
4-7 Multidimensional Steady-State Problems, 182
4-8 Splitting Up of Nonhomogeneous Problems into
     Simpler Problems, 185
     References, 187
     Problems, 187
     Notes, 189

Chapter 5

THE USE OF DUHAMEL'S THEOREM   194

5-1 The Statement of Duhamel's Theorem, 194
5-2 A Proof of Duhamel's Theorem, 197
5-3 Applications of Duhamel's Theorem, 199
     References, 206
     Problems, 206
     Notes, 208

Chapter 6

THE USE OF GREEN'S FUNCTION   209

6-1 Green's Function in the Solution of Nonhomogeneous,
     Time-Dependent Heat-Conduction Problems, 209
6-2 Determination of Green's Function, 216
6-3 Application of Green's Function in the Rectangular
     Coordinate System, 219
6-4 Applications of Green's Function in the Cylindrical
     Coordinate System, 226
6-5 Applications of Green's Function in the Spherical
     Coordinate System, 232
6-6 Product of Green's Functions, 239
     References, 240
     Problems, 240
     Notes, 245

Chapter 7

THE USE OF LAPLACE TRANSFORM   **246**

7-1 Definition of Laplace Transformation, 246
7-2 Properties of Laplace Transform, 248
7-3 The Inversion of Laplace Transform Using the
     Inversion Tables, 258
7-4 The Inversion of Laplace Transform by the
     Contour Integration Technique, 263
7-5 Application of Laplace Transform in the Solution of
     Time-Dependent Heat-Conduction Problems, 273
7-6 Approximations for Small and Large Times, 283
     References, 290
     Problems, 290
     Notes, 292

Chapter 8

ONE-DIMENSIONAL COMPOSITE MEDIUM   **294**

8-1 Solution of the Homogeneous Problem by the Generalized
     Orthogonal Expansion Technique, 295
8-2 Determination of Eigenfunctions and Eigenvalues, 300
8-3 Transformation of Nonhomogeneous Outer Boundary
     Conditions into Homogeneous Ones, 311
8-4 The Use of Green's Functions in the Solution of
     Nonhomogeneous Problems, 317
8-5 The Use of Laplace Transformation, 323
     References, 328
     Problems, 329
     Notes, 331

Chapter 9

APPROXIMATE ANALYTICAL METHODS   **335**

9-1 The Integral Method—Basic Concepts, 335
9-2 The Integral Method—Various Applications, 341
9-3 The Variational Principles, 358
9-4 The Ritz Method, 367
9-5 The Galerkin Method, 372

9-6 Partial Integration, 380
9-7 Time-Dependent Problems, 386
     References, 391
     Problems, 393
     Notes, 395

Chapter 10

PHASE-CHANGE PROBLEMS   397

10-1 Boundary Conditions at the Moving Interface, 399
10-2 Exact Solution of Phase-Change Problems, 406
10-3 Integral Method of Solution of Phase-Change Problems, 416
10-4 Moving Heat Source Method for the Solution of
      Phase-Change Problems, 423
10-5 Phase Change over a Temperature Range, 430
      References, 432
      Problems, 434
      Notes, 435

Chapter 11

NONLINEAR PROBLEMS   439

11-1 Transformation of a Dependent Variable—The
      Kirchhoff Transformation, 440
11-2 Linearization of a One-Dimensional Nonlinear
      Heat-Conduction Problem, 443
11-3 Transformation of an Independent Variable—The
      Boltzmann transformation, 448
11-4 Similarity Transformation via One-Parameter
      Group Theory, 452
11-5 Transformation into Integral Equation, 460
      References, 464
      Problems, 466
      Notes, 468

Chapter 12

NUMERICAL METHODS OF SOLUTION   471

12-1 Finite Difference Approximation of Derivatives
      Through Taylor's Series, 471

12-2 Finite-Difference Representation of Steady-State
      Heat-Conduction Problems, 477
12-3 Methods of Solving Simultaneous Linear
      Algebraic Equations, 484
12-4 Errors Involved in Numerical Solutions, 486
12-5 Finite Difference Representation of Time-Dependent
      Heat-Conduction Equation, 487
12-6 Applications of Finite-Difference Methods to
      Time-Dependent Heat Conduction Problems, 496
12-7 Finite Difference in Cylindrical and Spherical
      Coordinate Systems, 503
12-8 Variable Thermal Properties, 511
12-9 Curved Boundaries, 513
      References, 516
      Problems, 518

Chapter 13

INTEGRAL-TRANSFORM TECHNIQUE   **522**

13-1 The Use of Integral Transform in the Solution of
      Heat-Conduction Problems in Finite Regions, 523
13-2 Alternative Form of General Solution for Finite Regions, 532
13-3 Applications in the Rectangular Coordinate System, 536
13-4 Applications in the Cylindrical Coordinate System, 551
13-5 Applications in the Spherical Coordinate System, 568
13-6 Applications in the Solution of Steady-State Problems, 579
      References, 582
      Problems, 583
      Notes, 587

Chapter 14

**INTEGRAL-TRANSFORM TECHNIQUE FOR
COMPOSITE MEDIUM**   **594**

14-1 The Use of Integral Transform in the Solution of
      Heat-Conduction Problems in Finite Composite Regions, 594
14-2 One-Dimensional Case, 601
      References, 607
      Problems, 608
      Notes, 608

Chapter 15

HEAT CONDUCTION IN ANISOTROPIC MEDIUM   611

15-1   Heat Flux for Anisotropic Solids, 612
15-2   Heat-Conduction Equation for Anisotropic Solids, 614
15-3   Boundary Conditions, 615
15-4   Thermal-Resistivity Coefficients, 617
15-5   Transformation of Axes and Conductivity Coefficients, 618
15-6   Geometrical Interpretation of Conductivity Coefficients, 620
15-7   The Symmetry of Crystals, 625
15-8   One-Dimensional Steady-State Heat Conduction in
       Anisotropic Solids, 626
15-9   One-Dimensional Time-Dependent Heat Conduction in
       Anisotropic Solids, 629
15-10 Heat Conduction in an Orthotropic Medium, 631
15-11 Multidimensional Heat Conduction in an
       Anisotropic Medium, 638
       References, 646
       Problems, 647
       Notes, 649

Appendices 651

Appendix I   Roots of Transcendental Equations, 653
Appendix II   Error Functions, 656
Appendix III   Bessel Functions, 659
Appendix IV   Numerical Values of Legendre Polynomials of the
                First Kind, 674

Index   679

CHAPTER 1

HEAT CONDUCTION FUNDAMENTALS

The energy given up by the constituent particles such as atoms, molecules, or free electrons of the hotter regions of a body to those in cooler regions is called *heat*. Conduction is the mode of heat transfer in which energy exchange takes place in solids or in fluids in rest (i.e., no convective motion resulting from the displacement of the macroscopic portion of the medium) from the region of high temperature to the region of low temperature due to the presence of temperature gradient in the body. The heat flow cannot be measured directly, but the concept has physical meaning because it is related to the measurable scalar quantity called *temperature*. Therefore, once the temperature distribution $T(\mathbf{r}, t)$ within a body is determined as a function of position and time, then the heat flow in the body is readily computed from the laws relating heat flow to the temperature gradient. The science of heat conduction is principally concerned with the determination of temperature distribution within solids. In this chapter we present the basic laws relating the heat flow to the temperature gradient in the medium, the differential equation of heat conduction governing the temperature distribution in solids, the boundary conditions appropriate for the analysis of heat conduction problems, the rules of coordinate transformation needed to write the heat conduction equation in different orthogonal coordinate systems, and a general discussion of various methods of solution of the heat-conduction equation.

1-1 THE HEAT FLUX

The basic law that gives the relationship between the heat flow and the temperature gradient, based on experimental observations, is generally named after the French mathematical physicist Joseph Fourier [1] who used it in his analytic theory of heat. For a homogeneous, isotropic solid

1

(i.e., material in which thermal conductivity is independent of direction) the *Fourier law* is given in the form

$$\mathbf{q}(\mathbf{r}, t) = -k\nabla T(\mathbf{r}, t) \quad W/m^2 \tag{1-1}$$

where the temperature gradient is a vector normal to the isothermal surface, the *heat flux vector* $\mathbf{q}(\mathbf{r}, t)$ represents heat flow per unit time, per unit area of the isothermal surface in the direction of the decreasing temperature, and k is called the *thermal conductivity* of the material which is a positive, scalar quantity. Since the heat-flux vector $\mathbf{q}(\mathbf{r}, t)$ points in the direction of decreasing temperature, the minus sign is included in equation (1-1) to make the heat flow a positive quantity. When the heat flux is in W/m^2 and the temperature gradient in °C/m, the thermal conductivity k has units W/m °C. In the rectangular coordinate system, for example, equation (1-1) is written as

$$\mathbf{q}(x, y, z, t) = -\hat{\mathbf{i}}k\frac{\partial T}{\partial x} - \hat{\mathbf{j}}k\frac{\partial T}{\partial y} - \hat{\mathbf{k}}k\frac{\partial T}{\partial z} \tag{1-2}$$

where $\hat{\mathbf{i}}, \hat{\mathbf{j}}$, and $\hat{\mathbf{k}}$ are the unit direction vectors along the x, y, and z directions, respectively. Thus, the three components of the heat flux vector in the x, y, and z directions are given, respectively, by

$$q_x = -k\frac{\partial T}{\partial x}, \qquad q_y = -k\frac{\partial T}{\partial y}, \qquad \text{and} \qquad q_z = -k\frac{\partial T}{\partial z} \tag{1-3}$$

The general expressions for the heat flux vector $\mathbf{q}$ and for its components in other coordinate systems are given later in this section [i.e., see equations (1-20) and (1-21)]. Clearly, the heat flow rate for a given temperature gradient is directly proportional to the thermal conductivity k of the material. Therefore, in the analysis of heat conduction, the thermal conductivity of the material is an important property, which controls the rate of heat flow in the medium. There is a wide difference in the thermal conductivities of various engineering materials. The highest value is given by pure metals and the lowest value by gases and vapors; the amorphous insulating materials and inorganic liquids have thermal conductivities that lie in between. To give some idea of the order of magnitude of thermal conductivity for various materials we list below some typical values of k:

Metals	50 to 415 W/m °C
Alloys	12 to 120 W/m °C
Nonmetallic liquids	0.17 to 0.7 W/m °C
Insulating materials	0.03 to 0.17 W/m °C
Gases at atmospheric pressure	0.007 to 0.17 W/m °C

Thermal conductivity also varies with temperature. For most pure metals it

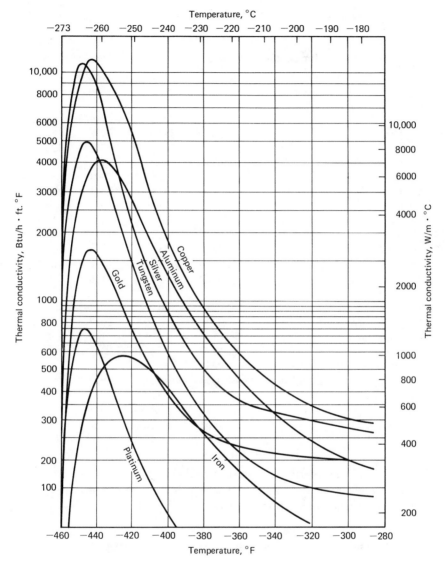

Fig. 1-1 Thermal conductivity of metals at low temperatures. (From Powell et al. [2].)

decreases with temperature, whereas for gases and insulating materials it increases with temperature. At very low temperatures, however, thermal conductivity varies very rapidly with temperature as shown in Fig. 1-1. A comprehensive compilation of thermal conductivities of material may be found in references [2–4]. We present in Table 1-1 the thermal conducti-

Table 1-1   Physical Properties of Metals and Nonmetals

Material	Temperature °C	$C_p \times 10^{-3}$ $\dfrac{\text{W·s}}{\text{kg·°C}}$	k $\dfrac{\text{W}}{\text{m·°C}}$	ρ $\dfrac{\text{kg}}{\text{m}^3}$	$\alpha \times 10^6$ $\dfrac{\text{m}^2}{\text{s}}$
Metals					
Aluminum	0	0.871	202.4	2719	85.9
Copper	0	0.381	387.6	8978	114.1
Gold	20	0.126	292.4	19,372	120.8
Iron, pure	0	0.435	62.3	7900	18.1
Cast iron ($c \simeq 4\%$)	20	0.417	51.9	7304	17.0
Lead	21	0.126	34.6	11,343	25.5
Mercury	0	0.138	8.36	13,660	4.44
Nickel	0	0.431	59.52	8930	15.5
Silver	0	0.234	418.7	10,539	170.4
Steel, mild	0	0.460	45.0	7884	12.4
Tungsten	0	0.134	159.2	19,372	61.7
Zinc	0	0.381	112.5	7176	41.3
Nonmetals					
Asbestos	0	1.047	0.151	579	0.258
Brick, fire clay	204	0.837	1.004	2317	0.516
Cork, ground	37	2.010	0.042	128	0.155
Glass, Pyrex		0.837	1.177	2413	0.594
Granite	0	0.796	2.768	2703	1.291
Ice	0	2.051	2.215	917	1.187
Oak, across grain	29	1.716	0.192	708	0.160
Pine, across grain	29	1.758	0.159	595	0.152
Quartz sand, dry		0.796	0.260	1657	0.206
Rubber, soft		1.884	0.173	1110	0.077

vity of typical engineering materials together with the specific heat C_p, density ρ, and the thermal diffusivity α, which are also important physical properties for heat conduction analysis.

1-2   THE DIFFERENTIAL EQUATION OF HEAT CONDUCTION

We now derive the differential equation of heat conduction for a stationary, homogeneous, isotropic solid with heat generation within the body. Heat generation may be due to nuclear, electrical, chemical, gamma-ray, or other sources that may be a function of time and/or position. The heat generation rate in the medium, generally specified as heat generation per unit time, per unit volume, is denoted by the symbol $g(\mathbf{r}, t)$, and if SI units are used given in the units W/m^3.

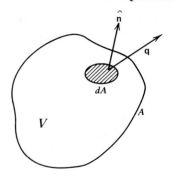

Fig. 1-2 Nomenclature for the derivation of the heat-conduction equation.

We consider the energy-balance equation for a small control volume V, illustrated in Fig. 1-2, stated as

$$
\begin{bmatrix}
\text{rate of heat entering} \\
\text{through the bounding} \\
\text{surfaces of } V
\end{bmatrix}
+
\begin{bmatrix}
\text{rate of energy} \\
\text{generation} \\
\text{in } V
\end{bmatrix}
=
\begin{bmatrix}
\text{rate of storage} \\
\text{of energy} \\
\text{in } V
\end{bmatrix}
\tag{1-4}
$$

Various terms in this equation are evaluated as

$$
\begin{bmatrix}
\text{rate of heat entering} \\
\text{through the bounding} \\
\text{surfaces of } V
\end{bmatrix}
= -\int_A \mathbf{q} \cdot \hat{\mathbf{n}}\, dA = -\int_V \nabla \cdot \mathbf{q}\, dv
\tag{1-5a}
$$

where A is the surface area of the volume element V, $\hat{\mathbf{n}}$ is the outward-drawn normal unit vector to the surface element dA, $\mathbf{q}$ is the heat flux vector at dA; here, the minus sign is included to ensure that the heat flow is into the volume element V, and the divergence theorem is used to convert the surface integral to volume integral. The remaining two terms are evaluated as

$$
(\text{rate of energy generation in } V) = \int_V g(\mathbf{r}, t)\, dv
\tag{1-5b}
$$

$$
(\text{rate of energy storage in } V) = \int_V \rho C_p \frac{\partial T(\mathbf{r}, t)}{\partial t}\, dv
\tag{1-5c}
$$

The substitution of equations (1-5) into equation (1-4) yields

$$
\int_V \left[-\nabla \cdot \mathbf{q}(\mathbf{r}, t) + g(\mathbf{r}, t) - \rho C_p \frac{\partial T(\mathbf{r}, t)}{\partial t} \right] dv = 0
\tag{1-6}
$$

Equation (1-6) is derived for an arbitrary small-volume element V within the solid, hence the volume V may be chosen so small as to remove the integral; we obtain

$$
-\nabla \cdot \mathbf{q}(\mathbf{r}, t) + g(\mathbf{r}, t) = \rho C_p \frac{\partial T(\mathbf{r}, t)}{\partial t}
\tag{1-7}
$$

Substituting $\mathbf{q}(\mathbf{r}, t)$ from equation (1-1) into equation (1-7), we obtain the *differential equation of heat conduction* for a stationary, homogeneous, isotropic solid with heat generation within the body as

$$\nabla \cdot [k\nabla T(\mathbf{r}, t)] + g(\mathbf{r}, t) = \rho C_p \frac{\partial T(\mathbf{r}, t)}{\partial t} \qquad (1\text{-}8)$$

When the thermal conductivity is assumed to be constant (i.e., independent of position and temperature), equation (1-8) simplifies to

$$\nabla^2 T(\mathbf{r}, t) + \frac{1}{k} g(\mathbf{r}, t) = \frac{1}{\alpha} \frac{\partial T(\mathbf{r}, t)}{\partial t} \qquad (1\text{-}9a)$$

where

$$\alpha = \frac{k}{\rho C_p} = \text{thermal diffusivity} \qquad (1\text{-}9b)$$

For a medium with uniform thermal conductivity and no heat generation in the medium, equations (1-9) become the diffusion or the *Fourier* equation

$$\nabla^2 T(\mathbf{r}, t) = \frac{1}{\alpha} \frac{\partial T(\mathbf{r}, t)}{\partial t} \qquad (1\text{-}10a)$$

and for steady-state, equation (1-10a) simplifies to the *Laplace* equation

$$\nabla^2 T(\mathbf{r}, t) = 0 \qquad (1\text{-}10b)$$

Here, the thermal diffusivity α is the property of the medium and has a dimension of length^2/time, which may be given in the units m^2/hr or m^2/s. The physical significance of thermal diffusivity is associated with the speed of propagation of heat into the solid during changes of temperature with time. The higher the thermal diffusivity, the faster is the propagation of heat in the medium. This statement is better understood by referring to the following specific heat-conduction problem. A semi-infinite medium in the region $x \geq 0$ is initially at a uniform temperature T_0 and for times $t > 0$ the boundary surface at $x = 0$ is kept at zero temperature. Clearly, the temperature in the body will vary with position and time. Suppose we are

Table 1-2 Effect of Thermal Diffusivity on the Rate of Heat Propagation into the Medium

Material	Silver	Copper	Steel	Glass	Cork
α, $10^6 \times$ m^2/s	170	103	12.9	0.59	0.155
Time	9.5 min	16.5 min	2.2 hr	2.00 days	77 days

interested in the time required for the temperature to decrease from its initial value T_0 to half of this value, $\frac{1}{2}T_0$, at a position, say, 30 cm from the boundary surface; Table 1-2 gives the time required for several different materials. It is apparent from these results that the larger the thermal diffusivity, the shorter is the time required for the applied heat to penetrate into the depth of the solid.

1-3 HEAT-CONDUCTION EQUATION IN DIFFERENT ORTHOGONAL COORDINATE SYSTEMS

The first step in the analytic solution of a heat-conduction problem for a given region is to choose an orthogonal coordinate system such that its coordinate surfaces coincide with the boundary surfaces of the region. For example, the rectangular coordinate system is used for rectangular bodies, the cylindrical and the spherical coordinate systems are used for bodies having shapes such as a cylinder and a sphere, respectively, and so on. Here we present the heat-conduction equation in the rectangular, cylindrical, and spherical coordinate systems and also give the general expression for writing this equation in other orthogonal curvilinear coordinate systems.

Equations (1-8) and (1-9) in the *rectangular coordinate system* (x, y, z), respectively, become

$$\frac{\partial}{\partial x}\left(k\frac{\partial T}{\partial x}\right) + \frac{\partial}{\partial y}\left(k\frac{\partial T}{\partial y}\right) + \frac{\partial}{\partial z}\left(k\frac{\partial T}{\partial z}\right) + g = \rho C_p \frac{\partial T}{\partial t} \qquad (1\text{-}11a)$$

$$\frac{\partial^2 T}{\partial x^2} + \frac{\partial^2 T}{\partial y^2} + \frac{\partial^2 T}{\partial z^2} + \frac{1}{k}g = \frac{1}{\alpha}\frac{\partial T}{\partial t} \qquad (1\text{-}11b)$$

In the *cylindrical (i.e., circular-cylinder) coordinate system* (r, ϕ, z) shown

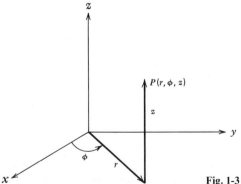

Fig. 1-3   Cylindrical coordinate system (r, ϕ, z).

in Fig. 1-3 they are given as

$$\frac{1}{r}\frac{\partial}{\partial r}\left(kr\frac{\partial T}{\partial r}\right)+\frac{1}{r^2}\frac{\partial}{\partial \phi}\left(k\frac{\partial T}{\partial \phi}\right)+\frac{\partial}{\partial z}\left(k\frac{\partial T}{\partial z}\right)+g=\rho C_p\frac{\partial T}{\partial t} \quad (1\text{-}12a)$$

$$\frac{1}{r}\frac{\partial}{\partial r}\left(r\frac{\partial T}{\partial r}\right)+\frac{1}{r^2}\frac{\partial^2 T}{\partial \phi^2}+\frac{\partial^2 T}{\partial z^2}+\frac{1}{k}g=\frac{1}{\alpha}\frac{\partial T}{\partial t} \quad (1\text{-}12b)$$

and in the *spherical coordinate system* (r,θ,ϕ) shown in Fig. 1-4 they become

$$\frac{1}{r^2}\frac{\partial}{\partial r}\left(kr^2\frac{\partial T}{\partial r}\right)+\frac{1}{r^2\sin\theta}\frac{\partial}{\partial \theta}\left(k\sin\theta\frac{\partial T}{\partial \theta}\right)+\frac{1}{r^2\sin^2\theta}\frac{\partial}{\partial \phi}\left(k\frac{\partial T}{\partial \phi}\right)+g$$

$$=\rho C_p\frac{\partial T}{\partial t} \quad (1\text{-}13a)$$

$$\frac{1}{r^2}\frac{\partial}{\partial r}\left(r^2\frac{\partial T}{\partial r}\right)+\frac{1}{r^2\sin\theta}\frac{\partial}{\partial \theta}\left(\sin\theta\frac{\partial T}{\partial \theta}\right)+\frac{1}{r^2\sin^2\theta}\frac{\partial^2 T}{\partial \phi^2}+\frac{1}{k}g=\frac{1}{\alpha}\frac{\partial T}{\partial t}$$

$$(1\text{-}13b)$$

In this book we shall be concerned particularly with the solution of heat conduction problems in the rectangular, cylindrical, and spherical coordinate systems; therefore, equations needed for such purposes are immediately obtained from equations (1-11) to (1-13) given above. The heat-conduction equations in other *orthogonal curvilinear coordinate systems* (i.e., a coordinate system in which the coordinate lines cut each other at right angles) are readily obtained by the coordinate transformation. Here we present a brief discussion of the transformation of the heat conduction equation into a general *orthogonal curvilinear coordinate system*. The reader is referred to references [5–7] for further details.

Let u_1, u_2, and u_3 be the three space coordinates, and $\hat{\mathbf{u}}_1, \hat{\mathbf{u}}_2$, and $\hat{\mathbf{u}}_3$ be the unit direction vectors in the u_1, u_2, and u_3 directions in a general ortho-

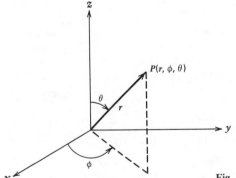

Fig. 1-4   Spherical coordinate system (r,ϕ,θ).

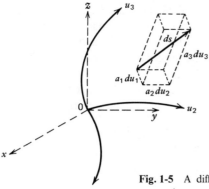

Fig. 1-5 A differential length ds in a curvilinear coordinate system (u_1, u_2, u_3).

gonal curvilinear coordinate system shown in Fig. 1-5. A differential length dS in the rectangular coordinate system (x, y, z) is given by

$$(dS)^2 = (dx)^2 + (dy)^2 + (dz)^2 \tag{1-14}$$

Let the functional relationship between orthogonal curvilinear coordinates (u_1, u_2, u_3) and the rectangular coordinates (x, y, z) be given as

$$x = X(u_1, u_2, u_3), \quad y = Y(u_1, u_2, u_3) \quad \text{and} \quad z = Z(u_1, u_2, u_3) \tag{1-15}$$

Then, the differential lengths dx, dy, and dz are obtained from Eqs. (1-15) by the differentiation

$$dx = \sum_{i=1}^{3} \frac{\partial X}{\partial u_i} du_i \tag{1-16a}$$

$$dy = \sum_{i=1}^{3} \frac{\partial Y}{\partial u_i} du_i \tag{1-16b}$$

$$dz = \sum_{i=1}^{3} \frac{\partial Z}{\partial u_i} du_i \tag{1-16c}$$

Substituting equations (1-16) into equation (1-14), and noting that the cross products must be zero when u_1, u_2, and u_3 are mutually orthogonal yields the following expression for the differential length dS in the orthogonal curvilinear coordinate system u_1, u_2, u_3

$$(dS)^2 = a_1^2(du_1)^2 + a_2^2(du_2)^2 + a_3^2(du_3)^2 \tag{1-17}$$

where

$$a_i^2 = \left(\frac{\partial x}{\partial u_i}\right)^2 + \left(\frac{\partial y}{\partial u_i}\right)^2 + \left(\frac{\partial z}{\partial u_i}\right)^2, \quad . \quad i = 1, 2, 3 \tag{1-18}$$

Here, the coefficients a_1, a_2, and a_3 are called the *scale factors*, which may be constants or functions of the coordinates. Thus, when the functional relationship between the rectangular and the orthogonal curvilinear system is available [i.e., as in equation (1-15)], then the scale factors a_i are evaluated by equation (1-18).

Once the scale factors are known, the gradient of temperature in the orthogonal curvilinear coordinate system (u_1, u_2, u_3) is given by

$$\nabla T = \hat{u}_1 \frac{1}{a_1} \frac{\partial T}{\partial u_1} + \hat{u}_2 \frac{1}{a_2} \frac{\partial T}{\partial u_2} + \hat{u}_3 \frac{1}{a_3} \frac{\partial T}{\partial u_3} \tag{1-19}$$

The expression defining the heat flux vector $\mathbf{q}$ becomes

$$\mathbf{q} = -k\nabla T = -k \sum_{i=1}^{3} \hat{u}_i \frac{1}{a_i} \frac{\partial T}{\partial u_i} \tag{1-20}$$

and the three components of the heat flux vector along the u_1, u_2, and u_3 coordinates are given by

$$q_i = -k \frac{1}{a_i} \frac{\partial T}{\partial u_i}, \qquad i = 1, 2, 3 \tag{1-21}$$

The divergence of the heat flux vector $\mathbf{q}$, in the orthogonal curvilinear coordinate system (u_1, u_2, u_3) is given by

$$\nabla \cdot \mathbf{q} = \frac{1}{a} \left[\frac{1}{\partial u_1} \left(\frac{a}{a_1} q_1 \right) + \frac{\partial}{\partial u_2} \left(\frac{a}{a_2} q_2 \right) + \frac{\partial}{\partial u_3} \left(\frac{a}{a_3} q_3 \right) \right] \tag{1-22a}$$

where

$$a = a_1 a_2 a_3 \tag{1-22b}$$

The differential equation of heat conduction in a general orthogonal curvilinear coordinate system is now obtained by substituting the results given by equations (1-21) and (1-22) into equation (1-7)

$$\frac{1}{a} \left[\frac{\partial}{\partial u_1} \left(k \frac{a}{a_1^2} \frac{\partial T}{\partial u_1} \right) + \frac{\partial}{\partial u_2} \left(k \frac{a}{a_2^2} \frac{\partial T}{\partial u_2} \right) + \frac{\partial}{\partial u_3} \left(k \frac{a}{a_3^2} \frac{\partial T}{\partial u_3} \right) \right] + g = \rho C_p \frac{\partial T}{\partial t} \tag{1-23}$$

The heat-conduction equations in the cylindrical and spherical coordinates given previously by equations (1-12) and (1-13) are readily obtainable as special cases from the general equation (1-23) if the appropriate values of the scale factors are introduced.

Length, Area, and Volume Relations

In the analysis of heat conduction problems integrations are generally required over a length, an area, or a volume. If such an operation is to be performed in an orthogonal curvilinear coordinate system, expressions are needed for a differential length dl, a differential area dA, and a differential volume dV. These relations are determined as now described.

In the case of rectangular coordinate system, a differential volume element dV is given by

$$dV = dx\,dy\,dz \tag{1-24a}$$

and the differential areas dA_x, dA_y, and dA_z cut from the planes $x = \text{constant}$, $y = \text{constant}$, and $z = \text{constant}$ are given, respectively, by

$$dA_x = dy\,dz, \qquad dA_y = dx\,dz, \qquad \text{and} \qquad dA_z = dx\,dy \tag{1-24b}$$

In the case of an orthogonal curvilinear coordinate system, the elementary lengths dl_1, dl_2, and dl_3 along the three coordinate axes u_1, u_2, and u_3 are given, respectively, by

$$dl_1 = a_1\,du_1, \qquad dl_2 = a_2\,du_2, \qquad \text{and} \qquad dl_3 = a_3\,du_3 \tag{1-25a}$$

Then, an elementary volume element dV is expressed as

$$dv = a_1 a_2 a_3\,du_1\,du_2\,du_3 = a\,du_1\,du_2\,du_3 \qquad \text{where } a \equiv a_1 a_2 a_3 \tag{1-25b}$$

The differential areas dA_1, dA_2, and dA_3 cut from the planes $u_1 = \text{constant}$, $u_2 = \text{constant}$, and $u_3 = \text{constant}$ are given, respectively, by

$$dA_1 = dl_2\,dl_3 = a_2 a_3\,du_2\,du_3, \qquad dA_2 = dl_1\,dl_3 = a_1 a_3\,du_1\,du_3 \qquad \text{and}$$
$$dA_3 = dl_1\,dl_2 = a_1 a_2\,du_1\,du_2 \tag{1-25c}$$

Example 1-1. Determine the scale factors for the cylindrical coordinate system (r, ϕ, z) and write the expressions for the heat flux components.

Solution. The functional relationships between the coordinates (r, ϕ, z) and the rectangular coordinates (x, y, z) are given by

$$x = r\cos\phi, \qquad y = r\sin\phi, \qquad z = z$$

Let

$$u_1 \equiv r, \qquad u_2 \equiv \phi, \qquad \text{and} \qquad u_3 \equiv z \tag{1-26}$$

The scale factors $a_1 \equiv a_r, a_2 \equiv a_\phi$, and $a_3 \equiv a_z$ for the (r, ϕ, z) coordinate system are determined by equation (1-18) as

$$a_1^2 \equiv a_r^2 = \left(\frac{\partial x}{\partial r}\right)^2 + \left(\frac{\partial y}{\partial r}\right)^2 + \left(\frac{\partial z}{\partial r}\right)^2 = \cos^2\phi + \sin^2\phi + 0 = 1$$

$$a_2^2 \equiv a_\phi^2 = \left(\frac{\partial x}{\partial \phi}\right)^2 + \left(\frac{\partial y}{\partial \phi}\right)^2 + \left(\frac{\partial z}{\partial \phi}\right)^2 = (-r\sin\phi)^2 + (r\cos\phi)^2 + 0 = r^2$$

$$a_3^2 \equiv a_z^2 = \left(\frac{\partial x}{\partial z}\right)^2 + \left(\frac{\partial y}{\partial z}\right)^2 + \left(\frac{\partial z}{\partial z}\right)^2 = 0 + 0 + 1 = 1$$

Hence the scale factors for the cylindrical coordinate system become

$$a_r = 1, \qquad a_\phi = r, \qquad a_z = 1, \qquad \text{and} \qquad a = r \qquad (1\text{-}27)$$

and the three components of the heat flux are given as

$$q_r = -k\frac{\partial T}{\partial r}, \qquad q_\phi = -\frac{k}{r}\frac{\partial T}{\partial \phi}, \qquad \text{and} \qquad q_z = -k\frac{\partial T}{\partial z} \qquad (1\text{-}27b)$$

Example 1-2. Determine the scale factors for the spherical coordinate system (r, ϕ, θ).

Solution. The functional relationships between the coordinates (r, ϕ, θ) and the rectangular coordinates (x, y, z) are given by

$$x = r\sin\theta\cos\phi, \qquad y = r\sin\theta\sin\phi, \qquad z = r\cos\theta \qquad (1\text{-}28)$$

Let

$$u_1 \equiv r, \qquad u_2 \equiv \phi, \qquad \text{and} \qquad u_3 \equiv \theta$$

Then, by utilizing equation (1-18), the scale factors $a_1 \equiv a_r, a_2 \equiv a_\phi$, and $a_3 \equiv a_\theta$ are determined as

$$a_1^2 \equiv a_r^2 = (\sin\theta\cos\phi)^2 + (\sin\theta\sin\phi)^2 + (\cos\theta)^2 = 1$$
$$a_2^2 \equiv a_\phi^2 = r^2\sin^2\theta\sin^2\phi + r^2\sin^2\theta\cos^2\phi + 0 = r^2\sin^2\theta$$
$$a_3^2 \equiv a_\theta^2 = r^2\cos^2\theta\cos^2\phi + r^2\cos^2\theta\sin^2\phi + r^2\sin^2\theta = r^2$$

Hence the scale factors become

$$a_r = 1, \qquad a_\phi = r\sin\theta, \qquad a_\theta = r, \qquad \text{and} \qquad a = r^2\sin\theta \qquad (1\text{-}29)$$

1-4 BOUNDARY CONDITIONS

The differential equation of heat conduction will have numerous solutions unless a set of boundary conditions and an initial condition (for the time-dependent problem) are prescribed. The initial condition specifies the temperature distribution in the medium at the origin of the time coordinate (that is, $t = 0$), and the boundary conditions specify the temperature or the heat flow at the boundaries of the region. For example, at a given boundary surface, the temperature distribution may be prescribed, or the heat-flux distribution may be prescribed, or there may be heat exchange by convection with an environment at a prescribed temperature. With this consideration, we use the terminology the boundary condition of the *first kind*, the *second kind*, and the *third kind*, respectively, to characterize these three situations at the boundaries. To formalize the mathematical representation, we present below a discussion of these three types of boundary conditions.

Boundary Condition of the First Kind

Temperature is prescribed along the boundary surface; for the general case it is a function of both time and position and is represented in the form

$$T = f_i(\mathbf{r}, t) \text{ on the boundary surface } S_i \qquad (1\text{-}30a)$$

Special cases include temperature at the boundary surface as a function of position only $f_i(\mathbf{r})$, or a function of time only $f_i(t)$, or a constant.

If the temperature at the boundary surface vanishes, we have

$$T = 0 \text{ on the boundary surface } S_i \qquad (1\text{-}30b)$$

This special case is called the *homogeneous boundary condition of the first kind*. A boundary surface that is kept at zero temperature satisfies homogeneous boundary conditions of the first kind. A boundary surface that is kept at a constant temperature T_0 also satisfies the homogeneous boundary condition of the first kind if the temperature is measured in excess of T_0.

Boundary Condition of the Second Kind

The normal derivative of temperature is prescribed at the boundary surface, and it may be a function of both time and position. It is given in the form

$$\frac{\partial T}{\partial n_i} = f_i(\mathbf{r}, t) \text{ on the boundary surface } S_i \qquad (1\text{-}31a)$$

where $\partial/\partial n_i$ denotes differentiation along the outward-drawn normal at the boundary surface S_i. This boundary condition is equivalent to that of prescribing the magnitude of the heat flux along the boundary surface, since the left-hand side becomes the heat flux at the surface S_i when both sides of equation (1-31a) are multiplied by the thermal conductivity of the material. If the normal derivative of temperature at the boundary surface vanishes, we have

$$\frac{\partial T}{\partial n_i} = 0 \text{ on the boundary } S_i \qquad (1\text{-}31b)$$

This special case is called the *homogeneous boundary condition of the second kind*. An insulated boundary condition satisfies this condition.

Boundary Condition of the Third Kind

A linear combination of the temperature and its normal derivative is prescribed at the boundary surface.

$$k_i \frac{\partial T}{\partial n_i} + h_i T = f_i(\mathbf{r}, t) \text{ on the boundary surface } S_i \qquad (1\text{-}32)$$

The boundary conditions of the first and second kinds that are discussed above are obtainable by setting k_i and h_i equal to zero, respectively, in equation (1-32). The physical significance of equation (1-32) is that the boundary surface under consideration dissipates heat by convection according to Newton's law of cooling (i.e., heat transfer is proportional to temperature difference) to a surrounding temperature that varies both with time and position along the boundary surface. To demonstrate this we write an energy balance for the boundary surface S_i shown in Fig. 1-6 as

$$-k_i \frac{\partial T}{\partial n_i}\bigg|_{S_i} = h_i(T\,|_{S_i} - T_a) \qquad (1\text{-}33a)$$

or

$$k_i \frac{\partial T}{\partial n_i} + h_i T = h_i T_a \equiv f_i(\mathbf{r}, t) \text{ on } S_i \qquad (1\text{-}33b)$$

which is in the same form as equation (1-32).

A special case of equation (1-32) is

$$k_i \frac{\partial T}{\partial n_i} + h_i T = 0 \text{ on } S_i \qquad (1\text{-}34)$$

which is called the *homogeneous boundary condition of the third kind*. The physical situation described by equation (1-34) is that of heat dissipation by convection from the boundary surface into a surrounding at zero temperature.

Three types of boundary conditions described above cover most cases of practical interest and they are all *linear boundary conditions*. There are also thermal radiation boundary conditions with heat transfer obeying the fourth-power temperature law, or the natural convection boundary condition with heat transfer proportional to the $\frac{5}{4}$ power of temperature difference.

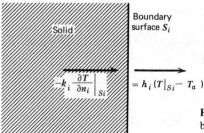

Fig. 1-6 Heat transfer by convection at the boundary surface s_i to an environment at temperature T_a.

Such boundary conditions are *nonlinear* because a power of temperature enters the boundary condition.

Boundary conditions associated with change of phase (i.e., melting, solidification, ablation) are also nonlinear boundary conditions. In this book we are concerned primarily with the solution of linear differential equations of heat conduction subject to the linear boundary conditions discussed above. Solutions of nonlinear problems will be treated later in a separate chapter.

1-5 DIMENSIONLESS HEAT-CONDUCTION PARAMETERS

The number of variables in a heat-conduction problem can be reduced by introducing dimensionless variables. To illustrate typical dimensionless variables and their physical significance, we consider the following one-dimensional, time-dependent heat-conduction problem for a slab, that is, $0 \leq x \leq L$.

$$\frac{\partial^2 T}{\partial x^2} + \frac{g}{k} = \frac{1}{\alpha} \frac{\partial T}{\partial t} \quad \text{in} \quad 0 < x < L, \quad \text{for} \quad t > 0 \quad \text{(1-35a)}$$

subject to the boundary and initial conditions

$$\frac{\partial T}{\partial x} = 0 \qquad \text{at } x = 0, \qquad \text{for } t > 0 \qquad \text{(1-35b)}$$

$$k \frac{\partial T}{\partial x} + hT = hT_\infty \qquad \text{at } x = L, \qquad \text{for } t > 0 \qquad \text{(1-35c)}$$

$$T = T_0 \qquad \text{in } 0 \leq x \leq L, \qquad \text{for } t = 0 \qquad \text{(1-35d)}$$

New dimensionless variables are defined as

$$X = \frac{x}{L} = \text{dimensionless space coordinate} \qquad \text{(1-36a)}$$

$$\theta = \frac{T - T_\infty}{T_0 - T_\infty} = \text{dimensionless temperature} \qquad \text{(1-36b)}$$

$$Bi \equiv \frac{hL}{k} = \text{Biot number} \qquad \text{(1-36c)}$$

$$G \equiv \frac{gL^2}{k(T_0 - T_\infty)} = \text{dimensionless heat generation} \qquad \text{(1-36d)}$$

$$\tau \equiv \frac{\alpha t}{L^2} = \text{dimensionless time or Fourier number} \equiv Fo \qquad \text{(1-36e)}$$

Then equations (1-35) become dimensionless as

$$\frac{\partial^2 \theta}{\partial X^2} + G = \frac{\partial \theta}{\partial \tau} \qquad \text{in } 0 < X < 1, \qquad \text{for } \tau > 0 \qquad (1\text{-}37a)$$

$$\frac{\partial \theta}{\partial X} = 0 \qquad \text{at } X = 0, \qquad \text{for } \tau > 0 \qquad (1\text{-}37b)$$

$$\frac{\partial \theta}{\partial X} + Bi\theta = 0 \qquad \text{at } X = 1, \qquad \text{for } \tau > 0 \qquad (1\text{-}37)$$

$$\theta = 1 \qquad \text{in } 0 \le X \le 1, \qquad \text{for } \tau = 0 \qquad (1\text{-}37d)$$

The Fourier number and the Biot number are two important dimensionless parameters that are frequently used in heat-conduction problems. The physical significance of the Fourier number is better envisioned if it is rearranged in the form

$$\tau = \frac{\alpha t}{L^2} = \frac{k(1/L)L^2}{\rho C_p L^3 / t} = \frac{\left[\begin{array}{l}\text{rate of heat-conduction} \\ \text{across } L \text{ in volume } L^3\end{array}\right]}{\left[\begin{array}{l}\text{rate of heat storage} \\ \text{in volume } L^3\end{array}\right]} \qquad (1\text{-}38)$$

Thus, the Fourier number is a measure of the rate of heat conduction in comparison with the rate of heat storage in a given volume element. Therefore, the larger the Fourier number, the deeper is the penetration of heat into a solid over a given period of time.

The physical significance of the Biot number is better understood if it is rearranged in the form

$$Bi = \frac{hL}{h} = \frac{h}{k/L} = \frac{\left[\begin{array}{l}\text{heat-transfer coefficient} \\ \text{at the surface of solid}\end{array}\right]}{\left[\begin{array}{l}\text{internal conductance of} \\ \text{solid across length } L\end{array}\right]} \qquad (1\text{-}39)$$

That is, the Biot number is the ratio of the heat-transfer coefficient to the unit conductance of a solid over the characteristic dimension. It can be used to establish a criteria under which the temperature distribution within a solid can be considered uniform during transients. For example, for solids in the shape of a slab, long cylinder, or sphere, with no internal heat generation, one-dimensional transient temperature distribution within the solid can be considered uniform with an error less than approximately 5% if $Bi \equiv hL_s/k < 0.1$, where L_s is a characteristic dimension defined as $L_s = $ volume/surface area.

1-6 HOMOGENEOUS AND NONHOMOGENEOUS PROBLEMS

For convenience in the analysis, the time-dependent boundary-value problems of heat conduction will be considered in two different groups: *homogeneous problems* and *nonhomogeneous problems*.

The problem will be referred to as a *homogeneous problem* when both the differential equation and the boundary conditions are homogeneous. The problem in the form

$$\nabla^2 T = \frac{1}{\alpha}\frac{\partial T}{\partial t} \qquad \text{in region } R, \qquad t > 0 \qquad (1\text{-}40\text{a})$$

$$k_i \frac{\partial T}{\partial n_i} + h_i T = 0 \qquad \text{on boundary } S_i, \qquad t > 0 \qquad (1\text{-}40\text{b})$$

$$T = F(\mathbf{r}) \qquad \text{in region } R, \qquad t = 0 \qquad (1\text{-}40\text{c})$$

will be referred to as the homogeneous problem because both the differential equation and the boundary condition are homogeneous. The boundary condition in Equation (1-40) could be a homogeneous boundary condition of the first or second kind.

The problem will be referred to as a *nonhomogeneous problem* if the differential equation, or the boundary conditions, or both are nonhomogeneous. For example, the boundary-value problem of heat-conduction in the form

$$\nabla^2 T + \frac{g(\mathbf{r}, t)}{k} = \frac{1}{\alpha}\frac{\partial T}{\partial t} \qquad \text{in region } R, \qquad t > 0 \qquad (1\text{-}41\text{a})$$

$$k_i \frac{\partial T}{\partial n_i} + h_i T = f_i(\mathbf{r}, t) \qquad \text{on boundary } S_i, \qquad t > 0 \qquad (1\text{-}41\text{b})$$

$$T = F(\mathbf{r}) \qquad \text{in region } R, \qquad t = 0 \qquad (1\text{-}41\text{c})$$

is nonhomogeneous because the differential equation and the boundary condition are nonhomogeneous [i.e., functions $g(\mathbf{r}, t)$ and $f_i(\mathbf{r}, t)$ do not include T as product].

The boundary-value problem of heat-conduction in the form

$$\nabla^2 T + \frac{g(\mathbf{r}, t)}{k} = \frac{1}{\alpha}\frac{\partial T}{\partial t} \qquad \text{in region } R, \qquad t > 0 \qquad (1\text{-}42\text{a})$$

$$k_i \frac{\partial T}{\partial n_i} + h_i T = 0 \qquad \text{on boundary } S_i, \qquad t > 0 \qquad (1\text{-}42\text{b})$$

$$T = F(\mathbf{r}) \qquad \text{in region } R, \qquad t = 0 \qquad (1\text{-}42\text{c})$$

is nonhomogeneous because the differential equation is nonhomogeneous.

1-7 METHODS OF SOLUTION OF HEAT-CONDUCTION PROBLEMS

Considerable amount of work is devoted in the literature on the development of exact, approximate, and numerical methods of solution of heat-conduction problems. The handling of nonlinear problems by analytic means is a complicated matter; no general theory is yet available to handle all types of nonlinear problems, because each nonlinear problem requires different techniques for its analytic treatment. The heat-conduction problem becomes nonlinear either due to the nonlinearity of the differential equation or the boundary conditions or both. On the other hand a variety of analytic methods have been developed for the analysis of a broad class of linear problems. In the following chapters we shall present in detail various analytic, approximate, and numerical methods of solution of heat-conduction problems. To provide an overall view of this subject, we now present a brief qualitative discussion of various methods of solution of heat-conduction problems.

Method of Separation of Variables

The method of separation of variables, perhaps, is the oldest method for the solution of a certain class of linear partial differential equations of mathematical physics. Introduced in the middle of the eighteenth century by Euler, d'Alembert, and Bernoulli, the theory and application of this method are well documented in numerous standard texts [6, 8, 9] on the solution of partial differential equations. The application of this method to the solution of linear, homogeneous boundary-value problems of heat conduction is rather straightforward. That is, the partial differential equation of heat conduction in the n independent variables is separated into n ordinary differential equations, and in this separation process $n - 1$ arbitrary separation constants are introduced. The resulting ordinary differential equations are solved and the complete solution is constructed by the linear superposition of all separated solutions. The unknown coefficients associated with the superposition are then determined. However, the solution of heat-conduction problems by the method of separation of variables is not as convenient if the problem is nonhomogeneous either due to the presence of the heat generation term in the differential equation or due to the non-homogeneity of boundary conditions or both.

Integral Transform Technique

The integral transform techniques provide a systematic and straightforward approach to the solution of a certain class of linear partial differential equations. The method is particularly suitable for the solution of both homogeneous and nonhomogeneous boundary value problems of heat conduction, since the second partial derivatives are readily removed from the differential equation by this method. It is for this reason, in the heat-conduction problem, the integral transformation is applied for the removal of partial derivatives with respect to the space variables. For example, the heat-conduction problem in the x, y, z, and t variables is reduced to an ordinary differential equation in the t variable by successive application of the integral transform for the removal of partial derivatives with respect to the x, y, and z variables. The resulting ordinary differential equation is then solved subject to the transformed initial condition for the problem. The triple transform of the temperature function determined in this manner is readily inverted successively with respect to the x, y, and z variables to obtain the desired solution for the problem. The inversion process is a straightforward matter since the inversion formulas are available at the onset of the problem

The integral transform technique derives its basis from the classical method of separation of variables. That is, the transform pairs needed for the solution of a given problem are developed by considering the representation of an arbitrary function, defined in the same region as for the problem, in terms of the separated solutions for the homogeneous part of the problem. Therefore, the method of separation of variables that will be presented in the following chapter will provide the necessary background for the development of appropriate transform pairs needed in the solution of heat-conduction problems by the integral transform technique. Because the method is very efficient in application, its use by the engineer and scientist has been greatly increased during the past decade. A discussion of the theory and application of the integral transform technique may be found in several texts [10–13].

Laplace Transform Technique

The Laplace transform technique has been widely used in the solution of transient problems of mathematical physics, because the partial derivative with respect to the time variable can be removed from the differential equation by the application of the Laplace transformation. In the case of one-dimensional, time-dependent, heat-conduction problem, for example, the problem is reduced to an ordinary differential equation in the space variable for the transform of the temperature function by the application of the Laplace transformation. When the ordinary differential equation is solved and the resulting transform is inverted, the desired solution for the temperature distribution is obtained. Although the application of the Laplace transform for the removal of the time derivative is a relatively simple matter, the inversion of the transformed function generally is not so straightforward, unless the desired inversion is available in the standard Laplace inversion tables. For transient linear heat-conduction problems involving more than one space variable, the Laplace transform may be used together with the integral transform to reduce the partial differential equation into an ordinary differential equation.

Approximate Analytic Methods

The analytic methods discussed above are suitable for the solution of linear heat-conduction problems in bodies having simple geometries such as slabs, rectangles, cylinders, spheres, and so on. The nonlinear problems can be treated analytically only for a limited number of simple situations. Therefore, numerous approximate analytic methods have been developed in the literature for the analysis of steady and transient heat-conduction problems in bodies having more complicated geometries or for situations when the differential equation or the boundary condition is nonlinear. The *integral method*, the variational formulation leading to the *Rayleigh-Ritz method* and the *Galerkin method*, among many others, are valuable to obtain approximate solutions to a broad class of engineering problems. However, the accuracy of an approximate analysis cannot be assessed unless the results are compared with the exact solution. The subject of approximate analysis, its application to the solution of various boundary-value problems of heat conduction and the accuracy of the resulting solutions will be discussed in a separate chapter devoted for this purpose.

Numerical Methods

For heat-conduction problems involving complicated boundary conditions, irregular boundaries and variable thermal properties, the exact solutions become impossible; or the approximate solutions may not be applicable or may not provide the desired degree of accuracy. The numerical methods of solution are useful for such situations. The *finite-difference* method is widely used in the solution of both transient and steady-state heat-conduction problems. The basic concept in this method is the approximation of partial derivatives at a given point by finite differences, thus converting the solution of the partial differential equation to the solution of a large number of coupled algebraic equations for temperatures at a selected number of nodal points within the region. The *Monte-Carlo* method of solution, based on the concepts of *probability* and *random walk*, has found only limited application in the solution of heat-conduction problems. More recently, the *finite element* method, has found numerous applications in the solution of heat-conduction problems. This method appears to handle the irregular boundaries or unusual specification of boundary conditions better than the finite-difference method. On the other hand, the representation of the heat-conduction problem in the finite difference form is a more straightforward matter than its representation in the finite-element formulation. Therefore, in a limited space available here, only the fundamentals of finite-difference representation of heat-conduction problems and their methods of solution will be presented.

The theory and application of various methods of solution of heat-conduction problems discussed above can be found in several texts [13–17].

REFERENCES

1. J. B. Fourier, *Theorie Analytique de la Chaleur*, Paris, 1822 (English translation by A. Freeman. Dover Publications, Inc., New York, 1955.)

2. R. W. Powell, C. Y. Ho, and P. E. Liley, Thermal Conductivity of Selected Materials, NSRDS-NBS 8, U.S. Department of Commerce, National Bureau of Standards, 1966.

3. *Thermophysical Properties of Matter*, Vols. 1–3, 1F1/Plenum Data Corporation, New York, 1969.

4. C. Y. Ho, R. W. Powell, and P. E. Liley, Thermal Conductivity of Elements, Vol. 1, First supplement to *J. Phys. Chem. Ref. Data* (1972).

5. P. Moon and D. E. Spencer, *Field Theory for Engineers*, Van Nostrand Company, Inc., Princeton, N.J., 1961.

6. M. P. Morse and H. Feshbach, *Methods of Theoretical Physics*, Part 1, McGraw-Hill Book Company, New York, 1953.

7. G. Arfken, *Mathematical Methods for Physicists*, Academic Press, New York, 1966.

8. R. V. Churchill, *Fourier Series and Boundary Value Problems*, McGraw-Hill Book Company, New York, 1963.

9. J. W. Dettman, *Mathematical Methods in Physics and Engineering*, McGraw-Hill Book Company, New York, 1962.

10. I. N. Sneddon, *Fourier Transforms*, McGraw-Hill Book Company, New York, 1951.

11. I. N. Sneddon, *The Use of Integral Transforms*, McGraw-Hill Book Company, New York, 1972.

12. C. J. Tranter, *Integral Transforms in Mathematical Physics*, John Wiley and Sons, Inc., New York, 1951.

13. M. N. Özışık, *Boundary Value Problems of Heat Conduction*, International Textbook Company, Scranton, Pa., 1968.

14. H. S. Carslaw and J. C. Jaeger, *Conduction of Heat in Solids*, Clarendon Press, London, 1959.

15. V. S. Arpaci, *Conduction Heat Transfer*, Addison-Wesley Publishing Co., Reading, Mass., 1966.

16. P. J. Schneider, *Conduction Heat Transfer*, Addison-Wesley Publishing Co., Reading, Mass., 1955.

17. A. V. Luikov, *Analytical Heat Diffusion Theory*, Academic Press, New York, 1968.

PROBLEMS

1-1 Verify that ∇T and $\nabla \cdot \mathbf{q}$ in the cylindrical coordinate system (r, ϕ, z) are given as

$$\nabla T = \hat{\mathbf{u}}_r \frac{\partial T}{\partial r} + \hat{\mathbf{u}}_\phi \frac{1}{r} \frac{\partial T}{\partial \phi} + \hat{\mathbf{u}}_z \frac{\partial T}{\partial z}$$

$$\nabla \cdot \mathbf{q} = \frac{1}{r} \frac{\partial}{\partial r}(r q_r) + \frac{1}{r} \frac{\partial q_\phi}{\partial \phi} + \frac{\partial q_z}{\partial z}$$

1-2 Verify that ∇T and $\nabla \cdot \mathbf{q}$ in the spherical coordinate system (r, ϕ, θ) are given as

$$\nabla T = \hat{\mathbf{u}}_r \frac{\partial T}{\partial r} + \hat{\mathbf{u}}_\phi \frac{1}{r \sin \theta} \frac{\partial T}{\partial \phi} + \hat{\mathbf{u}}_\theta \frac{1}{r} \frac{\partial T}{\partial \theta}$$

$$\nabla \cdot \mathbf{q} = \frac{1}{r^2} \frac{\partial}{\partial r}(r^2 q_r) + \frac{1}{r \sin \theta} \frac{\partial q_\phi}{\partial \phi} + \frac{1}{r \sin \theta} \frac{\partial}{\partial \theta}(q_\theta \sin \theta)$$

1-3 By using the appropriate scale factors in equation (1-23) show that the heat-conduction equation in the cylindrical and spherical coordinate systems are given by equations (1-12) and (1-13).

1-4 Obtain expressions for elemental areas dA cut from the surfaces $r = \text{constant}$, $\theta = \text{constant}$, and $z = \text{constant}$, also for an elemental volume element dV in the cylindrical coordinate system (r, θ, z).

1-5 Repeat the problem (1-4) for the spherical coordinate system (r, ϕ, θ).

1-6 The *prolate spheroidal* coordinate system (η, θ, ϕ) as illustrated in Fig. 1-7 consists of prolate spheroids $\eta = \text{constant}$, hyperboloids $\theta = \text{constant}$,

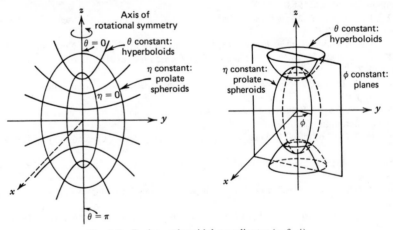

Fig. 1-7 Prolate spheroidal coordinates (η, θ, ϕ).

and planes ϕ = constant. Note that as $\eta \to 0$ spheroids become straight lines of length $2A$ on the z axis and as $\eta \to \infty$ spheroids become nearly spherical. For $\theta = 0$, hyperboloids degenerate into z axis from A to $+\infty$, and for $\theta = \pi$ hyperboloids degenerate into z axis from $-A$ to $-\infty$, and for $\theta = \pi/2$ hyperboloids become the xy-plane. If the coordinates (η, θ, ϕ) of the prolate spheroidal system are related to the rectangular coordinates by

$$x = A \sinh \eta \sin \theta \cos \phi$$

$$y = \sinh \eta \sin \theta \sin \phi$$

$$z = A \cosh \eta \cos \theta$$

show that the scale factors are given by

$$a_1 \equiv a_\eta = A(\sin^2 \theta + \sinh^2 \eta)^{1/2}$$

$$a_2 \equiv a_\theta = A(\sin^2 \theta + \sinh^2 \eta)^{1/2}$$

$$a_3 \equiv a_\phi = A \sinh \eta \sin \theta$$

1-7 Using the scale factors determined in the problem (1-6), show that the expression for $\nabla^2 T$ in the prolate spheroidal coordinates (η, θ, ϕ) is given as

$$\nabla^2 T = \frac{1}{A^2(\sinh^2 \eta + \sin^2 \theta)} \left[\frac{\partial^2 T}{\partial \eta^2} + \coth \eta \frac{\partial T}{\partial \eta} + \frac{\partial^2 T}{\partial \theta^2} + \cot \theta \frac{\partial T}{\partial \theta} \right]$$
$$+ \frac{1}{A^2 \sinh^2 \eta \sin^2 \theta} \frac{\partial^2 T}{\partial \phi^2}$$

1-8 Obtain expressions for elemental areas dA cut from the surfaces η = constant, θ = constant, and ϕ = constant, and also for an elemental volume element dV in the prolate spheroidal coordinate system (η, θ, ϕ) discussed above.

1-9 The coordinates (η, θ, ϕ) of an *oblate spheroidal* coordinate system are related to the rectangular coordinates by

$$x = A \cosh \eta \sin \theta \cos \phi$$

$$y = A \cosh \eta \sin \theta \sin \theta$$

$$z = A \sinh \eta \cos \theta$$

Show that the scale factors are given by

$$a_1^2 \equiv a_\eta^2 = A^2(\cosh^2 \eta - \sin^2 \theta)$$

$$a_2^2 \equiv a_\theta^2 = A^2(\cosh^2 \eta - \sin^2 \theta)$$

$$a_3^2 \equiv a_\phi^2 = A^2 \cosh^2 \eta \sin^2 \theta$$

1-10 Using the scale factors in the problem (1-9) show that the expression for $\nabla^2 T$ in the oblate spheroidal coordinate system (η, θ, ϕ) is given by

$$\nabla^2 T = \frac{1}{A^2 (\cosh^2 \eta - \sin^2 \theta)} \left[\frac{\partial^2 T}{\partial \eta^2} + \tanh \eta \frac{\partial T}{\partial \eta} + \frac{\partial^2 T}{\partial \theta^2} + \cot \theta \frac{\partial T}{\partial \theta} \right]$$

$$+ \frac{1}{A^2 \cosh^2 \eta \sin^2 \theta} \frac{\partial^2 T}{\partial \phi^2}$$

1-11 Show that the following three different forms of the differential operator in the spherical coordinate system are equivalent.

$$\frac{1}{r^2} \frac{d}{dr}\left(r^2 \frac{dT}{dr} \right) = \frac{1}{r} \frac{d^2}{dr^2}(rT) = \frac{d^2 T}{dr^2} + \frac{2}{r} \frac{dT}{dr}$$

1-12 Set up the mathematical formulation of the following heat conduction problems:

1. A slab in $0 \le x \le L$ is initially at a temperature $F(x)$. For times $t > 0$, the boundary at $x = 0$ is kept insulated and the boundary at $x = L$ dissipates heat by convection into a medium at zero temperature.

2. A semi-infinite region $0 \le x < \infty$ is initially at a temperature $F(x)$. For times $t > 0$, heat is generated in the medium at a constant rate of g_0 W/m^3, while the boundary at $x = 0$ is kept at zero temperature.

3. A solid cylinder $0 \le r \le b$ is initially at a temperature $F(r)$. For times $t > 0$, heat is generated in the medium at a rate of $g(r)$, W/m^3, while the boundary at $r = b$ dissipates heat by convection into a medium at zero temperature.

4. A solid sphere $0 \le r \le b$ is initially at temperature $F(r)$. For times $t > 0$, heat is generated in the medium at a rate of $g(r)$, W/m^3, while the boundary at $r = b$ is kept at a uniform temperature T_0.

CHAPTER 2

THE SEPARATION OF VARIABLES IN THE RECTANGULAR COORDINATE SYSTEM

The method of separation of variables has been widely used in the solution of heat-conduction problems. The homogeneous problems are readily handled with this method. The multidimensional steady-state heat-conduction problems with no generation can also be solved with this method if only one of the boundary conditions is nonhomogeneous; problems involving more than one nonhomogeneous boundary conditions can be split up into simpler problems each containing only one nonhomogeneous boundary condition. In this chapter we discuss the general problem of the separability of the heat-conduction equation; examine the separation in the rectangular coordinate system; determine the elementary solutions, the norms, and the eigenvalues of the resulting separated equations for different combinations of boundary conditions and present these results systematically in a tabulated form for ready reference; examine the solution of one and multidimensional homogeneous problems by the method of separation of variables; examine the solution of multidimensional steady-state heat-conduction problems with and without heat generation; and describe the splitting up of a nonhomogeneous problem into a set of simpler problems that can be solved by the separation of variable technique. The reader should consult references [1]–[4] for a discussion of the mathematical aspects of the method of separation of variables and references [5]–[8] for additional applications on the solution of heat-conduction problems.

2-1 METHOD OF SEPARATION OF VARIABLES

To illustrate the basic concepts associated with the method of separation of variables we consider a homogeneous boundary-value problem of heat

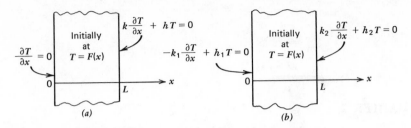

Fig. 2-1 Heat conduction in a slab.

conduction for a slab in $0 \le x \le L$. Initially the slab is at a temperature $T = F(x)$, and for times $t > 0$ the boundary surface at $x = 0$ is kept insulated while the boundary at $x = L$ dissipates heat by convection with a heat-transfer coefficient h into a medium at zero temperature. There is no heat generation in the medium. The mathematical formulation of this problem is given as (see Fig. 2-1a)

$$\frac{\partial^2 T(x,t)}{\partial x^2} = \frac{1}{\alpha}\frac{\partial T(x,t)}{\partial t} \qquad \text{in } 0 < x < L \qquad t > 0 \qquad (2\text{-}1a)$$

$$\frac{\partial T}{\partial x} = 0 \qquad \text{at } x = 0 \qquad t > 0 \qquad (2\text{-}1b)$$

$$k\frac{\partial T}{\partial x} + hT = 0 \qquad \text{at } x = L \qquad t > 0 \qquad (2\text{-}1c)$$

$$T = F(x) \qquad \text{for } t = 0 \qquad 0 \le x \le L \qquad (2\text{-}1d)$$

To solve this problem we assume the separation of function $T(x,t)$ into a space- and time-dependent functions in the form

$$T(x,t) = X(x)\Gamma(t) \qquad (2\text{-}2)$$

The substituting of equation (2-2) into equation (2-1a) yields

$$\frac{1}{X(x)}\frac{d^2 X(x)}{dx^2} = \frac{1}{\alpha \Gamma(t)}\frac{d\Gamma(t)}{dt} \qquad (2\text{-}3)$$

In this equation, the left-hand side is a function of the space variable x, alone, and the right-hand side of the time variable t, alone; the only way this equality holds if both sides are equal to the same constant, say $-\beta^2$; thus, we have

$$\frac{1}{X(x)}\frac{d^2 X(x)}{dx^2} = \frac{1}{\alpha \Gamma(t)}\frac{d\Gamma(t)}{dt} = -\beta^2 \qquad (2\text{-}4)$$

Then, the function $\Gamma(t)$ satisfies the differential equation

$$\frac{d\Gamma(t)}{dt} + \alpha\beta^2\Gamma(t) = 0 \tag{2-5}$$

which has a solution in the form

$$\Gamma(t) = e^{-\alpha\beta^2 t} \tag{2-6}$$

Here, we note that the negative sign chosen above for β^2 now ensures that the solution $\Gamma(t)$ approaches zero as time increases indefinitely because both α and t are positive quantities. This is consistent with the physical reality for the problem (2-1) in that the temperature tends to zero as $t \to \infty$.

The space-variable function $X(x)$ satisfies the differential equation

$$\frac{d^2 X(x)}{dx^2} + \beta^2 X(x) = 0 \qquad \text{in } 0 < x < L \tag{2-7a}$$

The boundary conditions for this equation are obtained by introducing the separated solution (2-2) into the boundary conditions (2-1b) and (2-1c); we find

$$\frac{dX}{dx} = 0 \qquad\qquad \text{at } x = 0 \tag{2-7b}$$

$$k\frac{dX}{dx} + hX = 0 \qquad \text{at } x = L \tag{2-7c}$$

The auxiliary problem defined by equations (2-7) is called an *eigenvalue problem*, because it has solutions only for certain values of the separation parameter $\beta = \beta_m, m = 1, 2, 3, \ldots$, which are called the *eigenvalues*; the corresponding solution $X(\beta_m, x)$ are called the *eigenfunctions* of the problem. When β is not an eigenvalue, that is, when $\beta \neq \beta_m$, the problem has trivial solutions (i.e., $X = 0$ if $\beta \neq \beta_m$). We now assume that these eigenfunctions $X(\beta_m, x)$ and the eigenvalues β_m are available and proceed to the solution of the above heat conduction problem. The complete solution for the temperature $T(x, t)$ is constructed by a linear superposition of the above separated elementary solutions in the form

$$T(x, t) = \sum_{m=1}^{\infty} c_m X(\beta_m, x) e^{-\alpha\beta_m^2 t} \tag{2-8}$$

This solution satisfies both the differential equation (2-1a) and the boundary conditions (2-1b) and (2-1c) of the heat-conduction problem, but it does not necessarily satisfy the initial condition (2-1d). Therefore, the application of the initial condition to equation (2-8) yields

$$F(x) = \sum_{m=1}^{\infty} c_m X(\beta_m, x) \qquad \text{in } 0 < x < L \tag{2-9}$$

This result is a representation of an arbitrary function $F(x)$ defined in the interval $0 < x < L$ in terms of the eigenfunctions $X(\beta_m, x)$ of the eigenvalue problem (2-7). The unknown coefficients c_m's can be determined by making use of the orthogonality of the eigenfunctions given as

$$\int_0^L X(\beta_m, x) X(\beta_n, x)\, dx = \begin{cases} 0 & \text{for } m \neq n \\ N(\beta_m) & \text{for } m = n \end{cases} \tag{2-10}$$

where, the *normalization integral* (or the *norm*), $N(\beta_m)$, is defined as

$$N(\beta_m) = \int_0^L [X(\beta_m, x)]^2\, dx \tag{2-11}$$

The eigenvalue problem given by equations (2-7) is a special case of a more general eigenvalue problem called the *Sturm-Liouville* problem. We present a discussion of the orthogonality property of the Sturm-Liouville problem in Note 1.*

To determine the coefficients c_m we operate on both sides of equation (2-9) by the operator $\int_0^L X(\beta_n, x)\, dx$ and utilize the orthogonality property given by equations (2-10); we find

$$c_m = \frac{1}{N(\beta_m)} \int_0^L X(\beta_m, x) F(x)\, dx \tag{2-12}$$

The substitution of equation (2-12) into equation (2-8) yields the solution for the temperature as

$$T(x, t) = \sum_{m=1}^{\infty} e^{-\alpha \beta_m^2 t} \frac{1}{N(\beta_m)} X(\beta_m, x) \int_0^L X(\beta_m, x') F(x')\, dx' \tag{2-13}$$

Thus the temperature distribution in the medium can be determined as a function of position and time from equation (2-13) once the explicit expressions are available for the eigenfunctions $X(\beta_m, x)$, the eigenvalues β_m and the norm $N(\beta_m)$. This matter will be discussed later in this chapter.

The method of separation of variables illustrated above for the solution of the one-dimensional homogeneous heat-conduction problem is now formally generalized to the solution of the following three-dimensional homogeneous problem

$$\nabla^2 T(\mathbf{r}, t) = \frac{1}{\alpha} \frac{\partial T(\mathbf{r}, t)}{\partial t} \qquad \text{in region } R, t > 0 \tag{2-14}$$

$$k_i \frac{\partial T}{\partial n_i} + h_i T = 0 \qquad \text{on boundary } S_i, t > 0 \tag{2-15a}$$

$$T(\mathbf{r}, t) = F(\mathbf{r}) \qquad \text{for } t = 0, \text{ in region } R \tag{2-15b}$$

*Notes are at the end of the chapter.

where $\partial/\partial n_i$ denotes differentiation along the outward-drawn normal to the boundary surface S_i and $\mathbf{r}$ denotes the general space coordinate. It is assumed that the region R has a number of continuous boundary surfaces $S_i, i = 1, 2, \ldots, s$ in number, such that each boundary surface S_i fits the coordinate surface of the chosen orthogonal coordinate system. Clearly the slab problem considered above is obtainable as a special case from this more general problem; that is, the slab has two continuous boundary surfaces one at $x = 0$ and the other at $x = L$. The boundary conditions for the slab problem are readily obtainable from the general boundary condition (2-15a) by choosing the coefficients h_i and k_i, accordingly.

To solve the above general problem we assume a separation in the form

$$T(\mathbf{r}, t) = \psi(\mathbf{r})\Gamma(t) \tag{2-16}$$

where function $\psi(\mathbf{r})$ is, in general, depends on three space variables. We substitute equation (2-16) into equation (2-14) and carry out the analysis with a similar argument as discussed above to obtain

$$\frac{1}{\psi(\mathbf{r})} \nabla^2 \psi(\mathbf{r}) = \frac{1}{\alpha\Gamma(t)} \frac{d\Gamma(t)}{dt} = -\lambda^2 \tag{2-17}$$

where λ is the separation variable. Clearly, the function $\Gamma(t)$ satisfies an ordinary differential equation of the same form as equation (2-5) and its solution is taken as $\exp(-\alpha\lambda^2 t)$. The space-variable function $\psi(\mathbf{r})$ satisfies the following auxiliary problem

$$\nabla^2 \psi(\mathbf{r}) + \lambda^2 \psi(\mathbf{r}) = 0 \qquad \text{in region } R \tag{2-18a}$$

$$k_i \frac{\partial \psi}{\partial n_i} + h_i \psi = 0 \qquad \text{on boundary } S_i \tag{2-18b}$$

where $i = 1, 2, \ldots, s$ in number. The differential equation (2-18a) is called the *Helmholtz* equation, and it is a partial differential equation, in general, in the three space variables. The solution of this partial differential equation is essential for the solution of the above heat-conduction problem. The *Helmholtz* equation (2-18a) can be solved by the method of separation of variables provided that its separation into a set or ordinary differential equation is possible. Therefore the separability of the Helmholtz equation has been studied in the literature and it has been shown that a simple separation of the Helmholtz equation (also of the Laplace equation) into ordinary differential equations is possible in eleven orthogonal coordinate system. We list in Table 2-1 these eleven orthogonal coordinate systems and also indicate the type of functions that may appear as solutions of the separated functions [1, 3, 9]. A detailed discussion of the separation of the Helmholtz equation will be presented in this chapter for the rectangular coordinate

Table 2-1   Orthogonal Coordinate Systems Allowing Simple
Separation of the Helmholtz and Laplace Equations*

Coordinate System	Functions that Appear in Solution
1 Rectangular	Exponential, circular, hyperbolic
2 Circular-cylinder	Bessel, exponential, circular
3 Elliptic-cylinder	Mathieu, circular
4 Parabolic-cylinder	Weber, circular
5 Spherical	Legendre, power, circular
6 Prolate spheroidal	Legendre, circular
7 Oblate spheroidal	Legendre, circular
8 Parabolic	Bessel, circular
9 Conical	Lamé, power
10 Ellipsoidal	Lamé
11 Paraboloidal	Baer

*From references [1, 3, 9].

system and in the following two chapters for the cylindrical and shperical coordinate systems. The reader should consult reference [10] for the definition of various functions listed in Table 2-1.

2-2   SEPARATION OF THE HEAT-CONDUCTION EQUATION IN THE RECTANGULAR COORDINATE SYSTEM

Consider the three-dimensional, homogeneous heat-conduction equation in the rectangular coordinate system

$$\frac{\partial^2 T}{\partial x^2} + \frac{\partial^2 T}{\partial y^2} + \frac{\partial^2 T}{\partial z^2} = \frac{1}{\alpha}\frac{\partial T}{\partial t} \qquad \text{where } T \equiv T(x, y, z, t) \qquad (2\text{-}19)$$

Assume a separation of variables in the form

$$T(x, y, z, t) = \psi(x, y, z)\Gamma(t) \qquad (2\text{-}20)$$

Equation (2-19) becomes

$$\frac{1}{\psi}\left(\frac{\partial^2 \psi}{\partial x^2} + \frac{\partial^2 \psi}{\partial y^2} + \frac{\partial^2 \psi}{\partial z^2}\right) = \frac{1}{\alpha\Gamma(t)}\frac{d\Gamma(t)}{dt} = -\lambda^2 \qquad (2\text{-}21)$$

Then, the separated functions $\Gamma(t)$ and ψ satisfy the equations

$$\frac{d\Gamma(t)}{dt} + \alpha\lambda^2\Gamma(t) = 0 \qquad (2\text{-}22)$$

$$\frac{\partial^2 \psi}{\partial x^2} + \frac{\partial^2 \psi}{\partial y^2} + \frac{\partial^2 \psi}{\partial z^2} + \lambda^2\psi = 0 \qquad (2\text{-}23)$$

Equation (2-23) is the Helmholtz equation; we assume a separation in the form

$$\psi(x, y, z) = X(x)Y(y)Z(z) \tag{2-24}$$

The substitution of equation (2-24) into equation (2-23) yields

$$\frac{1}{X}\frac{d^2X}{dx^2} + \frac{1}{Y}\frac{d^2Y}{dy^2} + \frac{1}{Z}\frac{d^2Z}{dz^2} + \lambda^2 = 0 \tag{2-25}$$

Here, since each term is a function of a single independent variable, the only way this equality is satisfied is if each term is equated to an arbitrary separation constant, say, in the form

$$\frac{1}{X}\frac{d^2X}{dx^2} = -\beta^2, \qquad \frac{1}{Y}\frac{d^2Y}{dy^2} = -\gamma^2, \qquad \text{and} \qquad \frac{1}{Z}\frac{d^2Z}{dz^2} = -\eta^2 \tag{2-26}$$

Then the separated equations become

$$\frac{d^2X}{dx^2} + \beta^2 X = 0 \tag{2-27a}$$

$$\frac{d^2Y}{dy^2} + \gamma^2 Y = 0 \tag{2-27b}$$

$$\frac{d^2Z}{dz^2} + \eta^2 Z = 0 \tag{2-27c}$$

where

$$\beta^2 + \gamma^2 + \eta^2 = \lambda^2 \tag{2-27d}$$

Clearly, the solutions of the separated equations for the functions X, Y, and Z are sines and cosines, and the solution of equation (2-22) for the function $\Gamma(t)$ is given as

$$\Gamma(t) = e^{-\alpha(\beta^2 + \gamma^2 + \eta^2)t} \tag{2-28}$$

The complete solution for the temperature $T(x, y, z, t)$ is constructed by a linear superposition of the separated solutions X, Y, Z, and Γ. When the region is finite, say, in the x direction, the separation constant β associated with it takes discrete values and the superposition of the separated solutions for the x variable is performed by summation over all permissible values of β_m. On the other hand, when the region is infinite or semi-infinite, the separation constant assumes all values from zero to infinity continuously and superposition is done by integration over all values of β. In the following sections we examine the explicit functional forms of the separated solutions for finite, semi-infinite, and infinite regions. The elementary solutions obtained in this manner are tabulated systematically for ready reference in the solution of heat-conduction problems by the method of separation of variables.

2-3 ONE-DIMENSIONAL HOMOGENEOUS PROBLEMS IN A FINITE MEDIUM

Here we consider the application of the method of separation of variables to the solution of the homogeneous boundary-value problem of heat-conduction for a slab. That is, a slab, $0 \leq x \leq L$, initially at a temperature $F(x)$, dissipates heat by convection for times $t > 0$ from its boundary surfaces into an environment at zero temperature as illustrated in Fig. 2-1b. For generality we assumed that the heat-transfer coefficients at the two boundaries are not the same. The mathematical formulation of this problem is given as

$$\frac{\partial^2 T(x,t)}{\partial x^2} = \frac{1}{\alpha}\frac{\partial T(x,t)}{\partial t} \qquad \text{in } 0 < x < L, \ t > 0 \qquad (2\text{-}29a)$$

$$-k_1\frac{\partial T}{\partial x} + h_1 T = 0 \qquad \text{at } x = 0, \ t > 0 \qquad (2\text{-}29b)$$

$$k_2\frac{\partial T}{\partial x} + h_2 T = 0 \qquad \text{at } x = L, \ t > 0 \qquad (2\text{-}29c)$$

$$T = F(x) \qquad \text{for } t = 0, \ \text{in } 0 \leq x \leq L \qquad (2\text{-}29d)$$

Clearly, the heat-conduction problem for a slab for other combinations of boundary conditions are readily obtainable as special cases from the problem considered here by setting any one of the coefficients k_1, k_2, h_1, and h_2 equal to zero. Nine different combinations of these boundary conditions are possible including the one given above.

We assume a separation in the form

$$T(x,t) = X(x)\Gamma(t) \qquad (2\text{-}30)$$

and separate the equation in a manner described above. The solution for the function $\Gamma(t)$ is given as

$$\Gamma(t) = e^{-\alpha\beta^2 t} \qquad (2\text{-}31)$$

and the space-variable function $X(\beta, x)$ satisfies the following eigenvalue problem

$$\frac{d^2 X(x)}{dx^2} + \beta^2 X(x) = 0 \qquad \text{in } 0 < x < L \qquad (2\text{-}32a)$$

$$-k_1 \frac{dX}{dx} + h_1 X = 0 \qquad \text{at } x = 0 \qquad (2\text{-}32\text{b})$$

$$k_2 \frac{dX}{dx} + h_2 X = 0 \qquad \text{at } x = L \qquad (2\text{-}32\text{c})$$

This problem is a special case of the Sturm-Liouville problem discussed in Note 1, with $p(x) = 1, w(x) = 1, q(x) = 0$, and $\lambda = \beta^2$. Then, the eigenfunctions $X(\beta_m, x)$ are orthogonal, that is

$$\int_0^L X(\beta_m, x) X(\beta_n, x) \, dx = \begin{cases} 0 & \text{for } m \neq n \\ N(\beta_m) & \text{for } m = n \end{cases} \qquad (2\text{-}33)$$

The solution of the problem (2-29) is now constructed as

$$T(x, t) = \sum_{m=1}^{\infty} c_m X(\beta_m, x) e^{-\alpha \beta_m^2 t} \qquad (2\text{-}34)$$

The application of the initial condition (2-29d) gives

$$F(x) = \sum_{m=1}^{\infty} c_m X(\beta_m, x) \qquad \text{in } 0 < x < L \qquad (2\text{-}35\text{a})$$

This is a representation of an arbitrary function $F(x)$ defined in the interval $0 < x < L$ in terms of the eigenfunction $X(\beta_m, x)$ of the eigenvalue problem (2-32). Suppose such a representation is permissible, the coefficients c_m can be determined by operating on both sides of equation (2-35a) by the operator $\int_0^L X(\beta_m, x) \, dx$ and utlizing the orthogonality property of the eigenfunctions. We find

$$c_m = \frac{1}{N(\beta_m)} \int_0^L X(\beta_m, x') F(x') \, dx' \qquad (2\text{-}35\text{b})$$

where the *norm* N is defined as

$$N(\beta_m) = \int_0^L [X(\beta_m, x)]^2 \, dx \qquad (2\text{-}35\text{c})$$

The substitution of equation (2-35b) into equation (2-34) yields the solution for the temperature $T(x, t)$ as

$$T(x, t) = \sum_{m=1}^{\infty} e^{-\alpha \beta_m^2 t} \frac{1}{N(\beta_m)} X(\beta_m, x) \int_0^L X(\beta_m, x') F(x') \, dx' \qquad (2\text{-}36)$$

This solution is valid for times $t > 0$; as $t \to 0$ it approaches to the initial value of the temperature in the medium. Therefore, by substituting $t = 0$ in equation (2-36), we obtain

$$F(x) = \sum_{m=1}^{\infty} \frac{1}{N(\beta_m)} X(\beta_m, x) \int_0^L X(\beta_m, x') F(x') dx' \qquad \text{in } 0 < x < L \quad (2\text{-}37)$$

This equation is a representation of an arbitrary function $F(x)$ defined in the interval $0 < x < L$ in terms of the eigenfunctions $X(\beta_m, x)$ of the eigenvalue problem given by equations (2-32). The general problem of determining under what conditions an arbitrary function $F(x)$ can be expanded in terms of such functions has been investigated [4, 11, 12] and the general conditions on the behavior of $F(x)$ have been established. It is shown that the series in equation (2-37) does converge to $F(x)$ at each point x on the interval $0 < x < L$ where $F(x)$ is continuous, provided that $F(x)$ and dF/dx are *sectionally continuous* on the interval $(0, L)$. (See reference [4], p. 54, or reference [11], p. 5, for the definition of sectionally continuous function.) Thus, the representation given by equation (2-37) is valid. Then, the solution given by equation (2-36) is the solution of the heat-conduction problem (2-29) since it satisfies the differential equation, its boundary and initial conditions.

To complete the solution (2-36), explicit expressions are needed for the eigenfunction $X(\beta_m, x)$, the eigenvalues β_m, and the norm $N(\beta_m)$. The details of their derivation are given in Note 2; we present the results here.

The eigenfunctions $X(\beta_m, x)$ of the eigenvalue problem (2-32) are given as

$$X(\beta_m, x) = \beta_m \cos \beta_m x + H_1 \sin \beta_m x \qquad (2\text{-}38a)$$

where the eigenvalues β_m are the roots of the following transcendental equation

$$\tan \beta_m L = \frac{\beta_m (H_1 + H_2)}{\beta_m^2 - H_1 H_2} \qquad (2\text{-}38b)$$

and the norm $N(\beta_m)$ is given by

$$N(\beta_m) = \frac{1}{2} \left[(\beta_m^2 + H_1^2) \left(L + \frac{H_2}{\beta_m^2 + H_2^2} \right) + H_1 \right] \qquad (2\text{-}38c)$$

where

$$H_1 \equiv \frac{h_1}{k_1} \qquad \text{and} \qquad H_2 \equiv \frac{h_2}{k_2} \qquad (2\text{-}39)$$

The results given by equations (2-38) are for the general case when the boundary conditions at $x = 0$ and $x = L$ are of the third kind as in equations (2-32). Eight other different combinations of boundary conditions are also possible; the results for such cases are obtainable from equations (2-38) by setting H_1, H_2 equal to zero or infinity. We list in Table 2-2 the eigenfunctions

Table 2-2 The Solution $X(\beta_m, x)$, the Norm $N(\beta_m)$ and the Eigenvalues β_m of the Differential Equation

$$\frac{d^2X(x)}{dx^2} + \beta^2 X(x) = 0 \quad \text{in} \quad 0 < x < L$$

Subject to the Boundary Conditions Shown in the Table

No	Boundary Condition at $x=0$	Boundary Condition at $x=L$	$X(\beta_m, x)$	$1/N(\beta_m)$	Eigenvalues β_m's are Positive Roots of
1	$-\dfrac{dX}{dx} + H_1 X = 0$	$\dfrac{dX}{dx} + H_2 X = 0$	$\beta_m \cos\beta_m x + H_1 \sin\beta_m x$	$2\left[(\beta_m^2 + H_1^2)\left(L + \dfrac{H_2}{\beta_m^2 + H_2^2}\right) + H_1\right]^{-1}$	$\tan\beta_m L = \dfrac{\beta_m(H_1 + H_2)}{\beta_m^2 - H_1 H_2}$
2	$-\dfrac{dX}{dx} + H_1 X = 0$	$\dfrac{dX}{dx} = 0$	$\cos\beta_m(L-x)$	$2\dfrac{\beta_m^2 + H_1^2}{L(\beta_m^2 + H_1^2) + H_1}$	$\beta_m \tan\beta_m L = H_1$
3	$-\dfrac{dX}{dx} + H_1 X = 0$	$X = 0$	$\sin\beta_m(L-x)$	$2\dfrac{\beta_m^2 + H_1^2}{L(\beta_m^2 + H_1^2) + H_1}$	$\beta_m \cot\beta_m L = -H_1$
4	$\dfrac{dX}{dx} = 0$	$\dfrac{dX}{dx} + H_2 X = 0$	$\cos\beta_m x$	$2\dfrac{\beta_m^2 + H_2^2}{L(\beta_m^2 + H_2^2) + H_2}$	$\beta_m \tan\beta_m L = H_2$
5	$\dfrac{dX}{dx} = 0$	$\dfrac{dX}{dx} = 0$	$*\cos\beta_m x$	$\dfrac{2}{L}$ for $\beta_m \neq 0$; $\dfrac{1}{L}$ for $\beta_0 = 0*$	$\sin\beta_m L = 0*$
6	$\dfrac{dX}{dx} = 0$	$X = 0$	$\cos\beta_m x$	$\dfrac{2}{L}$	$\cos\beta_m L = 0$
7	$X = 0$	$\dfrac{dX}{dx} + H_2 X = 0$	$\sin\beta_m x$	$2\dfrac{\beta_m^2 + H_2^2}{L(\beta_m^2 + H_2^2) + H_2}$	$\beta_m \cot\beta_m L = -H_2$
8	$X = 0$	$\dfrac{dX}{dx} = 0$	$\sin\beta_m x$	$\dfrac{2}{L}$	$\cos\beta_m L = 0$
9	$X = 0$	$X = 0$	$\sin\beta_m x$	$\dfrac{2}{L}$	$\sin\beta_m L = 0$

*For this particular case $\beta_0 = 0$ is also an eigenvalue corresponding to $X = 1$.

$X(\beta_m, x)$, the eigenvalues β_m, and the norm $N(\beta_m)$ of the differential equation (2-32a) for the nine different combinations of boundary conditions at $x = 0$ and $x = L$. We note that, in this table, for the case of boundary condition of the second kind both at $x = 0$ and $x = L$ (i.e., case 5), $\beta_0 = 0$ is also an eigenvalue corresponding to $X(\beta_0, x) = \text{constant} = 1$; the reader should consult Note 3 for a discussion of this special case.

The solution of the homogeneous heat-conduction problem for a slab given by equations (2-29) is immediately obtainable from equation (2-36) for the nine different combinations of boundary conditions at $x = 0$ and $x = L$ if $X(\beta_m, x), \beta_m$, and $N(\beta_m)$ are taken from Table 2-2 accordingly.

To give an idea of the distribution of the eigenvalues β_m of the transcendental equation (2-38b) we consider the case $H_1 = H_2 \equiv H$ and write this equation in the form

$$\cot \xi = \frac{1}{2}\left(\frac{\xi}{B} - \frac{B}{\xi}\right) \equiv Z \tag{2-40}$$

where $\xi = \beta L$ and $B = HL$. In this equation

$$Z = \frac{1}{2}\left(\frac{\xi}{B} - \frac{B}{\xi}\right)$$

represents a hyperbola whose center is at the origin and its asymptotes are $\xi = 0$ and $Z = \xi/2B$; the curves $Z = \cot \xi$ represents a set of cotangent curves as illustrated in Fig. 2-2. The values of ξ corresponding to the intersections of this hyperbola with the cotangent curves are the roots of the transcendental equation (2-40). Clearly there are an infinite number of such points, each successively located in intervals $(0 - \pi)$, $(\pi - 2\pi)$, $(2\pi - 3\pi)$, ... Because of symmetry, the negative roots are equal in absolute value to the positive ones; therefore, only the positive roots need to be considered in the solution since the solution remains unaffected by the sign of the root.

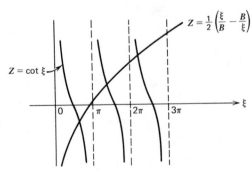

Fig. 2-2   Geometrical representation of the roots of $\cot \xi = (\frac{1}{2})[(\xi/B) - (B/\xi)]$.

The transcendental equation in the form

$$\xi \tan \xi = c \qquad (2\text{-}41a)$$

$$\xi \cot \xi = -c \qquad (2\text{-}41b)$$

also appear in Table 2-2. We present in Appendix I the first six roots of the transcendental equations (2-41) for different values of the parameter c. If more roots are needed, they can be calculated numerically. For example, to determine the roots of equation (2-41a), this equation is written in the form $\xi \tan \xi - c \equiv \varepsilon$ and calculations are performed with small increments in $\Delta \xi$ for each discrete value of ξ until ε changes sign. A root must lie somewhere in the interval $\Delta \xi$ over which ε changes sign. A *Newton-Raphson* method or the method of *Regula Falsi*, which are well documented in the texts on numerical analysis, may be used to determine to any desired degree of accuracy the value of ξ in the interval $\Delta \xi$ where $\varepsilon \to 0$. The reader should consult reference [13] for the computation of the roots of the transcendental equations by numerical means. Recently, analytic solutions have been developed [15] for the determination of the roots of the transcendental equations (2-41).

Example 2-1. A slab in $0 \le x \le L$ is initially at a temperature $F(x)$; for times $t > 0$, the boundary at $x = 0$ is kept insulated and the boundary at $x = L$ dissipates heat by convection into a medium at zero temperature, that is

$$\frac{\partial T}{\partial x} = 0 \quad \text{at} \quad x = 0 \quad \text{and} \quad \frac{\partial T}{\partial x} + H_2 T = 0 \quad \text{at} \quad x = L$$

Obtain an expression for the temperature distribution $T(x, t)$ in the slab. Also consider the case when $F(x) = T_0 = $ constant.

Solution. The boundary conditions for this problem correspond to case 4 in Table 2-2. Therefore, when the eigenfunctions $X(\beta_m, x)$ and the norm $N(\beta_m)$ are obtained from this table and introduced into equation (2-36), the solution becomes

$$T(x, t) = 2 \sum_{m=1}^{\infty} e^{-\alpha \beta_m^2 t} \frac{\beta_m^2 + H_2^2}{L(\beta_m^2 + H_2^2) + H_2} \cos \beta_m x \int_{x'=0}^{L} F(x') \cos \beta_m x' \, dx' \quad (2\text{-}42a)$$

where β_m's are the positive roots of

$$\beta_m \tan \beta_m L = H_2 \qquad (2\text{-}42b)$$

For the special case of $F(x) = T_0 = $ constant, the integration in equation

(2-42) can be performed and the solution reduces to

$$T(x,t) = 2T_0 \sum_{m=1}^{\infty} e^{-\alpha\beta_m^2 t} \frac{\beta_m^2 + H_2^2}{L(\beta_m^2 + H_2^2) + H_2} \frac{\sin \beta_m L}{\beta_m} \cos \beta_m x \qquad (2\text{-}43\text{a})$$

and by making use of the transcendental equation (2-42b) this result is written as

$$T(x,t) = 2T_0 \sum_{m=1}^{\infty} e^{-\alpha\beta_m^2 t} \frac{H_2}{L(\beta_m^2 + H_2^2) + H_2} \frac{\cos \beta_m x}{\cos \beta_m L} \qquad (2\text{-}43\text{b})$$

For times $t = 0$, equation (2-43b) simplifies to

$$1 = 2 \sum_{m=1}^{\infty} \frac{H_2}{L(\beta_m^2 + H_2^2) + H_2} \frac{\cos \beta_m x}{\cos \beta_m L} \qquad (2\text{-}44)$$

which is a formal representation of unity in the interval $0 < x < L$ in terms of the eigenfunctions $\cos \beta_m x$ of the considered heat-conduction problem.

Example 2-2. A slab, $0 \leq x \leq L$, is initially at a temperature $F(x)$, for times $t > 0$ the boundaries at $x = 0$ and $x = L$ are kept insulated, that is, $\partial T/\partial x = 0$ at $x = 0$ and $x = L$. Obtain an expression for the temperature distribution $T(x,t)$ in the slab.

Solution. The boundary conditions for this problem correspond to case 5 in Table 2-2. Obtaining $X(\beta_m, x)$ and $N(\beta_m)$ from this table and introducing them into equation (2-36) and noting that for this special case $\beta_0 = 0$ is also an eigenvalue, the solution of the problem becomes

$$T(x,t) = \frac{1}{L} \int_0^L F(x')\,dx' + \frac{2}{L} \sum_{m=1}^{\infty} e^{-\alpha\beta_m^2 t}$$

$$\cdot \cos \beta_m x \int_{x'=0}^{L} F(x') \cos \beta_m x'\,dx' \qquad (2\text{-}45)$$

where β_m's are the roots of $\sin \beta_m L = 0$ or given as $\beta_m = m\pi/L, m = 1, 2, 3, \ldots$. Here, the first term on the right-hand side of the equation results from the fact that $\beta_0 = 0$ is also an eigenvalue. The physical significance of this term is as follows: It represents the temperature in the solid as $t \to \infty$ (i.e., after the transients have passed); it is an arithmetic mean of the initial temperature over the region $0 \leq x \leq L$. This is to be expected by physical considerations, since heat cannot escape from the insulated boundaries, eventually the temperature equalizes over the region. See Chapter 13, equation (13-25b) for a more general expression for $T(x, \infty)$ when all boundaries of a finite region are insulated.

2-4 ONE-DIMENSIONAL HOMOGENEOUS PROBLEMS IN A SEMI-INFINITE MEDIUM

We now consider the solution of a homogeneous heat-conduction problem for a semi-infinite region. That is, a semi-infinite region, $0 \leq x < \infty$, is initially at a temperature $F(x)$ and for times $t > 0$ the boundary surface at $x = 0$ dissipates heat by convection into a medium at zero temperature as illustrated in Fig. 2-3. The mathematical formulation of this problem is given as

$$\frac{\partial^2 T(x,t)}{\partial x^2} = \frac{1}{\alpha}\frac{\partial T(x,t)}{\partial t} \qquad \text{in } 0 < x < \infty, \; t > 0 \qquad (2\text{-}46a)$$

$$-k_1 \frac{\partial T}{\partial x} + h_1 T = 0 \qquad \text{at } x = 0, \; t > 0 \qquad (2\text{-}46b)$$

$$T = F(x) \qquad \text{for } t = 0, \text{ in } 0 \leq x < \infty \qquad (2\text{-}46c)$$

We assume a separation in the form $T(x,t) = X(x)\Gamma(t)$; then, by separating the equations in a manner described previously, the solution for the function $\Gamma(t)$ is given as

$$\Gamma(t) = e^{-\alpha\beta^2 t} \qquad (2\text{-}47)$$

where β is the separation constant, and the space variable function $X(\beta, x)$ satisfies the following problem

$$\frac{d^2 X(x)}{dx^2} + \beta^2 X(x) = 0 \qquad \text{in } 0 < x < \infty \qquad (2\text{-}48a)$$

$$-k_1 \frac{dX(x)}{dx} + h_1 X(x) = 0 \qquad \text{at } x = 0 \qquad (2\text{-}48b)$$

The solution of equations (2-48) may be taken in the form

$$X(\beta, x) = \beta \cos \beta x + H_1 \sin \beta x \qquad (2\text{-}49a)$$

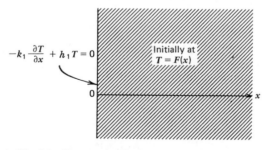

Fig. 2-3 Heat conduction in a semi-infinite region.

where

$$H_1 = \frac{h_1}{k_1} \tag{2-49b}$$

and the separation variable β assumes all values from zero to infinity continuously. The general solution for $T(x,t)$ is constructed by the superposition of all these elementary solutions by integrating over the value of β from zero to infinity

$$T(x,t) = \int_{\beta=0}^{\infty} c(\beta)e^{-\alpha\beta^2 t}(\beta \cos \beta x + H_1 \sin \beta x)\,d\beta \tag{2-50}$$

This solution satisfies the differential equation (2-46a) and its boundary condition (2-46b), but it does not necessarily satisfy the initial condition (2-46c). The application of the initial condition to equation (2-50) yields

$$F(x) = \int_{\beta=0}^{\infty} c(\beta)X(\beta,x)\,d\beta \qquad \text{in } 0 < x < \infty \tag{2-51}$$

where

$$X(\beta,x) = \beta \cos \beta x + H_1 \sin \beta x$$

This result is a representation of an arbitrary function $F(x)$ defined in the semi-infinite interval $0 < x < \infty$ in terms of the solution of the auxiliary problem defined by equations (2-48). A similar representation has been developed [11, p. 228] when solving the heat-conduction problem (2-46) by the Laplace transform technique, and that result may be expressed in the form

$$F(x) = \int_{\beta=0}^{\infty} X(\beta,x)\left[\frac{1}{N(\beta)}\int_{x'=0}^{\infty} X(\beta,x')F(x')\,dx'\right]d\beta \tag{2-52}$$

where

$$X(\beta,x) = \beta \cos \beta x + H_1 \sin \beta x \qquad \text{and} \qquad \frac{1}{N(\beta)} = \frac{2}{\pi}\frac{1}{\beta^2 + H_1^2}$$

The representation given by equation (2-52) is valid when $F(x)$ and dF/dx are sectionally continuous on each finite interval in the range $0 < x < \infty$, provided the integral $\int_0^{\infty} |F(x)|\,dx$ exists, if $F(x)$ is defined as its mean value at each point of discontinuity.

By comparing equations (2-51) and (2-52) we obtain the unknown coefficient $c(\beta)$ as

$$c(\beta) = \frac{1}{N(\beta)}\int_0^{\infty} X(\beta,x')F(x')\,dx' \tag{2-53}$$

where $N(\beta)$ and $X(\beta, x)$ are as defined previously. The substitution of equation (2-53) into equation (2-50) yields the solution for the heat-conduction problem (2-46) as

$$T(x, t) = \int_{\beta=0}^{\infty} e^{-\alpha\beta^2 t} \frac{1}{N(\beta)} X(\beta, x) \int_{x'=0}^{\infty} X(\beta, x')F(x')\, dx'\, d\beta \qquad (2\text{-}54)$$

where

$$X(\beta, x) = \beta \cos \beta x + H_1 \sin \beta x \qquad (2\text{-}55a)$$

$$\frac{1}{N(\beta)} = \frac{2}{\pi} \frac{1}{\beta^2 + H_1^2} \quad \text{and} \quad H_1 \equiv \frac{h_1}{k_1} \qquad (2\text{-}55b)$$

The functions $X(\beta, x)$ and $N(\beta)$ given by equations (2-55) are for a boundary condition of the third kind at $x = 0$. The boundary condition at $x = 0$ may also be of the second or the first kind. We list in Table 2-3 the functions $X(\beta, x)$ and $N(\beta)$ for these three different boundary conditions at $x = 0$. Thus, the solution of the homogeneous heat-conduction problem for a semi-infinite medium $0 \le x < \infty$ given by equations (2-46) is obtainable from equation (2-54) for the three different boundary conditions at $x = 0$ if $X(\beta, x)$ and $N(\beta)$ are taken from Table 2-3, accordingly.

Example 2-3. A semi-infinite region $0 \le x < \infty$ is initially at temperature $F(x)$. For time $t > 0$ the boundary at $x = 0$ is kept at zero temperature.

Table 2-3 The Solution $X(\beta, x)$ and the Norm $N(\beta)$ of the Differential Equation

$$\frac{d^2 X(x)}{dx^2} + \beta^2 X(x) = 0 \quad \text{in} \quad 0 < x < \infty$$

Subject to the Boundary Conditions Shown in the Table

No	Boundary Condition at $x = 0$	$X(\beta, x)$	$1/N(\beta)$
1	$-\dfrac{dX}{dx} + H_1 X = 0$	$\beta \cos \beta x + H_1 \sin \beta x$	$\dfrac{2}{\pi} \dfrac{1}{\beta^2 + H_1^2}$
2	$\dfrac{dX}{dx} = 0$	$\cos \beta x$	$\dfrac{2}{\pi}$
3	$X = 0$	$\sin \beta x$	$\dfrac{2}{\pi}$

Obtain an expression for the temperature distribution $T(x, t)$ in the medium. Also, examine the case when $F(x) = T_0 = \text{constant}$.

Solution. The boundary condition for this problem corresponds to case 3 in Table 2-3. Obtaining the functions $X(\beta, x)$ and $N(\beta)$ from this table and substituting in equation (2-54) the solution becomes

$$T(x, t) = \frac{2}{\pi} \int_{x'=0}^{\infty} F(x') \int_{\beta=0}^{\infty} e^{-\alpha\beta^2 t} \sin \beta x \sin \beta x' \, d\beta \, dx' \qquad (2\text{-}56)$$

The integration with respect to β is evaluated by making use of the following relations

$$2 \sin \beta x \sin \beta x' = \cos \beta(x - x') - \cos \beta(x + x') \qquad (2\text{-}57\text{a})$$

and from reference [16, , # 862.20] we have

$$\int_{\beta=0}^{\infty} e^{-\alpha\beta^2 t} \cos \beta(x - x') \, d\beta = \sqrt{\frac{\pi}{4\alpha t}} \cdot \exp\left[-\frac{(x - x')^2}{4\alpha t} \right] \qquad (2\text{-}57\text{b})$$

$$\int_{\beta=0}^{\infty} e^{-\alpha\beta^2 t} \cos \beta(x + x') \, d\beta = \sqrt{\frac{\pi}{4\alpha t}} \cdot \exp\left[-\frac{(x + x')^2}{4\alpha t} \right] \qquad (2\text{-}57\text{c})$$

Then

$$\frac{2}{\pi} \int_{\beta=0}^{\infty} e^{-\alpha\beta^2 t} \sin \beta x \sin \beta x' \, d\beta$$

$$= \frac{1}{(4\pi\alpha t)^{1/2}} \left[\exp\left(-\frac{(x - x')^2}{4\alpha t} \right) - \exp\left(-\frac{(x + x')^2}{3\alpha t} \right) \right] \qquad (2\text{-}57\text{d})$$

and the solution (2-56) becomes

$$T(x, t) = \frac{1}{(4\pi\alpha t)^{1/2}} \int_{x'=0}^{\infty} F(x') \left[\exp\left(-\frac{(x - x')^2}{4\alpha t} \right) - \exp\left(-\frac{(x + x')^2}{4\alpha t} \right) \right] dx'$$

$$(2\text{-}58)$$

For a constant initial temperature in the solid, $F(x) = T_0 = \text{constant}$, equation (2-58) becomes

$$\frac{T(x, t)}{T_0} = \frac{1}{(4\pi\alpha t)^{1/2}} \left[\int_{x'=0}^{\infty} \exp\left(-\frac{(x - x')^2}{4\alpha t} \right) dx' - \int_{x'=0}^{\infty} \exp\left(-\frac{(x + x')^2}{4\alpha t} \right) dx' \right]$$

$$(2\text{-}59)$$

Introducing the following new variables,

$$-\eta = \frac{x - x'}{\sqrt{4\alpha t}} \quad , \quad dx' = \sqrt{4\alpha t}\, d\eta \qquad \text{for the first integral}$$

$$\eta = \frac{x + x'}{\sqrt{4\alpha t}} \quad , \quad dx' = \sqrt{4\alpha t}\, d\eta \qquad \text{for the second integral}$$

equation (2-59) becomes

$$\frac{T(x,t)}{T_0} = \frac{1}{\sqrt{\pi}} \left[\int_{-x/\sqrt{4\alpha t}}^{\infty} e^{-\eta^2}\, d\eta - \int_{x/\sqrt{4\alpha t}}^{\infty} e^{-\eta^2}\, d\eta \right] \qquad (2\text{-}60)$$

Since $e^{-\eta^2}$ is symmetrical about $\eta = 0$, equation (2-60) is written in the form

$$\frac{T(x,t)}{T_0} = \frac{2}{\sqrt{\pi}} \int_{0}^{x/\sqrt{4\alpha t}} e^{-\eta^2}\, d\eta \qquad (2\text{-}61)$$

The right-hand side of equation (2-61) is called the *error function* of argument $x/\sqrt{4\alpha t}$ and the solution is expressed in the form

$$\frac{T(x,t)}{T_0} = \text{erf}\left(\frac{x}{\sqrt{4\alpha t}} \right) \qquad (2\text{-}62)$$

The values of the error functions are tabulated in Appendix II. Also included in this appendix is a brief discussion of the properties of the error function.

2-5 ONE-DIMENSIONAL HOMOGENEOUS PROBLEMS IN AN INFINITE MEDIUM

We now consider the homogeneous heat-conduction problem for a one-dimensional infinite medium, $-\infty < x < \infty$, which is initially at a temperature $F(x)$. We are interested in the determination of the temperature $T(x,t)$ of the medium for time $t > 0$. No boundary conditions are specified for the problem since the medium extends to infinity in both directions; but the problem consists of a boundedness condition on $T(x,t)$. The mathematical formulation is given as

$$\frac{\partial^2 T(x,t)}{\partial x^2} = \frac{1}{\alpha} \frac{\partial T(x,t)}{\partial t} \qquad \text{in} \ -\infty < x < \infty, \ t > 0 \qquad (2\text{-}63a)$$

$$T = F(x) \qquad \text{for } t = 0, \text{ in} -\infty < x < \infty \qquad (2\text{-}63b)$$

By separating the variables in the form $T(x,t) = X(x)\Gamma(t)$, the solution for the function $\Gamma(t)$ is given as

$$\Gamma(t) = e^{-\alpha\beta^2 t} \tag{2-64a}$$

and the function $X(x)$ satisfies the equation

$$\frac{d^2 X(x)}{dx^2} + \beta^2 X(x) = 0 \quad \text{in} \; -\infty < x < \infty \tag{2-64b}$$

Two linearly independent solutions of this equation are $\cos\beta x$ and $\sin\beta x$, corresponding to each value of β. As negative values of β generates no additional solutions, we consider only $\beta \geq 0$. The general solution of the heat-conduction problem is constructed by the superposition of $X(\beta, x)\Gamma(t)$ in the form

$$T(x, t) = \int_{\beta=0}^{\infty} e^{-\alpha\beta^2 t}[a(\beta)\cos\beta x + b(\beta)\sin\beta x]\, d\beta \tag{2-65}$$

The unknown coefficients $a(\beta)$ and $b(\beta)$ are to be determined so that for $t = 0$ this solution represents the initial temperature distribution $F(x)$ in the medium $-\infty < x < \infty$. The application of the initial condition to equation (2-65) yields

$$F(x) = \int_{\beta=0}^{\infty} [a(\beta)\cos\beta x + b(\beta)\sin\beta x]\, d\beta, \quad -\infty < x < \infty \tag{2-66a}$$

This equation is the Fourier formula for the integral representation of an arbitrary function $F(x)$ defined in the interval $-\infty < x < \infty$; the coefficients $a(\beta)$ and $b(\beta)$ are given as [4, p. 114; 14, p. 1]

$$a(\beta) = \frac{1}{\pi} \int_{x'=-\infty}^{\infty} F(x')\cos\beta x'\, dx' \tag{2-66b}$$

$$b(\beta) = \frac{1}{\pi} \int_{x'=-\infty}^{\infty} F(x')\sin\beta x'\, dx' \tag{2-66c}$$

Equations (2-66b, c) are substituted into equation (2-66a), the trigonometric terms are combined and the order of integration is changed. We obtain

$$F(x) = \int_{\beta=0}^{\infty} \left[\frac{1}{\pi} \int_{x'=-\infty}^{\infty} F(x')\cos\beta(x - x')\, dx' \right] d\beta \tag{2-66d}$$

The representation given by equation (2-66d) is valid if function $F(x)$ and dF/dx are sectionally continuous on every finite interval on the x axis, $F(x)$ is defined as its mean value at each point of discontinuity, and the integral $\int_{-\infty}^{\infty} |F(x)|\, dx$ exists [4, p. 115].

A comparison of the results in equations (2-66a) and (2-66d) implies that the coefficients are related by

$$[a(\beta)\cos\beta x + b(\beta)\sin\beta x] \equiv \frac{1}{\pi}\int_{x'=-\infty}^{\infty} F(x')\cos\beta(x-x')\,dx' \quad (2\text{-}67)$$

Then the solution given by equation (2-65) becomes

$$T(x,t) = \frac{1}{\pi}\int_{\beta=0}^{\infty} e^{-\alpha\beta^2 t}\int_{x'=-\infty}^{\infty} F(x')\cos\beta(x-x')\,dx'\,d\beta \quad (2\text{-}68)$$

In view of the integral [16, # 861.20]

$$\int_{\beta=0}^{\infty} e^{-\alpha\beta^2 t}\cos\beta(x-x')\,d\beta = \sqrt{\frac{\pi}{4\alpha t}}\exp\left[-\frac{(x-x')^2}{4\alpha t}\right] \quad (2\text{-}69)$$

The solution (2-68) takes the form

$$T(x,t) = \frac{1}{[4\pi\alpha t]^{1/2}}\int_{x'=-\infty}^{\infty} F(x')\exp\left[-\frac{(x-x')^2}{4\alpha t}\right]dx' \quad (2\text{-}70)$$

An Alternative Approach

The solution given by equation (2-70) may be constructed by noting that the function

$$\frac{1}{(4\pi\alpha t)^{1/2}}\exp\left[-\frac{(x-x')^2}{4\alpha t}\right]$$

is a particular solution of the heat-conduction equation (2-63a); this is readily verified by direct substitution into the differential equation. The equation being linear, its general solution can be constructed by the superposition of these solutions in the form

$$T(x,t) = \frac{1}{(4\pi\alpha t)^{1/2}}\int_{-\infty}^{\infty} c(x')\exp\left[-\frac{(x-x')^2}{4\alpha t}\right]dx' \quad (2\text{-}71a)$$

A new variable is defined as

$$\eta = \frac{x'-x}{(4\alpha t)^{1/2}} \quad \text{or} \quad x' = x + (4\alpha t)^{1/2}\eta \ \therefore\ dx' = (4\alpha t)^{1/2}\,d\eta$$

Then, the equation (2-71a) becomes

$$T(x,t) = \frac{1}{\sqrt{\pi}}\int_{-\infty}^{\infty} c[x+(4\alpha t)^{1/2}\eta]e^{-\eta^2}\,d\eta \quad (2\text{-}71b)$$

To determine the unknown coefficient we utilize the fact that for $t\to 0$ we should have $T(x,t) \to F(x)$; then equation (2-71b) reduces to

$$F(x) = \frac{c(x)}{\sqrt{\pi}} \int_{-\infty}^{\infty} e^{-\eta^2}\, d\eta = c(x)\,\text{erf}(\infty) = c(x) \tag{2-72}$$

Clearly, equation (2-71a) satisfies the initial condition (2-63b) for the problem if $c(x) = F(x)$; thus, the solution obtained with this alternative approach is identical to that given by equation (2-70).

Example 2-4. In a one-dimensional infinite medium $-\infty < x < \infty$, the region $-L < x < L$ is initially at a constant temperature T_0, and everywhere outside this region is at zero temperature. Obtain an expression for the temperature distribution $T(x,t)$ in the medium.

Solution. For this particular case the initial condition function is of the form

$$F(x) = \begin{cases} T_0 & \text{in} \quad -L < x < L \\ 0 & \text{everywhere outside this region} \end{cases}$$

and the solution (2-70) becomes

$$T(x,t) = \frac{T_0}{(4\pi\alpha t)^{1/2}} \int_{-L}^{L} \exp\left[-\frac{(x-x')^2}{4\alpha t} \right] dx' \tag{2-73}$$

A new variable is defined as

$$\eta = \frac{x-x'}{\sqrt{4\alpha t}} \quad \therefore\ dx' = -\sqrt{4\alpha t}\, d\eta$$

Then equation (2-73) becomes

$$T(x,t) = \frac{T_0}{2}\left[\frac{2}{\sqrt{\pi}} \int_{0}^{(L+x)/\sqrt{4\alpha t}} e^{-\eta^2}\, d\eta + \frac{2}{\sqrt{\pi}} \int_{0}^{(L-x)/\sqrt{4\alpha t}} e^{-\eta^2}\, d\eta \right] \tag{2-74a}$$

which is written in the form

$$\frac{T(x,t)}{T_0} = \frac{1}{2}\left[\text{erf}\left(\frac{L+x}{\sqrt{4\alpha t}} \right) + \text{erf}\left(\frac{L-x}{\sqrt{4\alpha t}} \right) \right] \quad \text{in } -\infty < x < \infty \tag{2-74b}$$

2-6 MULTIDIMENSIONAL HOMOGENEOUS PROBLEMS

Having established the eigenfunctions and the norms for the eigenvalue problems associated with the separation in one-dimensional finite, semi-infinite, and infinite regions, we are now in a position to apply the method of

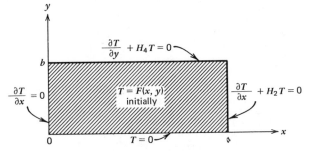

Fig. 2-4 Boundary and initial conditions for a rectangular region considered in Example 2-5.

separation of variables to the solution of multidimensional homogeneous boundary-value problems of heat conduction as illustrated with typical examples below.

Example 2-5. A rectangular region $0 \le x \le a, 0 \le y \le b$ is initially at temperature $F(x, y)$. For times $t > 0$ the boundary at $x = 0$ is kept insulated, the boundary at $y = 0$ is kept at zero temperature, and boundaries at $x = a$ and $y = b$ dissipate heat by convection into an environment at zero temperature as illustrated in Fig. 2-4. Obtain an expression for the temperature distribution $T(x, y, t)$ for times $t > 0$.

Solution. The mathematical formulation of the problem is given as

$$\frac{\partial^2 T}{\partial x^2} + \frac{\partial^2 T}{\partial y^2} = \frac{1}{\alpha}\frac{\partial T}{\partial t} \qquad \text{in } 0 < x < a,\ 0 < y < b,\ t > 0 \qquad (2\text{-}75a)$$

$$\frac{\partial T}{\partial x} = 0 \quad \text{at } x = 0; \qquad \frac{\partial T}{\partial x} + H_2 T = 0 \qquad \text{at } x = a \text{ for } t > 0 \quad (2\text{-}75b)$$

$$T = 0 \quad \text{at } y = 0; \qquad \frac{\partial T}{\partial y} + H_4 T = 0 \qquad \text{at } y = b \text{ for } t > 0 \quad (2\text{-}75c)$$

$$T = F(x, y) \qquad \text{for } t = 0, \text{ in the region} \qquad (2\text{-}75d)$$

Assuming a separation in the form

$$T(x, y, t) = \Gamma(t)X(x)Y(y) \qquad (2\text{-}76)$$

The separation equations for the $X(x)$ and $Y(y)$ functions become

$$\frac{d^2 X(x)}{dx^2} + \beta^2 X(x) = 0 \qquad \text{in } 0 < x < a \qquad (2\text{-}77a)$$

$$\frac{dX}{dx} = 0 \quad \text{at } x = 0; \qquad \frac{dX}{dx} + H_2 X = 0 \qquad \text{at } x = a \qquad (2\text{-}77b)$$

and

$$\frac{d^2Y(y)}{dy^2} + \gamma^2 Y(y) = 0 \qquad \text{in } 0 < y < b \tag{2-78a}$$

$$Y = 0 \quad \text{at } y = 0; \qquad \frac{dY}{dy} + H_4 Y = 0 \qquad \text{at } y = b \tag{2-78b}$$

and the solution for $\Gamma(t)$ is given as

$$\Gamma(t) = e^{-\alpha(\beta^2 + \gamma^2)t} \tag{2-79}$$

The complete solution for the problem is constructed as

$$T(x, y, t) = \sum_{m=1}^{\infty} \sum_{n=1}^{\infty} c_{mn} e^{-\alpha(\beta_m^2 + \gamma_n^2)t} X(\beta_m, x) Y(\gamma_n, y) \tag{2-80}$$

For $t = 0$ equation (2-80) becomes

$$F(x, y) = \sum_{m=1}^{\infty} \sum_{n=1}^{\infty} c_{mn} X(\beta_m, x) Y(\gamma_n, y) \qquad \text{in } 0 < x < a,\ 0 < y < b \tag{2-81}$$

The unknown coefficient c_{mn} is determined by operating on both sides of equation (2-81) successively by the operators

$$\int_0^a X(\beta_m, x)\, dx \qquad \text{and} \qquad \int_0^b Y(\gamma_n, y)\, dx$$

and utilizing the orthogonality of these eigenfunctions. We obtain

$$c_{mn} = \frac{1}{N(\beta_m)N(\gamma_n)} \int_{x'=0}^a \int_{y'=0}^b X(\beta_m, x') Y(\gamma_n, y') F(x', y')\, dx'\, dy' \tag{2-82}$$

where

$$N(\beta_m) \equiv \int_0^a X^2(\beta_m, x)\, dx \qquad \text{and} \qquad N(\gamma_n) \equiv \int_0^b Y^2(\gamma_n, y)\, dy$$

The substitution of equation (2-82) into equation (2-80) gives the solution of this problem as

$$T(x, y, t) = \sum_{m=1}^{\infty} \sum_{n=1}^{\infty} e^{-\alpha(\beta_m^2 + \gamma_n^2)t} \frac{1}{N(\beta_m)N(\gamma_n)} X(\beta_m, x) Y(\gamma_n, y) \int_0^a \int_0^b X(\beta_m, x')$$
$$\cdot Y(\gamma_n, y') F(x', y')\, dx'\, dy' \tag{2-83}$$

The eigenfunctions, the eigenvalues, and the norms appearing in equation (2-83) are immediately obtainable from Table 2-2; that is, $X(\beta_m, x)$ satisfying the eigenvalue problem (2-77) corresponds to case 4 and is given as

$$X(\beta_m, x) = \cos \beta_m x \tag{2-84a}$$

$$\frac{1}{N(\beta_m)} = 2 \frac{\beta_m^2 + H_2^2}{a(\beta_m^2 + H_2^2) + H_2} \tag{2-84b}$$

and β_m's are the positive roots of

$$\beta_m \tan \beta_m a = H_2 \tag{2-84c}$$

The function $Y(\gamma_n, y)$ satisfying the eigenvalue problem (2-78) corresponds to case 7 in Table 2-2; after replacing L by b, β by γ, and H_2 by H_4, we find

$$Y(\gamma_n, y) = \sin \gamma_n y \tag{2-85a}$$

$$\frac{1}{N(\gamma_n)} = 2 \frac{\gamma_n^2 + H_4^2}{b(\gamma_n^2 + H_4^2) + H_4} \tag{2-85b}$$

and γ_n's are the positive roots of

$$\gamma_n \cot \gamma_n b = - H_4 \tag{2-85c}$$

Introducing equations (2-84) and (2-85) into equation (2-83), the solution becomes

$$T(x, y, t) = 4 \sum_{m=1}^{\infty} \sum_{n=1}^{\infty} e^{-\alpha(\beta_m^2 + \gamma_n^2)t} \cdot \frac{\beta_m^2 + H_2^2}{a(\beta_m^2 + H_2^2) + H_2} \frac{\gamma_n^2 + H_4^2}{b(\gamma_n^2 + H_4^2) + H_4}$$

$$\cdot \cos \beta_m x \sin \gamma_n y \int_{x'=0}^{a} \int_{y'=0}^{b} \cos \beta_m x' \sin \gamma_n y' F(x', y') \, dx' \, dy' \tag{2-86}$$

where β_m and γ_n are the positive roots of the equations (2-84c) and (2-85c), respectively.

Example 2-6. A rectangular parallelepiped $0 \le x \le a, 0 \le y \le b, 0 \le z \le c$ is initially at temperature $F(x, y, z)$. For times $t > 0$ all boundary surfaces are kept at zero temperature. Obtain an expression for $T(x, y, z, t)$ for times $t > 0$.

Solution. The mathematical formulation of this problem is given as

$$\frac{\partial^2 T}{\partial x^2} + \frac{\partial^2 T}{\partial y^2} + \frac{\partial^2 T}{\partial z^2} = \frac{1}{\alpha} \frac{\partial T}{\partial t} \qquad \text{in } 0 < x < a, \ 0 < y < b, \ 0 < z < c, \text{ for } t > 0 \tag{2-87a}$$

$$T = 0 \qquad \text{on all boundaries, for } t > 0 \tag{2-87b}$$

$$T = F(x, y, z) \qquad \text{for } t = 0, \text{ in the region} \tag{2-87c}$$

Assuming a separation in the form $T(x, y, z, t) = \Gamma(t)X(x)Y(y)Z(z)$, the complete solution for $T(x, y, z, t)$ in terms of these separated functions is written as

$$T(x, y, z, t) = \sum_{m=1}^{\infty} \sum_{n=1}^{\infty} \sum_{p=1}^{\infty} c_{mnp} e^{-\alpha(\beta_m^2 + \gamma_n^2 + \eta_p^2)t} X(\beta_m, x) Y(\gamma_n, y) Z(\eta_p, z) \quad (2\text{-}88)$$

The application of the initial condition gives

$$F(x, y, z) = \sum_{m=1}^{\infty} \sum_{n=1}^{\infty} \sum_{p=1}^{\infty} c_{mnp} X(\beta_m, x) Y(\gamma_n, y) Z(\eta_p, z) \quad (2\text{-}89)$$

The unknown coefficient c_{mnp} is determined by operating on both sides of equation (2-89) successively by the operators

$$\int_0^a X(\beta_m, x)\, dx, \qquad \int_0^b Y(\gamma_n, y)\, dy, \qquad \text{and} \qquad \int_0^c Z(\eta_p, z)\, dz$$

and utilizing the orthogonality of these eigenfunctions. We obtain

$$c_{mnp} = \frac{1}{N(\beta_m)N(\gamma_n)N(\eta_p)} \int_{x'=0}^a \int_{y'=0}^b \int_{z'=0}^c X(\beta_m, x') Y(\gamma_n, y') Z(\eta_p, z')$$
$$\cdot F(x', y', z')\, dx'\, dy'\, dz' \quad (2\text{-}90)$$

where

$$N(\beta_m) \equiv \int_0^a X^2(\beta_m, x)\, dx, \quad N(\gamma_n) \equiv \int_0^b Y^2(\gamma_n, y)\, dy, \quad \text{and} \quad N(\eta_p) \equiv \int_0^c Z^2(\eta_p, z)\, dz$$

The substitution of equation (2-90) into equation (2-88) gives the solution as

$$T(x, y, z) = \sum_{m=1}^{\infty} \sum_{n=1}^{\infty} \sum_{p=1}^{\infty} e^{-\alpha(\beta_m^2 + \gamma_n^2 + \eta_p^2)t} \frac{1}{N(\beta_m)N(\gamma_n)N(\eta_p)} X(\beta_m, x) Y(\gamma_n, y) Z(\eta_p, z)$$
$$\int_{x=0}^a \int_{y=0}^b \int_{z=0}^c X(\beta_m, x') Y(\gamma_n, y') Z(\eta_p, z') F(x', y', z')\, dx'\, dy'\, dz' \quad (2\text{-}91)$$

Here, the functions X, Y, Z satisfy the eigenvalue problems whose solutions corresponds to those given by case 9 in Table 2-2. Therefore, from Table 2-2 we immediately obtain

$$X(\beta_m, x) = \sin \beta_m x, \qquad \frac{1}{N(\beta_m)} = \frac{2}{a} \qquad \text{and } \beta_m\text{'s are roots of } \sin \beta_m a = 0$$

$$Y(\gamma_n, y) = \sin \gamma_n y, \qquad \frac{1}{N(\gamma_n)} = \frac{2}{b} \qquad \text{and } \gamma_n\text{'s are roots of } \sin \gamma_n b = 0$$

$$Z(\eta_p, z) = \sin \eta_p z, \qquad \frac{1}{N(\eta_p)} = \frac{2}{c} \qquad \text{and } \eta_p\text{'s are roots of } \sin \eta_p c = 0$$

Hence, the solution (2-91) becomes

$$T(x, y, z, t) = \frac{8}{abc} \sum_{m=1}^{\infty} \sum_{n=1}^{\infty} \sum_{p=1}^{\infty} e^{-\alpha(\beta_m^2 + \gamma_n^2 + \eta_p^2)t} \cdot \sin \beta_m x \sin \gamma_n y \sin \eta_p z$$

$$\cdot \int_{x'=0}^{a} \int_{y'=0}^{b} \int_{z'=0}^{c} \sin \beta_m x' \sin \gamma_n y' \sin \eta_p z' F(x', y', z') \, dx' \, dy' \, dz'$$

$$(2\text{-}92)$$

where

$$\beta_m = \frac{m\pi}{a}, \qquad m = 1, 2, 3, \ldots$$

$$\gamma_n = \frac{n\pi}{b}, \qquad n = 1, 2, 3, \ldots$$

$$\eta_p = \frac{p\pi}{c}, \qquad p = 1, 2, 3, \ldots$$

Example 2-7. A semi-infinite rectangular strip $0 \le y \le b, 0 \le x < \infty$ is initially at temperature $F(x, y)$. For times $t > 0$ the boundaries at $x = 0$ and $y = b$ are kept at zero temperature and the boundary at $y = 0$ dissipates heat by convection into an environment at zero temperature as illustrated in Fig. 2-5. Obtain an expression for the temperature $T(x, y, t)$ for times $t > 0$.

Solution. The mathematical formulation of this problem is given as

$$\frac{\partial^2 T}{\partial x^2} + \frac{\partial^2 T}{\partial y^2} = \frac{1}{\alpha} \frac{\partial T}{\partial t} \qquad \text{in } 0 < x < \infty, \ 0 < y < b, \ t > 0 \qquad (2\text{-}93a)$$

$$T = 0 \qquad \text{at } x = 0, \ t > 0 \qquad (2\text{-}93b)$$

$$-\frac{\partial T}{\partial y} + H_1 T = 0 \qquad \text{at } y = 0, \ t > 0 \qquad (2\text{-}93c)$$

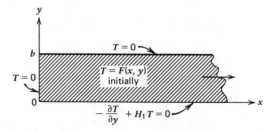

Fig. 2-5 Boundary and initial conditions for a semi-infinite strip considered in Example 2-7.

$$T = 0 \qquad\qquad \text{at } y = b, \ t > 0 \tag{2-93d}$$

$$T = F(x, y) \qquad\qquad \text{for } t = 0, \text{ in the region} \tag{2-93e}$$

Assuming separation, the general solution for $T(x, y, t)$ is written in the form

$$T(x, y, t) = \sum_{n=1}^{\infty} \int_{\beta=0}^{\infty} c_n(\beta) e^{-\alpha(\beta^2 + \gamma_n^2)t} X(\beta, x) Y(\gamma_n, y) \, d\beta \tag{2-94}$$

where $X(\beta, x)$ satisfies the auxiliary problem

$$\frac{d^2 X(x)}{dx^2} + \beta^2 X(x) = 0 \qquad \text{in } 0 < x < \infty \tag{2-95a}$$

$$X = 0 \qquad\qquad \text{at } x = 0 \tag{2-95b}$$

and $Y(\gamma_n, y)$ satisfies the eigenvalue problem

$$\frac{d^2 Y(y)}{dy^2} + \gamma^2 Y(y) = 0 \qquad \text{in } 0 < y < b \tag{2-96a}$$

$$-\frac{dY}{dy} + H_1 Y = 0 \qquad \text{at } y = 0 \tag{2-96b}$$

$$Y = 0 \qquad\qquad \text{at } y = b \tag{2-96c}$$

Here we note that the superposition of the elementary solutions $X(\beta, x)$ is made by integration over the separation variable β, because the region is semi-infinite in the x direction.

The application of the initial condition to equation (2-94) yields

$$F(x, y) = \sum_{n=1}^{\infty} \int_{\beta=0}^{\infty} c_n(\beta) X(\beta, x) Y(\gamma_n, y) \, d\beta \tag{2-97}$$

To determine the unknown coefficients $c_n(\beta)$ we first operate on both sides of equation (2-97) by the operator $\int_0^b Y(\gamma_n, y) \, dy$ and utilize the orthogonality of the eigenfunctions $Y(\gamma_n, y)$. We obtain

$$f^*(x) = \int_{\beta=0}^{\infty} c_n(\beta) X(\beta, x) \, d\beta \qquad \text{in } 0 < x < \infty \tag{2-98a}$$

where

$$f^*(x) \equiv \frac{1}{N(\gamma_n)} \int_{y=0}^{b} Y(\gamma_n, y) F(x, y) \, dy, \qquad N(\gamma_n) \equiv \int_0^b Y^2(\gamma_n, y) \, dy \tag{2-98b}$$

Equation (2-98a) is a representation of an arbitrary function $f^*(x)$, defined in the interval $0 < x < \infty$ in terms of the functions $X(\beta, x)$ which are the solution of the auxiliary problem (2-95). This representation is exactly of the same form as that given by equation (2-51); the coefficient of equation (2-51) is given by equation (2-53). Therefore, the unknown coefficient $c(\beta)$ in equation (2-98a) is determined according to equation (2-53); we obtain

$$c_n(\beta) = \frac{1}{N(\beta)} \int_{x=0}^{\infty} X(\beta, x) \left[\frac{1}{N(\gamma_n)} \int_{y=0}^{b} Y(\gamma_n, y) F(x, y) dy \right] dx \qquad (2\text{-}99)$$

The substitution of equation (2-99) into equation (2-94) gives the solution for $T(x, y, t)$ as

$$T(x, y, t) = \sum_{n=1}^{\infty} \int_{\beta=0}^{\infty} e^{-\alpha(\beta^2 + \gamma_n^2)t} \frac{1}{N(\beta)N(\gamma_n)} X(\beta, x) Y(\gamma_n, y).$$

$$\left[\int_{x'=0}^{\infty} \int_{y'=0}^{b} X(\beta, x') Y(\gamma_n, y') F(x', y') dx' dy' \right] d\beta \qquad (2\text{-}100)$$

The eigenfunctions $Y(\gamma_n, y)$, the norm $N(\gamma_n)$ and the eigenvalues γ_n for the y separation are immediately obtainable from case 3 of Table 2-2 by appropriate changes in the symbols. We find

$$Y(\gamma_n, y) = \sin \gamma_n (b - y) \qquad (2\text{-}101a)$$

$$\frac{1}{N(\gamma_n)} = 2 \frac{\gamma_n^2 + H_1^2}{b(\gamma_n^2 + H_1^2) + H_1} \qquad (2\text{-}101b)$$

and γ_n's are the positive roots of

$$\gamma_n \cot \gamma_n b = -H_1 \qquad (2\text{-}101c)$$

The function $X(\beta, x)$ and the norm $N(\beta)$ are obtained from case 3 of Table 2-3, as

$$X(\beta, x) = \sin \beta x \qquad (2\text{-}102a)$$

$$\frac{1}{N(\beta)} = \frac{2}{\pi} \qquad (2\text{-}102b)$$

Substituting equations (2-101) and (2-102) into equation (2-100) and after changing the orders of integration, we obtain

$$T(x, y, t) = \frac{4}{\pi} \sum_{n=1}^{\infty} e^{-\alpha \gamma_n^2 t} \frac{\gamma_n^2 + H_1^2}{b(\gamma_n^2 + H_1^2) + H_1} \sin \gamma_n (b - y).$$

$$\int_{x'=0}^{\infty} \int_{y'=0}^{b} F(x', y') \sin \gamma_n (b - y') dx' dy' \int_{\beta=0}^{\infty} e^{-\alpha \beta^2 t} \sin \beta x' \sin \beta x \, d\beta$$

$$(2\text{-}103)$$

The last integral with respect to β was evaluated previously and the result given by equation (2-57d); then equation (2-103) becomes

$$T(x, y, t) = \frac{1}{(\pi \alpha t)^{1/2}} \sum_{n=1}^{\infty} e^{-\alpha \gamma_n^2 t} \frac{\gamma_n^2 + H_1^2}{b(\gamma_n^2 + H_1^2) + H_1} \sin \gamma_n(b - y)$$

$$\int_{x'=0}^{\infty} \int_{y'=0}^{\infty} F(x', y') \sin \gamma_n(b - y') \left[\exp\left(-\frac{(x - x')^2}{4\alpha t} \right) \right.$$

$$\left. - \exp\left(-\frac{(x + x')^2}{4\alpha t} \right) \right] dx' \, dy' \tag{2-104}$$

2-7 PRODUCT SOLUTION

The solution of multidimensional homogeneous boundary-value problems of heat conduction can be written down very simply as the product of the solutions of one-dimensional problems if the initial temperature distribution in the medium is expressible as a product of single space variable functions. For example, for a two-dimensional problem it may be in the form $F(x, y) = F_1(x)F_2(y)$, or for a three-dimensional problem in the form $F(x, y, z) = F_1(x)F_2(y)F_3(z)$. Clearly, the case of uniform temperature initial condition also is expressible in the product form.

To illustrate this method we consider the following two-dimensional homogeneous heat-conduction problem for a rectangular region $0 \le x \le a$, $0 \le y \le b$:

$$\frac{\partial^2 T}{\partial x^2} + \frac{\partial^2 T}{\partial y^2} = \frac{1}{\alpha} \frac{\partial T}{\partial t} \qquad \text{in } 0 < x < a, \ 0 < y < b, \ t > 0 \tag{2-105a}$$

$$-k_1 \frac{\partial T}{\partial x} + h_1 T = 0 \qquad \text{at } x = 0, \ t > 0 \tag{2-105b}$$

$$k_2 \frac{\partial T}{\partial x} + h_2 T = 0 \qquad \text{at } x = a, \ t > 0 \tag{2-105c}$$

$$-k_3 \frac{\partial T}{\partial y} + h_3 T = 0 \qquad \text{at } y = 0, \ t > 0 \tag{2-105d}$$

$$k_4 \frac{\partial T}{\partial y} + h_4 T = 0 \qquad \text{at } y = b, \ t > 0 \tag{2-105e}$$

$$T = F_1(x)F_2(y) \qquad \text{for } t = 0, \text{ in the region} \tag{2-105f}$$

where

$$T \equiv T(x, y, t).$$

To solve this problem we consider the following two one-dimensional homogeneous heat-conduction problems for slabs $0 \leq x \leq a$ and $0 \leq y \leq b$, given as

$$\frac{\partial^2 T_1}{\partial x^2} = \frac{1}{\alpha} \frac{\partial T_1}{\partial t} \qquad\qquad \text{in } 0 < x < a, \ t > 0 \qquad (2\text{-}106a)$$

$$-k_1 \frac{\partial T_1}{\partial x} + h_1 T_1 = 0 \qquad \text{at } x = 0, \ t > 0 \qquad (2\text{-}106b)$$

$$k_2 \frac{\partial T_1}{\partial x} + h_2 T_1 = 0 \qquad \text{at } x = a, \ t > 0 \qquad (2\text{-}106c)$$

$$T_1 = F_1(x) \qquad\qquad \text{for } t = 0, \ \text{in } 0 \leq x \leq a \qquad (2\text{-}106d)$$

and

$$\frac{\partial^2 T_2}{\partial y^2} = \frac{1}{\alpha} \frac{\partial T_2}{\partial t} \qquad\qquad \text{in } 0 < y < b, \ t > 0 \qquad (2\text{-}107a)$$

$$-k_3 \frac{\partial T_2}{\partial y} + h_3 T_2 = 0 \qquad \text{at } y = 0, \ t > 0 \qquad (2\text{-}107b)$$

$$k_4 \frac{\partial T_2}{\partial y} + h_4 T_2 = 0 \qquad \text{at } y = b, \ t > 0 \qquad (2\text{-}107c)$$

$$T_2 = F_2(y) \qquad\qquad \text{for } t = 0, \ \text{in } 0 \leq y \leq b \qquad (2\text{-}107d)$$

Here we note that the boundary conditions for the problem (2-106) are the same as those given by equations (2-105b, c) and those for the problem (2-107) are the same as those given by equations (2-105d, e). Then the solution of the two-dimensional problem (2-105) is given as the product solution of the above one-dimensional problems as

$$T(x, y, t) = T_1(x, t) \cdot T_2(y, t) \qquad (2\text{-}108)$$

To prove the validity of this result we substitute equation (2-108) into equations (2-105) and utilize the equations (2-106) and (2-107). For example, the substitution of equation (2-108) into the differential equation (2-105a) gives

$$T_2 \frac{\partial^2 T_1}{\partial x^2} + T_1 \frac{\partial^2 T_2}{\partial y^2} = \frac{1}{\alpha} T_2 \frac{\partial T_1}{\partial t} + \frac{1}{\alpha} T_1 \frac{\partial T_2}{\partial t}$$

or

$$T_2 \left(\frac{\partial^2 T_1}{\partial x^2} - \frac{1}{\alpha} \frac{\partial T_1}{\partial t} \right) + T_1 \left(\frac{\partial^2 T_2}{\partial y^2} - \frac{1}{\alpha} \frac{\partial T_2}{\partial t} \right) = 0 \qquad (2\text{-}109)$$

Thus, the differential equation is satisfied in view of equations (2-106a) and (2-107a).

Similarly, the substitution of equation (2-107) into the boundary conditions (2-105) shows that they are also satisfied. Hence, equation (2-108) is the solution of the problem (2-105).

Example 2-8.   A semi-infinite corner, $0 \leq x < \infty$ and $0 \leq y < \infty$, is initially at a constant temperature T_0; for times $t > 0$ the boundaries at $x = 0$ and $y = 0$ are kept at zero temperatures. Obtain an expression for the temperature $T(x, y, t)$ in the region for times $t > 0$.

Solution.   The solution of this problem can be expressed as the product of the solutions of the following two one-dimensional problems: (1) $T_1(x, t)$, the solution for a semi-finite region $0 \leq x < \infty$ initially at a temperature $F_1(x) = 1$ and for times $t > 0$ the boundary surface at $x = 0$ is kept at zero temperature, and (2) $T_2(y, t)$, the solution for a semi-infinite region $0 \leq y < \infty$ initially at a temperature $F_2(y) = T_0$ and for times $t > 0$ the boundary at $y = 0$ is kept at zero temperature. Clearly, the initial condition for the two-dimensional problem is expressible as a product, $T_0 = 1 \cdot T_0$. The solution of such one-dimensional problem was considered previously in Example 2-3; thus obtaining these solutions from equation (2-62) we write

$$T_1(x, t) = \operatorname{erf}\left(\frac{x}{\sqrt{4\alpha t}} \right) \quad \text{and} \quad T_2(y, t) = T_0 \operatorname{erf}\left(\frac{y}{\sqrt{4\alpha t}} \right)$$

Then, the solution for the above two-dimensional problem becomes

$$T(x, y, t) = T_1(x, t) T_2(y, t) = T_0 \operatorname{erf}\left(\frac{x}{\sqrt{4\alpha t}} \right) \operatorname{erf}\left(\frac{y}{\sqrt{4\alpha t}} \right) \quad (2\text{-}110)$$

Example 2-9.   A rectangular region $0 \leq x \leq a, 0 \leq y \leq b$ is initially at a uniform temperature $F(x, y) = T_0$. For times $t > 0$, the boundaries at $x = 0$ and $y = 0$ are insulated and the boundaries at $x = a$ and $y = b$ dissipate heat by convection into an environment at zero temperature with a heat transfer coefficient h (or $H = h/k$). Figure 2-6 illustrates the boundary conditions for this problem. Obtain an expression for the temperature distribution $T(x, y, t)$ for times $t > 0$.

Solution.   The solution of this problem can be expressed as the product of the solutions of the following two slab problems: (1) $T_1(x, t)$, for a slab, $0 \leq x \leq a$, initially at a temperature $F(x) = 1$ and for times $t > 0$ the boundary at $x = 0$ is insulated and the boundary at $x = a$ dissipates heat by convection into an environment at zero temperature with a heat transfer coefficient

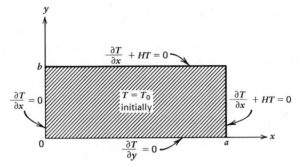

Fig. 2-6 Boundary and initial conditions for a rectangular region considered in Example 2-9.

h (or $H = h/k$); and (2) $T_2(y, t)$, for a slab, $0 \le y \le b$, initially at a temperature $F(y) = T_0$ and for times $t > 0$ the boundary at $y = 0$ is insulated and the boundary at $y = b$ dissipates heat by convection into an environment at zero temperature with a heat-transfer coefficient h (or $H = h/k$). These slab problems were solved previously in Example 2-1 and the solutions for $T_1(x, t)$ and $T_2(y, t)$ are readily obtainable from equation (2-43b) by appropriate changes in the parameters. We set $T_0 = 1, L = a$, and $H_2 = H$ to obtain

$$T_1(x, t) = 2 \sum_{m=1}^{\infty} e^{-\alpha \beta_m^2 t} \frac{H}{a(\beta_m^2 + H^2) + H} \frac{\cos \beta_m x}{\cos \beta_m a} \qquad (2\text{-}111a)$$

where β_m's are the positive roots of $\beta_m \tan \beta_m a = H$.
We set $L = b, H_2 = H, x = y$, and $\beta_m = \gamma_n$ to find

$$T_2(y, t) = 2T_0 \sum_{n=1}^{\infty} e^{-\alpha \gamma_n^2 t} \frac{H}{b(\gamma_n^2 + H^2) + H} \frac{\cos \gamma_n y}{\cos \gamma_n b} \qquad (2\text{-}111b)$$

where γ_n's are the positive roots of $\gamma_n \tan \gamma_n b = H$.
Then the solution of the above problem for the rectangular region becomes

$$T(x, y, t) = T_1(x, t) T_2(y, t) \qquad (2\text{-}111c)$$

$$T(x, y, t) = 4T_0 \sum_{m=1}^{\infty} \sum_{n=1}^{\infty} \frac{H^2 e^{-\alpha(\beta_m^2 + \gamma_n^2)t}}{[a(\beta_m^2 + H^2) + H][b(\gamma_n^2 + H^2) + H]} \frac{\cos \beta_m x \cos \gamma_n y}{\cos \beta_m a \cos \gamma_n b}$$
$$(2\text{-}111d)$$

2-8 MULTIDIMENSIONAL STEADY-STATE PROBLEMS WITH NO HEAT GENERATION

The multidimensional steady-state heat-conduction problem with no heat generation can be solved by the separation of variable technique when only one of the boundary conditions is nonhomogeneous. If the problem involves more than one nonhomogeneous boundary condition, it can be split up into a set of simpler problems each containing only one nonhomogeneous boundary condition; the method of separation of variables can then be used to solve the resulting simpler problems. Consider, for example the following steady-state problem subject to more than one nonhomogeneous boundary condition

$$\nabla^2 T(\mathbf{r}) = 0 \qquad \text{in region } R \qquad (2\text{-}112\text{a})$$

$$k_i \frac{\partial T}{\partial n_i} + h_i T = f_i \qquad \text{on boundary } S_i \qquad (2\text{-}112\text{b})$$

where, $\partial/\partial n_i$ is the derivative along the outward-drawn normal to the boundary surface $S_i, i = 1, 2, \ldots, s$ and s is the number of continuous boundary surfaces of the region, and f_i is the nonhomogeneous part of the boundary condition at the surface S_i. This problem can be split up into a set of simpler problems for the temperatures $T_j(\mathbf{r})$ in the form

$$\nabla^2 T_j(\mathbf{r}) = 0 \qquad \text{in region } R \qquad (2\text{-}113\text{a})$$

$$k_i \frac{\partial T_j}{\partial n_i} + h_i T_j = \delta_{ij} f_i \qquad \text{on boundary } S_i \qquad (2\text{-}113\text{b})$$

where

$$i = 1, 2, \ldots, s$$
$$j = 1, 2, \ldots, s$$
$$\delta_{ij} = \text{kronecker delta} = \begin{cases} 0 & \text{for} & i \neq j \\ 1 & \text{for} & i = j \end{cases}$$

Clearly, each of the steady-state problems given by equations (2-113) has only one nonhomogeneous boundary condition. Then, the solution of the heat-conduction problem (2-112) is obtained by the superposition of these simpler problems in the form

$$T(\mathbf{r}) = \sum_{j=1}^{s} T_j(\mathbf{r}) \qquad (2\text{-}114)$$

The validity of this result is readily verified by substituting equation (2-114) into equations (2-112) and utilizing equations (2-113).

Example 2-10. Obtain an expression for the steady-state temperature distribution $T(x, y)$ in a rectangular region $0 \leq x \leq a, 0 \leq y \leq b$ for the boundary conditions shown in Fig. 2-7.

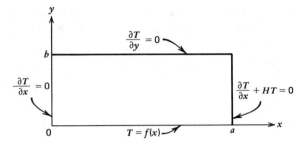

Fig. 2-7 Boundary conditions for a rectangular region considered in Example 2-10.

Solution. The mathematical formulation of the problem is given as

$$\frac{\partial^2 T(x, y)}{\partial x^2} + \frac{\partial^2 T(x, y)}{\partial y^2} = 0 \qquad \text{in } 0 < x < a, \; 0 < y < b \qquad (2\text{-}115a)$$

$$\frac{\partial T}{\partial x} = 0 \qquad \text{at } x = 0, \qquad\qquad \frac{\partial T}{\partial x} + HT = 0 \quad \text{at } x = a \quad (2\text{-}115b)$$

$$T = f(x) \qquad \text{at } y = 0, \qquad\qquad \frac{\partial T}{\partial y} = 0 \qquad\qquad \text{at } y = b \quad (2\text{-}115c)$$

In this problem the boundary condition at $y = 0$ is nonhomogeneous; looking ahead in the analysis we conclude that the nonhomogeneous part $f(x)$ of this boundary condition should be represented in terms of the separated solution $X(x)$ for the problem. Therefore, when separating the temperature in the form $T(x, y) = X(x)Y(y)$, the sign of the separation constant should be so chosen as to produce an eigenvalue problem for the function $X(x)$. With this consideration the separated problems become

$$\frac{d^2 X(x)}{dx^2} + \beta^2 X(x) = 0 \qquad \text{in } 0 < x < a \qquad (2\text{-}116a)$$

$$\frac{dX}{dx} = 0 \qquad\qquad \text{at } x = 0 \qquad (2\text{-}116b)$$

$$\frac{dX}{dx} + HX = 0 \qquad\qquad \text{at } x = a \qquad (2\text{-}116c)$$

and

$$\frac{d^2 Y(y)}{dy^2} - \beta^2 Y(y) = 0 \qquad \text{in } 0 < y < b \qquad (2\text{-}117a)$$

$$\frac{dY}{dy} = 0 \qquad\qquad \text{at } y = b \qquad (2\text{-}117b)$$

The solution of the eigenvalue problem (2-116) is immediately obtainable from Table 2-2 as case 4; by replacing L by a and H_2 by H we find

$$X(\beta_m, x) = \cos \beta_m x, \qquad \frac{1}{N(\beta_m)} = 2 \frac{\beta_m^2 + H^2}{a(\beta_m^2 + H^2) + H} \qquad (2\text{-}118a)$$

and β_m's are the positive roots of

$$\beta_m \tan \beta_m a = H \qquad (2\text{-}118b)$$

The solution of equations (2-117) is taken as

$$Y(\beta_m, y) = \cosh \beta_m(b - y) \qquad (2\text{-}118c)$$

The complete solution for $T(x, y)$ is constructed as

$$T(x, y) = \sum_{m=1}^{\infty} c_m \cosh \beta_m(b - y) \cos \beta_m x \qquad (2\text{-}119)$$

which satisfies the heat-conduction equation (2-115a) and its three homogeneous boundary conditions; the coefficients c_m should be so determined that this solution also satisfies the nonhomogeneous boundary condition. The application of the boundary condition at $y = 0$ yields

$$f(x) = \sum_{m=1}^{\infty} c_m \cosh \beta_m b \cos \beta_m x \qquad \text{in} \qquad 0 < x < a \qquad (2\text{-}120a)$$

The coefficients c_m are determined by utilizing the orthogonality of the functions $\cos \beta_m x$; we find

$$c_m = \frac{1}{N(\beta_m) \cosh \beta_m b} \int_0^a \cos \beta_m x' f(x') \, dx' \qquad (2\text{-}120b)$$

The substitution of this expression into equation (2-119) together with the value of $N(\beta_m)$ as given above, results in the solution

$$T(x, y) = 2 \sum_{m=1}^{\infty} \frac{\beta_m^2 + H^2}{a(\beta_m^2 + H^2) + H} \frac{\cosh \beta_m(b - y)}{\cosh \beta_m b} \cos \beta_m x \int_0^a \cos \beta_m x' f(x') \, dx'$$
$$(2\text{-}121)$$

where β_m's are the roots of equation (2-118b).

For the special case of $F(x) = T_0 = $ constant, the integral is readily performed; after combining the resulting solution with the results obtained from the transcendental equation (2-118b) the solution becomes

$$T(x, y) = 2T_0 H \sum_{m=1}^{\infty} \frac{1}{a(\beta_m^2 + H^2) + H} \frac{\cosh \beta_m(b - y)}{\cosh \beta_m b} \frac{\cos \beta_m x}{\cos \beta_m a} \qquad (2\text{-}122)$$

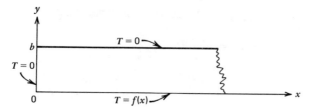

Fig. 2-8 Boundary conditions for a semi-infinite strip considered in Example 2-11.

Example 2-11. Obtain an expression for the steady-state temperature $T(x, y)$ in a semi-infinite strip $0 \leq y \leq b, 0 \leq x < \infty$ for the boundary conditions shown in Fig. 2-8.

Solution. The mathematical formulation of this problem is given as

$$\frac{\partial^2 T(x, y)}{\partial x^2} + \frac{\partial^2 T(x, y)}{\partial y^2} = 0 \qquad \text{in } 0 < y < b, \ 0 < x < \infty \qquad (2\text{-}123a)$$

$$T = 0 \qquad \text{at } x = 0 \qquad (2\text{-}123b)$$

$$T = f(x) \qquad \text{at } y = 0, \qquad T = 0 \text{ at } y = b \qquad (2\text{-}123c)$$

The separated equations for the functions $X(x)$ and $Y(y)$ are now constructed by considering the fact that the nonhomogeneous boundary condition function $f(x)$ defined in the interval $0 < x < \infty$ should be represented by the function $X(x)$. Then the separated problems become

$$\frac{d^2 X(x)}{dx^2} + \beta^2 X(x) = 0 \qquad \text{in } 0 < x < \infty \qquad (2\text{-}124a)$$

$$X = 0 \qquad \text{at } x = 0 \qquad (2\text{-}124b)$$

and

$$\frac{d^2 Y(y)}{dy^2} - \beta^2 Y(y) = 0 \qquad 0 < y < b \qquad (2\text{-}125a)$$

$$Y = 0 \qquad \text{at } y = b \qquad (2\text{-}125b)$$

The solution of the problem (2-124) is obtainable from Table 2-3, Case 3, as

$$X(\beta, x) = \sin \beta x \qquad \text{and} \qquad \frac{1}{N(\beta)} = \frac{2}{\pi} \qquad (2\text{-}126a)$$

and the solution of (2-125) is given as

$$Y(\beta, y) = \sinh \beta(b - y) \qquad (2\text{-}126b)$$

Then the complete solution for $T(x, y)$ is constructed as

$$T(x, y) = \int_{\beta=0}^{\infty} A(\beta) \sinh \beta(b - y) \sin \beta x \, d\beta \qquad (2\text{-}127)$$

If this solution should also satisfy the nonhomogeneous boundary condition at $y = 0$ for the above heat-conduction problem, we obtain

$$f(x) = \int_{\beta=0}^{\infty} A(\beta) \sinh \beta b \sin \beta x \, d\beta \qquad \text{in } 0 < x < \infty \qquad (2\text{-}128a)$$

This is a representation of function $f(x)$ defined in the interval $0 < x < \infty$; but it is a special case of the representation given by equation (2-51). The coefficient for equation (2-51) is given by equation (2-53). Therefore, the coefficient of equation (2-128a) is determined from the result in equation (2-53) as

$$A(\beta) \sinh \beta b = \frac{1}{N(\beta)} \int_{0}^{\infty} \sin \beta x' f(x') \, dx' \qquad (2\text{-}128b)$$

where

$$\frac{1}{N(\beta)} = \frac{2}{\pi}$$

as given previously. The substitution of $A(\beta)$ into equation (2-127) gives

$$T(x, y) = \frac{2}{\pi} \int_{\beta=0}^{\infty} \frac{\sinh \beta(b - y)}{\sinh \beta b} \sin \beta x \, d\beta \int_{x'=0}^{\infty} \sin \beta x' f(x') \, dx' \qquad (2\text{-}129a)$$

or changing the order of integration we obtain

$$T(x, y) = \frac{2}{\pi} \int_{x'=0}^{\infty} f(x') \, dx' \int_{\beta=0}^{\infty} \frac{\sinh \beta(b - y)}{\sinh \beta b} \sin \beta x \sin \beta x' \, d\beta \qquad (2\text{-}129b)$$

The integral with respect to β has been evaluated [14, Section 10.11]; then the solution for the temperature becomes

$$T(x, y) = \frac{1}{2b} \sin \frac{\pi y}{b} \int_{x'=0}^{\infty} f(x') \left[\frac{1}{\cos[\pi(b - y)/b] + \cosh[\pi(x - x')/b]} \right.$$
$$\left. - \frac{1}{\cos[\pi(b - y)/b] + \cosh[\pi(x + x')/b]} \right] dx' \qquad (2\text{-}130)$$

Example 2-12. Obtain an expression for the steady-state temperature $T(x, y)$ in an infinite strip $0 \le y \le b$, $-\infty < x < \infty$ for the boundary conditions shown in Fig. 2-9.

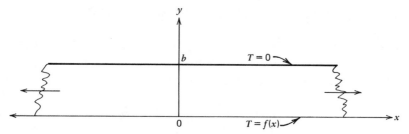

Fig. 2-9 Boundary conditions for an infinite strip considered in Example 2-12.

Solution. The mathematical formulation of this problem is given as

$$\frac{\partial^2 T(x, y)}{\partial x^2} + \frac{\partial^2 T(x, y)}{\partial y^2} = 0 \qquad \text{in } -\infty < x < \infty, \ 0 < y < b \quad (2\text{-}131\text{a})$$

$$T = f(x) \qquad \text{at } y = 0, \qquad\qquad T = 0 \qquad \text{at } y = b \qquad (2\text{-}131\text{b})$$

The separated problems are taken as

$$\frac{d^2 X(x)}{dx^2} + \beta^2 X(x) = 0 \qquad \text{in } -\infty < x < \infty \qquad (2\text{-}132\text{a})$$

and

$$\frac{d^2 Y(y)}{dy^2} - \beta^2 Y(y) = 0 \qquad \text{in } 0 < y < b \qquad (2\text{-}132\text{b})$$

$$Y(y) = 0 \qquad\qquad\qquad \text{at } y = b \qquad (2\text{-}132\text{c})$$

Then the general solution for $T(x, y)$ is constructed as

$$T(x, y) = \int_{\beta = 0}^{\infty} \sinh \beta(b - y)[A(\beta) \cos \beta x + B(\beta) \sin \beta x] \, d\beta \qquad (2\text{-}133)$$

If this solution should satisfy the boundary condition at $y = 0$, we obtain

$$f(x) = \int_{\beta = 0}^{\infty} \sinh \beta b [A(\beta) \cos \beta x + B(\beta) \sin \beta x] \, d\beta \qquad \text{in } -\infty < x < \infty$$

$$(2\text{-}134\text{a})$$

This is a representation of function $f(x)$ defined in the interval $-\infty < x < \infty$ in a form similar to that given by equation (2-66a); the coefficients of equation (2-66a) is given by equation (2-67). Then the coefficients of (2-134a) are obtained according to the relation given by equation (2-67). We find

$$\sinh \beta b [A(\beta) \cos \beta x + B(\beta) \sin \beta x] = \frac{1}{\pi} \int_{x' = -\infty}^{\infty} f(x') \cos \beta(x - x') \, dx' \quad (2\text{-}134\text{b})$$

The substitution of these coefficients into equation (2-133) yields

$$T(x, y) = \frac{1}{\pi} \int_{\beta=0}^{\infty} \frac{\sinh \beta(b-y)}{\sinh \beta b} \int_{x'=-\infty}^{\infty} f(x') \cos \beta(x-x') \, dx' \, d\beta \quad (2\text{-}135a)$$

or changing the order of integration we obtain

$$T(x, y) = \frac{1}{\pi} \int_{x'=-\infty}^{\infty} f(x') \int_{\beta=0}^{\infty} \frac{\sinh \beta(b-y)}{\sinh \beta b} \cos \beta(x-x') \, d\beta \, dx' \quad (2\text{-}135b)$$

The integral with respect to β is available in the integral tables [16, # 862.41]. Then the solution becomes

$$T(x, y) = \frac{1}{2b} \sin \frac{y\pi}{b} \int_{x'=-\infty}^{\infty} \frac{f(x')}{\cos[\pi(b-y)/b] + \cosh[\pi(x-x')/b]} \, dx' \quad (2\text{-}136)$$

Example 2-13.   Obtain an expression for the steady-state temperature $T(x, y)$ in a semi-infinite strip $0 \le y \le b, 0 \le x < \infty$ for the boundary conditions shown in Fig. 2-10.

Solution.   The mathematical formulation is given as

$$\frac{\partial^2 T(x, y)}{\partial x^2} + \frac{\partial^2 T(x, y)}{\partial y^2} = 0 \quad \text{in } 0 \le y < b, \ 0 < x < \infty \quad (2\text{-}137a)$$

$$T = f(y) \quad \text{at } x = 0 \quad (2\text{-}137b)$$

$$T = 0 \quad \text{at } y = 0, \quad T = 0 \quad \text{at } y = b \quad (2\text{-}137c)$$

The sign of the separation constant must be so chosen that the separation function $Y(y)$ results in an eigenvalue problem. Then the separated problems are taken as

$$\frac{d^2 Y(y)}{dy^2} + \gamma^2 Y(y) = 0 \quad \text{in } 0 < y < b \quad (2\text{-}138a)$$

$$Y = 0 \quad \text{at } y = 0, \quad Y = 0 \text{ at } y = b \quad (2\text{-}138b)$$

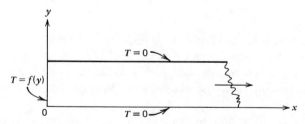

Fig. 2-10   Boundary conditions for a semi-infinite strip considered in Example 2-13.

and

$$\frac{d^2 X(x)}{dx^2} - \gamma^2 X(x) = 0 \qquad \text{in } 0 < x < \infty \tag{2-139}$$

The solution of equations (2-138) is obtainable from Table 2-2, case 9, as

$$Y(\gamma_n, y) = \sin \gamma_n y, \qquad N(\gamma_n) = \frac{b}{2} \tag{2-140a}$$

where γ_n's are the positive roots of $\sin \gamma_n b = 0$ or $\gamma_n = n\pi/b, n = 1, 2, 3, \dots$. The solution of (2-139) that does not diverge at infinity is

$$X(\gamma_n x) = e^{-\gamma_n x} \tag{2-140b}$$

Then the complete solution for $T(x, y)$ is constructed as

$$T(x, y) = \sum_{n=1}^{\infty} c_n e^{-\gamma_n x} \sin \gamma_n y \tag{2-141}$$

The application of the boundary condition at $x = 0$ gives

$$f(y) = \sum_{n=1}^{\infty} c_n \sin \gamma_n y \qquad \text{in } 0 < y < b \tag{2-142a}$$

The coefficients c_n are determined by utilizing the orthogonality of the eigenfunctions $\sin \gamma_n y$; we find

$$c_n = \frac{1}{N(\gamma_n)} \int_0^b \sin \gamma_n y' f(y') \, dy' \tag{2-142b}$$

The substitution of c_n into equation (2-141) together with the value of $N(\gamma_n)$ as given above results in

$$T(x, y) = \frac{2}{b} \sum_{n=1}^{\infty} e^{-\gamma_n x} \sin \gamma_n y \int_0^b \sin \gamma_n y' f(y') \, dy' \tag{2-143}$$

where

$$\gamma_n = \frac{n\pi}{b}, \qquad n = 1, 2, 3 \dots$$

For the special case of $f(y) = T_0 = $ constant, the integral is performed and the solution becomes

$$\frac{T(x, y)}{T_0} = \frac{4}{\pi} \sum_{n=\text{odd}}^{\infty} \frac{1}{n} e^{-\gamma_n x} \sin \gamma_n y \tag{2-144}$$

where only the odd values of n are considered in the summation because the terms for the even values of n vanish.

2-9 MULTIDIMENSIONAL STEADY-STATE PROBLEMS WITH HEAT GENERATION

The method of separation of variables is not so convenient for the solution of heat conduction problems with heat generation. However, by a suitable change of the dependent variable if the boundary-value problem of heat conduction *with* heat generation is transformed to a boundary-value problem of heat conduction *without* heat generation, the resulting problem may be solved by the separation of variable techniques. This procedure is equivalent to finding a *particular solution* of the nonhomogeneous differential equation of heat conduction so that it can be transformed into the homogeneous form. In this section we examine only the steady-state problems with heat generation, because, as it will be illustrated in the next section, a certain class of nonhomogeneous, time-dependent heat-conduction problems can be split up into a set of steady-state problems and a time-dependent homogeneous problem.

Consider the steady-state heat-conduction problem with heat generation given as

$$\nabla^2 T(x, y, z) + \frac{g}{k} = 0 \qquad \text{in region } R \qquad (2\text{-}145)$$

subject to a set of boundary conditions on the surfaces S_i of region R. We now write the general solution $T(x, y, z)$ of this nonhomogeneous equation as the sum of the general solution $\theta(x, y, z)$ of the corresponding homogeneous equation and an arbitrary particular solution $p(x, y, z)$ in the form

$$T(x, y, z) = \theta(x, y, z) + p(x, y, z) \qquad (2\text{-}146)$$

where, by our definition the function $\theta(x, y, z)$ satisfies the following homogeneous equation

$$\nabla^2 \theta(x, y, z) = 0 \qquad \text{in region } R \qquad (2\text{-}147)$$

The substitution of the transformation (2-146) into equation (2-145) and the use of equation (2-147) reveals that $p(x, y, z)$ is a particular solution of the equation

$$\nabla^2 p + \frac{g}{k} = 0 \qquad \text{in region } R \qquad (2\text{-}148)$$

We now summarize the above procedure: if a particular solution $p(x, y, z)$ of equation (2-145) [or equation (2-148)] is found, then a change of variable as defined by equation (2-146) tansforms the nonhomogeneous equation (2-145) into a homogeneous equation (2-147).

The functional form of a particular solution $p(x, y, z)$ of equation (2-145) depends on the functional form of the heat generation term $g(x, y, z)$. For the case $g = $ constant, a particular solution is readily obtained by inspection. For the case of $g = g(x, y)$, a procedure for the determination of a particular solution is discussed in reference [17]. We present in Table 2-4 some particular solutions of equation (2-145).

Example 2-14. Solve the following steady-state heat-conduction problem in a rectangular region $0 \leq x \leq a, 0 \leq y \leq b$ with heat generation in the medium at a constant rate $g(x, y) = g_0$.

$$\frac{\partial^2 T}{\partial x^2} + \frac{\partial^2 T}{\partial y^2} + \frac{1}{k}g_0 = 0 \qquad \text{in } 0 < x < a, \ 0 < y < b \qquad (2\text{-}149a)$$

$$\frac{\partial T}{\partial x} = 0 \text{ at } x = 0, \qquad\qquad \frac{\partial T}{\partial x} + HT = 0 \text{ at } x = a \qquad (2\text{-}149b)$$

$$\frac{\partial T}{\partial y} = 0 \text{ at } y = 0, \qquad\qquad \frac{\partial T}{\partial y} + HT = 0 \text{ at } y = b \qquad (2\text{-}149c)$$

Solution. A particular solution of equation (2-149a) for constant gene-

Table 2-4 Particular solutions $p(x, y, z)$ of the equation

$$\nabla^2 T(x, y, z) + \frac{1}{k}g = 0$$

T is a Function of	g^*	p
(x) or (x, y) or (x, y, z)	g_0	$-\dfrac{g_0}{k}\dfrac{x^2}{2}$
(x) or (x, y) or (x, y, z)	$g_0 x$	$-\dfrac{g_0}{k}\dfrac{x^3}{6}$
(x) or (x, y) or (x, y, z)	$g_0 x^2$	$-\dfrac{g_0}{k}\dfrac{x^4}{12}$
(x) or (x, y) or (x, y, z)	$g_0 x^n$	$-\dfrac{g_0}{k}\dfrac{x^{n+2}}{(n+1)(n+2)}$
(x, y) or (x, y, z)	$g_0\dfrac{x}{y^2}$	$\dfrac{g_0}{k} \cdot x \cdot \ln y$
(x, y) or (x, y, z)	$g_0\dfrac{y}{x^2}$	$\dfrac{g_0}{k} \cdot y \ln x$

$^*g_0$ is a constant.

ration is available from Table 2-4. Therefore a new variable $\theta(x, y)$ is defined as

$$T(x, y) = \theta(x, y) - \frac{g_0}{2k}x^2 + A \qquad (2\text{-}150)$$

The arbitrary constant A is introduced in order to simplify the transformed boundary conditions as it will be apparent later in the analysis.

The substitution of equation (2-150) into equations (2-149) yields the following problem for the function $\theta(x, y)$

$$\frac{\partial^2 \theta(x, y)}{\partial x^2} + \frac{\partial^2 \theta(x, y)}{\partial y^2} = 0 \qquad \text{in } 0 < x < a, \ 0 < y < b \qquad (2\text{-}151\text{a})$$

$$\frac{\partial \theta}{\partial x} = 0 \text{ at } x = 0, \qquad \frac{\partial \theta}{\partial x} + H\theta = H\left(\frac{g_0 a^2}{2k} + \frac{g_0 a}{Hk} - A\right) \text{ at } x = a$$

$$(2\text{-}151\text{b})$$

$$\frac{\partial \theta}{\partial y} = 0 \text{ at } y = 0, \qquad \frac{\partial \theta}{\partial y} + H\theta = H\left(\frac{g_0 x^2}{2k} - A\right) \qquad \text{at } y = b$$

$$(2\text{-}151\text{c})$$

Now, if we choose the constant A as

$$A = \frac{g_0 a^2}{2k} + \frac{g_0 a}{Hk} \qquad (2\text{-}152)$$

equations (2-151) become

$$\frac{\partial^2 \theta(x, y)}{\partial x^2} + \frac{\partial^2 \theta(x, y)}{\partial y^2} = 0 \qquad \text{in } 0 < x < a, \ 0 < y < b \qquad (2\text{-}153\text{a})$$

$$\frac{\partial \theta}{\partial x} = 0 \text{ at } x = 0, \qquad \frac{\partial \theta}{\partial x} + H\theta = 0 \quad \text{at } x = a \quad (2\text{-}153\text{b})$$

$$\frac{\partial \theta}{\partial y} = 0 \text{ at } y = 0, \qquad \frac{\partial \theta}{\partial y} + H\theta = f(x) \text{ at } y = b \quad (2\text{-}153\text{c})$$

where

$$f(x) \equiv H\left(\frac{g_0 x^2}{2k} - \frac{g_0 a^2}{2k} - \frac{g_0 a}{Hk}\right) \qquad (2\text{-}153\text{d})$$

The steady-state heat-conduction problem (2-153) for $\theta(x, y)$ has only one nonhomogeneous boundary condition at $y = b$ and can be solved by the method of separation of variables. Once $\theta(x, y)$ is known, the temperature $T(x, y)$ of problem (2-149) is determined from

$$T(x, y) = \theta(x, y) + \frac{g_0}{2k}(a^2 - x^2) + \frac{g_0 a}{Hk} \qquad (2\text{-}154)$$

2-10 SPLITTING UP OF NONHOMOGENEOUS PROBLEMS INTO SIMPLER PROBLEMS

When the heat-conduction problem is nonhomogeneous due to the non-homogeneity of the differential equation and/or the boundary conditions, it can be split up into a set of simpler problems that may be solved by the method of the separation of variables. Here we consider a nonhomogeneous problem in which the generation term and the nonhomogeneous parts of the boundary condition functions *do not depend on time.*

$$\nabla^2 T(\mathbf{r}, t) + \frac{1}{k}g(\mathbf{r}) = \frac{1}{\alpha}\frac{T(\mathbf{r}, t)}{\partial t} \qquad \text{in region } R, \ t > 0 \qquad (2\text{-}155a)$$

$$k_i \frac{\partial T}{\partial n_i} + h_i T = f_i(\mathbf{r}) \qquad \text{on boundary } S_i, \ t > 0 \qquad (2\text{-}155b)$$

$$T = F(\mathbf{r}) \qquad \text{for } t = 0, \text{ in region } R \qquad (2\text{-}155c)$$

where

$\dfrac{\partial}{\partial n_i}$ = derivative along the outward-drawn normal to the boundary surface $S_i (i = 1, 2, \ldots, s)$

s = number of continuous boundary surfaces of region R

Here we note that $g(\mathbf{r})$ and $f_i(\mathbf{r})$ *do not depend on time.* Clearly, many special cases are obtainable from the general problem given above. We shall now split up this problem into a number of simpler problems in the following manner:

1. A set of steady-state problems defined by the temperatures $T_{0j}(\mathbf{r})$, $j = 0, 1, 2, \ldots, s$.
2. A homogeneous time-dependent problem defined by the temperature $T_h(\mathbf{r}, t)$.

The temperatures $T_{0j}(\mathbf{r})$ are taken as the solutions of the following set of steady-state problems

$$\nabla^2 T_{0j}(\mathbf{r}) + \delta_{0j}\frac{1}{k}g(\mathbf{r}) = 0 \qquad \text{in region } R \qquad (2\text{-}156a)$$

$$k_i \frac{\partial T_{0j}}{\partial n_i} + h_i T_{0j} = \delta_{ij} f_i(\mathbf{r}) \qquad \text{on boundary } S_i \qquad (2\text{-}156b)$$

where

$i = 1, 2, \dots, s$

$j = 0, 1, 2, \dots, s$

s = number of continuous boundary surfaces of region R

δ_{ij} = kronecker delta = $\begin{cases} 0 & \text{for } i \neq j \\ 1 & \text{for } i = j \end{cases}$

The temperature $T_h(\mathbf{r}, t)$ is taken as the solution of the following homogeneous problem

$$\nabla^2 T_h(\mathbf{r}, t) = \frac{1}{\alpha} \frac{\partial T_h(\mathbf{r}, t)}{\partial t} \qquad \text{on region } R, \ t > 0 \qquad (2\text{-}157a)$$

$$k_i \frac{\partial T_h}{\partial n_i} + h_i T_h = 0 \qquad \text{on boundary } S_i \qquad (2\text{-}157b)$$

$$T_h = F(\mathbf{r}) - \sum_{j=0}^{s} T_{0j}(\mathbf{r}) \qquad \text{for } t = 0, \text{ in region } R \qquad (2\text{-}157c)$$

Then, the solution $T(\mathbf{r}, t)$ of the problem (2-155) is given in terms of the solutions of the above problems as

$$T(\mathbf{r}, t) = T_h(\mathbf{r}, t) + \sum_{j=0}^{s} T_{0j}(\mathbf{r}) \qquad (2\text{-}158)$$

The validity of equation (2-158) can be verified by substituting this equation into equation (2-155) and by utilizing equations (2-156) and (2-157).

We note that equations (2-156) corresponds to a set of steady-state heat-conduction problems. The function $T_{00}(\mathbf{r})$ for $j = 0$ corresponds to a steady-state heat-conduction problem with heat generation in the medium, but subject to all homogeneous boundary conditions. The functions $T_{01}(\mathbf{r})$, $T_{02}(\mathbf{r}), T_{03}(\mathbf{r}), \dots$ for $j = 1, 2, 3, \dots$, respectively, corresponds to heat-conduction problems with no heat generation, but only one of the boundary conditions, $i = j$, is nonhomogeneous.

The homogeneous problem given by equations (2-157) is the homogeneous version of the original problem (2-155), except the initial condition is modified by subtracting from it the sum of the solutions of the steady-state problems (2-156).

Clearly, the problems defined by equations (2-156) and (2-157), when given in the rectangular coordinate system, are soluble with the techniques discussed in this chapter. The more general case will be discussed in Chapter 13 in connection with the general method of solution of heat-conduction problems by the integral transform technique.

Example 2-15. A slab, $0 \le x \le L$, is initially at temperature $F(x)$. For times $t > 0$ the boundaries at $x = 0$ and $x = L$ are kept at constant temperatures T_1 and T_2, respectively. Obtain an expression for the temperature distribution $T(x, t)$ in the slab.

Solution. The mathematical formulation of this problem is given as

$$\frac{\partial^2 T}{\partial x^2} = \frac{1}{\alpha}\frac{\partial T}{\partial t} \qquad \text{in } 0 < x < L, \ t > 0 \qquad (2\text{-}159\text{a})$$

$$T = T_1 \qquad \text{at } x = 0, \ t > 0 \qquad (2\text{-}159\text{b})$$

$$T = T_2 \qquad \text{at } x = L, \ t > 0 \qquad (2\text{-}159\text{c})$$

$$T = F(x) \qquad \text{for } t = 0, \text{ in the region} \qquad (2\text{-}159\text{d})$$

Since the problem is one-dimensional, we split it into a steady-state problem for $T_s(x)$ given as

$$\frac{d^2 T_s}{dx^2} = 0 \qquad \text{in } 0 < x < L \qquad (2\text{-}160\text{a})$$

$$T_s = T_1 \qquad \text{at } x = 0 \qquad (2\text{-}160\text{b})$$

$$T_s = T_2 \qquad \text{at } x = L \qquad (2\text{-}160\text{c})$$

and to a homogeneous problem for $T_h(x, t)$ given by

$$\frac{\partial^2 T_h}{\partial x^2} = \frac{1}{\alpha}\frac{\partial T_h}{\partial t} \qquad \text{in } 0 < x < L, \ t > 0 \qquad (2\text{-}161\text{a})$$

$$T_h = 0 \qquad \text{at } x = 0 \text{ and } x = L, \text{ for } t > 0 \quad (2\text{-}161\text{b})$$

$$T_h = F(x) - T_s(x) \equiv f^*(x) \qquad \text{for } t = 0, \text{ in the region} \qquad (2\text{-}161\text{c})$$

Then, the solution for the original problem (2-159) is determined from

$$T(x, t) = T_s(x) + T_h(x, t) \qquad (2\text{-}162)$$

The solution of the steady-state problem (2-160) is given as

$$T_s(x) = T_1 + (T_2 - T_1)\frac{x}{L} \qquad (2\text{-}163)$$

The solution of the problem (2-161) is immediately written from equation (2-36) as

$$T_h(x,t) = \sum_{m=1}^{\infty} e^{-\alpha\beta_m^2 t} \frac{1}{N(\beta_m)} X(\beta_m x) \int_0^L X(\beta_m x') f^*(x') \, dx' \qquad (2\text{-}164)$$

where the eigenfunctions $X(\beta_m x)$, the norm $N(\beta_m)$ and the eigenvalues β_m are obtained from Table 2-2, Case 9, as

$$X(\beta_m, x) = \sin \beta_m x, \qquad \frac{1}{N(\beta_m)} = \frac{2}{L} \qquad (2\text{-}165a)$$

and β_m's are the roots of

$$\sin \beta_m L = 0 \qquad (2\text{-}165b)$$

and the initial condition function $f^*(x)$ is defined as

$$f^*(x) \equiv F(x) - T_s(x) = F(x) - T_1 - (T_2 - T_1)\frac{x}{L} \qquad (2\text{-}165c)$$

The solution $T(x,t)$ of the problem (2-159) is obtained by introducing equations (2-163) and (2-164) into equation (2-162). We find

$$T(x,t) = T_1 + (T_2 - T_1)\frac{x}{L} + \frac{2}{L} \sum_{m=1}^{\infty} e^{-\alpha\beta_m^2 t} \sin \beta_m x$$

$$\int_0^L \left[F(x') - T_1 - (T_2 - T_1)\frac{x'}{L} \right] \sin \beta_m x' \, dx' \qquad (2\text{-}166a)$$

Performing the integrations we obtain

$$T(x,t) = T_1 + (T_2 - T_1)\frac{x}{L} + \frac{2}{L} \sum_{m=1}^{\infty} e^{-\alpha\beta_m^2 t} \sin \beta_m x \int_0^L F(x') \sin \beta_m x' \, dx'$$

$$+ \frac{2}{L} \sum_{m=1}^{\infty} e^{-\alpha\beta_m^2 t} \frac{1}{\beta_m} \sin \beta_m x [T_2 \cos m\pi - T_1] \qquad (2\text{-}166b)$$

where $\cos m\pi = (-1)^m$ and $\beta_m = m\pi/L$.

Example 2-16. A slab, $0 \leq x \leq L$, is initially at temperature $F(x)$. For times $t > 0$, heat is generated in the solid at a constant rate of g_0 per unit volume, the boundary at $x = 0$ is kept insulated and the boundary at $x = L$ is kept at zero temperature. Obtain an expression for the temperature distribution $T(x,t)$ in the slab.

Solution. The mathematical formulation of this problem is given as

$$\frac{\partial^2 T}{\partial x^2} + \frac{1}{k}g_0 = \frac{1}{\alpha}\frac{\partial T}{\partial t} \qquad \text{in } 0 < x < L, \ t > 0 \qquad (2\text{-}167a)$$

$$\frac{\partial T}{\partial x} = 0 \qquad \text{at } x = 0, \ t > 0 \qquad (2\text{-}167b)$$

$$T = 0 \qquad \text{at } x = L, \ t > 0 \qquad (2\text{-}167c)$$

$$T = F(x) \qquad \text{for } t = 0 \text{ in } 0 \le x \le L \qquad (2\text{-}167d)$$

This problem is split up into a steady-state problem for $T_s(x)$ as

$$\frac{d^2 T_s}{dx^2} + \frac{1}{k}g_0 = 0 \qquad \text{in} \qquad 0 < x < L \qquad (2\text{-}168a)$$

$$\frac{dT_s}{dx} = 0 \quad \text{at } x = 0 \quad \text{and} \quad T_s = 0 \quad \text{at } x = L \qquad (2\text{-}168b)$$

and a homogeneous problem for $T_h(x, t)$ as

$$\frac{\partial^2 T_h}{\partial x^2} = \frac{1}{\alpha}\frac{\partial T_h}{\partial t} \qquad \text{in } 0 < x < L, \ t > 0 \qquad (2\text{-}169a)$$

$$\frac{\partial T_h}{\partial x} = 0 \quad \text{at } x = 0, \qquad T_h = 0 \quad \text{at } x = L \text{ for } t > 0 \quad (2\text{-}169b)$$

$$T_h = F(x) - T_s(x) \equiv f^*(x) \qquad \text{for } t = 0, \text{ in } 0 \le x \le L \qquad (2\text{-}169c)$$

Then, the solution of the original problem (2-167) is determined from

$$T(x, t) = T_s(x) + T_h(x, t) \qquad (2\text{-}170)$$

The solution of the steady-state problem (2-168) is

$$T_s(x) = \frac{1}{2k}g_0 L^2 \left(1 - \frac{x^2}{L^2}\right) \qquad (2\text{-}171)$$

and the solution of the homogeneous problem (2-169) is obtained as

$$T_h(x, t) = \frac{2}{L}\sum_{m=0}^{\infty} e^{-\alpha\beta_m^2 t}\cos\beta_m x \int_0^L f^*(x')\cos\beta_m x'\, dx' \qquad (2\text{-}172a)$$

where

$$f^*(x) \equiv F(x) - \frac{1}{2k}g_0 L^2 \left(1 - \frac{x^2}{L^2}\right) \qquad (2\text{-}172b)$$

and β_m's are the positive roots of

$$\cos\beta_m L = 0 \qquad \text{or} \qquad \beta_m = \frac{(2m+1)\pi}{2L}, \qquad m = 0, 1, 2\ldots \quad (2\text{-}172c)$$

Introducing equations (2-171) and (2-172) into (2-170) and performing the integrations we obtain

$$T(x,t) = \frac{g_0 L^2}{2k}\left(1 - \frac{x^2}{L^2}\right) + \frac{2}{L}\sum_{m=0}^{\infty} e^{-\alpha\beta_m^2 t}\cos\beta_m x \int_0^L F(x')\cos\beta_m x'\,dx'$$
$$- \frac{2g_0}{LK}\sum_{m=0}^{\infty}(-1)^m e^{-\alpha\beta_m^2 t}\frac{1}{\beta_m^3}\cos\beta_m x \qquad (2\text{-}173)$$

2-11   USEFUL TRANSFORMATIONS

In this section we present some transformations that are useful in reducing the differential equation into a more convenient form.

   1. We consider an equation containing convective and generation terms in the form

$$\frac{\partial T}{\partial t} = \alpha\frac{\partial^2 T}{\partial x^2} - \beta\frac{\partial T}{\partial x} + \gamma T + g \qquad (2\text{-}174)$$

where α, β, and γ are constants, $\beta(\partial T/\partial x)$ represents a convective diffusion and γT represents generation proportional to the local temperature. We define a new dependent variable $W(x,t)$ as

$$T(x,t) = W(x,t)\exp\left[\frac{\beta}{2\alpha}x - \left(\frac{\beta^2}{4\alpha} - \gamma\right)t\right] \qquad (2\text{-}175)$$

Then, under this transformation, equation (2-174) reduces to

$$\frac{\partial W}{\partial t} = \alpha\frac{\partial^2 W}{\partial x^2} + g\cdot\exp\left\{-\left[\frac{\beta}{2\alpha}x - \left(\frac{\beta^2}{4\alpha} - \gamma\right)t\right]\right\} \qquad (2\text{-}176)$$

which is easier to solve than equation (2-174). The boundary and the initial conditions for the problem should be transformed with the same transformation.

   2. We now generalize the above procedure to three-dimensional equation given as

$$\frac{\partial T}{\partial t} = \alpha\left(\frac{\partial^2 T}{\partial x^2} + \frac{\partial^2 T}{\partial y^2} + \frac{\partial^2 T}{\partial z^2}\right) - \beta_1\frac{\partial T}{\partial x} - \beta_2\frac{\partial T}{\partial y} - \beta_3\frac{\partial T}{\partial z} + \gamma T + g$$
$$(2\text{-}177)$$

where $\alpha, \beta_1, \beta_2, \beta_3$, and γ are constants. We define a new dependent variable

$W(x, y, z, t)$ as

$$T(x, y, z, t) = W(x, y, z, t) \exp\left[\frac{\beta_1}{2\alpha}x - \left(\frac{\beta_1^2}{4\alpha} - \gamma\right)t\right].$$

$$\cdot \exp\left[\frac{\beta_2}{2\alpha}y - \frac{\beta_2^2}{4\alpha}t\right] \cdot \exp\left[\frac{\beta_3}{2\alpha}z - \frac{\beta_3}{4\alpha}t\right] \quad (2\text{-}178)$$

Under this transformation equation (2-177) reduces to

$$\frac{\partial W}{\partial t} = \alpha\left(\frac{\partial^2 W}{\partial x^2} + \frac{\partial^2 W}{\partial y^2} + \frac{\partial^2 W}{\partial z^2}\right) + G \quad (2\text{-}179a)$$

where

$$G \equiv g \cdot \exp\left[-\frac{\beta_1}{2\alpha}x + \left(\frac{\beta_1^2}{4\alpha} - \gamma\right)t\right] \cdot \exp\left[-\frac{\beta_2}{2\alpha}y + \frac{\beta_2^2}{4\alpha}t\right]$$

$$\cdot \exp\left[-\frac{\beta_3}{2\alpha}z + \frac{\beta_3}{4\alpha}t\right] \quad (2\text{-}179b)$$

which is easier to solve than equation (2-177).

3. We consider an equation in the form

$$\frac{d}{dx}\left[k(x)\frac{dT}{dx}\right] + \beta(x)T = 0 \quad (2\text{-}180)$$

or in the expanded form as

$$\frac{d^2 T}{dx^2} + a(x)\frac{dT}{dx} + b(x)T = 0 \quad (2\text{-}181a)$$

where

$$a(x) \equiv \frac{1}{k(x)}\frac{dk(x)}{dx}, \qquad b(x) = \frac{\beta(x)}{k(x)} \quad (2\text{-}181b)$$

Equation (2-180) the steady-state heat conduction equation with space-dependent thermal conductivity. We define a new dependent variable $W(x)$ as [18, p. 109]

$$T(x) = W(x) \exp\left[-\frac{1}{2}\int_0^x a(x') dx'\right] \quad (2\text{-}182)$$

Under this transformation equation (2-181a) is transformed into

$$\frac{d^2 W}{dx^2} + \left[b(x) - \frac{1}{2}\frac{da(x)}{dx} - \frac{1}{4}a^2(x)\right]W = 0 \quad (2\text{-}183)$$

or introducing the definitions of $a(x)$ and $b(x)$ we obtain

$$\frac{d^2 W}{dx^2} + A(x)W = 0 \qquad (2\text{-}184\text{a})$$

where

$$A(x) \equiv \frac{\beta(x)}{k(x)} - \frac{1}{2}\frac{d}{dx}\left(\frac{1}{k}\frac{dk}{dx}\right) - \frac{1}{4}\left(\frac{1}{k}\frac{dk}{dx}\right)^2 \qquad (2\text{-}184\text{b})$$

The above transformation is valid provided $\int_0^x a(x')\,dx'$ is finite for finite x and the zeros of W is the same as the zeros of T.

Equation (2-184a) can be reduced to a first order equation if we define a new dependent variable $V(x)$ as

$$W(x) = e^{\int_0^x V(x')\,dx'} \qquad (2\text{-}185)$$

Under this transformation equation (2-184a) simplifies to

$$\frac{dV(x)}{dx} + V^2(x) + A(x) = 0 \qquad (2\text{-}186)$$

which is a Riccatti type equation.

REFERENCES

1. M. Philip Morse and H. Feshbach, *Methods of Theoretical Physics*, Part I, McGraw-Hill Book Co., New York, 1953.

2. John W. Dettman, *Mathematical Methods in Physics and Engineering*, McGraw-Hill Book Co., New York, 1962.

3. Parry Moon and Domino Eberle Spencer, *Field Theory for Engineers*, D. Van Nostrand Company, Inc., Princeton, N.J., 1961.

4. R. V. Churchill, *Fourier Series and Boundary Value Problems*, McGraw-Hill Book Co., New York, 1963.

5. H. S. Carslaw and J. C. Jaeger, *Conduction of Heat in Solids*, Oxford at the Clarendon Press, London, 1959.

6. V. S. Arpaci, *Conduction Heat Transfer*, Addison-Wesley Publishing Co., Reading, Mass., 1966.

7. M. N. Özişik, *Boundary Value Problems of Heat Conduction*, International Textbook Company, Scranton, Pa., 1968.

8. A. V. Luikov, *Analytical Heat Diffusion Theory*, Academic Press, New York, 1968.

9. Parry Moon and Domino Eberle Spencer, *Q. Appl. Math.* **16**, 1–10, 1956.

10. A. Erdelyi, W. Magnus, F. Oberhettinger, and F. G. Tricomi, *Higher Transcendental Functions*, McGraw-Hill Book Co., New York, 1953.

11. R. V. Churchill, *Operational Mathematics*, McGraw-Hill Book Co., New York, 1958.

12. E. C. Titchmarsh, *Eigenfunction Expansions*, Clarendon Press, London, 1962.

13. M. L. James, G. M. Smith and J. C. Wolford, *Applied Numerical Methods for Digital Computations with Fortrand and CSMP*, 2nd edition, IEP, New York, 1977.

14. E. C. Titchmarsh, *Fourier Integrals*, 2nd edition, Clarendon Press, London, 1962.

15. E. E. Burniston and C. E. Siewert, *Proc. Camb. Phil. Soc.* **73**, 111–118, 1973.

16. H. B. Dwight, *Tables of Integrals and Other Mathematical Data*, 4th ed., MacMillan Co., New York, 1957.

17. M. J. Moran, *A New Approach to Steady Heat Conduction in Regions with Generation, Fourth International Heat Transfer Conference*, Vol. C. 1.4, Paris, 1970, p. 1–10.

18. R. Bellman, *Stability Theory of Differential Equations*, McGraw-Hill Book Co., Inc., 1953.

PROBLEMS

2-1 A slab, $0 \le x \le L$, is initially at a temperature $F(x)$. For times $t > 0$ the boundaries at $x = 0$ and $x = L$ are kept at zero temperature. Derive an expression for the temperature $T(x, t)$ in the slab for times $t > 0$. Determine the temperature $T(x, t)$ for the special case $F(x) = T_0 = $ constant.

2-2 A slab, $0 \le x \le L$, is initially at a temperature $F(x)$. For times $t > 0$ the boundary surface at $x = 0$ is kept insulated and that at $x = L$ dissipates heat by convection into a medium at zero temperature with a heat transfer coefficient h. Obtain an expression for the temperature distribution $T(x, t)$ in the slab for times $t > 0$ and for the heat flux at the boundary surface $x = L$.

2-3 A slab, $0 \le x \le L$, is initially at a temperature $F(x)$. For times $t > 0$ the boundary surface at $x = 0$ is kept at zero temperature, whereas the boundary at $x = L$ dissipates heat by convection into a medium at zero temperature with a heat-transfer coefficient h. Obtain an expression for the temperature $T(x, t)$ in the slab and the heat flux at the boundary surface $x = L$ for times $t > 0$. Also consider the case when $F(x) = T_0 = $ constant.

2-4 A semi-infinite medium, $0 \le x < \infty$, is initially at zero temperature. For times $t > 0$ the boundary surface at $x = 0$ is kept at a constant temperature T_0. Obtain an expression for the temperature distribution $T(x, t)$ in the slab for times $t > 0$.

2-5 A semi-infinite medium, $0 \le x < \infty$, is initially at a uniform temperature T_0 and for times $t > 0$ it dissipates heat by convection from the boundary surface $x = 0$ into an environment at zero temperature. Obtain an expression for the temperature distribution $T(x, t)$ in the medium for times $t > 0$. Determine an expression for the heat flux at the surface $x = 0$.

2-6 In a one-dimensional infinite medium, $-\infty < x < \infty$, initially, the region $a < x < b$ is at a constant temperature T_0, and everywhere outside this region is at zero temperature. Obtain an expression for the temperature distribution $T(x, t)$ in the medium for times $t > 0$.

2-7 A rectangular region $0 \le x \le a, 0 \le y \le b$ is initially at a temperature $F(x, y)$. For times $t > 0$ it dissipates heat by convection from all its boundary surfaces into an environment at zero temperature. The heat transfer coefficient is the same for all the boundaries. Obtain an expression for the temperature distribution $T(x, y, t)$ in the region for times $t > 0$.

2-8   A region $x > 0, y > 0, z > 0$ is initially at a uniform temperature T_0. For times $t > 0$ all the boundaries are kept at zero temperature. Using the product solution obtain an expression for the temperature distribution $T(x, y, z, t)$ in the medium.

2-9   A region $x > 0, y > 0$ is initially at a uniform temperature T_0. For times $t > 0$, both boundaries dissipate heat by convection into an environment at zero temperature. The heat-transfer coefficients are the same for both boundaries. Using the product solution, obtain an expression for the temperature distribution $T(x, y, t)$ in the medium.

2-10   A rectangular region $0 \leq x \leq a, 0 \leq y \leq b$ is initially at a uniform temperature T_0. For times $t > 0$ the boundaries at $x = 0$ and $y = 0$ are kept at zero temperature and the boundaries at $x = a$ and $y = b$ dissipate heat by convection into an environment at zero temperature. The heat-transfer coefficients are the same for both of these boundaries. Using the product solution obtain an expression for the temperature distribution $T(x, y, t)$ in the medium for times $t > 0$.

2-11   A rectangular parallelepiped $0 \leq x \leq a, 0 \leq y \leq b, 0 \leq z \leq c$ is initially at a uniform temperature T_0. For times $t > 0$ the boundaries at $x = 0$, $y = 0$, and $z = 0$ are insulated and the boundaries at $x = a, y = b$, and $z = c$ are kept at zero temperature. Using the product solution obtain an expression for the temperature distribution $T(x, y, z, t)$ in the region.

2-12   Repeat problem (2-11) for the case when the boundaries at $x = a$, $y = b$, and $z = c$ dissipate heat by convection into an environment at zero temperature. Assume the heat transfer coefficients to be the same at all these boundaries.

2-13   Obtain an expression for the steady-state temperature distribution $T(x, y)$ in a semi-infinite strip $0 \leq x \leq a, 0 \leq y < \infty$, for the case when the boundary at $x = 0$ is kept at a temperature $f(y)$ and the boundaries at $y = 0$ and $x = a$ are kept at zero temperature.

2-14   Obtain an expression for the steady-state temperature distribution $T(x, y)$ in an infinite strip $0 \leq x \leq a, -\infty < y < \infty$, for the case when the boundary surface at $x = 0$ is kept at a temperature $f(y)$ and the boundary surface at $x = a$ is kept at zero temperature.

2-15   Obtain an expression for the steady-state temperature distribution $T(x, y)$ in a rectangular region $0 \leq x \leq a, 0 \leq y \leq b$ for the following boundary conditions: the boundary at $x = 0$ is kept insulated, the boundary at $y = 0$ is kept at a temperature $f(x)$ and the boundaries at $x = a$ and $y = b$ dissipate heat by convection into an environment at zero temperature. Assume the heat transfer coefficient to be the same for both boundaries.

2-16 Obtain an expression for the steady-state temperature distribution $T(x, y, z)$ in a rectangular parallelepiped $0 \leq x \leq a, 0 \leq y \leq b, 0 \leq z \leq c$ for the following boundary conditions: the boundary surfaces at $x = 0$ is kept at temperature T_0, the boundaries at $y = 0$ and $z = 0$ are kept insulated, the boundary at $x = a$ is kept at zero temperature, and the boundaries at $y = b$ and $z = c$ dissipate heat by convection into an environment at zero temperature. The heat-transfer coefficients are the same for all these surfaces.

2-17 Obtain an expression for the steady-state temperature distribution $T(x, y)$ in a rectangular region $0 \leq x \leq a$, $0 \leq y \leq b$ in which heat is generated at a constant rate $g(x, y) = g_0 = $ constant and subjected to the following boundary conditions: boundaries at $x = 0$ and $y = 0$ are kept insulated, whereas the boundaries at $x = a$ and $y = b$ are kept at zero temperature.

2-18 A slab, $0 \leq x \leq L$, is initially at zero temperature. For times $t > 0$ the boundary at $x = 0$ is kept insulated, the boundary at $x = L$ is kept at zero temperature, and there is heat generation within the solid at a constant rate of g_0. Obtain an expression for the temperature distribution $T(x, t)$ in the slab for times $t > 0$.

2-19 A semi-infinite medium $x \geq 0$ is initially at a uniform temperature T_0. For times $t > 0$ the boundary at $x = 0$ is kept at zero temperature and heat is generated within the solid at a constant rate of g_0. Obtain an expression for the temperature distribution $T(x, t)$ for times $t > 0$.

NOTES

1.   The properties of the following homogeneous boundary value problem, called a Sturm-Liouville problem, was first studied by J. C. F. Sturm and J. Liouville in Journal de Mathématique, 1836–1838. Here we present the orthogonality of the eigenfunctions

$$\frac{d}{dx}\left[p(x)\frac{d\psi(\lambda, x)}{dx} \right] + [q(x) + \lambda w(x)]\psi(\lambda, x) = 0 \qquad \text{in } a < x < b \quad \text{(1a)}$$

$$A_1 \frac{d\psi(\lambda, x)}{dx} + A_2\psi(\lambda, x) = 0 \qquad \text{at } x = a \qquad \text{(1b)}$$

$$B_1 \frac{d\psi(\lambda, x)}{dx} + B_2\psi(\lambda, x) = 0 \qquad \text{at } x = b \qquad \text{(1c)}$$

where the functions $p(x), q(x), w(x)$ and $dp(x)/dx$ are assumed to be real valued, and continuous, and $p(x) > 0$ and $w(x) > 0$ over the interval (a, b). The constants A_1, A_2, B_1, B_2 are real and independent of the parameter

λ. Let

$$L[\psi(\lambda, x)] \equiv \frac{d}{dx}\left[p(x)\frac{d\psi(\lambda, x)}{dx} \right] + q(x)\psi(\lambda, x) \tag{2}$$

We then write equation (1a) for any two eigenfunctions $\psi(\lambda_m, x)$ and $\psi(\lambda_n, x)$ as

$$L[\psi_m(x)] + \lambda_m w(x)\psi_m(x) = 0 \tag{3a}$$

$$L[\psi_n(x)] + \lambda_n w(x)\psi_n(x) = 0 \tag{3b}$$

where

$$\psi_n(x) \equiv \psi(\lambda_n x)$$

We multiply equation (3a) by $\psi_n(x)$ and equation (3b) by $\psi_m(x)$, then subtract the results

$$\frac{d}{dx}\left[p(\psi_n\psi'_m - \psi_m\psi'_n) \right] = (\lambda_n - \lambda_m)w\psi_m\psi_n \tag{4}$$

When both sides of equation (4) are integrated with respect to x from $x = a$ to $x = b$, the left-hand side vanishes in view of the homogeneous boundary conditions (1b) and (1c); we obtain

$$(\lambda_n - \lambda_m)\int_a^b w(x)\psi_m(x)\psi_n(x)\, dx = 0 \tag{5}$$

For $\lambda_n \neq \lambda_m$, equation (5) is satisfied if

$$\int_a^b w(x)\psi_m(x)\psi_n(x)\, dx = 0 \qquad \text{for } \lambda_n \neq \lambda_m \tag{6}$$

which proves that eigenfunctions of the Sturm-Liouville system are orthogonal with respect to the weighting function $w(x)$ in the interval (a, b).

2. The eigenfunctions $X(\beta_m, x) \equiv X_m$, the eigenvalues β_m and the norm $N(\beta_m)$ of the eigenvalue problem (2-32) are now determined. The boundary conditions (2-32b) and (2-32c) are written as

$$-X'_m + H_1 X_m = 0 \qquad \text{at } x = 0 \tag{1a}$$

$$X'_m + H_2 X_m = 0 \qquad \text{at } x = L \tag{1b}$$

where

$$H_1 \equiv \frac{h_1}{k_1} \qquad \text{and} \qquad H_2 \equiv \frac{h_2}{k_2}$$

The solution X_m of equation (2-32a) chosen as

$$X_m = \beta_m \cos \beta_m x + H_1 \sin \beta_m x \tag{2}$$

satisfies the boundary condition at $x = 0$. Equation (2) is substituted into the boundary condition at $x = L$ to yield

$$\tan \beta_m L = \frac{\beta_m (H_1 + H_2)}{\beta_m^2 - H_1 H_2} \tag{3}$$

Thus, if β_m's are chosen as the positive roots of this transcendental equation the solution (2) satisfies the boundary condition at $x = L$.

The norm is defined as

$$N(\beta_m) = \int_0^L X_m^2 \, dx \tag{4}$$

This integral is evaluated as now described. From the differential equation (2-32a) we have

$$\int_0^L X_m^2 \, dx = -\frac{1}{\beta_m^2} \int_0^L X_m X_m'' \, dx$$

$$= -\frac{1}{\beta_m^2} [X_m X_m']_0^L + \frac{1}{\beta_m^2} \int_0^L X_m'^2 \, dx \tag{5}$$

where primes denote differentiation with respect to x. Differentiating equation (2) we obtain

$$\frac{1}{\beta_m} X_m' = -\beta_m \sin \beta_m x + H_1 \cos \beta_m x \tag{6}$$

By squaring equations (2) and (6) and adding the results we have

$$\frac{1}{\beta_m^2} X_m'^2 + X_m^2 = \beta_m^2 + H_1^2 \tag{7}$$

We integrate this result from $x = 0$ to $x = L$

$$\int_0^L X_m^2 \, dx = (\beta_m^2 + H_1^2)L - \frac{1}{\beta_m^2} \int_0^L X_m'^2 \, dx \tag{8}$$

Add equations (5) and (8) and utilize the definition of norm as given by equation (4); we obtain

$$2N(\beta_m) = (\beta_m^2 + H_1^2)L - \frac{1}{\beta_m^2} [X_m X_m']_0^L \tag{9}$$

From equations (2) and (6) we, respectively, obtain

$$X_m|_{x=0} \equiv \beta_m \qquad \text{and} \qquad X_m'|_{x=0} = \beta_m H_1 \tag{10}$$

From the boundary condition (1b) we have

$$X_m X'_m\big|_{x=L} = -H_2 X_m^2\big|_{x=L} \tag{11}$$

The results (10) and (11) are utilized to evaluate $[X_m X'_m]_0^L$ as

$$[X_m X'_m]_0^L = -H_2 X_m^2\big|_{x=L} - \beta_m^2 H_1 \tag{12}$$

From equations (1b) and (7)

$$X_m^2\big|_{x=L} = \frac{\beta_m^2 + H_1^2}{1 + (H_2^2/\beta_m^2)} \tag{13}$$

Equation (13) is substituted into equation (12)

$$[X_m X'_m]_0^L = -H_2 \frac{\beta_m^2 + H_1^2}{1 + (H_2/\beta_m^2)} - \beta_m^2 H_1 \tag{14}$$

Equation (14) is introduced into equation (9)

$$2N(\beta_m) = (\beta_m^2 + H_1^2)\left(L + \frac{H_2}{\beta_m^2 + H_2^2}\right) + H_1 \tag{15a}$$

or

$$\frac{1}{N(\beta_m)} = 2\left[(\beta_m^2 + H_1^2)\left(L + \frac{H_2}{\beta_m^2 + H_2^2}\right) + H_1\right]^{-1} \tag{15b}$$

3. For a boundary condition of the second kind at both boundaries, the eigenvalue problem is given as

$$\frac{d^2 X(x)}{dx^2} + \beta_m^2 X(x) = 0 \qquad \text{in } 0 < x < L \tag{1a}$$

$$\frac{dX}{dx} = 0 \qquad\qquad \text{at } x = 0 \text{ and } x = L \tag{1b}$$

From equation (1a) we have

$$\beta^2 \int_0^L X^2(x)\,dx = -\left[X\frac{dX}{dx}\right]_0^L + \int_0^L \left(\frac{dX}{dx}\right)^2 dx \tag{2}$$

The first term on the right vanishes in view of the boundary conditions. Then $\beta_0 = 0$ is also an eigenvalue corresponding to the eigenfunction $X_0(x) = \text{constant} \neq 0$. For $X_0 = 1$, the norm N becomes

$$N = \int_0^L X_0^2\,dx = \int_0^L dx = L \tag{3}$$

CHAPTER 3

THE SEPARATION OF VARIABLES IN THE CYLINDRICAL COORDINATE SYSTEM

In this chapter we examine the separation of the homogeneous heat-conduction equation in the cylindrical coordinate system; determine the elementary solutions, the norms, and the eigenvalues of the separated problems for different combinations of boundary conditions and systematically tabulate the resulting expressions for ready reference; discuss the solution of the one- and multidimensional homogeneous problems by the method of separation of variables; examine the solutions of steady-state multidimensional problems with and without the heat generation in the medium; and illustrate the splitting up of nonhomogeneous problems into a set of simpler problems. The reader should consult references [1–3] for additional applications on the solution of heat-conduction problems in the cylindrical coordinate system.

3-1 SEPARATION OF HEAT-CONDUCTION EQUATION IN THE CYLINDRICAL COORDINATE SYSTEM

Consider the three-dimensional, homogeneous differential equation of heat conduction in the cylindrical coordinate system,

$$\frac{\partial^2 T}{\partial r^2} + \frac{1}{r}\frac{\partial T}{\partial r} + \frac{1}{r^2}\frac{\partial^2 T}{\partial \phi^2} + \frac{\partial^2 T}{\partial z^2} = \frac{1}{\alpha}\frac{\partial T}{\partial t} \tag{3-1}$$

where $T \equiv T(r, \phi, z, t)$. Assume a separation of variables in the form

$$T(r, \phi, z, t) = \psi(r, \phi, z)\Gamma(t) \tag{3-2}$$

Equation (3-1) becomes

$$\frac{1}{\psi}\left(\frac{\partial^2\psi}{\partial r^2}+\frac{1}{r}\frac{\partial\psi}{\partial r}+\frac{1}{r^2}\frac{\partial^2\psi}{\partial\phi^2}+\frac{\partial^2\psi}{\partial z^2}\right)=\frac{1}{\alpha\Gamma(t)}\frac{d\Gamma(t)}{dt}=-\lambda^2 \tag{3-3}$$

Then, the separated equations are taken as

$$\frac{d\Gamma(t)}{dt}+\alpha\lambda^2\Gamma(t)=0 \tag{3-4}$$

$$\frac{\partial^2\psi}{\partial r^2}+\frac{1}{r}\frac{\partial\psi}{\partial r}+\frac{1}{r^2}\frac{\partial^2\psi}{\partial\phi^2}+\frac{\partial^2\psi}{\partial z^2}+\lambda^2\psi=0 \tag{3-5}$$

Equation (3-5) is the Helmholtz equation; we assume a separation in the form

$$\psi(r,\phi,z)=R(r)\Phi(\phi)Z(z) \tag{3-6}$$

Then equation (3-5) becomes

$$\frac{1}{R}\left(\frac{d^2R}{dr^2}+\frac{1}{r}\frac{dR}{dr}\right)+\frac{1}{r^2}\frac{1}{\Phi}\frac{d^2\Phi}{d\phi^2}+\frac{1}{Z}\frac{d^2Z}{dz^2}+\lambda^2=0 \tag{3-7}$$

The only way this equality is satisfied is if each group of functions is equated to an arbitrary separation constant in the form

$$\frac{1}{Z}\frac{d^2Z}{dz^2}=-\eta^2,\quad \frac{1}{\Phi}\frac{d^2\Phi}{d\phi^2}=-v^2,\quad \text{and}\quad \frac{1}{R_v}\left(\frac{d^2R_v}{dr^2}+\frac{1}{r}\frac{dR_v}{dr}\right)-\frac{v^2}{r^2}=-\beta^2$$

$$\tag{3-8}$$

Then, the separated equations and their elementary solutions become

$$\frac{d^2Z}{dz^2}+\eta^2Z=0 \qquad\qquad Z(\eta,z):\ \sin\eta z\ \text{and}\ \cos\eta z \tag{3-9a}$$

$$\frac{d^2\Phi}{d\phi^2}+v^2\Phi=0 \qquad\qquad \Phi(v,\phi):\ \sin v\phi\ \text{and}\ \cos v\phi \tag{3-9b}$$

$$\frac{d^2R_v}{dr^2}+\frac{1}{r}\frac{dR_v}{dr}+\left(\beta^2-\frac{v^2}{r^2}\right)R_v=0\ \ R_v(\beta,r):\ J_v(\beta r)\ \text{and}\ Y_v(\beta r) \tag{3-9c}$$

and the function $\Gamma(t)$ satisfies equation (3-4), that is,

$$\frac{d\Gamma}{dt}+\alpha\lambda^2\Gamma=0 \qquad \Gamma(t):\ e^{-\alpha\lambda^2 t} \tag{3-9d}$$

where

$$\lambda^2=\beta^2+\eta^2 \tag{3-9e}$$

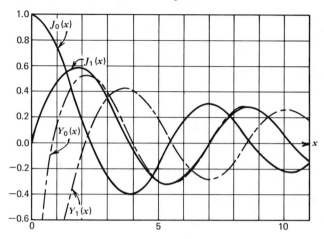

Fig. 3-1 $J_0(x)$, $Y_0(x)$ and $J_1(x)$, $Y_1(x)$ functions.

Here we note that the separation constant λ^2 does not include v^2 because of the nature of the separation. Equation (3-9c) is called *Bessel's differential equation* of order v, and its solutions, $J_v(\beta r)$ and $Y_v(\beta r)$, are the *Bessel functions* of order v of the first and second kind, respectively. Figure 3-1 shows $J_0(x)$, $J_1(x)$, $Y_0(x)$ and $Y_1(x)$ functions. The $Y_v(x)$ functions become infinite as x becomes zero; both $J_v(x)$ and $Y_v(x)$ functions have oscillatory behavior like trigonometric functions. A discussion of the properties of Bessel functions is given in Appendix III; the reader should consult references [4–7] for more information on Bessel functions.

The complete solution, $T(r, \phi, z, t)$, of equation (3-1) is constructed by the superposition of the elementary solutions of the above separated equations. The resulting separation and integration constants are determined by the application of the boundary conditions and initial condition and utilizing the orthogonality of the eigenfunctions (for finite regions) as it will be discussed in this chapter.

We now examine the separation of equation (3-1) for special cases.

1. *Temperature has no ϕ dependence.*   Equation (3-1) becomes

$$\frac{\partial^2 T}{\partial r^2} + \frac{1}{r}\frac{\partial T}{\partial r} + \frac{\partial^2 T}{\partial z^2} = \frac{1}{\alpha}\frac{\partial T}{\partial t} \tag{3-10}$$

The separated equations and their elementary solutions become

$$\frac{d^2 Z}{dz^2} + \eta^2 Z = 0 \qquad\qquad Z(\eta, z): \ \sin \eta z \text{ and } \cos \eta z \tag{3-11a}$$

$$\frac{d^2 R_0}{dr^2} + \frac{1}{r}\frac{dR_0}{dr} + \beta^2 R_0 = 0 \qquad R_0(\beta, r): \; J_0(\beta r) \text{ and } Y_0(\beta r) \qquad (3\text{-}11\text{b})$$

$$\frac{d\Gamma}{dt} + \alpha\lambda^2\Gamma = 0 \qquad\qquad \Gamma(t): \; e^{-\alpha\lambda^2 t} \qquad\qquad (3\text{-}11\text{c})$$

where

$$\lambda^2 = \beta^2 + \eta^2 \qquad (3\text{-}11\text{d})$$

We note that the solutions, $R_0(\beta, r)$, of equation (3-11b) are zero-order Bessel functions, because equation (3-10) has no ϕ dependence; hence, $v = 0$.

2. *Temperature has no z dependence.* Equation (3-1) becomes

$$\frac{\partial^2 T}{\partial r^2} + \frac{1}{r}\frac{\partial T}{\partial r} + \frac{1}{r^2}\frac{\partial^2 T}{\partial \phi^2} = \frac{1}{\alpha}\frac{\partial T}{\partial t} \qquad (3\text{-}12)$$

The separated equations and their elementary solutions become

$$\frac{d^2 \Phi}{d\phi^2} + v^2 \Phi = 0 \qquad\qquad \Phi(v, \phi): \; \sin v\phi \text{ and } \cos v\phi \qquad (3\text{-}13\text{a})$$

$$\frac{d^2 R_v}{dr^2} + \frac{1}{r}\frac{dR_v}{dr} + \left(\beta^2 - \frac{v^2}{r^2}\right)R_v = 0 \qquad R_v(\beta, r): \; J_v(\beta r) \text{ and } Y_v(\beta r) \qquad (3\text{-}13\text{b})$$

$$\frac{d\Gamma}{dt} + \alpha\lambda^2\Gamma = 0 \qquad\qquad \Gamma(t): \; e^{-\alpha\lambda^2 t} \qquad (3\text{-}13\text{c})$$

where

$$\lambda^2 = \beta^2 \qquad (3\text{-}13\text{d})$$

3. *Temperature has no time-dependence.* Equation (3-1) reduces to

$$\frac{\partial^2 T}{\partial r^2} + \frac{1}{r}\frac{\partial T}{\partial r} + \frac{1}{r^2}\frac{\partial^2 T}{\partial \phi^2} + \frac{\partial^2 T}{\partial z^2} = 0 \qquad (3\text{-}14)$$

The separated equations and their elementary solutions become

$$\frac{d^2 \Phi}{d\phi^2} + v^2 \Phi = 0 \qquad\qquad \Phi(v, \phi): \; \sin v\phi \text{ and } \cos v\phi \qquad (3\text{-}15\text{a})$$

$$\frac{d^2 Z}{dz^2} + \eta^2 Z = 0 \qquad\qquad Z(\eta, z): \; \sin \eta z \text{ and } \cos \eta z \qquad (3\text{-}15\text{b})$$

$$\frac{d^2 R_v}{dr^2} + \frac{1}{r}\frac{dR_v}{dr} - \left(\eta^2 + \frac{v^2}{r^2}\right)R_v = 0 \qquad R_v(\eta, r): \; I_v(\eta r) \text{ and } K_v(\eta r) \qquad (3\text{-}15\text{c})$$

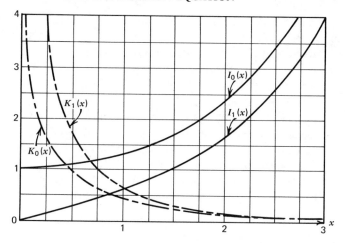

Fig. 3-2 $I_0(x)$, $K_0(x)$ and $I_1(x)$, $K_1(x)$ functions.

In this case the solution, $R_v(\eta, r)$, of equation (3-15c) involves the *modified Bessel functions of order v* of the first kind $I_v(\eta r)$ and of the second kind $K_v(\eta r)$. Figure 3-2 shows $I_0(x)$, $I_1(x)$, $K_0(x)$, and $K_1(x)$ functions. We note that $I_v(x)$ functions become infinite as $x \to \infty$ and $K_v(x)$ functions become infinite as $x \to 0$. A discussion of the properties of modified Bessel functions and their numerical values are given in Appendix III.

There is another possibility for the separation of equation (3-14), obtainable by replacing η^2 by $-\eta^2$ in equations (3-15b) and (3-15c). In this case, the elementary solutions for the Z separation are taken as $e^{-\eta z}$, $e^{\eta z}$ or $\sinh \eta z$, $\cosh \eta z$; the equation for the R separation becomes *Bessel's differential equation* of order v and its solutions are taken as: $J_v(\eta r)$, $Y_v(\eta r)$.

4. *The temperature has no t and z dependence.* Then equation (3-1) simplifies to

$$\frac{\partial^2 T}{\partial r^2} + \frac{1}{r} \frac{\partial T}{\partial r} + \frac{1}{r^2} \frac{\partial^2 T}{\partial \phi^2} = 0 \qquad (3\text{-}16)$$

The separated equations and their elementary solutions become

$$\frac{d^2 \Phi}{d\phi^2} + v^2 \Phi = 0 \qquad \Phi(v, \phi): \sin v\phi \text{ and } \cos v\phi \qquad (3\text{-}17a)$$

$$\frac{d^2 R}{dr^2} + \frac{1}{r} \frac{dR}{dr} - \frac{v^2}{r^2} R = 0 \qquad R(r): \begin{cases} r^v \text{ and } r^{-v} \text{ for } v \neq 0 \\ c_1 + c_2 \ln r \text{ for } v = 0 \end{cases} \qquad (3\text{-}17b)$$

We note that for this particular case the equation for the function $R(r)$ is *Euler's homogeneous* differential equation.

In the solution of the heat conduction problem by the method of separation of variables, if Bessel functions $J_v(\beta r)$ or $Y_v(\beta r)$ appear as elementary solutions of the separated equations, it may be necessary to represent the initial condition function or the nonhomogeneous part of the boundary condition function in terms of the Bessel functions. Therefore, we devote the next section to a discussion of the representation of an arbitrary function $F(r)$ in terms of the Bessel functions in a finite, a semi-infinite, and an infinite interval. The resulting eigenfunctions, eigenvalues, and the norms associated with such expansions will be systematically tabulated for various combinations of boundary conditions, for ready reference, as has been done in the previous chapter. The reader should consult references [8–12] for further discussion of the representation of an arbitrary function in terms of the Bessel functions.

3-2 REPRESENTATION OF AN ARBITRARY FUNCTION IN TERMS OF BESSEL FUNCTIONS

In the previous chapter we discussed the representation of an arbitrary function defined in a finite, semi-infinite or infinite interval in terms of the trigonometric functions in connection with the solution of the heat-conduction problem in the rectangular coordinate system. We now present similar representations of an arbitrary function $F(r)$ in terms of the Bessel functions for the regions $0 \le r \le b$, $a \le r \le b$, and $0 \le r < \infty$.

Region $0 \le r \le b$

We consider the representation of an arbitrary function $F(r)$ defined in a finite interval $0 \le r < b$ in terms of the eigenfunctions $R_v(\beta_m, r)$ of the following eigenvalue problem

$$\frac{d^2R_v(r)}{dr^2} + \frac{1}{r}\frac{dR_v(r)}{dr} + \left(\beta^2 - \frac{v^2}{r^2}\right)R_v(r) = 0 \qquad \text{in } 0 \le r < b \quad (3\text{-}18\text{a})$$

$$\frac{dR_v}{dr} + HR_v = 0 \qquad\qquad\qquad\qquad \text{at } r = b \qquad (3\text{-}18\text{b})$$

As it will be apparent later in this chapter, the eigenvalue problem of this type is encountered in the solution of heat-conduction problem for a solid cylinder $0 \le r \le b$ with temperature varying with the ϕ angle. For generality, the boundary condition at $r = b$ is chosen of the third kind. The boundary conditions of the second and the first kinds are obtainable from equation (3-18b) by setting $H = 0$ and $H \to \infty$, respectively.

The eigenvalue problem given by equation (3-18) is a special case of the Sturm-Liouville problem discussed previously, hence the eigenfunctions $R_v(\beta_m, r)$ are orthogonal in the interval $0 \le r < b$ with respect to the weighting function $w = r$. That is

$$\int_0^b r R_v(\beta_m, r) R_v(\beta_n, r)\, dr = \begin{cases} 0 & \text{for } m \ne n \\ N(\beta_m) & \text{for } m = n \end{cases} \tag{3-19}$$

We now consider the representation of an arbitrary function $F(r)$ defined in the finite interval $0 \le r < b$ in terms of the eigenfunctions $R_v(\beta_m, r)$ in the form

$$F(r) = \sum_{m=1}^{\infty} c_m R_v(\beta_m, r) \qquad \text{in } 0 \le r < b \tag{3-20}$$

The unknown coefficients c_m are determined by operating on both sides of equation (3-20) by the operator $\int_0^b r R_v(\beta_n, r)\, dr$ and utilizing the orthogonality relation (3-19). We find

$$c_m = \frac{1}{N(\beta_m)} \int_0^b r R_v(\beta_m, r) F(r)\, dr \tag{3-21a}$$

where the norm is

$$N(\beta_m) = \int_0^b r R_v^2(\beta_m, r)\, dr \tag{3-21b}$$

The substitution of equation (3-21a) into (3-20) gives this expansion as

$$F(r) = \sum_{m=1}^{\infty} \frac{1}{N(\beta_m)} R_v(\beta_m, r) \int_0^b r' R_v(\beta_m, r') F(r')\, dr' \qquad \text{in } 0 \le r < b \tag{3-22}$$

The conditions under which an arbitrary function $F(r)$ defined in a finite interval $0 \le r < b$ can be represented as given by equation (3-22) are similar to those discussed in the previous chapter in connection with the representation given by equation (2-37).

The integral (3-21b) defining the norm can be evaluated by utilizing the following indefinite integral of Bessel functions [4, p. 135; 5, p. 110]

$$\int r G_v^2(\beta r)\, dr = \tfrac{1}{2} r^2 [G_v^2(\beta r) - G_{v-1}(\beta r) G_{v+1}(\beta r)] \tag{3-23a}$$

$$= \tfrac{1}{2} r^2 \left[G_v'^2(\beta r) + \left(1 - \frac{v^2}{\beta^2 r^2}\right) G_v^2(\beta r) \right] \tag{3-23b}$$

where $G_v(\beta r)$ is any Bessel function of the first or second kind of order v.

Having established the formal representation of an arbitrary function $F(r)$ as given by equation (3-22), we now determine explicit expressions for the eigenfunctions $R_v(\beta_m, r)$, the norm $N(\beta_m)$, and the eigenvalues β_m of the eigenvalue problem (3-18) for boundary conditions of the first, second, and third kind at $r = b$.

Boundary Condition at $r = b$ is of the Third Kind. The general solution of equation (3-18a) consists of $J_\nu(\beta r)$ and $Y_\nu(\beta r)$ functions. The solution that remains finite at $r = 0$ is taken as

$$R_\nu(\beta_m, r) = J_\nu(\beta_m r) \tag{3-24}$$

since the $Y_\nu(\beta_m r)$ function becomes infinite at $r = 0$. If this solution should satisfy the boundary condition (3-18b), β_m's should be the positive roots of the following transcendental equation

$$\beta_m J_\nu'(\beta_m b) + H J_\nu(\beta_m b) = 0 \tag{3-25}$$

where we defined

$$J_\nu'(\beta_m b) \equiv \left[\frac{d}{dr} J_\nu(r) \right]_{r = \beta_m b} \tag{3-26}$$

here H and ν are real constants and [4, p. 597]

$$\nu + \tfrac{1}{2} \geq 0 \tag{3-27}$$

It is to be noted that *when prime is used to denote the derivative of Bessel functions (the first or second kind) it will imply a derivative in a sense as defined by equation* (3-26). Finally, the norm $N(\beta_m)$ is evaluated according to equations (3-21b), (3-23b), and (3-24) as

$$N(\beta_m) = \frac{b^2}{2} \left[J_\nu'^2(\beta_m b) + \left(1 - \frac{\nu^2}{\beta_m^2 b^2} \right) J_\nu^2(\beta_m b) \right] \tag{3-28a}$$

In view of the transcendental equation (3-25), this relation may be written in the alternative form as

$$N(\beta_m) = \frac{b^2}{2} \left[\frac{H^2}{\beta_m^2} + \left(1 - \frac{\nu^2}{\beta_m^2 b^2} \right) \right] J_\nu^2(\beta_m b) \tag{3-28b}$$

Boundary Condition at $r = b$ is of the Second Kind. For this special case we have $H = 0$ and the boundary condition (3-18b) reduces to $dR_\nu/dr = 0$ at $r = b$. The solution of equation (18a) is taken as

$$R_\nu(\beta_m, r) = J_\nu(\beta_m r) \tag{3-29}$$

and the eigenvalues β_m are the positive roots of

$$J_\nu'(\beta_m b) = 0 \tag{3-30}$$

The norm $N(\beta_m)$ is determined from equation (3-23b) as

$$N(\beta_m) = \frac{b^2}{2}\left(1 - \frac{v^2}{\beta_m^2 b^2}\right) J_v^2(\beta_m b) \qquad \text{for } \beta_m \neq 0 \qquad (3\text{-}31a)$$

When the boundary condition at $r = b$ is of the second kind, $\beta_0 = 0$ is also an eigenvalue for $v = 0$; then the corresponding eigenfunction and the norm for this special case are

$$R_0(\beta_0 r) = 1 \quad \text{and} \quad N(\beta_0) = \int_0^b r \, dr = \frac{b^2}{2} \qquad \text{for } \beta_0 = 0 \quad (3\text{-}31b)$$

See *Note* 1 for a discussion of $\beta_0 = 0$.

Boundary Condition at $r = b$ is of the First Kind. For this case we have $H \to \infty$, hence the boundary condition (3-18b) reduces to $R_v(\beta_m, b) = 0$. The solution of equation (3-18a) is taken as

$$R_v(\beta_m, r) = J_v(\beta_m r) \qquad (3\text{-}32)$$

and the eigenvalues β_m's are the positive roots of

$$J_v(\beta_m b) = 0 \qquad (3\text{-}33)$$

The norm $N(\beta_m)$ is obtained from equation (3-23b) as

$$N(\beta_m) = \frac{b^2}{2} J_v'^2(\beta_m b) \qquad (3\text{-}34)$$

We summarize in Table 3-1 the above results for the eigenfunctions $R_v(\beta_m, r)$, the norms $N(\beta_m)$, and the eigenvalues β_m of the eigenvalue problem (3-18) for the boundary conditions of the first, second, and third kind at $r = b$. The results given in this table will be used in the solution of heat-conduction problems for a solid cylinder $0 \leq r \leq b$ when temperature varies with azimuth angle ϕ. For problems with aximuthal symmetry, the eigenvalue problem (3-18) is applicable with $v = 0$. Therefore, the results in Table 3-1 are also applicable for heat-conduction problems for a solid cylinder with azimuthally symmetric temperature if we set $v = 0$ in these results.

Region $a \leq r \leq b$

We now consider the representation of an arbitrary function $F(r)$ defined in a finite interval $a \leq r \leq b$ in terms of the eigenfunctions of the following eigenvalue problem

$$\frac{d^2 R_v(r)}{dr^2} + \frac{1}{r}\frac{dR_v(r)}{dr} + \left(\beta^2 - \frac{v^2}{r^2}\right) R_v(r) = 0 \qquad \text{in } a < r < b \qquad (3\text{-}35a)$$

Table 3-1 The Eigenfunctions $R_\nu(\beta_m, r)$, the Norm $N(\beta_m)$, and the Eigenvalues β_m of the Differential Equation

$$\frac{d^2 R_\nu}{dr^2} + \frac{1}{r}\frac{dR_\nu}{dr} + \left(\beta^2 - \frac{\nu^2}{r^2}\right) R_\nu = 0 \quad \text{in} \quad 0 \le r < b$$

Subject to the Shown Boundary Conditions

No	Boundary Condition at $r = b$	$R_\nu(\beta_m, r)$	$\dfrac{1}{N(\beta_m)}$	Eigenvalues β_m's are the Positive Roots of
1	$\dfrac{dR_\nu}{dr} + HR_\nu = 0$	$J_\nu(\beta_m r)$	$\dfrac{2}{J_\nu^2(\beta_m b)} \cdot \dfrac{\beta_m^2}{b^2(H^2 + \beta_m^2) - \nu^2}$	$\beta_m J'_\nu(\beta_m b) + HJ_\nu(\beta_m b) = 0$
2	$\dfrac{dR_\nu}{dr} = 0$	$J_\nu(\beta_m r)^*$	$\dfrac{2}{J_\nu^2(\beta_m b)} \cdot \dfrac{\beta_m^2}{b^2\beta_m^2 - \nu^2}$ *	$J'_\nu(\beta_m b) = 0^*$
3	$R_\nu = 0$	$J_\nu(\beta_m r)$	$\dfrac{2}{b^2 J_\nu'^2(\beta_m b)}$	$J_\nu(\beta_m b) = 0$

*For this particular case $\beta_0 = 0$ is also an eigenvalue with $\nu = 0$; then the corresponding eigenfunction is $R_0 = 1$ and the norm $1/N(\beta_0) = 2/b^2$.

$$-\frac{dR_v}{dr} + H_1 R_v = 0 \qquad\qquad \text{at } r = a \qquad (3\text{-}35b)$$

$$\frac{dR_v}{dr} + H_2 R_v = 0 \qquad\qquad \text{at } r = b \qquad (3\text{-}35c)$$

The eigenvalue problem of this type is encountered in the solution of heat-conduction problems for a hollow cylinder $a \le r \le b$ when temperature varies with the azimuth angle ϕ. For generality, the boundary conditions are chosen both of the third kind. Other combinations of boundary conditions are obtainable by setting the coefficients H_1, H_2 equal to zero or infinity. Thus, nine different combinations are possible. The eigenvalue problem (3-35) for $v = 0$ is encountered in the solution of heat-conduction problems with azimuthally symmetric temperature.

Equations (3-35) are a special case of the Sturm-Liouville problem, hence the eigenfunctions $R_v(\beta_m, r)$ have the following orthogonality property

$$\int_a^b r R_v(\beta_m, r) R_v(\beta_n, r)\, dr = \begin{cases} 0 & \text{for } m \ne n \\ N(\beta_m) & \text{for } m = n \end{cases} \qquad (3\text{-}36a)$$

where

$$N(\beta_m) \equiv \int_a^b r R_v^2(\beta_m, r)\, dr \qquad (3\text{-}36b)$$

Now we consider the representation of an arbitrary function $F(r)$ defined in the interval $a < r < b$ in terms of the eigenfunctions $R_v(\beta_m, r)$ of the above eigenvalue problem (3-35) in the form

$$F(r) = \sum_{m=1}^{\infty} c_m R_v(\beta_m, r) \qquad \text{in } a < r < b \qquad (3\text{-}37)$$

The unknown coefficients c_m are determined by following a procedure described previously; then the representation (3-37) becomes

$$F(r) = \sum_{m=1}^{\infty} \frac{1}{N(\beta_m)} R_v(\beta_m, r) \int_a^b r' R_v(\beta_m, r') F(r')\, dr' \qquad \text{in } a < r < b \quad (3\text{-}38)$$

The conditions under which an arbitrary function $F(r)$ can be represented as in equation (3-38) are similar to those discussed in the previous chapter in connection with the representation given by equation (2-37).

We now examine the determination of the eigenfunctions $R_v(\beta_m, r)$, the norm $N(\beta_m)$ and the eigenvalues β_m of the expansion (3-38) for the nine different combinations of the boundary conditions (3-35b) and (3-35c). Instead of performing the analysis for each of these cases separately, the general case with boundary conditions of the third kind at $r = a$ and $r = b$

as given by equation (3-35) will be solved first. The solutions for other possible combinations of boundary conditions will be obtained from this general result by setting H_1, H_2 equal to zero or infinity.

Let $R_\nu(\beta_m, r)$ be the eigenfunctions of the eigenvalue problem given by equations (3-35). If the function $R_\nu(\beta_m, r)$ is chosen as

$$R_\nu(\beta_m, r) = S_\nu J_\nu(\beta_m r) - V_\nu Y_\nu(\beta_m r) \tag{3-39}$$

where

$$S_\nu \equiv \beta_m Y_\nu'(\beta_m b) + H_2 Y_\nu(\beta_m b) \tag{3-40a}$$

$$V_\nu \equiv \beta_m J_\nu'(\beta_m b) + H_2 J_\nu(\beta_m b) \tag{3-40b}$$

the differential equation (3-35a) and the boundary condition (3-35b) are both satisfied. If this solution should also satisfy the boundary condition (3-35c), the eigenvalues β_m's should be the positive roots of the following transcendental equation

$$S_\nu U_\nu - V_\nu W_\nu = 0 \tag{3-41}$$

where

$$U_\nu \equiv \beta_m J_\nu'(\beta_m a) - H_1 J_\nu(\beta_m a) \tag{3-42a}$$

$$W_\nu \equiv \beta_m Y_\nu'(\beta_m a) - H_1 Y_\nu(\beta_m a) \tag{3-42b}$$

with S_ν and V_ν defined as above. The result given by equation (3-41) is obtained by substituting the solution (3-39) into the boundary condition (3-35c).

The norm $N(\beta_m)$ defined by equation (3-36b) can now be written as

$$N(\beta_m) = \int_a^b r [S_\nu J_\nu(\beta_m r) - V_\nu Y_\nu(\beta_m r)]^2 \, dr$$

$$= S_\nu^2 \int_a^b r J_\nu^2(\beta_m r) \, dr - 2 S_\nu V_\nu \int_a^b r J_\nu(\beta_m r) Y_\nu(\beta_m r) \, dr + V_\nu^2 \int_a^b r Y_\nu^2(\beta_m r) \, dr \tag{3-43}$$

Various integrals in this expression can be evaluated by utilizing the wronskian relationship for the Bessel functions [8, p. 18]

$$J_\nu(\beta r) Y_\nu'(\beta r) - Y_\nu(\beta r) J_\nu'(\beta r) = \frac{2}{\pi \beta r} \tag{3-44}$$

and the indefinite integral of the product of two Bessel functions expressed in the form [10, Eq. (9)]

$$\int r G_\nu(\beta r) \bar{G}_\nu(\beta r) \, dr = \frac{r^2}{2} \left\{ G_\nu'(\beta r) \bar{G}_\nu'(\beta r) + \left[1 - \left(\frac{\nu}{\beta r} \right)^2 \right] G_\nu(\beta r) \bar{G}_\nu(\beta r) \right\} \tag{3-45a}$$

where $G_\nu(\beta r)$ and $\bar{G}_\nu(\beta r)$ can be any Bessel function of the first or second kind. It is to be noted that equation (3-45a) has been obtained by utilizing the recurrence relationships from the following indefinite integral [4, p. 134; 5, p. 110]

$$\int r G_\nu(\beta r)\bar{G}_\nu(\beta r)\,dr = \tfrac{1}{4}r^2\big[2G_\nu(\beta r)\bar{G}_\nu(\beta r) - G_{\nu-1}(\beta r)\bar{G}_{\nu+1}(\beta r)$$
$$- G_{\nu+1}(\beta r)\bar{G}_{\nu-1}(\beta r)\big] \tag{3-45b}$$

We note that the indefinite integrals (3-23) are special cases of the integrals (3-45).

The integral in the norm $N(\beta_m)$ defined by equation (3-43) can be performed by utilizing the relations (3-44) and (3-45) as described in Note 2. We present below the resulting expression for the norm $N(\beta_m)$ when the boundary conditions at $r = a$ and $r = b$ are both of the third kind.

$$\frac{1}{N(\beta_m)} = \frac{\pi^2}{2}\,\frac{\beta_m^2 U_\nu^2}{B_2 U_\nu^2 - B_1 V_\nu^2} \tag{3-46}$$

where

$$B_1 \equiv H_1^2 + \beta_m^2\left[1 - \left(\frac{\nu}{\beta_m a}\right)^2\right] \tag{3-47a}$$

$$B_2 \equiv H_2^2 + \beta_m^2\left[1 - \left(\frac{\nu}{\beta_m b}\right)^2\right] \tag{3-47b}$$

$$U_\nu \equiv \beta_m J_\nu'(\beta_m a) - H_1 J_\nu(\beta_m a) \tag{3-47c}$$

$$V_\nu \equiv \beta_m J_\nu'(\beta_m b) + H_2 J_\nu(\beta_m a) \tag{3-47d}$$

We summarize in Table 3-2 the eigenfunctions $R_\nu(\beta_m, r)$, the norm $N(\beta_m)$ and the eigenvalues β_m of the eigenvalue problem (3-35) for the nine different combinations of the boundary conditions at $r = a$ and $r = b$. We note that for the case of boundary condition of the second kind at both $r = a$ and $r = b$ (i.e., case 5), $\beta_0 = 0$ is also an eigenvalue with $\nu = 0$. This result is obtainable with an analysis similar to that given in Note 1.

The results presented in Table 3-2 will be needed in the solution of heat-conduction problems for a hollow cylinder $a \le r \le b$ when the temperature varies with the azimuth angle ϕ. For problems with azimuthally symmetric temperature (i.e., no dependence on the ϕ angle), the eigenvalue problem (3-35) is also applicable with $\nu = 0$. Therefore, the results in Table 3-2 are also applicable for the solution of heat-conduction problems in a hollow cylinder with azimuthally symmetric temperature if we set $\nu = 0$ in these results.

Table 3-2 The Solution $R_\nu(\beta_m, r)$, the Norm $N(\beta_m)$ and the Eigenvalues β_m of the Differential Equation

$$\frac{d^2R(r)}{dr^2} + \frac{1}{r}\frac{dR(r)}{dr} + \left(\beta^2 - \frac{\nu^2}{r^2}\right)R(r) = 0 \quad \text{in} \quad a < r < b$$

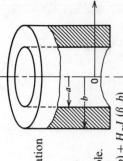

Subject to the Boundary Conditions Shown in the Table. The following notation is used in this Table.

$S_\nu \equiv \beta_m Y'_\nu(\beta_m b) + H_2 Y_\nu(\beta_m b)$, $\quad U_\nu \equiv \beta_m J'_\nu(\beta_m a) - H_1 J_\nu(\beta_m a)$, $\quad V_\nu \equiv \beta_m J'_\nu(\beta_m b) + H_2 J_\nu(\beta_m b)$

$W_\nu \equiv \beta_m Y'_\nu(\beta_m a) - H_1 Y_\nu(\beta_m a)$, $\quad B_1 \equiv H_1^2 + \beta_m^2\left[1 - \left(\frac{\nu}{\beta_m a}\right)^2\right]$, $\quad B_2 \equiv H_2^2 + \beta_m^2\left[1 - \left(\frac{\nu}{\beta_m b}\right)^2\right]$

No.	Boundary Condition at $r = a$	Boundary Condition at $r = b$	$R_\nu(\beta_m, r)$ and $1/N(\beta_m)$	β_m's are the positive roots of
1	$-\dfrac{dR}{dr} + H_1 R = 0$	$\dfrac{dR}{dr} + H_2 R = 0$	$R_\nu(\beta_m, r) = S_\nu J_\nu(\beta_m r) - V_\nu Y_\nu(\beta_m r)$ $\dfrac{1}{N(\beta_m)} = \dfrac{\pi^2}{2}\,\dfrac{\beta_m^2 U_\nu^2}{B_2 U_\nu^2 - B_1 V_\nu^2}$	$S_\nu U_\nu - V_\nu W_\nu = 0$
2	$-\dfrac{dR}{dr} + H_1 R = 0$	$\dfrac{dR}{dr} = 0$	$R_\nu(\beta_m, r) = J_\nu(\beta_m r)Y'_\nu(\beta_m b) - J'_\nu(\beta_m b)Y_\nu(\beta_m r)$ $\dfrac{1}{N(\beta_m)} = \dfrac{\pi^2}{2}\,\dfrac{\beta_m^2 U_\nu^2}{\left[1 - \left(\frac{\nu}{\beta_m b}\right)^2\right]\left[U_\nu^2 - B_1 J'^2_\nu(\beta_m b)\right]}$	$U_\nu Y'_\nu(\beta_m b) - W_\nu J'_\nu(\beta_m b) = 0$
3	$-\dfrac{dR}{dr} + H_1 R = 0$	$R = 0$	$R_\nu(\beta_m, r) = J_\nu(\beta_m r)Y_\nu(\beta_m b) - J_\nu(\beta_m b)Y_\nu(\beta_m r)$ $\dfrac{1}{N(\beta_m)} = \dfrac{\pi^2}{2}\,\dfrac{\beta_m^2 U_\nu^2}{\left[U_\nu^2 - B_1 J_\nu^2(\beta_m b)\right]}$	$U_\nu Y_\nu(\beta_m b) - W_\nu J_\nu(\beta_m b) = 0$
4	$\dfrac{dR}{dr} = 0$	$\dfrac{dR}{dr} + H_2 R = 0$	$R_\nu(\beta_m, r) = S_\nu J_\nu(\beta_m r) - V_\nu Y_\nu(\beta_m r)$ $\dfrac{1}{N(\beta_m)} = \dfrac{\pi^2}{2}\,\dfrac{\beta_m^2 J'^2_\nu(\beta_m a)}{B_2 J'^2_\nu(\beta_m a) - \left[1 - \left(\frac{\nu}{\beta_m a}\right)^2\right]V_\nu^2}$	$S_\nu J'_\nu(\beta_m a) - V_\nu Y'_\nu(\beta_m a) = 0$

			$R_v(\beta_m, r)$	$\dfrac{1}{N(\beta_m)}$	
5	$\dfrac{dR}{dr} = 0$	$\dfrac{dR}{dr} = 0$	$R_v(\beta_m, r) = J_v(\beta_m r)Y'_v(\beta_m b) - J'_v(\beta_m b)Y_v(\beta_m r)$	$\dfrac{1}{N(\beta_m)} = \dfrac{\pi^2}{2} \dfrac{\beta_m^2 J_v'^2(\beta_m a)}{\left[1-\left(\dfrac{\nu}{\beta_m b}\right)^2\right]J_v'^2(\beta_m a) - \left[1-\left(\dfrac{\nu}{\beta_m a}\right)^2\right]J_v'^2(\beta_m b)}$	$J'_v(\beta_m a)Y'_v(\beta_m b) - J'_v(\beta_m b)Y'_v(\beta_m a) = 0^*$
6	$\dfrac{dR}{dr} = 0$	$R = 0$	$R_v(\beta_m, r) = J_v(\beta_m r)Y_v(\beta_m b) - J_v(\beta_m b)Y_v(\beta_m r)$	$\dfrac{1}{N(\beta_m)} = \dfrac{\pi^2}{2} \dfrac{\beta_m^2 J_v^2(\beta_m a)}{J_v'^2(\beta_m a) - \left[1-\left(\dfrac{\nu}{\beta_m a}\right)^2\right]J_v^2(\beta_m b)}$	$J'_v(\beta_m a)Y_v(\beta_m b) - J_v(\beta_m b)Y'_v(\beta_m a) = 0$
7	$R = 0$	$R = 0$	$R_v(\beta_m, r) = S_v J_v(\beta_m r) - V_v Y_v(\beta_m r)$	$\dfrac{1}{N(\beta_m)} = \dfrac{\pi^2}{2} \dfrac{\beta_m^2 J_v^2(\beta_m a)}{B_{2v} J_v^2(\beta_m a) - V_v^2}$	$S_v J_v(\beta_m a) - V_v Y_v(\beta_m a) = 0$
8	$\dfrac{dR}{dr} = 0$	$R = 0$	$R_v(\beta_m, r) = J_v(\beta_m r)Y'_v(\beta_m b) - J'_v(\beta_m b)Y_v(\beta_m r)$	$\dfrac{1}{N(\beta_m)} = \dfrac{\pi^2}{2} \dfrac{\beta_m^2 J_v^2(\beta_m a)}{\left[1-\left(\dfrac{\nu}{\beta_m b}\right)^2\right]J_v^2(\beta_m a) - J_v'^2(\beta_m b)}$	$J_v(\beta_m a)Y'_v(\beta_m b) - J'_v(\beta_m b)Y_v(\beta_m a) = 0$
9	$R = 0$	$R = 0$	$R_v(\beta_m, r) = J_v(\beta_m r)Y_v(\beta_m b) - J_v(\beta_m b)Y_v(\beta_m r)$	$\dfrac{1}{N(\beta_m)} = \dfrac{\pi^2}{2} \dfrac{J_v^2(\beta_m a)}{J_v^2(\beta_m a) - J_v^2(\beta_m b)}$	$J_v(\beta_m a)Y_v(\beta_m b) - J_v(\beta_m b)Y_v(\beta_m a) = 0$

*For this particular case $\beta_0 = 0$ is also an eigenvalue with $\nu = 0$; the corresponding eigenfunction is $R_0(\beta_0, r) = 1$ and the norm $1/N(\beta_0) = 2/(b^2 - a^2)$.

Region $0 \leq r < \infty$

We now consider the representation of an arbitrary function $F(r)$ defined in the infinite interval $0 \leq r < \infty$ in terms of the solutions of the following differential equation

$$\frac{d^2 R_v(r)}{dr^2} + \frac{1}{r}\frac{dR_v(r)}{dr} + \left(\beta^2 - \frac{v^2}{r^2}\right)R_v(r) = 0 \qquad \text{in } 0 \leq r < \infty \quad (3\text{-}48)$$

subject to the condition that $R_v(r)$ remains finite at $r = 0$. Expansions of this type will be needed in the solution of heat-conduction problems for a region $0 \leq r < \infty$ in the cylindrical coordinate system.

The solution of equation (3-48) that remains finite at $r = 0$ is

$$R_v(\beta, r) = J_v(\beta r) \qquad (3\text{-}49)$$

An arbitrary function $F(r)$ defined in the interval $0 \leq r < \infty$ can be represented in terms of $J_v(\beta r)$ functions for $v \geq -\frac{1}{2}$ in the form $[8, \text{p. } 88; 9, \text{p. } 52; 4, \text{p. } 453]$

$$F(r) = \int_{\beta=0}^{\infty} r^{1/2}\beta J_v(\beta r)\, d\beta \int_{r'=0}^{\infty} r'^{1/2}J_v(\beta r')F(r')\, dr' \qquad 0 \leq r < \infty \quad (3\text{-}50)$$

if the integral $\int_0^\infty F(r')\, dr'$ is absolutely convergent, and if the function $F(r)$ is of bounded variation in the neighborhood of the point r.

If we now replace $F(r)$ by $r^{1/2}F(r)$ in the representation (3-50), we obtain

$$F(r) = \int_{\beta=0}^{\infty} \beta J_v(\beta r)\, d\beta \int_{r'=0}^{\infty} r'J_v(\beta r')F(r')\, dr' \qquad 0 \leq r < \infty \quad (3\text{-}51)$$

which is the representation of a function $F(r)$ in the interval $0 \leq r < \infty$ that will be needed for the solution of heat-conduction problems in an infinite region $0 \leq r < \infty$.

Region $a < r < \infty$

We now examine the representation of an arbitrary function $F(r)$ defined in the interval $a < r < \infty$ in terms of the solutions of the following problem

$$\frac{d^2 R_0(r)}{dr^2} + \frac{1}{r}\frac{dR_0(r)}{dr} + \beta^2 R_0(r) = 0 \qquad \text{in } a < r < \infty \quad (3\text{-}52a)$$

$$-\frac{dR_0}{dr} + HR_0 = 0 \qquad \text{at } r = a \quad (3\text{-}52b)$$

such a representation is needed in the solution of heat-conduction problems in the region $a \leq r < \infty$ in the cylindrical coordinate system for an azimuthally symmetric temperature (i.e., temperature does not depend on ϕ).

The representation of an arbitrary function $F(r)$ in the region $a < r < \infty$ in terms of the solutions $R_0(\beta, r)$ of the problem (3-52) is considered in reference [11] and his results can be written formally in the form

$$F(r) = \int_{\beta = 0}^{\infty} \frac{1}{N(\beta)} \beta R_0(\beta, r) \, d\beta \int_{r' = a}^{\infty} r' R_0(\beta, r') F(r') \, dr' \quad \text{in } a < r < \infty \quad (3\text{-}53)$$

Here, the norm $N(\beta)$, the function $R_0(\beta, r)$ depend on the type of the boundary condition at $r = a$; that is, whether it is of the first, second, or the third kind. We present the expressions for $R_0(\beta, r)$ and $N(\beta)$ for three different types of boundary conditions at $r = a$.

The Boundary Condition at $r = a$ is of the Third Kind. The solution of equation (3-52a) satisfying the boundary condition (3-52b) is taken as

$$R_0(\beta, r) = J_0(\beta r)[\beta Y_1(\beta a) + H Y_0(\beta a)] - Y_0(\beta r)[\beta J_1(\beta a) + H J_0(\beta a)] \quad (3\text{-}54a)$$

and the norm $N(\beta)$ is given by

$$N(\beta) = [\beta J_1(\beta a) + H J_0(\beta a)]^2 + [\beta Y_1(\beta a) + H Y_0(\beta a)]^2 \quad (3\text{-}54b)$$

The Boundary Condition at $r = a$ is of the Second Kind. For this special case we have $H = 0$. The solution of equation (3-52a) satisfying this boundary condition is taken as

$$R_0(\beta, r) = J_0(\beta r) Y_1(\beta a) - Y_0(\beta r) J_1(\beta a) \quad (3\text{-}55a)$$

and the norm becomes

$$N(\beta) = J_1^2(\beta a) + Y_1^2(\beta a) \quad (3\text{-}55b)$$

The Boundary Condition at $r = a$ is of the First Kind. For this special case we have $H \to \infty$. The solution of equation (3-52a) satisfying this boundary condition is taken as

$$R_0(\beta, r) = J_0(\beta r) Y_0(\beta a) - Y_0(\beta r) J_0(\beta a) \quad (3\text{-}56a)$$

and the corresponding norm becomes

$$N(\beta) = J_0^2(\beta a) + Y_0^2(\beta a) \quad (3\text{-}56b)$$

We summarize in Table 3-3 the foregoing results for $R_0(\beta, r)$ and $N(\beta)$ for the boundary conditions of the first, second, and third kind at $r = a$.

3-3 HOMOGENEOUS PROBLEMS IN (r, t) VARIABLES

Having established the representation of an arbitrary function $F(r)$ in terms of the solutions of Bessel's differential equation as discussed in the previous

Table 3-3 The solution $R_0(\beta, r)$, the Norm $N(\beta)$ of the Differential Equation

$$\frac{dR^2(r)}{dr^2} + \frac{1}{r}\frac{dR(r)}{dr} + \beta^2 R(r) = 0 \quad \text{in} \quad a < r < \infty$$

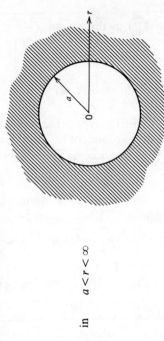

Subject to the Shown Boundary Condition

No	Boundary Condition at $r = a$	$R_0(\beta, r)$ and $1/N(\beta)$
1	$-\dfrac{dR}{dr} + HR = 0$	$R_0(\beta, r) = J_0(\beta r)[\beta Y_1(\beta a) + HY_0(\beta a)] - Y_0(\beta r)[\beta J_1(\beta a) + HJ_0(\beta a)]$ $\dfrac{1}{N(\beta)} = \{[\beta J_1(\beta a) + HJ_0(\beta a)]^2 + [\beta Y_1(\beta a) + HY_0(\beta a)]^2\}^{-1}$
2	$\dfrac{dR}{dr} = 0$	$R_0(\beta, r) = J_0(\beta r)Y_1(\beta a) - Y_0(\beta r)J_1(\beta a)$ $\dfrac{1}{N(\beta)} = [J_1^2(\beta a) + Y_1^2(\beta a)]^{-1}$
3	$R = 0$	$R_0(\beta, r) = J_0(\beta r)Y_0(\beta a) - Y_0(\beta r)J_0(\beta a)$ $\dfrac{1}{N(\beta)} = [J_0^2(\beta a) + Y_0^2(\beta a)]^{-1}$

section, the solution of the one-dimensional homogeneous heat-conduction problems in the (r, t) variables becomes a very straightforward matter as it will now be illustrated. We consider the problems for each of the regions $0 \le r \le b, a \le r \le b, 0 \le r < \infty$, and $a \le r < \infty$ separately.

Problems for Region $0 \le r \le b$

Example 3-1. A solid cylinder, $0 \le r \le b$, is initially at a temperature $F(r)$; for times $t > 0$ the boundary surface at $r = b$ dissipates heat by convection into a medium at zero temperature as illustrated in Fig. 3-3a. Obtain an expression for the temperature distribution $T(r, t)$ for times $t > 0$.

Solution. The mathematical formulation of this problem is taken as

$$\frac{\partial^2 T}{\partial r^2} + \frac{1}{r}\frac{\partial T}{\partial r} = \frac{1}{\alpha}\frac{\partial T(r, t)}{\partial t} \qquad \text{in } 0 \le r < b, \ t > 0 \tag{3-57a}$$

$$\frac{\partial T}{\partial r} + HT = 0 \qquad \text{at } r = b, \qquad t > 0 \tag{3-57b}$$

$$T = F(r) \qquad \text{for } t = 0 \qquad \text{in } 0 \le r \le b \tag{3-57c}$$

subject to the condition that temperature remains finite at $r = 0$. Separating the variables it can be shown that the solution for the time-variable function is given as

$$\Gamma(t) = e^{-\alpha\beta_m^2 t} \tag{3-58}$$

and the space variable function $R(\beta_m, r)$ satisfies the following eigenvalue

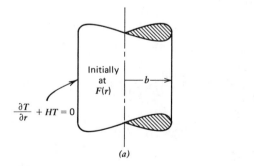
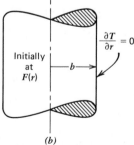

(a)   (b)

Fig. 3-3 Boundary and initial conditions for a solid cylinder considered in (a) Example 3-1 and (b) Example 3-2.

problem

$$\frac{d^2 R_0(r)}{dr^2} + \frac{1}{r}\frac{dR_0(r)}{dr} + \beta^2 R_0(r) = 0 \qquad \text{in } 0 \le r < b \qquad (3\text{-}59a)$$

$$\frac{dR_0}{dr} + HR_0 = 0 \qquad\qquad\qquad \text{at } r = b \qquad (3\text{-}59b)$$

The complete solution for $T(r, t)$ is constructed as

$$T(r, t) = \sum_{m=1}^{\infty} c_m e^{-\alpha \beta_m^2 t} R_0(\beta_m, r) \qquad (3\text{-}60)$$

The application of the initial condition gives

$$F(r) = \sum_{m=1}^{\infty} c_m R_0(\beta_m, r) \qquad \text{in } 0 \le r < b \qquad (3\text{-}61)$$

This is an expansion of an arbitrary function $F(r)$ defined in the interval $0 \le r < b$ in the same form as given by equation (3-20). The unknown coefficients c_m are determined by utilizing the orthogonality of the eigenfunction as given by equation (3-19). Then, the solution for the problem becomes

$$T(r, t) = \sum_{m=1}^{\infty} \frac{1}{N(\beta_m)} e^{-\alpha \beta_m^2 t} R_0(\beta_m, r) \int_0^b r' R_0(\beta_m, r') F(r')\, dr' \qquad (3\text{-}62)$$

where $R_0(\beta_m, r)$, $N(\beta_m)$ and the eigenvalues β_m are immediately obtainable from Table 3-1, Case 1, by setting $v = 0$, because the eigenvalue problem (3-59) is a special case of the general problem (3-18) with $v = 0$. Then the solution (3-62) takes the form

$$T(r, t) = \frac{2}{b^2} \sum_{m=1}^{\infty} e^{-\alpha \beta_m^2 t} \frac{\beta_m^2 J_0(\beta_m r)}{(\beta_m^2 + H^2) J_0^2(\beta_m b)} \int_0^b r' J_0(\beta_m r') F(r')\, dr' \quad (3\text{-}63)$$

where β_m's are the positive roots of

$$\beta_m J_0'(\beta_m b) + H J_0(\beta_m b) = 0 \qquad \text{or } \beta_m J_1(\beta_m b) = H J_0(\beta_m b) \qquad (3\text{-}64)$$

For the special case of $F(r) = T_0 = $ constant, the solution (3-63) reduces to

$$T(r, t) = \frac{2 T_0}{b} \sum_{m=1}^{\infty} e^{-\alpha \beta_m^2 t} \frac{\beta_m J_0(\beta_m r) J_1(\beta_m b)}{(\beta_m^2 + H^2) J_0^2(\beta_m b)} \qquad (3\text{-}65a)$$

$$= \frac{2 H T_0}{b} \sum_{m=1}^{\infty} e^{-\alpha \beta_m^2 t} \frac{J_0(\beta_m r)}{(\beta_m^2 + H^2) J_0(\beta_m b)} \qquad (3\text{-}65b)$$

where we utilized equation (3-64) to obtain the alternative form given by equation (3-65b)

Example 3-2. A solid cylinder, $0 \le r \le b$, is initially at a temperature

$F(r)$; for times $t > 0$ the boundary surface at $r = b$ is kept insulated as illustrated in Fig. 3-3b. Obtain an expression for the temperature distribution $T(r, t)$ for times $t > 0$.

Solution. The solution for this problem is written formally exactly in the same form as that given by equation (3-62); but, $R_0(\beta_m, r)$, $N(\beta_m)$ and eigenvalues β_m are taken from Table 3-1, Case 2, by setting $v = 0$. We obtain

$$T(r, t) = \frac{2}{b^2} \int_{r'=0}^{b} r' F(r') \, dr' + \frac{2}{b^2} \sum_{m=1}^{\infty} e^{-\alpha \beta_m^2 t}$$
$$\cdot \frac{J_0(\beta_m r)}{J_0^2(\beta_m b)} \int_{r'=0}^{b} r' J_0(\beta_m r') F(r') \, dr' \qquad (3\text{-}66a)$$

where β_m's are the positive roots of

$$J_0'(\beta_m b) = 0 \qquad \text{or} \qquad J_1(\beta_m b) = 0 \qquad (3\text{-}66b)$$

The first term on the right-hand side of equation (3-66a) is due to the fact that $\beta_0 = 0$ is also an eigenvalue for this special case. The region being insulated, heat cannot escape from the boundaries, hence the temperature, after the transients have passed, becomes the average of the initial temperature distribution over the cross-section of the cylinder as given by the first term on the right-hand side of equation (3-66a). See Chapter 13, equation (13-25b) for a more general expression for $T(r, \infty)$ when all boundaries of a finite region are insulated.

Example 3-3. A solid cylinder, $0 \le r \le b$, is initially at a temperature $F(r)$; for times $t > 0$ the boundary surface at $r = b$ is kept at zero temperature. Obtain an expression for the temperature distribution $T(r, t)$ for times $t > 0$.

Solution. The solution is written formally exactly in the same form as that given by equation (3-62); but, $R_0(\beta_m, r)$, $N(\beta_m)$ and eigenvalues β_m are taken from Table 3-1, Case 3, by setting $v = 0$. We obtain

$$T(r, t) = \frac{2}{b^2} \sum_{m=1}^{\infty} e^{-\alpha \beta_m^2 t} \frac{J_0(\beta_m r)}{J_1^2(\beta_m b)} \int_{r'=0}^{b} r' J_0(\beta_m r') F(r') \, dr' \qquad (3\text{-}67a)$$

where β_m's are the positive roots of

$$J_0(\beta_m b) = 0 \qquad (3\text{-}67b)$$

For the case of constant initial temperature $F(r) = T_0$, equation (3-67a) becomes

$$T(r, t) = \frac{2T_0}{b} \sum_{m=1}^{\infty} e^{-\alpha \beta_m^2 t} \frac{J_0(\beta_m r)}{\beta_m J_1(\beta_m b)} \qquad (3\text{-}68)$$

Problems for Region $a \le r \le b$

Example 3-4. A hollow cylinder, $a \le r \le b$, is initially at a temperature $F(r)$; for times $t > 0$ the boundary surfaces at $r = a$ and $r = b$ dissipate heat by convection into environments at zero temperature as illustrated in Fig. 3-4. Obtain an expression for the temperature distribution $T(r, t)$ for times $t > 0$.

Solution. The mathematical formulation of the problem is given as

$$\frac{\partial^2 T}{\partial r^2} + \frac{1}{r}\frac{\partial T}{\partial r} = \frac{1}{\alpha}\frac{\partial T}{\partial t} \qquad \text{in } a < r < b, \ t > 0 \qquad (3\text{-}69a)$$

$$-\frac{\partial T}{\partial r} + H_1 T = 0 \qquad \text{at } r = a, \ t > 0 \qquad (3\text{-}69b)$$

$$\frac{\partial T}{\partial r} + H_2 T = 0 \qquad \text{at } r = b, \ t > 0 \qquad (3\text{-}69c)$$

$$T = F(r) \qquad \text{for } t = 0, \ \text{in the region} \qquad (3\text{-}69d)$$

Separating the variables it can be shown that the solution for the time variable function is given by $\exp(-\alpha\beta_m^2 t)$, and the space variable function $R_0(\beta_m, r)$ is the solution of the following eigenvalue problem

$$\frac{d^2 R_0}{dr^2} + \frac{1}{r}\frac{dR_0}{dr} + \beta_m^2 R_0 = 0 \qquad \text{in } a < r < b \qquad (3\text{-}70a)$$

$$-\frac{dR_0}{dr} + H_1 R_0 = 0 \qquad \text{at } r = a \qquad (3\text{-}70b)$$

$$\frac{dR_0}{dr} + H_2 R_0 = 0 \qquad \text{at } r = b \qquad (3\text{-}70c)$$

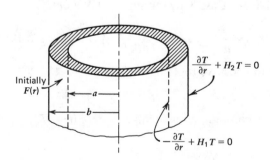

Fig. 3-4 Boundary and initial conditions for a hollow cylinder considered in Example 3-4.

Then, the complete solution for $T(r, t)$ is written as

$$T(r, t) = \sum_{m=1}^{\infty} c_m e^{-\alpha \beta_m^2 t} R_0(\beta_m, r) \tag{3-71}$$

The application of the initial condition (3-69d) yields

$$F(r) = \sum_{m=1}^{\infty} c_m R_0(\beta_m, r) \quad \text{in } a < r < b \tag{3-72}$$

This is an expansion of an arbitrary function $F(r)$ defined in the interval $a < r < b$ in terms of the eigenfunctions $R_0(\beta_m, r)$ of the eigenvalue problem (3-70); it is similar to the expansion given by equation (3-37) with $v = 0$. The unknown coefficients c_m are readily determined by utilizing the orthogonality of the eigenfunctions as given by equations (3-36). Then, the solution for the temperature $T(r, t)$ is written as

$$T(r, t) = \sum_{m=1}^{\infty} \frac{1}{N(\beta_m)} e^{-\alpha \beta_m^2 t} R_0(\beta_m, r) \int_a^b r' R_0(\beta_m, r') F(r') \, dr' \tag{3-73}$$

where the eigenfunctions $R_0(\beta_m, r)$, eigenvalues β_m, and the norm $N(\beta_m)$ are obtained from Table 3-2, Case 1, by setting $v = 0$, because the eigenvalue problem (3-70) is a special case of the general problem (3-35) with $v = 0$. We find

$$R_0(\beta_m, r) = S_0 J_0(\beta_m r) - V_0 Y_0(\beta_m r) \tag{3-74a}$$

$$\frac{1}{N(\beta_m)} = \frac{\pi^2}{2} \frac{\beta_m^2 U_0^2}{B_2 U_0^2 - B_1 V_0^2} \tag{3-74b}$$

β_m's are the positive roots of

$$S_0 U_0 - V_0 W_0 = 0 \tag{3-75}$$

where

$$S_0 = \beta_m Y_0'(\beta_m b) + H_2 Y_0(\beta_m b), \quad U_0 = \beta_m J_0'(\beta_m a) - H_1 J_0(\beta_m a) \tag{3-76a}$$

$$V_0 = \beta_m J_0'(\beta_m b) + H_2 J_0(\beta_m b), \quad W_0 = \beta_m Y_0'(\beta_m a) - H_1 Y_0(\beta_m a) \tag{3-76c}$$

$$B_1 = H_1^2 + \beta_m^2, \quad B_2 = H_2^2 + \beta_m^2 \tag{3-76c}$$

Example 3-5. A hollow cylinder, $a \leq r \leq b$, is initially at a temperature $F(r)$; for times $t > 0$ the boundary surfaces at $r = a$ and $r = b$ are kept at zero temperature. Obtain an expression for the temperature distribution $T(r, t)$ for times $t > 0$.

Solution. This is a special case of the general problem considered above in Example 3-4. The solution for $T(r, t)$ is given in the same form as equation (3-73), that is

$$T(r, t) = \sum_{m=1}^{\infty} \frac{1}{N(\beta_m)} e^{-\alpha \beta_m^2 t} R_0(\beta_m, r) \int_a^b r' R_0(\beta_m, r') F(r') \, dr' \qquad (3\text{-}77)$$

where $R_0(\beta_m, r)$, $N(\beta_m)$ and the eigenvalues β_m are obtained from Table 3-2, Case 9, by setting $v = 0$. Then, the solution becomes

$$T(r, t) = \frac{\pi^2}{2} \sum_{m=1}^{\infty} \frac{\beta_m^2 J_0^2(\beta_m a)}{J_0^2(\beta_m a) - J_0^2(\beta_m b)} e^{-\alpha \beta_m^2 t} R_0(\beta_m, r) \int_a^b r' R_0(\beta_m, r') F(r') \, dr' \quad (3\text{-}78a)$$

where

$$R_0(\beta_m, r) = J_0(\beta_m r) Y_0(\beta_m b) - J_0(\beta_m b) Y_0(\beta_m r) \qquad (3\text{-}78b)$$

and β_m's are the positive roots of

$$J_0(\beta_m a) Y_0(\beta_m b) - J_0(\beta_m b) Y_0(\beta_m a) = 0 \qquad (3\text{-}79)$$

For the special case of $F(r') = T_0 = $ constant, the integral in equation (3-78a) is evaluated, the resulting expression is simplified by utilizing the wronskian relationship given by equation (3-44) for $v = 0$ and the transcendental equation (3-79). Then the temperature distribution is given by

$$T(r, t) = T_0 \pi \sum_{m=1}^{\infty} e^{-\alpha \beta_m^2 t} \frac{J_0(\beta_m a)}{J_0(\beta_m a) + J_0(\beta_m b)} R_0(\beta_m, r) \qquad (3\text{-}80)$$

where $R_0(\beta_m, r)$ as given by equation (3-78b).

Problems for Region $0 \le r < \infty$

Example 3-6.   An infinite region $0 \le r < \infty$ is initially at a temperature $F(r)$. Obtain an expression for the temperature distribution $T(r, t)$ for times $t > 0$

Solution.   The heat-conduction problem is given by

$$\frac{\partial^2 T}{\partial r^2} + \frac{1}{r} \frac{\partial T}{\partial r} = \frac{1}{\alpha} \frac{\partial T}{\partial t} \qquad \text{in } 0 \le r < \infty, \ t > 0 \qquad (3\text{-}81a)$$

$$T = F(r) \qquad \qquad \text{for } t = 0, \text{ in the region} \qquad (3\text{-}18b)$$

and subject to the condition that temperature remains finite at $r = 0$. Separating the variables it can be shown that the solution for the time variable function is given by $\exp(-\alpha \beta^2 t)$, where β is the separation variable, and the space variable function $R_0(\beta, r)$ is the solution of the following problem.

$$\frac{d^2 R_0}{dr^2} + \frac{1}{r}\frac{dR_0}{dr} + \beta^2 R_0 = 0 \quad \text{in } 0 \le r < \infty \tag{3-82}$$

subject to the condition that $R_0(\beta, r)$ remains finite at $r = 0$ the solution of equation (3-82) which is finite at $r = 0$ is

$$R_0(\beta, r) = J_0(\beta r) \tag{3-83}$$

Then, the complete solution for $T(r, t)$ is constructed as

$$T(r, t) = \int_{\beta=0}^{\infty} c(\beta) e^{-\alpha\beta^2 t} J_0(\beta r)\, d\beta \tag{3-84}$$

The application of the initial condition (3-81b) yields

$$F(r) = \int_{\beta=0}^{\infty} c(\beta) J_0(\beta r)\, d\beta \quad \text{in } 0 \le r < \infty \tag{3-85}$$

This is an expansion of an arbitrary function $F(r)$ defined in the interval $0 \le r < \infty$ in terms of $J_0(\beta r)$ functions. Such a representation was given in the previous section by equation (3-51) in terms of $J_\nu(\beta r)$ functions. Therefore, by setting $\nu = 0$ in equation (3-51) we obtain

$$F(r) = \int_{\beta=0}^{\infty} \beta J_0(\beta r)\, d\beta \int_{r'=0}^{\infty} r' J_0(\beta r') F(r')\, dr' \quad \text{in } 0 \le r < \infty \tag{3-86}$$

By comparing equations (3-85) and (3-86) we find the coefficient $c(\beta)$ as

$$c(\beta) \equiv \beta \int_{r'=0}^{\infty} r' J_0(\beta r') F(r')\, dr' \tag{3-87}$$

The substitution of equation (3-87) into equation (3-84) yields

$$T(r, t) = \int_{\beta=0}^{\infty} e^{-\alpha\beta^2 t} \beta J_0(\beta r)\, d\beta \int_{r'=0}^{\infty} r' J_0(\beta r') F(r')\, dr' \tag{3-88}$$

By changing the order of integration and making use of the following integral [Appendix III, equation (24)]

$$\int_{\beta=0}^{\infty} e^{-\alpha\beta^2 t} \beta J_0(\beta r) J_0(\beta r')\, d\beta = \frac{1}{2\alpha t} \exp\left(-\frac{r^2 + r'^2}{4\alpha t}\right) I_0\left(\frac{rr'}{2\alpha t}\right) \tag{3-89}$$

The solution (3-88) becomes

$$T(r, t) = \frac{1}{2\alpha t} \int_{r'=0}^{\infty} r' \exp\left(-\frac{r^2 + r'^2}{4\alpha t}\right) F(r') I_0\left(\frac{rr'}{2\alpha t}\right) dr' \tag{3-90}$$

For the special case of

$$F(r) = \begin{cases} T_0, \text{ constant} & \text{for } 0 < r < b \\ 0 & \text{for } r > b \end{cases} \qquad (3\text{-}91)$$

the solution (3-90) becomes

$$\frac{T(r,t)}{T_0} = \frac{1}{2\alpha t} \exp\left(-\frac{r^2}{4\alpha t}\right) \int_{r'=0}^{b} r' \exp\left(-\frac{r'^2}{4\alpha t}\right) I_0\left(\frac{rr'}{2\alpha t}\right) dr' \equiv P \quad (3\text{-}92)$$

This integral, which is called a *P function*, has been numerically evaluated and the results are tabulated [13].

Problems for Region $a \le r < \infty$

Example 3-7. A region $a \le r < \infty$ in the cylindrical coordinate system is initially at a temperature $F(r)$; for times $t > 0$ the boundary surface at $r = a$ is kept at zero temperature. Obtain an expression for the temperature distribution $T(r, t)$ in the region for times $t > 0$.

Solution. The heat-conduction problem is given by

$$\frac{\partial^2 T}{\partial r^2} + \frac{1}{r}\frac{\partial T}{\partial r} = \frac{1}{\alpha}\frac{\partial T}{\partial t} \qquad \text{in } a < r < \infty, \ t > 0 \qquad (3\text{-}93a)$$

$$T = 0 \qquad \text{at } r = a, \ t > 0 \qquad (3\text{-}93b)$$

$$T = F(r) \qquad \text{for } t = 0, \text{ in the region} \qquad (3\text{-}93c)$$

By separating the variables it can be shown that the time variable function is given by $\exp(-\alpha\beta^2 t)$ and the space variable function $R_0(\beta, r)$ is the solution of the following problem

$$\frac{d^2 R_0}{dr^2} + \frac{1}{r}\frac{dR_0}{dr} + \beta^2 R_0 = 0 \qquad \text{in } a < r < \infty \qquad (3\text{-}94a)$$

$$R_0 = 0 \qquad \text{at } r = a \qquad (3\text{-}94b)$$

Then, the complete solution for $T(r, t)$ is constructed as

$$T(r,t) = \int_{\beta=0}^{\infty} c(\beta)e^{-\alpha\beta^2 t} R_0(\beta, r)\, d\beta \qquad (3\text{-}95)$$

The application of the initial condition (3-93c) yields

$$F(r) = \int_{\beta=0}^{\infty} c(\beta) R_0(\beta, r)\, d\beta \qquad \text{in } a < r < \infty \qquad (3\text{-}96)$$

This is an expansion of an arbitrary function $F(r)$ defined in the interval

$a < r < \infty$ in terms of the solutions of the problem (3-93). Such an expansion was given previously as given by equation (3-53) for a more general case. By comparing equation (3-96) with equation (3-53), we obtain the expansion coefficient $c(\beta)$ as

$$c(\beta) \equiv \frac{1}{N(\beta)} \beta \int_{r'=a}^{\infty} r' R_0(\beta, r') F(r') \, dr' \tag{3-97}$$

The substitution of equation (3-97) into equation (3-95) gives

$$T(r, t) = \int_{\beta=0}^{\infty} \frac{\beta}{N(\beta)} e^{-\alpha\beta^2 t} R_0(\beta, r) \, d\beta \int_{r'=a}^{\infty} r' R_0(\beta, r') F(r') \, dr' \tag{3-98}$$

When the functions $R_0(\beta, r)$ and $N(\beta)$ are obtained from Table 3-3, Case 3, the solution (3-98) becomes

$$T(r, t) = \int_{\beta=0}^{\infty} \frac{\beta}{J_0^2(\beta a) + Y_0^2(\beta a)} e^{-\alpha\beta^2 t} [J_0(\beta r) Y_0(\beta a) - Y_0(\beta r) J_0(\beta a)] \, d\beta$$

$$\cdot \int_{r'=a}^{\infty} r' [J_0(\beta r') Y_0(\beta a) - Y_0(\beta r') J_0(\beta a)] F(r') \, dr' \tag{3-99}$$

Example 3-8. A region $a \le r < \infty$ in the cylindrical coordinate system is initially at a temperature $F(r)$; for times $t > 0$ the boundary at $r = a$ dissipates heat by convection into a medium at zero temperature. Obtain an expression for the temperature distribution $T(r, t)$ for times $t > 0$.

Solution. The heat-conduction problem is given by

$$\frac{\partial^2 T}{\partial r^2} + \frac{1}{r} \frac{\partial T}{\partial r} = \frac{1}{\alpha} \frac{\partial T}{\partial t} \qquad \text{in } a < r < \infty, \ t > 0 \tag{3-100a}$$

$$-\frac{\partial T}{\partial r} + HT = 0 \qquad \text{at } r = a, \ t > 0 \tag{3-100b}$$

$$T = F(r) \qquad \text{for } t = 0 \ \text{ in } a \le r < \infty \tag{3-100c}$$

By carrying out the analysis as described in the previous example, the solution is written in the form as given by equation (3-98), that is,

$$T(r, t) \int_{\beta=0}^{\infty} \frac{\beta}{N(\beta)} e^{-\alpha\beta^2 t} R_0(\beta, r) \, d\beta \int_{r'=a}^{\infty} r' R_0(\beta, r') F(r') \, dr' \tag{3-101}$$

where the functions $R_0(\beta, r)$ and $N(\beta)$ are obtained from Table 3-3, Case 1, as

$$R_0(\beta, r) = J_0(\beta r)[\beta Y_1(\beta a) + H Y_0(\beta a)] - Y_0(\beta r)[\beta J_1(\beta a) + H J_0(\beta a)] \tag{3-102a}$$

$$N(\beta) = [\beta J_1(\beta a) + H J_0(\beta a)]^2 + [\beta Y_1(\beta a) + H Y_0(\beta a)]^2 \tag{3-102b}$$

3-4 HOMOGENEOUS PROBLEMS IN (r, z, t) VARIABLES

The general solution of the homogeneous problems of heat conduction in (r, z, t) variables is constructed by the superposition of the separated solutions $\Gamma(t)$, $R_0(\beta, r)$ and $Z(\eta, z)$ for the t, r, and z variables, respectively. The analysis is a straightforward matter because explicit expressions for the separated solutions are available in tabulated form for all possible combinations of boundary conditions. That is, the functions $R_0(\beta_m, r)$, the norm $N(\beta_m)$, and the eigenvalues β_m for finite regions (i.e., $0 \leq r \leq a$ and $a \leq r \leq b$) are obtainable from Tables 3-1 and 3-2 by setting $v = 0$; and the corresponding expressions for a semi-infinite region $a \leq r < \infty$ are obtainable from Table 3-3. Similarly, the expressions defining the functions $Z(\eta_p, z)$, the norm $N(\eta_p)$ and the eigenvalues η_p for a finite region $0 \leq z \leq c$ are available in Table 2-2 and the corresponding expressions for a semi-infinite region $0 \leq z < \infty$ are obtainable from Table 2-3. We illustrate below the application with several representative examples.

Example 3-9. A hollow cylinder of finite length, in the region $a \leq r \leq b$, $0 \leq z \leq c$, is initially at a temperature $F(r, z)$. For times $t > 0$, the boundaries at $r = a$ and $r = b$ are kept at zero temperatures, the boundary at $z = 0$ is insulated, and the boundary at $z = c$ is dissipating heat by convection into a medium at zero temperature as illustrated in Fig. 3-5. Obtain an expression for the temperature distribution $T(r, z, t)$ for times $t > 0$.

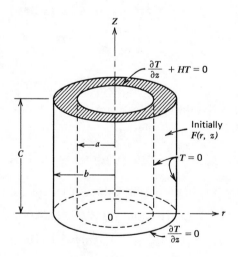

Fig. 3-5 Boundary and initial conditions for a hollow cylinder considered in Example 3-9.

Solution. The mathematical formulation of the problem is given as

$$\frac{\partial^2 T}{\partial r^2} + \frac{1}{r}\frac{\partial T}{\partial r} + \frac{\partial^2 T}{\partial z^2} = \frac{1}{\alpha}\frac{\partial T}{\partial t} \quad \text{in } a<r<b,\ 0<z<c,\ t>0 \quad (3\text{-}103)$$

$$T = 0 \qquad\qquad \text{at } r=a,\ r=b,\ t>0 \qquad (3\text{-}104\text{a})$$

$$\frac{\partial T}{\partial z} = 0 \qquad\qquad \text{at } z=0,\ t>0 \qquad (3\text{-}104\text{b})$$

$$\frac{\partial T}{\partial z} + HT = 0 \qquad\qquad \text{at } z=c,\ t>0 \qquad (3\text{-}104\text{c})$$

$$T = F(r,z) \qquad\qquad \text{for } t=0,\ \text{in the region} \qquad (3\text{-}104\text{d})$$

The separation of variables lead to a set of equations as given by equations (3-11); the separated solutions are taken as

$$e^{-\alpha(\beta_m^2+\eta_p^2)t}, \qquad R_0(\beta_m,r), \qquad \text{and} \qquad Z(\eta_p,z) \qquad (3\text{-}105)$$

Here, the eigenvalues β_m and η_p are discrete because the regions in the r and z directions are both finite. The complete solution for $T(r,z,t)$ is constructed as

$$T(r,z,t) = \sum_{m=1}^{\infty}\sum_{p=1}^{\infty} c_{mp}R_0(\beta_m,r)Z(\eta_p,z)e^{-\alpha(\beta_m^2+\eta_p^2)t} \qquad (3\text{-}106)$$

The application of the initial condition (3-104d) yields

$$F(r,z) = \sum_{m=1}^{\infty}\sum_{p=1}^{\infty} c_{mp}R_0(\beta_m,r)Z(\eta_p,z) \quad \text{in } a<r<b,\ 0<z<c \quad (3\text{-}107)$$

The coefficients c_{mp} are determined by operating on both sides of equation (3-107) successively by the operators

$$\int_a^b rR_0(\beta_{m'},r)\,dr \qquad \text{and} \qquad \int_0^c Z(\eta_{p'},z)\,dz \qquad (3\text{-}108)$$

and utilizing the orthogonality of these eigenfunctions. We obtain

$$c_{mp} = \frac{1}{N(\beta_m)N(\eta_p)} \int_{r=a}^b \int_{z=0}^c rR_0(\beta_m,r)Z(\eta_p,z)F(r,z)\,dr\,dz \qquad (3\text{-}109)$$

Then the solution (3-106) becomes

$$T(r,z,t) = \sum_{m=1}^{\infty}\sum_{p=1}^{\infty} \frac{e^{-\alpha(\beta_m^2+\eta_p^2)t}}{N(\beta_m)N(\eta_p)}R_0(\beta_m,r)Z(\eta_p,z)\int_{r'=a}^b\int_{z'=0}^c r'R_0(\beta_m,r')$$
$$\cdot Z(\eta_p,z')F(r',z')\,dz'\,dr' \qquad (3\text{-}110)$$

where the eigenfunctions $R_0(\beta_m,r)$, the norm $N(\beta_m)$ and the eigenvalues β_m

are obtained from Table 3-2, Case 9, by setting $v = 0$. We find

$$R_0(\beta_m, r) = J_0(\beta_m r) Y_0(\beta_m b) - J_0(\beta_m b) Y_0(\beta_m r) \tag{3-111a}$$

$$\frac{1}{N(\beta_m)} = \frac{\pi^2}{2} \frac{\beta_m^2 J_0^2(\beta_m a)}{J_0^2(\beta_m a) - J_0^2(\beta_m b)} \tag{3-111b}$$

and β_m's are the positive roots of

$$J_0(\beta_m a) Y_0(\beta_m b) - J_0(\beta_m b) Y_0(\beta_m a) = 0 \tag{3-111c}$$

The eigenfunctions $Z(\eta_p, z)$, the norm $N(\eta_p)$ and the eigenvalues η_p are obtained from Table 2-2, Case 4, by making appropriate changes in the symbols. We find

$$Z(\eta_p, z) = \cos \eta_p z \tag{3-112a}$$

$$\frac{1}{N(\eta_p)} = 2 \frac{\eta_p^2 + H^2}{c(\eta_p^2 + H^2) + H} \tag{3-112b}$$

and η_p's are the positive roots of

$$\eta_p \tan \eta_p c = H \tag{3-112c}$$

Example 3-10. A solid cylinder, $0 \le r \le b, 0 \le z < \infty$, is initially at temperature $F(r, z)$. For times $t > 0$, the boundaries are kept at zero temperature as illustrated in Fig. 3-6. Obtain an expression for the temperature distribution $T(r, z, t)$ in the cylinder for times $t > 0$.

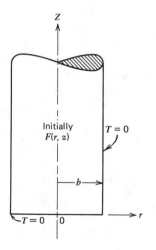

Fig. 3-6 Boundary and initial conditions for a solid cylinder considered in Example 3-10.

Solution. The mathematical formulation of the problem is given as

$$\frac{\partial^2 T}{\partial r^2} + \frac{1}{r}\frac{\partial T}{\partial r} + \frac{\partial^2 T}{\partial z^2} = \frac{1}{\alpha}\frac{\partial T}{\partial t} \qquad \text{in } 0 \le r < b, \ 0 < z < \infty, \ t > 0 \qquad (3\text{-}113)$$

$$T = 0 \qquad\qquad\qquad \text{at } r = b, \ z = 0 \text{ for } t > 0 \qquad (3\text{-}114a)$$

$$T = F(r, z) \qquad\qquad \text{for } t = 0, \text{ in the region} \qquad (3\text{-}114b)$$

The separated solutions are taken as

$$e^{-\alpha(\beta_m^2 + \eta^2)t}, \qquad R_0(\beta_m, r), \qquad \text{and} \qquad Z(\eta, z) \qquad (3\text{-}115)$$

Here we note that the eigenvalues β_m are discrete because the region in the r direction is finite, but the separation constant η takes all values from zero to infinity because the region in the z direction is semi-infinite.

The complete solution for $T(r, z, t)$ is constructed as

$$T(r, z, t) = \sum_{m=1}^{\infty} \int_{\eta=0}^{\infty} c_m(\eta) R_0(\beta_m, r) Z(\eta, z) e^{-\alpha(\beta_m^2 + \eta^2)t} \, d\eta \qquad (3\text{-}116)$$

The application of the initial condition (3-114b) yields

$$F(r, z) = \sum_{m=1}^{\infty} \int_{\eta=0}^{\infty} c_m(\eta) R_0(\beta_m, r) Z(\eta, z) \, d\eta \qquad \text{in } 0 \le r < b, \ 0 < z < \infty \qquad (3\text{-}117)$$

Both sides of equation (3-117) are operated on by the operator

$$\int_{r=0}^{b} r R_0(\beta_{m'}, r) \, dr \qquad (3\text{-}118)$$

and the orthogonality of $R_0(\beta_m, r)$ functions is utilized. We obtain

$$f^*(z) = \int_{\eta=0}^{\infty} c_m(\eta) Z(\eta, z) \, d\eta \qquad \text{in } 0 < z < \infty \qquad (3\text{-}119a)$$

where we defined

$$f^*(z) \equiv \frac{1}{N(\beta_m)} \int_{r'=0}^{b} r R_0(\beta_m, r) F(r, z) \, dr \qquad (3\text{-}119b)$$

The representation given by equation (3-119a) is exactly the same as that given by equation (2-51) for a semi-infinite region. Therefore, the unknown coefficient $c_m(\eta)$ is determined according to the result in equation (2-53); we find

$$c_m(\eta) \equiv \frac{1}{N(\eta)} \int_{z=0}^{\infty} Z(\eta, z) f^*(z) \, dz \qquad (3\text{-}120)$$

The substitution of equation (3-120) together with equation (3-119b) into equation (3-116) gives the solution for $T(r, z, t)$ in the form

$$T(r, z, t) = \sum_{m=1}^{\infty} \int_{\eta=0}^{\infty} \frac{e^{-\alpha(\beta_m^2 + \eta^2)t}}{N(\beta_m)N(\eta)} R_0(\beta_m, r)Z(\eta, z) d\eta \int_{r'=0}^{b} \int_{z'=0}^{\infty} r' R_0(\beta_m, r')$$
$$\cdot Z(\eta, z')F(r', z') dz' dr' \tag{3-121}$$

The eigenfunctions $R_0(\beta_m, r)$, the norm $N(\beta_m)$, and the eigenvalues β_m are obtained from Table 3-1, Case 3, by setting $v = 0$; we find

$$R_0(\beta_m, r) = J_0(\beta_m r), \qquad \frac{1}{N(\beta_m)} = \frac{2}{b^2 J_0'^2(\beta_m b)} = \frac{2}{b^2 J_1^2(\beta_m b)} \tag{3-122a}$$

and β_m's are the positive roots of

$$J_0(\beta_m b) = 0 \tag{3-122b}$$

The functions $Z(\eta, z)$ and $N(\eta)$ are obtained from Table 2-3, Case 3, as

$$Z(\eta, z) = \sin \eta z \quad \text{and} \quad \frac{1}{N(\eta)} = \frac{2}{\pi} \tag{3-123}$$

When the results in equations (3-122) and (3-123) are introduced into equation (3-121) and the order of integration is changed we obtain

$$T(r, z, t) = \frac{4}{\pi b^2} \sum_{m=1}^{\infty} \frac{J_0(\beta_m r)}{J_1^2(\beta_m b)} e^{-\alpha\beta_m^2 t} \int_{r'=0}^{b} \int_{z'=0}^{\infty} r' J_0(\beta_m r')F(r'z') dz' dr'$$
$$\cdot \int_{\eta=0}^{\infty} e^{-\alpha\eta^2 t} \sin \eta z \sin \eta z' d\eta \tag{3-124}$$

The last integral with respect to η is similar to the one given by equation (2-57d); then this integral is evaluated as

$$\frac{2}{\pi} \int_{\eta=0}^{\infty} e^{-\alpha\eta^2 t} \sin \eta z \sin \eta z' d\eta = \frac{1}{(4\pi\alpha t)^{1/2}}$$
$$\cdot \left[\exp\left(-\frac{(z - z')^2}{4\alpha t} \right) - \exp\left(-\frac{(z + z')^2}{4\alpha t} \right) \right] \tag{3-125}$$

and this result is introduced into equation (3-124).

3-5   HOMOGENEOUS PROBLEMS IN (r, ϕ, t) VARIABLES

In the analysis of heat-conduction problems involving (r, ϕ, t) variables, the following two situations require different considerations: (1) the range of ϕ variable is $0 \le \phi \le 2\pi$ as in the case of a *full cylinder*; in this case no boundary conditions are prescribed at ϕ except the requirement that the temperature should be periodic in ϕ with period 2π, and (2) the range of ϕ variable is $0 \le \phi \le \phi_0 < 2\pi$ as in the case of a *portion of a cylinder*; in this case boundary conditions should be prescribed at $\phi = 0$ and $\phi = \phi_0$. The analysis of heat-conduction problems for these two cases are discussed below.

Problems of Full Cylinder, $0 \le \phi \le 2\pi$

The separation of the heat-conduction equation in (r, ϕ, t) variables results in the elementary solutions $R_\nu(\beta, r), \Phi(\nu, \phi)$ and $\Gamma(t)$. We have already determined the explicit forms of the functions $R_\nu(\beta_m, r)$, the norms $N(\beta_m)$, and the eigenvalues β_m and tabulated them in Tables 3-1 and 3-2 for different types of boundary conditions. In the problems of full cylinder the range of ϕ variables lies in $0 \le \phi \le 2\pi$ and the temperature is periodic in ϕ with period 2π. Then the function $\Phi(\phi)$ satisfies the following problem:

$$\frac{d^2\Phi}{d\phi^2} + \nu^2\Phi = 0 \qquad \text{in } 0 \le \phi \le 2\pi \tag{3-126a}$$

and the solution of which may be taken as

$$\Phi(\nu, \phi) = A_\nu \sin \nu\phi + B_\nu \cos \nu\phi \tag{3-126b}$$

We now examine the representation of a function $F(\phi)$ that is periodic in ϕ with period 2π in terms of $\Phi(\nu, \phi)$ functions in the form

$$F(\phi) = \sum_\nu (A_\nu \sin \nu\phi + B_\nu \cos \nu\phi) \qquad \text{in } 0 \le \phi \le 2\pi \tag{3-127}$$

The condition that $F(\phi)$ is periodic in ϕ with period 2π requires that the separation constants ν should be taken integral, that is

$$\nu = 0, 1, 2, 3 \ldots \tag{3-128}$$

To determine the coefficients A_ν, we operate on both sides of equation (3-127) by the operator $\int_0^{2\pi} \sin \nu'\phi \, d\phi$ and utilize the orthogonality of functions $\sin \nu\phi$. We obtain

$$A_\nu = \frac{1}{\pi} \int_0^{2\pi} F(\phi) \sin \nu\phi \, d\phi \qquad \text{for } \nu = 0, 1, 2, 3 \ldots \tag{3-129}$$

since $\int_0^{2\pi} \sin^2 \nu\phi \, d\phi = \pi$ and the integrals of the product of $\sin \nu\phi$, $\cos \nu\phi$ vanish. To determine the coefficients B_ν we operate on both sides of equation (3-127) by the operator $\int_0^{2\pi} \cos \nu'\phi \, d\phi$ and utilize the orthogonality of functions $\cos v\phi$. We find

$$
B_v = \begin{cases}
\dfrac{1}{\pi} \int\limits_0^{2\pi} F(\phi) \cos v\phi \, d\phi & \text{for } v = 1, 2, 3 \ldots \tag{3-130a} \\[3mm]
\dfrac{1}{2\pi} \int\limits_0^{2\pi} F(\phi) \, d\phi & \text{for } v = 0 \tag{3-130b}
\end{cases}
$$

Since $\int_0^{2\pi} \cos^2 v\phi \, d\phi$ is equal to π for $v = 1, 2, 3, \ldots$ and equal to 2π for $v = 0$.

The substitution of the above expressions for A_v and B_v into equation (3-127) yields the representation in the form

$$
\begin{aligned}
F(\phi) &= \frac{1}{2\pi} \int\limits_0^{2\pi} F(\phi')\, d\phi' + \frac{1}{\pi} \sum_{v=1}^{\infty} \int\limits_0^{2\pi} F(\phi')(\sin v\phi \sin v\phi' + \cos v\phi \cos v\phi')\, d\phi' \\
&= \frac{1}{2\pi} \int\limits_0^{2\pi} F(\phi')\, d\phi' + \frac{1}{\pi} \sum_{v=1}^{\infty} \int\limits_0^{2\pi} F(\phi') \cos v(\phi - \phi')\, d\phi'
\end{aligned} \tag{3-131a}
$$

This representation may be written more compactly in the form

$$
F(\phi) = \frac{1}{\pi} \sum_v \int\limits_0^{2\pi} F(\phi') \cos v(\phi - \phi')\, d\phi' \qquad \text{in } 0 \le \phi \le 2\pi \tag{3-131b}
$$

where

$$
v = 0, 1, 2, 3 \ldots
$$

and replace π by 2π for $v = 0$. If we compare the representations given by equations (3-127) and (3-131b) we conclude that

$$
[A_v \sin v\phi + B_v \cos v\phi] \equiv \frac{1}{\pi} \int\limits_0^{2\pi} F(\phi') \cos v(\phi - \phi')\, d\phi' \tag{3-132}
$$

where

$$
v = 0, 1, 2, 3 \ldots
$$

and replace π by 2π for $v = 0$. These results will be utilized in the solution of homogeneous heat-conduction problems in the (r, ϕ, t) variables for the full cylinder as illustrated with the examples below.

Example 3-11. A solid cylinder, $0 \le r \le b$, $0 \le \phi \le 2\pi$ is initially at temperature $F(r, \phi)$. For times $t > 0$, heat is dissipated by convection from the boundary surface at $r = b$ into an environment at zero temperature. Obtain an expression for the temperature distribution $T(r, \phi, t)$ in the cylinder.

Solution. The mathematical formulation of this problem is given as

$$\frac{\partial^2 T}{\partial r^2} + \frac{1}{r}\frac{\partial T}{\partial r} + \frac{1}{r^2}\frac{\partial^2 T}{\partial \phi^2} = \frac{1}{\alpha}\frac{\partial T}{\partial t} \qquad \text{in } 0 \le r < b,\ 0 \le \phi \le 2\pi,\ t > 0 \quad (3\text{-}133\text{a})$$

$$\frac{\partial T}{\partial r} + HT = 0 \qquad\qquad\qquad \text{at } r = b,\ t > 0 \qquad\qquad (3\text{-}133\text{b})$$

$$T = F(r, \phi) \qquad\qquad\qquad \text{for } t = 0, \text{ in the region} \qquad (3\text{-}133\text{c})$$

The separated solutions are taken as

$$e^{-\alpha\beta_m^2 t}, \qquad \Phi(v, \phi) = A \sin v\phi + B \cos v\phi, \qquad R_v(\beta_m, r)$$

The complete solution of $T(r, \phi, t)$ is constructed by the superposition of these elementary solutions as

$$T(r, \phi, t) = \sum_{m=1}^{\infty} \sum_{v=0}^{\infty} e^{-\alpha\beta_m^2 t}(A_{mv} \sin v\phi + B_{mv} \cos v\phi)R_v(\beta_m, r) \quad (3\text{-}134)$$

The application of the initial condition (3-133c) gives

$$F(r, \phi) = \sum_{m=1}^{\infty} \sum_{v}(A_{mv} \sin v\phi + B_{mv} \cos v\phi)R_v(\beta_m, r) \qquad \text{in } 0 \le r < b,\ 0 \le \phi \le 2\pi$$

$$(3\text{-}135)$$

We now operate on both sides of this expression by the operator

$$\int_0^b rR_v(\beta_{m'}, r)\, dr$$

and utilize the orthogonality property of the functions $R_v(\beta_m, r)$. We obtain

$$f(\phi) = \sum_v (A_{mv} \sin v\phi + B_{mv} \cos v\phi)N(\beta_m) \qquad \text{in } 0 \le \phi \le 2\pi \quad (3\text{-}136\text{a})$$

where we defined

$$f(\phi) \equiv \int_0^b rR_v(\beta_m, r)F(r, \phi)\, dr \qquad\qquad (3\text{-}136\text{b})$$

Equation (3-136a) is representation of a function $f(\phi)$ periodic in ϕ with period 2π similar to the representation considered by equation (3-127). We recall that the coefficients of equation (3-127) are given by equation (3-132). Therefore, the coefficients of equation (3-136a) are immediately obtainable from the result given by equation (3-132) as

$$[A_{mv} \sin v\phi + B_{mv} \cos v\phi]N(\beta_m) \equiv \frac{1}{\pi} \int_{\phi=0}^{2\pi} f(\phi')\cos v(\phi - \phi')\, d\phi' \quad (3\text{-}137)$$

where

$$v = 0, 1, 2, 3 \dots$$

and replace π by 2π for $v = 0$. The substitution of equation (3-137) together with equation (3-136b) into equation (3-134) gives the temperature distribution as

$$T(r, \phi, t) = \frac{1}{\pi} \sum_{m=1}^{\infty} \sum_{v=0}^{\infty} \frac{e^{-\alpha \beta_m^2 t}}{N(\beta_m)} R_v(\beta_m, r)$$

$$\cdot \int_{\phi'=0}^{2\pi} \int_{r'=0}^{b} r' R_v(\beta_m, r') \cos v(\phi - \phi') F(r', \phi') \, dr' \, d\phi'$$

(3-138)

where

$$v = 0, 1, 2, 3 \dots$$

and replace π by 2π for $v = 0$. The eigenfunctions $R_v(\beta_m, r)$, the norm $N(\beta_m)$, and the eigenvalues β_m are obtained from Table 3-1, Case 1, as

$$R_v(\beta_m, r) = J_v(\beta_m r), \qquad \frac{1}{N(\beta_m)} = \frac{2}{J^2(\beta_m b)} \frac{\beta_m^2}{b^2(H^2 + \beta_m^2) - v^2} \quad (3\text{-}139a)$$

and β_m's are the positive roots of

$$\beta_m J_v'(\beta_m b) + H J_v(\beta_m b) = 0 \qquad (3\text{-}139b)$$

Example 3-12. Repeat Example 3-11 for the case when the boundary surface at $r = b$ is kept at zero temperature.

Solution. The mathematical formulation of this problem is similar to the one given above by equations (3-133) except the boundary condition (3-133b) should be replaced by the boundary condition $T = 0$ at $r = b$. Therefore, the general solution given above by equation (3-138) is also applicable for this case provided that the functions defining $R_v(\beta_m, r)$, $N(\beta_m)$, and β_m are obtained from Table 3-1, Case 3, as

$$R(\beta_m, r) = J_v(\beta_m r), \qquad \frac{1}{N(\beta_m)} = \frac{2}{b^2 J_v'^2(\beta_m b)} \qquad (3\text{-}140a)$$

and β_m's are the roots of

$$J_v(\beta_m b) = 0 \qquad (3\text{-}140b)$$

The substitution of equations (3-140) into equation (3-138) gives the solution as

$$T(r, \phi, t) = \frac{2}{\pi b^2} \sum_{m=1}^{\infty} \sum_{v} \frac{e^{-\alpha \beta_m^2 t}}{J_v'^2(\beta_m b)} J_v(\beta_m r)$$

$$\cdot \int_{\phi'=0}^{2\pi} \int_{r'=0}^{b} r' J_v(\beta_m r') \cos v(\phi - \phi') F(r', \phi') \, dr' \, d\phi' \qquad (3\text{-}141)$$

where

$$v = 0, 1, 2, 3 \dots$$

and replace π by 2π for $v = 0$, β_m's are the roots of $J_v(\beta_m b) = 0$.

Example 3-13. A hollow cylinder $a \le r \le b$, $0 \le \phi \le 2\pi$, is initially at temperature $F(r, \phi)$. For times $t > 0$, the boundary surfaces at $r = a$ and $r = b$ are kept at zero temperature as shown in Fig. 3-7. Obtain an expression for the temperature distribution $T(r, \phi, t)$ in the cylinder for times $t > 0$.

Solution. The mathematical formulation of this problem is given as

$$\frac{\partial^2 T}{\partial r^2} + \frac{1}{r}\frac{\partial T}{\partial t} + \frac{1}{r^2}\frac{\partial^2 T}{\partial \phi^2} = \frac{1}{\alpha}\frac{\partial T}{\partial t} \qquad \text{in } a < r < b, \ 0 \le \phi \le 2\pi, \ t > 0 \quad (3\text{-}142a)$$

$$T = 0 \qquad \qquad \text{at } r = a, \ r = b, \ t > 0 \qquad (3\text{-}142b)$$

$$T = F(r, \phi) \qquad \qquad \text{for } t = 0, \ \text{in the region} \qquad (3\text{-}142c)$$

This problem can be solved by following a procedure similar to that described in Example 3-11. The resulting expression for $T(r, \phi, t)$ is of the same form as given by equation (3-138) except the limits of integration with respect to

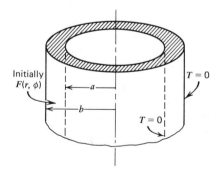

Fig. 3-7 Boundary and initial conditions for a hollow cylinder considered in Example 3-13.

r is now from $r' = a$ to $r' = b$; that is

$$T(r, \phi, t) = \frac{1}{\pi} \sum_{m=1}^{\infty} \sum_{v=0}^{\infty} \frac{e^{-\alpha\beta_m^2 t}}{N(\beta_m)} R_v(\beta, r)$$

$$\cdot \int_{\phi'=0}^{2\pi} \int_{r'=a}^{b} r' R_v(\beta_m, r') \cos v(\phi - \phi') F(r', \phi') dr' d\phi' \quad (3\text{-}143)$$

where

$$v = 0, 1, 2, 3 \ldots$$

and replace π by 2π for $v = 0$. Here, $R_v(\beta_m, r)$, $N(\beta_m)$, and β_m's are obtained from Table 3-2, Case 9, as

$$R_v(\beta_m, r) = J_v(\beta_m r) Y_v(\beta_m b) - J_v(\beta_m b) Y_v(\beta_m r) \quad (3\text{-}144\text{a})$$

$$\frac{1}{N(\beta_m)} = \frac{\pi^2}{2} \frac{\beta_m^2 J_v^2(\beta_m a)}{J_v^2(\beta_m a) - J_v^2(\beta_m b)} \quad (3\text{-}144\text{b})$$

and β_m's are the positive roots of

$$J_v(\beta_m a) Y_v(\beta_m b) - J_v(\beta_m b) Y_v(\beta_m a) = 0 \quad (3\text{-}144\text{c})$$

Problems of Portion of a Cylinder, $0 \le \phi \le \phi_0 < 2\pi$

The separation of the heat-conduction equation results in the elementary solutions $R_v(\beta_m, r)$, $\Phi(v, \phi)$, and $\Gamma(t)$. The functions $R_v(\beta_m, r)$, the norms $N(\beta_m)$, and the eigenvalues β_m are obtainable from Tables 3-1 and 3-2. The function $\Phi(v, \phi)$ satisfies the following problem

$$\frac{d^2\Phi}{d\phi^2} + v^2\Phi = 0 \qquad \text{in } 0 < \phi < \phi_0(\phi_0 < 2\pi) \quad (3\text{-}145)$$

subject to prescribed boundary conditions at $\phi = 0$ and $\phi = \phi_0$, which may be of the first, second, or third kind. Clearly, the problem given by equation (3-145) is similar to the eigenvalue problem (2-32) considered in Chapter 2 for the solution of the slab problem. Therefore, the functions $\Phi(v, \phi)$, the norms $N(v)$, and the eigenvalues v for different combinations of boundary conditions at $\phi = 0$ and $\phi = \phi_0 < 2\pi$ are obtainable from the results listed in Table 2-2. We illustrate the application with the examples below.

Example 3-14.   The portion of a solid cylinder, $0 \le r \le b, 0 \le \phi \le \phi_0 < 2\pi$ is initially at temperature $F(r, \phi)$. For times $t > 0$ the boundaries at $r = b$, $\phi = 0$ and $\phi = \phi_0$ are kept at zero temperature as illustrated in Fig. 3-8. Obtain an expression for the temperature distribution $T(r, \phi, t)$ for times $t > 0$.

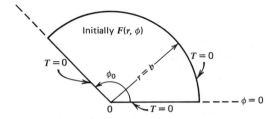

Fig. 3-8 Boundary and initial conditions for a portion of a cylinder considered in Example 3-14.

Solution. The mathematical formulation of this problem is given as

$$\frac{\partial^2 T}{\partial r^2} + \frac{1}{r}\frac{\partial T}{\partial r} + \frac{1}{r^2}\frac{\partial^2 T}{\partial \phi^2} = \frac{1}{\alpha}\frac{\partial T}{\partial t} \qquad \text{in } 0 \le r < b, \ 0 < \phi < \phi_0, \ t > 0 \quad (3\text{-}146a)$$

$$T = 0 \qquad\qquad\qquad\qquad \text{at } r = b, \ \phi = 0, \ \phi = \phi_0, \ t > 0 \quad (3\text{-}146b)$$

$$T = F(r, \phi) \qquad\qquad\qquad \text{for } t = 0, \text{ in the region} \qquad\qquad (3\text{-}146c)$$

The separated solutions are taken as

$$e^{-\alpha\beta_m^2 t}, \qquad \Phi(v, \phi), \qquad \text{and} \qquad R_v(\beta_m, r)$$

where $\Phi(v, \phi)$ is the solution of equation (3-145) subject to the boundary conditions $\Phi(v, \phi) = 0$ at $\phi = 0$ and $\phi = \phi_0$; the function $R_v(\beta_m, r)$ is the solution of the Bessel's differential equation subject to the boundary conditions $R_v(\beta_m, r) = 0$ at $r = b$, and $R_v(\beta_m, r)$ should remain finite at $r = 0$.

The complete solution for $T(r, \phi, t)$ is constructed by the superposition of these separated solutions as

$$T(r, \phi, t) = \sum_{m=1}^{\infty} \sum_{v} c_{mv} R_v(\beta_m, r)\Phi(v, \phi)e^{-\alpha\beta_m^2 t} \qquad (3\text{-}147)$$

The application of the initial condition (3-146c) gives

$$F(r, \phi) = \sum_{m=1}^{\infty} \sum_{v} c_{mv} R_v(\beta_m, r)\Phi(v, \phi) \qquad \text{in } 0 \le r < b, \ 0 < \phi < \phi_0 \quad (3\text{-}148)$$

To determine the coefficients c_{mv}, both sides of equation (3-148) are operated on successively by the operators

$$\int_{\phi=0}^{\phi_0} \Phi(v', \phi)\,d\phi \qquad \text{and} \qquad \int_{r=0}^{b} r R_v(\beta_{m'}, r)\,dr$$

and the orthogonality property of these eigenfunctions are utilized. We find

$$c_{mv} = \frac{1}{N(\beta_m)N(v)} \int_{r=0}^{b}\int_{\phi=0}^{\phi_0} r R_v(\beta_m, r)\Phi(v, \phi)F(r, \phi)\,d\phi\,dr \qquad (3\text{-}149)$$

This result is now introduced into equation (3-147) to obtain the solution for $T(r, \phi, t)$ in the form

$$
T(r, \phi, t) = \sum_{m=1}^{\infty} \sum_{v} \frac{e^{-\alpha \beta_m^2 t}}{N(\beta_m)N(v)} R_v(\beta_m, r) \Phi(v, \phi)
$$

$$
\cdot \int_{r'=0}^{b} \int_{\phi'=0}^{\phi_0} r' R_v(\beta_m, r') \Phi(v, \phi') F(r', \phi') \, d\phi' \, dr' \qquad (3\text{-}150)
$$

where $R_v(\beta_m, r)$, $N(\beta_m)$, and β_m's are obtained from Table 3-1, Case 3, as

$$
R_v(\beta_m, r) = J_v(\beta_m r), \qquad \frac{1}{N(\beta_m)} = \frac{2}{b^2 J_v'^2(\beta_m b)} \qquad (3\text{-}151a)
$$

and β_m's are the positive roots of

$$
J_v(\beta_m b) = 0 \qquad (3\text{-}151b)
$$

The expressions defining $\Phi(v, \phi)$, $N(v)$, and v are obtained from Table 2-2, Case 9, by appropriate change of the notation. We find

$$
\Phi(v, \phi) = \sin v\phi, \qquad \frac{1}{N(v)} = \frac{2}{\phi_0} \qquad (3\text{-}152a)
$$

and v's are the roots of

$$
\sin v\phi_0 = 0 \qquad (3\text{-}152b)
$$

When the results given by equations (3-151) and (3-152) are introduced into equation (3-147) the solution becomes

$$
T(r, \phi, t) = \frac{4}{b^2 \phi_0} \sum_{m=1}^{\infty} \sum_{v} e^{-\alpha \beta_m^2 t} \frac{J_v(\beta_m r)}{J_v'^2(\beta_m b)} \sin v\phi
$$

$$
\cdot \int_{r'=0}^{b} \int_{\phi'=0}^{\phi_0} r' J_v(\beta_m r') \sin v\phi' F(r', \phi') \, d\phi' \, dr' \qquad (3\text{-}153)
$$

where β_m's are roots of $J_v(\beta_m b) = 0$, and v's are given by

$$
v = \frac{n\pi}{\phi_0}, \qquad n = 1, 2, 3 \ldots
$$

For the special case of $F(r, \phi) = T_0 = $ constant, the solution (3-153) becomes

$$
T(r, \phi, t) = \frac{8T_0}{b^2 \phi_0} \sum_{m=1}^{\infty} \sum_{v} e^{-\alpha \beta_m^2 t} \frac{J_v(\beta_m r)}{J_v'^2(\beta_m b)} \frac{\sin v\phi}{v} \int_{r'=0}^{b} r' J_v(\beta_m r') \, dr' \quad (3\text{-}154)
$$

where β_m's are the roots of $J_v(\beta b) = 0$, and v's are given by

$$
v = \frac{(2n-1)\pi}{\phi_0}, \qquad n = 1, 2, 3 \ldots
$$

3-6 HOMOGENEOUS PROBLEMS IN (r, ϕ, z, t) VARIABLES

The general solution of the homogeneous heat-conduction problem in (r, ϕ, z, t) variables is constructed by the superposition of all permissible elementary solutions; the resulting expansion coefficients are then determined by a procedure described previously. The analysis is straightforward because all the elementary solutions are now available and systematically tabulated for all possible combinations of boundary conditions. The application is illustrated with the following examples.

Example 3-15.   A solid cylinder, $0 \le r \le b, 0 \le \phi \le 2\pi, 0 \le z \le c$, is initially at a temperature $F(r, \phi, z)$. For times $t > 0$ the boundary at $z = 0$ is insulated, the boundary at $z = c$ is kept at zero temperature, and the boundary at $r = b$ dissipates heat by convection into a medium at zero temperature as illustrated in Fig. 3-9. Obtain an expression for the temperature distribution $T(r, \phi, z, t)$ for times $t > 0$.

Solution.   The mathematical formulation of this problem is given as

$$\frac{\partial^2 T}{\partial r^2} + \frac{1}{r}\frac{\partial T}{\partial r} + \frac{1}{r^2}\frac{\partial^2 T}{\partial \phi^2} + \frac{\partial^2 T}{\partial z^2} = \frac{1}{\alpha}\frac{\partial T}{\partial t} \qquad \text{in } 0 \le r < b, 0 \le \phi \le 2\pi, \\ 0 < z < c, t > 0 \qquad (3\text{-}155)$$

$$\frac{\partial T}{\partial r} + HT = 0 \qquad \text{at } r = b, t > 0 \qquad (3\text{-}156a)$$

$$\frac{\partial T}{\partial z} = 0 \qquad \text{at } z = 0, t > 0 \qquad (3\text{-}156b)$$

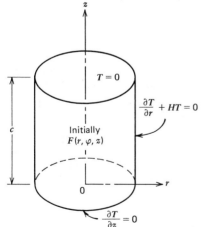

Fig. 3-9 Boundary and initial conditions for a solid cylinder considered in Example 3-15.

$$T = 0 \qquad\qquad\qquad \text{at } z = c, \; t > 0 \qquad (3\text{-}156c)$$

$$T = F(r, \phi, z) \qquad\qquad \text{for } t = 0, \text{ in the region } (3\text{-}156d)$$

The elementary solutions are taken as

$$e^{-\alpha(\beta_m^2 + \eta_p^2)t}, \qquad R_\nu(\beta_m, r), \qquad Z(\eta_p, z), \qquad (A \sin \nu\phi + B \cos \nu\phi)$$

The complete solution for $T(r, \phi, z, t)$ is constructed by the linear super-position of these elementary solutions as

$$T(r, \phi, z, t) = \sum_{m=1}^{\infty} \sum_{p=1}^{\infty} \sum_{\nu} R_\nu(\beta_m, r) Z(\eta_p, z)$$
$$\cdot [A_{mp\nu} \sin \nu\phi + B_{mp\nu} \cos \nu\phi] e^{-\alpha(\beta_m^2 + \eta_p^2)t} \qquad (3\text{-}157)$$

The application of the initial condition yields

$$F(r, \phi, z) = \sum_{m=1}^{\infty} \sum_{p=1}^{\infty} \sum_{\nu} R_\nu(\beta_m, r) Z(\eta_p, z) [A_{mp\nu} \sin \nu\phi + B_{mp\nu} \cos \nu\phi] \qquad (3\text{-}158)$$

To determine the coefficients, we operate on both sides of this equation successively by the operators

$$\int_0^b r R_\nu(\beta_{m'}, r) \, dr \qquad \text{and} \qquad \int_0^c Z(\eta_{p'}, z) \, dz$$

and utilize the orthoganility of the eigenfunctions $R_\nu(\beta_m, r)$ and $Z(\eta_p, r)$. We find

$$f(\phi) = \sum_{\nu} N(\beta_m) N(\eta_p) [A_{mp\nu} \sin \nu\phi + B_{mp\nu} \cos \nu\phi] \qquad \text{in } 0 \le \phi \le 2\pi \quad (3\text{-}159a)$$

where we defined

$$f(\phi) \equiv \int_{z=0}^{c} \int_{r=0}^{b} r R_\nu(\beta_m, r) Z(\eta_p, z) F(r, \phi, z) \, dr \, dz \qquad (3\text{-}159b)$$

Equation (3-159a) is a representation of function $f(\phi)$ periodic in ϕ with period 2π similar to the representation considered in equation (3-127); the coefficients of equation (3-127) are given by equation (3-132). Therefore, the coefficients of equation (3-159a) are obtained from the result in equation (3-132) as

$$N(\beta_m) N(\eta_p) [A_{mp\nu} \sin \nu\phi + B_{mp\nu} \cos \nu\phi] \equiv \frac{1}{\pi} \int_{\phi'=0}^{2\pi} f(\phi') \cos \nu(\phi - \phi') \, d\phi' \qquad (3\text{-}160)$$

where

$$\nu = 0, 1, 2, 3 \ldots$$

and replace π by 2π for $\nu = 0$. The substitution of equation (3-160) into equation (3-157) together with equation (3-159b) gives the temperature distribution in the form

$$T(r,\phi,z,t) = \frac{1}{\pi} \sum_{m=1}^{\infty} \sum_{p=1}^{\infty} \sum_{\nu=0}^{\infty} \frac{e^{-\alpha(\beta_m^2 + \eta_p^2)t}}{N(\beta_m)N(\eta_p)} R_\nu(\beta_m, r)Z(\eta_p, z)$$

$$\cdot \int_{\phi'=0}^{2\pi} \int_{z'=0}^{b} \int_{r'=0}^{b} r' R_\nu(\beta_m, r')Z(\eta_p, z') \cos \nu(\phi - \phi')F(r', \phi', z')dr'\, dz'\, d\phi'$$

$$(3\text{-}161)$$

where

$$\nu = 0, 1, 2, 3 \dots$$

and replace π by 2π for $\nu = 0$. The expressions defining $R_\nu(\beta_m, r)$, $N(\beta_m)$, and β_m are obtained from Table 3-1, Case 1, as

$$R_\nu(\beta_m, r) = J_\nu(\beta_m r), \qquad \frac{1}{N(\beta_m)} = \frac{2}{J_\nu^2(\beta_m b)} \frac{\beta_m^2}{b^2(H^2 + \beta_m^2) - \nu^2} \quad (3\text{-}162a)$$

and β_m's are the positive roots of

$$\beta_m J_\nu'(\beta_m b) + H J_\nu(\beta_m b) = 0 \qquad (3\text{-}162b)$$

and the expressions defining $Z(\eta_p, z)$, $N(\eta_p)$ and η_p are obtained from Table 2-2, Case 6, by making appropriate changes in the symbols. We find

$$Z(\eta_p, z) = \cos \eta_p z, \qquad \frac{1}{N(\eta_p)} = \frac{2}{c} \qquad (3\text{-}163a)$$

and η_p's are the roots of

$$\cos \eta_p c = 0 \quad \left(\text{or } \eta_p = \frac{(2p-1)\pi}{2c}, p = 1, 2, 3 \dots \right) \qquad (3\text{-}163b)$$

Example 3-16. A portion of a hollow cylinder, $a \le r \le b$, $0 \le \phi \le \phi_0(< 2\pi)$, $0 \le z \le c$, as illustrated in Fig. 3-10 is initially at temperature $F(r, \phi, z)$. For times $t > 0$ all boundary surfaces are kept at zero temperature. Obtain an expression for the temperature distribution $T(r, \phi, z, t)$ for times $t > 0$.

Solution. The mathematical formulation of the problem is given as

$$\frac{\partial^2 T}{\partial r^2} + \frac{1}{r}\frac{\partial T}{\partial r} + \frac{1}{r^2}\frac{\partial^2 T}{\partial \phi^2} + \frac{\partial^2 T}{\partial z^2} = \frac{1}{\alpha}\frac{\partial T}{\partial t} \quad \begin{array}{l} \text{in } a \le r < b, \ 0 < z < c, \\ 0 < \phi < \phi_0(< 2\pi), t > 0 \end{array} \quad (3\text{-}164)$$

$$T = 0 \qquad \qquad \text{at all boundaries, } t > 0 \qquad (3\text{-}165a)$$

$$T = F(r, \phi, z) \qquad \qquad \text{for } t = 0, \text{ in the region} \qquad (3\text{-}165b)$$

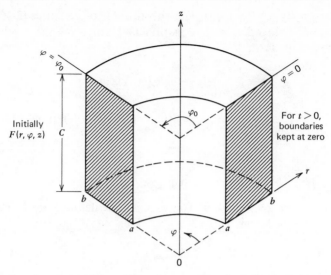

Fig. 3-10 Boundary and initial conditions for a portion of a hollow cylinder considered in Example 3-16.

The elementary solutions are taken as

$$e^{-\alpha(\beta_m^2 + \eta_p^2)t}, \qquad R_\nu(\beta_m, r), \qquad Z(\eta_p, z), \qquad \Phi(\nu, \phi)$$

and the complete solution for $T(r, \phi, z, t)$ is constructed by the superposition of these elementary solutions as

$$T(r, \phi, z, t) = \sum_{m=1}^{\infty} \sum_{p=1}^{\infty} \sum_{\nu} c_{mp\nu} R_\nu(\beta_m, r) Z(\eta_p, z) \Phi(\nu, \phi) e^{-\alpha(\beta_m^2 + \eta_p^2)t} \quad (3\text{-}166)$$

The application of the initial condition yields

$$F(r, \phi, z) = \sum_{m=1}^{\infty} \sum_{p=1}^{\infty} \sum_{\nu} c_{mp\nu} R_\nu(\beta_m, r) Z(\eta_p, z) \Phi(\nu, \phi)$$
$$\text{in } a < r < b, \ 0 < z < c, \ 0 < \phi < \phi_0 \quad (3\text{-}167)$$

To determine the expansion coefficients $c_{mp\nu}$ we operate on both sides of this expression successively by the operators

$$\int_a^b r R_\nu(\beta_{m'}, r)\, dr, \qquad \int_0^c Z(\eta_{p'}, z)\, dz, \qquad \text{and} \qquad \int_0^{\phi_0} \Phi(\nu', \phi)\, d\phi$$

and utilize the orthogonality property of these eigenfunctions. We obtain

$$c_{mn\nu} = \frac{1}{N(\beta_m) N(\eta_p) N(\nu)} \int_{r=a}^{b} \int_{z=0}^{c} \int_{\phi=0}^{\phi_0} r R_\nu(\beta_m, r) Z(\eta_p, z) \Phi(\nu, \phi) F(r, \phi, z)\, dr\, dz\, d\phi$$
$$(3\text{-}168)$$

Introducing equation (3-168) into equation (3-166) the solution for the temperature distribution becomes

$$T(r,\phi,z,t) = \sum_{m=1}^{\infty} \sum_{n=1}^{\infty} \sum_{v} \frac{e^{-\alpha(\beta_m^2 + \eta_p^2)t}}{N(\beta_m)N(\eta_p)N(v)} R_v(\beta_m,r)Z(\eta_p,z)\Phi(v,\phi)$$

$$\cdot \int_{r'=a}^{b} \int_{z'=0}^{c} \int_{\phi'=0}^{\phi_0} r' R_v(\beta_m,r')Z(\eta_p,z')\Phi(v,\phi')F(r',\phi',z')\,d\phi'\,dz'\,dr'$$

$$(3\text{-}169)$$

The expressions defining $R_v(\beta_m,r)$, $N(\beta_m)$, and β_m are obtained from Table 3-2, Case 9, as

$$R_v(\beta_m,r) = J_v(\beta_m r)Y_v(\beta_m b) - J_v(\beta_m b)Y_v(\beta_m r) \qquad (3\text{-}170a)$$

$$\frac{1}{N(\beta_m)} = \frac{\pi^2}{2} \frac{\beta_m^2 J_v^2(\beta_m a)}{J_v^2(\beta_m a) - J_v^2(\beta_m b)} \qquad (3\text{-}170b)$$

and β_m's are the positive roots of

$$J_v(\beta_m a)Y_v(\beta_m b) - J_v(\beta_m b)Y_v(\beta_m a) = 0 \qquad (3\text{-}170c)$$

The expressions defining $Z(\eta_p,z)$, $N(\eta_p)$, and η_p are obtained from Table 2-2, Case 9, as

$$Z(\eta_p,z) = \sin \eta_p z, \qquad \frac{1}{N(\eta_p)} = \frac{2}{c} \qquad (3\text{-}171a)$$

and η_p's are the roots of

$$\sin \eta_p c = 0 \quad \left(\text{or } \eta_p = \frac{p\pi}{c}, \qquad p = 1,2,3\ldots\right) \qquad (3\text{-}171b)$$

The expressions for $\Phi(v,\phi)$, $N(v)$, and v are also obtained from Table 2-2, Case 9, as

$$\Phi(v,\phi) = \sin v\phi, \qquad \frac{1}{N(v)} = \frac{2}{\phi_0} \qquad (3\text{-}172a)$$

and v's are the roots of

$$\sin v\phi_0 = 0 \qquad (3\text{-}172b)$$

3-7 PRODUCT SOLUTION

The basic principles of product solution described in the previous chapter (Section 2-7) are also applicable for the solution of multidimensional homogeneous problems of heat conduction in the cylindrical coordinate system. That is, if the initial temperature distribution is expressible as a product of single-space variable functions, the solution of the multidimensional homogeneous problem can be written down as the product of the solutions of one-dimensional problems. To illustrate the concept, we consider the two-dimensional homogeneous heat-conduction problem of Example 3-9 for an initial condition given in the product form as $F(r,z) = F_1(r)F_2(z)$. Then, the solution $T(r,z,t)$ of this two-dimensional, time-dependent problem can be written as a product in the form

$$T(r,z,t) = T_1(r,t)T_2(z,t) \tag{3-173}$$

where the functions $T_1(r,t)$ and $T_2(z,t)$ are the solutions of the following two one-dimensional homogeneous problems:

$$\frac{\partial^2 T_1}{\partial r^2} + \frac{1}{r}\frac{\partial T_1}{\partial r} = \frac{1}{\alpha}\frac{\partial T_1}{\partial t} \qquad \text{in } a < r < b, \ t > 0 \tag{3-174a}$$

$$T_1 = 0 \qquad \text{at } r = a \text{ and } r = b, \ t > 0 \tag{3-174b}$$

$$T_1 = F_1(r) \qquad \text{for } t = 0, \text{ in } a \le r \le b \tag{3-174c}$$

and

$$\frac{\partial^2 T_2}{\partial z^2} = \frac{1}{\alpha}\frac{\partial T_2}{\partial t} \qquad \text{in } 0 < z < c, \ t > 0 \tag{3-175a}$$

$$\frac{\partial T_2}{\partial z} = 0 \qquad \text{at } z = 0, \ t > 0 \tag{3-175b}$$

$$\frac{\partial T_2}{\partial z} + HT_2 = 0 \qquad \text{at } z = c, \ t > 0 \tag{3-175c}$$

$$T_2 = F(z) \qquad \text{for } t = 0, \text{ in } 0 \le z \le c \tag{3-175d}$$

The solutions of the problems (3-174) and (3-175) are given, respectively, as

$$T_1(r,t) = \sum_{m=1}^{\infty} \frac{e^{-\alpha\beta_m^2 t}}{N(\beta_m)} R_0(\beta_m, r) \int_{r'=a}^{b} r'R_0(\beta_m, r')F_1(r')\,dr' \tag{3-176}$$

and

$$T_2(z,t) = \sum_{p=1}^{\infty} \frac{e^{-\alpha\eta_p^2 t}}{N(\eta_p)} Z(\eta_p, z) \int_{z'=0}^{c} Z(\eta_p, z')F_2(z')\,dz' \tag{3-177}$$

where the expressions defining $R_0(\beta_m, r)$, $N(\beta_m)$, and β_m are obtainable from Table 3-2, Case 9, by setting $v = 0$, and $Z(\eta_p, z)$, $N(\eta_p)$, and η_p are obtainable from Table 2-2, Case 4. Introducing the solutions (3-176) and (3-177) into equation (3-173), the solution for the two-dimensional problem becomes

$$T(r, z, t) = \sum_{m=1}^{\infty} \sum_{p=1}^{\infty} \frac{e^{-\alpha(\beta_m^2 + \eta_p^2)t}}{N(\beta_m)N(\eta_p)} R_0(\beta_m, r)Z(\eta_p, z)$$

$$\cdot \int_{r'=a}^{b} \int_{z'=0}^{c} r'R_0(\beta_m, r')Z(\eta_p, z')F_1(r')F_2(z')\, dz'\, dr' \qquad (3\text{-}178)$$

This solution is indeed exactly the same as that given by equation (3-110) for an initial condition $F(r, z) = F_1(r)F_2(z)$, and various eigenfunctions, eigenvalues, and the norms are the same as those given by equations (3-111) and (3-112).

3-8 MULTIDIMENSIONAL STEADY-STATE PROBLEMS WITH NO HEAT GENERATION

The multidimensional steady-state heat-conduction problem with no heat generation can be solved by the separation of variables if only one of the boundary conditions is nonhomogeneous. If the problem involves more than one nonhomogeneous boundary condition, it can be split up into a set of simpler problems each containing only one nonhomogeneous boundary condition as discussed in Section 2-8. To illustrate the application we consider the following examples.

Example 3-17. Obtain an expression for the steady-state temperature distribution $T(r, z)$ in a solid cylinder $0 \le r \le b$, $0 \le z \le c$, when the boundary surface at $z = 0$ is kept at a temperature $f(r)$, boundary at $z = c$ is kept at zero temperature, and that at $r = b$ dissipates heat by convection into a medium at zero temperature.

Solution. The mathematical formulation of the problem is given as

$$\frac{\partial^2 T}{\partial r^2} + \frac{1}{r}\frac{\partial T}{\partial r} + \frac{\partial^2 T}{\partial z^2} = 0 \qquad \text{in } 0 \le r < b,\ 0 < z < c \qquad (3\text{-}179a)$$

$$\frac{\partial T}{\partial r} + HT = 0 \qquad\qquad \text{at } r = b \qquad (3\text{-}179b)$$

$$T = f(r) \qquad\qquad \text{at } z = 0 \qquad (3\text{-}179c)$$

$$T = 0 \qquad\qquad \text{at } z = c \qquad (3\text{-}179d)$$

In this problem the boundary condition at $z = 0$ is nonhomogeneous; looking ahead in the analysis we conclude that the nonhomogeneous part $f(r)$ of the boundary condition should be represented in terms of the separated solutions $R_0(\beta_m, r)$. Therefore, in separating the variables the sign of the separation constant should be so chosen as to produce an eigenvalue problem for the functions $R_0(\beta_m, r)$. With this consideration the separated equations are taken as

$$\frac{d^2 R_0}{dr^2} + \frac{1}{r}\frac{dR_0}{dr} + \beta^2 R_0 = 0 \qquad \text{in } 0 \le r < b \qquad (3\text{-}180a)$$

$$\frac{dR_0}{dr} + HR_0 = 0 \qquad \text{at } r = b \qquad (3\text{-}180b)$$

and

$$\frac{d^2 Z}{dz^2} - \beta^2 Z = 0 \qquad \text{in } 0 < z < c \qquad (3\text{-}181a)$$

$$Z = 0 \qquad \text{at } z = c \qquad (3\text{-}181b)$$

Then, the solution for $T(r, z)$ is constructed as

$$T(r, z) = \sum_{m=1}^{\infty} A_m \sinh \beta_m (c - z) R_0(\beta_m, r) \qquad (3\text{-}182)$$

The application of the boundary condition at $z = 0$ gives

$$f(r) = \sum_{m=1}^{\infty} A_m \sinh \beta_m c R_0(\beta_m, r) \qquad \text{in } 0 \le r < b \qquad (3\text{-}183)$$

where, the coefficients A_m are determined as

$$A_m = \frac{1}{N(\beta_m)\sinh \beta_m c} \int_0^b r R_0(\beta_m, r) f(r)\, dr \qquad (3\text{-}184)$$

Introducing equation (3-184) into equation (3-182) the solution becomes

$$T(r, z) = \sum_{m=1}^{\infty} \frac{1}{N(\beta_m)} \frac{\sinh \beta_m (c - z)}{\sinh \beta_m c} R_0(\beta_m, r) \int_0^b r' R_0(\beta_m, r') f(r')\, dr' \quad (3\text{-}185)$$

where the expressions defining the functions $R_0(\beta_m, r)$, $N(\beta_m)$, and β_m are obtained from Table 3-1, Case 1, by setting $\nu = 0$. We find

$$R_0(\beta_m, r) = J_0(\beta_m r), \qquad \frac{1}{N(\beta_m)} = \frac{2}{J_0^2(\beta_m b)} \frac{\beta_m^2}{b^2(H^2 + \beta_m^2)} \qquad (3\text{-}186a)$$

and β_m's are the positive roots of

$$\beta_m J_0'(\beta_m b) + HJ_0(\beta_m b) = 0 \qquad \text{or } \beta_m J_1(\beta_m b) = HJ_0(\beta_m b) \quad (3\text{-}186b)$$

For the special case of $f(r) = T_0 = $ constant, the integral in equation (3-185) is performed and the solution becomes

$$\frac{T(r,z)}{T_0} = \frac{2}{b} \sum_{m=1}^{\infty} \frac{\beta_m J_1(\beta_m b)}{J_0^2(\beta_m b)(H^2 + \beta_m^2)} \frac{\sinh \beta_m(c-z)}{\sinh \beta_m c} J_0(\beta_m r) \qquad (3\text{-}187a)$$

or, by utilizing equation (3-186b), we find

$$\frac{T(r,z)}{T_0} = \frac{2}{b} \sum_{m=1}^{\infty} \frac{H}{H^2 + \beta_m^2} \frac{\sinh \beta_m(c-z)}{\sinh \beta_m c} \frac{J_0(\beta_m r)}{J_0(\beta_m b)} \qquad (3\text{-}187b)$$

Example 3-18. Obtain an expression for the steady-state temperature distribution $T(r,\phi)$ in a solid cylinder $0 \le r \le b, 0 \le \phi \le 2\pi$, which is subjected to convective heat transfer at the boundary surface $r = b$ with an environment whose temperature varies around the circumference.

Solution. The mathematical formulation of this problem is given as

$$\frac{\partial^2 T}{\partial r^2} + \frac{1}{r}\frac{\partial T}{\partial r} + \frac{1}{r^2}\frac{\partial^2 T}{\partial \phi^2} = 0 \qquad \text{in } 0 \le r < b, \ 0 \le \phi \le 2\pi \quad (3\text{-}188a)$$

$$\frac{\partial T}{\partial r} + HT = f(\phi) \qquad\qquad \text{at } r = b \qquad\qquad\qquad (3\text{-}188b)$$

The separated equations and their elementary solutions are as given by equations (3-17). The general solution for $T(r,\phi)$ is constructed in terms of these solutions as

$$T(r,\phi) = \sum_{\nu} r^{\nu}(C_{\nu} \sin \nu\phi + D_{\nu} \cos \nu\phi) \qquad (3\text{-}189)$$

where we excluded the elementary solutions $r^{-\nu}$ and $\ln r$ because they diverge at $r = 0$. This solution is introduced into the boundary condition (3-188b); we find

$$\sum_{\nu} b^{\nu-1}(\nu + Hb)(C_{\nu} \sin \nu\phi + D_{\nu} \cos \nu\phi) = f(\phi) \qquad \text{in } 0 \le \phi \le 2\pi \quad (3\text{-}190)$$

This equation is a representation of function $f(\phi)$ periodic in ϕ with period 2π similar to the representation considered in equation (3-127); the coefficients of equation (3-127) are given by equation (3-132). Therefore, by comparing equation (3-190) with equations (3-127) and (3-132) we conclude that the coefficients are given by

$$b^{\nu-1}(\nu + Hb)(C_{\nu} \sin \nu\phi + D_{\nu} \cos \nu\phi) \equiv \frac{1}{\pi} \int_{\phi'=0}^{2\pi} f(\phi') \cos \nu(\phi - \phi')d\phi' \quad (3\text{-}191)$$

where
$$\nu = 0, 1, 2, 3, \ldots$$

and replace π by 2π for $\nu = 0$. When these coefficients are introduced into equation (3-189), the solution for the temperature becomes

$$T(r,\phi) = \frac{b}{\pi} \sum_{v} \left(\frac{r}{b}\right)^{v} \frac{1}{v + Hb} \int_{\phi'=0}^{2\pi} f(\phi') \cos v(\phi - \phi') d\phi' \qquad (3\text{-}192)$$

where $v = 0, 1, 2, 3, \ldots$

and replace π by 2π for $v = 0$.

Example 3-19. Obtain an expression for the steady-state temperature $T(r,z)$ in a solid cylinder $0 \le r \le b, 0 \le z \le c$, when the boundary at $r = b$ is at temperature $f(z)$ and the boundaries at $z = 0$ and $z = c$ are at zero temperature.

Solution. The mathematical formulation of this problem is given as

$$\frac{\partial^2 T}{\partial r^2} + \frac{1}{r}\frac{\partial T}{\partial r} + \frac{\partial^2 T}{\partial z^2} = 0 \quad \text{in } 0 \le r < b,\ 0 < z < c \qquad (3\text{-}193a)$$

$$T = f(z) \qquad\qquad \text{at } r = b \qquad\qquad (3\text{-}193b)$$

$$T = 0 \qquad\qquad \text{at } z = 0 \text{ and } z = c \qquad (3\text{-}193c)$$

The separated equations are taken as

$$\frac{d^2 Z}{dz^2} + \eta^2 Z = 0 \qquad \text{in } 0 < z < c \qquad\qquad (3\text{-}194a)$$

$$Z = 0 \qquad\qquad \text{at } z = 0 \text{ and } z = c \qquad (3\text{-}194b)$$

and

$$\frac{d^2 R_0}{dr^2} + \frac{1}{r}\frac{dR_0}{dr} - \eta^2 R_0 = 0 \qquad \text{in } 0 \le r < b \qquad (3\text{-}195)$$

We note that the sign of the separation constant is so chosen as to produce an eigenvalue problem for $Z(\eta, z)$, because the boundary condition function $f(z)$ should be represented in terms of $Z(\eta, z)$. The general solution for $T(r,z)$ is constructed as

$$T(r,z) = \sum_{m=1}^{\infty} A_m I_0(\eta_m r) Z(\eta_m, z) \qquad (3\text{-}196)$$

The application of the boundary condition (3-193b) yields

$$f(z) = \sum_{m=1}^{\infty} A_m I_0(\eta_m b) Z(\eta_m, z) \qquad \text{in } 0 < z < c \qquad (3\text{-}197)$$

The coefficients A_m are determined as

$$A_m = \frac{1}{I_0(\eta_m b)N(\eta_m)} \int_0^c Z(\eta_m, z)f(z)\,dz \tag{3-198}$$

Introducing equation (3-198) into equation (3-196) the solution becomes

$$T(r,z) = \sum_{m=1}^{\infty} \frac{1}{N(\eta_m)} \frac{I_0(\eta_m r)}{I_0(\eta_m b)} Z(\eta_m, z) \int_0^c Z(\eta_m, z')f(z')\,dz' \tag{3-199}$$

where $Z(\eta_m, z)$, $N(\eta_m)$, and η_m are obtained from Table 2-2, Case 9, as

$$Z(\eta_m, z) = \sin \eta_m z, \qquad \frac{1}{N(\eta_m)} = \frac{2}{c} \tag{3-200a}$$

and η_m's are the roots of

$$\sin \eta_m c = 0 \tag{3-200b}$$

Substituting equation (3-200) into equation (3-199) we find

$$T(r,z) = \frac{2}{c} \sum_{m=1}^{\infty} \frac{I_0(\eta_m r)}{I_0(\eta_m b)} \sin \eta_m z \int_0^c \sin \eta_m z' f(z')\,dz' \tag{3-201}$$

where

$$\eta_m = \frac{m\pi}{c}$$

3-9 MULTIDIMENSIONAL STEADY-STATE PROBLEMS WITH HEAT GENERATION

As discussed in Section 2-9 in the previous chapter, if a particular solution $p(r, \phi, z)$ of the equation

$$\nabla^2 T(r, \phi, z) + \frac{1}{k} g(r, \phi, z) = 0 \tag{3-202}$$

can be found, then a change of variable in the form

$$T(r, \phi, z) = \theta(r, \phi, z) + p(r, \phi, z) \tag{3-203}$$

transforms the nonhomogeneous equation (3-202) into the Laplace's equation for $\theta(r, \phi, z)$ as

$$\nabla^2 \theta(r, \phi, z) = 0 \tag{3-204}$$

Table 3-4   Particular solutions $p(r, \phi, z)$
of equation $\nabla^2 T(r, \phi, z) + (1/k)g = 0$

T is a function of	g^*	p
(r) or (r, ϕ) or (r, z) or (r, ϕ, z)	g_0	$-\dfrac{g_0}{k}\dfrac{r^2}{4}$
(r) or (r, ϕ) or (r, z) or (r, ϕ, z)	$g_0 r$	$-\dfrac{g_0}{k}\dfrac{r^3}{9}$
(r) or (r, ϕ) or (r, z) or (r, ϕ, z)	$g_0 r^2$	$-\dfrac{g_0}{k}\dfrac{r^4}{16}$
(r) or (r, ϕ) or (r, z) or (r, ϕ, z)	$g_0 r^n$	$-\dfrac{g_0}{k}\dfrac{r^{n+2}}{(n+2)^2}$

$*g_0$ is a constant and n is an integer.

The Laplace's equation subject to nonhomogeneous boundary conditions can be solved by the method of separation of variables. Some particular solutions of equation (3-202) are given in Table 3-4.

Example 3-20.   Obtain an expression for the steady-state temperature distribution $T(r, z)$ in a solid cylinder $0 \le r \le b, 0 \le z \le c$, with heat generation at a constant rate of g_0 per unit volume, while all boundaries are kept at zero temperature.

Solution.   The mathematical formulation of this problem is given as

$$\frac{\partial^2 T}{\partial r^2} + \frac{1}{r}\frac{\partial T}{\partial r} + \frac{\partial^2 T}{\partial z^2} + \frac{1}{k}g_0 = 0 \qquad \text{in } 0 \le r < b, \ 0 < z < c \quad \text{(3-205a)}$$

$$T = 0 \qquad\qquad\qquad \text{at } r = b, \ z = 0, \text{ and } z = c \text{ (3-205b)}$$

A particular solution of equation (3-205a) is available in Table 3-4 and Table 2-4; a new variable $\theta(r, z)$ is defined as

$$T(r, z) = \theta(r, z) - \frac{g_0 z^2}{2k} + Az \qquad\qquad (3-206)$$

where the arbitrary constant A is introduced to allow simplification of boundary conditions by proper choice of the value of this constant. Introducing equation (3-206) into equations (3-205) we obtain

$$\frac{\partial^2 \theta}{\partial r^2} + \frac{1}{r}\frac{\partial \theta}{\partial r} + \frac{\partial^2 \theta}{\partial z^2} = 0 \qquad \text{in } 0 \le r < b, \ 0 < z < c \qquad (3\text{-}207a)$$

$$\theta = \frac{g_0 z^2}{2k} - Az \qquad \text{at } r = b \qquad (3\text{-}207b)$$

$$\theta = 0 \qquad \text{at } z = 0 \qquad (3\text{-}207c)$$

$$\theta = \frac{g_0 c^2}{2k} - Ac \qquad \text{at } z = c \qquad (3\text{-}207d)$$

If we chose the constant A as

$$A = \frac{g_0 c}{2k} \qquad (3\text{-}208)$$

The transformation (3-206) becomes

$$T(r, z) = \theta(r, z) + \frac{g_0}{2k} z(c - z) \qquad (3\text{-}209)$$

and the problem (3-207) simplifies to

$$\frac{\partial^2 \theta}{\partial r^2} + \frac{1}{r}\frac{\partial \theta}{\partial r} + \frac{\partial^2 \theta}{\partial z^2} = 0 \qquad \text{in } 0 \le r < b, \ 0 < z < c \qquad (3\text{-}210a)$$

$$\theta = \frac{g_0}{2k} z(z - c) \equiv f(z) \qquad \text{at } r = b \qquad (3\text{-}210b)$$

$$\theta = 0 \qquad \text{at } z = 0, \ z = c \qquad (3\text{-}210c)$$

The problem (3-210) is exactly the same as considered in Example 3-19; hence its solution is obtainable from the solution (3-201) as

$$\theta(r, z) = \frac{2}{c} \sum_{m=1}^{\infty} \frac{I_0(\eta_m r)}{I_0(\eta_m b)} \sin \eta_m z \int_0^c \sin \eta_m z' f(z') \, dz' \qquad (3\text{-}211a)$$

where

$$\eta_m = \frac{m\pi}{c}, \qquad f(z) = \frac{g_0}{2k} z(z - c) \qquad (3\text{-}211b)$$

Performing the integration and introducing equation (3-211a) into equation (3-209) we find

$$T(r, z) = \frac{g_0}{2k} z(c - z) - \frac{4g_0 c^2}{\pi^3 k} \sum_{m=0}^{\infty} \frac{1}{(2m + 1)^3} \frac{I_0(\xi_m r)}{I_0(\xi_m b)} \sin \xi_m z \qquad (3\text{-}212)$$

where

$$\xi_m = \frac{(2m+1)\pi}{c}.$$

3-10 SPLITTING-UP OF NONHOMOGENEOUS PROBLEMS INTO SIMPLER PROBLEMS

When the heat-conduction problem is nonhomogeneous due to the non-homogeneity of the differential equation and/or the boundary conditions, it can be split into a set of simpler problems, as discussed in the Section 2-10, if the generation term and the nonhomogeneous part of the boundary conditions *do not depend on time.*

Example 3-21. A solid cylinder, $0 \le r \le b$, is initially at temperature $F(r)$. For times $t > 0$, heat is generated within the solid at a constant rate of g_0 and the boundary surface at $r = b$ is kept at zero temperature. Obtain an expression for the temperature distribution $T(r, t)$ in the cylinder for times $t > 0$.

Solution. The mathematical formulation of this problem is given as

$$\frac{\partial^2 T}{\partial r^2} + \frac{1}{r}\frac{\partial T}{\partial r} + \frac{1}{k}g_0 = \frac{1}{\alpha}\frac{\partial T}{\partial t} \qquad \text{in } 0 \le r < b, \ t > 0 \qquad (3\text{-}213\text{a})$$

$$T = 0 \qquad\qquad\qquad \text{at } r = b, \ t > 0 \qquad (3\text{-}213\text{b})$$

$$T = F(r) \qquad\qquad\qquad \text{for } t = 0, \text{ in the region} \qquad (3\text{-}213\text{c})$$

This problem is split into a steady-state problem for $T_s(r)$ as

$$\frac{d^2 T_s}{dr^2} + \frac{1}{r}\frac{dT_s}{dr} + \frac{1}{k}g_0 = 0 \qquad \text{in } 0 \le r < b \qquad (3\text{-}214\text{a})$$

$$T = 0 \qquad\qquad\qquad \text{at } r = b \qquad (3\text{-}214\text{b})$$

and into a homogeneous problem for $T_h(r, t)$ as

$$\frac{\partial^2 T_h}{\partial r^2} + \frac{1}{r}\frac{\partial T_h}{\partial r} = \frac{1}{\alpha}\frac{\partial T_h}{\partial t} \qquad \text{in } 0 \le r < b, \ t > 0 \qquad (3\text{-}215\text{a})$$

$$T = 0 \qquad\qquad\qquad \text{at } r = b, \ t > 0 \qquad (3\text{-}215\text{b})$$

$$T = F(r) - T_s(r) \qquad\qquad \text{for } t = 0, \text{ in the region} \qquad (3\text{-}215\text{c})$$

Then, the solution $T(r, t)$ of the original problem (3-213) is obtained as

$$T(r, t) = T_s(r) + T_h(r, t) \tag{3-216}$$

The steady-state problem is readily solved

$$T_s(r) = \frac{g_0}{4k}(b^2 - r^2) \tag{3-217}$$

The homogeneous problem (3-215) is exactly the same as considered in Example 3-3; hence its solution is immediately obtained from equation (3-67) as

$$T_h(r, t) = \frac{2}{b^2} \sum_{m=1}^{\infty} e^{-\alpha \beta_m^2 t} \frac{J_0(\beta_m r)}{J_1^2(\beta_m b)} \int_0^b r' J_0(\beta_m r')[F(r') - T_s(r')] dr' \tag{3-218a}$$

where β_m's are the roots of

$$J_0(\beta_m b) = 0 \tag{3-218b}$$

When the results in equations (3-217) and (3-218) are introduced into equation (3-216) and some of the integrals are performed, we obtain

$$T(r, t) = \frac{g_0(b^2 - r^2)}{4k} - \frac{2g_0}{bk} \sum_{m=1}^{\infty} e^{-\alpha \beta_m^2 t} \frac{J_0(\beta_m r)}{\beta_m^3 J_1(\beta_m b)}$$
$$+ \frac{2}{b^2} \sum_{m=1}^{\infty} e^{-\alpha \beta_m^2 t} \frac{J_0(\beta_m r)}{J_1^2(\beta_m b)} \int_0^b r' J_0(\beta_m r') F(r') dr' \tag{3-219}$$

Example 3-22. A solid cylinder is initially at temperature $F^*(r)$. For times $t > 0$ heat is generated in the region at a constant rate of g_0 per unit volume and the boundary surface at $r = b$ is subjected to convection with an environment at temperature T_∞. Obtain an expression for the temperature distribution $T(r, t)$ in the solid for times $t > 0$.

Solution. The mathematical formulation of this problem is given as

$$\frac{\partial^2 T}{\partial r^2} + \frac{1}{r}\frac{\partial T}{\partial r} + \frac{g_0}{k} = \frac{1}{\alpha}\frac{\partial T}{\partial t} \qquad \text{in } 0 \le r < b, \ t > 0 \tag{3-220a}$$

$$\frac{\partial T}{\partial r} + HT = HT_\infty \qquad \text{at } r = b, \ t > 0 \tag{3-220b}$$

$$T = F^*(r) \qquad \text{for } t = 0, \ \text{in } 0 \le r \le b \tag{3-220c}$$

and the temperature should remain finite at $r = 0$. This problem is split into a steady-state problem for $T_s(r)$ as

$$\frac{d^2 T_s}{dr^2} + \frac{1}{r}\frac{dT_s}{dr} + \frac{g_0}{k} = 0 \qquad \text{in } 0 \le r < b \qquad (3\text{-}221a)$$

$$\frac{dT_s}{dr} + HT_s = HT_\infty \qquad \text{at } r = b \qquad (3\text{-}221b)$$

and into a homogeneous problem for $T_h(r, t)$ as

$$\frac{\partial^2 T_h}{\partial r^2} + \frac{1}{r}\frac{\partial T_h}{\partial r} = \frac{1}{\alpha}\frac{\partial T_h}{\partial t} \qquad \text{in } 0 \le r < b,\ t > 0 \qquad (3\text{-}222a)$$

$$\frac{\partial T_h}{\partial r} + HT_h = 0 \qquad \text{at } r = b,\ t > 0 \qquad (3\text{-}222b)$$

$$T_h = F^*(r) - T_s(r) \equiv F(r) \qquad \text{for } t = 0,\ \text{in } 0 \le r \le b \qquad (3\text{-}222c)$$

Then, the solution of the problem (3-220) is given by

$$T(r, t) = T_s(r) + T_h(r, t) \qquad (3\text{-}223)$$

The solution $T_s(r)$ of the steady-state problem (3-221) is a straightforward matter. The homogeneous problem (3-222) is exactly the same as the problem (3-57) considered in example (3-1); therefore, the solution of $T_h(r, t)$ is obtainable from equation (3-63) by setting in that equation $F(r) = F^*(r) - T_s(r)$.

REFERENCES

1.   H. S. Carslaw and J. C. Jaeger, *Conduction of Heat in Solids*, Clarendon Press, London, 1959.
2.   A. V. Luikov, *Analytical Heat Diffusion Theory*, Academic Press, New York, 1968.
3.   P. Moon and D. E. Spencer, *Field Theory for Engineers*, D. Van Nostrand Company, Inc., Princeton, N.J., 1961.
4.   G. N. Watson, *A Treatise on the Theory of Bessel Functions*, 2nd. ed., Cambridge University Press, London, 1966.
5.   N. W. McLachlan, *Bessel Functions for Engineers*, 2nd ed., Clarendon Press, London, 1961.
6.   E. T. Whittaker and G. N. Watson, *A Course of Modern Analysis*, Cambridge University Press, London, 1965.
7.   M. Abramowitz and I. A. Stegun, *Handbook of Mathematical Functions*, National Bureau of Standards, Applied Mathematic Series 55, U.S. Government Printing Office, Washington, D.C., 20402, 1964.
8.   E. C. Titchmarsh, *Eigenfunction Expansions*, Part I, Clarendon Press, London, 1962.
9.   I. N. Sneddon, *Fourier Transforms*, McGraw-Hill Book Company, Inc., New York, 1951.
10.   G. Cinelli, *Int. J. Eng. Sci.* **3**, 539–559, 1965.

11. S. Goldstein, *Proc. Lond. Math. Soc. (2)* **34**, 51–88, 1932.
12. E. C. Titchmarsh, *Proc. Lond. Math. Soc. (2)* **22**, 15–28, 1923.
13. J. I. Masters, *J. Chem. Phys.*, **23**, 1865–1874, 1955.

PROBLEMS

3-1 A hollow cylinder, $a \leq r \leq b$, is initially at a temperature $F(r)$. For times $t > 0$ the boundaries at $r = a$ and $r = b$ are kept insulated. Obtain an expression for temperature distribution $T(r, t)$ in the solid for times $t > 0$.

3-2 A region $a \leq r < \infty$ in the cylindrical coordinate system is initially at a temperature $F(r)$. For times $t > 0$ the boundary at $r = a$ is kept insulated. Obtain an expression for the temperature distribution $T(r, t)$ in the region for times $t > 0$.

3-3 A solid cylinder, $0 \leq r \leq b, 0 \leq z \leq c$, is initially at temperature $F(r, z)$. For times $t > 0$, the boundary at $z = 0$ is insulated, the boundary at $z = c$ is dissipating heat by convection into a medium at zero temperature, and the boundary at $r = b$ is kept at zero temperature. Obtain an expression for the temperature distribution $T(r, z, t)$ in the solid for times $t > 0$.

3-4 A semi-infinite solid cylinder, $0 \leq r \leq b, 0 \leq z < \infty$, is initially at temperature $F(r, z)$. For times $t > 0$, the boundary at $z = 0$ is kept insulated and the boundary at $r = b$ is dissipating heat by convection into a medium at zero temperature. Obtain an expression for the temperature distribution $T(r, z, t)$ in the solid for times $t > 0$.

3-5 A semi-infinite hollow cylinder, $a \leq r \leq b, 0 \leq z < \infty$, is initially at temperature $F(r, z)$. For times $t > 0$, the boundaries at $z = 0, r = a$, and $r = b$ are all kept at zero temperature. Obtain an expression for the temperature distribution $T(r, z, t)$ in the solid for times $t > 0$.

3-6 A solid cylinder, $0 \leq r \leq b, 0 \leq \phi \leq 2\pi$, is initially at temperature $F(r, \phi)$. For times $t > 0$, the boundary at $r = b$ is kept insulated. Obtain an expression for the temperature distribution $T(r, \phi, t)$ in the solid for times $t > 0$.

3-7 A hollow cylinder, $a \leq r \leq b, 0 \leq \phi \leq 2\pi$, is initially at temperature $F(r, \phi)$. For times $t > 0$, the boundaries at $r = a$ and $r = b$ are kept insulated. Obtain an expression for the temperature distribution $T(r, \phi, t)$ in the region for times $t > 0$.

3-8 A portion of a solid cylinder $0 \leq r \leq b, 0 \leq \phi \leq \phi_0 (< 2\pi)$ is initially at temperature $F(r, \phi)$. For times $t > 0$, the boundary at $r = b$ dissipates heat by convection into a medium at zero temperature, the boundaries at $\phi = 0$ and $\phi = \phi_0$ are kept at zero temperature. Obtain an expression for the temperature distribution $T(r, \phi, t)$ in the solid for times $t > 0$.

3-9 A portion of a hollow cylinder $a \leq r \leq b, 0 \leq \phi \leq \phi_0 < 2\pi$ is initially at temperature $F(r, \phi)$. For times $t > 0$, the boundaries at $r = a, r = b, \phi = 0$, and $\phi = \phi_0$ are all kept at zero temperature. Obtain an expression for the temperature distribution $T(r, \phi, t)$ in the solid for times $t > 0$.

3-10   Repeat problem 3-9 for the case when the boundaries at $r = a$, $r = b, \phi = 0$ and $\phi = \phi_0$ for all kept insulated.

3-11   A solid cylinder $0 \le r \le b, 0 \le z \le c, 0 \le \phi \le 2\pi$, is initially at temperature $F(r, \phi, z)$. For times $t > 0$, the boundary at $z = 0$ is kept insulated, the boundaries at $z = c$ and $r = b$ are kept at zero temperature. Obtain an expression for the temperature distribution $T(r, z, \phi, t)$ in the solid for times $t > 0$.

3-12   A portion of a hollow cylinder, $a \le r \le b, 0 \le \phi \le \phi_0 < 2\pi, 0 \le z \le c$, as illustrated in Fig. 3-10 is initially at temperature $F(r, \phi, z)$. For times $t > 0$, the boundary surface at $z = 0$ is kept insulated, the boundary at $z = c$ dissipates heat by convection into an environment at zero temperature, and the remaining boundaries are kept at zero temperature. Obtain an expression for temperature distribution $T(r, \phi, z, t)$ in the solid for times $t > 0$.

3-13   Solve Problem 3-3 by using product solution for the case solid is initially at a uniform temperature T_0.

3-14   Obtain an expression for the steady-state temperature distribution $T(r, z)$ in a solid cylinder, $0 \le r \le b, 0 \le z \le c$, when the boundary at $z = 0$ is kept at temperature $F(r)$, and there is convection into a medium at zero temperature from the surfaces $r = b$ and $z = c$. Assume heat-transfer coefficients to be the same for both of these surfaces.

3-15   Obtain an expression for the steady-state temperature distribution $T(r, z)$ in a hollow cylinder $a \le r \le b, 0 \le z \le c$, when the boundary at $r = a$ is kept at temperature $F(z)$ and other boundaries at $r = b, z = 0$, and $z = c$ are kept at zero temperature.

3-16   Obtain an expression for the steady-state temperature $T(r, z)$ in a hollow cylinder $a \le r \le b, 0 \le z \le c$, when the heat flux into the surface at $r = a$ is $f(z)$ [i.e., $-k(\partial T/\partial r) = f(z)$ at $r = a$] and the other boundaries at $r = b, z = 0$ and $z = c$ are kept at zero temperature.

3-17   Obtain an expression for the steady-state temperature distribution $T(r, \phi)$ in a solid cylinder $0 \le r \le b, 0 \le \phi \le 2\pi$, when the boundary at $r = b$ is subjected to a prescribed temperature distribution $f(\phi)$.

3-18   Obtain an expression for the steady-state temperature distribution $T(r, z)$ in a solid, semi-infinite cylinder $0 \le r \le b, 0 \le z < \infty$, when the boundary at $r = b$ is kept at prescribed temperature $f(z)$ and the boundary at $z = 0$ is kept at zero temperature.

3-19   Obtain an expression for the steady-state temperature distribution $T(r, z)$ in a solid, semi-infinite cylinder $0 \le r \le b, 0 \le z < \infty$, when the boundary at $z = 0$ is kept at temperature $f(r)$ and the boundary at $r = b$ dissipates heat by convection into a medium at zero temperature.

3-20   Obtain an expression for the steady-state temperature distribution $T(r, z)$ in a hollow cylinder $a \leq r \leq b, 0 \leq z \leq c$, in which heat is generated at a constant rate of g_0 per unit volume, the boundary at $r = a$ is kept insulated and the other boundaries at $r = b, z = 0$, and $z = c$ are kept at zero temperature.

NOTES

1.   Consider the eigenvalue problem

$$\frac{1}{r}\frac{d}{dr}\left[r\frac{dR(r)}{dr}\right] + \left(\beta^2 - \frac{v^2}{r^2}\right)R(r) = 0 \qquad \text{in } 0 \leq r < b \tag{1a}$$

$$\frac{dR}{dr} = 0 \quad \text{at } r = b \tag{1b}$$

From equation (1a) for $v = 0$ we find

$$\beta^2 \int_0^b rR^2(r)\,dr = -\int_0^b R\frac{d}{dr}\left[r\frac{dR}{dr}\right]dr \tag{2}$$

Integrating the right-hand side by parts we obtain

$$\beta^2 \int_0^b rR^2(r)\,dr = -\left[rR\frac{dR}{dr}\right]_0^b + \int_0^b r\left(\frac{dR}{dr}\right)^2 dr \tag{3}$$

The first term on the right vanishes in view of the boundary condition (1b); then

$$\beta^2 = \frac{1}{N}\int_0^b r\left(\frac{dR}{dr}\right)^2 dr \qquad \text{where} \qquad N \equiv \int_0^b rR^2\,dr \tag{4}$$

Clearly, $\beta_0 = 0$ is also an eigenvalue corresponding to $R_0(\beta_0, r) =$ constant $\neq 0$. Then, for $R_0(\beta_0, r) = 1$ the corresponding norm becomes

$$N(\beta_0) = \frac{b^2}{2} \tag{5}$$

2.   The norm $N(\beta_m)$ given by equation (3-43) is

$$N(\beta_m) = S_v^2 \int_a^b rJ_v^2(\beta_m r)\,dr - 2S_v V_v \int_a^b rJ_v(\beta_m r)Y_v(\beta_m r)\,dr + V_v^2 \int_0^b rY_v^2(\beta_m r)\,dr \tag{1}$$

Various integrals in this expression are evaluated by utilizing the indefinite integral (3-45a); we obtain

$$N(\beta_m) = S_v^2 \frac{b^2}{2} \left\{ J_v'^2(\beta_m b) + \left[1 - \left(\frac{v}{\beta_m b} \right)^2 \right] J_v^2(\beta_m b) \right\}$$

$$- S_v^2 \frac{a^2}{2} \left\{ J_v'^2(\beta_m a) + \left[1 - \left(\frac{v}{\beta_m a} \right)^2 \right] J_v^2(\beta_m a) \right\}$$

$$- 2S_v V_v \frac{b^2}{2} \left\{ J_v'(\beta_m b) Y_v'(\beta_m b) + \left[1 - \left(\frac{v}{\beta_m b} \right)^2 \right] J_v(\beta_m b) Y_v(\beta_m b) \right\}$$

$$+ 2S_v V_v \frac{a^2}{2} \left\{ J_v'(\beta_m a) Y_v'(\beta_m a) + \left[1 - \left(\frac{v}{\beta_m a} \right)^2 \right] J_v(\beta_m a) Y_v(\beta_m a) \right\}$$

$$+ V_v^2 \frac{b^2}{2} \left\{ Y_v'(\beta_m b) + \left[1 - \left(\frac{v}{\beta_m b} \right)^2 \right] Y_v^2(\beta_m b) \right\}$$

$$- V_v^2 \frac{a^2}{2} \left\{ Y_v'(\beta_m a) + \left[1 - \left(\frac{v}{\beta_m a} \right)^2 \right] Y_v^2(\beta_m a) \right\} \qquad (2)$$

This result is now rearranged as

$$N(\beta_m) = \frac{b^2}{2} A_1 - \frac{a^2}{2} A_2 + \frac{b^2}{2} \left[1 - \left(\frac{v}{\beta_m b} \right)^2 \right] A_3 - \frac{a^2}{2} \left[1 - \left(\frac{v}{\beta_m a} \right)^2 \right] A_4 \quad (3)$$

where

$$A_1 \equiv [S_v J_v'(\beta_m b) - V_v Y_v'(\beta_m b)]^2 \qquad (4a)$$

$$A_2 \equiv [S_v J_v'(\beta_m a) - V_v Y_v'(\beta_m a)]^2 \qquad (4b)$$

$$A_3 \equiv [S_v J_v(\beta_m b) - V_v Y_v(\beta_m b)]^2 \qquad (4c)$$

$$A_4 \equiv [S_v J_v(\beta_m a) - V_v Y_v(\beta_m a)]^2 \qquad (4d)$$

where

$$S_v \equiv \beta_m Y_v'(\beta_m b) + H_2 Y_v(\beta_m b) \qquad (5a)$$

$$V_v \equiv \beta_m J_v'(\beta_m b) + H_2 J_v(\beta_m b) \qquad (5b)$$

The values of S_v and V_v are substituted into equations (4), and the resulting expressions are simplified by means of the wronkian relationship (3-44). We find

$$A_1 = \left(\frac{2H_2}{\pi \beta_m b} \right)^2, \qquad A_2 = \frac{V_v^2}{U_v^2} \left(\frac{2H_1}{\pi \beta_m a} \right)^2 \qquad (6a)$$

$$A_3 = \left(\frac{2}{\pi b} \right)^2, \qquad A_4 = \frac{V_v^2}{U_v^2} \left(\frac{2}{\pi a} \right)^2 \qquad (6b)$$

When equations (6) are introduced into equation (3), the norm becomes

$$N(\beta_m) = \frac{2}{\pi\beta_m^2}\left\{H_2 + \beta_m^2\left[1 - \left(\frac{v}{\beta_m b}\right)^2\right]\right\}$$
$$- \frac{2}{\pi\beta_m^2}\left(\frac{V_v}{U_v}\right)^2\left\{H_1^2 + \beta_m^2\left[1 - \left(\frac{v}{\beta_m a}\right)^2\right]\right\} \tag{7}$$

or

$$\frac{1}{N(\beta_m)} = \frac{\pi^2}{2}\frac{\beta_m^2 U_v^2}{B_2 U_v^2 - B_1 V_v^2} \tag{8a}$$

where

$$B_1 \equiv H_1^2 + \beta_m^2\left[1 - \left(\frac{v}{\beta_m a}\right)^2\right] \quad\text{and}\quad B_2 \equiv H_2^2 + \beta_m^2\left[1 - \left(\frac{v}{\beta_m b}\right)^2\right] \tag{8b}$$

which is the same expression as given by equation (3-46).

CHAPTER 4

THE SEPARATION OF VARIABLES IN THE SPHERICAL COORDINATE SYSTEM

In this chapter we present the separation of the homogeneous heat-conduction equation in the spherical coordinate system; give a brief discussion of the properties of the Legendre functions and the representation of a function in terms of the Legendre functions; discuss the solution of the homogeneous problems involving $(r, t), (r, \mu, t)$, and (r, μ, ϕ, t) variables by the method of separation of variables; examine the solution of the multi-dimensional steady-state problems, and illustrate the splitting up of non-homogeneous problems into a set of simpler problems. The reader should consult references [1–5] for further application of the method of separation of variables to the solution of homogeneous heat-conduction problems in the spherical coordinate system.

4-1 SEPARATION OF THE HEAT-CONDUCTION EQUATION IN THE SPHERICAL COORDINATE SYSTEM

Consider the three-dimensional, homogeneous heat-conduction equation in the spherical coordinate system (r, θ, ϕ) given as

$$\frac{\partial^2 T}{\partial r^2} + \frac{2}{r}\frac{\partial T}{\partial r} + \frac{1}{r^2 \sin\theta}\frac{\partial}{\partial\theta}\left(\sin\theta\frac{\partial T}{\partial\theta}\right) + \frac{1}{r^2 \sin^2\theta}\frac{\partial^2 T}{\partial\phi^2} = \frac{1}{\alpha}\frac{\partial T}{\partial t} \tag{4.1}$$

where $T \equiv T(r, \theta, \phi, t)$. This equation is put into a more convenient form by defining a new independent variable

$$\mu = \cos\theta \tag{4.2}$$

Equation (4.1) becomes

$$\frac{\partial^2 T}{\partial r^2} + \frac{2}{r}\frac{\partial T}{\partial r} + \frac{1}{r^2}\frac{\partial}{\partial \mu}\left[(1-\mu^2)\frac{\partial T}{\partial \mu}\right] + \frac{1}{r^2(1-\mu^2)}\frac{\partial^2 T}{\partial \phi^2} = \frac{1}{\alpha}\frac{\partial T}{\partial t} \qquad (4.3)$$

where $T \equiv T(r, \mu, \phi, t)$. If we define a new dependent variable V as

$$V = r^{1/2}T \qquad (4\text{-}4)$$

equation (4-3) becomes

$$\frac{\partial^2 V}{\partial r^2} + \frac{1}{r}\frac{\partial V}{\partial r} - \frac{1}{4}\frac{V}{r^2} + \frac{1}{r^2}\frac{\partial}{\partial \mu}\left[(1-\mu^2)\frac{\partial V}{\partial \mu}\right] + \frac{1}{r^2(1-\mu^2)}\frac{\partial^2 V}{\partial \phi^2} = \frac{1}{\alpha}\frac{\partial V}{\partial t} \qquad (4\text{-}5)$$

If we assume a separation of variables in the form

$$V(r, \mu, \phi, t) = \Gamma(t)R(r)M(\mu)\Phi(\phi) \qquad (4\text{-}6)$$

The resulting separated equations become

$$\frac{d\Gamma(t)}{dt} + \alpha\lambda^2\Gamma(t) = 0 \qquad (4\text{-}7a)$$

$$\frac{d^2\Phi(\phi)}{d\phi^2} + m^2\Phi(\phi) = 0 \qquad (4\text{-}7b)$$

$$\frac{d^2R}{dr^2} + \frac{1}{r}\frac{dR}{dr} + \left[\lambda^2 - \left(n+\frac{1}{2}\right)^2\frac{1}{r^2}\right]R = 0 \qquad (4\text{-}7c)$$

$$\frac{d}{d\mu}\left[(1-\mu^2)\frac{dM}{d\mu}\right] + \left[n(n+1) - \frac{m^2}{1-\mu^2}\right]M = 0 \qquad (4\text{-}7d)$$

Equation (4-7c) is the Bessel's differential equation of order $(n + \frac{1}{2})$ which has solutions $J_{n+1/2}(\lambda r)$ and $Y_{n+1/2}(\lambda r)$. When the order of the Bessel function is not zero or positive integer, the solution $Y_{n+1/2}(\lambda r)$ can be replaced by $J_{-n-1/2}(\lambda r)$ as discussed in Appendix III. The differential equation (4-7d) is called *Legendre's associated differential equation*, its solutions $P_n^m(\mu)$ and $Q_n^m(\mu)$ are called *associated Legendre functions of degree n and order m, of the first and second kind*, respectively. We present a brief discussion of the Legendre functions in the next section.

The elementary solutions of the separated equations (4-7) can be summarized as

$$\Gamma(t): \ e^{-\alpha\lambda^2 t} \qquad (4\text{-}8a)$$

$$\Phi(\phi): \ \sin m\phi \ \text{and} \ \cos m\phi \qquad (4\text{-}8b)$$

$$R(r): \ J_{n+1/2}(\lambda r) \ \text{and} \ Y_{n+1/2}(\lambda r)\left[\text{or} \ J_{-n-1/2}(\lambda r)\right] \qquad (4\text{-}8c)$$

$$M(\mu): \ P_n^m(\mu) \ \text{and} \ Q_n^m(\mu) \qquad (4\text{-}8d)$$

We now examine the separation of equation (4-3) for special cases.

1. *Temperature has no ϕ-dependence.*   Equation (4-3) reduces to

$$\frac{\partial^2 T}{\partial r^2} + \frac{2}{r}\frac{\partial T}{\partial r} + \frac{1}{r^2}\frac{\partial}{\partial \mu}\left[(1 - \mu^2)\frac{\partial T}{\partial \mu}\right] = \frac{1}{\alpha}\frac{\partial T}{\partial t} \tag{4-9a}$$

$$V = r^{1/2}T \tag{4-9b}$$

Equation (4-9a) is transformed into

$$\frac{\partial^2 V}{\partial r^2} + \frac{1}{r}\frac{\partial V}{\partial r} - \frac{1}{4}\frac{V}{r^2} + \frac{1}{r^2}\frac{\partial}{\partial \mu}\left[(1 - \mu^2)\frac{\partial V}{\partial \mu}\right] = \frac{1}{\alpha}\frac{\partial V}{\partial t} \tag{4-9c}$$

The separation of equation (4-9c) results in the following equations

$$\frac{d\Gamma(t)}{dt} + \alpha\lambda^2\Gamma(t) = 0 \tag{4-10a}$$

$$\frac{d^2R}{dr^2} + \frac{1}{r}\frac{dR}{dr} + \left[\lambda^2 - \left(n + \frac{1}{2}\right)^2\frac{1}{r^2}\right]R = 0 \tag{4-10b}$$

$$\frac{d}{d\mu}\left[(1 - \mu^2)\frac{dM}{d\mu}\right] + n(n + 1)M = 0 \tag{4-10c}$$

The elementary solutions of these equations are taken as

$$\Gamma(t):\ e^{-\alpha\lambda^2 t} \tag{4-11a}$$

$$R(r):\ J_{n+1/2}(\lambda r) \quad \text{and} \quad Y_{n+1/2}(\lambda r)\left[\text{or } J_{-n-1/2}(\lambda r)\right] \tag{4-11b}$$

$$M(\mu):\ P_n(\mu) \quad \text{and} \quad Q_n(\mu) \tag{4-11c}$$

We note that when the temperature is independent of the azimuth angle ϕ, the separated equation (4-10c) for the function $M(\mu)$ becomes the Legendre's differential equation. The solutions $P_n(\mu)$ and $Q_n(\mu)$ are called the Legendre functions of degree n, of the first and second kind, respectively.

2. *Temperature is independent of time.*   Assuming $T \equiv T(r, \mu, \phi)$, equation (4-3) reduces to

$$\frac{\partial^2 T}{\partial r^2} + \frac{2}{r}\frac{\partial T}{\partial r} + \frac{1}{r^2}\frac{\partial}{\partial \mu}\left[(1 - \mu^2)\frac{\partial T}{\partial \mu}\right] + \frac{1}{r^2(1 - \mu^2)}\frac{\partial^2 T}{\partial \phi^2} = 0 \tag{4-12}$$

For this case we separate the variables as

$$T(r, \mu, \phi) = R(r)M(\mu)\Phi(\phi)$$

The resulting separated equations become

$$\frac{d^2\Phi}{d\phi^2} + m^2\Phi = 0 \tag{4-13a}$$

$$\frac{d^2R}{dr^2} + \frac{2}{r}\frac{dR}{dr} - \frac{n(n+1)}{r^2}R = 0 \tag{4-13b}$$

$$\frac{d}{d\mu}\left[(1-\mu^2)\frac{dM}{d\mu}\right] + \left[n(n+1) - \frac{m^2}{1-\mu^2}\right]M = 0 \tag{4-13c}$$

and their elementary solutions are taken as

$$\Phi(\phi): \quad \sin m\phi \qquad \text{and} \qquad \cos m\phi \tag{4-13d}$$

$$R(r): \quad r^n \qquad \text{and} \qquad r^{-n-1} \tag{4-13e}$$

$$M(\mu): \quad P_n^m(\mu) \qquad \text{and} \qquad Q_n^m(\mu) \tag{4-13f}$$

For this special case the separated equation (4-13b) for the function $R(r)$ is an *Euler-Cauchy* type differential equation which has solutions r^n and r^{-n-1}.

3. *Temperature is a function of r and μ variables only.* When $T \equiv T(r,\mu)$, equation(4-3) reduces to

$$\frac{\partial^2 T}{\partial r^2} + \frac{2}{r}\frac{\partial T}{\partial r} + \frac{1}{r^2}\frac{\partial}{\partial \mu}\left[(1-\mu^2)\frac{\partial T}{\partial \mu}\right] = 0 \tag{4-14}$$

The separation of this equation by setting $T(r,\mu) = R(r)M(\mu)$ leads to the following separated equations

$$\frac{d^2R}{dr^2} + \frac{2}{r}\frac{dR}{dr} - \frac{n(n+1)}{r^2}R = 0 \tag{4-15a}$$

$$\frac{d}{d\mu}\left[(1-\mu^2)\frac{dM}{d\mu}\right] + n(n+1)M = 0 \tag{4-15b}$$

and their elementary solutions are taken as

$$R(r): \quad r^n \qquad \text{and} \qquad r^{-n-1} \tag{4-15c}$$

$$M(\mu): \quad P_n(\mu) \qquad \text{and} \qquad Q_n(\mu) \tag{4-15d}$$

4. *Temperature is a function of r and t.* When $T \equiv T(r,t)$ equation (4-3) reduces to

$$\frac{\partial^2 T}{\partial r^2} + \frac{2}{r}\frac{\partial T}{\partial r} = \frac{1}{\alpha}\frac{\partial T}{\partial t} \tag{4-16a}$$

or

$$\frac{1}{r}\frac{\partial^2}{\partial r^2}(rT) = \frac{1}{\alpha}\frac{\partial T}{\partial t} \tag{4-16b}$$

A new dependent variable is defined as

$$U(r, t) = rT(r, t) \tag{4-16c}$$

Then equation (4-16b) is transformed into

$$\frac{\partial^2 U}{\partial r^2} = \frac{1}{\alpha} \frac{\partial U}{\partial t} \tag{4-17}$$

which is now the one-dimensional, time-dependent heat-conduction equation in the rectangular coordinate system and the separation of which has already been considered in Chapter 2.

Once the elementary solutions of the heat-conduction equation are available, the general solution is constructed by the superposition of the elementary solutions.

4-2   LEGENDRE FUNCTIONS AND LEGENDRE'S ASSOCIATED FUNCTIONS

In this section we present a brief discussion of the properties of the Legendre functions and Legendre's associated functions. The reader should consult references [5–14] for detailed treatment of this subject.

Legendre Functions

It has been shown that the separation of the heat-conduction equation for azimuthally symmetric temperature (i.e., temperature independent of ϕ) results in the Legendre's differential equation for $M(\mu)$ as

$$\frac{d}{d\mu}\left[(1 - \mu^2)\frac{dM}{d\mu} \right] + n(n + 1)M = 0 \tag{4-18}$$

This differential equation is a special case of the Sturm-Liouville equation discussed in Chapter 2, with $p(\mu) = 1 - \mu^2, q(\mu) = 0, w(\mu) = 1$, and $\lambda = n(n + 1)$. Clearly, the separation constants $n(n + 1)$ are the eigenvalues, in which n, in general, is any number; depending on the nature of the problem n can be a positive integer or fractional. In heat-conduction problems for a sphere the maximum range of the polar angle θ is from 0 to π; then, the corresponding range of μ from 1 to -1 covers all cases of interest.

According to the theory of linear differential equations, equation (4-18) has two linearly independent solutions. These solutions, denoted by the symbols $P_n(\mu)$ and $Q_n(\mu)$ are called *Legendre functions of degree n, of the first and second kind, respectively*. These solutions are in the form of series that converge for all $|\mu| < 1$, but the problem of convergence arises at the points

$\mu = \pm 1$ that are generally contained in the problems of sphere. For example the range of the μ variable for a full sphere include the points $\mu = \pm 1$, or for the part of a sphere cut out by the cone $\theta = \theta_0$ include one of these points, say, $\mu = 1$. With this consideration we now examine the solutions of equation (4-18) for the regions $-1 \le \mu \le 1$ and $\mu_0 \le \mu \le 1$ where $\mu_0 > -1$.

The Region $-1 \le \mu \le 1$.   This region is encountered in the problems of full sphere. The solution $Q_n(\mu)$ is infinite at $\mu = \pm 1$ for all values of n; therefore, in the problems of full sphere it is always excluded from the solution on the physical grounds. $P_n(\mu)$ function is infinite at $\mu = \pm 1$ unless n is an integer; for integer values of n the series defining the function $P_n(\mu)$ terminates at a finite number of terms, hence the Legendre function $P_n(\mu)$ becomes the *Legendre Polynomial* $P_n(\mu)$ for the integer values of n. The Legendre polynomial $P_n(\mu)$ is a polynomial of degree n in μ, and convergent in the interval $-1 \le \mu \le 1$. The first few of the Legendre polynomials are given as [5, p. 86; 7, p. 151]

$$P_0(\mu) = 1 \qquad\qquad\qquad P_1(\mu) = \mu$$
$$P_2(\mu) = \tfrac{1}{2}(3\,\mu^2 - 1) \qquad\qquad P_3(\mu) = \tfrac{1}{2}(5\,\mu^3 - 3\,\mu)$$
$$P_4(\mu) = \tfrac{1}{8}(35\,\mu^4 - 30\,\mu^2 + 3) \qquad P_5(\mu) = \tfrac{1}{8}(63\,\mu^5 - 70\,\mu^3 + 15\,\mu)$$
$$P_6(\mu) = \tfrac{1}{16}(231\,\mu^6 - 315\,\mu^4 + 105\,\mu^2 - 5) \qquad P_7(\mu) = \tfrac{1}{16}(429\,\mu^7 - 639\,\mu^5$$
$$+ 315\,\mu^3 - 35\,\mu)$$
$$P_8(\mu) = \tfrac{1}{128}(6435\,\mu^8 - 12012\,\mu^6 + 6930\,\mu^4 - 1260\,\mu^2 + 35) \qquad (4\text{-}19)$$

Any other $P_n(\mu)$, when n is a positive integer, is obtainable from the following recurrence relation

$$(n + 1)P_{n+1}(\mu) - (2n + 1)\mu P_n(\mu) + nP_{n-1}(\mu) = 0 \qquad (4\text{-}20)$$

The Legendre polynomials $P_n(\mu)$ are also obtainable from the Rodrigues' formula [15]

$$P_n(\mu) = \frac{1}{2^n n!} \frac{d^n}{d\mu^n}(\mu^2 - 1)^n \qquad (4\text{-}21)$$

This formula is of great use to evaluate definite integrals involving Legendre polynomials. We present in Appendix IV numerical values of the first seven of the Legendre polynomials $P_n(\mu)$. Figure 4-1 shows a plot of the first four of the Legendre polynomials.

The Region $\mu_0 \le \mu \le 1$.   The region $\mu_0 \le \mu \le 1$, where $\mu_0 > -1$, is encountered in the solution of heat-conduction problems for the part of the sphere cut out by the cone $\theta = \theta_0$ as illustrated in Fig. 4-2. For such cases the region includes the point $\mu = 1$ and a boundary condition is specified at

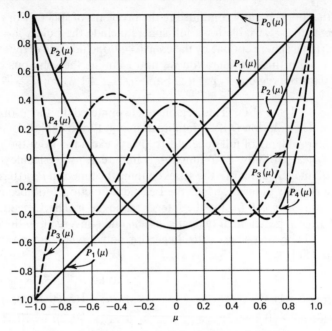

Fig. 4-1   Legendre polynomials $p_n(\mu)$ for $n = 0, 1, 2, 3, 4$.

the surface $\mu = \mu_0$. The solution $Q_n(\mu)$ being infinite at $\mu = 1$ for all values of n, it is excluded from the solution on the physical grounds. The Legendre polynomials given by equations (4-19) generally are not suitable; because, to satisfy the boundary condition at the surface $\mu = \mu_0$ it may be required that n should be chosen as noninteger. With this consideration we need an alternative expression defining the function $P_n(\mu)$ such that it will remain finite in the region $\mu_0 \leq \mu \leq 1$ where $\mu_0 > -1$, and will admit both noninteger and integer values of n in order to satisfy the requirement of the boundary

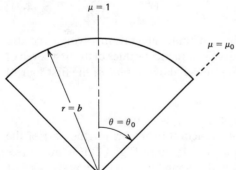

Fig. 4-2   A part of a sphere cut out by the cone $\theta = \theta_0$.

condition at the surface $\mu = \mu_0$. For such cases, the Legendre function $P_n(\mu)$ defined as a *hypergeometric series* in powers of $(1 - \mu)$ is a suitable solution; because, it remains finite in the range $\mu_0 \leq \mu \leq 1$ and admits both integer and noninteger values of n. It is given as [5, p. 104; 6, p. 132; 13, p. 59]

$$P_n(\mu) = F\left(-n, n+1, 1, \frac{1-\mu}{2}\right) = 1 + \sum_{r=1}^{\infty} \frac{(-n)_r(n+1)_r}{(1)_r r!}\left(\frac{1-\mu}{2}\right)^r \quad (4\text{-}22a)$$

$$= 1 + \sum_{r=1}^{\infty} \frac{[(-n)(-n+1)\ldots(-n+r-1)][(n+1)(n+2)\ldots(n+r)]}{(r!)^2 2^r}$$

$$\cdot (1-\mu)^r \quad (4\text{-}22b)$$

where

$$(\alpha)_r \equiv \alpha(\alpha+1)(\alpha+2)\ldots(\alpha+r-1).$$

This solution is also referred to [6, p. 312] as Murphy's expression of $P_n(\mu)$ as a hypergeometric series. A brief discussion of hypergeometric series is given in Note 1.

The solution given by equation (4-22) has a value 1 at $\mu = 1$ for all values of n, whether integer or not. When n is not an integer the series is finite in the interval $\mu_0 \leq \mu \leq 1$, and the values of n are determined from the requirement that the boundary condition at $\mu = \mu_0$ is satisfied. When n is a positive integer $(n = 0, 1, 2, 3, \ldots)$, the series (4-22) has a finite number of terms and $P_n(\mu)$ becomes a polynomial of degree n in powers of $(1 - \mu)$. We note that the series given by equation (4-22b) remains invariant if n is replaced by $-n-1$; we find

$$P_n(\mu) = P_{-n-1}(\mu) \quad (4\text{-}23)$$

Legendre's Associated Functions

We have seen that if the temperature depends among other variables on μ and ϕ variables, the separation of the heat-conduction equation results in the Legendre's associated differential equation for the separated function $M(\mu)$ in the form

$$\frac{d}{d\mu}\left[(1-\mu^2)\frac{dM}{d\mu}\right] + \left[n(n+1) - \frac{m^2}{1-\mu^2}\right]M = 0 \quad (4\text{-}24)$$

The two solutions $P_n^m(\mu)$ and $Q_n^m(\mu)$ of this differential equation are known as the associated Legendre functions of degree n and order m, of the first and second kinds, respectively. Here the order m of these functions has resulted from the separation constant associated with the separation of the ϕ variable, therefore its values depend on the range of the ϕ variable. When the range of

ϕ is $0 \leq \phi \leq 2\pi$, the values of m are taken as positive integers ($m = 0, 1, 2, 3, \dots$) to satisfy the physical requirement that the temperature remain periodic in ϕ with period 2π. The values n can be a positive integer or nonintegral depending on the range of μ. In the problems of a full sphere, the range of μ is $-1 \leq \mu \leq 1$ and in the problems of the part of sphere cut out by the cone $\theta = \theta_0$ as illustrated in Fig. 4-2, its range is $\mu_0 \leq \mu \leq 1$ where $\mu_0 > -1$. Therefore, we consider below the admissible solutions of equation (4-24) for these two ranges of μ separately.

The Region $-1 \leq \mu \leq 1$.   For the problems of full sphere in the region $1 \leq \mu \leq 1$, the functions $Q_n^m(\mu)$ are inadmissible as solutions on the physical grounds because they become infinite at $\mu = \pm 1$ for all values of n, whether integer or not. If m is a positive integer and n being unrestricted, it can be shown that the solution $P_n^m(\mu)$ given by equation (4-24) can be expressed in terms of the $P_n(\mu)$ functions as [5, p. 116; 12, p. 53]

$$P_n^m(\mu) = (-1)^m (1 - \mu^2)^{m/2} \frac{d^m}{d\mu^m} P_n(\mu) \qquad (4\text{-}25)$$

The function $P_n^m(\mu)$ defined in this manner in the range $-1 \leq \mu \leq 1$ is also referred to as Ferrers' associated Legendre function of degree n and order m of the first kind. Ferrer used the notation $T_n^m(\mu)$ for $P_n^m(\mu)$; such notation is used in some texts [6, 13]. Also in some texts $P_n^m(\mu)$ functions are defined as given by equation (4-25), but omitting the factor $(-1)^m$ on the right-hand side [6, 11].

We have seen that $P_n(\mu)$ functions become infinite at $\mu = \pm 1$ unless n is chosen as positive integer. Therefore, the solutions $P_n^m(\mu)$ of equation (4-24) remain finite over the range $-1 \leq \mu \leq 1$ if m and n are chosen as positive integers (i.e., $m, n = 0, 1, 2, 3, \dots$). When n is positive integer, $P_n(\mu)$ is a polynomial of degree n in μ, then the mth derivative of equation (4-25) vanish for $m > n$; therefore we must have $m \leq n$. Also, for $m = 0$ equation (4-25) gives

$$P_n^0(\mu) = P_n(\mu) \qquad (4\text{-}26)$$

$P_n^m(\mu)$ functions can be determined from equation (4-25) since the Legendre polynomials $P_n(\mu)$ are known; we present below the first few of $P_n^m(\mu)$ functions

$$P_1^1(\mu) = -(1 - \mu^2)^{1/2} \qquad P_2^1(\mu) = -3(1 - \mu^2)^{1/2} \mu$$
$$P_2^2(\mu) = 3(1 - \mu^2) \qquad P_3^1(\mu) = -\tfrac{3}{2}(1 - \mu^2)^{1/2}(5\mu^2 - 1)$$
$$P_3^2(\mu) = 15\mu(1 - \mu^2) \qquad P_3^3(\mu) = -15(1 - \mu^2)^{3/2} \qquad (4\text{-}27)$$

Here $P_n^0(\mu)$ are not included because they are the same as Legendre polynomials $P_n(\mu)$.

The recurrence formula among $P_n^m(\mu)$ functions is given as [5, p. 304; 11,

p. 360; 12, p. 62]

$$(n - m + 1)P_{n+1}^m(\mu) - (2n + 1)P_n^m(\mu) + (n + m)P_{n-1}^m(\mu) = 0 \qquad (4\text{-}28)$$

For $m = 0$, this expression reduces to the recurrence relation (4-20) for the Legendre polynomials.

The Region $\mu_0 \le \mu \le 1$, where $\mu_0 > -1$.   The functions $Q_n^m(\mu)$ are inadmissible as solutions because they become infinite at $\mu = 1$ for all values of n, whether integer or not. The other solution must be so chosen that it remains finite in the range $\mu_0 \le \mu \le 1$, where $\mu_0 > -1$, and accept as the degree unrestricted values of n (i.e., not necessarily integer) in order to satisfy the requirement of the boundary condition specified at the surface $\mu = \mu_0$. With this consideration the solution admissible for the part of the sphere in the range $\mu_0 \le \mu \le 1$, where $\mu_0 > -1$, and $0 \le \phi \le 2\pi$ is taken as the generalized Legendre function $P_n^{-m}(\mu)$ defined as [5, p. 288; 14, p. 112]

$$P_n^{-m}(\mu) = \frac{1}{\Gamma(m + 1)}\left(\frac{1 - \mu}{1 + \mu}\right)^{m/2} F\left(-n, n + 1, 1 + m, \frac{1 - \mu}{2}\right) \qquad (4\text{-}29a)$$

$$= \frac{1}{\Gamma(m + 1)}\left(\frac{1 - \mu}{1 + \mu}\right)^{m/2}\left[1 + \sum_{r=1}^{\infty}\frac{(-n)_r(n + 1)_r}{r!(1 + m)_r}\left(\frac{1 - \mu}{2}\right)^r\right] \qquad (4\text{-}29b)$$

where

$$(\alpha)_r \equiv \alpha(\alpha + 1)(\alpha + 2)\ldots(\alpha + r - 1) \qquad (4\text{-}30a)$$

and $\Gamma(m + 1)$ is the gamma function such that for integer values of m it is determined from

$$\Gamma(m + 1) = m! \qquad (4\text{-}30b)$$

Clearly, for $m = 0$, the solution (4-29) reduces to the hypergeometric series form of the $P_n(\mu)$ function given in powers of $(1 - \mu)$ by equation (4-22). In equation (4-29), m's are positive integers, zero being included, n is unrestricted and its value is determined from the requirement that the boundary condition at the surface $\mu = \mu_0$ is satisfied. From equation (4-29a) it follows that $P_{-n-1}^{-m}(\mu) = P_n^{-m}(\mu)$, so that this function is symmetrical about $n = -\frac{1}{2}$; therefore n's can take values greater than $-\frac{1}{2}$. It is to be noted that this solution is singular at $\mu = -1$ and therefore is inadmissible for the problem of the whole sphere.

If $(-m)$ is replaced by m, equation (4-29a) becomes

$$P_n^m(\mu) = \frac{1}{\Gamma(1 - m)}\left(\frac{1 + \mu}{1 - \mu}\right)^{m/2} F\left(-n, n + 1, 1 - m, \frac{1 - \mu}{2}\right) \qquad (4\text{-}31)$$

This solution is singular at $\mu = 1$; it is admissible in the range $-1 \le \mu \le \mu_0$, where $\mu_0 < 1$.

The functions $P_n^{-m}(\mu)$ and $P_n^m(\mu)$ in the range $-1 < \mu < 1$ are not independent; they are related to each other by

$$P_n^{-m}(\mu) = (-1)^m \frac{\Gamma(n-m+1)}{\Gamma(n+m+1)} P_n^m(\mu) \tag{4-32}$$

where m is integer, n is unrestricted.

4-3 REPRESENTATION OF AN ARBITRARY FUNCTION IN TERMS OF LEGENDRE FUNCTIONS

In the solution of heat conduction problems for a sphere or a hemisphere or a part of a sphere cut out by the cone $\theta = \theta_0$, the representation is needed of an arbitrary function $F(\mu)$ defined in the interval $-1 \leq \mu \leq 1$ or $0 \leq \mu \leq 1$ or $\mu_0 \leq \mu \leq 1$, where $\mu_0 > -1$, in terms of the Legendre functions. Here we present a brief discussion of such representations.

Representation in Region $-1 \leq \mu \leq 1$

This region is encountered in the problems of the full sphere; we consider the following two cases:

The Representation of $F(\mu)$. When temperature depends on μ but it is azimuthally symmetric, the representation of an arbitrary function $F(\mu)$ defined in the interval $-1 \leq \mu \leq 1$ is needed in terms of the Legendre polynomials $P_n(\mu), n = 0, 1, 2, \ldots$, in the form

$$F(\mu) = \sum_{n=0}^{\infty} c_n P_n(\mu) \quad \text{in} \quad -1 \leq \mu \leq 1 \tag{4-33}$$

To determine the coefficients c_n we utilize the following orthogonality of the Legendre polynomials [5, p. 88; 12, p. 51]

$$\int_{-1}^{1} P_n(\mu) P_{n'}(\mu) \, d\mu = \begin{cases} 0 & \text{for } n \neq n' \\ N(n) & \text{for } n = n' \end{cases} \tag{4-34a}$$

where

$$N(n) \equiv \int_{-1}^{1} [P_n(\mu)]^2 \, d\mu = \frac{2}{2n+1} \tag{4-34b}$$

If it is assumed that the series on the right of equation (4-33) can be integrated term by term over the range $-1 \leq \mu \leq 1$, we operate on both sides of equation (4-33) by the operator $\int_{-1}^{1} P_{n'}(\mu) \, d\mu$ and utilize the above orthogonality relation. We obtain

$$c_n = \frac{1}{N(n)} \int_{-1}^{1} P_n(\mu) F(\mu) \, d\mu \qquad (4\text{-}35)$$

The substitution of equation (4-35) into (4-33) yields

$$F(\mu) = \sum_{n=0}^{\infty} \frac{1}{N(n)} P_n(\mu) \int_{-1}^{1} P_n(\mu') F(\mu') \, d\mu' \qquad \text{in } -1 \le \mu \le 1 \quad (4\text{-}36a)$$

where

$$N(n) = \frac{2}{2n+1}, \qquad n = 0, 1, 2, 3 \dots \qquad (4\text{-}36b)$$

A discussion of the validity of such an expansion can be found in reference [5].

The Representation of $F(\mu, \phi)$. The representation of this type is generally needed in the problems of full sphere when the temperature is a function of both μ and ϕ variables. Consider a function $F(\mu, \phi)$ defined in the interval $-1 \le \mu \le 1, 0 \le \phi \le 2\pi$ to be represented in terms of the elementary solutions

$$P_n^m(\mu) \quad \text{and} \quad (A \cos m\phi + B \sin m\phi)$$

where m, n are positive integers, zero being included, with $m \le n$, in the form

$$F(\mu, \phi) = \sum_{n=0}^{\infty} \left[A_n P_n(\mu) + \sum_{m=1}^{n} (A_{nm} \cos m\phi + B_{nm} \sin m\phi) P_n^m(\mu) \right] \qquad (4\text{-}37a)$$

or

$$F(\mu, \phi) = \sum_{n=0}^{\infty} \sum_{m=0}^{n} (A_{nm} \cos m\phi + B_{nm} \sin m\phi) P_n^m(\mu)$$
$$\text{in } -1 \le \mu \le 1, 0 \le \phi \le 2\pi \qquad (4\text{-}37b)$$

where

$$n, m = 0, 1, 2, \dots \qquad \text{and} \qquad m \le n$$

To determine the coefficients A_{nm} and B_{nm} we utilize the orthogonality of the associated Legendre functions $P_n^m(\mu)$ in the interval $-1 \le \mu \le 1$ given as [5, p. 117; 6, p. 324; 12, p. 54; 14, p. 184]

$$\int_{-1}^{1} P_n^m(\mu) P_{n'}^m(\mu) \, d\mu = \begin{cases} 0 & \text{for } n \ne n' \\ \dfrac{2}{2n+1} \dfrac{(n+m)!}{(n-m)!} & \text{for } n = n' \end{cases} \qquad (4\text{-}38)$$

where n, n', m are positive integer, zero being included and $m \le n$.

To determine the coefficients B_{nm} we operate on both sides of equation (4-37b) successively by the operators

$$\int_0^{2\pi} \sin m'\phi \, d\phi \quad \text{and} \quad \int_{-1}^1 P_n^m(\mu) \, d\mu \tag{4-39}$$

and utilize the orthogonality properties of trigonometric functions. We obtain

$$B_{nm} = \frac{1}{\pi N(m,n)} \int_{\phi'=0}^{2\pi} \int_{\mu'=-1}^1 \sin m\phi' P_n^m(\mu') F(\mu',\phi') \, d\mu' \, d\phi' \tag{4-40a}$$

where

$$N(m,n) = \int_{-1}^1 [P_n^m(\mu)]^2 \, d\mu = \frac{2}{2n+1} \frac{(n+m)!}{(n-m)!}, \, m \le n \tag{4-40b}$$

To determine the coefficients A_{nm} we operate on both sides of equation (4-37b) successively by the operators

$$\int_0^{2\pi} \cos m'\phi \, d\phi \quad \text{and} \quad \int_{-1}^1 P_n^m(\mu) \, d\mu$$

and utilize the orthogonality properties of trigonometric functions. We obtain

$$A_{nm} = \frac{1}{\pi N(m,n)} \int_{\phi'=0}^{2\pi} \int_{\mu'=-1}^1 \cos m\phi' P_n^m(\mu') F(\mu',\phi') \, d\mu' \, d\phi' \tag{4-41}$$

where π *should be replaced by* 2π *for* $m = 0$ and $N(m,n)$ is given by equation (4-40b).

When the coefficients A_{nm} and B_{nm} as determined above are introduced into equation (4-37b) and the trigonometric terms are combined as

$$\cos m\phi \cos m\phi' + \sin m\phi \sin m\phi' = \cos m(\phi - \phi') \tag{4-42}$$

the representation (4-37b) becomes

$$F(\mu,\phi) = \frac{1}{\pi} \sum_{n=0}^\infty \sum_{m=0}^n \frac{P_n^m(\mu)}{N(m,n)} \int_{\phi'=0}^{2\pi} \int_{\mu'=-1}^1 F(\mu',\phi') P_n^m(\mu') \cos m(\phi - \phi') \, d\mu' \, d\phi' \tag{4-43}$$

where π *should be replaced by* 2π *for* $m = 0$. By comparing equations (4-37b) and (4-43) we write

$$[A_{nm} \cos m\phi + B_{nm} \sin m\phi]$$

$$\equiv \frac{1}{\pi N(m,n)} \int_{\phi'=0}^{2\pi} \int_{\mu'=-1}^1 F(\mu',\phi') P_n^m(\mu') \cos m(\phi - \phi') \, d\mu' \, d\phi' \tag{4-44}$$

where π *should be replaced by* 2π *for* $m = 0$.

Equation (4-43) is now written more explicitly in the form

$$F(\mu, \phi) = \frac{1}{4\pi} \sum_{n=0}^{\infty} (2n + 1) P_n(\mu) \int_{\phi'=0}^{2\pi} \int_{\mu'=-1}^{1} F(\mu', \phi') P_n(\mu') \, d\mu' \, d\phi'$$

$$+ \frac{1}{2\pi} \sum_{n=0}^{\infty} \sum_{m=1}^{n} (2n + 1) \frac{(n-m)!}{(n+m)!} P_n^m(\mu)$$

$$\cdot \int_{\phi'=0}^{2\pi} \int_{\mu'=-1}^{1} F(\mu', \phi') P_n^m(\mu') \cos[m(\phi - \phi')] \, d\mu' \, d\phi' \qquad (4\text{-}45)$$

$$\text{in } -1 \le \mu \le 1, 0 \le \phi \le 2\pi$$

This representation is valid for all values of μ and ϕ in the range $-1 \le \mu \le 1$, $0 \le \phi \le 2\pi$, provided that the function $F(\mu, \phi)$ satisfies the conditions that would have to be satisfied if it were to be developed into a Fourier's series.

Representation in Region $0 \le \mu \le 1$

This region is encountered in the problems of the hemisphere as illustrated in Fig. 4-3. When temperature is azimuthally symmetric but depends on the μ variable among other variables, it may be necessary to represent an arbitrary function $F(\mu)$ defined in the interval $0 \le \mu \le 1$ in terms of the $P_n(\mu)$ functions in the form

$$F(\mu) = \sum_{n} c_n P_n(\mu) \quad \text{in} \quad 0 < \mu \le 1 \qquad (4\text{-}46)$$

Here, the values of n should be so chosen that the boundary condition at $\mu = 0$ is satisfied. We consider this expansion for the following two different boundary conditions at $\mu = 0$, the base of the hemisphere.
1. For a boundary condition of the *first kind* at $\mu = 0$ we have

$$P_n(\mu) = 0 \quad \text{at} \quad \mu = 0 \qquad (4\text{-}47)$$

This requirement is satisfied if $P_n(\mu)$ is chosen as the Legendre polynomials

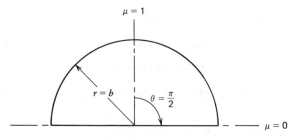

Fig. 4-3 Coordinates for a hemisphere.

with n being *odd positive integer* (i.e., $n = 1, 3, 5 \ldots$). This is apparent from the definition of Legendre polynomials given by equation (4-19).

2. For a boundary condition of the *second kind* at $\mu = 0$ we have

$$\frac{dP_n(\mu)}{d\mu} = 0 \qquad \text{at} \qquad \mu = 0 \tag{4-48}$$

This requirement is satisfied if $P_n(\mu)$ is chosen as the Legendre polynomial with n being *even positive integers*, zero being included (i.e., $n = 0, 2, 4, 6 \ldots$). This is apparent from the definition of the Legendre polynomials given by equation (4-19).

To determine the coefficients c_n in equation (4-46), we utilize the following orthogonality of Legendre polynomials in the interval $0 \leq \mu \leq 1$ [5, p. 109; 6, p. 306; 7, p. 172]

$$\int_0^1 P_n(\mu)P_{n'}(\mu)\,d\mu = \begin{cases} 0 & \text{if } n, n' \text{ both } even \text{ or both } odd, n \neq n' \\[2mm] \dfrac{1}{2n+1} & \text{if } n = n' \\[4mm] \dfrac{(-1)^{(n+n'+1)/2}n!n'!}{2^{n+n'-1}(n-n')(n+n'+1)\left(\dfrac{n}{2}!\right)^2\left(\dfrac{n'-1}{2}!\right)^2} \end{cases} \tag{4-49}$$

$$\text{if } n \text{ even, } n' \text{ odd}$$

where n and n' are positive integers.

The coefficients c_n are now determined by operating on both sides of equation (4-46) by the operator $\int_0^1 P_{n'}(\mu)\,d\mu$ and utilizing the above orthogonality relations. We find

$$c_n = \frac{1}{N(n)}\int_0^1 F(\mu')P_n(\mu')\,d\mu' \tag{4-50a}$$

where

$$N(n) \equiv \int_0^1 [P_n(\mu)]^2\,d\mu = \frac{1}{2n+1} \tag{4-50b}$$

and the values of n are chosen as

$n = 1, 3, 5 \ldots$ for boundary condition of the *first kind* at $\mu = 0$

$n = 0, 2, 4 \ldots$ for boundary condition of the *second kind* at $\mu = 0$

Introducing the coefficients c_n into equation (4-46), the representation of $F(\mu)$ becomes

$$F(\mu) = \sum_n (2n+1)P_n(\mu)\int_{\mu'=0}^1 F(\mu')P_n(\mu')\,d\mu' \qquad \text{in } 0 < \mu \leq 1 \tag{4-51}$$

where the values of n depend on the type of the boundary condition at the surface $\mu = 0$ as follows:

1. When the boundary condition at $\mu = 0$ is of the *first kind* take $n = 1, 3, 5, 7, \ldots$, that is, odd positive integers

2. When the boundary condition at $\mu = 0$ is of the *second kind* take $n = 0, 2, 4, 6 \ldots$, that is, even positive integers, zero being included.

Representation in Region $\mu_0 \leq \mu \leq 1$

This region is encountered in the problems of the part of the sphere cut out by the cone $\theta = \theta_0$ as illustrated in Fig. 4-2. For the general case of temperature being a function of both μ and ϕ variables among others, it may be necessary to represent an arbitrary function $F(\mu, \phi)$ defined in the interval $\mu_0 \leq \mu \leq 1, 0 \leq \phi \leq 2\pi$, where $\mu_0 > -1$, in terms of the elementary solutions

$$P_n^{-m}(\mu) \qquad \text{and} \qquad (A \cos m\phi + B \sin m\phi)$$

where m is positive integer (i.e., $m = 0, 1, 2, 3 \ldots$) and n is unrestricted. The representation of $F(\mu, \phi)$ may be written in the form

$$F(\mu, \phi) = \sum_{m=0}^{\infty} \sum_{n} P_n^{-m}(\mu) [A_{mn} \cos m\phi + B_{mn} \sin m\phi]$$
$$\text{in } 0 \leq \phi \leq 2\pi, \mu_0 \leq \mu \leq 1, \text{ where } \mu_0 > -1 \qquad (4\text{-}52)$$

Here the function $P_n^{-m}(\mu)$ is as defined by equation (4-29), m's are taken as positive integers, and the values of n are determined from the requirement of the boundary condition at the surface $\mu = \mu_0$. In the present analysis we consider the following two different types of boundary conditions. (1). For a boundary condition of the *first kind* at $\mu = \mu_0$ we should satisfy the requirement

$$P_n^{-m}(\mu_0) = 0 \qquad (4\text{-}53a)$$

and (2). For a boundary condition of the *second kind* at $\mu = \mu_0$ we should satisfy

$$\left. \frac{dP_n^{-m}(\mu)}{d\mu} \right|_{\mu = \mu_0} = 0 \qquad (4\text{-}53b)$$

Then, the values of n are the roots of equation (4-53a) or (4-53b) depending on whether the boundary condition at $\mu = \mu_0$ is of the first kind or the second kind, respectively. The numerical values of n as the roots of equations (4-53) have been calculated [16] by regarding these equations as equations in n; only those values of n greater than $-\frac{1}{2}$ are to be considered. In Table 4-1

Table 4-1 The numerical values of n obtained as the roots of equation $P_n^m(\mu_0) = 0^*$

$\theta_0 = \pi/4$ or $\mu_0 = 0.7071$			$\theta_0 = \pi/6$ or $\mu_0 = 0.8660$			$\theta_0 = \pi/12$ or $\mu_0 = 0.9659$		
$m = 0$	1	2	$m = 0$	1	2	$m = 0$	1	2
6.52	4.40	1.52	10.03	6.83	2.96	20.60	14.14	4.77
10.51	8.44	6.15	16.02	12.91	9.39	32.55	26.30	19.21
14.51	12.46	10.28	22.01	18.93	15.62	44.53	38.36	31.67
18.50	16.47	14.34	28.01	24.95	21.72	56.53	50.39	43.90
22.50	20.47	18.37	34.01	30.96	27.78	68.52	62.41	56.03

*From B. Pal, reference [16].

we present the first five values of n as the roots of the transcendental equation $P_n^m(\mu_0) = 0$ for different values of m and μ_0.

To determine the coefficients A_{mn} and B_{mn} in the representation (4-52) we need the following orthogonality relation for the functions $P_n^{-m}(\mu)$

$$\int_{\mu_0}^{1} P_n^{-m}(\mu) P_{n'}^{-m}(\mu) \, d\mu = \begin{cases} 0 & \text{if } n \neq n' \\ N(m, n) & \text{if } n = n' \end{cases} \tag{4-54a}$$

where n and n' are the two different roots of equation (4-53a) or (4-53b), greater than $-\frac{1}{2}$, m's are positive integers ($m = 0, 1, 2 \ldots$) and the norm $N(m, n)$ is defined as

$$N(m, n) \equiv \int_{\mu = \mu_0}^{1} [P_n^{-m}(\mu)]^2 \, d\mu \tag{4-54b}$$

The integral defining the norm can be performed and the result depends on whether the boundary condition at $\mu = \mu_0$ is of the first or the second kind. We present below the resulting expressions for $N(m, n)$ for the boundary conditions of the first and second kind at $\mu = \mu_0$.

$$N(m, n) = -\frac{1 - \mu_0^2}{2n + 1} \left[\frac{d}{dn} P_n^{-m}(\mu) \frac{d}{d\mu} P_n^{-m}(\mu) \right]_{\mu = \mu_0} \tag{4-55a}$$

when the boundary condition is of the first kind, that is

$$P_n^{-m}(\mu) \big|_{\mu = \mu_0} = 0 \tag{4-55b}$$

and

$$N(m, n) = \frac{1 - \mu_0^2}{2n + 1} \left[P_n^{-m}(\mu) \frac{d^2 P_n^{-m}(\mu)}{dn \, d\mu} \right]_{\mu = \mu_0} \tag{4-56a}$$

when the boundary condition is of the second kind, that is

$$\frac{dP_n^{-m}(\mu)}{d\mu}\bigg|_{\mu=\mu_0} = 0 \tag{4-56b}$$

The reader should consult to *Note* 2 for the derivation of the results given by equations (4-54) through (4-56).

To determine the coefficients B_{mn} we operate on both sides of equation (4-52) successively by the operators

$$\int_0^{2\pi} \sin m'\phi \, d\phi \qquad \text{and} \qquad \int_{\mu_0}^1 P_{n'}^{-m}(\mu) \, d\mu$$

and utilize the orthogonality relations given by equations (4-39) and (4-54). We obtain

$$B_{mn} = \frac{1}{\pi N(m,n)} \int_{\phi'=0}^{2\pi} \int_{\mu=\mu_0}^1 \sin m\phi' P_n^{-m}(\mu')F(\mu',\phi') \, d\mu' \, d\phi' \tag{4-57}$$

To determine the coefficients A_{mn} we operate on both sides of equation (4-52) successively by the operators

$$\int_0^{2\pi} \cos m'\phi \, d\phi \qquad \text{and} \qquad \int_{\mu_0}^1 P_{n'}^{-m}(\mu) \, d\mu$$

and utilize the orthogonality relations given by equations (4-39) and (4-54) to obtain

$$A_{mn} = \frac{1}{\pi N(m,n)} \int_{\phi'=0}^{2\pi} \int_{\mu'=\mu_0}^1 \cos m\phi' P_n^{-m}(\mu')F(\mu',\phi') \, d\mu' \, d\phi' \tag{4-58}$$

where π *should be replaced by* 2π *for* $m = 0$.

When the coefficient A_{mn} and B_{mn} as determined above are introduced into the representation (4-52) and the trigonometric terms are combined according to equation (4-42) we obtain

$$F(\mu,\phi) = \frac{1}{\pi} \sum_{m=0}^{\infty} \sum_n \frac{P_n^{-m}(\mu)}{N(m,n)} \int_{\phi'=0}^{2\pi} \int_{\mu'=\mu_0}^1 F(\mu',\phi')P_n^{-m}(\mu')\cos[m(\phi-\phi')]d\mu'\,d\phi'$$
$$\text{in } 0 \le \phi \le 2\pi, \, \mu_0 \le \mu \le 1, \, \mu_0 > -1 \tag{4-59}$$

where π *should be replaced by* 2π *for* $m = 0$. In this representation, when the boundary condition at $\mu = \mu_0$ is of the first kind, $N(m,n)$ is given by equation (4-55a) and n's are the roots of equation (4-55b), greater than $-\frac{1}{2}$; when the boundary condition at $\mu = \mu_0$ is of the second kind, $N(m,n)$ is given by equation (4-56a) and n's are the roots of equation (4-56b), greater than $-\frac{1}{2}$.

By comparing equations (4-52) and (4-59) we note that, an alternative expression defining the coefficient can be written as

$$[A_{mn}\cos m\phi + B_{mn}\sin m\phi]$$

$$\equiv \frac{1}{\pi N(m,n)} \int_{\phi'=0}^{2\pi} \int_{\mu'=\mu_0}^{1} F(\mu',\phi')P_n^{-m}(\mu')\cos[m(\phi-\phi')]d\mu'd\phi'$$

$$(4\text{-}60)$$

where π *should be replaced by* 2π *for* $m = 0$, and other quantities are as defined above.

4-4 HOMOGENEOUS PROBLEMS IN (r,t) VARIABLES

The heat-conduction problem for a sphere involving (r,t) variables can be transformed into a problem of a slab or a semi-infinite medium by the transformation of the dependent variable as in equation (4-16c). Then, the resulting problem can be solved readily by the techniques described in Chapter 2. For generality, we present here the transformation of the non-homogeneous problem.

Solid Sphere $0 \le r \le b$

Consider the heat-conduction problem in a solid sphere $0 \le r \le b$, with heat generation and subject to nonhomogeneous boundary condition of the third kind at the boundary surface $r = b$ as illustrated in Fig. 4-4. The mathematical formulation of the problem is given as

$$\frac{1}{r}\frac{\partial^2}{\partial r^2}(rT) + \frac{1}{k}g(r) = \frac{1}{\alpha}\frac{\partial T}{\partial t} \qquad \text{in } 0 \le r < b,\ t > 0 \qquad (4\text{-}61a)$$

$$\frac{\partial T}{\partial r} + HT = f \qquad \text{at } r = b,\ t > 0 \qquad (4\text{-}61b)$$

$$T = F(r) \qquad \text{for } t = 0,\ \text{in } 0 \le r \le b \qquad (4\text{-}61c)$$

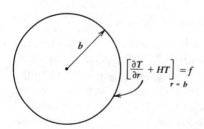

$$\left[\frac{\partial T}{\partial r} + HT\right]_{r=b} = f$$

Fig. 4-4 Boundary condition for a solid sphere.

A new dependent variable $U(r, t)$ is defined as

$$U(r, t) = rT(r, t) \tag{4-62}$$

Then equations (4-61) are transformed to

$$\frac{\partial^2 U}{\partial r^2} + \frac{rg(r)}{k} = \frac{1}{\alpha} \frac{\partial U}{\partial t} \qquad \text{in } 0 < r < b, \ t > 0 \tag{4-63a}$$

$$U = 0 \qquad \text{at } r = 0, \ t > 0 \tag{4-63b}$$

$$\frac{\partial U}{\partial r} + \left(H - \frac{1}{b} \right) U = bf \quad \text{at } r = b, \ t > 0 \tag{4-63c}$$

$$U = rF(r) \qquad \text{for } t = 0, \text{ in } 0 \le r \le b \tag{4-63d}$$

The problem given by equations (4-63) is the problem of heat conduction in a slab $0 \le r \le b$, which can readily be solved by the application of the techniques described in Chapter 2. We now illustrate the application with the examples given below.

Example 4-1. A solid sphere of radius $r = b$ is initially at temperature $F(r)$ and for times $t > 0$ the boundary surface at $r = b$ dissipates heat by convection into a medium at zero temperature. Obtain an expression for the temperature distribution $T(r, t)$ in the sphere for times $t > 0$.

Solution. The mathematical formulation of this problem is given as

$$\frac{1}{r} \frac{\partial^2}{\partial r^2}(rT) = \frac{1}{\alpha} \frac{\partial T}{\partial t} \qquad \text{in } 0 \le r < b, \ t > 0 \tag{4-64a}$$

$$\frac{\partial T}{\partial r} + HT = 0 \qquad \text{at } r = b, \ t > 0 \tag{4-64b}$$

$$T = F(r) \qquad \text{for } t = 0, \text{ in } 0 \le r \le b \tag{4-64c}$$

When this solution is transformed by the transformation $U(r, t) = rT(r, t)$, the transformed system becomes

$$\frac{\partial^2 U}{\partial r^2} = \frac{1}{\alpha} \frac{\partial U}{\partial t} \qquad \text{in } 0 < r < b, \ t > 0 \tag{4-65a}$$

$$U = 0 \qquad \text{at } r = 0, \ t > 0 \tag{4-65b}$$

$$\frac{\partial U}{\partial r} + \left(H - \frac{1}{b} \right) U = 0 \qquad \text{at } r = b, \ t > 0 \tag{4-65c}$$

$$U = rF(r) \qquad \text{for } t = 0, \text{ in } 0 \le r \le b \tag{4-65d}$$

This is a homogeneous heat-conduction problem for a slab $0 \leq r \leq b$ and the solution for $U(r,t)$ is readily obtainable by the approach described in Chapter 2. After the transformation of the solution for $U(r,t)$ to $T(r,t)$ we obtain

$$T(r,t) = \frac{2}{r} \sum_{m=1}^{\infty} e^{-\alpha\beta_m^2 t} \frac{\beta_m^2 + K^2}{b(\beta_m^2 + K^2) + K} \sin \beta_m r \int_{r'=0}^{b} r'F(r') \sin \beta_m r' \, dr' \qquad (4\text{-}66a)$$

where

$$K \equiv H - \frac{1}{b} \qquad (4\text{-}66b)$$

and β_m's are the positive roots of

$$\beta_m b \cot \beta_m b + bK = 0 \qquad (4\text{-}66c)$$

The roots of this transcendental equation are real if $bK > -1$ (see Appendix I, the table for the roots of $\xi \cot \xi + c = 0$). When the value of K as defined above introduced into this inequality we find $(bH - 1) > -1$, which implies that $H > 0$. This result is consistent with the requirement on the physical grounds that in the original sphere problem (4-64) we should have $H > 0$. Therefore, in the pseudo problem (4-65) the coefficient $(Hb - 1)$ may be negative, but the quantity Hb is always positive.

Insulated Boundary

When the boundary at $r = b$ is insulated, we have $H = 0$ in equations (4-64b) and (4-64c). For this special case $\beta_0 = 0$ is also an eigenvalue. Then the term

$$\frac{3}{b^3} \int_0^b r^2 F(r) \, dr$$

resulting from the eigenvalue $\beta_0 = 0$ should be added on the right-hand side of equation (4-66a). This term implies that after the transients have passed, the steady-state temperature in the medium is the mean of the initial temperature distribution $F(r)$ over the volume of the insulated sphere (see Note 3 for further discussion of this matter).

Hollow Sphere $a \leq r \leq b$

We now consider the problem of heat conduction in a hollow sphere $a \leq r \leq b$, with heat generation and subject to nonhomogeneous boundary conditions of the third kind at $r = a$ and $r = b$ as illustrated in Fig. 4-5. The mathematical

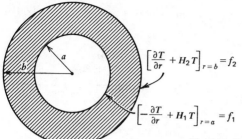

$$\left[\frac{\partial T}{\partial r} + H_2 T\right]_{r=b} = f_2$$

$$\left[-\frac{\partial T}{\partial r} + H_1 T\right]_{r=a} = f_1$$

Fig. 4-5 Boundary conditions for a hollow sphere.

formulation of the problem is given as

$$\frac{1}{r}\frac{\partial^2}{\partial r^2}(rT) + \frac{1}{k}g(r) = \frac{1}{\alpha}\frac{\partial T}{\partial t} \qquad \text{in } a < r < b, \ t > 0 \qquad (4\text{-}67a)$$

$$-\frac{\partial T}{\partial r} + H_1 T = f_1 \qquad \text{at } r = a, \ t > 0 \qquad (4\text{-}67b)$$

$$\frac{\partial T}{\partial r} + H_2 T = f_2 \qquad \text{at } r = b, \ t > 0 \qquad (4\text{-}67c)$$

$$T = F(r) \qquad \text{for } t = 0, \text{ in } a \le r \le b \qquad (4\text{-}67d)$$

A new dependent variable is now defined as

$$U(r, t) = rT(r, t) \qquad (4\text{-}68)$$

Then equations (4-67) are transformed into

$$\frac{\partial^2 U}{\partial r^2} + \frac{rg(r)}{k} = \frac{1}{\alpha}\frac{\partial U}{\partial t} \qquad \text{in } a < r < b, \ t > 0 \qquad (4\text{-}69a)$$

$$-\frac{\partial U}{\partial r} + \left(H_1 + \frac{1}{a}\right)U = af_1 \qquad \text{at } r = a, \ t > 0 \qquad (4\text{-}69b)$$

$$\frac{\partial U}{\partial r} + \left(H_2 - \frac{1}{b}\right)U = bf_2 \qquad \text{at } r = b, \ t > 0 \qquad (4\text{-}69c)$$

$$U = rF(r) \qquad \text{for } t = 0, \text{ in } a \le r \le b \qquad (4\text{-}69d)$$

If a shift in the space coordinate is introduced as

$$x = r - a \qquad (4\text{-}70)$$

the system (4-69) becomes

$$\frac{\partial^2 U}{\partial x^2} + \frac{(a + x)g(x + a)}{k} = \frac{1}{\alpha}\frac{\partial U}{\partial t} \qquad \text{in } 0 < x < L, \ t > 0 \qquad (4\text{-}71a)$$

$$-\frac{\partial U}{\partial x} + K_1 U = af_1 \qquad\qquad \text{at } x = 0, \ t > 0 \qquad (4\text{-}71b)$$

$$\frac{\partial U}{\partial x} + K_2 U = bf_2 \qquad\qquad \text{at } x = L, \ t > 0 \qquad (4\text{-}71c)$$

$$U = (x + a)F(x + a) \qquad\qquad \text{for } t = 0, \text{ in } 0 \le x \le L \qquad (4\text{-}71d)$$

where

$$K_1 = H_1 + \frac{1}{a}, \qquad K_2 = H_2 - \frac{1}{b}, \qquad \text{and} \qquad L = b - a \qquad (4\text{-}72)$$

which is a problem of heat conduction for a slab, $0 \le x \le L$, and can be solved by the techniques described in Chapter 2. We illustrate the application with examples given below.

Example 4-2. A hollow sphere $a \le r \le b$ is initially at a temperature $F(r)$, for times $t > 0$ heat is dissipated by convection from the boundaries at $r = a$ and $r = b$ into an environment at zero temperature. Obtain an expression for the temperature distribution $T(r, t)$ in the sphere for times $t > 0$.

Solution. This problem is a special case of the problem (4-67) with $g(r) = 0$ and $f_1 = f_2 = 0$. Therefore the governing differential equation is obtained from equations (4-67) by setting

$$g(r) = 0, \qquad f_1 = 0, \qquad \text{and} \qquad f_2 = 0 \qquad (4\text{-}73)$$

Then the transformation of this heat-conduction problem by the transformations

$$U(r, t) = rT(r, t) \qquad \text{and} \qquad x = r - a \qquad (4\text{-}74)$$

results in equations for $U(x, t)$ as given by the system (4-71), with $g = 0$, $f_1 = 0$, and $f_2 = 0$, which is a homogeneous heat-conduction problem for a slab and can readily be solved by the method described in Chapter 2. When the solution for $U(x, t)$ is obtained and transformed back to $T(r, t)$ by the transformation (4-70) and (4-68), the solution for the considered sphere problem becomes

$$T(r, t) = \frac{1}{r} \sum_{m=1}^{\infty} e^{-\alpha \beta_m^2 t} \frac{1}{N(\beta_m)} R(\beta_m, r) \int_{r'=a}^{b} r' F(r') R(\beta_m, r') \, dr' \qquad (4\text{-}75)$$

where $R(\beta_m, r)$, $N(\beta_m)$, and β_m's are obtained from Table 2-2, Case 1, as

$$R(\beta_m, r) = \beta_m \cos \beta_m (r - a) + K_1 \sin \beta_m (r - a) \qquad (4\text{-}76a)$$

$$\frac{1}{N(\beta_m)} = \frac{2}{(\beta_m^2 + K_1^2)[(b - a) + K_2/(\beta_m^2 + K_2^2)] + K_1} \qquad (4\text{-}76b)$$

where

$$K_1 \equiv H_1 + \frac{1}{a}, \qquad K_2 = H_2 - \frac{1}{b} \tag{4-76c}$$

and β_m's are the positive roots of

$$\tan \beta_m (b - a) = \frac{\beta_m (K_1 + K_2)}{\beta_m^2 - K_1 K_2} \tag{4-76d}$$

Insulated Boundaries

When both boundaries at $r = a$ and $r = b$ are insulated, we have $H_1 = H_2 = 0$. For this special case $\beta_0 = 0$ is also an eigenvalue. Then the term

$$\frac{3}{b^3 - a^3} \int_a^b r^2 F(r)\, dr$$

resulting from the zero eigenvalue should be added on the right-hand side of equation (4-75). This term implies that, after the transients have passed, the steady-state temperature in the medium is the mean of the initial temperature distribution $F(r)$ over the volume of the insulated sphere. The validity of this result can be verified by a derivation similar to that given in Note 3. Also, see Chapter 13, equation (13-25b) for a more general expression for $T(r, \infty)$ when all boundaries of a finite region are insulated.

Example 4-3. A hollow sphere, $a \le r \le b$, is initially at temperature $F(r)$. For times $t > 0$, the boundaries at $r = a$ and $r = b$ are kept at zero temperature. Obtain an expression for the temperature distribution $T(r, t)$ in the sphere for times $t > 0$.

Solution. The mathematical formulation of the problem is given as

$$\frac{1}{r} \frac{\partial^2}{\partial r^2} (rT) = \frac{1}{\alpha} \frac{\partial T}{\partial t} \qquad \text{in } a < r < b, \ t > 0 \tag{4-77a}$$

$$T = 0 \qquad \text{at } r = a \text{ and } r = b, \ t > 0 \tag{4-77b}$$

$$T = F(r) \qquad \text{for } t = 0, \text{ in } a \le r \le b \tag{4-77c}$$

This system is now transformed successively by the application of the transformations

$$U(r, t) = rT(r, t) \qquad \text{and} \qquad x = r - a \tag{4-78}$$

We obtain

$$\frac{\partial^2 U}{\partial x^2} = \frac{1}{\alpha} \frac{\partial U}{\partial t} \qquad \text{in } 0 < x < (b - a), \ t > 0 \tag{4-79a}$$

$$U = 0 \qquad\qquad\qquad \text{at } x = 0 \text{ and } x = b - a,\ t > 0 \qquad (4\text{-}79\text{b})$$

$$U = (x + a)F(x + a) \qquad \text{for } t = 0,\ \text{in } 0 \le x \le b - a \qquad (4\text{-}79\text{c})$$

This equation for $U(x,t)$ is readily solved as described in Chapter 2, and after the transformation to $T(r,t)$ according to equation (4-78) we find

$$T(r,t) = \frac{2}{r(b-a)} \sum_{m=1}^{\infty} e^{-\alpha\beta_m^2 t} \sin \beta_m(r-a) \int_{r'=a}^{b} r'F(r') \sin \beta_m(r'-a)\,dr' \qquad (4\text{-}80\text{a})$$

where β_m's are the roots of

$$\sin \beta_m(b-a) = 0 \qquad\qquad\qquad\qquad (4\text{-}80\text{b})$$

or

$$\beta_m = \frac{m\pi}{b-a}, \qquad m = 1, 2, 3 \dots \qquad\qquad (4\text{-}80\text{c})$$

4-5   HOMOGENEOUS PROBLEMS IN (r, μ, t) VARIABLES

In this section we illustrate with examples the application of the method of the separation of variables to the solution of homogeneous heat-conduction problems involving (r, μ, t) variables.

Problem of a Full Sphere

Example 4-4. Obtain an expression for the temperature distribution $T(r, \mu, t)$ in a solid sphere, $-1 \le \mu \le 1, 0 \le r \le b$, which is initially at a temperature $F(r, \mu)$ and for times $t > 0$ boundary surface at $r = b$ is kept at zero temperature

Solution.   The mathematical formulation of this problem is given as

$$\frac{\partial^2 T}{\partial r^2} + \frac{2}{r}\frac{\partial T}{\partial r} + \frac{1}{r^2}\frac{\partial}{\partial \mu}\left[(1-\mu^2)\frac{\partial T}{\partial \mu}\right] = \frac{1}{\alpha}\frac{\partial T}{\partial t} \quad \text{in } 0 \le r < b,\ -1 \le \mu \le 1,$$
$$t > 0 \qquad (4\text{-}81\text{a})$$

$$T = 0 \qquad\qquad\qquad\qquad\qquad \text{at } r = b,\ \text{for } t > 0 \qquad (4\text{-}81\text{b})$$

$$T = F(r, \mu) \qquad\qquad\qquad\qquad \text{for } t = 0,\ \text{in the sphere} \qquad (4\text{-}81\text{c})$$

Defining a new dependent variable $V(r, \mu, t)$ as

$$V = r^{1/2}T \qquad\qquad\qquad\qquad\qquad (4\text{-}82)$$

the problem (4-81) is transformed into [see equation (4-9c)]

$$\frac{\partial^2 V}{\partial r^2} + \frac{1}{r} \frac{\partial V}{\partial r} - \frac{1}{4} \frac{V}{r^2} + \frac{1}{r^2} \frac{\partial}{\partial \mu} \left[(1 - \mu^2) \frac{\partial V}{\partial \mu} \right] = \frac{1}{\alpha} \frac{\partial V}{\partial t} \tag{4-83a}$$

$$\text{in } 0 \leq r < b, \; -1 \leq \mu \leq 1, \; t > 0 \tag{4-83a}$$

$$V = 0 \qquad \text{at } r = b, \; t > 0 \tag{4-83b}$$

$$V = r^{1/2} F(r, \mu) \qquad \text{for } t = 0, \text{ in the sphere} \tag{4-83c}$$

The elementary solutions of equation (4-83a) are given by equations (4-11). The solutions $Q_n(\mu)$ become infinite at $\mu = \pm 1$ and $Y_{n+1/2}(\lambda r) \left[\text{or } J_{-n-1/2}(\lambda r) \right]$ become infinite at $r = 0$; therefore they are inadmissible as solutions on the physical grounds. Then, the elementary solutions that are admissible for this problem include

$$e^{-\alpha \lambda^2 t}, \qquad J_{n+1/2}(\lambda r), \qquad \text{and} \qquad P_n(\mu)$$

where $P_n(\mu)$ is the Legendre polynomial as defined by equation (4-19) with $n = 0, 1, 2, 3, \ldots$. The complete solution for $V(r, \mu, t)$ is constructed as

$$V(r, \mu, t) = \sum_{n=0}^{\infty} \sum_{p=1}^{\infty} c_{np} e^{-\alpha \lambda_{np}^2 t} J_{n+1/2}(\lambda_{np} r) P_n(\mu) \tag{4-84}$$

where the coefficients c_{np} and the eigenvalues λ_{np} are to be so determined that the boundary condition (4-83b) and the initial condition (4-83c) are satisfied. If λ_{np}'s are taken as the positive roots of

$$J_{n+1/2}(\lambda_{np} b) = 0 \tag{4-85}$$

the boundary condition at $r = b$ is satisfied. The application of the initial condition (4-83c) gives

$$r^{1/2} F(r, \mu) = \sum_{n=0}^{\infty} \sum_{p=1}^{\infty} c_{np} J_{n+1/2}(\lambda_{np} r) P_n(\mu) \qquad \text{in } 0 \leq r < b, \; -1 \leq \mu \leq 1 \tag{4-86}$$

To determine the coefficients c_{np} we operate on both sides of equation (4-86) successively by the operators

$$\int_{-1}^{1} P_{n'}(\mu) \, d\mu \qquad \text{and} \qquad \int_{0}^{b} r J_{n+1/2}(\lambda_{np'} r) \, dr$$

and utilize the orthogonality relations (4-34) for the Legendre polynomials and (3-19) for the Bessel functions. We obtain

$$c_{np} = \frac{1}{N(n) N(\lambda_{np})} \int_{r=0}^{b} \int_{\mu=-1}^{1} r^{3/2} J_{n+1/2}(\lambda_{np} r) P_n(\mu) F(r, \mu) \, d\mu \, dr \tag{4-87a}$$

where the norms are defined as

$$N(n) \equiv \int_{-1}^{1} [P_n(\mu)]^2 d\mu \quad \text{and} \quad N(\lambda_{np}) \equiv \int_0^b r J_{n+1/2}^2(\lambda_{np} r) dr \quad (4\text{-}87b)$$

The coefficient c_{np} as given above is introduced into equation (4-84) and the resulting expression is transformed to $T(r, \mu, t)$ by the transformation (4-82). We find

$$T(r, \mu, t) = \sum_{n=0}^{\infty} \sum_{p=1}^{\infty} \frac{1}{N(n)N(\lambda_{np})} e^{-\alpha\lambda_{np}^2 t} r^{-1/2} J_{n+1/2}(\lambda_{np} r) P_n(\mu)$$

$$\cdot \int_{r'=0}^{b} \int_{\mu'=-1}^{1} r'^{3/2} J_{n+1/2}(\lambda_{np} r') P_n(\mu') F(r', \mu') d\mu' dr' \quad (4\text{-}88)$$

where λ_{np}'s are the positive roots of

$$J_{n+1/2}(\lambda_{np} b) = 0 \quad (4\text{-}89a)$$

the norm $N(n)$ is obtained from equation (4-34b) as

$$N(n) = \frac{2}{2n+1} \quad (4\text{-}89b)$$

and the norm $N(\lambda_{np})$ is obtained from equation (3-23) by utilizing the condition (4-89a) as

$$N(\lambda_{np}) = -\frac{b^2}{2} J_{n-1/2}(\lambda_{np} b) J_{n+3/2}(\lambda_{np} b) \quad \text{if (3-23a) is used} \quad (4\text{-}89c)$$

$$= \frac{b^2}{2} [J'_{n+1/2}(\lambda_{np} b)]^2 \quad \text{if (3-23b) is used} \quad (4\text{-}89d)$$

and n's are positive integers, zero being included.

We note that the eigenfunctions $J_{n+1/2}(\lambda_{np} r)$, the norm $N(\lambda_{np})$ given by equation (4-89d) and the expression (4-89a) for the eigenvalues λ_{np} are the same as those obtainable from Table 3-1, Case 3, with $v = n + \frac{1}{2}$. Therefore, Tables 3-1 and 3-2 are useful for the determination of the eigenvalues, the eigenfunctions, and the norms associated with the r variable in the solution of equation (4-83a) for a solid and hollow sphere, respectively.

Problem of a Hemisphere

Example 4-5. Obtain an expression for the temperature distribution $T(r, \mu, t)$ in a solid hemisphere, $0 \le \mu \le 1, 0 \le r \le b$, which is initially at a temperature $F(r, \mu)$ and for times $t > 0$ the boundary surfaces at $r = b$ and $\mu = 0$ are kept at zero temperature as illustrated in Fig. 4-6.

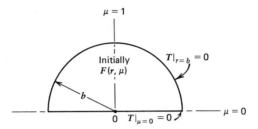

Fig. 4-6 Boundary and initial conditions for a hemisphere in Example 4-5.

Solution. The mathematical formulation of this problem is given as

$$\frac{\partial^2 T}{\partial r^2} + \frac{2}{r}\frac{\partial T}{\partial r} + \frac{1}{r^2}\frac{\partial}{\partial \mu}\left[(1 - \mu^2)\frac{\partial T}{\partial \mu}\right] = \frac{1}{\alpha}\frac{\partial T}{\partial t}$$

$$\text{in } 0 \leq r < b, 0 < \mu \leq 1, \text{ for } t > 0 \quad (4\text{-}90a)$$

$$T = 0 \qquad\qquad \text{at } r = b \text{ and } \mu = 0, \text{ for } t > 0 \quad (4\text{-}90b)$$

$$T = F(r, \mu) \qquad\qquad \text{for } t = 0, \text{ in the hemisphere} \quad (4\text{-}90c)$$

A new variable $V(r, \mu, t)$ is defined as

$$V = r^{1/2}T \quad (4\text{-}91)$$

Then, the problem (4-90) is transformed into

$$\frac{\partial^2 V}{\partial r^2} + \frac{1}{r}\frac{\partial V}{\partial r} - \frac{1}{4}\frac{V}{r^2} + \frac{1}{r^2}\frac{\partial}{\partial \mu}\left[(1 - \mu^2)\frac{\partial V}{\partial \mu}\right] = \frac{1}{\alpha}\frac{\partial V}{\partial t}$$

$$\text{in } 0 \leq r < b, 0 < \mu \leq 1, \text{ for } t > 0 \quad (4\text{-}92a)$$

$$V = 0 \qquad\qquad \text{at } r = b \text{ and } \mu = 0, \text{ for } t > 0 \quad (4\text{-}92b)$$

$$V = r^{1/2}F(r, \mu) \qquad\qquad \text{for } t = 0, \text{ in the hemisphere} \quad (4\text{-}92c)$$

The elementary solutions of equation (4-92a) that are admissible for this problem are

$$e^{-\alpha\lambda^2 t}, \qquad J_{n+1/2}(\lambda r), \qquad \text{and} \qquad P_n(\mu) \quad (4\text{-}93)$$

where $P_n(\mu)$ is the Legendre polynomial as defined by equation (4-19). To satisfy the boundary condition of the first kind at the surface $\mu = 0$ (i.e., the base of the hemisphere) the degree n should be taken as *odd positive integer* (i.e., $n = 1, 3, 5, \ldots$) for reasons discussed in Section 4-3. Then, the complete solution for $V(r, \mu, t)$ is constructed as

$$V(r, \mu, t) = \sum_{n=1,3,5,\ldots}^{\infty} \sum_{p=1}^{\infty} c_{np}e^{-\alpha\lambda_{np}^2 t}J_{n+1/2}(\lambda_{np}r)P_n(\mu) \quad (4\text{-}94)$$

which satisfies the boundary condition at $\mu = 0$. It will also satisfy the boundary condition at $r = b$ if λ_{np}'s are taken as the positive roots of

$$J_{n+1/2}(\lambda_{np}b) = 0 \tag{4-95}$$

The application of the initial condition (4-92c) to the solution (4-94) gives

$$r^{1/2}F(r, \mu) = \sum_{n=1,3,5,\dots}^{\infty} \sum_{p=1}^{\infty} c_{np}J_{n+1/2}(\lambda_{np}r)P_n(\mu)$$
$$\text{in } 0 \leq r < b, 0 < \mu \leq 1 \tag{4-96}$$

To determine the coefficients c_{np} we operate on both sides of equation (4-96) successively by the operators

$$\int_0^1 P_{n'}(\mu)\,d\mu \quad \text{and} \quad \int_0^b rJ_{n+1/2}(\lambda_{np'}r)\,dr$$

where $n' = 1, 3, 5, \dots$ and utilize the orthogonality relations (4-49) and (3-19). We obtain

$$c_{np} = \frac{1}{N(n)N(\lambda_{np})} \int_{r=0}^b \int_{\mu=0}^1 r^{3/2}J_{n+1/2}(\lambda_{np}r)P_n(\mu)F(r,\mu)\,d\mu\,dr \tag{4-97a}$$

where the norms are defined as

$$N(n) \equiv \int_0^1 [P_n(\mu)]^2\,d\mu \quad \text{and} \quad N(\lambda_{np}) \equiv \int_0^b rJ_{n+1/2}^2(\lambda_{np}r)\,dr \tag{4-97b}$$

The coefficient c_{np} as given above is introduced into equation (4-94) and the resulting expression is transformed into $T(r, \mu, t)$ by the transformation (4-91). We obtain

$$T(r, \mu, t) = \sum_{n=1,3,5,\dots}^{\infty} \sum_{p=1}^{\infty} \frac{1}{N(n)N(\lambda_{np})} e^{-\alpha\lambda_{np}^2 t} r^{-1/2}J_{n+1/2}(\lambda_{np}r)P_n(\mu)$$
$$\cdot \int_{r'=0}^b \int_{\mu'=0}^1 r'^{3/2}J_{n+1/2}(\lambda_{np}r')P_n(\mu')F(r',\mu')\,d\mu'\,dr' \tag{4-98}$$

where the eigenvalues λ_{np} are the positive roots of

$$J_{n+1/2}(\lambda_{np}b) = 0 \tag{4-99a}$$

$N(n)$ is determined from equation (4-49) as

$$N(n) = \frac{1}{2n+1} \tag{4-99b}$$

and $N(\lambda_{np})$ is obtained from equation (3-23a) by utilizing the result (4-99a) as

$$N(\lambda_{np}) = -\frac{b^2}{2} J_{n-1/2}(\lambda_{np}b)J_{n+3/2}(\lambda_{np}b) \tag{4-99c}$$

and n's are odd positive integers, that is, $n = 1, 3, 5, \dots$.

Example 4-6. Obtain an expression for the temperature distribution $T(r, \mu, t)$ in a hemisphere, $0 \le \mu \le 1, 0 \le r \le b$, which is initially at temperature $F(r, \mu)$ and for times $t > 0$ the boundary surface at $r = b$ is kept insulated and the boundary surface at $\mu = 0$ (i.e., the base of the sphere) is kept at zero temperature as illustrated in Fig. 4-7.

Solution. This problem is similar to the one considered in Example 4-5 except the boundary surface at $r = b$ is now insulated. The differential equation is the same as that equation (4-90a); therefore we give only the boundary and initial conditions

$$T = 0 \qquad \text{at } \mu = 0 \text{ (the base), } t > 0 \qquad (4\text{-}100a)$$

$$\frac{\partial T}{\partial r} = 0 \qquad \text{at } r = b \text{ (spherical surface), } t > 0 \qquad (4\text{-}100b)$$

$$T = F(r, \mu) \qquad \text{for } t = 0, \text{ in the hemisphere} \qquad (4\text{-}100c)$$

If this problem is transformed with the transformation (4-91), the differential equation is transformed to that given by equation (4-92a) and the boundary and initial conditions (4-99) are transformed into

$$V = 0 \qquad \text{at } \mu = 0 \text{ (the base), } t > 0 \qquad (4\text{-}101a)$$

$$\frac{\partial V}{\partial r} - \frac{1}{2b} V = 0 \qquad r = b, t > 0 \qquad (4\text{-}101b)$$

$$V = r^{1/2} F(r, \mu) \qquad \text{for } t = 0, \text{ in the hemisphere} \qquad (4\text{-}101c)$$

The elementary solutions of this problem are the same as those given by equation (4-93) and the complete solution for $\overset{\smallsmile}{V}(r, \mu, t)$ is constructed as

$$V(r, \mu, t) = \sum_{n = 1,3,5,\ldots}^{\infty} \sum_{p=1}^{\infty} c_{np} e^{-\alpha \lambda_{np}^2 t} J_{n+1/2}(\lambda_{np} r) P_n(\mu) \qquad (4\text{-}102)$$

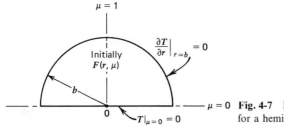

Fig. 4-7 Boundary and initial conditons for a hemisphere in Example 4-6.

If the eigenvalues λ_{np} are taken as the positive roots of

$$\frac{d}{dr}J_{n+1/2}(\lambda_{np}b) - \frac{1}{2b}J_{n+1/2}(\lambda_{np}b) = 0 \qquad (4\text{-}103a)$$

or

$$\lambda_{np}J'_{n+1/2}(\lambda_{np}b) - \frac{1}{2b}J_{n+1/2}(\lambda_{np}b) = 0 \qquad (4\text{-}103b)$$

the boundary condition (4-101b) at $r = b$ is satisfied. The application of the initial condition (4-101c) to equation (4-102) gives

$$r^{1/2}F(r,\mu) = \sum_{n=1,3,5,\ldots}^{\infty} \sum_{p=1}^{\infty} c_{np}J_{n+1/2}(\lambda_{np}r)P_n(\mu) \qquad (4\text{-}104)$$

To determine the coefficients c_{np} we operate on both sides of this equation successively by the operators

$$\int_0^1 P_{n'}(\mu)\,d\mu \qquad \text{and} \qquad \int_0^b rJ_{n+1/2}(\lambda_{np'}r)\,dr$$

where $n' = 1, 3, 5, \ldots$ and utilize the orthogonality relations (4-49) and (3-19). We obtain

$$c_{np} = \frac{1}{N(n)N(\lambda_{np})} \int_{r=0}^{b} \int_{\mu=0}^{1} r^{3/2}J_{n+1/2}(\lambda_{np}r)P_n(\mu)F(r,\mu)\,d\mu\,dr \qquad (4\text{-}105a)$$

where

$$N(n) \equiv \int_0^1 [P_n(\mu)]^2\,d\mu \qquad \text{and} \qquad N(\lambda_{np}) \equiv \int_0^b rJ_{n+1/2}^2(\lambda_{np}r)\,dr \qquad (4\text{-}105b)$$

The coefficient c_{np} as given above is introduced into equation (4-102) and the resulting solution is transformed into $T(r,\mu,t)$ by the transformation (4-91). We obtain

$$T(r,\mu,t) = \sum_{n=1,3,5,\ldots}^{\infty} \sum_{p=1}^{\infty} \frac{1}{N(n)N(\lambda_{np})}e^{-\alpha\lambda_{np}^2 t}r^{-1/2}J_{n+1/2}(\lambda_{np}r)P_n(\mu)$$

$$\cdot \int_{r'=0}^{b} \int_{\mu'=0}^{1} r'^{3/2}J_{n+1/2}(\lambda_{np}r')P_n(\mu')F(r',\mu')\,d\mu'\,dr' \qquad (4\text{-}106)$$

where the eigenvalues λ_{np}'s are the positive roots of

$$\lambda_{np}J'_{n+1/2}(\lambda_{np}b) - \frac{1}{2b}J_{n+1/2}(\lambda_{np}b) = 0 \qquad (4\text{-}107a)$$

the norm $N(n)$ is obtained from equation (4-49) as

$$N(n) = \frac{1}{2n + 1} \qquad (4\text{-}107\text{b})$$

The norm $N(\lambda_{np})$ is determined from equation (3-23a) as

$$N(\lambda_{np}) = \tfrac{1}{2}b^2 \big[J_{n+1/2}^2(\lambda_{np}b) - J_{n-1/2}(\lambda_{np}b) J_{n+3/2}(\lambda_{np}b) \big] \qquad (4\text{-}107\text{c})$$

and n's are *odd positive integers* (i.e., $n = 1, 3, 5, \ldots$).

We note that the general form of the solution (4-106) is exactly the same as that of equation (4-98) of the previous example except the expressions defining the eigenvalues λ_{np} and the norm $N(\lambda_{np})$ are different. The eigenfunctions $J_{n+1/2}(\lambda_{np}r)$, the eigenvalues λ_{np}, and the norm $N(\lambda_{np})$ if determined by using equation (3-23b) are the same as those obtainable from Table 3-1, Case 1, by setting

$$v = n + \tfrac{1}{2}, \; H = -\frac{1}{2b} \text{ and } \lambda_{np} = \beta_m.$$

All Boundaries Insulated

When all the boundary surfaces of the region are insulated, the analysis is performed in a similar manner to those illustrated above with other boundary conditions; but for this special case $\lambda_{0,0} = 0$ is also an eigenvalue. Then the term

$$\frac{\displaystyle\int_{\text{Region}} F(r, \mu) r^2 \, dr \, d\mu}{\displaystyle\int_{\text{Region}} r^2 \, dr \, d\mu}$$

that results from the zero eigenvalue should be added to the solution. This term implies that, after the transients have passed, the steady-state temperature in the medium is the mean of the initial distribution $F(r, \mu)$ over the volume of the insulated region. The validity of the above expression can be proved by a discussion similar to that given in Note 3. Also, see equation (13-25b) for the more general expression for $T(r, \infty)$ when all boundaries of a finite region are insulated.

4-6 HOMOGENEOUS PROBLEMS IN (r, μ, ϕ, t) VARIABLES

In this section we illustrate with examples the solution of the homogeneous problems of heat conduction involving (r, μ, ϕ, t) variables.

Problem of a Full Sphere

Example 4-7. A solid sphere of radius $r = b$ is initially at temperature $F(r,\mu,\phi)$. For times $t > 0$ the boundary surface at $r = b$ is kept at zero temperature. Obtain an expression for the temperature distribution $T(r,\mu,\phi,t)$ in the sphere for times $t > 0$.

Solution. The mathematical formulation of this problem is given as

$$\frac{\partial^2 T}{\partial r^2} + \frac{2}{r}\frac{\partial T}{\partial r} + \frac{1}{r^2}\frac{\partial}{\partial \mu}\left[(1 - \mu^2)\frac{\partial T}{\partial \mu}\right] + \frac{1}{r^2(1 - \mu^2)}\frac{\partial^2 T}{\partial \phi^2} = \frac{1}{\alpha}\frac{\partial T}{\partial t}$$

$$\text{in } 0 \leq r < b, \, -1 \leq \mu \leq 1, 0 \leq \phi \leq 2\pi \text{ for } t > 0 \quad (4\text{-}108\text{a})$$

$$T = 0 \qquad \text{at } r = b, \text{ for } t > 0 \tag{4-108b}$$

$$T = F(r,\mu,\phi) \qquad \text{for } t = 0, \text{ in the sphere} \tag{4-108c}$$

A new variable $V(r,\mu,\phi,t)$ is defined as

$$V = r^{1/2}T \tag{4-109}$$

The problem (4-108) is transformed into

$$\frac{\partial^2 V}{\partial r^2} + \frac{1}{r}\frac{\partial V}{\partial r} - \frac{1}{4}\frac{V}{r^2} + \frac{1}{r^2}\frac{\partial}{\partial \mu}\left[(1 - \mu^2)\frac{\partial V}{\partial \mu}\right] + \frac{1}{r^2(1 - \mu^2)}\frac{\partial^2 V}{\partial \phi^2} = \frac{1}{\alpha}\frac{\partial V}{\partial t}$$

$$\text{in } 0 \leq r < b, \, -1 \leq \mu \leq 1, 0 \leq \phi \leq 2\pi, \text{ for } t > 0 \quad (4\text{-}110\text{a})$$

$$V = 0 \qquad \text{at } r = b, \text{ for } t > 0 \tag{4-110b}$$

$$V = r^{1/2}F(r,\mu,\phi) \quad \text{for } t = 0, \text{ in the sphere} \tag{4-110c}$$

The elementary solution of equation (4-110a) that are admissible on the physical grounds are [see equations (4-8)]

$$e^{-\alpha\lambda^2 t}, \qquad J_{n+1/2}(\lambda r), \qquad P_n^m(\mu), \qquad (A\cos m\phi + B\sin m\phi) \quad (4\text{-}111)$$

where $P_n^m(\mu)$ is the associated Legendre function of the first kind defined by equation (4-25), with n and m being positive integers (i.e., $n, m = 0, 1, 2, 3 \ldots$) and $m \leq n$. The choice of m as positive integer satisfies the requirement that the temperature T (or V) is periodic with period 2π in the interval $0 \leq \phi \leq 2\pi$. Then the complete solution for $V(r,\mu,\phi,t)$ is constructed as

$$V(r,\mu,\phi,t) = \sum_{n=0}^{\infty} \sum_{p=1}^{\infty} \sum_{m=0}^{n} e^{-\alpha\lambda_{np}^2 t} J_{n+1/2}(\lambda_{np}r)P_n^m(\mu)$$
$$\cdot (A_{mnp}\cos m\phi + B_{mnp}\sin m\phi) \tag{4-112}$$

This solution satisfies the differential equation (4-110a) and remains bounded in the region $-1 \leq \mu \leq 1, 0 \leq \phi \leq 2\pi$, and $0 \leq r \leq b$. If the eigenvalues λ_{np} are chosen as the positive roots of

$$J_{n+1/2}(\lambda_{np}b) = 0 \tag{4-113}$$

it also satisfies the boundary condition at $r = b$. The expansion coefficients A_{mnp} and B_{mnp} are to be determined so that the initial condition for the problem is satisfied. The application of the initial condition (4-110c) to equation (4-112) gives

$$r^{1/2}F(r, \mu, \phi) = \sum_{n=0}^{\infty} \sum_{p=1}^{\infty} \sum_{m=0}^{n} J_{n+1/2}(\lambda_{np}r)P_n^m(\mu)(A_{mnp} \cos m\phi + B_{mnp} \sin m\phi)$$
$$\text{in} \ -1 \leq \mu \leq 1, 0 \leq \phi \leq 2\pi, 0 \leq r \leq b \tag{4-114}$$

To determine the coefficients we operate on both sides of equation (4-114) by the operator

$$\int_0^b r J_{n+1/2}(\lambda_{np'}r) \, dr \tag{4-115}$$

and utilize the orthogonality relation (3-19). We obtain

$$f(\mu, \phi) = \sum_{n=0}^{\infty} \sum_{m=0}^{n} P_n^m(\mu)[A_{mnp} \cos m\phi + B_{mnp} \sin m\phi]N(\lambda_{np})$$
$$\text{in} \ -1 \leq \mu \leq 1, 0 \leq \phi \leq 2\pi \tag{4-116a}$$

where

$$f(\mu, \phi) \equiv \int_0^b r^{3/2}F(r, \mu, \phi)J_{n+1/2}(\lambda_{np}r) \, dr \tag{4-116b}$$

$$N(\lambda_{np}) \equiv \int_0^b r J_{n+1/2}^2(\lambda_{np}r) \, dr = -\frac{b^2}{2}J_{n-1/2}(\lambda_{np}b)J_{n+3/2}(\lambda_{np}b) \tag{4-116c}$$

here we utilized equation (3-23a) together with equation (4-113) to evaluate the norm $N(\lambda_{np})$.

Equation (4-116a) is a representation of a function $f(\mu, \phi)$ defined in the interval $-1 \leq \mu \leq 1, 0 \leq \phi \leq 2\pi$ in terms of $P_n^m(\mu)$, $\sin m\phi$ and $\cos m\phi$. Such an expansion was considered previously in equation (4-37b) and the expansion coefficients were given by equation (4-44). Therefore, the expansion coefficients in equation (4-116a) are obtained from equation (4-44) as

$$N(\lambda_{np})[A_{mnp} \cos m\phi + B_{mnp} \sin n\phi] \equiv \frac{1}{\pi N(m, n)} \int_{\phi'=0}^{2\pi} \int_{\mu'=-1}^{1} f(\mu', \phi')$$
$$\cdot P_n^m(\mu')\cos[m(\phi - \phi')] \, d\mu' \, d\phi' \tag{4-117a}$$

where π *should be replaced by* 2π *for* $m = 0$, and the norm $N(m, n)$ is as given by equation (4-40b)

$$N(m,n) \equiv \int_{-1}^{1} [P_n^m(\mu)]^2 \, d\mu = \left(\frac{2}{2n+1}\right)\frac{(n+m)!}{(n-m)!} \qquad (4\text{-}117b)$$

The coefficients given by equations (4-117) are introduced into equation (4-112) and the resulting expression is transformed into $T(r,\mu,\phi,t)$ by the transformation (4-109). We obtain

$$T(r,\mu,\phi,t) = \frac{1}{\pi} \sum_{n=0}^{\infty} \sum_{p=1}^{\infty} \sum_{m=0}^{n} \frac{e^{-\alpha \lambda_{np}^2 t}}{N(m,n)N(\lambda_{np})} r^{-1/2} J_{n+1/2}(\lambda_{np}r)P_n^m(\mu)$$

$$\cdot \int_{r'=0}^{b} \int_{\mu'=-1}^{1} \int_{\phi'=0}^{2\pi} r'^{3/2} J_{n+1/2}(\lambda_{np}r')P_n^m(\mu') \cos m(\phi - \phi')$$

$$\cdot F(r',\mu',\phi') \, d\phi' \, d\mu' \, dr' \qquad (4\text{-}118a)$$

where, π *should be replaced by* 2π *for* $m = 0$, and the eigenvalues λ_{np} are the positive roots of

$$J_{n+1/2}(\lambda_{np}b) = 0 \qquad (4\text{-}118b)$$

the norms $N(m,n)$ and $N(\lambda_{np})$ are given by

$$N(m,n) = \left(\frac{2}{2n+1}\right)\frac{(n+m)!}{(n-m)!} \qquad (4\text{-}118c)$$

$$N(\lambda_{np}) = -\frac{b^2}{2} J_{n-1/2}(\lambda_{np}b) J_{n+3/2}(\lambda_{np}r) \qquad (4\text{-}118b)$$

and n,m are positive integers, zero being included.

It is to be noted that, if equation (3-23b) is used together with equation (4-113) the alternative form of the norm $N(\lambda_{np})$ would be

$$N(\lambda_{np}) = \frac{b^2}{2} J_{n+1/2}'^2(\lambda_{np}b) \qquad (4\text{-}119)$$

In the above solution the eigenfunctions $J_{n+1/2}(\lambda_{np}r)$, the equation (4-118b) for the eigenvalues λ_{np}, and the norm $N(\lambda_{np})$ given by equation (4-119) are the same as those obtainable from Table 3-1, Case 3, by setting $v \equiv n + 1/2$ and $\lambda_{np} \equiv \beta_m$.

Problem of a Portion of a Sphere

Example 4-8.   The part of the sphere cut out by the cone $\theta = \theta_0$, as illustrated in Fig. 4-2, is initially at temperature $F(r,\mu,\phi)$. For times $t > 0$, all the surfaces are kept at zero temperature. Obtain an expression for the temperature distribution $T(r,\mu,\phi,t)$.

Solution. The mathematical formulation of this problem is given as

$$\frac{\partial^2 T}{\partial r^2} + \frac{2}{r}\frac{\partial T}{\partial r} + \frac{1}{r^2}\frac{\partial}{\partial \mu}\left[(1-\mu^2)\frac{\partial T}{\partial \mu}\right] + \frac{1}{r^2(1-\mu^2)}\frac{\partial^2 T}{\partial \phi^2} = \frac{1}{\alpha}\frac{\partial T}{\partial t} \qquad (4\text{-}120a)$$

$$\text{in } 0 \le r < b, \ \mu_0 < \mu \le 1, \ 0 \le \phi \le 2\pi, \ \text{for } t > 0$$

$$T = 0 \qquad \text{at } r = b \text{ and } \mu = \mu_0, \text{ for } t > 0 \qquad (4\text{-}120b)$$

$$T = F(r, \mu, \phi) \qquad \text{for } t = 0, \text{ in the region} \qquad (4\text{-}120c)$$

A new variable $V(r, \mu, \phi, t)$ is defined as

$$V = r^{1/2}T \qquad (4\text{-}121)$$

The problem (4-120) is transformed into

$$\frac{\partial^2 V}{\partial r^2} + \frac{1}{r}\frac{\partial V}{\partial r} - \frac{1}{4}\frac{V}{r^2} + \frac{1}{r^2}\frac{\partial}{\partial \mu}\left[(1-\mu^2)\frac{\partial V}{\partial \mu}\right] + \frac{1}{r^2(1-\mu^2)}\frac{\partial^2 V}{\partial \phi^2} = \frac{1}{\alpha}\frac{\partial V}{\partial t}$$

$$\text{in } 0 \le r < b, \ \mu_0 < \mu \le 1, \ 0 \le \phi \le 2\pi, \ \text{for } t > 0 \quad (4\text{-}122a)$$

$$V = 0 \qquad \text{at } r = b \text{ and } \mu = \mu_0, \text{ for } t > 0 \qquad (4\text{-}122b)$$

$$V = r^{1/2}F(r, \mu, \phi) \quad \text{for } t = 0, \text{ in the region} \qquad (4\text{-}122c)$$

The elementary solutions of equation (4-122a) that are admissible for the problem on the physical grounds include

$$e^{-\alpha\lambda^2 t}, \qquad J_{n+1/2}(\lambda r), \ P_n^{-m}(\mu), \qquad (A\cos m\phi + B\sin m\phi) \quad (4\text{-}123)$$

where the function $P_n^{-m}(\mu)$ is the *generalized Legendre function of the first kind* as defined by equation (4-29), with m being a positive integer ($m = 0, 1, 2, 3, \ldots$) and n being unrestricted taking values greater than $-\frac{1}{2}$. The choice of m as positive integer satisfies the requirement that T (or V) is periodic with period 2π in the interval $0 \le \phi \le 2\pi$. Then, the complete solution for $V(r, \mu, \phi, t)$ is constructed as

$$V(r, \mu, \phi, t) = \sum_n \sum_p \sum_{m=0}^{\infty} e^{-\alpha\lambda_{np}^2 t} J_{n+1/2}(\lambda_{np}r)P_n^{-m}(\mu)$$

$$\cdot (A_{mnp}\cos m\phi + B_{mnp}\sin m\phi) \qquad (4\text{-}124)$$

This solution satisfies the boundary condition $V = 0$ at $r = b$ if λ_{np}'s are the positive roots of

$$J_{n+1/2}(\lambda_{np}b) = 0 \qquad (4\text{-}125)$$

It also satisfies the boundary condition $V = 0$ at $\mu = \mu_0$ if n's are the roots, greater than $-\frac{1}{2}$, of the equation

$$P_n^{-m}(\mu_0) = 0 \qquad (4\text{-}126)$$

The expansion coefficients A_{mnp} and B_{mnp} are to be determined so that the initial condition is satisfied. The application of the initial condition (4-122c) to equation (4-124) gives

$$r^{1/2}F(r,\mu,\phi) = \sum_n \sum_p \sum_{m=0}^{\infty} J_{n+1/2}(\lambda_{np}r)P_n^{-m}(\mu)(A_{mnp}\cos m\phi + B_{mnp}\sin m\phi)$$

$$\text{in } \mu_0 < \mu \leq 1, \ 0 \leq \phi \leq 2\pi, \ 0 \leq r \leq b \qquad (4\text{-}127)$$

To determine the expansion coefficients we operate on both sides of equation (4-127) by the operator

$$\int_0^b rJ_{n+1/2}(\lambda_{np'}r)\,dr \qquad (4\text{-}128)$$

and utilize the orthogonality relation (3-19). We obtain

$$f(\mu,\phi) = \sum_n \sum_{m=0}^{\infty} P_n^{-m}(\mu)[A_{mnp}\cos m\phi + B_{mnp}\sin m\phi]N(\lambda_{np})$$

$$\text{in } \mu_0 < \mu \leq 1, \ 0 \leq \phi \leq 2\pi \qquad (4\text{-}129a)$$

where

$$f(\mu,\phi) \equiv \int_0^b r^{3/2}F(r,\mu,\phi)J_{n+1/2}(\lambda_{np}r)\,dr \qquad (4\text{-}129b)$$

$$N(\lambda_{np}) \equiv \int_0^b rJ_{n+1/2}^2(\lambda_{np}r)\,dr = \tfrac{1}{2}b^2[J'_{n+1/2}(\lambda_{np}b)]^2 \qquad (4\text{-}129c)$$

and we utilized equation (3-23b) together with equation (4-125) to evaluate the norm $N(\lambda_{np})$.

Equation (4-129a) is a representation of a function $f(\mu,\phi)$ defined in the interval $\mu_0 < \mu \leq 1, 0 \leq \phi \leq 2\pi$, subject to the condition $P_n^{-m}(\mu_0) = 0$, in terms of the functions $P_n^{-m}(\mu)$, $\cos m\phi$ and $\sin m\phi$. Such a representation was considered in equation (4-52) and the resulting expansion coefficients were given by equation (4-60). Therefore, the expansion coefficients in equation (4-129a) are readily obtained from equation (4-60) as

$$N(\lambda_{np})[A_{mnp}\cos m\phi + B_{mnp}\sin m\phi] \equiv \frac{1}{\pi N(m,n)}$$

$$\cdot \int_{\phi'=0}^{2\pi} \int_{\mu'=\mu_0}^{1} f(\mu',\phi')P_n^{-m}(\mu')$$

$$\cdot \cos m(\phi - \phi')\,d\mu'\,d\phi' \qquad (4\text{-}130a)$$

where π *should be replaced by* 2π *for* $m = 0$, and the norm $N(m,n)$ subject to the condition $P_n^{-m}(\mu_0) = 0$ is obtained from equation (4-55a) as

$$N(m, n) = -\frac{1 - \mu_0^2}{2n + 1} \frac{d}{dn} P_n^{-m}(\mu_0) \frac{d}{d\mu_0} P_n^{-m}(\mu_0) \qquad (4\text{-}130\text{b})$$

We now introduce the coefficients given by equation (4-130) into equation (4-124) and transform the resulting expression into $T(r, \mu, \phi, t)$ by the transformation (4-121). We obtain

$$T(r, \mu, \phi, t) = \frac{1}{\pi} \sum_n \sum_p \sum_{m=0}^{\infty} \frac{e^{-\alpha \lambda_{np}^2 t}}{N(m, n) N(\lambda_{np})} r^{-1/2} J_{n+1/2}(\lambda_{np} r) P_n^{-m}(\mu)$$

$$\cdot \int_{r'=0}^{b} \int_{\mu'=\mu_0}^{1} \int_{\phi'=0}^{2\pi} r'^{3/2} J_{n+1/2}(\lambda_{np} r') P_n^{-m}(\mu') \cos m(\phi - \phi')$$

$$\cdot F(r', \mu', \phi') \, d\phi' \, d\mu' \, dr' \qquad (4\text{-}131\text{a})$$

where π *should be replaced by* 2π *for* $m = 0$, the eigenvalues λ_{np}'s are the positive roots of

$$J_{n+1/2}(\lambda_{np} b) = 0 \qquad (4\text{-}131\text{b})$$

n's are the roots, greater than $-\frac{1}{2}$, of the equation

$$P_n^{-m}(\mu_0) = 0 \qquad (4\text{-}131\text{c})$$

The norms $N(m, n)$ and $N(\lambda_{np})$ are given by

$$N(m, n) = -\frac{1 - \mu_0^2}{2n + 1} \frac{d}{dn} P_n^{-m}(\mu_0) \frac{d}{d\mu_0} P_n^{-m}(\mu_0) \qquad (4\text{-}131\text{d})$$

$$N(\lambda_{np}) = \frac{b^2}{2} \left[J'_{n+1/2}(\lambda_{np} b) \right]^2 \qquad (4\text{-}131\text{e})$$

and m's are positive integers $(m = 0, 1, 2, 3 \ldots)$.

All Boundaries Insulated

When all boundary surfaces of the finite region are insulated, the analysis is performed in a similar manner to those illustrated above with other boundary conditions; but for this special case, zero is also an eigenvalue. Then the term

$$\frac{\displaystyle\int_{\text{Region}} F(r, \mu, \phi) r^2 \, dr \, d\mu \, d\phi}{\displaystyle\int_{\text{Region}} r^2 \, dr \, d\mu \, d\phi}$$

resulting from the zero eigenvalue should be added to the solution. This term implies that, after the transients have passed, the steady-state temperature in the medium is the mean of the initial distribution $F(r, \mu, \phi)$ over the volume of the insulated region. The validity of this result can be proved by a discussion similar to that given in Note 3 at the end of this chapter.

4-7 MULTIDIMENSIONAL STEADY-STATE PROBLEMS

The multidimensional steady-state heat-conduction equation with heat generation can be transformed into the Laplace's equation as discussed previously in Sections 2–9 and 3–9 if a particular solution of the non-homogeneous equation is found. The resulting problem, if it involves more than one nonhomogeneous boundary condition, is split up into a set of simpler problems each containing only one nonhomogeneous boundary condition. The complete solution of the original problem is obtained by summing up the solutions of the simpler problems. Therefore, in this section we illustrate with examples the solution of multidimensional, steady-state heat-conduction equation with no heat generation subject to only one nonhomogeneous boundary condition by the method of separation of variables.

Example 4-9. Determine the steady-state temperature distribution $T(r, \mu, \phi)$ in a solid sphere of radius $r = b$ with its boundary surface at $r = b$ is kept at temperature $f(\mu, \phi)$.

Solution. The mathematical formulation of this problem is given as

$$\frac{\partial^2 T}{\partial r^2} + \frac{2}{r} \frac{\partial T}{\partial r} + \frac{1}{r^2} \frac{\partial}{\partial \mu} \left[(1 - \mu^2) \frac{\partial T}{\partial \mu} \right] + \frac{1}{r^2(1 - \mu^2)} \frac{\partial^2 T}{\partial \phi^2} = 0$$

$$\text{in } 0 \le r < b, \ -1 \le \mu \le 1, \ 0 \le \phi \le 2\pi \quad (4\text{-}132a)$$

$$T = f(\mu, \phi) \qquad \text{at } r = b \qquad (4\text{-}132b)$$

The elementary solutions of equation (4-132a) are given by equations (4-13d, e, f). The solutions r^{-n-1} and $Q_n^m(\mu)$ are to be excluded, because the former becomes infinite at $r = 0$ and the latter at $\mu = \pm 1$. Then the solutions that are admissible include

$$r^n, \qquad P_n^m(\mu), \qquad \text{and} \qquad (A \cos m\phi + B \sin m\phi) \qquad (4\text{-}133)$$

where $P_n^m(\mu)$ is the associated Legendre function of the first kind as defined by equation (4-25), with n and m being positive integers (i.e., $n, m = 0, 1, 2 \ldots$) and $m \le n$. The choice of m as positive integer satisfies the requirement that the temperature T is periodic with period 2π in the region $0 \le \phi \le 2\pi$. The complete solution for $T(r, \mu, \phi)$ is constructed as

$$T(r, \mu, \phi) = \sum_{n=0}^{\infty} \sum_{m=0}^{n} r^n P_n^m(\mu)(A_{mn} \cos m\phi + B_{mn} \sin m\phi) \qquad (4\text{-}134)$$

which satisfies the differential equation (4-132a) and remains finite in the region $-1 \le \mu \le 1, 0 \le \phi \le 2\pi, 0 \le r < b$. The coefficients A_{mn} and B_{mn} are to be determined so that the boundary condition at $r = b$ is satisfied. The application of the boundary condition (4-132b) gives

$$f(\mu, \phi) = \sum_{n=0}^{\infty} \sum_{m=0}^{n} P_n^m(\mu)(A_{mn} \cos m\phi + B_{mn} \sin m\phi)b^n$$
$$\text{in } -1 \le \mu \le 1, \ 0 \le \phi \le 2\pi \qquad (4\text{-}135)$$

Equation (4-135) is a representation of a function $f(\mu, \phi)$ defined in the interval $-1 \le \mu \le 1, 0 \le \phi \le 2\pi$ in terms of the functions $P_n^m(\mu)$, $\sin m\phi$ and $\cos m\phi$. Such a representation was considered previously in equation (4-37b) and the expansion coefficients were given by equation (4-44). Therefore, the coefficients in equation (4-135) are obtained from equation (4-44) as

$$[A_{mn} \cos m\phi + B_{mn} \sin m\phi] \equiv \frac{1}{\pi N(m, n)} \int_{\phi'=0}^{2\pi} \int_{\mu'=-1}^{1} \frac{f(\mu', \phi')}{b^n} P_n^m(\mu')$$
$$\cdot \cos[m(\phi - \phi')] d\mu' d\phi' \qquad (4\text{-}136a)$$

where π *should be replaced by* 2π *for* $m = 0$, and the norm $N(m, n)$ is as given by equation (4-40b)

$$N(m, n) \equiv \int_{-1}^{1} [P_n^m(\mu)]^2 d\mu = \frac{2}{2n+1} \frac{(n+m)!}{(n-m)!} \qquad (4\text{-}136a)$$

When the coefficients given by equation (4-136a) are introduced into equation (4-134) the solution becomes

$$T(r, \mu, \phi) = \frac{1}{\pi} \sum_{n=0}^{\infty} \sum_{m=0}^{n} \frac{2n+1}{2} \frac{(n-m)!}{(n+m)!} \left(\frac{r}{b}\right)^n P_n^m(\mu)$$
$$\cdot \int_{\phi'=0}^{2\pi} \int_{\mu'=-1}^{1} P_n^m(\mu') \cos m(\phi - \phi') f(\mu', \phi') d\mu' d\phi' \qquad (4\text{-}137)$$

where π *should be replaced by* 2π *for* $m = 0$, $m = 0, 1, 2, 3, \ldots, n = 0, 1, 2, 3, \ldots$, $m \le n$.

Example 4-10. Determine the steady-state temperature distribution $T(r, \mu)$ in a solid hemisphere of radius $r = b$, in the region $0 \le r \le b, 0 \le \mu \le 1$, with its spherical surface at $r = b$ kept at temperature $f(\mu)$ and its base at $\mu = 0$ is insulated as illustrated in Fig. 4-8.

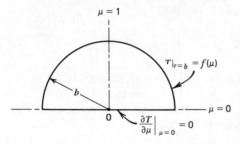

Fig. 4-8 Boundary conditions for a hemisphere in Example 4-10.

Solution. The mathematical formulation of the problem is given as

$$\frac{\partial^2 T}{\partial r^2} + \frac{2}{r}\frac{\partial T}{\partial r} + \frac{1}{r^2}\frac{\partial}{\partial \mu}\left[(1-\mu^2)\frac{\partial T}{\partial \mu}\right] = 0 \qquad \text{in } 0 \le r < b,\, 0 < \mu \le 1 \quad (4\text{-}138a)$$

$$\frac{\partial T}{\partial \mu} = 0 \qquad\qquad\qquad \text{at } \mu = 0 \qquad\qquad (4\text{-}138b)$$

$$T = f(\mu) \qquad\qquad\qquad \text{at } r = b \qquad\qquad (4\text{-}138c)$$

The elementary solutions of equation (4-138a) are given by equations (4-15c,d). The solutions r^{-n-1} and $Q_n(\mu)$ are inadmissible, because the former becomes infinite at $r = 0$ and the latter becomes infinite at $\mu = 1$. Then, the elementary solutions that are admissible are taken as

$$r^n \quad \text{and} \quad P_n(\mu) \qquad\qquad\qquad (4\text{-}139)$$

where $P_n(\mu)$ is the Legendre polynomial as defined by equations (4-19). The complete solution for $T(r, \mu)$ is constructed as

$$T(r, \mu) = \sum_n c_n r^n P_n(\mu) \qquad\qquad\qquad (4\text{-}140)$$

The application of the boundary condition at $r = b$ gives

$$f(\mu) = \sum_n c_n b^n P_n(\mu) \qquad \text{in } 0 \le \mu \le 1 \qquad (4\text{-}141)$$

This is a representation of a function $f(\mu)$ defined in the interval $0 \le \mu \le 1$ in terms of the Legendre polynomials. Such a representation was considered previously in equation (4-46) and the expansion coefficients were given by equation (4-50). Therefore, the coefficients c_n in equation (4-141) are readily obtained from equations (4-50) as

$$c_n = \frac{1}{N(n)} \int_0^1 \frac{f(\mu')}{b^n} P_n(\mu')\, d\mu' \qquad\qquad (4\text{-}142a)$$

where

$$Nn \equiv \int_0^1 [P_n(\mu)]^2 \, d\mu = \frac{1}{2n+1} \tag{4-142b}$$

$$n = 0, 2, 4, \ldots \tag{4-142c}$$

for the boundary condition of the *second kind* at $\mu = 0$. Introducing c_n into equation (4-140) the solution becomes

$$T(r, \mu) = \sum_{n=0,2,4,\ldots}^{\infty} (2n+1) \left(\frac{r}{b}\right)^n P_n(\mu) \int_{\mu'=0}^1 f(\mu') P_n(\mu') \, d\mu' \tag{4-143}$$

or if n is replaced by $2n$, this result is written as

$$T(r, \mu) = \sum_{n=0}^{\infty} (4n+1) \left(\frac{r}{b}\right)^{2n} P_{2n}(\mu) \int_{\mu'=0}^1 f(\mu') P_{2n}(\mu') \, d\mu' \tag{4-144}$$

in equation (4-144) we have $n = 0, 1, 2, 3, \ldots$.

4-8 SPLITTING-UP OF NONHOMOGENEOUS PROBLEMS INTO SIMPLER PROBLEMS

When the heat-conduction problem is nonhomogeneous due to the non-homogeneity of the differential equation and/or the boundary condition, it can be split up into a set of simpler problems as discussed in Section 2-10 if the heat-generation term and the nonhomogeneous part of the boundary conditions *do not depend on time*. Such simpler problems can be solved by the method of separation of variables; then the solution of the original problem is obtained by summing up the solutions of the simpler problems. In this section we illustrate this approach with an example in the spherical coordinate system.

Example 4-11. A solid sphere of radius $r = b$ is initially at a temperature $F(r)$. For times $t > 0$, heat is generated in the sphere at a constant rate of g_0 per unit volume, and the boundary surface at $r = b$ is kept at zero temperature. Obtain an expression for the temperature distribution $T(r, t)$ in the sphere.

Solution. The mathematical formulation of this problem is given as

$$\frac{1}{r} \frac{\partial^2}{\partial r^2} (rT) + \frac{1}{k} g_0 = \frac{1}{\alpha} \frac{\partial T}{\partial t} \qquad \text{in } 0 \le r < b, t > 0 \tag{4-145a}$$

$$T = 0 \qquad \text{at } r = b, t > 0 \tag{4-145b}$$

$$T = F(r) \qquad \text{for } t = 0, \text{ in } 0 \le r \le b \tag{4-145c}$$

A new variable $U(r,t)$ is defined as

$$U = rT \tag{4-146}$$

Then, equations (4-145) are transformed into

$$\frac{\partial^2 U}{\partial r^2} + \frac{rg_0}{k} = \frac{1}{\alpha}\frac{\partial U}{\partial t} \qquad \text{in } 0 < r < b, t > 0 \tag{4-147a}$$

$$U = 0 \qquad\qquad \text{at } r = 0,\ t > 0 \tag{4-147b}$$

$$U = 0 \qquad\qquad \text{at } r = b,\ t > 0 \tag{4-147c}$$

$$U = rF(r) \qquad\qquad \text{for } t = 0, \text{ in the sphere} \tag{4-147d}$$

This problem is now split up into a steady-state problem for the function $U_s(r)$ given by the equations

$$\frac{d^2 U_s}{dr^2} + \frac{rg_0}{k} = 0 \qquad \text{in } 0 < r < b \tag{4-148a}$$

$$U_s = 0 \qquad\qquad \text{at } r = 0 \tag{4-148b}$$

$$U_s = 0 \qquad\qquad \text{at } r = b \tag{4-148c}$$

and into a homogeneous problem for the function $U_h(r,t)$ given by the equations

$$\frac{\partial^2 U_h}{\partial r^2} = \frac{1}{\alpha}\frac{\partial U_h}{\partial t} \qquad \text{in } 0 < r < b,\ t > 0 \tag{4-149a}$$

$$U_h = 0 \qquad\qquad \text{at } r = 0,\ t > 0 \tag{4-149b}$$

$$U_h = 0 \qquad\qquad \text{at } r = b,\ t > 0 \tag{4-149c}$$

$$U_h = rF(r) - U_s(r) \quad \text{for } t = 0, \text{ in } 0 \le r \le b \tag{4-149c}$$

Then the solution of the problem (4-147) is determined from

$$U(r,t) = U_s(r) + U_h(r,t) \tag{4-150}$$

and the solution of the problem (4-145) becomes

$$T(r,t) = \frac{1}{r}[U_s(r) + U_h(r,t)] \tag{4-151}$$

Clearly, the solution of the steady-state problem (4-148) is

$$U_s(r) = \frac{g_0 r}{6k}(b^2 - r^2) \tag{4-152}$$

and the solution of the homogeneous problem (4-149) is readily obtained as

$$U_h(r,t) = \frac{2}{b} \sum_{m=1}^{\infty} e^{-\alpha\lambda_m^2 t} \sin\beta_m r \int_{r'=0}^{b} \left[r'F(r') - U_s(r') \right] \sin\beta_m r' \, dr' \quad (4\text{-}153)$$

where

$$\beta_m = \frac{m\pi}{b}, \qquad m = 1, 2, 3, \ldots$$

REFERENCES

1. H. S. Carslaw and J. C. Jaeger, *Conduction of Heat in Solids*, Clarendon Press, London, 1959.

2. M. N. Özışık, *Boundary Value Problems of Heat Conduction*, International Textbook Co., Scranton, P., 1968.

3. A. V. Luikov, *Analytical Heat Diffusion Theory*, Academic Press, New York, 1968.

4. J. Crank, *The Mathematics of Diffusion*, Clarendon Press, London, 1957.

5. T. M. MacRobert, *Spherical Harmonics*, 3rd. ed., Pergamon Press, New York, 1967.

6. E. T. Whittaker and G. N. Watson, *A Course of Modern Analysis*, Cambridge University Press London, 1965.

7. W. E. Byerly, *Fourier's Series and Spherical, Cylindrical and Ellipsoidal Harmonics*, Dover Publications Inc., New York, 1959.

8. M. Abramowitz and I. A. Stegun, *Handbook of Mathematical Functions*, National Bureau of Standards, Applied Mathematic Series 55, U.S. Government Printing Office, Washington, D.C., 20402, 1964.

9. E. W. Hobson, *The Theory of Spherical and Ellipsoidal Harmonics*, Cambridge University Press, 1932.

10. G. Sansone, *Orthogonal Functions*, Interscience Publishers, Inc., New York, 1959.

11. H. Bateman, *Partial Differential Equations of Mathematical Physics*, Dover Publications, New York, 1944.

12. W. Magnus and F. Oberhettinger, *Formulas and Theorems for the Special Functions of Mathematical Physics*, Chelsea Publishing Co., New York, 1949.

13. I. N. Sneddon, *Special Functions of Mathematical Physics and Chemistry*, Oliver and Boyd, London, 1961.

14. E. W. Barnes, *Quart. J. Pure Apl. Math.* **39**, 97–204, 1908.

15. O. Rodrigues, *Corr. Ec. Roy. Polytech.* **III**, 1816.

16. Bholanath Pal, *Bull. Calcutta Math. Soc.* **9**, 85–95, 1917; Part II in **10**, 187–194, 1918.

PROBLEMS

4-1 By making use of the Rodrigues' formula given by equation (4-21) show that the integral

$$I \equiv \int_{-1}^{1} f(\mu)P_n(\mu)\, d\mu$$

when performed by repeated integrations by parts can be expressed in the form

$$I = (-1)^n \frac{1}{2^n n!} \int_{-1}^{1} (\mu^2 - 1)^n \frac{d^n f(\mu)}{d\mu^n} d\mu$$

4-2 Consider the heat-conduction problem for a spherical cavity $a \leq r < \infty$ given in the form

$$\frac{1}{r} \frac{\partial^2}{\partial r^2}(rT) + \frac{g(r)}{k} = \frac{1}{\alpha} \frac{\partial T}{\partial t} \qquad \text{in } a < r < \infty, \; t > 0$$

$$-\frac{\partial T}{\partial r} + HT = f_1 \qquad \text{at } r = a, \; t > 0$$

$$T = F(r) \qquad \text{for } t = 0, \; \text{in } a \leq r < \infty$$

By utilizing the transformations $U = rT$ and $x = r - a$, transform the above problem to the problem of heat conduction in a semi-infinite medium in the rectangular coordinate system.

4-3 A hollow sphere $a \leq r \leq b$ is initially at temperature $F(r)$. For times $t > 0$ the boundary surface at $r = a$ is kept insulated and the boundary at $r = b$ dissipates heat by convection into a medium at zero temperature. Obtain an expression for the temperature distribution $T(r, t)$ in the sphere.

4-4 A solid sphere of radius $r = b$ is initially at a temperature $F(r)$. For times the boundary surface at $r = b$ is kept at zero temperature. Obtain an expression for the temperature distribution $T(r, t)$ in the sphere for times $t > 0$.

4-5 Obtain an expression for the temperature distribution $T(r, \mu, t)$ in a solid sphere of radius $r = b$ which is initially at temperature $F(r, \mu)$ and for times $t > 0$ the boundary surface at $r = b$ is kept insulated.

4-6 Obtain an expression for the temperature distribution $T(r, \mu, t)$ in a solid hemisphere, $0 \leq \mu \leq 1, 0 \leq r \leq b$, which is initially at temperature $F(r, \mu)$ and for times $t > 0$ the boundary at the spherical surface $r = b$ is kept at zero temperature and at the base $\mu = 0$ is kept insulated.

4-7 A solid sphere of radius $r = b$ is initially at a temperature $F(r, \mu, \phi)$. For times $t > 0$ the boundary surface $r = b$ dissipates heat by convection into a medium at zero temperature. Obtain an expression for the temperature distribution $T(r, \mu, \phi, t)$ in the sphere for times $t > 0$.

4-8 Solve Problem (4-7) for the case when the boundary surface at $r = b$ is kept insulated.

4-9 The part of the sphere cut out by the cone $\theta = \theta_0$ as illustrated in Fig. 4-2 is initially at temperature $F(r, \mu)$. For times $t > 0$, all the boundary surfaces are kept at zero temperature. Obtain an expression for the temperature distribution $T(r, \mu, t)$ for times $t > 0$.

4-10 The portion of the sphere cut out by the cone $\theta = \theta_0$ as illustrated in Fig. 4-2 is initially at temperature $F(r, \mu, \phi)$. For times $t > 0$, the boundary surface at $r = b$ is kept insulated and the boundary surface at $\mu = \mu_0$ is kept at zero temperature. Obtain an expression for the temperature distribution $T(r, \mu, \phi, t)$ for times $t > 0$.

4-11   Solve the Problem (4-10) for the case when the boundary surface at $r = b$ is kept at zero temperature and the boundary surface at $\mu = \mu_0$ is kept insulated.

4-12   Solve the problem (4-10) for the case when the boundary surface at $r = b$ is kept at temperature T_0 and the boundary surface at $\mu = \mu_0$ is kept insulated.

4-13   Determine the steady-state temperature distribution $T(r, \mu)$ in a solid hemisphere of radius $r = b$, in the region $0 \le r \le b, 0 \le \mu \le 1$, with its spherical surface at $r = b$ kept at temperature $f(\mu)$ and its base at $\mu = 0$ is kept at zero temperature.

4-14   Obtain an expression for the steady-state temperature $T(r, \mu)$ in a solid sphere of radius $r = b$ when the boundary surface at $r = b$ is kept at T_0 for $0 < \mu < 1$ and at zero temperature for $-1 < \mu < 0$.

4-15   A solid sphere of radius $r = b$ is initially at a uniform temperature $F(r)$. For times $t > 0$ the boundary surface at $r = b$ is kept at a constant temperature T_b. Obtain an expression for the temperature distribution $T(r, t)$ in the sphere.

4-16   A solid sphere of radius $r = b$ is initially at temperature $F(r)$. For times $t > 0$, the heat transfer at the boundary surface $r = b$ is given by $(\partial T / \partial r) + HT = f_b$, where f_b is constant. Obtain an expression for the temperature distribution $T(r, t)$ in the sphere.

4-17   A hollow sphere $a \le r \le b$ is initially at temperature $F(r)$. For times $t > 0$, heat is generated in the region at a constant rate of g_0 per unit volume and the boundary surfaces at $r = a$ and $r = b$ are kept at uniform temperatures T_a and T_b, respectively. Obtain an expression for the temperature distribution $T(r, t)$ in the sphere.

NOTES

1.   The hypergeometric function $F(\alpha, \beta, \gamma, x)$ is defined by means of the hypergeometric series as

$$F(\alpha, \beta, \gamma, x) = 1 + \frac{\alpha \cdot \beta}{1 \cdot \gamma} x + \frac{[\alpha(\alpha + 1)][\beta(\beta + 1)]}{1 \cdot 2 \cdot \gamma(\gamma + 1)} x^2$$
$$+ \frac{[\alpha(\alpha + 1)(\alpha + 2)][\beta(\beta + 1)(\beta + 2)]}{1 \cdot 2 \cdot 3 \cdot \gamma(\gamma + 1)(\gamma + 2)} x^3 + \dots \quad (1)$$

or

$$F(\alpha, \beta, \gamma, x) = 1 + \sum_{r=1}^{\infty} \frac{(\alpha)_r (\beta)_r}{r!(\gamma)_r} x^r \tag{2}$$

where

$$(\alpha)_r \equiv \alpha(\alpha + 1)(\alpha + 2)\ldots(\alpha + r - 1) \tag{3}$$

which is absolutely convergent if $|x| < 1$. If $|x| = 1$, it converges absolutely if $\gamma - \alpha - \beta > 0$.

If x is replaced by $(1 - \mu)$, then the series is convergent at $\mu = 1$ and has a value 1 at $\mu = 1$.

From the definition given by equation (2) it is obvious that

$$F(\alpha, \beta, \gamma, x) = F(\beta, \alpha, \gamma, x) \tag{4}$$

$$F(\alpha, \beta, \gamma, 0) = 1 \tag{5}$$

The derivative of $F(\gamma, \beta, \gamma, x)$ with respect to x is given as

$$\frac{d}{dx} F(\alpha, \beta, \gamma, x) = \frac{\alpha\beta}{\gamma} F(\alpha + 1, \beta + 1, \gamma + 1, x) \tag{6}$$

The generalization of this result to the mth derivative gives

$$\frac{d^m}{dx^m} F(\alpha, \beta, \gamma, x) = \frac{(\alpha)_m (\beta)_m}{(\gamma)_m} F(\alpha + m, \beta + m, \gamma + m, x) \tag{7}$$

and

$$\left[\frac{d^m}{dx^m} F(\alpha, \beta, \gamma, x) \right]_{x=0} = \frac{(\alpha)_m (\beta)_m}{(\gamma)_m}$$

where

$$(\alpha_m) \equiv \alpha(\alpha + 1)(\alpha + 2)\ldots(\alpha + m - 1), \text{ etc.}$$

Here we used the notation $F(\alpha, \beta, \gamma, x)$ to denote the hypergeometric series; the notation ${}_2F_1(\alpha, \beta, \gamma, x)$ has also been used in some texts.

2. The proof of the orthogonality relation for the $P_n^{-m}(\mu)$ functions, given by equations (4-54) is as follows. Let,

$$M(\mu) \equiv P_n^{-m}(\mu) \quad \text{and} \quad M'(\mu) \equiv P_{n'}^{-m}(\mu) \tag{1}$$

These functions satisfy the Legendre's associated differential equation

$$\frac{d}{d\mu} \left[(1 - \mu^2) \frac{dM}{d\mu} \right] + \left[n(n + 1) - \frac{m^2}{1 - \mu^2} \right] M = 0 \tag{2}$$

$$\frac{d}{d\mu} \left[(1 - \mu^2) \frac{dM'}{d\mu} \right] + \left[n'(n' + 1) - \frac{m^2}{1 - \mu^2} \right] M' = 0 \tag{3}$$

Multiply the first equation by M', the second by M, subtract and integrate between the limits μ_0 and 1; we obtain

$$[n'(n'+1) - n(n+1)]\int_{\mu_0}^{1} MM' d\mu = \int_{\mu_0}^{1} M' \frac{d}{d\mu}\left[(1-\mu^2)\frac{dM}{d\mu}\right]$$
$$- M\frac{d}{d\mu}\left[(1-\mu^2)\frac{dM'}{d\mu}\right] d\mu \qquad (4a)$$

or

$$(n'-n)(n'+n+1)\int_{\mu_0}^{1} MM' d\mu = \left[(1-\mu^2)\left(M'\frac{dM}{d\mu} - M\frac{dM'}{d\mu}\right)\right]_{\mu_0}^{1} \qquad (4b)$$

The right-hand side vanishes at the upper limit; then

$$(n'-n)(n'+n+1)\int_{\mu_0}^{1} MM' d\mu = -(1-\mu_0^2)\left[M'\frac{dM}{d\mu} - M\frac{dM'}{d\mu}\right]_{\mu=\mu_0} \qquad (5)$$

When n, n' are the two different roots of equation

$$\left[P_n^{-m}(\mu)\right]_{\mu=\mu_0} = 0 \qquad (6a)$$

or when n, n' are the two different roots of the equation

$$\left[\frac{dP_n^{-m}(\mu)}{d\mu}\right]_{\mu=\mu_0} = 0 \qquad (6b)$$

the right-hand side of equation (5) vanishes and we obtain

$$\int_{\mu_0}^{1} P_n^{-m}(\mu)P_{n'}^{-m}(\mu) d\mu = 0 \qquad \text{for } n \neq n' \qquad (7)$$

which is the orthogonality relation given by equation (4-54a). To determine the norm, we should evaluate equation (5) for $n' \to n$; to perform this calculation we consider below separately the cases of the boundary condition of the first kind given by equation (6a) and the boundary condition of the second kind given by equation (6b).

1. *The boundary condition of $\mu = \mu_0$ is of the first kind.* We have

$$\left[P_n^{-m}(\mu)\right]_{\mu=\mu_0} = 0 \qquad (8)$$

then, as $n' \to n$, equation (5) is written as

$$N(m,n) \equiv \int_{\mu_0}^{1} \left[P_n^{-m}(\mu)\right]^2 d\mu = -\frac{1-\mu_0^2}{2n+1}\lim_{n' \to n}\left\{\frac{1}{n'-n}\left[P_{n'}^{-m}\frac{dP_n^{-m}}{d\mu}\right]_{\mu=\mu_0}\right\} \qquad (9)$$

To evaluate the limit as $n' \to n$, we differentiate the numerator and denominator with respect to n' and obtain

$$N(m,n) = -\frac{1-\mu_0^2}{2n+1}\left[\frac{dP_n^{-m}(\mu)}{dn}\frac{dP_n^{-m}(\mu)}{d\mu}\right]_{\mu=\mu_0} \tag{10}$$

which is the result given by equation (4-55).

2. *Boundary condition at $\mu = \mu_0$ is of the second kind.* We have

$$\left[\frac{dP_n^{-m}(\mu)}{d\mu}\right]_{\mu=\mu_0} = 0 \tag{11}$$

then, as $n' \to n$, equation (5) is written as

$$N(m,n) \equiv \int_{\mu_0}^1 [P_n^{-m}(\mu)]^2\,d\mu = \frac{1-\mu_0^2}{2n+1}\lim_{n'\to n}\left\{\frac{1}{n'-n}\left[P_n^{-m}(\mu)\frac{dP_{n'}^{-m}(\mu)}{d\mu}\right]_{\mu=\mu_0}\right\} \tag{12}$$

To evaluate the limit as $n' \to n$ we differentiate numerator and denominator with respect to n' and obtain

$$N(m,n) = \frac{1-\mu_0^2}{2n+1}\left[P_n^{-m}(\mu)\frac{d^2P_n^{-m}(\mu)}{dn\,d\mu}\right]_{\mu=\mu_0} \tag{13}$$

which is the result given by equation (4-56).

3. Equations (4-65) for $H = 0$ becomes

$$\frac{\partial^2 U}{\partial r^2} = \frac{1}{\alpha}\frac{\partial U}{\partial t} \qquad \text{in } 0 < r < b,\ t > 0 \tag{1a}$$

$$U = 0 \qquad \text{at } r = 0,\ t > 0 \tag{1b}$$

$$\frac{\partial U}{\partial r} - \frac{1}{b}U = 0 \qquad \text{at } r = b,\ t > 0 \tag{1c}$$

$$U = rF(r) \qquad \text{for } t = 0,\ \text{in } 0 \le r \le b \tag{1d}$$

Appropriate eigenvalue problem for the solution of this system is given as

$$\frac{d^2R_m}{dr^2} + \beta_m^2 R_m = 0 \qquad \text{in } 0 < r < b \tag{2a}$$

$$R_m = 0 \qquad \text{at } r = 0 \tag{2b}$$

$$\frac{dR_m}{dr} - \frac{1}{b}R_m = 0 \qquad \text{at } r = b \tag{2c}$$

The solution of system (1) is obtainable according to equation (2-13) of

Chapter 2 as

$$U(r,t) = \sum_{m=0}^{\infty} e^{-\alpha \beta_m^2 t} \frac{1}{N(\beta_m)} R(\beta_m, r) \int_0^b R(\beta_m, r') r' F(r') \, dr' \tag{3a}$$

where

$$N(\beta_m) = \int_0^b [R(\beta_m, r)]^2 \, dr \tag{3b}$$

and $m = 0, 1, 2, 3, \ldots$. For $\beta_m \neq 0$, the eigenvalues β_m and the eigenfunctions $R(\beta_m, r)$ are obtainable from Table 2-2 of Chapter 2. However, for $\beta_m = 0$, equations (2) have a solution $R(\beta_m, r) = r$. Then, the solution (3) includes a term corresponding to the zero eigenvalue and takes the form

$$U(r,t) = \frac{r \int_0^b r'^2 F(r') \, dr'}{\int_0^b r'^2 \, dr'} + \sum_{m=1}^{\infty} \frac{e^{-\alpha \beta_m^2 t}}{N(\beta_m)} R(\beta_m, r) \int_0^b R(\beta_m, r') r' F(r') \, dr' \tag{4}$$

$U(r,t)$ being related to the temperature by $U(r,t) = rT(r,t)$, equation (4) becomes

$$T(r,t) = \frac{3}{b^3} \int_0^b r^2 F(r) \, dr + \frac{1}{r} \sum_{m=1}^{\infty} \frac{e^{-\alpha \beta_m^2 t}}{N(\beta_m)} R(\beta_m, r) \int_0^b R(\beta_m, r') r' F(r') \, dr' \tag{5}$$

Thus, the first term on the right is the mean of the initial temperature distribution over the volume of the sphere.

CHAPTER 5

THE USE OF DUHAMEL'S THEOREM

The solution of a heat-conduction problem with time-dependent boundary conditions and/or time-dependent heat generation can be related to the solution of the same problem with time-independent boundary conditions and/or heat generation by means of Duhamel's theorem. A proof of Duhamel's theorem is given in several references [1; 2, p. 162; 3, p. 30]. Here we present a statement of Duhamel's theorem, give its proof, and illustrate its application in the solution of heat-conduction problems with time-dependent boundary conditions and/or heat generation.

5-1 THE STATEMENT OF DUHAMEL'S THEOREM

Consider the three-dimensional, nonhomogeneous heat-conduction problem in a region R with time-dependent boundary condition and heat generation given in the form

$$\nabla^2 T(\mathbf{r}, t) + \frac{1}{k}g(\mathbf{r}, t) = \frac{1}{\alpha}\frac{\partial T(\mathbf{r}, t)}{\partial t} \qquad \text{in region } R, \ t > 0 \qquad (5\text{-}1a)$$

$$k_i\frac{\partial T}{\partial n_i} + h_i T = f_i(\mathbf{r}, t) \qquad \text{on boundary } S_i, \ t > 0 \qquad (5\text{-}1b)$$

$$T(\mathbf{r}, t) = F(\mathbf{r}) \qquad \text{for } t = 0, \text{ in region } R \qquad (5\text{-}1c)$$

where $\partial/\partial n_i$ is the derivative along outward-drawn normal to the boundary surface $S_i, i = 1, 2, \ldots, s$ and s being the number of continuous boundary surfaces of the region R. Here k_i and h_i are coefficients that are assumed to be constant. By setting $k_i = 0$ we obtain boundary condition of the first kind, and by setting $h_i = 0$ we obtain boundary condition of the second kind.

The problem given by equations (5-1) cannot be solved by the techniques described in the previous chapters because the nonhomogeneous terms

$g(\mathbf{r}, t)$ and $f_i(\mathbf{r}, t)$ depend on time. Therefore, instead of solving this problem directly, we express its solution in terms of the solution of the simpler auxiliary problem as now defined. Let $\Phi(\mathbf{r}, t, \tau)$ be the solution of problem (5-1) on the assumption that the nonhomogeneous terms $g(\mathbf{r}, \tau)$ and $f_i(\mathbf{r}, \tau)$ do not depend on time; namely, the variable τ is merely a parameter but not a time variable. Then, $\Phi(\mathbf{r}, t, \tau)$ is the solution of the following simpler auxiliary problem

$$\nabla^2 \Phi(\mathbf{r}, t, \tau) + \frac{1}{k} g(\mathbf{r}, \tau) = \frac{1}{\alpha} \frac{\partial \Phi(\mathbf{r}, t, \tau)}{\partial t} \qquad \text{in region } R, \ t > 0 \qquad (5\text{-}2a)$$

$$k_i \frac{\partial \Phi(\mathbf{r}, t, \tau)}{\partial n_i} + h_i \Phi(\mathbf{r}, t, \tau) = f_i(\mathbf{r}, \tau) \qquad \text{on boundary } S_i, \ t > 0 \quad (5\text{-}2b)$$

$$\Phi(\mathbf{r}, t, \tau) = F(\mathbf{r}) \qquad \text{for } t = 0, \text{ in region } R \qquad (5\text{-}2c)$$

where $\partial/\partial n_i$ and S_i as defined previously, and the function $\Phi(\mathbf{r}, t, \tau)$ depends on τ because $g(\mathbf{r}, \tau)$ and $f_i(\mathbf{r}, \tau)$ depend on τ.

The problem (5-2) can be solved with the techniques described in the previous chapters because $g(\mathbf{r}, \tau)$ and $f(\mathbf{r}, \tau)$ do not depend on time. Suppose the solution $\Phi(\mathbf{r}, t, \tau)$ of the auxiliary problem (5-2) is available. Then, Duhamel's theorem relates the solution $T(\mathbf{r}, t)$ of the problem (5-1) to the solution $\Phi(\mathbf{r}, t, \tau)$ of the problem (5-2) by the following integral expression

$$T(\mathbf{r}, t) = \frac{\partial}{\partial t} \int_{\tau=0}^{t} \Phi(\mathbf{r}, t - \tau, \tau) \, d\tau \qquad (5\text{-}3)$$

This result can be expressed in the alternative form by performing the differentiation under the integral sign; we obtain

$$T(\mathbf{r}, t) = F(\mathbf{r}) + \int_{\tau=0}^{t} \frac{\partial}{\partial t} \Phi(\mathbf{r}, t - \tau, \tau) \, d\tau \qquad (5\text{-}4)$$

since

$$\Phi(\mathbf{r}, t - \tau, \tau)\big|_{\tau=t} = \Phi(\mathbf{r}, 0, \tau) = F(\mathbf{r})$$

We now examine some special cases of Duhamel's theorem given by equation (5-4).

1. *Initial temperature zero.* For this special case we have $F(\mathbf{r}) = 0$ and equation (5-4) reduces to

$$T(\mathbf{r}, t) = \int_{\tau=0}^{t} \frac{\partial}{\partial t} \Phi(\mathbf{r}, t - \tau, \tau) \, d\tau \qquad (5\text{-}5)$$

2. *Initial temperature zero, problem has only one nonhomogeneity.* The solid is initially at zero temperature and the problem involves only one non-homogeneous term. Namely, if there is heat generation, all the boundary conditions for the problem are homogeneous; or, if there is no heat generation in the medium, only one of the boundary conditions is nonhomogeneous. For example, we consider a problem in which there is no heat generation, but one of the boundary conditions, say, the one at the boundary surface S_1 is nonhomogeneous.

$$\nabla^2 T(\mathbf{r}, t) = \frac{1}{\alpha} \frac{\partial T(\mathbf{r}, t)}{\partial t} \qquad \text{in region } R, \ t > 0 \tag{5-6a}$$

$$k_i \frac{\partial T}{\partial n_i} + h_i T = \delta_{1i} f_i(t) \qquad \text{on boundary } S_i, \ t > 0 \tag{5-6b}$$

$$T(\mathbf{r}, t) = 0 \qquad \text{for } t = 0, \ \text{in region } R \tag{5-6c}$$

where $i = 1, 2, \ldots, s$ and δ_{1i} is the kronecker delta defined as

$$\delta_{1i} = \begin{cases} 0 & i \neq 1 \\ 1 & i = 1 \end{cases}$$

The corresponding auxiliary problem is taken as

$$\nabla^2 \Phi(\mathbf{r}, t) = \frac{1}{\alpha} \frac{\partial \Phi(\mathbf{r}, t)}{\partial t} \qquad \text{in region } R, \ t > 0 \tag{5-7a}$$

$$k_i \frac{\partial \Phi}{\partial n_i} + h_i \Phi = \delta_{1i} \qquad \text{on boundary } S_i, \ t > 0 \tag{5-7b}$$

$$\Phi(\mathbf{r}, t) = 0 \qquad \text{for } t = 0, \ \text{in region } R \tag{5-7c}$$

Then, the solution $T(\mathbf{r}, t)$ of the problem (5-6) is related to the solution $\Phi(\mathbf{r}, t)$ of the problem (5-7) by

$$T(\mathbf{r}, t) = \int_{\tau=0}^{t} f(\tau) \frac{\partial \Phi(\mathbf{r}, t - \tau)}{\partial t} d\tau \tag{5-8}$$

The validity of this result is apparent from the fact that if $\Phi(\mathbf{r}, t, \tau)$ is the solution of the problem (5-7) for a boundary condition $\delta_{1i} f_i(\tau)$, then $\Phi(\mathbf{r}, t, \tau)$ is related to $\Phi(\mathbf{r}, t)$ by

$$\Phi(\mathbf{r}, t, \tau) = f(\tau) \Phi(\mathbf{r}, t) \tag{5-9}$$

When equation (5-9) is introduced into equation (5-5), the result (5-8) is obtained.

5-2 A PROOF OF DUHAMEL'S THEOREM

A proof of Duhamel's theorem is given in reference [1] by using the Laplace transform technique. In this book, the Laplace transform technique is considered in a later chapter. However, the presentation of the proof of Duhamel's theorem here does not pose any difficulty, because only few elementary properties of the Laplace transform is needed for this purpose. Therefore, before starting the analysis we summarize below those properties of the Laplace transformation that are needed for this proof.

The Laplace transform with respect to time of a function $H(t)$ is defined as

$$\mathscr{L}[H(t)] \equiv \bar{H}(s) = \int_0^\infty e^{-st} H(t)\, dt \qquad (5\text{-}10)$$

where s is the Laplace transform variable and the bar is used as an abreviation to denote the transform. The Laplace transform of the derivative $dH(t)/dt$ is given by

$$\mathscr{L}\left[\frac{dH(t)}{dt}\right] = s\bar{H}(s) - H(0) \qquad (5\text{-}11)$$

where $H(0)$ is the value of $H(t)$ at time $t = 0^+$. The Laplace transform of a constant c is given as

$$\mathscr{L}[c] \equiv \bar{c} = \frac{c}{s} \qquad (5\text{-}12)$$

Then, the Laplace transform of equations (5-1) becomes

$$\nabla^2 \bar{T}(\mathbf{r}, s) + \frac{1}{k}\bar{g}(\mathbf{r}, s) = \frac{1}{\alpha}\left[s\bar{T}(\mathbf{r}, s) - F(\mathbf{r})\right] \qquad \text{in region } R \qquad (5\text{-}13a)$$

$$k_i\frac{\partial \bar{T}}{\partial n_i} + h_i\bar{T} = \bar{f}_i(\mathbf{r}, s) \qquad \text{on } S_i \qquad (5\text{-}13b)$$

where $\bar{T}(\mathbf{r}, s)$ is the Laplace transform of the function $T(\mathbf{r}, t)$. Similarly, the Laplace transform of equations (5-2), noting $g(\mathbf{r}, \tau)$ and $f_i(\mathbf{r}, \tau)$ are independent of time, yields

$$\nabla^2 \bar{\Phi}(\mathbf{r}, s, \tau) + \frac{1}{sk}g(\mathbf{r}, \tau) = \frac{1}{\alpha}\left[s\bar{\Phi}(\mathbf{r}, s, \tau) - F(\mathbf{r})\right] \qquad \text{in region } R \qquad (5\text{-}14a)$$

$$k_i\frac{\partial \bar{\Phi}}{\partial n_i} + h_i\bar{\Phi} = \frac{1}{s}f_i(\mathbf{r}.\,\tau) \qquad \text{on } S_i \qquad (5\text{-}14b)$$

We now operate on both sides of equations (5-14) by the operator

$$\int_0^\infty e^{-s\tau} d\tau$$

and utilize the definition of the Laplace transform given by equation (5-10). We obtain

$$\nabla^2 \bar{\bar{\Phi}}(\mathbf{r}, s) + \frac{1}{sk} \bar{g}(\mathbf{r}, s) = \frac{1}{\alpha}\left[s\bar{\bar{\Phi}}(\mathbf{r}, s) - \frac{F(\mathbf{r})}{s} \right] \qquad \text{in region } R \qquad (5\text{-}15a)$$

$$k_i \frac{\partial \bar{\bar{\Phi}}}{\partial n_i} + h_i \bar{\bar{\Phi}} = \frac{1}{s} \bar{f}_i(\mathbf{r}, s) \qquad\qquad\qquad \text{on } S_i \qquad (5\text{-}15b)$$

since $\bar{\bar{\Phi}}(\mathbf{r}, s, s) = \bar{\bar{\Phi}}(\mathbf{r}, s)$; here the double transform is defined as

$$\bar{\bar{\Phi}}(\mathbf{r}, s) = \int_0^\infty \int_0^\infty e^{-(\tau+t)s} \Phi(\mathbf{r}, t, \tau) \, dt \, d\tau \qquad (5\text{-}16)$$

We multiply both sides of equations (5-15) by s and rearrange it in the form

$$\nabla^2 [s\bar{\bar{\Phi}}(\mathbf{r}, s)] + \frac{1}{k}\bar{g}(\mathbf{r}, s) = \frac{1}{\alpha}\{s[s\bar{\bar{\Phi}}(\mathbf{r}, s)] - F(\mathbf{r})\} \qquad \text{in region } R \qquad (5\text{-}19a)$$

$$k_i \frac{\partial}{\partial n_i}(s\bar{\bar{\Phi}}) + h_i(s\bar{\bar{\Phi}}) = \bar{f}_i(\mathbf{r}, s) \qquad\qquad\qquad \text{on } S_i \qquad (5\text{-}19b)$$

A comparison of equations (5-13) and (5-19) reveals that they are identical problems if the function $\bar{T}(\mathbf{r}, s)$ is taken identical to $s\bar{\bar{\Phi}}(\mathbf{r}, s)$; namely, if

$$\bar{T}(\mathbf{r}, s) = s\bar{\bar{\Phi}}(\mathbf{r}, s) \qquad (5\text{-}20)$$

Introducing equation (5-16) into (5-20), we obtain

$$\bar{T}(\mathbf{r}, s) = s \int_0^\infty \int_0^\infty e^{-(\tau+t)s} \Phi(\mathbf{r}, t, \tau) \, dt \, d\tau \qquad (5\text{-}21a)$$

or

$$\mathscr{L}[T(\mathbf{r}, t)] = s \int_0^\infty \int_0^\infty e^{-(\tau+t)s} \Phi(\mathbf{r}, t, \tau) \, dt \, d\tau \qquad (5\text{-}21b)$$

To invert this result into the time domain t we now make use of the following properties of the Laplace transform.

Consider a function $\Phi(\mathbf{r}, t, \tau)$. The *generalized convolution* $\Phi^*(\mathbf{r}, t)$ of this function is defined as [1, p. 276]

$$\Phi^*(\mathbf{r}, t) \equiv \int_{\tau=0}^{t} \Phi(\mathbf{r}, t - \tau, \tau) \, d\tau \qquad (5\text{-}22)$$

The Laplace transform of this generalized convolution $\Phi^*(\mathbf{r}, t)$ is given as [1]

$$\mathscr{L}[\Phi^*(\mathbf{r}, t)] \equiv \bar{\Phi}^*(\mathbf{r}, s) = \int_0^\infty \int_0^\infty e^{-(t+\tau)s}\Phi(\mathbf{r}, t, \tau)\,dt\,d\tau \tag{5-23}$$

By comparing the integral term on the right-hand side of equation (5-21b) with that in equation (5-23), we note that equation (5-21b) can be written as

$$\mathscr{L}[T(\mathbf{r}, t)] = s\bar{\Phi}^*(\mathbf{r}, s) \tag{5-24}$$

By comparing the right-hand side of equation (5-24) with that of equation (5-11) and noting that $\Phi^*(\mathbf{r}, 0) = 0$ by equation (5-22), we write equation (5-24) as

$$\mathscr{L}[T(\mathbf{r}, t)] = \mathscr{L}\left[\frac{\partial\Phi^*(\mathbf{r}, t)}{\partial t}\right] \tag{5-25}$$

This result is now inverted as

$$T(\mathbf{r}, t) = \frac{\partial\Phi^*(\mathbf{r}, t)}{\partial t} \tag{5-26}$$

Finally, by introducing equation (5-22) into equation (5-26) we obtain

$$T(\mathbf{r}, t) = \frac{\partial}{\partial t}\int_{\tau=0}^t \Phi(\mathbf{r}, t-\tau, \tau)\,d\tau \tag{5-27}$$

which is the Duhamel's theorem given by equation (5-3).

5-3 APPLICATIONS OF DUHAMEL'S THEOREM

We now illustrate with examples the application of Duhamel's theorem for the solution of heat-conduction problems with time-dependent boundary conditions and/or heat-generation term.

Example 5-1. A semi-infinite solid, $0 \leq x < \infty$, is initially at zero temperature. For times $t > 0$ the boundary surface at $x = 0$ is kept at temperature $f(t)$. Obtain an expression for the temperature distribution $T(x, t)$ in the solid for times $t > 0$.

Solution. The mathematical formulation of this problem is given as

$$\frac{\partial^2 T(x, t)}{\partial x^2} = \frac{1}{\alpha}\frac{\partial T(x, t)}{\partial t} \qquad \text{in } 0 < x < \infty,\ t > 0 \tag{5-28a}$$

$$T(x, t) = f(t) \qquad \text{at } x = 0,\ t > 0 \tag{5-28b}$$

$$T(x, t) = 0 \qquad \text{for } t = 0,\ \text{in } 0 \leq x < \infty \tag{5-28c}$$

The auxiliary problem is taken as

$$\frac{\partial^2 \Phi(x,t)}{\partial x^2} = \frac{1}{\alpha}\frac{\partial \Phi(x,t)}{\partial t} \qquad \text{in } 0 < x < \infty, \ t > 0 \qquad (5\text{-}29\text{a})$$

$$\Phi(x,t) = 1 \qquad\qquad\qquad \text{at } x = 0, \ t > 0 \qquad (5\text{-}29\text{b})$$

$$\Phi(x,t) = 0 \qquad\qquad\qquad \text{for } t = 0, \text{ in } 0 \le x < \infty \qquad (5\text{-}29\text{c})$$

Then the solution of the problem (5-28) is given in terms of the solution of the problem (5-29), by the Duhamel's theorem (5-8) as

$$T(x,t) = \int_{\tau=0}^{t} f(\tau)\frac{\partial \Phi(x, t-\tau)}{\partial t}\,d\tau \qquad (5\text{-}30)$$

The solution $\Phi(x,t)$ of the auxiliary problem (5-29) is obtainable from the solution $T(x,t)$ given by equation (2-62) by the relation $\Phi(x,t) = 1 - T(x,t)$, and setting in equation (2-62) $T_0 = 1$. Thus we obtain

$$\Phi(x,t) = 1 - \text{erf}\left(\frac{x}{\sqrt{4\alpha t}}\right) = \text{erfc}\left(\frac{x}{\sqrt{4\alpha t}}\right) = \frac{2}{\sqrt{\pi}}\int_{x/\sqrt{4\alpha t}}^{\infty} e^{-\xi^2}\,d\xi \qquad (5\text{-}31)$$

Then,

$$\frac{\partial \Phi(x, t-\tau)}{\partial t} = \frac{x}{\sqrt{4\pi\alpha}(t-\tau)^{3/2}}\exp\left[-\frac{x^2}{4\alpha(t-\tau)}\right] \qquad (5\text{-}32)$$

Introducing equation (5-32) into equation (5-30) the solution of the problem (5-28) becomes

$$T(x,t) = \frac{x}{\sqrt{4\pi\alpha}}\int_{\tau=0}^{t}\frac{f(\tau)}{(t-\tau)^{3/2}}\exp\left[-\frac{x^2}{4\alpha(t-\tau)}\right]d\tau \qquad (5\text{-}33)$$

This result can be put into a different form by defining a new variable as

$$\eta = \frac{x}{\sqrt{4\alpha(t-\tau)}} \qquad (5\text{-}34\text{a})$$

$$t - \tau = \frac{x^2}{4\alpha\eta^2} \qquad \text{and} \qquad d\tau = \frac{2}{\eta}(t-\tau)\,d\eta \qquad (5\text{-}34\text{b})$$

Introducing equations (5-34) into equation (5-33), we obtain

$$T(x,t) = \frac{2}{\sqrt{\pi}}\int_{x/\sqrt{4\alpha t}}^{\infty} e^{-\eta^2}f\left(t - \frac{x^2}{4\alpha\eta^2}\right)d\eta \qquad (5\text{-}35)$$

We now consider a special case of solution (5-35): If the surface temperature is a periodic function of time in the form

$$f(t) = T_0 \cos(\omega t - \beta) \tag{5-36}$$

The solution (3-5) becomes

$$\frac{T(x,t)}{T_0} = \frac{2}{\sqrt{\pi}} \int_{x/\sqrt{4\alpha t}}^{\infty} e^{-\eta^2} \cos\left[\omega\left(t - \frac{x^2}{4\alpha\eta^2} \right) - \beta \right] d\eta \tag{5-37a}$$

or

$$\frac{T(x,t)}{T_0} = \frac{2}{\sqrt{\pi}} \int_0^{\infty} e^{-\eta^2} \cos\left[\omega\left(t - \frac{x^2}{4\alpha\eta^2} \right) - \beta \right] d\eta$$

$$- \frac{2}{\sqrt{\pi}} \int_0^{x/\sqrt{4\alpha t}} e^{-\eta^2} \cos\left[\omega\left(t - \frac{x^2}{4\alpha\eta^2} \right) - \beta \right] d\eta \tag{5-37b}$$

The first definite integral can be evaluated [3, p. 65]; then

$$\frac{T(x,t)}{T_0} = \exp\left[-x\left(\frac{\omega}{2\alpha}\right)^{1/2} \right] \cos\left[\omega t - x\left(\frac{\omega}{2\alpha}\right)^{1/2} - \beta \right]$$

$$- \frac{2}{\sqrt{\pi}} \int_0^{x/\sqrt{4\alpha t}} e^{-\eta^2} \cos\left[\omega\left(t - \frac{x^2}{4\alpha\eta^2} \right) - \beta \right] d\eta \tag{5-38}$$

Here the second term on the right represents the transients that die away as $t \to \infty$, and the first term represents the steady oscillations of temperature in the medium after the transients have passed.

Example 5-2. A slab, $0 \le x \le L$, is initially at zero temperature. For times $t > 0$ the boundary surfaces at $x = 0$ and $x = L$ are kept at temperatures $f_1(t)$ and $f_2(t)$, respectively. Obtain an expression for the temperature distribution $T(x,t)$ in the slab for times $t > 0$.

Solution. The mathematical formulation of this problem is given as

$$\frac{\partial^2 T(x,t)}{\partial x^2} = \frac{1}{\alpha}\frac{\partial T(x,t)}{\partial t} \qquad \text{in } 0 < x < L, \ t > 0 \tag{5-39a}$$

$$T(x,t) = f_1(t) \qquad \text{at } x = 0, \ t > 0 \tag{5-39b}$$

$$T(x,t) = f_2(t) \qquad \text{at } x = L, \ t > 0 \tag{5-39c}$$

$$T(x,t) = 0 \qquad \text{for } t = 0, \ \text{in } 0 \le x \le L \tag{5-39d}$$

The auxiliary problem is taken as

$$\frac{\partial^2 \Phi(x,t,\tau)}{\partial x^2} = \frac{1}{\alpha}\frac{\partial \Phi(x,t,\tau)}{\partial t} \qquad \text{in } 0 < x < L, \ t > 0 \tag{5-40a}$$

$$\Phi(x,t,\tau) = f_1(\tau) \qquad\qquad \text{at } x = 0, \ t > 0 \qquad (5\text{-}40b)$$

$$\Phi(x,t,\tau) = f_2(\tau) \qquad\qquad \text{at } x = L, \ t > 0 \qquad (5\text{-}40c)$$

$$\Phi(x,t,\tau) = 0 \qquad\qquad \text{for } t = 0, \text{ in } 0 \le x \le L \qquad (5\text{-}40d)$$

where $f_1(\tau)$ and $f_2(\tau)$ are considered independent of time. The solution of the auxiliary problem (5-40) is obtainable from the solution (2-166b) by setting in that equation $T_1 = f_1(\tau)$, $T_2 = f_2(\tau)$, and $F(x) = 0$. We find

$$\Phi(x,t,\tau) = f_1(\tau)\left[1 - \frac{x}{L} - \frac{2}{L}\sum_{m=1}^{\infty} e^{-\alpha\beta_m^2 t}\frac{1}{\beta_m}\sin\beta_m x\right]$$

$$+ f_2(\tau)\left[\frac{x}{L} + \frac{2}{L}\sum_{m=1}^{\infty} e^{-\alpha\beta_m^2 t}\frac{1}{\beta_m}\sin\beta_m x \cos m\pi\right] \qquad (5\text{-}41)$$

where

$$\beta_m = \frac{m\pi}{L} \qquad \text{and} \qquad \cos m\pi = (-1)^m$$

Then

$$\Phi(x,t-\tau,\tau) = f_1(\tau)\left[1 - \frac{x}{L} - \frac{2}{L}\sum_{m=1}^{\infty} e^{-\alpha\beta_m^2(t-\tau)}\frac{1}{\beta_m}\sin\beta_m x\right]$$

$$+ f_2(\tau)\left[\frac{x}{L} + \frac{2}{L}\sum_{m=1}^{\infty} e^{-\alpha\beta_m^2(t-\tau)}\frac{(-1)^m}{\beta_m}\sin\beta_m x\right] \qquad (5\text{-}42)$$

and by Duhamel's theorem (5-4), the solution of problem (5-39) is given as

$$T(x,t) = \int_{\tau=0}^{t} \frac{\partial}{\partial t}\Phi(x,t-\tau,\tau)\,d\tau \qquad (5\text{-}43)$$

Introducing equation (5-42) into equation (5-43) we obtain

$$T(x,t) = \frac{2\alpha}{L}\sum_{m=1}^{\infty}\beta_m\sin\beta_m x\int_{\tau=0}^{t} e^{-\alpha\beta_m^2(t-\tau)}f_1(\tau)\,d\tau$$

$$- \frac{2\alpha}{L}\sum_{m=1}^{\infty}(-1)^m\beta_m\sin\beta_m x\int_{\tau=0}^{t} e^{-\alpha\beta_m^2(t-\tau)}f_2(\tau)\,d\tau \qquad (5\text{-}44)$$

where $\beta_m = m\pi/L$. This solution seems to vanish at $x = 0$ and $x = L$, instead of converging to the boundary-condition functions $f_1(t)$ and $f_2(t)$ at these locations. The reason for this is that the terms associated with the boundary-condition functions are in the form of Fourier series that are not uniformly convergent at these locations. This difficulty can be alleviated by integrating equation (5-44) by parts and replacing such series by their equivalent closed-form expressions as now described.

We write equation (5-44) in the form

$$T(x,t) = \frac{2\alpha}{L} \sum_{m=1}^{\infty} \beta_m \sin \beta_m x I_1(t) - \frac{2\alpha}{L} \sum_{m=1}^{\infty} (-1)^m \beta_m \sin \beta_m x I_2(t) \quad (5\text{-}45)$$

where

$$I_i(t) \equiv \int_0^t f_i(\tau) e^{-\alpha\beta_m^2(t-\tau)} d\tau, \qquad i = 1 \text{ or } 2 \quad (5\text{-}46)$$

The integral term is evaluated by parts as

$$I_i(t) = e^{-\alpha\beta_m^2 t} \int_0^t f_i(\tau) \frac{1}{\alpha\beta_m^2} d(e^{\alpha\beta_m^2 \tau})$$

$$= \frac{1}{\alpha\beta_m^2} e^{-\alpha\beta_m^2 t} \left\{ [f_i(\tau) e^{\alpha\beta_m^2 \tau}]_0^t - \int_0^t e^{\alpha\beta_m^2 \tau} df_i(\tau) \right\}$$

$$= \frac{1}{\alpha\beta_m^2} \left[f_i(t) - f_i(0) e^{-\alpha\beta_m^2 t} - \int_0^t e^{-\alpha\beta_m^2(t-\tau)} df_i(\tau) \right] \quad (5\text{-}47)$$

Equation (5-47) is introduced into equation (5-45)

$$T(x,t) = f_1(t) \frac{2}{L} \sum_{m=1}^{\infty} \frac{\sin \beta_m x}{\beta_m} - f_2(t) \frac{2}{L} \sum_{m=1}^{\infty} (-1)^m \frac{\sin \beta_m x}{\beta_m}$$

$$- \frac{2}{L} \sum_{m=1}^{\infty} \frac{\sin \beta_m x}{\beta_m} \left[f_1(0) e^{-\alpha\beta_m^2 t} + \int_0^t e^{-\alpha\beta_m^2(t-\tau)} df_1(\tau) \right]$$

$$+ \frac{2}{L} \sum_{m=1}^{\infty} (-1)^m \frac{\sin \beta_m x}{\beta_m} \left[f_2(0) e^{-\alpha\beta_m^2 t} + \int_0^t e^{-\alpha\beta_m^2(t-\tau)} df_2(\tau) \right] \quad (5\text{-}48)$$

Closed-form expressions can readily be obtained for the first two series on the right-hand side of equation (5-48) as explained in Note 1. The same results can also be obtained from the reference [4, p. 96, case 508 and 509] as

$$\frac{2}{L} \sum_{m=1}^{\infty} \frac{\sin \beta_m x}{\beta_m} = 1 - \frac{x}{L} \quad \text{and} \quad -\frac{2}{L} \sum_{m=1}^{\infty} (-1)^m \frac{\sin \beta_m x}{\beta_m} = \frac{x}{L} \quad (5\text{-}49)$$

Introducing equations (5-49) into (5-48), the solution becomes

$$T(x,t) = \left(1 - \frac{x}{L}\right) f_1(t) + \frac{x}{L} f_2(t)$$

$$- \frac{2}{L} \sum_{m=1}^{\infty} \frac{\sin \beta_m x}{\beta_m} \left[f_1(0) e^{-\alpha\beta_m^2 t} + \int_0^t e^{-\alpha\beta_m^2(t-\tau)} df_1(\tau) \right]$$

$$+ \frac{2}{L} \sum_{m=1}^{\infty} (-1)^m \frac{\sin \beta_m x}{\beta_m} \left[f_2(0) e^{-\alpha\beta_m^2 t} + \int_0^t e^{-\alpha\beta_m^2(t-\tau)} df_2(\tau) \right] \quad (5\text{-}50)$$

The solution given in this form clearly shows that at $x = 0$ and $x = L$ this solution reduces to $f_1(t)$ and $f_2(t)$, respectively.

Example 5-3. A solid cylinder, $0 \leq r \leq b$, is initially at zero temperature. For times $t > 0$ the boundary surface at $r = b$ is kept at temperature $T = f(t)$, which varies with time. Obtain an expression for the temperature distribution $T(r, t)$ in the cylinder for times $t > 0$.

Solution. The mathematical formulation of this problem is given as

$$\frac{\partial^2 T(r,t)}{\partial r^2} + \frac{1}{r}\frac{\partial T(r,t)}{\partial r} = \frac{1}{\alpha}\frac{\partial T(r,t)}{\partial t} \qquad \text{in } 0 \leq r < b, \ t > 0 \qquad (5\text{-}51\text{a})$$

$$T = f(t) \qquad\qquad\qquad \text{at } r = b, \ t > 0 \qquad (5\text{-}51\text{b})$$

$$T = 0 \qquad\qquad\qquad \text{for } t = 0, \text{ in } 0 \leq r \leq b \quad (5\text{-}51\text{c})$$

and the auxiliary problem is taken as

$$\frac{\partial^2 \Phi(r,t)}{\partial r^2} + \frac{1}{r}\frac{\partial \Phi(r,t)}{\partial r} = \frac{1}{\alpha}\frac{\partial \Phi(r,t)}{\partial t} \qquad \text{in } 0 \leq r < b, \ t > 0 \qquad (5\text{-}52\text{a})$$

$$\Phi = 1 \qquad\qquad\qquad \text{at } r = b, \ t > 0 \qquad (5\text{-}52\text{b})$$

$$\Phi = 0 \qquad\qquad\qquad \text{for } t = 0, \text{ in } 0 \leq r \leq b \quad (5\text{-}52\text{c})$$

Then, the solution of the problem (5-51) can be written in terms of the solution of the auxiliary problem (5-52) by Duhamel's (5-8) as

$$T(r,t) = \int_{\tau=0}^{t} f(\tau)\frac{\partial \Phi(r, t-\tau)}{\partial t}\,d\tau \qquad (5\text{-}53)$$

If $\psi(r, t)$ is the solution of the problem for a solid cylinder, $0 \leq r \leq b$, initially at temperature unity and for times $t > 0$, the boundary surface at $r = b$ is kept at zero temperature, then the solution for $\psi(r, t)$ is obtainable from the solution (3-68) by setting $T_0 = 1$ in that equation; we find

$$\psi(r,t) = \frac{2}{b}\sum_{m=1}^{\infty} e^{-\alpha\beta_m^2 t}\frac{J_0(\beta_m r)}{\beta_m J_1(\beta_m b)} \qquad (5\text{-}54\text{a})$$

where β_m's are the positive roots of

$$J_0(\beta_m b) = 0 \qquad (5\text{-}54\text{b})$$

The solution $\Phi(r, t)$ of the auxiliary problem (5-52) is obtainable from the solution $\psi(r, t)$ given by equation (5-54) as

$$\Phi(r,t) = 1 - \psi(r,t) = 1 - \frac{2}{b}\sum_{m=1}^{\infty} e^{-\alpha\beta_m^2 t}\frac{J_0(\beta_m r)}{\beta_m J_1(\beta_m b)} \qquad (5\text{-}55)$$

Introducing equation (5-55) into equation (5-53), the solution of the problem (5-51) becomes

$$T(r,t) = \frac{2\alpha}{b} \sum_{m=1}^{\infty} e^{-\alpha\beta_m^2 t} \beta_m \frac{J_0(\beta_m r)}{J_1(\beta_m b)} \int_0^t e^{\alpha\beta_m^2 \tau} f(\tau)\, d\tau \tag{5-56}$$

where β_m's are the roots of $J_0(\beta_m b) = 0$.

The solution for $T(r,t)$ given by equation (5-56) does not explicity show that $T(r,t) \to f(t)$ as $r \to b$. This result can be expressed in an alternative form by integrating the integral term by parts as has been done in the previous example. We obtain

$$T(r,t) = f(t)\cdot\frac{2}{b} \sum_{m=1}^{\infty} \frac{J_0(\beta_m r)}{\beta_m J_1(\beta_m b)}$$
$$- \frac{2}{b} \sum_{m=1}^{\infty} \frac{J_0(\beta_m r)}{\beta_m J_1(\beta_m b)}\left[f(0)e^{-\alpha\beta_m^2 t} + \int_0^t e^{-\alpha\beta_m^2(t-\tau)}\, df(\tau) \right] \tag{5-57}$$

We note that the solution (5-54a) for $t = 0$ should be equal to the initial temperature $\psi(r,0) = 1$; thus

$$1 = \frac{2}{b} \sum_{m=1}^{\infty} \frac{J_0(\beta_m r)}{\beta_m J_1(\beta_m b)} \tag{5-58}$$

which gives the desired closed-form expression for first series on the right-hand side of equation (5-57). Then, the solution (5-57) is written as

$$T(r,t) = f(t) - \frac{2}{b} \sum_{m=1}^{\infty} \frac{J_0(\beta_m r)}{\beta_m J_1(\beta_m b)}\left[f(0)e^{-\alpha\beta_m^2 t} + \int_0^t e^{-\alpha\beta_m^2(t-\tau)}\, df(\tau) \right] \tag{5-59}$$

The solution given in this form clearly shows that $T(r,t) = f(t)$ at $r = b$.

Example 5-4. A solid cylinder, $0 \le r \le b$, is initially at zero temperature. For times $t > 0$ heat is generated in the solid at a rate of $g(t)$ per unit volume and the boundary surface at $r = b$ is kept at zero temperature. Obtain an expression for the temperature distribution $T(r,t)$ in the cylinder for times $t > 0$.

Solution. The mathematical formulation of this problem is given as

$$\frac{\partial^2 T(r,t)}{\partial r^2} + \frac{1}{r}\frac{\partial T(r,t)}{\partial r} + \frac{g(t)}{k} = \frac{1}{\alpha}\frac{\partial T(r,t)}{\partial t} \qquad \text{in } 0 \le r < b,\ t > 0 \tag{5-60a}$$

$$T = 0 \qquad\qquad\qquad\qquad \text{at } r = b,\ t > 0 \tag{5-60b}$$

$$T = 0 \qquad\qquad\qquad\qquad \text{for } t = 0,\ \text{in } 0 \le r \le b \tag{5-60c}$$

and the auxiliary problem is taken as

$$\frac{\partial^2 \Phi(r,t)}{\partial r^2} + \frac{1}{r}\frac{\partial \Phi(r,t)}{\partial r} + \frac{1}{k} = \frac{1}{\alpha}\frac{\partial \Phi(r,t)}{\partial t} \qquad \text{in } 0 \le r < b, \ t > 0 \qquad (5\text{-}61a)$$

$$\Phi = 0 \qquad\qquad\qquad\qquad \text{at } r = b, \ t > 0 \qquad (5\text{-}61b)$$

$$\Phi = 0 \qquad\qquad\qquad\qquad \text{for } t = 0, \ \text{in } 0 \le r \le b \qquad (5\text{-}61c)$$

Then, the solution of the problem (5-60) is related to the solution of the auxiliary problem (5-61) by Duhamel's theorem as

$$T(r,t) = \int_{\tau=0}^{t} g(\tau)\frac{\partial \Phi(r,t-\tau)}{\partial t}d\tau \qquad (5\text{-}62)$$

The solution of the auxiliary problem (5-61) is obtainable from equation (3-219) by setting $g_0 = 1$ and $F(r) = 0$; we find

$$\Phi(r,t) = \frac{b^2 - r^2}{4k} - \frac{2}{bk}\sum_{m=1}^{\infty} e^{-\alpha\beta_m^2 t}\frac{J_0(\beta_m r)}{\beta_m^3 J_1(\beta_m b)} \qquad (5\text{-}63a)$$

where β_m's are the positive roots of

$$J_0(\beta_m b) = 0 \qquad (5\text{-}63b)$$

Introducing equation (5-63) into (5-62) we obtain

$$T(r,t) = \frac{2\alpha}{bk}\sum_{m=1}^{\infty} e^{-\alpha\beta_m^2 t}\frac{J_0(\beta_m r)}{\beta_m J_1(\beta_m b)}\int_{\tau=0}^{t} g(\tau)e^{\alpha\beta_m^2 \tau}d\tau \qquad (5\text{-}64)$$

REFERENCES

1. R. C. Bartels and R. V. Churchill, *Bull. Am. Math. Soc.* **48**, 276–282, 1942.
2. I. N. Sneddon, *Fourier Transforms*, McGraw-Hill Book Co., New York, 1951.
3. H. S. Carslaw and J. C. Jaeger, *Conduction of Heat in Solids*, Clarendon Press, London, 1959.
4. L. B. W. Jolley, *Summation of Series*, Dover Publications, Inc., New York, 1961.

PROBLEMS

5-1 Prove that Duhamel's theorem given by equation (5-3) is also applicable for the solution of more general heat-conduction problem given as

$$\nabla\cdot[k(\mathbf{r})\nabla T] + g(\mathbf{r},t) = \rho c_p\frac{\partial T(\mathbf{r},t)}{\partial t} \qquad \text{in region } R, t > 0$$

$$k_i \frac{\partial T}{\partial n_i} + h_i T = f_i(\mathbf{r}, t) \qquad\qquad \text{on boundary } S_i,\, t > 0$$

$$T(\mathbf{r}, t) = F(\mathbf{r}) \qquad\qquad \text{for } t = 0,\, \text{in region } R$$

if the auxiliary problem is taken as

$$\nabla \cdot \left[k(\mathbf{r}) \nabla \Phi(\mathbf{r}, t, \tau) \right] + g(\mathbf{r}, \tau) = \rho c_p \frac{\partial \Phi(\mathbf{r}, t, \tau)}{\partial t} \qquad \text{in region } R,\, t > 0$$

$$k_i \frac{\partial \Phi}{\partial n_i} + h_i \Phi = f_i(\mathbf{r}, \tau) \qquad\qquad \text{on boundary } S_i,\, t > 0$$

$$\Phi(\mathbf{r}, t, \tau) = F(r) \qquad\qquad \text{for } t = 0,\, \text{in region } R$$

5-2 A semi-infinite solid, $0 \le x < \infty$, is initially at zero temperature. For times $t > 0$, the boundary surface at $x = 0$ is kept at temperature $T = T_0 t$, where T_0 is a constant. Using Duhamel's theorem obtain an expression for the temperature distribution $T(x, t)$ in the region for times $t > 0$.

5-3 A slab, $0 \le x \le L$, is initially at zero temperature. For times $t > 0$ the boundary at $x = 0$ is kept insulated and the convection boundary condition at $x = L$ is given as $(\partial T / \partial x) + HT = f(t)$, where $f(t)$ is a function of time. Obtain an expression for the temperature distribution $T(x, t)$ in the slab for times $t > 0$.

5-4 A solid cylinder, $0 \le r \le b$, is initially at zero temperature. For times $t > 0$ the boundary condition at $r = b$ is given as $\partial T / \partial r + HT = f(t)$, where $f(t)$ is a function of time. Obtain an expression for the temperature distribution $T(r, t)$ in the cylinder for times $t > 0$.

5-5 A solid sphere, $0 \le r \le b$, is initially at zero temperature, for times $t > 0$ the boundary surface $r = b$ is kept at temperature $f(t)$, which varies with time. Obtain an expression for the temperature distribution $T(r, t)$ in the sphere.

5-6 A solid cylinder, $0 \le r \le b$, is initially at zero temperature. For times $t > 0$, heat is generated in the solid at a rate of $g(t)$ per unit volume whereas the boundary surface at $r = b$ dissipates heat by convection into a medium at zero temperature. Obtain an expression for the temperature distribution $T(r, t)$ in the cylinder for times $t > 0$.

5-7 A rectangular region $0 \le x \le a$, $0 \le y \le b$ is initially at zero temperature. For times $t > 0$ the boundaries at $x = 0$ and $y = 0$ are kept insulated, the boundaries at $x = a$ and $y = b$ are kept at zero temperature while heat is generated in the region at a rate of $g(t)$ per unit volume. Obtain an expression for the temperature distribution in the region using Duhamel's theorem.

NOTES

1. We consider the following steady-state problem

$$\frac{d^2 T}{dx^2} = 0 \quad \text{in } 0 < x < L \tag{1a}$$

$$T = 1 \quad \text{at } x = 0 \tag{1b}$$

$$T = 0 \quad \text{at } x = L \tag{1c}$$

The solution of this problem is

$$T(x) = 1 - \frac{x}{L} \tag{2a}$$

If this problem is solved by the integral-transform technique (the integral transform technique will be presented in Chapter 13), the solution is given as

$$T(x) = \frac{2}{L} \sum_{m=1}^{\infty} \frac{\sin \beta_m x}{\beta_m} \quad \text{where} \quad \beta_m = \frac{m\pi}{L} \tag{2b}$$

The equivalence of solutions (2a) and (2b) yields

$$\frac{2}{L} \sum_{m=1}^{\infty} \frac{\sin \beta_m x}{\beta_m} = 1 - \frac{x}{L} \tag{3}$$

which is the result given by equation (5-49).
  Similarly we consider the problem

$$\frac{d^2 T}{dx^2} = 0 \quad \text{in } 0 < x < L \tag{4a}$$

$$T = 0 \quad \text{at } x = 0 \tag{4b}$$

$$T = 1 \quad \text{at } x = L \tag{4c}$$

The Solution of this problem is $T(x) = x/L$. If this problem is also solved by the integral transform technique and the two results are equated we obtain

$$-\frac{2}{L} \sum_{m=1}^{\infty} (-1)^m \frac{\sin \beta_m x}{\beta_m} = \frac{x}{L} \tag{5}$$

CHAPTER 6

THE USE OF GREEN'S FUNCTION

The use of Green's function in the solution of partial differential equations of mathematical physics can be found in several references [1–6]. In this chapter we present the method of solution of the time-dependent heat-conduction equation with heat generation, subject to nonhomogeneous boundary conditions and an initial condition in terms of Green's function. The method is quite general in that all nonhomogeneous problems are handled in the same manner and the solutions for the one-, two-, or three-dimensional problems are presented formally in a very compact form. The principal difficulty in the use of Green's function approach appears to be the determination of the appropriate Green's function for a given problem, because it depends on the type of coordinate system, the boundary conditions and the extent of the region (i.e., finite, semi-infinite, or infinite). To alleviate this difficulty we present a straightforward and systematic approach for the construction of Green's function. That is, we show that the construction of Green's function for a given problem is related to the solution of the homogeneous part of that problem. Then, the methods of solution of the homogeneous problems considered in Chapters 2, 3, and 4 form the basis for the construction of Green's function. The application is now illustrated with examples.

6-1 GREEN'S FUNCTION IN THE SOLUTION OF NONHOMOGENEOUS, TIME-DEPENDENT HEAT-CONDUCTION PROBLEMS

We consider the following three-dimensional nonhomogeneous boundary value problem of heat conduction:

$$\nabla^2 T(\mathbf{r}, t) + \frac{1}{k} g(\mathbf{r}, t) = \frac{1}{\alpha} \frac{\partial T(\mathbf{r}, t)}{\partial t} \qquad \text{in region } R, t > 0 \qquad (6\text{-}1a)$$

$$k_i \frac{\partial T}{\partial n_i} + h_i T = f_i(\mathbf{r}, t) \qquad\qquad \text{on boundary } S_i, t > 0 \qquad (6\text{-}1b)$$

$$T(\mathbf{r}, t) = F(\mathbf{r}) \qquad\qquad \text{for } t = 0, \text{ in region } R \qquad (6\text{-}1c)$$

where $\partial/\partial n_i$ denotes differentiation along the outward-drawn normal to the boundary surface $S_i, i = 1, 2, \ldots, s$ and s is the number of continuous boundary surfaces of the region. For generality it is assumed that the generation term $g(\mathbf{r}, t)$ and the boundary-condition function $f_i(\mathbf{r}, t)$ vary both with position and time. Here, k_i and h_i are coefficients that are considered constants. By setting $k_i = 0$ we obtain a boundary condition of the first kind and by setting $h_i = 0$ we obtain a boundary condition of the second kind.

To solve the above heat-conduction problem we consider the following auxiliary problem for the same region R:

$$\nabla^2 G(\mathbf{r}, t | \mathbf{r}', \tau) + \frac{1}{\alpha} \delta(\mathbf{r} - \mathbf{r}') \delta(t - \tau) = \frac{1}{\alpha} \frac{\partial G}{\partial t} \qquad \text{in region } R, t > \tau \qquad (6\text{-}2a)$$

$$k_i \frac{\partial G}{\partial n_i} + h_i G = 0 \qquad\qquad \text{on } S_i, \ t > \tau \qquad (6\text{-}2b)$$

and subject to the condition

$$G(\mathbf{r}, t | \mathbf{r}', \tau) = 0 \qquad \text{if } t < \tau \qquad (6\text{-}2c)$$

where $\delta(\mathbf{r} - \mathbf{r}')$ is the three-dimensional delta function for the space variable, that is, $\delta(x - x')\delta(y - y')\delta(z - z')$ for (x, y, z) coordinates, and so forth, and $\delta(t - \tau)$ is the delta function for the time variable. See Note 1 for a discussion of the properties of delta function. Here, the function $G(\mathbf{r}, t | \mathbf{r}', \tau)$ is called a *Green's function*. We note that the auxiliary problem satisfied by the Green's function has homogeneous boundary conditions that are the homogeneous version of those for the original problem (6-1), and has an impulsive point heat source and zero initial condition (i.e., medium at zero temperature for times $t < \tau$). Then, the *three-dimensional Green's function* $G(\mathbf{r}, t | \mathbf{r}', \tau)$ *satisfying the problem* (6-2) *represents the temperature distribution in the region R, which is initially at zero temperature and subjected to homogeneous boundary conditions, due to an impulsive point heat source of strength unity located at $\mathbf{r}'$ and releasing its heat spontaneously at time τ.* The significance of the notation $G(\mathbf{r}, t | \mathbf{r}', \tau)$ is as follows: The first part of the argument "$\mathbf{r}, t$" refers to the *effect*, namely, the temperature at the location $\mathbf{r}$ at time t in the medium; the second part "$\mathbf{r}', \tau$" refers to the *impulse*, namely, the impulsive (i.e., instantaneous) point heat source located at $\mathbf{r}'$ releasing its heat spontaneously at time τ. Therefore, the physical significance of this notation can be illustrated symbolically by writing it in the form

$$G(\mathbf{r}, t | \mathbf{r}', \tau) \equiv G\,(\text{effect} | \text{impulse}) \tag{6-3}$$

The units of the source term in equation (6-2a) need some explanation. In this equation, the heat source is an *instantaneous point heat source* of unit-strength in degrees Centigrade × cubic meter (or degrees Farenheit × cubic foot). The physical significance of this instantaneous point heat source in relation to the term $g(\mathbf{r}, t)/k$ in equation (6-1a) is envisioned better by expressing $g(\mathbf{r}, t)/k$ in different forms as

$$S(r, t) \equiv \frac{g(\mathbf{r}, t)}{k} \tag{6-4a}$$

$$= \frac{1}{k} g_i(\mathbf{r})\delta(t - \tau) = \frac{1}{\alpha}\left[\frac{g_i(\mathbf{r})}{\rho c_p}\right]\delta(t - \tau) \tag{6-4b}$$

$$= \frac{1}{k} g_{ip}\delta(\mathbf{r} - \mathbf{r}')\delta(t - \tau) = \frac{1}{\alpha}\left[\frac{g_{ip}}{\rho c_p}\right]\delta(r - \mathbf{r}')\delta(t - \tau) \tag{6-4c}$$

where

$g(\mathbf{r}, t)$ = distributed heat source, W/m³ (or Btu/hr ft³)
$g_i(\mathbf{r})$ = instantaneous distributed heat source, Ws/m³ (or Btu/ft³)
g_{ip} = instantaneous point heat source, W·s (or Btu)
$\dfrac{g_{ip}}{\rho c_p}$ = instantaneous point heat source, °C·m³ (or °F·ft³)

Therefore, the instantaneous point heat source of unit strength in equation (6-2a) is equivalent to a source $g_{ip}/\rho c_p = 1\ °\text{C·m}^3$. This definition has the advantage that an initial distribution of temperature $T(\mathbf{r}, 0) = F(\mathbf{r})$ in a medium may be regarded as an instantaneous distributed heat source releasing its heat at time $t = 0$ in the amount of

$$g_i(\mathbf{r}) \equiv \rho c_p F(\mathbf{r})\ \text{Ws/m}^3\ (\text{or Btu/ft}^3) \tag{6-5}$$

over the entire region; conversely, an instantaneous source of strength $g_i(r)$ Ws/m³ releasing its heat at time $t = 0$ can be considered as an initial distribution $F(\mathbf{r}) = g_i(\mathbf{r})/\rho c_p = \alpha g_i(\mathbf{r})/k$. This matter will be illustrated with examples later in this chapter.

The Green's function $G(\mathbf{r}, t | \mathbf{r}', \tau)$ satisfying the auxiliary problem (6-2) obeys the following reciprocity relation [2, p. 858]:

$$G(\mathbf{r}, t | \mathbf{r}', \tau) = G(\mathbf{r}', -\tau | \mathbf{r}, -t) \tag{6-6}$$

This reciprocity relation implies that the *effect* at **r** at time t due to an *impulse* (i.e., instantaneous point heat source) at **r**' released at a time τ (i.e., $\tau < t$)

is equal to the *effect* at $\mathbf{r}'$ at a time $-\tau$ due to an *impulse* at $\mathbf{r}$ started at time $-t$. This reciprocity relation will be useful in the analysis later in this section.

Suppose the Green's function $G(\mathbf{r}, t | \mathbf{r}', \tau)$ satisfying the auxiliary problem (6-2) is known. Then our aim in this analysis is to express the general solution of the nonhomogeneous, time-dependent heat-conduction problem (6-1) in terms of the Green's function satisfying the auxiliary problem (6-2). In the following analysis we derive the general expression for the solution $T(\mathbf{r}, t)$ of problem (6-1) in terms of the Green's function $G(\mathbf{r}, t | \mathbf{r}', \tau)$ satisfying problem (6-2).

In view of the reciprocity relation (6-6), we write equation (6-2a) in terms of the function $G(\mathbf{r}', -\tau | \mathbf{r}, -t)$; it takes the form

$$\nabla_0^2 G + \frac{1}{\alpha}\delta(\mathbf{r}' - \mathbf{r})\delta(\tau - t) = -\frac{1}{\alpha}\frac{\partial G}{\partial \tau} \qquad \text{in region } R \qquad (6\text{-}7)$$

where ∇_0^2 is the Laplacian in the variable $\mathbf{r}'$ and the minus sign on the right-hand side results from the replacement of t by $-\tau$.

In the heat conduction (6-1a) we replace t by τ and $\mathbf{r}$ by $\mathbf{r}'$ to obtain

$$\nabla_0^2 T + \frac{1}{k}g(\mathbf{r}', \tau) = \frac{1}{\alpha}\frac{\partial T(\mathbf{r}', \tau)}{\partial \tau} \qquad \text{in region } R \qquad (6\text{-}8)$$

We multiply equation (6-7) by T, equation (6-8) by G, and subtract

$$(G\nabla_0^2 T - T\nabla_0^2 G) + \frac{1}{k}g(\mathbf{r}', \tau)G - \frac{1}{\alpha}\delta(\mathbf{r}' - \mathbf{r})\delta(\tau - t)T$$

$$= \frac{1}{\alpha}\frac{\partial}{\partial \tau}(GT) \qquad (6\text{-}9)$$

We integrate equation (6-9) with respect to $\mathbf{r}'$ over the region R and with respect to τ from 0 to $t^* = t + \varepsilon$, where ε is arbitrarily small.

$$\int\limits_{\tau=0}^{t^*} d\tau \int\limits_R (G\nabla_0^2 T - T\nabla_0^2 G)\,dv' + \frac{1}{k}\int\limits_{\tau=0}^{t^*} d\tau \int\limits_R g(\mathbf{r}', \tau)\,G\,dv' - \frac{1}{\alpha}T(\mathbf{r}, t^*)$$

$$= \frac{1}{\alpha}\int\limits_R [GT]_{\tau=0}^{\tau=t^*}\,dv'. \qquad (6\text{-}10)$$

The first volume integral on the left-hand side is changed to surface integral by employing Green's theorem; we obtain (see Note 2 for the Green's theorem)

$$\int\limits_R (G\nabla_0^2 T - T\nabla_0^2 G)\,dv' = \sum\limits_{i=1}^{S} \int\limits_{S_i} \left(G\frac{\partial T}{\partial n_i} - T\frac{\partial G}{\partial n_i}\right)dS_i \qquad (6\text{-}11a)$$

where $\partial/\partial n_i$ denotes differentiation along the outward drawn normal to the boundary surface $S_i, i = 1, 2, \ldots, s$ and s is the number of continuous boundary surfaces of the region R. The term $[GT]$ on the right-hand side of equation (6-10) is evaluated at the limits; we find

$$[GT]_{\tau=0}^{t^*} = -GT\big|_{\tau=0} = -G\big|_{\tau=0}F(\mathbf{r}) \tag{6-11b}$$

since $T\big|_{\tau=0} = F(\mathbf{r})$ and at the upper limit $t^* = t + \varepsilon$ we have $G(\mathbf{r}, t\,|\,\mathbf{r}', t^*) = 0$ by definition, that is, for $t^* > t$, $G(\mathbf{r}, t\,|\,\mathbf{r}', t^*)$ is zero because the time for the *effect* is earlier than the time for *impulse*. Introducing equations (6-11) into equation (6-10) and letting $\varepsilon \to 0$, we obtain

$$T(\mathbf{r}, t) = \int_R G\big|_{\tau=0}F(\mathbf{r}')\,dv' + \frac{\alpha}{k}\int_{\tau=0}^{t} d\tau \int_R Gg(\mathbf{r}', \tau)\,dv'$$

$$+ \alpha \int_{\tau=0}^{t} d\tau \sum_{i=1}^{s} \int_{S_i} \left(G\frac{\partial T}{\partial n_i} - T\frac{\partial G}{\partial n_i} \right) dS_i \tag{6-12}$$

where

$$G \equiv G(\mathbf{r}, t\,|\,\mathbf{r}', \tau)$$
$$G\big|_{\tau=0} \equiv G(\mathbf{r}, t\,|\,\mathbf{r}', 0).$$

The last term on the right-hand side of equation (6-12) is now evaluated by making use of the boundary conditions (6-1b) and (6-2b). Namely, multiplying (6-1b) by G and (6-2b) by T and subtracting, we find

$$G\frac{\partial T}{\partial n_i} - T\frac{\partial G}{\partial n_i} = \frac{1}{k_i}G\big|_{S_i}f_i(\mathbf{r}, t) \tag{6-13}$$

where $G\big|_{S_i}$ refer to the value of the Green's function evaluated at the boundary surface S_i. Substituting equation (6-13) into equation (6-12), we obtain the solution $T(\mathbf{r}, t)$ of the three-dimensional heat conduction problem (6-1) in terms of the Green's function $G(\mathbf{r}, t\,|\,\mathbf{r}', \tau)$ satisfying the problem (6-2) as

$$T(\mathbf{r}, t) = \int_R G(\mathbf{r}, t\,|\,\mathbf{r}', \tau)\big|_{\tau=0}F(\mathbf{r}')\,dv'$$

$$+ \frac{\alpha}{k}\int_{\tau=0}^{t} d\tau \int_R G(\mathbf{r}, t\,|\,\mathbf{r}', \tau)g(\mathbf{r}', \tau)\,dv'$$

$$+ \alpha \int_{\tau=0}^{t} d\tau \sum_{i=1}^{s} \int_{S_i} G(\mathbf{r}, t\,|\,\mathbf{r}', \tau)\big|_{\mathbf{r}'=\mathbf{r}_i}\frac{1}{k_i}f_i(\mathbf{r}, t)\,ds_i \tag{6-14}$$

where R refers to the entire volume of the region considered; S_i refers to the boundary surface S_i of the region $R, i = 1, 2, \ldots, s$ and s in number continuous boundary surfaces; and dv' and ds_i' refer to differential volume and surface elements, respectively, in the $\mathbf{r}'$ variable.

For generality, the solution (6-14) is given for boundary condition of the *third kind* at all boundaries of the region. If the boundary condition is of the *second kind*, say, at the boundary surface $i = j$, we set $h_j = 0$ in equations (6-1b) and (6-2b) for that particular boundary surface. For such cases, the general form of the solution (6-14) remains the same, but the Green's function G is the solution of the auxiliary problem (6-2) subject to the modified boundary conditions.

If the boundary condition is of the *first kind*, say, at a boundary surface $i = j$, we set $k_j = 0$ in equations (6-1b) and (6-2b) for that particular boundary surface; but, we cannot set $k_j = 0$ in equation (6-14) because k_j is in the denominator. This difficulty can be avoided if the following change is made in the last term in equation (6-14): Replace

$$\frac{1}{k_j} G\Big|_{\mathbf{r}' = \mathbf{r}_j}$$

by

$$-\frac{1}{h_j} \frac{\partial G}{\partial n_j}\bigg|_{\mathbf{r}' = \mathbf{r}_j} \tag{6-16}$$

for the boundary surface S_j for which $k_j = 0$. Here, $\partial/\partial n_j$ is the normal derivative at the boundary S_j in the outward direction. The validity of this replacement is apparent if the boundary condition (6-1b) is arranged in the form:

$$\frac{1}{k_i} G\Big|_{S_i} = -\frac{1}{h_i} \frac{\partial G}{\partial n_i}\bigg|_{S_i} \qquad i = 1, 2, \ldots, s. \tag{6-17}$$

The general solution of the heat-conduction problem (6-1) as given by equation (6-14) in terms of Green's functions consists of three different terms. The physical significance of these three terms is as follows: The *first* term is for the effects of the initial temperature distribution $F(\mathbf{r})$; the *second* term is for the effects of the distributed heat source $g(\mathbf{r}, t)$; and the *third* term is for the effects of the nonhomogeneity $f_i(\mathbf{r}, t)$ of the boundary conditions.

The foregoing analysis is presented, for generality, for a three-dimensional temperature field. The two- and one-dimensional cases are readily obtainable from the three-dimensional solution (6-14) as given below.

Two-Dimensional Problems

The problems defined by equations (6-1) and (6-2) are also applicable for the two-dimensional case, if ∇^2 is treated as a two-dimensional Laplacian operator and $\delta(\mathbf{r} - \mathbf{r}')$ as a two-dimensional delta function, that is, $\delta(\mathbf{r} - \mathbf{r}') \equiv \delta(x - x')\,\delta(y - y')$ in the (x, y) coordinate system, and so forth.

In the case of two-dimensional temperature field the solution (6-14) reduces to

$$T(\mathbf{r}, t) = \int_A G(\mathbf{r}, t | \mathbf{r}', \tau)\big|_{\tau = 0} F(\mathbf{r}') \, dA'$$

$$+ \frac{\alpha}{k} \int_{\tau = 0}^{t} d\tau \int_A G(\mathbf{r}, t | \mathbf{r}', \tau) g(\mathbf{r}', \tau) \, dA' \qquad (6\text{-}18)$$

$$+ \alpha \int_{\tau = 0}^{t} d\tau \sum_{i = 1}^{s} \int_{\substack{\text{Boundary} \\ \text{path } i}} G(\mathbf{r}, t | \mathbf{r}', \tau)\big|_{\mathbf{r}' = \mathbf{r}_i} \frac{1}{k_i} f_i \, dl_i$$

where A is the area of the region under consideration, dl_i is the differential length along the boundary path of the boundary $i, i = 1, 2, \ldots, s$, and s is the number of continuous boundary paths of the region A. For a boundary condition of the *first kind* at the boundary, say, $i = j$, the term $(1/k_j)G\big|_{\mathbf{r}' = \mathbf{r}_j}$ should be replaced by $- (1/h_j)(\partial G/\partial n_j)\big|_{\mathbf{r}' = \mathbf{r}_j}$ for the boundary $i = j$ in accordance with equation (6-16).

One-Dimensional Problems

For the one-dimensional temperature field, the problems defined by equations (6-1) and (6-2) are applicable if ∇^2 is considered as one-dimensional Laplacian operator and $\delta(\mathbf{r} - \mathbf{r}')$ as one-dimensional delta function, that is, $\delta(\mathbf{r} - \mathbf{r}') = \delta(x - x')$ for the (x) coordinate, etc.

For a one-dimensional temperature field, say, in the x variable, equation (6-14) reduces to

$$T(x, t) = \int_L x'^P G(x, t | x', \tau)\big|_{\tau = 0} F(x') \, dx'$$

$$+ \frac{\alpha}{k} \int_{\tau = 0}^{t} d\tau \int_L x'^P G(x, t | x', \tau) \big| g(x', \tau) \, dx' \qquad (6\text{-}19)$$

$$+ \alpha \int_{\tau = 0}^{t} d\tau \sum_{i = 1}^{2} [x'^P G(x, t | x', \tau)]_{x' = x_i} \frac{1}{k_i} f_i$$

where x'^P is the Sturm-Liouville weight function such that

$$P = \begin{cases} 0 & \text{slab} \\ 1 & \text{cylinder} \\ 2 & \text{sphere} \end{cases}$$

Here L refers to the length of the one-dimensional region and $G(x, t | x', \tau)\big|_{x' = x_i'}$ refers to the value of G evaluated at the boundary points $x' = x_i'$. For a boundary condition of the *first kind* at the boundary, say, $i = j$, the term $(1/k_j)G\big|_{x' = x_j'}$ should be replaced by $- (1/h_j)(\partial G/\partial n_j)\big|_{x' = x_j'}$ for the boundary $i = j$ in accordance with equation (6-16).

Equations (6-14), (6-18), and (6-19) are the general solutions of the non-homogeneous heat-conduction problem (6-1) for the three-, two-, and one-dimensional cases, respectively, in terms of the Green's function. Here we note that these solutions are not always uniformly convergent, because of the terms involving the nonhomogeneous part of the boundary condition functions. To elaborate this matter, we recall the use of Duhamel's theorem in examples (5-2) and (5-3) in the solution of the heat-conduction problem involving nonhomogeneous boundary conditions. In these examples, the solutions did not seem to satisfy the boundary conditions in the form as obtained by Duhamel's theorem. This difficulty was alleviated by integrating by parts and replacing those series that were not uniformly convergent by their equivalent closed-form expressions. Similar difficulties may also arise in the above solutions, because of the terms involving the nonhomogeneous part of the boundary-condition functions. Therefore, it is desirable to replace those parts that converge slowly by their corresponding closed-form expressions. This matter and the determination of Green's function will be illustrated with examples in the following sections.

6-2 DETERMINATION OF GREEN'S FUNCTION

Appropriate Green's functions are needed to solve the nonhomogeneous heat-conduction problems with the Green's function approach discussed in the previous section. We now present a method of determining Green's functions.

First, we consider the following homogeneous boundary-value problem of heat conduction:

$$\nabla^2 T(\mathbf{r}, t) = \frac{1}{\alpha} \frac{\partial T(\mathbf{r}, t)}{\partial t} \qquad \text{in region } R, \ t > 0 \qquad (6\text{-}20a)$$

$$\frac{\partial T}{\partial n_i} + H_i T = 0 \qquad \text{on } S_i, \ t > 0 \qquad (6\text{-}20b)$$

$$T(\mathbf{r}, t) = F(\mathbf{r}) \qquad \text{for } t = 0, \ \text{in region } R \qquad (6\text{-}20c)$$

The appropriate Green's function $G(\mathbf{r}, t \,|\, \mathbf{r}', \tau)$ needed for the solution of this problem satisfies the following auxiliary problem:

$$\nabla^2 G + \frac{1}{\alpha} \delta(\mathbf{r} - \mathbf{r}') \delta(t - \tau) = \frac{1}{\alpha} \frac{\partial G}{\partial t} \qquad \text{in region } R, \ t > \tau \qquad (6\text{-}21a)$$

$$\frac{\partial G}{\partial n_i} + H_i G = 0 \qquad \text{on } S_i, \ t > \tau \qquad (6\text{-}21b)$$

and subject to the condition

$$G = 0 \qquad \text{for } t < \tau \tag{6-21c}$$

where we defined $H_i \equiv h_i/k_i$.

According to equation (6-14), the solution $T(\mathbf{r}, t)$ of the problem (6-20) is given in terms of the Green's function G, satisfying the problem (6-21), as

$$T(\mathbf{r}, t) = \int_R G(\mathbf{r}, t | \mathbf{r}', \tau)|_{\tau = 0} F(\mathbf{r}') \, dv'. \tag{6-22}$$

The homogeneous heat-conduction problem (6-20) can readily be solved by the method of separation of variables as discussed in Chapters 2 to 4. Suppose the problem (6-20) is solved in this manner and the solution is expressed formally in the form

$$T(\mathbf{r}, t) = \int_R [K(\mathbf{r}, \mathbf{r}', t)] F(\mathbf{r}') \, dv \tag{6-23}$$

where the integration is over the entire region of the considered problem, and the term $K(\mathbf{r}, \mathbf{r}', t)$ is used to denote symbolically all the summations or integrations over the eigenfunctions, norms, and so forth. A comparison of equations (6-22) and (6-23) implies that

$$G(\mathbf{r}, t | \mathbf{r}', \tau)|_{\tau = 0} = K(\mathbf{r}, \mathbf{r}', t) \tag{6-24}$$

Thus, we conclude that $G(\mathbf{r}, t | \mathbf{r}', \tau)|_{\tau = 0}$ can be determined by solving the homogeneous part of the heat-conduction problem, arranging it in the form given by equation (6-23) and comparing the resulting expression with equation (6-22).

To solve a nonhomogeneous boundary-value problem of heat conduction by the Green's function technique, we also need to know the Green's function $G(\mathbf{r}, t | \mathbf{r}', \tau)$, as apparent from equation (6-14). Then, our task reduces to the determination of $G(\mathbf{r}, t | \mathbf{r}', \tau)$ when $G(\mathbf{r}, t | \mathbf{r}', \tau)|_{\tau = 0}$ is available. In reference [6, Chapter 5], the nonhomogeneous boundary-value problem of heat conduction (6-1) is solved both by the integral transform technique and the Green's function technique, and by comparing the resulting solutions the general forms of $G(\mathbf{r}, t | \mathbf{r}', \tau)$ and $G(\mathbf{r}, t | \mathbf{r}', \tau)|_{\tau = 0}$ are determined. A scrutiny of those results reveals that $G(\mathbf{r}, t | \mathbf{r}', \tau)$ can be determined from $G(\mathbf{r}, t | \mathbf{r}', \tau)|_{\tau = 0}$, merely by replacing t by $(t - \tau)$ in the latter. This conclusion forms the basis of our approach for the determination of the Green's function as now summarized.

To determine the Green's function $G(\mathbf{r}, t | \mathbf{r}', \tau)$ needed for the solution of a nonhomogeneous boundary-value problem of heat conduction, we need to consider only the homogeneous version of the same problem in the form given by equations (6-20). This homogeneous problem is readily solved by the method of separation of variables, the solution is expressed formally in the form given by equation (6-23) and $G(\mathbf{r},t|\mathbf{r}',\tau)|_{\tau=0}$ is determined by comparing this solution with that given by equation (6-22). Then, the desired Green's function $G(\mathbf{r},t|\mathbf{r}',\tau)$ is determined by replacing t by $(t-\tau)$ in the expression for $G(\mathbf{r},t|\mathbf{r}',\tau)|_{\tau=0}$. This procedure is now illustrated with the following simple example.

Example 6-1. Determine the Green's function appropriate for the solution of the following nonhomogeneous heat-conduction problem for a solid cylinder:

$$\frac{1}{r}\frac{\partial}{\partial r}\left(r\frac{\partial T}{\partial r}\right)+\frac{1}{k}g(r,t)=\frac{1}{\alpha}\frac{\partial T}{\partial t} \qquad \text{in } 0 \le r < b,\ t > 0 \qquad (6\text{-}25a)$$

$$T = f(t) \qquad\qquad\qquad \text{at } r = b,\ t > 0 \qquad (6\text{-}25b)$$

$$T = F(r) \qquad\qquad\qquad \text{for } t = 0,\ \text{in } 0 \le r \le b \quad (6\text{-}25c)$$

Solution. To determine the desired Green's function we consider the homogeneous version of the problem defined by equations (6-25) for the same region given as

$$\frac{1}{r}\frac{\partial}{\partial r}\left(r\frac{\partial \psi}{\partial r}\right)=\frac{1}{\alpha}\frac{\partial \psi}{\partial t} \qquad \text{in } 0 \le r < b,\ t > 0 \qquad (6\text{-}26a)$$

$$\psi = 0 \qquad\qquad\qquad\qquad \text{at } r = b,\ t > 0 \qquad (6\text{-}26b)$$

$$\psi = F(r) \qquad\qquad\qquad \text{for } t = 0,\ \text{in } 0 \le r \le b \quad (6\text{-}26c)$$

This homogeneous problem can readily be solved by the method of separation of variables; or its solution is immediately obtainable from equation (3-67) of Example 3-3. We write this solution in the same general form as given by equation (6-23), namely, as

$$\psi(r,t) = \int_{r'=0}^{b}\left[\frac{2}{b^2}\sum_{m=1}^{\infty}e^{-\alpha\beta_m^2 t}\frac{1}{J_1^2(\beta_m b)}r'J_0(\beta_m r)J_0(\beta_m r')\right]F(r')\,dr' \quad (6\text{-}27)$$

where β_m's are the roots of $J_0(\beta_m b) = 0$.

The solution of the homogeneous problem (6-26) in terms of Green's function is given, according to equation (6-22), as

$$\psi(r,t) = \int_{r'=0}^{b} G(r,t|r',\tau)|_{\tau=0}F(r')\,dr' \qquad (6\text{-}28)$$

By comparing the two solutions (6-27) and (6-28) we find

$$G(r,t|r',\tau)|_{\tau=0} = \frac{2}{b^2}\sum_{m=1}^{\infty}e^{-\alpha\beta_m^2 t}\frac{1}{J_1^2(\beta_m b)}r'J_0(\beta_m r)J_0(\beta_m r'). \qquad (6\text{-}29)$$

Then, replacing t by $(t - \tau)$ we obtain the desired Green's function as

$$G(r,t\,|\,r',\tau) = \frac{2}{b^2} \sum_{m=1}^{\infty} e^{-\alpha\beta_m^2(t-\tau)} \frac{1}{J_1^2(\beta_m b)} r' J_0(\beta_m r) J_0(\beta_m r'). \qquad (6\text{-}30)$$

In the following sections we illustrate the application of Green's function technique for the solution of nonhomogeneous boundary-value problems of heat conduction in the rectangular, cylindrical, and spherical coordinate systems.

6-3 APPLICATIONS OF GREEN'S FUNCTION IN THE RECTANGULAR COORDINATE SYSTEM

In this section we illustrate with examples the application of the Green's function technique in the solution of nonhomogeneous boundary-value problems of heat conduction in the rectangular coordinate system. For convenience in the determination of Green's function we consider, as examples, those problems for which solutions are available in Chapter 2 for their homogeneous part.

Example 6-2. An infinite medium $-\infty < x < \infty$ is initially at temperature $F(x)$; for times $t > 0$ there is heat generation within the solid at a rate of $g(x, t)$ per unit time, per unit volume. Obtain an expression for the temperature distribution $T(x, t)$ for times $t > 0$ by the Green's function technique.

Solution. The mathematical formulation of this problem is given as

$$\frac{\partial^2 T(x,t)}{\partial x^2} + \frac{1}{k}g(x,t) = \frac{1}{\alpha}\frac{\partial T}{\partial t} \qquad \text{in} \ -\infty < x < \infty, \ t > 0 \qquad (6\text{-}31a)$$

$$T = F(x) \qquad\qquad \text{for } t = 0, \text{ in the region} \qquad (6\text{-}31b)$$

To determine the Green's function we consider the homogeneous version of this problem given as

$$\frac{\partial^2 \psi(x,t)}{\partial x^2} = \frac{1}{\alpha}\frac{\partial \psi(x,t)}{\partial t} \qquad \text{in} \ -\infty < x < \infty, \ t > 0 \qquad (6\text{-}32a)$$

$$\psi = F(x) \qquad\qquad \text{for } t = 0, \text{ in the region} \qquad (6\text{-}32b)$$

The solution of this homogeneous problem is obtainable from equation (2-70) as

$$\psi(x,t) = \int_{x'=-\infty}^{\infty} \left[(4\pi\alpha t)^{-1/2} \exp\left(-\frac{(x-x')^2}{4\alpha t} \right) \right] F(x')\,dx'. \qquad (6\text{-}33)$$

The solution of the problem (6-32) can be written in terms of Green's function, according to equation (6-22), as

$$\psi(x,t) = \int_{x'=-\infty}^{\infty} G(x,t\,|\,x',\tau)\big|_{\tau=0} F(x')\,dx' \tag{6-34}$$

A comparison of equations (6-33) and (6-34) yields

$$G(x,t\,|\,x',\tau)\big|_{\tau=0} = (4\pi\alpha t)^{-1/2} \exp\left(-\frac{(x-x')^2}{4\alpha t}\right) \tag{6-35}$$

The desired Green's function is obtained by replacing t by $(t-\tau)$ in equation (6-35); we find

$$G(x,t\,|\,x',\tau) = [4\pi\alpha(t-\tau)]^{-1/2} \exp\left(-\frac{(x-x')^2}{4\alpha(t-\tau)}\right) \tag{6-36}$$

Then the solution of the nonhomogeneous problem (6-31), according to equation (6-19), is given as

$$T(x,t) = (4\pi\alpha t)^{-1/2} \int_{x'=-\infty}^{\infty} \exp\left[-\frac{(x-x')^2}{4\alpha t}\right] F(x')\,dx'$$
$$+ \frac{\alpha}{k} \int_{\tau=0}^{t} d\tau \int_{x'=-\infty}^{\infty} [4\pi\alpha(t-\tau)]^{-1/2} \exp\left[-\frac{(x-x')^2}{4\alpha(t-\tau)}\right] g(x',\tau)\,dx'. \tag{6-37}$$

We now examine some special cases of the solution (6-37).

1. There is no heat generation. By setting $g(x',\tau)=0$, equation (6-37) reduces to

$$T(x,t) = (4\pi\alpha t)^{-1/2} \int_{x'=-\infty}^{\infty} \exp\left[-\frac{(x-x')^2}{4\alpha t}\right] F(x')\,dx' \tag{6-38}$$

which is the same as that given by equation (2-70).

2. Medium is initially at zero temperature, an instantaneous distributed heat source of strength $g_i(x)$ Ws/m^3 (or Btu/ft^3) releases its heat spontaneously at time $t=0$. By setting

$$F(x) = 0, \qquad g(x,t) = g_i(x)\delta(t-0) \tag{6-39}$$

equation (6-37) reduces to

$$T(x,t) = (4\pi\alpha t)^{-1/2} \int_{x'=-\infty}^{\infty} \exp\left[-\frac{(x-x')^2}{4\alpha t}\right] \left[\frac{\alpha}{k} g_i(x')\right] dx' \tag{6-40}$$

A comparison of equations (6-38) and (6-40) reveals that

$$F(x') \equiv \frac{\alpha}{k} g_i(x') = \frac{1}{\rho c_p} g_i(x') \tag{6-41}$$

which is in agreement with the result given by equation (6-5). Equation (6-41) implies that the heat-conduction problem for an instantaneous distributed heat source $g_i(x)$ releasing its heat at time $t = 0$ is equivalent to an initial value problem with the initial temperature distribution as given by equation (6-41).

3.   Medium is initially at zero temperature; for times $t > 0$ a plane heat source of strength $g_s(t)$ W/m^2 (or Btu/hr ft^2) situated at $x = a$ releases its heat continuously. By setting

$$F(x) = 0, \qquad g(x, t) = g_s(t)\delta(x - a) \tag{6-42}$$

equation (6-37) reduces to

$$T(x, t) = \frac{\alpha}{k} \int_{\tau=0}^{t} [4\pi\alpha(t - \tau)]^{-1/2} \exp\left[-\frac{(x - a)^2}{4\alpha(t - \tau)} \right] g_s(\tau) d\tau \tag{6-43}$$

Example 6-3.   A slab, $0 \le x \le L$, is initially at temperature $F(x)$. For times $t > 0$, the boundaries at $x = 0$ and $x = L$ are maintained at temperatures $f_1(t)$ and $f_2(t)$ respectively, whereas heat is generated in the medium at a rate of $g(x, t)$ W/m^3 (or Btu/hr ft^3). Obtain an expression for the temperature distribution $T(x, t)$ in the slab for times $t > 0$.

Solution.   The mathematical formulation of this problem is given as

$$\frac{\partial^2 T(x, t)}{\partial x^2} + \frac{1}{k} g(x, t) = \frac{1}{\alpha} \frac{\partial T(x, t)}{\partial t} \qquad \text{in } 0 < x < L, \ t > 0 \tag{6-44a}$$

$$T = f_1(t) \qquad\qquad \text{at } x = 0, \ t > 0 \tag{6-44b}$$

$$T = f_2(t) \qquad\qquad \text{at } x = L, \ t > 0 \tag{6-44c}$$

$$T = F(x) \qquad\qquad \text{for } t = 0, \text{ in } 0 \le x \le L \tag{6-44d}$$

To determine the appropriate Green's function, we consider the homogeneous version of this problem as

$$\frac{\partial^2 \psi(x, t)}{\partial x^2} = \frac{1}{\alpha} \frac{\partial \psi(x, t)}{\partial t} \qquad \text{in } 0 < x < L, \ t > 0 \tag{6-45a}$$

$$\psi = 0 \qquad\qquad \text{at } x = 0 \text{ and } x = L, \ t > 0 \tag{6-45b}$$

$$\psi = F(x) \qquad\qquad \text{for } t = 0, \text{ in } 0 \le x \le L \tag{6-45c}$$

The problem (6-45) is exactly the same as that given by equations (2-161), and its solution is obtainable from equations (2-164) and (2-165a, b) as

$$\psi(x,t) = \int_{x'=0}^{L} \left[\frac{2}{L} \sum_{m=1}^{\infty} e^{-\alpha \beta_m^2 t} \sin \beta_m x \sin \beta_m x' \right] F(x')\,dx' \qquad (6\text{-}46)$$

where

$$\beta_m = \frac{m\pi}{L}, \qquad m = 1, 2, 3, \ldots$$

Also, the solution of problem (6-45) in terms of Green's function is given, according to equation (6-22), as

$$\psi(x,t) = \int_{x'=0}^{L} G(x,t|x',\tau)\big|_{\tau=0} F(x')\,dx' \qquad (6\text{-}47)$$

A comparison of equations (6-46) and (6-47) gives

$$G(x,t|x',\tau)\big|_{\tau=0} = \frac{2}{L} \sum_{m=1}^{\infty} e^{-\alpha \beta_m^2 t} \sin \beta_m x \sin \beta_m x' \qquad (6\text{-}48)$$

The desired Green's function is obtained by replacing t by $(t-\tau)$ in equation (6-48); we find

$$G(x,t|x',\tau) = \frac{2}{L} \sum_{m=1}^{\infty} e^{-\alpha \beta_m^2 (t-\tau)} \sin \beta_m x \sin \beta_m x' \qquad (6\text{-}49)$$

Then the solution of the nonhomogeneous problem (6-44) is given in terms of the above Green's function, according to equation (6-19), as

$$\begin{aligned}
T(x,t) = {} & \int_{x'=0}^{L} G(x,t|x',\tau)\big|_{\tau=0} F(x')\,dx' \\[4pt]
& + \frac{\alpha}{k} \int_{\tau=0}^{t} d\tau \int_{x'=0}^{L} G(x,t|x',\tau) g(x',\tau)\,dx' \\[4pt]
& + \alpha \int_{\tau=0}^{t} \frac{\partial G(x,t|x',\tau)}{\partial x'}\bigg|_{x'=0} f_1(\tau)\,d\tau \\[4pt]
& - \alpha \int_{\tau=0}^{t} \frac{\partial G(x,t|x',\tau)}{\partial x'}\bigg|_{x'=L} f_2(\tau)\,d\tau \qquad (6\text{-}50)
\end{aligned}$$

We note that in the problem (6-44) the boundary conditions are both of the first kind. Therefore, in the solution (6-50), we made replacements according to equation (6-16) in the terms involving the boundary-condition functions $f_1(\tau)$ and $f_2(\tau)$. Namely, we replaced $G|_{x'=0}$ by $+(\partial G/\partial x')|_{x'=0}$ for the terms involving $f_1(\tau)$ and $G|_{x'=L}$ by $-(\partial G/\partial x')|_{x'=L}$ for the term involving $f_2(\tau)$. It is to be noted that the positive sign for the term $+(\partial G/\partial x')|_{x'=0}$ is due to the fact that the outward drawn normal at the boundary surface $x = 0$ is in the negative x direction.

Introducing the above expression for the Green's function into equation (6-50) we obtain the solution in the form

$$
\begin{aligned}
T(x,t) = & \frac{2}{L} \sum_{m=1}^{\infty} e^{-\alpha \beta_m^2 t} \sin \beta_m x \int_{x'=0}^{L} \sin \beta_m x' F(x')\, dx' \\
& + \frac{\alpha}{k} \frac{2}{L} \sum_{m=1}^{\infty} e^{-\alpha \beta_m^2 t} \sin \beta_m x \int_{\tau=0}^{t} e^{\alpha \beta_m^2 t}\, d\tau \int_{x'=0}^{L} \sin \beta_m x' g(x', \tau)\, dx' \\
& + \alpha \frac{2}{L} \sum_{m=1}^{\infty} e^{-\alpha \beta_m^2 t} \beta_m \sin \beta_m x \int_{\tau=0}^{t} e^{\alpha \beta_m^2 \tau} f_1(\tau)\, d\tau \\
& - \alpha \frac{2}{L} \sum_{m=1}^{\infty} (-1)^m e^{-\alpha \beta_m^2 t} \beta_m \sin \beta_m x \int_{\tau=0}^{t} e^{\alpha \beta_m^2 \tau} f_2(\tau)\, d\tau \qquad (6\text{-}51)
\end{aligned}
$$

where

$$
\beta_m = \frac{m\pi}{L}, \qquad m = 1, 2, 3, \ldots
$$

The special case of this solution for $F(x) = 0$ and $g(x,t) = 0$ is exactly the same as that given by equation (5-44) of the solution of problem (5-39) obtained by Duhamel's method.

The solution (6-51) appears to vanish at the two boundaries $x = 0$ and $x = L$, instead of yielding the boundary conditions functions $f_1(t)$ and $f_2(t)$ at these locations. The reason for this is that these two terms involve series that are not uniformly convergent at the location $x = 0$ and $x = L$. This difficulty can be alleviated by integrating by parts the last two terms in equation (6-51), and replacing the resulting series expressions by their equivalent closed-form expressions. The details of this portion of the analysis is exactly the same as that considered in equations (5-45) to (5-50). Therefore, the alternative form of solution (6-51) that is uniformly convergent at $x = 0$ and $x = L$ is obtained by replacing the last two terms in this equation by the expression given by equation (5-50).

We now examine some special cases of solution (6-51):

1. The medium is initially at zero temperature. The boundaries at $x = 0$ and $x = L$ are kept at zero temperature for times $t > 0$, and a distributed heat source of strength $g_i(x)$ Ws/m^3 (or Btu/ft^3) releases its heat spontaneously at time $t = 0$.

For this special case we set

$$
F(x) = 0, \qquad f_1(t) = 0, \qquad f_2(t) = 0, \qquad \text{and} \qquad g(x,t) = g_i(x)\delta(t - 0) \quad (6\text{-}52)
$$

Then, the solution (6-51) reduces to

$$T(x,t) = \frac{2}{L} \sum_{m=1}^{\infty} e^{-\alpha\beta_m^2 t} \sin \beta_m x \int_{x'=0}^{L} \left[\frac{\alpha}{k} g_i(x') \right] \sin\beta_m x' \, dx'. \tag{6-53}$$

A comparison of this solution with the first term in equation (6-51) reveals that the problem of heat conduction for an instantaneous distributed heat source $g_i(x)$ Ws/m^3 releasing its heat at time $t = 0$ is equivalent to the problem in which the medium is initially at a temperature

$$F(x') \equiv \frac{\alpha}{k} g_i(x') = \frac{1}{\rho c_p} g_i(x') \tag{6-54}$$

2. Medium is initially at zero temperature; for times $t > 0$ boundaries at $x = 0$ and $x = L$ are kept at zero temperature and a plane heat source of strength $g_s(t)$ W/m^2 (or Btu/hr ft^2) situated at $x = a(< L)$ releases its heat continuously. For this case we set

$$F(x) = f_1(t) = f_2(t) = 0 \quad \text{and} \quad g(x,t) = g_s(t)\delta(x-a) \tag{6-55}$$

Then equation (6-51) reduces to

$$T(x,t) = \frac{2\alpha}{kL} \sum_{m=1}^{\infty} e^{-\alpha\beta_m^2 t} \sin \beta_m x \sin \beta_m a \int_{\tau=0}^{t} e^{\alpha\beta_m^2 \tau} g_s(\tau) \, d\tau \tag{6-56}$$

where

$$\beta_m = \frac{m\pi}{L}, \qquad m = 1, 2, 3, \ldots$$

Example 6-4. A rectangular parallelepiped, $0 \le x \le a, 0 \le y \le b, 0 \le z \le c$, is initially at temperature $F(x,y,z)$. For times $t > 0$ heat is generated in the medium at a rate of $g(x,y,z,t)$ W/m^3 (or Btu/hr ft^3) while the boundary surfaces are kept at zero temperature. Obtain an expression for the temperature distribution in the solid for times $t > 0$.

Solution. The mathematical formulation of this problem is given as

$$\frac{\partial^2 T}{\partial x^2} + \frac{\partial^2 T}{\partial y^2} + \frac{\partial^2 T}{\partial z^2} + \frac{1}{k} g(x,y,z,t) = \frac{1}{\alpha} \frac{\partial T}{\partial t}$$

$$\text{in } 0 < x < a, \ 0 < y < b, \ 0 < z < c, \text{ for } t > 0 \tag{6-57a}$$

$$T = 0 \qquad \text{at all boundaries, for } t > 0 \tag{6-57b}$$

$$T = F(x,y,z) \qquad \text{for } t = 0, \text{ in the region} \tag{6-57c}$$

To determine the appropriate Green's function, we consider the homogeneous version of this problem as

$$\frac{\partial^2 \psi}{\partial x^2} + \frac{\partial^2 \psi}{\partial y^2} + \frac{\partial^2 \psi}{\partial z^2} = \frac{1}{\alpha} \frac{\partial \psi}{\partial t}$$

$$\text{in } 0 < x < a, \ 0 < y < b, \ 0 < z < c, \text{ for } t > 0 \quad \text{(6-58a)}$$

$$\psi = 0 \qquad\qquad \text{at all boundaries, for } t > 0 \qquad\qquad \text{(6-58b)}$$

$$\psi = F(x, y, z) \qquad \text{for } t = 0, \text{ in the region.} \qquad\qquad \text{(6-58c)}$$

The problem (6-58) is the same as that given by equations (2-87); its solution is obtainable from equation (2-92) as

$$\psi(x, y, z, t) = \int_{x'=0}^{a} \int_{y'=0}^{b} \int_{z'=0}^{c} \left[\frac{8}{abc} \sum_{m=1}^{\infty} \sum_{n=1}^{\infty} \sum_{p=1}^{\infty} e^{-\alpha(\beta_m^2 + \gamma_n^2 + \eta_p^2)t} \right.$$

$$\left. \cdot \sin \beta_m x \sin \gamma_n y \sin \eta_p z \sin \beta_m x' \sin \gamma_n y' \sin \eta_p z' \right]$$

$$\cdot F(x', y', z') \, dx' \, dy' \, dz' \qquad\qquad \text{(6-59)}$$

where

$$\beta_m = \frac{m\pi}{a}, \qquad \gamma_n = \frac{n\pi}{b}, \qquad \eta_p = \frac{p\pi}{c}, \qquad \text{with } (m, n, p) = 1, 2, 3, 4 \dots$$

Also the solution of the problem (6-58) in terms of Green's function is given, according to equation (6-22), as

$$\psi(x, y, z, t) = \int_{x'=0}^{a} \int_{y'=0}^{b} \int_{z'=0}^{c} G(x, y, z, t \,|\, x', y', z', \tau)\Big|_{\tau=0}$$

$$\cdot F(x', y', z') \, dx' \, dy' \, dz' \qquad\qquad \text{(6-60)}$$

A comparison of equations (6-59) and (6-60) gives

$$G(x, y, z, t \,|\, x', y', z', \tau)\Big|_{\tau=0} = \frac{8}{abc} \sum_{m=1}^{\infty} \sum_{n=1}^{\infty} \sum_{p=1}^{\infty} e^{-\alpha(\beta_m^2 + \gamma_n^2 + \eta_p^2)t}$$

$$\cdot \sin \beta_m x \sin \gamma_n y \sin \eta_p z$$

$$\cdot \sin \beta_m x' \sin \gamma_n y' \sin \eta_p z' \qquad\qquad \text{(6-61)}$$

The desired Green's function is obtained by replacing t by $(t - \tau)$ in equation (6-61); we find

$$G(x, y, z, t \,|\, x', y', z', \tau) = \frac{8}{abc} \sum_{m=1}^{\infty} \sum_{n=1}^{\infty} \sum_{p=1}^{\infty} e^{-\alpha(\beta_m^2 + \gamma_n^2 + \eta_p^2)(t - \tau)}$$

$$\cdot \sin \beta_m x \sin \gamma_n y \sin \eta_p z$$

$$\cdot \sin \beta_m x' \sin \gamma_n y' \sin \eta_p z'. \qquad\qquad \text{(6-62)}$$

Then the solution of the nonhomogeneous problem (6-57) is given in terms of the above Green's function, according to equation (6-14), as

$$
\begin{aligned}
T(x,y,z,t) = \int\limits_{x'=0}^{a} \int\limits_{y'=0}^{b} \int\limits_{z'=0}^{c} & \left. G(x,y,z,t\,|\,x',y',z',\tau)\right|_{\tau=0} \\
& \cdot F(x',y',z')\,dx'\,dy'\,dz' \\
+ \frac{\alpha}{k} \int\limits_{\tau=0}^{t} d\tau \int\limits_{x'=0}^{a} & \int\limits_{y'=0}^{b} \int\limits_{z'=0}^{c} \\
& \cdot G(x,y,z,t\,|\,x',y',z',\tau)g(x',y',z',\tau)\,dx'\,dy'\,dz' \qquad (6\text{-}63)
\end{aligned}
$$

where the Green's function is as defined above.

6-4   APPLICATIONS OF GREEN'S FUNCTION IN THE CYLINDRICAL COORDINATE SYSTEM

In this section we illustrate with examples the application of Green's function in the solution of nonhomogeneous boundary-value problems of heat conduction in the cylindrical coordinate system. For convenience in the determination of Green's function, we have chosen those problems for which solutions are available in Chapter 3 for their homogeneous part.

Example 6-5.   A solid cylinder, $0 \le r \le b$, is initially at temperature $F(r)$. For times $t > 0$ there is heat generation in the medium at a rate of $g(r,t)\ \mathrm{W/m^3}$ (or $\mathrm{Btu/hr\ ft^3}$) while the boundary surface at $r = b$ is kept at temperature $f(t)$. Obtain an expression for the temperature distribution $T(r,t)$ in the cylinder for times $t > 0$.

Solution.   The mathematical formulation of this problem is given as

$$
\frac{\partial^2 T}{\partial r^2} + \frac{1}{r}\frac{\partial T}{\partial r} + \frac{1}{k}g(r,t) = \frac{1}{\alpha}\frac{\partial T}{\partial t} \qquad \text{in } 0 \le r < b,\ t > 0 \qquad (6\text{-}64a)
$$

$$
T = f(t) \qquad\qquad\qquad\qquad \text{at } r = b,\ \text{for } t > 0 \qquad (6\text{-}64b)
$$

$$
T = F(r) \qquad\qquad\qquad\qquad \text{for } t = 0,\ \text{in } 0 \le r \le b \qquad (6\text{-}64c)
$$

To determine the appropriate Green's function, we consider the homogeneous version of this problem as

$$
\frac{\partial^2 \psi}{\partial r^2} + \frac{1}{r}\frac{\partial \psi}{\partial r} = \frac{1}{\alpha}\frac{\partial \psi}{\partial t} \qquad \text{in } 0 \le r < b,\ t > 0 \qquad (6\text{-}65a)
$$

$$
\psi = 0 \qquad\qquad\qquad\qquad \text{at } r = b,\ t > 0 \qquad (6\text{-}65b)
$$

$$
\psi = F(r) \qquad\qquad\qquad\qquad \text{for } t = 0,\ \text{in } 0 \le r \le b \qquad (6\text{-}65c)
$$

The problem (6-65) is the same as that considered in Example 3-3. Its solution is obtainable from equation (3-67) as

$$\psi(r,t) = \int_{r'=0}^{b} r' \left[\frac{2}{b^2} \sum_{m=1}^{\infty} e^{-\alpha\beta_m^2 t} \frac{J_0(\beta_m r)}{J_1^2(\beta_m b)} J_0(\beta_m r') \right] F(r') \, dr' \qquad (6\text{-}66)$$

where β_m's are positive roots of $J_0(\beta_m b) = 0$. Also the solution of problem (6-65) in terms of Green's function is given, according to equation (6-19), as

$$\psi(r,t) = \int_{r'=0}^{b} r' G(r,t \,|\, r', \tau)\big|_{\tau=0} F(r') \, dr' \qquad (6\text{-}67)$$

where r' is the Sturm-Liouville weight function. A comparison of equations (6-66) and (6-67) yields

$$G(r,t \,|\, r', \tau)\big|_{\tau=0} = \frac{2}{b^2} \sum_{m=1}^{\infty} e^{-\alpha\beta_m^2 t} \frac{J_0(\beta_m r)}{J_1^2(\beta_m b)} J_0(\beta_m r') \qquad (6\text{-}68)$$

The desired Green's function is obtained by replacing t by $(t - \tau)$ in equation (6-68); we find

$$G(r,t \,|\, r', \tau) = \frac{2}{b^2} \sum_{m=1}^{\infty} e^{-\alpha\beta_m^2 (t-\tau)} \frac{J_0(\beta_m r)}{J_1^2(\beta_m b)} J_0(\beta_m r'). \qquad (6\text{-}69)$$

Then the solution of the nonhomogeneous problem (6-64) in terms of the above Green's function is given, according to equation (6-19), as

$$\begin{aligned}
T(r,t) = {} & \int_{r'=0}^{b} r' G(r,t \,|\, r', \tau)\big|_{\tau=0} F(r') \, dr' \\
& + \frac{\alpha}{k} \int_{\tau=0}^{t} d\tau \int_{r'=0}^{b} r' G(r,t \,|\, r', \tau) g(r', \tau) \, dr' \\
& - \alpha \int_{\tau=0}^{t} \left[r' \frac{\partial G}{\partial r'} \right]_{r'=b} \cdot f(\tau) \, d\tau
\end{aligned} \qquad (6\text{-}70)$$

Here since the boundary condition at $r = b$ is of the first kind, we replaced $[G]_{r'=b}$ by $-[\partial G/\partial r']_{r'=b}$ according to equation (6-16).

Introducing the above Green's function into equation (6-70) and noting that

$$\left[r' \frac{\partial G}{\partial r'} \right]_{r'=b} = -\frac{2}{b} \sum_{m=1}^{\infty} e^{-\alpha\beta_m^2 (t-\tau)} \beta_m \frac{J_0(\beta_m r)}{J_1(\beta_m b)} \qquad (6\text{-}71)$$

we obtain

$$T(r,t) = \frac{2}{b^2} \sum_{m=1}^{\infty} e^{-\alpha\beta_m^2 t} \frac{J_0(\beta_m r)}{J_1^2(\beta_m b)} \int_{r'=0}^{b} r' J_0(\beta_m r') F(r') \, dr'$$

$$+ \frac{2\alpha}{kb^2} \sum_{m=1}^{\infty} e^{-\alpha\beta_m^2 t} \frac{J_0(\beta_m r)}{J_1^2(\beta_m b)} \int_{\tau=0}^{t} e^{\alpha\beta_m^2 \tau} d\tau$$

$$\int_{r'=0}^{b} r' J_0(\beta_m r') g(r', \tau) dr' \tag{6-72}$$

$$+ \frac{2\alpha}{b} \sum_{m=1}^{\infty} e^{-\alpha\beta_m^2 t} \beta_m \frac{J_0(\beta_m r)}{J_1(\beta_m b)} \int_{\tau=0}^{t} e^{\alpha\beta_m^2 \tau} f(\tau) d\tau$$

where β_m's are the positive roots of $J_0(\beta_m b) = 0$.

In this solution the first term on the right-hand side is for the effects of the initial condition function $F(r)$, and it is the same as that given by equation (3-67). The second term is for the effects of the heat generation function $g(r, t)$. The last term is for the effects of the boundary condition function $f(t)$; this term is the same as the solution given by equation (5-56), which was obtained by Duhamel's method. The above solution (6-72) appears to vanish at the boundary $r = b$ instead of yielding the boundary condition function $f(t)$. The reason for this is that the last term in equation (6-72) involves a series that is not uniformly convergent at $r = b$. This difficulty can be alleviated by integrating the last term by parts as it has been done in equation (5-57), and replacing the resulting series by its closed-form expression as given by equation (5-58). We shall not repeat this procedure here because it is exactly the same as those described by equations (5-56) through (5-59). Therefore, the last term in equation (6-72) can be replaced by equation (5-59). Then the alternative form of solution (6-72), which yields the proper boundary condition at $r = b$, becomes

$$T(r, t) = \frac{2}{b^2} \sum_{m=1}^{\infty} e^{-\alpha\beta_m^2 t} \frac{J_0(\beta_m r)}{J_1^2(\beta_m b)} \int_{r'=0}^{b} r' J_0(\beta_m r') F(r') dr'$$

$$+ \frac{2\alpha}{kb^2} \sum_{m=1}^{\infty} e^{-\alpha\beta_m^2 t} \frac{J_0(\beta_m r)}{J_1^2(\beta_m b)} \int_{\tau=0}^{t} e^{\alpha\beta_m^2 \tau} d\tau$$

$$\int_{r'=0}^{b} r' J_0(\beta_m r') g(r', \tau) dr'$$

$$+ f(t) - \frac{2}{b} \sum_{m=1}^{\infty} \frac{J_0(\beta_m r)}{\beta_m J_1(\beta_m b)} \left[f(0) e^{-\alpha\beta_m^2 t} + \int_0^t e^{-\alpha\beta_m^2 (t-\tau)} df(\tau) \right] \tag{6-73}$$

where β_m's are the positive roots of $J_0(\beta_m b) = 0$.

Clearly, several special cases are obtainable from this solution. We now examine some of them.

1. Cylinder is initially at zero temperature; there is no heat generation, the boundary surface at $r = b$ is maintained at a constant temperature T_b.

For this special case we set in equation (6-73)

$$F(r) = 0, \qquad g(r, t) = 0, \qquad \text{and} \qquad f(t) = T_b.$$

Then equation (6-73) reduces to

$$T(r, t) = T_b - \frac{2T_b}{b} \sum_{m=1}^{\infty} \frac{J_0(\beta_m r)}{\beta_m J_1(\beta_m b)} e^{-\alpha \beta_m^2 t}. \tag{6-74}$$

2. Cylinder has zero initial temperature, zero surface temperature, but heat is generated within the solid at a constant rate of g_0 W/m^3.

By setting in equation (6-73), $F(r) = 0$, $f(t) = 0$, and $g(r, t) = g_0$, we obtain

$$T(r, t) = \frac{2g_0}{kb} \sum_{m=1}^{\infty} \frac{J_0(\beta_m r)}{\beta_m^3 J_1(\beta_m b)} - \frac{2g_0}{kb} \sum_{m=1}^{\infty} e^{-\alpha \beta_m^2 t} \frac{J_0(\beta_m r)}{\beta_m^3 J_1(\beta_m b)}. \tag{6-75a}$$

For $t \to \infty$, the second term on the right-hand side vanishes and the first term must be equal to the steady-state temperature distribution in the cylinder, namely,

$$T(r, \infty) = \frac{2g_0}{kb} \sum_{m=1}^{\infty} \frac{J_0(\beta_m r)}{\beta_m^3 J_1(\beta_m b)} \equiv \frac{g_0(b^2 - r^2)}{4k} \tag{6-75b}$$

Introducing (6.75b) into (6.75a), the solution becomes

$$T(r, t) = \frac{g_0(b^2 - r^2)}{4k} - \frac{2g_0}{kb} \sum_{m=1}^{\infty} e^{-\alpha \beta_m^2 t} \frac{J_0(\beta_m r)}{\beta_m^3 J_1(\beta_m b)} \tag{6-75c}$$

which is the same as solution (3-219) for $F(r) = 0$.

3. Cylinder has zero initial temperature, zero surface temperature, but there is a line heat source of strength $g_L(t)$ W/m (or Btu/hr ft) situated along the center line of the cylinder and releasing its heat continuously for times $t > 0$.

For this special case we set in equation (6-73)

$$F(r) = 0, \qquad f(t) = 0, \qquad \text{and} \qquad g(r', \tau) = g_L(\tau) \frac{1}{2\pi r'} \delta(r' - 0)$$

Then, equation (6-73) reduces to

$$T(r, t) = \frac{\alpha}{k\pi b^2} \sum_{m=1}^{\infty} e^{-\alpha \beta_m^2 t} \frac{J_0(\beta_m r)}{J_1^2(\beta_m b)} \int_{\tau=0}^{t} e^{\alpha \beta_m^2 \tau} g_L(\tau) \, d\tau \tag{6-76}$$

4. Cylinder has zero initial temperature, zero surface temperature, but there is an instantaneous volume heat source of strength $g_i(r)$ Ws/m^3 (or Btu/ft^3) which releases its heat spontaneously at time $t = 0$.

For this case we set in equation (6-73)

$$F(r) = 0, \qquad f(t) = 0, \qquad \text{and} \qquad g(r', \tau) = g_i(r')\delta(\tau - 0)$$

Then equation (6-73) reduces to

$$T(r, t) = \frac{2}{b^2} \sum_{m=1}^{\infty} e^{-\alpha\beta_m^2 t} \frac{J_0(\beta_m r)}{J_1^2(\beta_m b)} \int_{r'=0}^{b} r' J_0(\beta_m r') \frac{\alpha g_i(r')}{k} dr' \qquad (6-77)$$

A comparison of this solution with the first term in equation (6-73) reveals that

$$\frac{\alpha g_i(r)}{k} \equiv F(r)$$

Namely, an instantaneous volume heat source of strength $g_i(r)$ Ws/m^3 releasing its heat spontaneously at time $t = 0$ is equivalent to an initial temperature distribution $\alpha g_i(r)/k$.

Example 6-6. A hollow cylinder, $a \leq r \leq b$, is initially at temperature $F(r)$. For times $t > 0$ there is heat generation in the medium at a rate of $g(r, t)$ W/m^3 (or Btu/hr ft^3) while the boundary surfaces at $r = a$ and $r = b$ are kept at zero temperatures. Obtain an expression for the temperature distribution $T(r, t)$ in the cylinder for times $t > 0$.

Solution. The mathematical formulation of this problem is given as

$$\frac{\partial^2 T}{\partial r^2} + \frac{1}{r}\frac{\partial T}{\partial r} + \frac{1}{k}g(r, t) = \frac{1}{\alpha}\frac{\partial T}{\partial t} \qquad \text{in } a < r < b, \ t > 0 \qquad (6\text{-}78a)$$

$$T = 0 \qquad\qquad\qquad \text{at } r = a, \ r = b, \ t > 0 \qquad (6\text{-}78b)$$

$$T = F(r) \qquad\qquad\qquad \text{for } t = 0, \ \text{in the region} \qquad (6\text{-}78c)$$

To determine the appropriate Green's function, we consider the homogeneous version of this problem as

$$\frac{\partial^2 \psi}{\partial r^2} + \frac{1}{r}\frac{\partial \psi}{\partial r} = \frac{1}{\alpha}\frac{\partial \psi}{\partial t} \qquad \text{in } a < r < b, \ t > 0 \qquad (6\text{-}79a)$$

$$\psi = 0 \qquad\qquad\qquad \text{at } r = a, \ r = b, \ t > 0 \qquad (6\text{-}79b)$$

$$\psi = F(r) \qquad\qquad\qquad \text{for } t = 0, \ \text{in the region} \qquad (6\text{-}79c)$$

The problem (6-79) is the same as that considered in Example 3-5; the solution is obtainable from equation (3-78) as

$$
\psi(r,t) = \int_{r'=a}^{b} r' \left[\frac{\pi^2}{2} \sum_{m=1}^{\infty} e^{-\alpha\beta_m^2 t} \frac{\beta_m^2 J_0^2(\beta_m a)}{J_0^2(\beta_m a) - J_0^2(\beta_m b)} \right.
$$
$$
\left. \cdot R_0(\beta_m r) R_0(\beta_m r') \right] F(r') \, dr' \tag{6-80a}
$$

where

$$
R_0(\beta_m, r) = J_0(\beta_m r) Y_0(\beta_m b) - J_0(\beta_m b) Y_0(\beta_m r) \tag{6-80b}
$$

and β_m's are the positive roots of

$$
J_0(\beta_m a) Y_0(\beta_m b) - J_0(\beta_m b) Y_0(\beta_m a) = 0 \tag{6-80c}
$$

Also the solution of the problem (6-79) in terms of Green's function is given, according to equation (6-19) as

$$
\psi(r,t) = \int_{r'=a}^{b} r' G(r,t \,|\, r', \tau)|_{\tau=0} F(r') \, dr' \tag{6-81}
$$

A comparison of equations (6-80b) and (6-81) yields

$$
G(r,t \,|\, r', \tau)|_{\tau=0} = \frac{\pi^2}{2} \sum_{m=1}^{\infty} e^{-\alpha\beta_m^2 t} \frac{\beta_m^2 J_0(\beta_m a)}{J_0^2(\beta_m a) - J_0^2(\beta_m b)} R_0(\beta_m r) R_0(\beta_m r'). \tag{6-82}
$$

The desired Green's function is obtained by replacing t by $(t - \tau)$ in equation (6-82); we find

$$
G(r,t \,|\, r', \tau) = \frac{\pi^2}{2} \sum_{m=1}^{\infty} e^{-\alpha\beta_m^2 (t - \tau)} \frac{\beta_m^2 J_0(\beta_m a)}{J_0^2(\beta_m a) - J_0^2(\beta_m b)} R_0(\beta_m r) R_0(\beta_m r'). \tag{6-83}
$$

Then the solution of the above nonhomogeneous problem (6-78) in terms of this Green's function is given, according to equation (6-19), as

$$
T(r,t) = \int_{r'=a}^{b} r' G(r,t \,|\, r', \tau)|_{\tau=0} F(r') \, dr'
$$
$$
+ \frac{\alpha}{k} \int_{\tau=0}^{t} d\tau \int_{r'=a}^{b} r' G(r,t \,|\, r', \tau) g(r', \tau) \, dr' \tag{6-84}
$$

Introducing the foregoing Green's function into equation (6-84), the solution of the problem (6-78) becomes

$$
T(r,t) = \frac{\pi^2}{2} \sum_{m=1}^{\infty} e^{-\alpha\beta_m^2 t} \frac{\beta_m^2 J_0(\beta_m a)}{J_0^2(\beta_m a) - J_0^2(\beta_m b)} R_0(\beta_m r)
$$
$$
\cdot \int_{r'=a}^{b} r' R_0(\beta_m r') F(r') \, dr' \tag{6-85}
$$

$$+ \frac{\pi^2 \alpha}{2k} \sum_{m=1}^{\infty} e^{-\alpha \beta_m^2 t} \frac{\beta_m^2 J_0(\beta_m a)}{J_0^2(\beta_m a) - J_0^2(\alpha_m b)} R_0(\beta_m r)$$

$$\cdot \int_{\tau=0}^{t} e^{\alpha \beta_m^2 \tau} d\tau \int_{r'=a}^{b} r' R_0(\beta_m r') g(r', \tau) dr'$$

where $R_0(\beta_m, r)$ as given by equation (6-80b) and β_m's are the roots of the transcendental equation (6-80c). Clearly, several special cases are obtainable from the solution (6-85).

6-5   APPLICATIONS OF GREEN'S FUNCTION IN THE SPHERICAL COORDINATE SYSTEM

In this section we illustrate with examples the application of Green's function in the solution of nonhomogeneous boundary-value problems of heat conduction in the spherical coordinate system. For convenience in the determination of Green's function we have chosen those examples for which solutions are available in Chapter 4 for their homogeneous parts.

Example 6-7.   A hollow sphere $a \le r \le b$, is initially at temperature $F(r)$. For time $t > 0$ heat is generated within the sphere at a rate of $g(r, t)$ W/m³ (or Btu/hr ft³) while the boundaries at $r = a$ and $r = b$ are kept at zero temperature. Obtain an expression for the temperature distribution $T(r, t)$ in the sphere for times $t > 0$.

Solution.   The mathematical formulation of this problem is given as

$$\frac{1}{r} \frac{\partial^2}{\partial r^2}(rT) + \frac{1}{k}g(r, t) = \frac{1}{\alpha} \frac{\partial T}{\partial t} \qquad \text{in } a < r < b, \ t > 0 \qquad (6\text{-}86\text{a})$$

$$T = 0 \qquad \text{at } r = a \text{ and } r = b, \ t > 0 \quad (6\text{-}86\text{b})$$

$$T = F(r) \qquad \text{for } t = 0, \text{ in } a \le r \le b \qquad (6\text{-}86\text{c})$$

To determine the Green's function we consider the homogeneous version of this problem as

$$\frac{1}{r} \frac{\partial^2}{\partial r^2}(r\psi) = \frac{1}{\alpha} \frac{\partial \psi}{\partial t} \qquad \text{in } a < r < b, \ t > 0 \qquad (6\text{-}87\text{a})$$

$$\psi = 0 \qquad \text{at } r = a \text{ and } r = b, \ t > 0 \qquad (6\text{-}87\text{b})$$

$$\psi = F(r) \qquad \text{for } t = 0, \text{ in } a \le r \le b \qquad (6\text{-}87\text{c})$$

This homogeneous problem is the same as that considered in Example 4-3;

its solution is obtainable from equations (4-80) as

$$\psi(r,t) = \int_{r'=a}^{b} r'^2 \left[\frac{2}{r'r(b-a)} \sum_{m=1}^{\infty} e^{-\alpha\beta_m^2 t} \sin \beta_m(r'-a) \sin \beta_m(r-a) \right] F(r') dr'$$

(6-88a)

where β_m's are the positive roots of

$$\sin \beta_m(b-a) = 0$$

(6-88b)

or

$$\beta_m = \frac{m\pi}{b-a}, \qquad m = 1, 2, 3 \ldots$$

(6-88c)

The solution of the problem (6-87) in terms of Green's function is given, according to equation (6-22), as

$$\psi(r,t) = \int_{r'=a}^{b} r'^2 G(r,t|r',\tau)\big|_{\tau=0} F(r') dr'$$

(6-89)

where r'^2 is the Sturm-Liouville weight function. A comparison of equations (6-88a) and (6-89) gives

$$G(r,t|r',\tau)\big|_{\tau=0} = \frac{2}{r'r(b-a)} \sum_{m=1}^{\infty} e^{-\alpha\beta_m^2 t} \cdot \sin \beta_m(r'-a) \sin \beta_m(r-a).$$

(6-90)

The desired Green's function is obtained by replacing t by $(t-\tau)$ in equation (6-90); we find

$$G(r,t|r',\tau) = \frac{2}{r'r(b-a)} \sum_{m=1}^{\infty} e^{-\alpha\beta_m^2(t-\tau)} \cdot \sin \beta_m(r'-a) \sin \beta_m(r-a)$$

(6-91)

Then the solution of the nonhomogeneous problem (6-86) in terms of Green's function is given, according to equation (6-19), as

$$T(r,t) = \int_{r'=a}^{b} r'^2 G(r,t|r',\tau)\big|_{\tau=0} F(r') dr'$$

$$+ \frac{\alpha}{k} \int_{\tau=0}^{t} d\tau \int_{r'=a}^{b} r'^2 G(r,t|r',\tau) g(r',\tau) dr'$$

(6-92)

Introducing the above Green's function into equation (6-92), the solution becomes

$$T(r,t) = \frac{2}{r(b-a)} \sum_{m=1}^{\infty} e^{-\alpha\beta_m^2 t} \sin \beta_m(r-a) \int_{r'=a}^{b} r' \sin \beta_m(r'-a) F(r') dr'$$

$$+\frac{\alpha}{k}\frac{2}{r(b-a)}\sum_{m=1}^{\infty}e^{-\alpha\beta_m^2 t}\sin\beta_m(r-a)\int_{\tau=0}^{t}e^{\alpha\beta_m^2\tau}\,d\tau \qquad (6\text{-}93a)$$

$$\int_{r'=a}^{b}r'\sin\beta_m(r'-a)g(r',\tau)\,dr'$$

where β_m's are the positive roots of

$$\sin\beta_m(b-a)=0 \qquad (6\text{-}93b)$$

We now consider some special cases of the solution (6-93).

1. The medium is initially at zero temperature, the heat source is a spherical surface heat source of radius r_1 (i.e., $a < r_1 < b$) of total strength $g_s(t)$ W (or Btu/hr) which releases its heat continuously for times $t > 0$.

In this case we set in equation (6-93a)

$$F(r')=0, \qquad g(r',\tau)=g_s(\tau)\frac{1}{4\pi r'^2}\delta(r'-r_1) \qquad (6\text{-}94)$$

and perform the integration with respect to the variable r'. We find

$$T(r,t)=\frac{\alpha}{k}\frac{1}{2\pi r r_1(b-a)}\sum_{m=1}^{\infty}e^{-\alpha\beta_m^2 t}\sin\beta_m(r-a)$$

$$\cdot\sin\beta_m(r_1-a)\int_{\tau=0}^{t}e^{\alpha\beta_m^2\tau}g_s(\tau)\,d\tau \qquad (6\text{-}95a)$$

where

$$\beta_m=\frac{m\pi}{b-a}, \qquad m=1,2,3\dots \qquad (6\text{-}95b)$$

2. The medium is initially at zero temperature, the heat source is an instantaneous spherical surface heat source of radius r_1 (i.e., $a < r_1 < b$) of total strength g_{si} Ws (or Btu), which releases its heat spontaneously at time $t = 0$.

In this case we set in equation (6-93a)

$$F(r')=0, \qquad g(r',\tau)=g_{si}\frac{1}{4\pi r'^2}\delta(r'-r_1)\delta(\tau-0) \qquad (6\text{-}96)$$

and perform the integrations with respect to the variables r' and τ. We find

$$T(r,t)=\frac{\alpha}{k}\frac{1}{2\pi r r_1(b-a)}\sum_{m=1}^{\infty}e^{-\alpha\beta_m^2 t}\sin\beta_m(r-a)\sin\beta_m(r_1-a)g_{si} \qquad (6\text{-}97a)$$

where

$$\beta_m = \frac{m\pi}{b-a}, \qquad m = 1, 2, 3 \ldots \tag{6-97b}$$

Example 6-8. A solid sphere $0 \le r \le b$ is initially at zero temperature. For times $t > 0$ heat is generated within the sphere at a rate of $g(r, t)$ W/m³ (or Btu/hr ft³) while the boundary surface at $r = b$ is kept at zero temperature. Obtain an expression for the temperature distribution in the sphere by the Green's function approach.

Solution. The mathematical formulation of this problem is given as

$$\frac{1}{r}\frac{\partial^2}{\partial r^2}(rT) + \frac{1}{k}g(r, t) = \frac{1}{\alpha}\frac{\partial T}{\partial t} \qquad \text{in } 0 \le r \le b, \ t > 0 \tag{6-98a}$$

$$T = 0 \qquad \qquad \text{at } r = b, \ t > 0 \tag{6-98b}$$

$$T = 0 \qquad \qquad \text{for } t = 0, \ \text{in } 0 \le r \le b \tag{6-98c}$$

To determine the Green's function we consider the following homogeneous problem:

$$\frac{1}{r}\frac{\partial^2}{\partial r^2}(r\psi) = \frac{1}{\alpha}\frac{\partial \psi}{\partial t} \qquad \text{in } 0 \le r < b, \ t > 0 \tag{6-99a}$$

$$\psi = 0 \qquad \qquad \text{at } r = b, \ t > 0 \tag{6-99b}$$

$$\psi = F(r) \qquad \qquad \text{for } t = 0, \ \text{in } 0 \le r \le b \tag{6-99c}$$

The solution of the problem (6-99) is obtainable by converting it to a slab problem or directly from the solution (4-66) by setting $K \to \infty$. We find

$$\psi(r, t) = \int_{r'=0}^{b} r'^2 \left[\frac{2}{r'rb} \sum_{m=1}^{\infty} e^{-\alpha\beta_m^2 t} \sin \beta_m r' \sin \beta_m r \right] F(r') \, dr' \tag{6-100a}$$

where β_m's are the positive roots of

$$\sin \beta_m b = 0 \tag{6-100b}$$

or

$$\beta_m = \frac{m\pi}{b}, \qquad m = 1, 2, 3 \ldots$$

Also the solution of the problem (6-99) in terms of Green's function is given, according to equation (6-22), as

$$\psi(r, t) = \int_{r'=0}^{b} r'^2 G(r, t \,|\, r', \tau)\big|_{\tau=0} F(r') \, dr'$$

A comparison of equations (6-100a) and (6-101) gives

$$G(r,t\,|\,r',\tau)\big|_{\tau=0} = \frac{2}{r'rb} \sum_{m=1}^{\infty} e^{-\alpha\beta_m^2 t} \cdot \sin \beta_m r' \sin \beta_m r \qquad (6\text{-}102)$$

The desired Green's function is obtained by replacing t by $(t - \tau)$ in equation (6-102)

$$G(r,t\,|\,r',\tau) = \frac{2}{r'rb} \sum_{m=1}^{\infty} e^{-\alpha\beta_m^2(t-\tau)} \sin \beta_m r' \sin \beta_m r \qquad (6\text{-}103)$$

Then the solution of the nonhomogeneous problem (6-98) in terms of Green's function is given, according to equation (6-19), as

$$T(r,t) = \frac{\alpha}{k} \int_{\tau=0}^{t} d\tau \int_{r'=0}^{b} r'^2 G(r,t\,|\,r',\tau)g(r',\tau)\,dr' \qquad (6\text{-}104)$$

Introducing the Green's function given by equation (6-103) into equation (6-104), the solution of the problem (6-98) becomes

$$T(r,t) = \frac{\alpha}{k}\frac{2}{br} \sum_{m=1}^{\infty} e^{-\alpha\beta_m^2 t} \sin \beta_m r \int_{\tau=0}^{t} e^{\alpha\beta_m^2 \tau}\,d\tau \int_{r'=0}^{b}$$
$$\cdot r' \sin \beta_m r' g(r',\tau)\,dr' \qquad (6\text{-}105)$$

where

$$\beta_m = \frac{m\pi}{b}, \qquad m = 1, 2, 3 \ldots$$

We now consider some special cases of the solution (6-105).

1.   The heat source is an instantaneous volume heat source of strength $g_i(r)$ Ws/m^3 (or Btu/ft^3) that releases its heat spontaneously at time $t = 0$.
By setting in equation (6-105)

$$g(r',\tau) = g_i(r)\delta(\tau - 0) \qquad (6\text{-}106)$$

and performing the integration with respect to the variable τ we obtain

$$T(r,t) = \frac{\alpha}{k}\frac{2}{br} \sum_{m=1}^{\infty} e^{-\alpha\beta_m^2 t} \sin \beta_m r \int_{r'=0}^{b} r'g_i(r') \sin \beta_m r'\,dr' \qquad (6\text{-}107)$$

2.   The heat source is an instantaneous point heat source of strength g_{pi} Ws (or Btu), which is situated at the center of the sphere and releases its heat spontaneously at time $t = 0$.
By setting in equation (6-105)

$$g(r',\tau) = \frac{g_{pi}}{4\pi r'^2}\delta(r' - 0)\delta(\tau - 0) \qquad (6\text{-}108)$$

and performing the integrations with respect to the variables r' and τ we obtain

$$T(r,t) = \frac{\alpha}{k}\frac{1}{2rb^2} \sum_{m=1}^{\infty} e^{-\alpha\beta_m^2 t} m \sin \beta_m r \cdot g_{Pi} \tag{6-109}$$

where $\beta_m = m\pi/b$.

Example 6-9. A solid sphere of radius $r = b$ is initially at temperature $F(r,\mu)$. For times $t > 0$ heat is generated in the sphere at a rate of $g(r,\mu,t)$ W/m^3 (or Btu/hr ft^3), while the boundary surface at $r = b$ is kept at zero temperature. Obtain an expression for the temperature distribution $T(r,\mu,t)$ in the sphere for times $t > 0$.

Solution. The mathematical formulation of this problem is given as

$$\frac{\partial^2 T}{\partial r^2} + \frac{2}{r}\frac{\partial T}{\partial r} + \frac{1}{r^2}\frac{\partial}{\partial \mu}\left[(1-\mu^2)\frac{\partial T}{\partial \mu}\right] + \frac{1}{k}g(r,\mu,t) = \frac{1}{\alpha}\frac{\partial T}{\partial t} \tag{6-110a}$$

$$\text{in } 0 \le r < b, \; -1 \le \mu \le 1, \; t > 0$$

$$T = 0 \qquad \text{at } r = b, \; t > 0 \tag{6-110b}$$

$$T = F(r,\mu) \qquad \text{for } t = 0, \text{ in the sphere} \tag{6-110c}$$

To determine the Green's function, we consider the homogeneous version of this problem as

$$\frac{\partial^2 \psi}{\partial r^2} + \frac{2}{r}\frac{\partial \psi}{\partial r} + \frac{1}{r^2}\frac{\partial}{\partial \mu}\left[(1-\mu^2)\frac{\partial \psi}{\partial \mu}\right] = \frac{1}{\alpha}\frac{\partial \psi}{\partial t} \tag{6-111a}$$

$$\text{in } 0 \le r < b, \; -1 \le \mu \le 1, \text{ for } t > 0$$

$$\psi = 0 \qquad \text{at } r = b, \; t > 0 \tag{6-111b}$$

$$\psi = F(r,\mu) \qquad \text{for } t = 0, \text{ in the sphere} \tag{6-111c}$$

This homogeneous problem is the same as that considered in Example 4-4; the solution is obtainable from equation (4-88) as

$$\psi(r,\mu,t) = \int_{r'=0}^{b} \int_{\mu'=-1}^{1} r'^2 \left[\sum_{n=0}^{\infty} \sum_{p=1}^{\infty} \frac{1}{N(n)N(\lambda_{np})} e^{-\alpha\lambda_{np}^2 t} \right.$$

$$\cdot (r'r)^{-1/2} J_{n+1/2}(\lambda_{np}r)P_n(\mu)J_{n+1/2}(\lambda_{np}r')P_n(\mu') \Bigg]$$

$$\cdot F(r',\mu')\,d\mu'\,dr' \tag{6-112a}$$

where λ_{np}'s are the positive roots of

$$J_{n+1/2}(\lambda_{np}b) = 0 \tag{6-112b}$$

and the norms $N(n)$ and $N(\lambda_{np})$ are given as

$$N(n) = \frac{2}{2n+1} \tag{6-112c}$$

$$N(\lambda_{np}) = -\frac{b^2}{2} J_{n-1/2}(\lambda_{np}b) J_{n+3/2}(\lambda_{np}b). \tag{6-112d}$$

The solution of the problem (6-111) in terms of Green's function is given, according to equation (6-22), as

$$\psi(r,\mu,t) = \int\limits_{r'=0}^{b} \int\limits_{\mu'=-1}^{1} r'^2 G(r,\mu,t\,|\,r',\mu',\tau)\big|_{\tau=0} F(r',\mu')\,d\mu'\,dr'. \tag{6-113}$$

A comparison of equations (6-112a) and (6-113) yields

$$G(r,\mu,t\,|\,r',\mu',\tau)\big|_{\tau=0} = \sum_{n=0}^{\infty} \sum_{p=1}^{\infty} \frac{1}{N(n)N(\lambda_{np})} e^{-\alpha\lambda_{np}^2 t}$$
$$(r'r)^{-1/2} J_{n+1/2}(\lambda_{np}r) P_n(\mu) J_{n+1/2}(\lambda_{np}r') P_n(\mu') \tag{6-114}$$

The desired Green's function is obtained by replacing t by $(t - \tau)$ in equation (6-114); we find

$$G(r,\mu,t\,|\,r',\mu',\tau) = \sum_{n=0}^{\infty} \sum_{p=1}^{\infty} \frac{1}{N(n)N(\lambda_{np})} e^{-\alpha\lambda_{np}^2(t-\tau)} \tag{6-115}$$
$$\cdot (r'r)^{-1/2} J_{n+1/2}(\lambda_{np}r) P_n(\mu) J_{n+1/2}(\lambda_{np}r') P_n(\mu')$$

Then the solution of the nonhomogeneous problem (6-110) in terms of this Green's function is given, according to equation (6-18), as

$$T(r,\mu,t) = \int\limits_{r'=0}^{b} \int\limits_{\mu'=-1}^{1} r'^2 G(r,\mu,t\,|\,r',\mu',\tau)\big|_{\tau=0} F(r',\mu')\,d\mu'\,dr'$$
$$+ \frac{\alpha}{k} \int\limits_{\tau=0}^{t} d\tau \int\limits_{r'=0}^{b} \int\limits_{\mu'=-1}^{1} r'^2 G(r,\mu,t\,|\,r',\mu',\tau)$$
$$\cdot g(r',\mu',\tau)\,d\mu'\,dr' \tag{6-116}$$

Introducing the above Green's function into (6-116), the solution becomes

$$T(r,\mu,t) = \sum_{n=0}^{\infty} \sum_{p=1}^{\infty} \frac{1}{N(n)N(\lambda_{np})} e^{-\alpha\lambda_{np}^2 t} r^{-1/2} J_{n+1/2}(\lambda_{np}r) P_n(\mu)$$
$$\cdot \int\limits_{r'=0}^{b} \int\limits_{u'=-1}^{1} r'^{3/2} J_{n+1/2}(\lambda_{np}r') P_n(\mu') F(r',\mu')\,d\mu'\,dr'$$

$$+\frac{\alpha}{k}\sum_{n=0}^{\infty}\sum_{p=1}^{\infty}\frac{1}{N(n)N(\lambda_{np})}e^{-\alpha\lambda_{np}^{2}t}r^{-1/2}J_{n+1/2}(\lambda_{np}r)P_{n}(\mu)$$

$$\cdot\int_{\tau=0}^{t}e^{\alpha\lambda_{np}^{2}\tau}\,d\tau\int_{r'=0}^{b}\int_{\mu'=-1}^{1}r'^{3/2}J_{n+1/2}(\lambda_{np}r')P_{n}(\mu')$$

$$\cdot g(r',\mu',\tau)\,d\mu'\,dr' \tag{6-117}$$

Clearly several special cases are obtainable from this solution.

6-6   PRODUCT OF GREEN'S FUNCTIONS

We have shown in Section 2-7 that the solution of multidimensional, homogeneous boundary-value problems of heat conduction can be constructed as the product solutions of one-dimensional problems if the initial temperature distribution is expressible as a product of single variable functions. In a similar manner a multidimensional Green's function can be constructed as a product of one-dimensional Green's functions. This result follows from the facts that (1) the Green's function satisfy the heat-conduction equation for an impulsive heat source, subject to homogeneous boundary conditions, and (2) the problem for an impulsive heat source can be recast as a problem with a specified initial temperature distribution. We have already illustrated in Examples (6-2) case 2, (6-3) case 1 and (6-5) case 4 that an impulsive heat source of strength g_i Ws/m^3, releasing its heat spontaneously at time $t=0$ is equivalent to an initial temperature distribution $\alpha g_i/k$.

To illustrate the construction of Green's function as a product of one-dimensional Green's function, we refer to Example 6-4 for the problem of rectangular parallelepiped, $0 \le x \le a$, $0 \le y \le b$, $0 \le z \le c$, whose boundaries are kept at zero temperature. The three-dimensional Green's function for this problem is given by equation (6-62) as

$$G(x,y,z,t|x',y',z',\tau)=\frac{8}{abc}\sum_{m=1}^{\infty}\sum_{n=1}^{\infty}\sum_{p=1}^{\infty}e^{-\alpha(\beta_m^2+\gamma_n^2+\eta_p^2)(t-\tau)}$$
$$\cdot\sin\beta_m x\sin\gamma_n y\sin\eta_p z\sin\beta_m x'\sin\gamma_n y'\sin\eta_p z' \tag{6-118}$$

which can be written as a product of three one-dimensional Green's functions in the form

$$G(x,y,z,t|x',y',z',\tau)=G_1(x,t|x',\tau)\cdot G_2(y,t|y',\tau)$$
$$\cdot G_3(z,t|z',\tau) \tag{6-119}$$

where

$$G_1(x,t|x',\tau)=\frac{2}{a}\sum_{m=1}^{\infty}e^{-\alpha\beta_m^2(t-\tau)}\sin\beta_m x\sin\beta_m x' \tag{6-120a}$$

$$G_2(y,t\,|\,y',\tau) = \frac{2}{b} \sum_{n=1}^{\infty} e^{-\gamma_n^2(t-\tau)} \sin \gamma_n y \sin \gamma_n y' \qquad (6\text{-}120\mathrm{b})$$

$$G_3(z,t\,|\,z',\tau) = \frac{2}{c} \sum_{p=1}^{\infty} e^{-\eta_p^2(t-\tau)} \sin \eta_p z \sin \eta_p z' \qquad (6\text{-}120\mathrm{c})$$

Clearly, G_1, G_2, and G_3 are Green's functions for slabs $0 \le x \le a$, $0 \le y \le b$, and $0 \le z \le c$, respectively, whose boundaries are kept at zero temperature.

REFERENCES

1. H. S. Carslaw and J. C. Jaeger, *Conduction of Heat in Solids*, Clarendon Press, London, 1959.

2. P. M. Morse and H. Feshbach, *Methods of Theoretical Physics*, McGraw-Hill Book Company, Inc., New York, 1953.

3. I. N. Sneddon, *Partial Differential Equations*, McGraw-Hill Book Company, Inc., New York, 1957.

4. J. W. Dettman, *Mathematical Methods in Physics and Engineering*, McGraw-Hill Book Company, Inc., New York, 1962.

5. R. Courant and D. Hilbert, *Methods of Mathematical Physics*, Interscience Publishers, New York, 1953.

6. M. N. Özışık, *Boundary Value Problems of Heat Conduction*, International Textbook Company, Scranton, P., 1968.

PROBLEMS

6-1 A semi-infinite region $0 \le x < \infty$ is initially at temperature $F(x)$. For times $t > 0$, boundary surface at $x = 0$ is kept at zero temperature and heat is generated within the solid at a rate of $g(x,t)\,\mathrm{W/m^3}$. Determine the Green's function for this problem, and using this Green's function obtain an expression for the temperature distribution $T(x,t)$ within the medium for times $t > 0$.

6-2 Repeat problem (6-1) for the case when the boundary surface at $x = 0$ is kept insulated.

6-3 A slab, $0 \le x \le L$, is initially at temperature $F(x)$. For times $t > 0$, heat is generated within the slab at a rate of $g(x,t)\,\mathrm{W/m^3}$, boundary surface at $x = 0$ is kept insulated and the boundary surface at $x = L$ dissipates heat by convection into a medium at zero temperature. Using the Green's function approach, obtain an expression for the temperature distribution $T(x,t)$ in the slab for times $t > 0$.

6-4 Using the Green's function approach solve the following heat-conduction problem for a rectangular region $0 \leq x \leq a, 0 \leq y \leq b$:

$$\frac{\partial^2 T}{\partial x^2} + \frac{\partial^2 T}{\partial y^2} + \frac{1}{k}g(x,y,t) = \frac{1}{\alpha}\frac{\partial T}{\partial t} \qquad \text{in } 0 < x < a, \ 0 < y < b, \ t > 0$$

$$\frac{\partial T}{\partial x} = 0 \qquad\qquad\qquad\qquad \text{at } x = 0, \ t > 0$$

$$\frac{\partial T}{\partial x} + H_2 T = 0 \qquad\qquad\qquad \text{at } x = a, \ t > 0$$

$$T = 0 \qquad\qquad\qquad\qquad\qquad \text{at } y = 0, \ t > 0$$

$$\frac{\partial T}{\partial y} + H_4 T = 0 \qquad\qquad\qquad \text{at } y = b, \ t > 0$$

$$T = F(x,y) \qquad\qquad\qquad\qquad \text{for } t = 0, \ \text{in the region}$$

6-5 Solve the following heat-conduction problem by using Green's function approach:

$$\frac{\partial^2 T}{\partial x^2} + \frac{\partial^2 T}{\partial y^2} + \frac{1}{k}g(x,y,t) = \frac{1}{\alpha}\frac{\partial T}{\partial t} \qquad \text{in } 0 < x < \infty, \ 0 < y < b, \ t > 0$$

$$T = 0 \qquad\qquad\qquad\qquad\qquad \text{at } x = 0, \ t > 0$$

$$-\frac{\partial T}{\partial y} + H_1 T = 0 \qquad\qquad\qquad \text{at } y = 0, \ t > 0$$

$$T = 0 \qquad\qquad\qquad\qquad\qquad \text{at } y = b, \ t > 0$$

$$T = F(x,y) \qquad\qquad\qquad\qquad \text{for } t = 0, \ \text{in the region}$$

6-6 Solve the following heat-conduction problem by using Green's function approach:

$$\frac{\partial^2 T}{\partial x^2} + \frac{1}{k}g(x,t) = \frac{1}{\alpha}\frac{\partial T}{\partial t} \qquad \text{in } 0 < x < L, \ t > 0$$

$$T = 0 \qquad\qquad\qquad\qquad\qquad \text{at } x = 0, \ t > 0$$

$$\frac{\partial T}{\partial x} + HT = 0 \qquad\qquad\qquad \text{at } x = L, \ t > 0$$

$$T = F(x) \qquad\qquad\qquad\qquad \text{for } t = 0, \ \text{in } 0 \leq x \leq L$$

6-7 A rectangular region $0 \leq x \leq a, 0 \leq y \leq b$ is initially at temperature $F(x,y)$. For times $t > 0$, heat is generated within the solid at a rate of $g(x,y,t)$

W/m^3, while all boundaries are kept at zero temperature. Obtain an expression for the temperature distribution $T(x, y, t)$ in the region for times $t > 0$.

6-8 A three-dimensional infinite medium, $-\infty < x < \infty$, $-\infty < y < \infty$, $-\infty < z < \infty$, is initially at temperature $F(x, y, z)$. For times $t > 0$ heat is generated in the medium at a rate of $g(x, y, z, t)$ W/m^3. Using Green's function approach obtain an expression for the temperature distribution $T(x, y, z, t)$ in the region for times $t > 0$. Also consider the following special cases:

1. The heat source is a point heat source of strength $g_p(t)$ W situated at the location (x_1, y_1, z_1), that is, $g(x, y, z, t) = g_p(t)\delta(x - x_1)\delta(y - y_1)$ $\delta(z - z_1)$ releases its heat for times $t > 0$.

2. The heat source is an instantaneous point heat source of strength g_{pi} Ws, which releases its heat spontaneously at time $t = 0$, at the location (x_1, y_1, z_1), that is, $g(x, y, z, t) = g_{pi}\delta(t - 0)\delta(x - x_1)\delta(y - y_1)$ $\delta(z - z_1)$.

6-9 Solve the following heat-conduction problem for a solid cylinder $0 \le r \le b$ by Green's function approach:

$$\frac{\partial^2 T}{\partial r^2} + \frac{1}{r}\frac{\partial T}{\partial r} + \frac{1}{k}g(r, t) = \frac{1}{\alpha}\frac{\partial T}{\partial t} \qquad \text{in } 0 \le r < b, \; t > 0$$

$$\frac{\partial T}{\partial r} + HT = 0 \qquad \text{at } r = b, \; t > 0$$

$$T = F(r) \qquad \text{for } t = 0, \text{ in } 0 \le r \le b$$

6-10 Solve the following heat-conduction problem by Green's function approach:

$$\frac{\partial^2 T}{\partial r^2} + \frac{1}{r}\frac{\partial T}{\partial r} + \frac{1}{k}g(r, t) = \frac{1}{\alpha}\frac{\partial T}{\partial t} \qquad \text{in } 0 \le r < \infty, \; t > 0$$

$$T = F(r) \qquad \text{for } t = 0, \text{ in the region}$$

Also consider the following special case: Medium initially at zero temperature, the heat source is an instantaneous line-heat source of strength $g_{L,i}$ Ws/m (or Btu/ft) situated along the z axis and releases its heat spontaneously at time $t = 0$, that is,

$$g(r, t) = \frac{g_{L,i}}{2\pi r}\delta(r - 0)\delta(t - 0)$$

6-11 Solve the following heat-conduction problem by Green's function approach:

$$\frac{\partial^2 T}{\partial r^2} + \frac{1}{r}\frac{\partial T}{\partial r} + \frac{1}{k}g(r, t) = \frac{1}{\alpha}\frac{\partial T}{\partial t} \qquad \text{in } a < r < \infty, \; t > 0$$

$$T = 0 \qquad\qquad\qquad\quad \text{at } r = a,\ t > 0$$

$$T = F(r) \qquad\qquad\qquad \text{for } t = 0, \text{ in the region}$$

6-12 Repeat problem (6-11) for the boundary condition:

$$-\frac{\partial T}{\partial r} + HT = 0 \qquad \text{at } r = a$$

6-13 Solve the following heat-conduction problem for a hollow cylinder by Green's function approach:

$$\frac{\partial^2 T}{\partial r^2} + \frac{1}{r}\frac{\partial T}{\partial r} + \frac{\partial^2 T}{\partial z^2} + \frac{1}{k}g(r,z,t) = \frac{1}{\alpha}\frac{\partial T}{\partial t} \qquad \text{in } a < r < b,\ 0 < z < c,\ t > 0$$

$$T = 0 \qquad\qquad\qquad\qquad \text{at } r = a,\ r = b,\ t > 0$$

$$\frac{\partial T}{\partial z} = 0 \qquad\qquad\qquad\qquad \text{at } z = 0,\ t > 0$$

$$\frac{\partial T}{\partial z} + HT = 0 \qquad\qquad\qquad \text{at } z = c,\ t > 0$$

$$T = F(r,z) \qquad\qquad\qquad \text{for } t = 0, \text{ in the region}$$

6-14 Solve the following heat-conduction problem for a solid cylinder by Green's function approach:

$$\frac{\partial^2 T}{\partial r^2} + \frac{1}{r}\frac{\partial T}{\partial r} + \frac{1}{r^2}\frac{\partial^2 T}{\partial \phi^2} + \frac{1}{k}g(r,\phi,t) = \frac{1}{\alpha}\frac{\partial T}{\partial t} \qquad \text{in } 0 \le r < b,\ 0 \le \phi \le 2\pi,\ t > 0$$

$$\frac{\partial T}{\partial r} + HT = 0 \qquad\qquad\qquad \text{at } r = b,\ t > 0$$

$$T = 0 \qquad\qquad\qquad\qquad \text{for } t = 0, \text{ in the region}$$

6-15 Repeat problem (6-14) for the case when the boundary surface at $r = b$ is kept at zero temperature.

6-16 Solve the following heat-conduction problem by Green's function approach:

$$\frac{\partial^2 T}{\partial r^2} + \frac{1}{r}\frac{\partial T}{\partial r} + \frac{1}{r^2}\frac{\partial^2 T}{\partial \phi^2} + \frac{1}{k}g(r,\phi,t) = \frac{1}{\alpha}\frac{\partial T}{\partial t}$$

$$\text{in } 0 \le r < b,\ 0 < \phi < \phi_0,\ (\phi_0 < 2\pi)t > 0$$

$$T = 0 \qquad \text{at } r = b,\ \phi = 0,\ \phi = \phi_0,\ t > 0$$

$$T = 0 \qquad \text{for } t = 0, \text{ in the region}$$

6-17   A solid sphere $0 \leq r \leq b$ is initially at temperature $F(r)$. For times $t > 0$ heat is generated in the sphere at a rate of $g(r, t)$ W/m^3 (or Btu/hr ft^3) while the boundary surface at $r = b$ dissipates heat by convection into a medium at zero temperature. Obtain an expression for the temperature distribution in the sphere.

6-18   Solve the following heat-conduction problem for a solid hemisphere:

$$\frac{\partial^2 T}{\partial r^2} + \frac{2}{r}\frac{\partial T}{\partial r} + \frac{1}{r^2}\frac{\partial}{\partial \mu}\left[(1 - \mu^2)\frac{\partial T}{\partial \mu}\right] + \frac{1}{k}g(r, \mu, t) = \frac{1}{\alpha}\frac{\partial T}{\partial t}$$

$$\text{in } 0 \leq r < b, \ 0 < \mu \leq 1, \ \text{for } t > 0$$

$T = 0$ at $r = b$ and $\mu = 0$, for $t > 0$

$T = F(r, \mu)$ for $t = 0$, in the hemisphere

6-19   Solve the following heat-conduction problem for a hemisphere:

$$\frac{\partial^2 T}{\partial r^2} + \frac{2}{r}\frac{\partial T}{\partial r} + \frac{1}{r^2}\frac{\partial}{\partial \mu}\left[(1 - \mu^2)\frac{\partial T}{\partial \mu}\right] + \frac{1}{k}g(r, \mu, t) = \frac{1}{\alpha}\frac{\partial T}{\partial t}$$

$$\text{in } 0 \leq r < b, \ 0 < \mu \leq 1, \ \text{for } t > 0$$

$\dfrac{\partial T}{\partial r} = 0$ at $r = b$, $t > 0$

$T = 0$ at $\mu = 0$, $t > 0$

$T = F(r, \mu)$ for $t = 0$, in the hemisphere.

6-20   Solve the following heat-conduction problem for a hollow sphere using Green's function

$$\frac{1}{r}\frac{\partial^2}{\partial r^2}(rT) + \frac{1}{k}g(r, t) = \frac{1}{\alpha}\frac{\partial T}{\partial t}   \qquad \text{in } a < r < b, \ t > 0$$

$-\dfrac{\partial T}{\partial r} + H_1 T = 0$ at $r = a$, $t > 0$

$\dfrac{\partial T}{\partial r} + H_2 T = 0$ at $r = b$, $t > 0$

$T = F(r)$ for $t = 0$, in $a \leq r \leq b$

Also consider the following special case: The heat source is an instantaneous, spherical surface heat source of radius r_1 (i.e., $a < r_1 < b$) of total strength g_{si} Ws (or Btu) which releases its heat spontaneously at time $t = 0$, i.e.,

$g(r, t)$ can be taken as

$$g(r', \tau) = g_{si} \frac{1}{4\pi r'^2} \delta(r' - r_1)\delta(\tau - 0)$$

6-21   Construct the Green's function for a region $0 \le x \le a$, $-\infty < y < \infty$, whose boundaries are kept at zero temperature, as a product of one-dimensional Green's functions for the regions $0 \le x \le a$ and $-\infty < y < \infty$.

6-22   Construct the Green's function for a hollow cylinder $a \le r \le b$, $0 \le z \le c$, whose boundaries are kept at zero temperature as a product of one-dimensional Green's functions for the regions $a \le r \le b$ and $0 \le z \le c$.

NOTES

1.   The *Dirac delta function*, which is usually called the *delta function* has the following properties:

$$\delta(x - b) = 0 \qquad \text{everywhere } x \ne b, \tag{1}$$

$$\int_{-\infty}^{\infty} \delta(x)\, dx = 1, \qquad \int_{-\infty}^{\infty} F(x)\delta(x - b)\, dx = F(b) \tag{2}$$

$$f(x)\delta(x - b) = f(b)\delta(x - b) \tag{3}$$

2.   The second form of Green's theorem is given as

$$\iiint_V [\phi_1 \nabla^2 \phi_2 - \phi_2 \nabla^2 \phi_1]\, dV = \iint_S \hat{\mathbf{n}} \cdot (\phi_1 \nabla \phi_2 - \phi_2 \nabla \phi_1)\, ds \tag{1}$$

where $\hat{\mathbf{n}}$ is the outward drawn normal unit direction vector. We note that the product $\hat{\mathbf{n}} \cdot \nabla \phi$ is the derivative of ϕ in the direction $\hat{\mathbf{n}}$. Hence we may write

$$\hat{\mathbf{n}} \cdot \nabla \phi = \frac{\partial \phi}{\partial n} \tag{2}$$

where $\partial/\partial n$ denotes differentiation along the outward-drawn normal to the boundary surface. Then equation (1) is written as

$$\iiint_V [\phi_1 \nabla^2 \phi_2 - \phi_2 \nabla^2 \phi_1]\, dV = \iint_S \left(\phi_1 \frac{\partial \phi_2}{\partial n} - \phi_2 \frac{\partial \phi_1}{\partial n} \right) ds \tag{3}$$

CHAPTER 7

THE USE OF LAPLACE TRANSFORM

The method of Laplace transform has been widely used in the solution of time-dependent heat-conduction problems, because the partial derivative with respect to the time variable can be removed from the differential equation of heat conduction by the application of Laplace transformation. Although the application of Laplace transform for the removal of the partial derivative is a relatively straightforward matter, the inversion of the trans-formed solution generally is rather involved unless the inversion is available in the standard Laplace transform tables.

In this chapter we present a brief description of the basic operational properties of the Laplace transformation, the inversion techniques, and illustrate with numerous examples its application in the solution of heat-conduction problems. The reader should consult references [1–7] for a more detailed discussion of the Laplace transform theory and references [8–12] for further applications of the Laplace transformation in the solution of heat-conduction problems.

7-1 DEFINITION OF LAPLACE TRANSFORMATION

Consider a function $F^*(t)$ defined as

$$F^*(t) = \begin{cases} e^{-\gamma t}F(t) & \text{for } t > 0 \\ 0 & \text{for } t < 0 \end{cases} \tag{7-1}$$

where γ is a positive constant such that the integral $\int_0^\infty F^*(t)\,dt$ does converge. Here the function $F^*(t)$ is considered to satisfy the requirement of the Fourier theorem, hence it can be represented in the form of a Fourier integral as [13, p. 3]

$$F^*(t) = \frac{1}{2\pi} \int_{\beta=-\infty}^{\infty} e^{-i\beta t}\,d\beta \int_{t'=0}^{\infty} e^{i\beta t'}F^*(t')\,dt' \tag{7-2}$$

where the integration over the variable t' is taken from 0 to ∞ instead of $-\infty$ to ∞, since the function $F^*(t)$ is identically zero for $t < 0$ by equation (7-1).

The substitution of $F^*(t)$ from equation (7-1) into (7-2) yields

$$F(t) = \frac{1}{2\pi} \int_{\beta=-\infty}^{\infty} e^{(\gamma-i\beta)t} \, d\beta \int_{t'=0}^{\infty} e^{-(\gamma-i\beta)t'} F(t') \, dt' \tag{7-3}$$

Now, a new complex variable s is defined as

$$s = \gamma - i\beta \quad \text{and} \quad d\beta = -\frac{ds}{i} \tag{7-4}$$

Then, equation (7-3) becomes

$$F(t) = \frac{1}{2\pi i} \int_{s=\gamma-i\infty}^{\gamma+i\infty} e^{st} \, ds \int_{t'=0}^{\infty} e^{-st'} F(t') \, dt' \tag{7-5}$$

This result is now written as the *Laplace transform* and the *inversion formula* for function $F(t)$ in the form

$$\text{Laplace transform}: \quad \mathscr{L}[F(t)] \equiv \bar{F}(s) = \int_{t'=0}^{\infty} e^{-st'} F(t') \, dt' \tag{7-6a}$$

$$\text{Inversion formula}: \quad F(t) = \frac{1}{2\pi i} \int_{s=\gamma-i\infty}^{\gamma+i\infty} e^{st} \bar{F}(s) \, ds \tag{7-6b}$$

Thus, the Laplace transform of a function $F(t)$ consists of multiplying the function $F(t)$ by e^{-st} and integrating it over t from 0 to ∞. The inversion formula consists of the complex integration as defined by equation (7-6b).

Some remarks on the existence of the Laplace transform of a function $F(t)$ as defined by equation (7-6a) might be in order to illustrate the significance of this matter. For example, the integral (7-6a) may not exist because, (1) $F(t)$ may have infinite discontinuities for some values of t, or (2) $F(t)$ may have singularity as $t \to 0$, or (3) $F(t)$ may diverge exponentially for large t. The conditions for the existence of the Laplace transform defined by equation (7-6a) may be summarized as:

1. Function $F(t)$ is continuous or piecewise continuous in any interval $t_1 \leq t \leq t_2$, for $t_1 > 0$.
2. $t^n |F(t)|$ is bounded as $t \to 0^+$ for some number n when $n < 1$.
3. Function $F(t)$ is of exponential order, namely, $e^{-\gamma t} |F(t)|$ is bounded for some positive number γ as $t \to \infty$.

For example, $F(t) = e^{t^2}$ is *not* of exponential order, that is, $e^{-\gamma t} \cdot e^{t^2}$ is unbounded at $t \to \infty$ for all values of γ, hence its Laplace transform *does not* exist. The Laplace transform of a function $F(t) = t^n$, when $n \le -1$, does not exist because of condition (2), that is $\int_0^\infty e^{-st} t^n \, dt$ for $n \le -1$ diverges at the origin.

Example 7-1. Determine the Laplace transform of the following functions: $F(t) = 1, t, e^{\pm at}$ and t^n with $n > -1$ but not necessarily integer.

Solution. According to the definition of the Laplace transform given by equation (7-6a), the Laplace transforms of these functions are given as

$$F(t) = 1: \quad \bar{F}(s) = \int_0^\infty 1 \cdot e^{-st} \, dt = -\frac{1}{s} e^{-st} \Big|_0^\infty = \frac{1}{s} \tag{7-7a}$$

$$F(t) = t: \quad \bar{F}(s) = \int_0^\infty t e^{-st} \, dt = \frac{1}{s^2} \tag{7-7b}$$

$$F(t) = e^{\pm at}: \quad \bar{F}(s) = \int_0^\infty e^{\pm at} e^{-st} \, dt = \int_0^\infty e^{-(s \mp a)t} \, dt = \frac{1}{s \mp a} \tag{7-7c}$$

$$F(t) = t^n, n > -1: \quad \bar{F}(s) = \int_0^\infty t^n e^{-st} \, dt$$

Now let $\xi = st$ and $d\xi = s \, dt$; then

$$\bar{F}(s) = s^{-n-1} \int_0^\infty \xi^n e^{-\xi} \, d\xi = \frac{\Gamma(n+1)}{s^{n+1}} \tag{7-7d}$$

where the integral $\int_0^\infty \xi^n e^{-\xi} \, d\xi$ is the *gamma function*, $\Gamma(n+1)$. The gamma function has the property $\Gamma(n+1) = n\Gamma(n)$; if n is an integer, we have $\Gamma(n+1) = n!$.

7-2 PROPERTIES OF LAPLACE TRANSFORM

Here we present some of the properties of Laplace transform that are useful in the solution of heat-conduction problems with Laplace transformation.

Linear Property

If $\bar{F}(s)$ and $\bar{G}(s)$ are the Laplace transform of functions $F(t)$ and $G(t)$ with respect to the t variable respectively, we may write

$$\mathscr{L}[c_1 F(t) + c_2 G(t)] = c_1 \bar{F}(s) + c_2 \bar{G}(s) \tag{7-8}$$

where c_1 and c_2 are any constants.

Example 7-2. By utilizing the linear property of the Laplace transform and the Laplace transform of $e^{\pm at}$ as given by equation (7-7c), determine the Laplace transform of the functions $\cosh at$ and $\sinh at$.

Solution. For $\cosh at$ we write

$$F_1(t) \equiv \cosh at = \tfrac{1}{2}(e^{at} + e^{-at}) \tag{7-9a}$$

$$\bar{F}_1(s) = \frac{1}{2}\left(\frac{1}{s-a} + \frac{1}{s+a}\right) = \frac{s}{s^2 - a^2} \tag{7-9b}$$

Similarly

$$F_2(t) \equiv \sinh at = \tfrac{1}{2}(e^{at} - e^{-at}) \tag{7-10a}$$

$$\bar{F}_2(s) = \frac{1}{2}\left(\frac{1}{s-a} - \frac{1}{s+a}\right) = \frac{a}{s^2 - a^2} \tag{7-10b}$$

Laplace Transform of Derivatives

The Laplace transform of the first derivative $dF(t)/dt$ of a function $F(t)$ is readily obtained by utilizing the definition of the Laplace transform and integrating it by parts.

$$\mathscr{L}[F'(t)] = \int_0^\infty F'(t)e^{-st}\,dt = \left[F(t)e^{-st}\right]_0^\infty + s\int_0^\infty F(t)e^{-st}\,dt$$

$$\mathscr{L}[F'(t)] = s\bar{F}(s) - F(0) \tag{7-11}$$

where the prime denotes differentiation with respect to t and $F(0)$ indicates the value of $F(t)$ at $t = 0^+$, namely as we approach zero from the positive side. Thus, the Laplace transform of the first derivative of a function is equal to multiplying the transform of the function by s and subtracting from it the value of this function at $t = 0^+$.

This result is now utilized to determine the Laplace transform of the second derivative of a function $F(t)$ as

$$\mathscr{L}[F''(t)] = s\mathscr{L}[F'(t)] - F'(0) = s[s\bar{F}(s) - F(0)] - F'(0)$$
$$= s^2\bar{F}(s) - sF(0) - F'(0) \tag{7-12}$$

Similarly, the Laplace transform of the third derivative becomes

$$\mathscr{L}[F'''(t)] = s^3\bar{F}(s) - s^2F(0) - sF'(0) - F''(0) \tag{7-13}$$

In general, the Laplace transform of the nth derivative is given as

$$\mathscr{L}[F^{(n)}(t)] = s^n\bar{F}(s) - s^{n-1}F(0) - s^{n-2}F^{(1)}(0) - s^{n-3}F^{(2)}(0) - \ldots - F^{(n-1)}(0) \tag{7-14}$$

where

$$F^{(n)}(t) \equiv \frac{d^n F(t)}{dt^n}$$

Laplace Transform of Integrals

The Laplace transform of the integral $\int_0^t F(\tau)\,d\tau$ of a function $F(t)$ is determined as now described.
Let

$$g(t) \equiv \int_0^t F(\tau)\,d\tau \qquad (7\text{-}15a)$$

then

$$g'(t) = F(t) \qquad (7\text{-}15b)$$

We take the Laplace transform of both sides of equation (7-15b) and utilize the result in equation (7-11) to obtain

$$s\bar{g}(s) = \bar{F}(s) \qquad (7\text{-}16)$$

since $g(0) = 0$. After rearranging, we find

$$\bar{g}(s) \equiv \mathscr{L}\left[\int_0^t F(\tau)\,d\tau\right] = \frac{1}{s}\bar{F}(s) \qquad (7\text{-}17)$$

This procedure is repeated to obtain the Laplace transform of the double integration of a function $F(t)$

$$\mathscr{L}\left[\int_0^t \int_0^{\tau_2} F(\tau_1)\,d\tau_1\,d\tau_2\right] = \frac{1}{s^2}\bar{F}(s) \qquad (7\text{-}18)$$

In general, the Laplace transform of the nth integral of a function $F(t)$ is given as

$$\mathscr{L}\left[\int_0^t \dots \int_0^{\tau_2} F(\tau_1)\,d\tau_1 \dots d\tau_n\right] = \frac{1}{s^n}\bar{F}(s) \qquad (7\text{-}19)$$

Change of Scale

Let $\bar{F}(s)$ be the Laplace transform of a function $F(t)$. Then, the Laplace transforms of functions $F(at)$ and $F[(1/a)t]$, where a is a real, positive constant, are determined as

$$\mathscr{L}[F(at)] = \int_0^\infty F(at)e^{-st}\,dt = \frac{1}{a}\int_0^\infty F(u)e^{-(s/a)u}\,du = \frac{1}{a}\bar{F}\left(\frac{s}{a}\right) \qquad (7\text{-}20a)$$

where we set $u = at$. Similarly,

$$\mathscr{L}\left[F\left(\frac{1}{a}t\right)\right] = \int_0^\infty F\left(\frac{t}{a}\right)e^{-st}\,dt = a\int_0^\infty F(u)e^{-asu}\,du = a\bar{F}(as) \quad (7\text{-}20b)$$

where we set $u = t/a$.

Example 7-3. The Laplace transform of $\cosh t$ is given as $\mathscr{L}[\cosh t] = s/(s^2 - 1)$. By utilizing the "change of scale" property, determine the Laplace transform of the function $\cosh at$ and $\cosh(t/a)$.

Solution. By utilizing equation (7-20a) we obtain

$$\mathscr{L}[\cosh at] = \frac{1}{a}\frac{(s/a)}{(s/a)^2 - 1} = \frac{s}{s^2 - a^2} \quad (7\text{-}21a)$$

and by utilizing equation (7-20b) we find

$$\mathscr{L}\left[\cosh\frac{t}{a}\right] = a\frac{as}{(as)^2 - 1} = \frac{s^2}{s^2 - (1/a)^2} \quad (7\text{-}21b)$$

Shift Property

When the Laplace transform $\bar{F}(s)$ of a function $F(t)$ is known, the shift property enables us to write the Laplace transform of a function "$e^{\pm at}F(t)$", where a is a constant; that is

$$\mathscr{L}[e^{\pm at}F(t)] = \int_0^\infty e^{-st}e^{\pm at}F(t)\,dt = \int_0^\infty e^{-(s\mp a)t}F(t)\,dt$$
$$= \bar{F}(s \mp a) \quad (7\text{-}22)$$

Example 7-4. The Laplace transform of $\cos bt$ is given as $\mathscr{L}[\cos bt] = s/(s^2 + b^2)$. By utilizing the "shift property" determine the Laplace transform of the function $e^{-at}\cdot\cos bt$.

Solution. By equation (7-22) we immediately write

$$\mathscr{L}[e^{-at}\cos bt] = \frac{s+a}{(s+a)^2 + b^2} \quad (7\text{-}23)$$

Laplace Transform of Translated Function

The unit step function (or the Heaviside unit function) is useful in denoting the translation of a function. Figure 7-1 shows the physical significance of

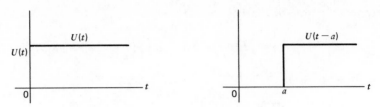

Fig. 7-1   Definition of the unit step functions $U(t)$ and $U(t-a)$.

the unit step functions $U(t)$ and $U(t-a)$; namely

$$U(t) = \begin{cases} 1 & t > 0 \\ 0 & t < 0 \end{cases} \qquad (7\text{-}24a)$$

$$U(t-a) = \begin{cases} 1 & t > a \\ 0 & t < a \end{cases} \qquad (7\text{-}24b)$$

We now consider a function $F(t)$ defined for $t > 0$ as illustrated in Fig. 7-2a and the translation of this function from $t = 0$ to $t = a$ as illustrated in Fig. 7-2b. The translated function $U(t-a) \cdot F(t-a)$ represents the function $F(t)$ defined for $t > 0$, translated by an amount $t = a$ in the positive t direction; namely

$$U(t-a)F(t-a) = \begin{cases} F(t-a) & \text{for } t > a \\ 0 & \text{for } t < a \end{cases} \qquad (7\text{-}25)$$

The Laplace transform of this translated function is determined as

$$\mathcal{L}[U(t-a)F(t-a)] = \int_{0}^{\infty} e^{-st} U(t-a)F(t-a)\,dt$$

$$= \int_{t=a}^{\infty} e^{-st} F(t-a)\,dt$$

$$= \int_{\eta=0}^{\infty} e^{-s(a+\eta)} F(\eta)\,d\eta = e^{-as} \int_{\eta=0}^{\infty} e^{-s\eta} F(\eta)\,d\eta$$

$$= e^{-as}\bar{F}(s) \qquad (7\text{-}26)$$

where a new variable η is defined as $\eta = t - a$. This result shows that the Laplace transform of a translated function $U(t-a)\,F(t-a)$ is equal to the Laplace transform $\bar{F}(s)$ of the function $F(t)$ multiplied by e^{-as}.

Similarly, the Laplace transform of a unit step function $U(t-a)$ is given by

$$\mathcal{L}[U(t-a)] = e^{-as}\frac{1}{s} \qquad (7\text{-}27)$$

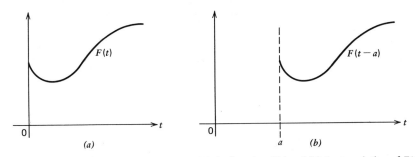

Fig. 7-2 The translation of a function $F(t)$: (a) the function $F(t)$ and (b) the translation of $F(t)$ from $t = 0$ to $t = a$.

Example 7-6. Determine the Laplace transform of the following function

$$F(t) = \begin{cases} 0 & \text{for } t < 0 \\ 1 & \text{for } 0 < t < 1 \\ 5 & \text{for } 1 < t < 4 \\ 2 & \text{for } 4 < t < 6 \\ 0 & \text{for } t > 6 \end{cases} \qquad (7\text{-}29)$$

which is illustrated in Fig. 7-3.

Solution. The function given by equation (7-29) is represented in terms of the unit step functions as

$$F(t) = U(t - 0) + 4U(t - 1) - 3U(t - 4) - 2U(t - 6) \qquad (7\text{-}30a)$$

and the Laplace transform of this function becomes

$$\bar{F}(s) = \frac{1}{s} + 4e^{-s}\frac{1}{s} - 3e^{-4s}\frac{1}{s} - 2e^{-6s}\frac{1}{s} \qquad (7\text{-}30b)$$

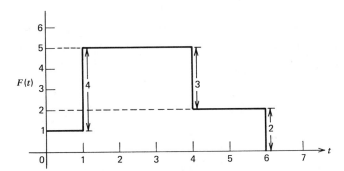

Fig. 7-3 The function defined by equation (7-29).

Laplace Transform of Delta Function

The delta function $\delta(x)$ is defined to be zero everywhere except at $x = 0$ such that

$$\delta(x) = 0, \qquad x \neq 0 \tag{7-31a}$$

and

$$\int_{-\infty}^{\infty} \delta(x)\,dx = 1 \tag{7-31b}$$

The Laplace transform of the delta function $\delta(x)$ is given by

$$\mathscr{L}[\delta(x)] \equiv \bar{\delta}(s) = \int_0^{\infty} e^{-sx}\delta(x)\,dx = 1 \tag{7-32}$$

Laplace Transform of Convolution

Let $f(t)$ and $g(t)$ be two functions of t defined for $t > 0$. The *convolution integral* or briefly the *convolution* of these two functions is denoted by the notation $f * g$ and defined by the equation

$$f * g = \int_0^t f(t - \tau)g(\tau)\,d\tau \tag{7-33a}$$

$$= \int_0^t f(\tau)g(t - \tau)\,d\tau \tag{7-33b}$$

Thus we have the relation $f * g = g * f$. The Laplace transform of the convolution $f * g$ is given by

$$\mathscr{L}[f * g] \equiv \overline{f * g} = \bar{f}(s)\bar{g}(s) \tag{7-34}$$

That is, the Laplace transform of the convolution is equal to the product of the Laplace transforms $\bar{f}(s)$ and $\bar{g}(s)$ of these two functions. The validity of the result given by equation (7-34) can be proved as follows.

$$\bar{f}(s)\bar{g}(s) = \left[\int_0^{\infty} e^{-s\eta}f(\eta)\,d\eta \right]\left[\int_0^{\infty} e^{-s\tau}g(\tau)\,d\tau \right]$$

$$= \int_0^{\infty} \int_0^{\infty} e^{-s(\eta + \tau)}f(\eta)g(\tau)\,d\eta\,d\tau$$

$$= \int_0^{\infty} g(\tau)\left[\int_{\eta=0}^{\infty} e^{-s(\eta + \tau)}f(\eta)\,d\eta \right] d\tau \tag{7-35a}$$

we defined a new variable t as

$$t = \eta + \tau, \qquad dt = d\eta \quad \text{and} \quad d\eta\, d\tau = J\left(\frac{\eta, \tau}{t, \tau}\right) dt\, d\tau = dt\, d\tau,$$

since the Jacobian, $J[(\eta, \tau)/(t, \tau)]$, for the transformation is equal to unity. The limits of integration in the new (t, τ) domain become

first over t : from $t = \tau$ to ∞

second over τ : from $\tau = 0$ to ∞

Figure 7-4 shows the area of integration in the (t, τ) domain (i.e., the hatched area). Then equation (7-35a) becomes

$$\bar{f}(s)\bar{g}(s) = \int_{\tau=0}^{\infty} g(\tau)\left[\int_{t=\tau}^{\infty} e^{-st}f(t - \tau)\, dt\right] d\tau \qquad (7\text{-}35b)$$

The order of integration in equation (7-35b) can be changed, provided that the integration remains over the same hatched area shown in Fig. 7-4. That is,

first over τ : from $\tau = 0$ to t

second over t : from $t = 0$ to ∞

Now changing the order of integration according to this rule, equation (7-35b) becomes

$$\bar{f}(s)\bar{g}(s) = \int_{t=0}^{\infty} e^{-st}\left[\int_{\tau=0}^{t} f(t - \tau)g(\tau)\, d\tau\right] dt$$

$$= \int_{t=0}^{\infty} e^{-st}[f * g]\, dt = \overline{f * g} \equiv \mathscr{L}[f * g] \qquad (7\text{-}35c)$$

which proves the validity of equation (7-34).

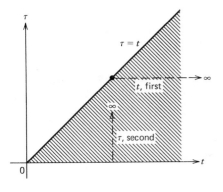

Fig. 7-4 The order and limits of integration in equation (7-35b).

Laplace Transform of Generalized Convolution

The *generalized convolution* of a function $\Phi(t, \tau)$ is defined in reference [14] by the equation

$$\Phi^*(t) = \int_0^t \Phi(t - \tau, \tau) \, d\tau \qquad (7\text{-}36\text{a})$$

and the Laplace transform of this generalized convolution $\Phi^*(t)$ is given by [14]

$$\mathscr{L}[\Phi^*(t)] \equiv \overline{\Phi^*}(s) = \int_0^\infty \int_0^\infty e^{-(t+\tau)s} \Phi(t, \tau) \, d\tau \, dt \qquad (7\text{-}36\text{b})$$

The reader should consult the original reference for proof of this result. The Laplace transform of the generalized convolution was used for the proof of Duhamel's theorem.

Derivatives of Laplace Transform

We now derive an expression for the derivative of the Laplace transform of a function. Consider the Laplace transform $\bar{F}(s)$ of a function $F(t)$ given as

$$\bar{F}(s) = \int_0^\infty e^{-st} F(t) \, dt \qquad (7\text{-}37)$$

By differentiating both sides of equation (7-37) with respect to s we obtain

$$\frac{d\bar{F}(s)}{ds} \equiv \bar{F}'(s) = \int_0^\infty (-t) e^{-st} F(t) \, dt$$

$$\bar{F}'(s) = \mathscr{L}[(-t)F(t)] \qquad (7\text{-}38\text{a})$$

or by differentiating equation (7-37) n times we obtain

$$\frac{d^n \bar{F}(s)}{ds^n} \equiv \bar{F}^{(n)}(s) = \mathscr{L}[(-t)^n F(t)], \quad n = 1, 2, 3 \dots \qquad (7\text{-}38\text{b})$$

Thus, the nth differentiation of the Laplace transform $\bar{F}(s)$ is equal to the Laplace transform of $(-t)^n F(t)$. This relation is useful in finding the inverse transforms with the aid of partial fractions and in many applications.

Example 7-7. The Laplace transform of $F(t) = \sin \beta t$ is given as $\bar{F}(s) = \beta/(s^2 + \beta^2)$. Determine the Laplace transform of the function "$t \sin \beta t$."

Solution. By applying the formula (7-38a) we write

$$\mathscr{L}[(-t)F(t)] = \frac{d}{ds}\bar{F}(s)$$

$$\mathscr{L}[-t\sin\beta t] = \frac{d}{ds}\left[\frac{\beta}{s^2 + \beta^2}\right] = -\frac{2s\beta}{(s^2 + \beta^2)^2} \qquad (7\text{-}39a)$$

or

$$\mathscr{L}[t\sin\beta t] = \frac{2\beta s}{(s^2 + \beta^2)^2} \qquad \text{for } s > 0 \qquad (7\text{-}39b)$$

The Integration of Laplace Transform

We now derive an expression for the integration of the Laplace transform of a function. Consider the Laplace transform of a function $F(t)$ given by

$$\bar{F}(s) = \int_0^\infty e^{-st}F(t)\,dt \qquad (7\text{-}40)$$

We integrate both sides of this equation with respect to s from s to b and obtain

$$\int_s^b \bar{F}(s')\,ds' = \int_s^b \int_0^\infty e^{-s't}F(t)\,dt\,ds'$$

$$= \int_0^\infty F(t)\left[\int_s^b e^{-s't}\,ds'\right]dt = \int_0^\infty \frac{F(t)}{t}(e^{-st} - e^{-bt})\,dt \qquad (7\text{-}41)$$

If the function $F(t)$ is such that $F(t)/t$ exists as $t \to 0$, the integral uniformly converges. Then, letting $b \to \infty$, equation (7-41) becomes

$$\int_s^\infty \bar{F}(s')\,ds' = \int_0^\infty \left[\frac{F(t)}{t}\right]e^{-st}\,dt \equiv \mathscr{L}\left[\frac{F(t)}{t}\right] \qquad (7\text{-}42)$$

Thus, the integration of the Laplace transform $\bar{F}(s)$ of a function $F(t)$ with respect to s from s to ∞, is equal to the Laplace transform of the function $F(t)/t$. This result is useful in the determination of the Laplace transform of the function $F(t)/t$ when the Laplace transform $\bar{F}(s)$ of the function $F(t)$ is known.

Example 7-8. The Laplace transform of $\sin\beta t$ is given as $\beta/(s^2 + \beta^2)$. Determine the Laplace transform of $(1/t)\sin\beta t$.

Solution. We utilize the formula (7-42)

$$\mathscr{L}\left[\frac{F(t)}{t}\right] = \int_s^\infty \bar{F}(s')\,ds'$$

Introducing the function as given above we obtain

$$\mathscr{L}\left[\frac{\sin \beta t}{t}\right] = \int_s^\infty \frac{\beta}{s'^2 + \beta^2}\,ds' = \left[\tan^{-1}\frac{s'}{\beta}\right]_s^\infty = \frac{\pi}{2} - \tan^{-1}\left(\frac{s}{\beta}\right) \quad (7\text{-}43)$$

7-3   THE INVERSION OF LAPLACE TRANSFORM
USING THE INVERSION TABLES

In heat-conduction problems, the Laplace transformation is generally applied to the time variable. Therefore, an important step in the final analysis is the inversion of the transformed function from the Laplace variable s domain to the actual time variable t domain. To facilitate such analysis comprehensive tables have been prepared for the inversion of the Laplace transform of a large class of functions [7]. We present in Table 7-1 the Laplace transform of various functions which are useful in the analysis of heat-conduction problems.

If the Laplace transform $\bar{F}(s)$ of a function $F(t)$ is expressible in the form

$$\bar{F}(s) = \frac{G(s)}{H(s)} \tag{7-44}$$

where $G(s)$ and $H(s)$ are polynomials with no common factor, with $G(s)$ being lower degree than $H(s)$, and the factors of $H(s)$ are all linear and distinct, then equation (7-44) can be expressed in the form

$$\bar{F}(s) = \frac{G(s)}{H(s)} = \frac{c_1}{s - a_1} + \frac{c_2}{s - a_2} + \dots + \frac{c_n}{s - a_n} \tag{7-45}$$

Here c_i's are independent of s. Then, by the theory of partial fractions c_i's are determined as

$$c_i = \lim_{s \to a_i} \left[(s - a_i)\bar{F}(s)\right] \tag{7-46}$$

Clearly, if a function $\bar{F}(s)$ is expressible in partial fractions as in equations (7-45), its inversion is readily obtained by the use of the Laplace transform table.

Also, there are many occasions that the transformed function $\bar{F}(s)$ will not appear in the standard transform tables. In such cases it will be necessary to use the inversion formula (7-6b) to determine the function. Such an

Table 7-1 A Table of Laplace Transform of Functions

No	$\bar{F}(s)$	$F(t)$
1	$\dfrac{1}{s}$	1
2	$\dfrac{1}{s^2}$	t
3	$\dfrac{1}{s^n}\,(n = 1, 2, 3, \ldots)$	$\dfrac{t^{n-1}}{(n-1)!}$
4	$\dfrac{1}{\sqrt{s}}$	$\dfrac{1}{\sqrt{\pi t}}$
5	$s^{-3/2}$	$2\sqrt{t/\pi}$
6	$s^{-(n+1/2)}(n = 1, 2, 3, \ldots)$	$\dfrac{2^n}{[1\cdot3\cdot5\cdot\ldots\cdot(2n-1)]\sqrt{\pi}}t^{n-1/2}$
7	$\dfrac{1}{s^n}\,(n > 0)$	$\dfrac{1}{\Gamma(n)}t^{n-1}$
8	$\dfrac{1}{s+a}$	e^{-at}
9	$\dfrac{1}{(s+a)^n}\,(n = 1, 2, 3, \ldots)$	$\dfrac{t^{n-1}e^{-at}}{(n-1)!}$
10	$\dfrac{\Gamma(k)}{(s+a)^k}\,(k > 0)$	$t^{k-1}e^{-at}$
11	$\dfrac{1}{(s+a)(s+b)}\,(a \neq b)$	$\dfrac{e^{-at}-e^{-bt}}{b-a}$
12	$\dfrac{s}{(s+a)(s+b)}\,(a \neq b)$	$\dfrac{ae^{-at}-be^{-bt}}{a-b}$
13	$\dfrac{1}{s^2+a^2}$	$\dfrac{1}{a}\sin at$
14	$\dfrac{s}{s^2+a^2}$	$\cos at$
15	$\dfrac{1}{s^2-a^2}$	$\dfrac{1}{a}\sinh at$
16	$\dfrac{s}{s^2-a^2}$	$\cosh at$
17	$\dfrac{1}{s(s^2+a^2)}$	$\dfrac{1}{a^2}(1-\cos at)$

Table 7-1 *(Continued)*

No	$\bar{F}(s)$	$F(t)$
18	$\dfrac{1}{s^2(s^2 + a^2)}$	$\dfrac{1}{a^3}(at - \sin at)$
19	$\dfrac{1}{(s^2 + a^2)^2}$	$\dfrac{1}{2a^3}(\sin at - at\cos at)$
20	$\dfrac{s}{(s^2 + a^2)^2}$	$\dfrac{t}{2a}\sin at$
21	$\dfrac{s^2}{(s^2 + a^2)^2}$	$\dfrac{1}{2a}(\sin at + at\cos at)$
22	$\dfrac{s^2 - a^2}{(s^2 + a^2)^2}$	$t\cos at$
23	$\dfrac{1}{\sqrt{s} + a}$	$\dfrac{1}{\sqrt{\pi t}} - ae^{a^2 t}\operatorname{erfc} a\sqrt{t}$
24	$\dfrac{\sqrt{s}}{s - a^2}$	$\dfrac{1}{\sqrt{\pi t}} + ae^{a^2 t}\operatorname{erf} a\sqrt{t}$
25	$\dfrac{\sqrt{s}}{s + a^2}$	$\dfrac{1}{\sqrt{\pi t}} - \dfrac{2a}{\sqrt{\pi}}e^{-a^2 t}\displaystyle\int_0^{a\sqrt{t}} e^{\lambda^2}\,d\lambda$
26	$\dfrac{1}{\sqrt{s}(s - a^2)}$	$\dfrac{1}{a}e^{a^2 t}\operatorname{erf} a\sqrt{t}$
27	$\dfrac{1}{\sqrt{s}(s + a^2)}$	$\dfrac{2}{a\sqrt{\pi}}e^{-a^2 t}\displaystyle\int_0^{a\sqrt{t}} e^{\lambda^2}\,d\lambda$
28	$\dfrac{b^2 - a^2}{(s - a^2)(b + \sqrt{s})}$	$e^{a^2 t}[b - a\operatorname{erf} a\sqrt{t}] - be^{b^2 t}\operatorname{erfc} b\sqrt{t}$
29	$\dfrac{1}{\sqrt{s}(\sqrt{s} + a)}$	$e^{a^2 t}\operatorname{erfc} a\sqrt{t}$
30	$\dfrac{1}{(s + a)\sqrt{s + b}}$	$\dfrac{1}{\sqrt{b - a}}e^{-at}\operatorname{erf}(\sqrt{b - a}\sqrt{t})$
31	$\dfrac{\sqrt{s + 2a}}{\sqrt{s}} - 1$	$ae^{-at}[I_1(at) + I_0(at)]$
32	$\dfrac{1}{\sqrt{s + a}\sqrt{s + b}}$	$e^{-(a+b)t/2}I_0\left(\dfrac{a - b}{2}t\right)$
33	$\dfrac{1}{\sqrt{s^2 + a^2}}$	$J_0(at)$

Table 7-1 *(Continued)*

No	$\bar{F}(s)$	$F(t)$
34	$\dfrac{(\sqrt{s^2 + a^2} - s)^v}{\sqrt{s^2 + a^2}} \ (v > -1)$	$a^v J_v(at)$
35	$\dfrac{(s - \sqrt{s^2 - a^2})^v}{\sqrt{s^2 - a^2}} \ (v > -1)$	$a^v I_v(at)$
36	$\dfrac{1}{s} e^{-ks}$	$u(t - k)$
37	$\dfrac{1}{s^2} e^{-ks}$	$(t - k)u(t - k)$
38	$\dfrac{1}{s} e^{-k/s}$	$J_0(2\sqrt{kt})$
39	$\dfrac{1}{s^\mu} e^{-k/s} \ (\mu > 0)$	$\left(\dfrac{t}{k}\right)^{(\mu - 1)/2} J_{\mu - 1}(2\sqrt{kt})$
40	$\dfrac{1}{s^\mu} e^{-k/s} \ (\mu > 0)$	$\left(\dfrac{t}{k}\right)^{(\mu - 1)/2} I_{\mu - 1}(2\sqrt{kt})$
41	$e^{-k\sqrt{s}} \ (k > 0)$	$\dfrac{k}{2\sqrt{\pi t^3}} \exp\left(-\dfrac{k^2}{4t}\right)$
42	$\dfrac{1}{s} e^{-k\sqrt{s}} (k \geq 0)$	$\operatorname{erfc} \dfrac{k}{2\sqrt{t}}$
43	$\dfrac{1}{\sqrt{s}} e^{-k\sqrt{s}} \ (k \geq 0)$	$\dfrac{1}{\sqrt{\pi t}} \exp\left(-\dfrac{k^2}{4t}\right)$
44	$\dfrac{1}{s^{3/2}} e^{-k\sqrt{s}} \ (k \geq 0)$	$2\sqrt{\dfrac{t}{\pi}} \exp\left(-\dfrac{k^2}{4t}\right) - k \operatorname{erfc} \dfrac{k}{2\sqrt{t}}$ $= 2\sqrt{t}\, i\operatorname{erfc} \dfrac{k}{2\sqrt{t}}$
45	$\dfrac{1}{s^{1+n/2}} e^{-k\sqrt{s}} \ (n = 0, 1, 2, \ldots, k \geq 0)$	$(4t)^{n/2} i^n \operatorname{erfc} \dfrac{k}{2\sqrt{t}}$
46	$\dfrac{e^{-k\sqrt{s}}}{a + \sqrt{s}} (k \geq 0)$	$\dfrac{1}{\sqrt{\pi t}} \exp\left(-\dfrac{k^2}{4t}\right) - a e^{ak} e^{a^2 t}$ $\times \operatorname{erfc}\left(a\sqrt{t} + \dfrac{k}{2\sqrt{t}}\right)$
47	$\dfrac{e^{-k\sqrt{s}}}{\sqrt{s}(a + \sqrt{s})} (k \geq 0)$	$e^{ak} e^{a^2 t} \operatorname{erfc}\left(a\sqrt{t} + \dfrac{k}{2\sqrt{t}}\right)$

Table 7-1 *(Continued)*

No	$\bar{F}(s)$	$F(t)$
48	$\dfrac{e^{-k\sqrt{s(s+a)}}}{\sqrt{s(s+a)}}$ $(k \geq 0)$	$e^{-at/2}I_0(\tfrac{1}{2}a\sqrt{t^2-k^2})u(t-k)$
49	$\dfrac{e^{-k\sqrt{s^2+a^2}}}{\sqrt{s^2+a^2}}$ $(k \geq 0)$	$J_0(a\sqrt{t^2-k^2})u(t-k)$
50	$\dfrac{e^{-k\sqrt{s^2+a^2}}}{\sqrt{s^2-a^2}}$ $(k \geq 0)$	$I_0(a\sqrt{t^2-k^2})u(t-k)$
51	$\dfrac{ae^{-k\sqrt{s}}}{s(a+\sqrt{s})}$ $(k \geq 0)$	$-e^{ak}e^{a^2t}\,\mathrm{erfc}\left(a\sqrt{t}+\dfrac{k}{2\sqrt{t}}\right)+\mathrm{erfc}\,\dfrac{k}{2\sqrt{t}}$
52	$\dfrac{1}{s^2}e^{-k\sqrt{s}}$	$4ti^2\,\mathrm{erfc}\left(\dfrac{k}{2\sqrt{t}}\right)=\left(t+\dfrac{k^2}{2}\right)$ $\times\,\mathrm{erfc}\left(\dfrac{k}{2\sqrt{t}}\right)-k\left(\dfrac{t}{\pi}\right)^{1/2}\exp\left(-\dfrac{k^2}{4t}\right)$
53	$\dfrac{1}{s}\ln s$	$-\gamma-\ln t\,(\gamma=0.57721\,56649\ldots$ Euler's constant)
54	$\ln\dfrac{s+a}{s+b}$	$\dfrac{1}{t}(e^{-bt}-e^{-at})$
55	$\ln\dfrac{s^2+a^2}{s^2}$	$\dfrac{2}{t}(1-\cos at)$
56	$\ln\dfrac{s^2-a^2}{s^2}$	$\dfrac{2}{t}(1-\cosh at)$
57	$K_0(ks)\,(k>0)$	$\dfrac{1}{\sqrt{t^2-k^2}}u(t-k)$
58	$K_0(k\sqrt{s})\,(k>0)$	$\dfrac{1}{2t}\exp\left(-\dfrac{k^2}{4t}\right)$
59	$\dfrac{1}{\sqrt{s}}K_1(k\sqrt{s})\,(k>0)$	$\dfrac{1}{k}\exp\left(-\dfrac{k^2}{4t}\right)$

inversion is generally performed by the method of contour integration and the calculus of residues. This matter will be discussed in the following section.

Example 7-9. Determine the function whose Laplace transform is

$$\bar{F}(s) = \frac{b^2}{s(s^2 + b^2)}.$$

Solution. This function is not available in the Laplace transform table in this form; but it can be expressible in partial fractions as

$$\bar{F}(s) = \frac{b^2}{s(s^2 + b^2)} = \frac{c_1}{s} + \frac{c_2 s + c_3}{s^2 + b^2} \qquad (7\text{-}47a)$$

Then

$$b^2 = c_1 b^2 + c_3 s + (c_1 + c_2)s^2$$

Equating the coefficients of like powers of s we obtain $c_1 = 1, c_2 = -1$, and $c_3 = 0$. Hence

$$\bar{F}(s) = \frac{1}{s} - \frac{s}{s^2 + b^2} \qquad (7\text{-}47b)$$

Each term on the right-hand side is readily inverted using Table 7-1, cases 1 and 14; we find

$$F(t) = 1 - \cos bt \qquad (7\text{-}48)$$

7-4 THE INVERSION OF LAPLACE TRANSFORM BY THE CONTOUR INTEGRATION TECHNIQUE

When the Laplace transform $\bar{F}(s)$ of a function $F(t)$ is known, the function is determined by means of the inversion formula (7-6b); namely

$$F(t) = \frac{1}{2\pi i} \int_{s = \gamma - i\infty}^{\gamma + i\infty} e^{st} \bar{F}(s)\, ds \qquad (7\text{-}49)$$

The significance of this formula is that the integration is to be performed in the complex s plane along the infinite line $x = \gamma$ as illustrated in Fig. 7-5. In this equation the constant γ is so chosen that all singularities of the function $\bar{F}(s)$ lie to the left of the line $x = \gamma$. In many instances the integral in equation (7-49) is performed by the method of *contour integration* of complex variable functions and utilizing the results from the *theorem of residues*. Therefore,

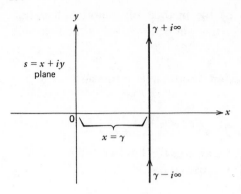

Fig. 7-5 The path of integration in the inversion formula.

we present below a brief discussion of contour integration and the theorem of residues before proceeding to the application of the inversion.

Contour Integration and the Residue Theorem

Let C be the contour of a region in the complex s plane and $F(s)$ be a complex variable function that is *analytic* inside this region except for a number of *poles* at locations $s_k, k = 1, 2, \ldots, N$ as illustrated in Fig. 7-6. (See Note 1 for the definition of an analytic function and the poles.) Then, the integration of the function $F(s)$ around the contour C in the *counterclockwise* (i.e., positive) direction is equal to "$2\pi i$ times the sum of the residues at the poles,"

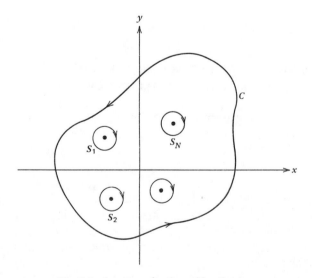

Fig. 7-6 A contour for the residue theorem.

namely

$$\oint_C F(s)\,ds = 2\pi i \sum_{k=1}^{N} \mathrm{res}(s_k) \qquad (7\text{-}50)$$

where res (s_k) denotes the residue of the integrand $F(s)$ at the pole $s = s_k$. This relationship is known as the *residue theorem* and its proof is available in the standard texts on complex variables.

Determination of Residues

Consider a function $F(s)$ that is analytic and single valued in a region of a complex s plane except at a point $s = a$ where it has a pole of order n. Near the point $s = a$, the function $F(s)$ may be expanded in the *Laurent series* in the form

$$F(s) = A_0 + A_1(s - a) + A_2(s - a)^2 + \ldots + \frac{B_1}{(s - a)} + \frac{B_2}{(s - a)^2} + \ldots + \frac{B_n}{(s - a)^n}$$

$$(7\text{-}51)$$

In this expression, the coefficient B_1, which is the coefficient of $1/(s - a)$, is called the *residue of the function* $F(s)$ at $s = a$ and is denoted by res $(s = a)$. The reason for this is that, if both sides of equation (7-51) is integrated around a closed contour C surrounding the point $s = a$ and the following fact is utilized

$$\oint_C (s - a)^n\,ds = \begin{cases} 0 & n \neq -1 \\ 2\pi i & n = -1 \end{cases} \qquad (7\text{-}52)$$

it is found that all the terms on the right-hand side of equation (7-51) vanish except the term involving the coefficient B_1. Thus we obtain

$$\oint_C F(s)\,ds = 2\pi i B_1 \qquad (7\text{-}53)$$

To determine the residue B_1, we multiply both sides of equation (7-51) by $(s - a)^n$, differentiate with respect to s, $(n - 1)$ times and set $s = a$, to obtain

$$B_1 \equiv \mathrm{res}(s = a) = \frac{1}{(n - 1)!}\left[\frac{d^{n-1}}{ds^{n-1}}\{(s - a)^n F(s)\}\right]_{s=a} \qquad (7\text{-}54)$$

Thus, equation (7-54) gives the residue of $F(s)$ at the point $s = a$ where the function $F(s)$ has an nth order pole.

When the function $F(s)$ has a *simple pole* (i.e., $n = 1$) at the point $s = a$, equation (7-54) simplifies to

$$\mathrm{res}(s = a) = [(s - a)F(s)]_{s=a} = \lim_{s \to a}[(s - a)F(s)] \qquad (7\text{-}55)$$

Example 7-10. Determine the residues of the function $F(s) = se^s/(s-a)^3$ at the triple pole $s = a$.

Solution. This function has a third-order pole at $s = a$; we use formula (7-54) with $n = 3$.

$$\text{res}(s = a) = \frac{1}{2!}\left[\frac{d^2}{ds^2}\{(s-a)^3 F(s)\}\right]_{s=a}$$

$$= \frac{1}{2!}\left[\frac{d^2}{ds^2}(se^s)\right]_{s=a} \tag{7-56a}$$

Noting that
$(d^2/ds^2)(se^s) = (2 + s)e^s$, we obtain

$$\text{res}(s = a) = \tfrac{1}{2}\left[e^s(2 + s)\right]_{s=a} = (1 + \tfrac{1}{2}a)e^a \tag{7-56b}$$

Example 7-11. A function $F(s)$ can be expressed in the fractional form as

$$F(s) = \frac{N(s)}{s^r M(s)} \tag{7-57}$$

where $M(s)$ has simple roots at $s = a_k, k = 1, 2, 3, \ldots, m$, while $N(a_k) \neq 0$, $N(0) \neq 0$ and $M(0) \neq 0$. Obtain an expression for the residues $\text{res}(s = a_k)$ of the function $F(s)$ at the poles $s = a_k, k = 1, 2, \ldots, m$.

Solution. The function $F(s)$ has only simple poles at $s = a_k, k = 1, 2, \ldots, m$. Therefore, to determine the residues at $s = a_k$ we apply the formula (7-55) as

$$\sum_{k=1}^{m} \text{res}(s = a_k) = \sum_{k=1}^{m} \lim_{s \to a_k}\left[(s - a_k)\frac{N(s)}{s^r M(s)}\right] \tag{7-58}$$

Noting that $M(a_k) \to 0$, we apply the L'Hospital's rule and obtain

$$\sum_{k=1}^{m} \text{res}(s = a_k) = \sum_{k=1}^{m} \frac{N(a_k)}{a_k^r[dM(s)/ds]_{s=a_k}} \tag{7-59}$$

This result will be useful in the inversion of Laplace transform in heat conduction applications.

Evaluation of the Inversion Integral

The contour integration technique and the residue theorem stated above are now applied to evaluate the integral in the inversion formula

$$F(t) = \frac{1}{2\pi i} \int_{s=\gamma-i\infty}^{\gamma+i\infty} e^{st}\bar{F}(s)\,ds \tag{7-60}$$

Depending on the type of singularities of the function $\bar{F}(s)$ a suitable contour is chosen on the complex s plane to evaluate this integral. In the following discussion we consider only two different types of contours, referred to as *case* 1 and *case* 2 to evaluate this integral. These two types of contours are sufficiently general for the inversion of transforms encountered in most heat conduction applications. The reader should consult reference [4] for a discussion of other types of contours.

CASE 1: Only Singularities of $\bar{F}(s)$ are the Poles

Let the transformed function $\bar{F}(s)$ be analytic in the complex s plane except for a finite (or an enumerably infinite) number of poles at the points $s = s_1$, $s_2, \ldots, s_k, \ldots$, all of which lie to the left of the line $x = \gamma$ in Fig. 7-5. We construct a circle of radius $|s| = R$, which lies to the left of the line $x = \gamma$, and enclose all singularities of the function $\bar{F}(s)$ as illustrated in Fig. 7-7. We now consider the integration of the function "$e^{st}\bar{F}(s)$" around the contour $ABB'CA'A$ of Fig. 7-7 in the counterclockwise direction. According to the residue theorem given by equation (7-50), this integral is equal to $2\pi i$ times the residues of $e^{st}\bar{F}(s)$ at the poles, that is

$$\oint_{\substack{\text{contour} \\ ABCA}} e^{st}\bar{F}(s)\,ds = 2\pi i \sum_{k=1}^{N} \text{res}(s_k) \qquad (7\text{-}61)$$

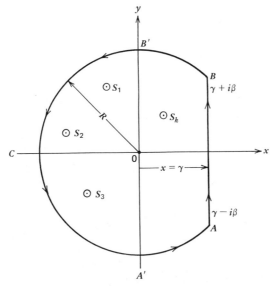

Fig. 7-7 Contour for the inversion problem considered as CASE 1.

The path of this contour is made up the line segment AB joining the points $\gamma - i\beta$ and $\gamma + i\beta$, and the circular are BCA. Therefore we write equation (7-61) as

$$\frac{1}{2\pi i} \int_{\gamma - i\beta}^{\gamma + i\beta} e^{st}\bar{F}(s)\, ds + \frac{1}{2\pi i} \int_{\substack{arc \\ BCA}} e^{st}\bar{F}(s)\, ds = \sum_{k=1}^{N} res(s_k) \qquad (7\text{-}62)$$

If we let the radius of the circle $R \to \infty$ as well as $N \to \infty$, then $\beta \to \infty$ and equation (7-62) is written as

$$\lim_{\beta \to \infty} \frac{1}{2\pi i} \int_{\gamma - i\beta}^{\gamma + i\beta} e^{st}\bar{F}(s)\, ds + \lim_{R \to \infty} \frac{1}{2\pi i} \int_{\substack{arc \\ BCA}} e^{st}\bar{F}(s)\, ds = \sum_{k=1}^{\infty} res(s_k) \qquad (7\text{-}63)$$

Clearly, the first integral on the left-hand side is the same as the inversion formula (7-60), hence it represents the function $F(t)$. Then, equation (7-63) is written as

$$F(t) = \sum_{k=1}^{\infty} res\,(s_k) - \frac{1}{2\pi i} \lim_{R \to \infty} \int_{\substack{arc \\ BCA}} e^{st}\bar{F}(s)\, ds \qquad (7\text{-}64)$$

If the function $\bar{F}(s)$ is such that

$$\lim_{R \to \infty} \int_{\substack{arc \\ BCA}} e^{st}\bar{F}(s)\, ds \to 0 \qquad (7\text{-}65)$$

Then, the inversion formula (7.64) reduces to

$$F(t) = \sum_{k=1}^{\infty} res\,(s_k) \qquad (7\text{-}66)$$

For heat-conduction problems considered in this book, the function $\bar{F}(s)$ is such that the integral around the contour BCA vanish as $R \to \infty$; thus, the inversion formula reduces to *the sum of the residues at the poles of the integrand*, as given by equation (7-66). A discussion of the conditions on $\bar{F}(s)$ leading to the result in equation (7-65) is given in several references [2, p. 193; 6; 10]. Briefly, the sufficient condition is that

$$|\bar{F}(s)| < \frac{M}{s^k} = \frac{M}{R^k} \qquad (7\text{-}67)$$

where M and k are positive constants.

Example 7-12. Determine the function $F(t)$ whose Laplace transform is given by $\bar{F}(s) = 1/(s^2 + \beta^2)$, where β is real and positive.

Solution.   The function $\bar{F}(s)$ has two simple poles at $s = \pm i\beta$, that is

$$\bar{F}(s) = \frac{1}{s^2 + \beta^2} = \frac{1}{(s - i\beta)(s + i\beta)} \tag{7-68}$$

Therefore, the function is of order $0(R^{-2})$ as $R \to \infty$; then the integral around the contour BCA in Fig. 7-7 vanishes as $R \to \infty$ and the inversion formula reduces to that given by equation (7.66)

$$F(t) = \sum_{k=1}^{2} \text{res}(s_k) \tag{7-69a}$$

Since the function $\bar{F}(s)$ has only simple poles, its residues at these poles are determined according to equation (7-55) as

$$\text{res}(s_1) = \text{res}(s = i\beta) = \lim_{s \to i\beta} \left[(s - i\beta) \frac{e^{st}}{s^2 + \beta^2} \right] = \left[\frac{e^{st}}{s + i\beta} \right]_{s = i\beta} = \frac{e^{i\beta t}}{2i\beta}$$

$$\text{res}(s_2) = \text{res}(s = -i\beta) = \lim_{s \to -i\beta} \left[(s + i\beta) \frac{e^{st}}{s^2 + \beta^2} \right] = \left[\frac{e^{st}}{s - i\beta} \right]_{s = -i\beta} = \frac{e^{-i\beta t}}{-2i\beta}$$

Then,

$$F(t) = \sum_{k=1}^{2} \text{res}(s_k) = \frac{e^{i\beta t}}{2i\beta} - \frac{e^{-i\beta t}}{2i\beta} = \frac{1}{\beta} \frac{e^{i\beta t} - e^{-i\beta t}}{2i}$$

$$F(t) = \frac{\sin \beta t}{\beta} \tag{7-69b}$$

We note that this result is also obtainable by rearranging $\bar{F}(s)$ as $\bar{F}(s) = (1/\beta)[\beta/(s^2 + \beta^2)]$ and noting that the inversion of $\beta/(s^2 + \beta^2)$ is $\sin \beta t$.

CASE 2: $\bar{F}(s)$ has One Branch Point at $s = 0$

We now consider a situation in which the function $\bar{F}(s)$ is analytic in the complex s plane except for a number of isolated singularities at the points $s = s_1, s_2, \ldots, s_k, \ldots$, all of which lie to the left of the line $x = \gamma$, and in addition the function $\bar{F}(s)$ has a branch point at $s = 0$. (See Note 2 for a discussion of branch point and branch cut.) Usually, in the problems of heat conduction in a semi-infinite region the function $\bar{F}(s)$ has a branch point at $s = 0$. When the function has a branch point at $s = 0$, it is multivalued at $s = 0$. To make the function single valued (i.e., analytic) we introduce a *branch cut* from the branch point $s = 0$, including the branch point, to infinity. The direction of the branch cut is arbitrary, as long as we stay to the left of the line $x = \gamma$. For the present problem we have chosen this branch cut from the point

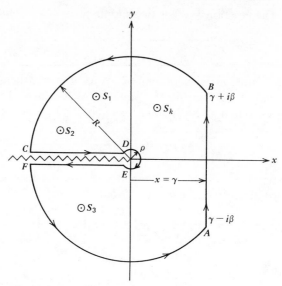

Fig. 7-8   Contour for the inversion problem considered as CASE 2.

$s = 0$ to infinity along the negative real axis as illustrated in Fig. 7-8. The desired contour is now constructed by drawing a large circle of radius R to enclose all singularities of the function $\bar{F}(s)$, a small circle of radius ρ around the center 0, and the paths CD and EF above and below the cut, respectively, as shown in Fig. 7-8. The integration of the function $e^{st}\bar{F}(s)$ around this contour in the counterclockwise direction is given according to the residue theorem (7-50) as

$$\frac{1}{2\pi i} \oint_{\substack{\text{around the} \\ \text{contour}}} e^{st}\bar{F}(s)\,ds = \sum_{k=1}^{N} \text{res}\,(s_k) \qquad (7\text{-}70)$$

We now let $R \to \infty$, $N \to \infty$, and $\rho \to 0$, and rewrite this integral by separating the contour into several parts as illustrated in Fig. 7-8.

$$\lim_{\substack{R \to \infty \\ \rho \to 0}} \frac{1}{2\pi i}\left[\int_{\substack{\text{line} \\ AB}} + \int_{\substack{\text{arcs} \\ BC \text{ and} \\ FA}} + \int_{\substack{\text{lines} \\ CD \text{ and} \\ EF}} + \int_{\substack{\text{small} \\ \text{circle} \\ \rho}} \right][e^{st}\bar{F}(s)\,ds] = \sum_{k=1}^{\infty} \text{res}\,(s_k) \qquad (7\text{-}71)$$

Various integrals in equation (7-71) are evaluated as now described.

Line AB.   As $R \to \infty$, this integral is equivalent to the inversion formula (7-60), hence is gives the function $F(t)$. That is

$$\lim_{R \to \infty} \frac{1}{2\pi i} \int_{\substack{\text{line} \\ AB}} e^{st}\bar{F}(s)\,ds \to \frac{1}{2\pi i} \int_{\gamma - i\infty}^{\gamma + i\infty} e^{st}\bar{F}(s)\,ds = F(t) \qquad (7\text{-}72a)$$

Arcs BC and FA.   If the function $\bar{F}(s)$ is such that the integral around the large arcs *BC* and *FA* vanishes as $R \to \infty$, we write

$$\lim_{\substack{R \to \infty}} \frac{1}{2\pi i} \int_{\substack{\text{arcs} \\ BC \text{ and} \\ FA}} e^{st}\bar{F}(s)\,ds \to 0 \qquad (7\text{-}72b)$$

Most functions considered in this book satisfy such conditions.

Lines CD and EF.   To evaluate the integrals along the paths *CD* and *EF* we set

$$s = xe^{i\pi} \quad \text{and} \quad ds = dxe^{i\pi} \qquad \text{for the line } CD$$

$$s = xe^{-i\pi} \quad \text{and} \quad ds = dxe^{-i\pi} \qquad \text{for the line } EF$$

where x and dx signify $|x|$ and $|dx|$, respectively. Then the integrals along the paths *CD* and *EF* are written, respectively, as

$$\lim_{\substack{R \to \infty \\ \rho \to \infty}} \frac{1}{2\pi i} \int_{C \to \infty}^{D \to 0} e^{-xt}\bar{F}(xe^{i\pi})\,dx = \frac{1}{2\pi i} \int_{0}^{\infty} e^{-xt}\bar{F}(xe^{i\pi})\,dx \qquad (7\text{-}72c)$$

$$\lim_{\substack{R \to \infty \\ \rho \to 0}} \frac{1}{2\pi i} \int_{E \to 0}^{F \to \infty} e^{-xt}\bar{F}(xe^{-i\pi})\,dx = -\frac{1}{2\pi i} \int_{0}^{\infty} e^{-xt}\bar{F}(xe^{-i\pi})\,dx \qquad (7\text{-}72d)$$

where x signifies $|x|$.

Small circle ρ.   To evaluate the integral around the small circle of radius ρ we write

$$s = \rho e^{i\theta} \quad \text{and} \quad ds = i\rho e^{i\theta}\,d\theta$$

Then, the integral around this circle is written as

$$\frac{1}{2\pi i} \int_{\substack{\text{small} \\ \text{circle } \rho}} e^{st}\bar{F}(s)\,ds = \frac{1}{2\pi i} \int_{D \to \pi}^{E \to -\pi} e^{\rho e^{i\theta}t}\bar{F}(\rho e^{i\theta})(i\rho e^{i\theta}\,d\theta)$$

$$= -\frac{1}{2\pi} \int_{-\pi}^{\pi} e^{\rho e^{i\theta}t}\bar{F}(\rho e^{i\theta})\rho e^{i\theta}\,d\theta \qquad (7\text{-}72e)$$

Now introducing equations (7-72) into equation (7-71), and rearranging, we obtain

$$F(t) = \sum_{k=1}^{\infty} \text{res}\,(s_k) + \frac{1}{2\pi i} \int_{0}^{\infty} e^{-xt}[\bar{F}(xe^{-i\pi}) - \bar{F}(xe^{i\pi})]\,dx$$

$$+ \lim_{\rho \to 0} \frac{1}{2\pi} \int_{-\pi}^{\pi} e^{\rho e^{i\theta}} \cdot \bar{F}(\rho e^{i\theta}) \cdot \rho e^{i\theta}\,d\theta \qquad (7\text{-}73)$$

which is valid if $\bar{F}(s)$ is such that the integrals around the arcs BC and FA vanish as $R \to \infty$. Here x signifies $|x|$.

Example 7-13. Determine the function $F(t)$ whose Laplace transform is given by

$$\bar{F}(s) = e^{-\alpha\sqrt{s}} \tag{7-74}$$

Solution. This function has a branch point at the origin where it is multivalued. It can be made single valued, hence analytic, by introducing a branch cut from $s = 0$ to infinity, including the point $s = 0$. Then the inversion problem is equivalent to that considered as CASE 2 with the contour of Fig. 7-8, and the inversion formula (7-73) can be used since the integrals around the large arcs BC and FA vanish as $R \to \infty$. In addition, the integral around the small circle of radius ρ vanish as $\rho \to 0$ and the summation over the residues is not needed because the function $\bar{F}(s)$ has no isolated poles in the s plane. Thus, the inversion formula (7-73) reduces to

$$F(t) = \frac{1}{2\pi i} \int_0^\infty e^{-xt}[\bar{F}(xe^{-i\pi}) - \bar{F}(xe^{i\pi})]\,dx \tag{7-75}$$

where

$$\bar{F}(xe^{-i\pi}) = e^{-\alpha\sqrt{s}}\Big|_{s=xe^{-i\pi}} = e^{-\alpha\sqrt{x}\cdot e^{-i(\pi/2)}} = e^{i\alpha\sqrt{x}} \tag{7-76a}$$

$$\bar{F}(xe^{i\pi}) = e^{-\alpha\sqrt{s}}\Big|_{s=xe^{i\pi}} = e^{-\alpha\sqrt{x}\cdot e^{i(\pi/2)}} = e^{-i\alpha\sqrt{x}} \tag{7-76b}$$

since $e^{\pm i(\pi/2)} = \pm i$. Equation (7-75) becomes

$$F(t) = \frac{1}{\pi} \int_0^\infty e^{-xt}\left[\frac{e^{i\alpha\sqrt{x}} - e^{-i\alpha\sqrt{x}}}{2i}\right] dx$$

$$= \frac{1}{\pi} \int_0^\infty e^{-xt} \sin(\alpha\sqrt{x})\,dx \tag{7-77}$$

This integral is available [15, p. 236, #861.32]; then

$$F(t) = \alpha\left(\frac{1}{4\pi t^3}\right)^{1/2} e^{-\alpha^2/4t} \tag{7-78}$$

Example 7-14. Determine the function $F(t)$ whose Laplace transform is

$$\bar{F}(s) = \frac{1}{s} e^{-\alpha\sqrt{s}} \tag{7-79}$$

The transform of this form is encountered in the solution of the heat-conduction problem for a semi-infinite medium subject to a constant temperature at the boundary surface $x = 0$ as will be illustrated in Example 7-15, CASE 1.

Solution. This function has a branch point at the origin; therefore we invert it according to CASE 2 and the contour shown in Fig. 7-8. We use the inversion formula (7-73) because the integrals around the large arcs BC and FA vanish as $R \to \infty$. The summation over the residues is not needed because the function $\bar{F}(s)$ has no poles other than $s = 0$, which is already removed from the s plane by the branch cut. Then, equation (7-73) becomes

$$F(t) = \frac{1}{2\pi i} \int_0^\infty e^{-xt} [\bar{F}(xe^{-i\pi}) - \bar{F}(xe^{i\pi})] \, dx$$

$$+ \lim_{\rho \to 0} \frac{1}{2\pi} \int_{-\pi}^\pi e^{\rho e^{i\theta}} \bar{F}(\rho e^{i\theta}) \rho e^{i\theta} \, d\theta \qquad (7\text{-}80)$$

We note that, in this case, the integral around the small circle does not vanish as $\rho \to 0$. Various terms in equation (7-80) are evaluated as discussed in Note 3 and equation (7-80) becomes

$$F(t) = -\frac{1}{\pi} \int_0^\infty \frac{e^{-xt}}{x} \frac{e^{i\alpha\sqrt{x}} - e^{-i\alpha\sqrt{x}}}{2i} \, dx + \frac{1}{2\pi} \lim_{\rho \to 0} \int_{-\pi}^\pi e^{\rho e^{i\theta}} \cdot e^{-\alpha\sqrt{\rho} e^{i(\theta/2)}} \, d\theta \qquad (7\text{-}81a)$$

or

$$F(t) = -\frac{1}{\pi} \int_0^\infty \frac{1}{x} e^{-xt} \sin(\alpha\sqrt{x}) \, dx + \frac{1}{2\pi} \int_{-\pi}^\pi d\theta \qquad (7\text{-}81b)$$

$$F(t) = 1 - \frac{1}{\pi} \int_0^\infty \frac{1}{x} e^{-xt} \sin(\alpha\sqrt{x}) \, dx \qquad (7\text{-}81c)$$

The integral is available [15,p. 236, # 861.22]; then

$$F(t) = 1 - \mathrm{erf}\left(\frac{\alpha}{2\sqrt{t}}\right) = \mathrm{erfc}\left(\frac{\alpha}{2\sqrt{t}}\right) \qquad (7\text{-}82)$$

We note that the transform (7-79) and its inversion (7-82) is of the same form as that given in Table 7-1, case 42.

7-5 APPLICATION OF LAPLACE TRANSFORM IN THE SOLUTION OF TIME-DEPENDENT HEAT-CONDUCTION PROBLEMS

In this section we illustrate with representative examples the use of Laplace transform technique in the solution of time-dependent heat-conduction problems. In this approach, the Laplace transform is applied to remove the partial derivative with respect to the time variable, the resulting equation is solved for the transform of temperature, and the transform is inverted to recover the solution for the temperature distribution. The approach is straightforward in principle, but generally the inversion is difficult unless the transform is available in the Laplace transform tables. In the following examples, typical heat-conduction problems are solved both by using the Laplace transform table and the contour integration technique to invert the transform.

Example 7-15. A semi-infinite medium, $x \geq 0$, is initially at zero temperature. For times $t > 0$, the boundary surface at $x = 0$ is subjected to a temperature $T = f(t)$ which varies with time. Obtain an expression for the temperature distribution $T(x, t)$ in the medium for times $t > 0$.

Solution. The mathematical formulation of this problem is given as

$$\frac{\partial^2 T(x,t)}{\partial x^2} = \frac{1}{\alpha} \frac{\partial T(x,t)}{\partial t} \qquad \text{in } 0 < x < \infty, \ t > 0 \qquad (7\text{-}83a)$$

$$T(x,t) = f(t) \qquad \text{at } x = 0, \ t > 0 \qquad (7\text{-}83b)$$

$$T(x,t) = 0 \qquad \text{as } x \to \infty, \ t > 0 \qquad (7\text{-}83c)$$

$$T(x,t) = 0 \qquad \text{for } t = 0, \ \text{in } x \geq 0 \qquad (7\text{-}83d)$$

We recall that this problem was solved in Example 5-1 by the application of Duhamel's method. Here the Laplace transform technique is used to solve the same problem, and the standard Laplace transform table is utilized to invert the resulting transform.

Taking the Laplace transform of equations (7-83) we obtain

$$\frac{d^2 \bar{T}(x,s)}{dx^2} - \frac{s}{\alpha} \bar{T}(x,s) = 0 \qquad \text{in } 0 < x < \infty \qquad (7\text{-}84a)$$

$$\bar{T}(x,s) = \bar{f}(s) \qquad \text{at } x = 0 \qquad (7\text{-}84b)$$

$$\bar{T}(x,s) = 0 \qquad \text{as } x \to \infty \qquad (7\text{-}84c)$$

The solution of equations (7-84) is given as

$$\bar{T}(x,s) = \bar{f}(s) \cdot \bar{g}(x,s) \qquad (7\text{-}85a)$$

where

$$\bar{g}(x,s) \equiv e^{-x\sqrt{s/\alpha}} \qquad (7\text{-}85b)$$

Since the functional form of $\bar{f}(s)$ is not explicitly specified, it is better to make use of the convolution property of the Laplace transform given by equation (7-34) to invert this transform. Namely, in view of equation (7-34), we write the result in equation (7-85a) as

$$\bar{T}(x,s) = \bar{f}(s) \cdot \bar{g}(x,s) = \mathscr{L}\big[f(t) * g(x,t) \big] \qquad (7\text{-}86)$$

The inversion of this result gives

$$T(x, t) = f(t) * g(x, t) \tag{7-87a}$$

and utilizing the definition of the convolution $f * g$ given by equation (7-33b), equation (7-87a) is written as

$$T(x, t) = \int_0^t f(\tau)g(x, t - \tau)\,d\tau \tag{7-87b}$$

To complete the solution of this problem we need to know the function $g(x, t)$. However, the Laplace transform $\bar{g}(x, s)$ of this function given by equation (7-85b); then, the function $g(x, t)$ can be determined by the inversion of this transform. The transform $\bar{g}(x, s)$ readily inverted by utilizing Table 7-1, case 41; we find

$$g(x, t) = \frac{x}{2\sqrt{\pi \alpha t^3}}\, e^{-x^2/4\alpha t} \tag{7-87c}$$

After replacing t by $(t - \tau)$ in this result, we introduce it into equation (7-87b) to obtain the desired solution as

$$T(x, t) = \frac{x}{\sqrt{4\pi\alpha}} \int_{\tau=0}^t \frac{f(\tau)}{(t - \tau)^{3/2}} \exp\left[\frac{-x^2}{4\alpha(t - \tau)}\right] d\tau \tag{7-88}$$

This result is the same as that given by equation (5-33) which was obtained by utilizing the Duhamel's theorem.

The temperature $T(x, t)$ can be determined from equation (7-88) for any specified form of the function $f(t)$ by performing the integration. Sometimes it is easier to introduce the transform $\bar{f}(s)$ of the function $f(t)$ into equation (7-85a) and then invert the result rather than performing the integration in equation (7-88). This matter is now illustrated for some special cases of function $f(t)$.

1. $f(t) = T_0 = constant.$ Then, the transform of $f(t) = T_0$ is $\bar{f}(s) = T_0/s$. Introducing this result into equation (7-85) we obtain

$$\bar{T}(x, s) = \frac{T_0}{s}\, e^{-x\sqrt{s/\alpha}} \tag{7-89a}$$

We note that this transform is of the same form as that given by equation (7-79) considered in Example 7-14 and the inversion is given by equation (7-82); or the transform (7-89a) is readily inverted by utilizing Table 7-1, case 42. We obtain

$$T(x, t) = T_0 \operatorname{erfc}(x/\sqrt{4\alpha t}) \tag{7-89b}$$

2. $f(t) = T_0 t^{1/2}.$ The transform of this function is obtained from

Table 7-1, case 5 as $\bar{f}(s) = T_0(\sqrt{\pi}/2)s^{-3/2}$. Introducing this result into equation (7-85) we obtain

$$\bar{T}(x,s) = T_0 \frac{\sqrt{\pi}}{2} s^{-3/2} e^{-x\sqrt{s/\alpha}} \tag{7-90a}$$

This result is inverted by utilizing Table 7-1, case 44; we find

$$T(x,t) = T_0 \left[t^{1/2} e^{-x^2/4\alpha t} - \frac{x}{2}\sqrt{\frac{\pi}{\alpha}} \operatorname{erfc} \frac{x}{\sqrt{4\alpha t}} \right] \tag{7-90b}$$

Example 7-16.   A semi-infinite medium, $0 \leq x < \infty$, is initially at zero temperature. For times $t > 0$, the boundary surface at $x = 0$ is subjected to convection with an environment at temperature T_∞. Obtain an expression for the temperature distribution $T(x, t)$ in the solid for times $t > 0$.

Solution.   The mathematical formulation of the problem is given as

$$\frac{\partial^2 T(x,t)}{\partial x^2} = \frac{1}{\alpha} \frac{\partial T(x,t)}{\partial t} \qquad \text{in } 0 < x < \infty, \ t > 0 \tag{7-91a}$$

$$-k\frac{\partial T}{\partial x} + hT = hT_\infty \qquad \text{at } x = 0, \ t > 0 \tag{7-91b}$$

$$T = 0 \qquad \text{as } x \to \infty, \ t > 0 \tag{7-91c}$$

$$T = 0 \qquad \text{for } t = 0, \text{ in } 0 \leq x < \infty \tag{7-91d}$$

The Laplace transform of equations (7-91) becomes

$$\frac{d^2 \bar{T}(x,s)}{dx^2} - \frac{s}{\alpha}\bar{T}(x,s) = 0 \qquad \text{in } 0 < x < \infty \tag{7-92a}$$

$$-k\frac{d\bar{T}}{dx} + h\bar{T} = \frac{1}{s}hT_\infty \qquad \text{at } x = 0 \tag{7-92b}$$

$$\bar{T} = 0 \qquad \text{as } x \to \infty \tag{7-92c}$$

The solution of equations (7-92) is

$$\frac{\bar{T}(x,s)}{T_\infty} = H\sqrt{\alpha}\,\frac{e^{-(x/\sqrt{\alpha})\sqrt{s}}}{s(H\sqrt{\alpha} + \sqrt{s})} \tag{7-93}$$

where $H \equiv h/k$. The inversion of this result is available in Table 7-1, case 51; then the solution becomes

$$\frac{T(x,t)}{T_\infty} = \operatorname{erfc}\left(\frac{x}{\sqrt{4\alpha t}}\right) - e^{Hx + H^2\alpha t} \operatorname{erfc}\left(H\sqrt{\alpha t} + \frac{x}{\sqrt{4\alpha t}}\right) \tag{7-94}$$

Example 7-17. A slab, $0 \leq x \leq L$, is initially at zero temperature. For times $t > 0$, the boundary at $x = 0$ is subjected to a prescribed temperature $T = f_1(t)$, which varies with time, while the boundary surface at $x = L$ is kept at zero temperature. Obtain an expression for the temperature distribution in the slab for times $t > 0$.

Solution. The mathematical formulation of this problem is given as

$$\frac{\partial^2 T(x,t)}{\partial x^2} = \frac{1}{\alpha} \frac{\partial T(x,t)}{\partial t} \qquad \text{in } 0 < x < L, \ t > 0 \qquad (7\text{-}95\text{a})$$

$$T(x,t) = f_1(t) \qquad \text{at } x = 0, \ t > 0 \qquad (7\text{-}95\text{b})$$

$$T(x,t) = 0 \qquad \text{at } x = L, \ t > 0 \qquad (7\text{-}95\text{c})$$

$$T(x,t) = 0 \qquad \text{for } t = 0, \text{ in } 0 \leq x \leq L \qquad (7\text{-}95\text{d})$$

We recall that a more general case of this problem was solved in Example 5-2 by the application of the Duhamel's method. Here, we solve this problem by the Laplace transform technique and invert the resulting transform by the inversion formula using the contour integration technique.

Taking the Laplace transform of equations (7-95) we obtain

$$\frac{d^2 \bar{T}(x,s)}{dx^2} - \frac{s}{\alpha} \bar{T}(x,s) = 0 \qquad \text{in } 0 < x < L \qquad (7\text{-}96\text{a})$$

$$\bar{T}(x,s) = \bar{f}_1(s) \qquad \text{at } x = 0 \qquad (7\text{-}96\text{b})$$

$$\bar{T}(x,s) = 0 \qquad \text{at } x = L \qquad (7\text{-}96\text{c})$$

The solution of equations (7-96) is given as

$$\bar{T}(x,s) = \bar{f}_1(s) \cdot \bar{g}(x,s) \qquad (7\text{-}97\text{a})$$

where

$$\bar{g}(x,s) \equiv \frac{\sinh\left[(L-x)\sqrt{s/\alpha}\right]}{\sinh(L\sqrt{s/\alpha})} \qquad (7\text{-}97\text{b})$$

Here, the functional form of $\bar{f}_1(s)$ is not specified explicitly. Therefore, we make use of the Laplace transform of a convolution to invert this transform. In view of equation (7-34), we write equation (7-97a) as

$$\bar{T}(x,s) = \bar{f}_1(s) \cdot \bar{g}(x,s) = \mathscr{L}\left[f_1(t) * g(x,t)\right] \qquad (7\text{-}98)$$

The inversion of this result gives

$$T(x,t) = f_1(t) * g(x,t) \qquad (7\text{-}99)$$

and by utilizing the definition of the convolution $f_1 * g$, we write this result as

$$T(x, t) = \int_0^t f_1(\tau) g(x, t - \tau) \, d\tau \tag{7-100}$$

To complete the solution we need to know the function $g(x, t)$. The Laplace transform of this function is given by equation (7-97b); therefore $\bar{g}(x, s)$ to be inverted to recover the function $g(x, t)$. The transform $\bar{g}(x, s)$ is not available in the standard Laplace transform tables. Therefore, we resort to the inversion formula to perform the inversion. By applying the inversion formula (7-6b) we write

$$g(x, t) = \frac{1}{2\pi i} \int_{s = \gamma - i\infty}^{\gamma + i\infty} e^{st} \frac{\sinh\left[(L - x)\sqrt{s/\alpha}\right]}{\sinh(L\sqrt{s/\alpha})} \, ds \tag{7-101}$$

We note that the denominator $\sinh(L\sqrt{s/\alpha})$ has infinite number of zeros when $\sqrt{s/\alpha}$ is purely imaginary. Therefore by setting $\sqrt{s/\alpha} = i\beta$, we write

$$\sinh(L\sqrt{s/\alpha}) = \sinh(i\beta L) = i \sin \beta L = 0 \tag{7-102a}$$

The zeros of $\sin \beta L$ occurs at

$$\beta_n L = n\pi \qquad \text{or} \qquad \beta_n = \frac{n\pi}{L}, \qquad n = 1, 2, 3 \ldots \tag{7-102b}$$

then the poles are at the locations

$$\sqrt{s_n/\alpha} = i\beta_n \qquad \text{or} \qquad s_n = -\alpha\beta_n^2, \qquad n = 1, 2, 3 \ldots \tag{7-102c}$$

Thus, the integrand in equation (7-101) is analytic in the s plane except for simple poles at $s_n = -\alpha\beta_n^2$. The inversion problem corresponds to that considered as CASE 1 with the contour shown in Fig. 7-7. We note that the integration of the integrand around the contour BCA of Fig. 7-7 vanishes then the inversion formula (7-101) reduces to that given by equation (7-66) namely

$$g(x, t) = \sum_{n=1}^{\infty} \text{res}(s_n) \tag{7-103}$$

where $\text{res}(s_n)$ denotes the residues of the integrand at the poles $s_n = -\alpha\beta_n^2$. To determine the residues, we write the integrand of equation (7-101) in the form

$$(\text{Integrand}) = \frac{N(s)}{M(s)} \tag{7-104a}$$

where

$$N(s) = e^{st} \sinh\left[(L - x)\sqrt{\frac{s}{\alpha}} \right] \qquad (7\text{-}104\text{b})$$

$$M(s) = \sinh\left(L\sqrt{\frac{s}{\alpha}} \right) \qquad (7\text{-}104\text{c})$$

$M(s)$ has simple roots at $s_n = -\alpha\beta_n^2, \beta_n = n\pi/L, n = 1, 2, 3 \ldots$. The function defined by equations (7-104) is of the same form as equation (7-57) with $r = 0$ considered in Example 7-11. Then, the residues are determined according to equation (7-59); we write

$$g(x, t) = \sum_{n=1}^{\infty} \text{res}(s_n) = \sum_{n=1}^{\infty} \frac{N(s_n)}{[dM(s)/ds]_{s=s_n}} \qquad (7\text{-}105\text{a})$$

where

$$s_n = -\alpha\beta_n^2 \qquad (7\text{-}105\text{b})$$

$$N(s_n) = e^{-\alpha\beta_n^2 t} \sinh\left[i\beta_n(L - x) \right] = -i(-1)^n e^{-\alpha\beta_n^2 t} \sin \beta_n x \qquad (7\text{-}105\text{c})$$

$$\left[\frac{dM(s)}{ds} \right]_{s=s_n} = \left[\frac{d}{ds} \sinh\left(L\sqrt{\frac{s}{\alpha}} \right) \right]_{s=s_n} = (-1)^n \frac{L}{2i\alpha\beta_n} \qquad (7\text{-}105\text{d})$$

Thus, the function $g(x, t)$ becomes

$$g(x, t) = \frac{2\alpha}{L} \sum_{n=1}^{\infty} e^{-\alpha\beta_n^2 t} \beta_n \sin \beta_n x \qquad (7\text{-}105\text{e})$$

We replace t by $(t - \tau)$ in equation (7-105e) and introduce it to equation (7-100) to obtain the solution for the temperature as

$$T(x, t) = \frac{2\alpha}{L} \sum_{n=1}^{\infty} \beta_n \sin \beta_n x \int_{\tau=0}^{t} f_1(\tau) e^{-\alpha\beta_n^2 (t-\tau)} \, d\tau \qquad (7\text{-}106)$$

where

$$\beta_n = \frac{n\pi}{L}$$

We note that this solution is the same as that given by equation (5-44) for $f_2(\tau) = 0$, which was obtained by the Duhamel's method.

We now consider a special case of equation (7-106).

1. $f_1(t) = T_1 = constant.$ For this special case equation (7-106) reduces to

$$\frac{T(x, t)}{T_1} = \frac{2}{L} \sum_{n=1}^{\infty} \frac{\sin \beta_n x}{\beta_n} (1 - e^{-\alpha\beta_n^2 t}) \qquad (7\text{-}107\text{a})$$

Noting that, for $t \to \infty$, the solution (7-107a) becomes the steady-state solution which is equal to $T(x, \infty) = T_1(1 - x/L)$; we obtain

$$1 - \frac{x}{L} = \frac{2}{L} \sum_{n=1}^{\infty} \frac{\sin \beta_n x}{\beta_n} \tag{7-107b}$$

Introducing (7-107b) into (7-107a), the solution for the case $f_1(\tau) = T_1$ becomes

$$\frac{T(x, t)}{T_1} = \left(1 - \frac{x}{L}\right) - \frac{2}{L} \sum_{n=1}^{\infty} e^{-\alpha \beta_n^2 t} \frac{\sin \beta_n x}{\beta_n} \tag{7-107c}$$

where

$$\beta_n = \frac{n\pi}{L}$$

We note that the solution (7-107c) is the same as that given by equation (2-166b) for $T_2 = 0$ and $F(x) = 0$.

Example 7-18.   A solid cylinder, $0 \le r \le b$, is initially at zero temperature. For times $t > 0$, the boundary surface at $r = b$ is kept at temperature $f(t)$, which varies with time. Obtain an expression for the temperature distribution $T(r, t)$ in the cylinder for times $t > 0$.

Solution.   The mathematical formulation of this problem is given as

$$\frac{1}{r} \frac{\partial}{\partial r}\left(r \frac{\partial T}{\partial r}\right) = \frac{1}{\alpha} \frac{\partial T}{\partial t} \qquad \text{in } 0 \le r < b, \ t > 0 \tag{7-108a}$$

$$T(r, t) = f(t) \qquad\qquad \text{at } r = b, \ t > 0 \tag{7-108b}$$

$$T(r, t) = 0 \qquad\qquad \text{for } t = 0, \text{ in } 0 \le r \le b \tag{7-108c}$$

We solved this problem in Example 5-3, by the application of the Duhamel's method. Here we solve it by the Laplace transform technique.

Taking the Laplace transform of equations (7-108) we obtain

$$\frac{1}{r} \frac{d}{dr}\left[r \frac{d\bar{T}(r, s)}{dr}\right] - \frac{s}{\alpha} \bar{T}(r, s) = 0 \qquad \text{in } 0 \le r < b \tag{7-109a}$$

$$\bar{T}(r, s) = \bar{f}(s) \qquad\qquad \text{at } r = b \tag{7-109b}$$

The solution of equation (7-109) that remains finite at $r = 0$ is

$$\bar{T}(r, s) = \bar{f}(s) \cdot \bar{g}(r, s) \tag{7-110a}$$

where

$$\bar{g}(r,s) = \frac{I_0(r\sqrt{s/\alpha})}{I_0(b\sqrt{s/\alpha})} \tag{7-110b}$$

We now make use of the relation (7-34) on the Laplace transform of a convolution and write equation (7-110a) as

$$\bar{T}(r,s) = \bar{f}(s)\cdot\bar{g}(r,s) = \mathscr{L}[f(t)*g(r,t)] \tag{7-111}$$

and inverting this result we obtain

$$T(r,t) = f(t)*g(r,t) = \int_0^t f(\tau)g(r,t-\tau)\,d\tau \tag{7-112}$$

To complete this solution the function $g(r,t)$ is needed. The Laplace transform of this function is available by equation (7-110b); by the application of the inversion formula (7-6b) we write

$$g(r,t) = \frac{1}{2\pi i}\int_{s=\gamma-i\infty}^{\gamma+i\infty} e^{st}\frac{I_0(r\sqrt{s/\alpha})}{I_0(b\sqrt{s/\alpha})}\,ds \tag{7-113}$$

The integrand is a single-valued function of s except for the infinite number of poles due to the denominator, which occurs when $\sqrt{s/\alpha}$ is purely imaginary. Namely, by setting

$$\sqrt{\frac{s}{\alpha}} = i\beta \qquad \text{or} \qquad s = -\alpha\beta^2 \tag{7-114a}$$

we write the denominator as

$$I_0(b\sqrt{s/\alpha}) = I_0(i\beta b) = J_0(\beta b) \tag{7-114b}$$

Thus zeros of the denominator occur at

$$J_0(\beta b) = 0 \tag{7-114c}$$

and the poles of the integrand in equation (7-113) occur at

$$s_n = -\alpha\beta_n^2 \tag{7-114d}$$

where β_n's are the roots of equation (7-114c). Then, the inversion problem corresponds to that considered as CASE 1 with the contour shown in Fig. 7-7. We also note that the integration of the integrand around the contour BCA of Fig. 7-7 vanishes; then the inversion formula (7-113) reduces to that given by equation (7-66), namely

$$g(r,t) = \sum_{n=1}^{\infty} \text{res}(s_n) \tag{7-115}$$

where $\mathrm{res}(s_n)$ denotes the residues of the integrand at the poles $s = s_n$. To determine the residues we write the integrand in the form

$$\text{(Integrand)} = \frac{N(s)}{M(s)} \tag{7-116a}$$

where

$$N(s) = e^{st} I_0\left(r\sqrt{\frac{s}{\alpha}}\right) \tag{7-116b}$$

$$M(s) = I_0\left(b\sqrt{\frac{s}{\alpha}}\right) \tag{7-116c}$$

and $M(s)$ has simple roots at $s_n = -\alpha\beta_n^2$ where β_n's are the roots of equation (7-114c). The function defined by equations (7-116) is of the same form as that given by equation (7-57) with $r = 0$. Then, the residues are determined according to equation (7-59), that is

$$g(r, t) = \sum_{n=0}^{\infty} \mathrm{res}(s_n) = \sum_{n=1}^{\infty} \frac{N(s_n)}{[dM(s)/ds]_{s=s_n}} \tag{7-117}$$

where $\sqrt{s_n/\alpha} = i\beta_n$ or $s_n = -\alpha\beta_n^2$. When these calculations are performed, we obtain

$$g(r, t) = \frac{2\alpha}{b} \sum_{n=1}^{\infty} e^{-\alpha\beta_n^2 t} \beta_n \frac{J_0(r\beta_n)}{J_1(b\beta_n)} \tag{7-118}$$

We now replace t by $(t - \tau)$ in equation (7-118) and introduce it into equation (7-112) to obtain the solution for the temperature distribution $T(r, t)$ as

$$T(r, t) = \frac{2\alpha}{b} \sum_{n=1}^{\infty} \beta_n \frac{J_0(r\beta_n)}{J_1(b\beta_n)} \int_0^t f(\tau) e^{-\alpha\beta_n^2(t-\tau)} \, d\tau \tag{7-119}$$

where β_n's are the positive roots of

$$J_0(\beta_n b) = 0 \tag{7-120}$$

We note that this solution is exactly the same as that given by equation (5-56), which was obtained by the application of the Duhamel's theorem.

We now consider a special case of function $f(t)$.

1. $f(t) = T_0 = \text{constant}$. The integration with respect to τ is readily performed and equation (7-119) reduces to

$$\frac{T(r, t)}{T_0} = \frac{2}{b} \sum_{n=1}^{\infty} \frac{1}{\beta_n} \frac{J_0(r\beta_n)}{J_1(b\beta_n)} (1 - e^{-\alpha\beta_n^2 t}) \tag{7-121}$$

Noting that for $t \to \infty$, $T(r,t)$ becomes the steady-state temperature which is equal to T_0, equation (7-21) gives

$$1 = \frac{2}{b} \sum_{n=1}^{\infty} \frac{1}{\beta_n} \frac{J_0(r\beta_n)}{J_1(b\beta_n)} \tag{7-122}$$

Introducing this result into equation (7-121) we obtain

$$\frac{T(r,t)}{T_0} = 1 - \frac{2}{b} \sum_{n=1}^{\infty} e^{-\alpha\beta_n^2 t} \frac{J_0(r\beta_n)}{\beta_n J_1(b\beta_n)} \tag{7-123}$$

where β_n's are the roots of $J_0(\beta_n b) = 0$.

7-6 APPROXIMATIONS FOR SMALL AND LARGE TIMES

The solutions of time-dependent heat-conduction problems for finite regions, such as slabs or cylinders of finite radius, are in the form of series which converge rapidly for large values of t, but converge very slowly for the small values of t. Therefore, such solutions are not suitable for numerical computations for very small values of time. For example, the solution of the slab problem given by equation (7-107c) converges very slowly for the values of $\alpha t/L^2$ less than approximately 0.02. On the other hand, for the problems of infinite regions, the integrals become more difficult to compute for large times. Therefore, it is desirable to develop alternative forms of the solution that will converge for small or large times.

When the Laplace transform is applied to the time variable, it transforms the equation in t into an equation in s. Therefore, it is instructive to examine the values of t in the time domain with the corresponding values of s in the Laplace transform domain. With this objective in mind we now examine the Laplace transform of some of some functions.

Consider a function $F(t)$ that is represented as a polynomial in t in the form

$$F(t) = \sum_{k=0}^{n} a_k \frac{t^k}{k!} = a_0 + a_1 \frac{t}{1!} + a_2 \frac{t^2}{2!} + \ldots + a_n \frac{t^n}{n!} \tag{7-124}$$

Since the function has only a finite number of terms, we can take its Laplace transform term by term to obtain

$$\bar{F}(s) = \sum_{k=0}^{n} a_k \frac{1}{s^{k+1}} = a_0 \frac{1}{s} + a_1 \frac{1}{s^2} + \ldots + a_n \frac{1}{s^{n+1}} \tag{7-125}$$

according to the transform Table 7-1, case 3.

The coefficients a_0 and a_n may be determined from equation (7-124) and (7-125) as

$$a_0 = \lim_{t \to 0} F(t) = \lim_{s \to \infty} s\bar{F}(s) \qquad (7\text{-}126a)$$

$$a_n = n! \lim_{t \to \infty} \frac{F(t)}{t^n} = \lim_{s \to 0} s^{n+1} \bar{F}(s) \qquad (7\text{-}126b)$$

The relations given by equations (7-126) indicate that the large values of s in the Laplace transform domain corresponds to small values of t in the time domain. Although the results given above are derived for a function $F(t)$, which is a polynomial, they are also applicable for other types of functions. Consider, for example, the following function and its transform

$$F(t) = \cosh kt \qquad \text{and} \qquad \bar{F}(s) = \frac{s}{s^2 - k^2} \qquad (7\text{-}127a)$$

which satisfies the relation

$$\lim_{t \to 0} \cosh kt = \lim_{s \to \infty} s \frac{s}{s^2 - k^2} \qquad (7\text{-}127b)$$

and this result is similar to that given by equation (7-126a).

These facts can be utilized to obtain an approximate solution for the function $F(t)$ valid for small times (or large times) from the knowledge of its transform evaluated for large values of s (or small values of s) as illustrated in several references [16; 4, pp. 82–85; 6; 8]; that is the transform of the desired function can be expanded as an asymptotic series and then inverted term by term. For example, in the problems of slab of finite thickness, the transform of temperature $\bar{T}(x, s)$ contains hyperbolic functions of $\sqrt{s/\alpha}$ as given by equation (7-97). These hyperbolic functions may be expanded in a series of negative exponentials of $\sqrt{s/\alpha}$ and the resulting expression is then inverted term by term. The solution obtained in this manner will converge fast for small time. In the problems of a solid cylinder of finite radius, for example, the transform of temperature involves Bessel functions of $\sqrt{s/\alpha}$ as shown in equation (7-110). Then, the procedure consists of using asymptotic expansion of Bessel functions in order to obtain a form involving negative exponentials of $\sqrt{s/\alpha}$ with coefficients that are series in $(1/\sqrt{s/\alpha})$. The resulting expression is then inverted term by term. The solutions obtained in this manner will converge fast. Many examples of this procedure is given in reference [16]. In an analogous manner, to obtain solutions that are rapidly convergent for large values of time, the transform may be expanded in ascending powers of s and the resulting expression is inverted term by term. We illustrate the procedure with representative examples.

Example 7-19. A slab, $0 \le x \le L$, is initially of zero temperature. For times $t > 0$, the boundary at $x = 0$ is kept insulated and the boundary at $x = L$ is kept at constant temperature T_0. Obtain an expression for the temperature distribution $T(x, t)$ which is useful for small values of time.

Solution. The mathematical formulation of this problem is given as

$$\frac{\partial^2 T(x, t)}{\partial x^2} = \frac{1}{\alpha} \frac{\partial T(x, t)}{\partial t} \qquad \text{in } 0 < x < L, \ t > 0 \qquad (7\text{-}128a)$$

$$\frac{\partial T}{\partial x} = 0 \qquad \text{at } x = 0, \ t > 0 \qquad (7\text{-}128b)$$

$$T = T_0 \qquad \text{at } x = L, \ t > 0 \qquad (7\text{-}128c)$$

$$T = 0 \qquad \text{for } t = 0, \text{ in } 0 \le x \le L \qquad (7\text{-}128d)$$

The Laplace transform of the equations (7-128) is

$$\frac{d^2 \bar{T}(x, s)}{dx^2} - \frac{s}{\alpha} \bar{T}(x, s) = 0 \qquad \text{in } 0 \le x \le L \qquad (7\text{-}129a)$$

$$\frac{d\bar{T}}{dx} = 0 \qquad \text{at } x = 0 \qquad (7\text{-}129b)$$

$$\bar{T} = \frac{T_0}{s} \qquad \text{at } x = L \qquad (7\text{-}129c)$$

The solution of equations (7-129) is

$$\frac{\bar{T}(x, s)}{T_0} = \frac{\cosh(x\sqrt{s/\alpha})}{s \cosh(L\sqrt{s/\alpha})} \qquad (7\text{-}130)$$

The inversion of this transform in this form yields a solution for $T(x, t)$ which is slowly convergent for small values of time. To obtain a solution applicable for very small times we expand this transform as an asymptotic series in negative exponentials of $\sqrt{s/\alpha}$ as given below.

$$\frac{\bar{T}(x, s)}{T_0} = \frac{e^{x\sqrt{s/\alpha}} + e^{-x\sqrt{s/\alpha}}}{s[e^{L\sqrt{s/\alpha}} + e^{-L\sqrt{s/\alpha}}]}$$

$$= \frac{1}{s}[e^{-(L-x)\sqrt{s/\alpha}} + e^{-(L+x)\sqrt{s/\alpha}}][1 + e^{-2L\sqrt{s/\alpha}}]^{-1} \qquad (7\text{-}131)$$

The last term is expanded in binomial series

$$\frac{\bar{T}(x,s)}{T_0} = \frac{1}{s}[e^{-(L-x)\sqrt{s/\alpha}} + e^{-(L+x)\sqrt{s/\alpha}}]\left[\sum_{n=0}^{\infty}(-1)^n e^{-2Ln\sqrt{s/\alpha}}\right] \qquad (7\text{-}132)$$

$$= \frac{1}{s}\sum_{n=0}^{\infty}(-1)^n e^{-[L(1+2n)-x]\sqrt{s/\alpha}} + \frac{1}{s}\sum_{n=0}^{\infty}(-1)^n e^{-[L(1+2n)+x]\sqrt{s/\alpha}}$$

The inversion of this transform is available in Table 7-1, case 42. Inverting term by term we obtain

$$\frac{T(x,t)}{T_0} = \sum_{n=0}^{\infty}(-1)^n \operatorname{erfc}\left(\frac{L(1+2n)-x}{\sqrt{4\alpha t}}\right) + \sum_{n=0}^{\infty}(-1)^n \operatorname{erfc}\left(\frac{L(1+2n)+x}{\sqrt{4\alpha t}}\right)$$

$$(7\text{-}133)$$

which converges fast for small values of t.

Example 7-20.   A slab, $0 \le x \le L$, is initially at uniform temperature T_0. For times $t > 0$, the boundary surface at $x = 0$ is kept insulated and the boundary at $x = L$ dissipates heat by convection into an environment of zero temperature. Obtain an expression for the temperature distribution $T(x,t)$ which is useful for small times.

Solution.   The mathematical formulation of this problem is given as

$$\frac{\partial^2 T(x,t)}{\partial x^2} = \frac{1}{\alpha}\frac{\partial T(x,t)}{\partial t} \qquad \text{in } 0 < x < L,\ t > 0 \qquad (7\text{-}134a)$$

$$\frac{\partial T}{\partial x} = 0 \qquad\qquad\qquad \text{at } x = 0,\ t > 0 \qquad (7\text{-}134b)$$

$$\frac{\partial T}{\partial x} + HT = 0 \qquad\qquad \text{at } x = L,\ t > 0 \qquad (7\text{-}134c)$$

$$T = T_0 \qquad\qquad\qquad \text{for } t = 0,\ \text{in } 0 \le x \le L \qquad (7\text{-}134d)$$

The Laplace transform of these equations give

$$\frac{d^2 \bar{T}(x,s)}{dx^2} - \frac{s}{\alpha}\bar{T}(x,t) = 0 \qquad \text{in } 0 < x < L \qquad (7\text{-}135a)$$

$$\frac{d\bar{T}}{dx} = 0 \qquad\qquad\qquad \text{at } x = 0 \qquad (7\text{-}135b)$$

$$\frac{d\bar{T}}{dx} + H\bar{T} = 0 \qquad\qquad \text{at } x = L \qquad (7\text{-}135c)$$

The solution of equations (7-135) is

$$\frac{\bar{T}(x,s)}{T_0} = \frac{1}{s} - H \frac{\cosh(x\sqrt{s/\alpha})}{s\left[\sqrt{\frac{s}{\alpha}}\sinh\left(L\sqrt{\frac{s}{\alpha}}\right) + H\cosh\left(L\sqrt{\frac{s}{\alpha}}\right)\right]} \tag{7-136}$$

If this transform is inverted by the contour integration technique, the resulting solution will be the same as that given by equation (2-43b) of Example 2-1. However, such a solution converges very slowly for small times. Therefore, we expand this transform as an asymptotic series in negative exponentials and then invert it term by term. The procedure is as follows.

$$\frac{\bar{T}(x,s)}{T_0} = \frac{1}{s} - H \frac{e^{x\sqrt{s/\alpha}} + e^{-x\sqrt{s/\alpha}}}{s\left[\sqrt{s/\alpha}(e^{L\sqrt{s/\alpha}} - e^{L\sqrt{s/\alpha}}) + H(e^{L\sqrt{s/\alpha}} + e^{-L\sqrt{s/\alpha}})\right]}$$

$$= \frac{1}{s} - \frac{H}{s} \frac{e^{-(L-x)\sqrt{s/\alpha}} + e^{-(L+x)\sqrt{s/\alpha}}}{H + \sqrt{s/\alpha}} \left[1 + \frac{H - \sqrt{s/\alpha}}{H + \sqrt{s/\alpha}} e^{-2L\sqrt{s/\alpha}}\right]^{-1} \tag{7-137}$$

Expanding the last term in the bracket in binomial series we obtain

$$\frac{\bar{T}(x,s)}{T_0} = \frac{1}{s} - \frac{H}{s} \frac{e^{-(L-x)\sqrt{s/\alpha}} + e^{-(L+x)\sqrt{s/\alpha}}}{H + \sqrt{s/\alpha}} \left[\sum_{n=0}^{\infty} (-1)^n \left(\frac{H - \sqrt{s/\alpha}}{H + \sqrt{s/\alpha}}\right)^n e^{-2Ln\sqrt{s/\alpha}}\right]$$

$$\tag{7-138a}$$

or

$$\frac{\bar{T}(x,s)}{T_0} = \frac{1}{s} - \frac{H}{s} \frac{e^{-(L-x)\sqrt{s/\alpha}} + e^{-(L+x)\sqrt{s/\alpha}}}{H + \sqrt{s/\alpha}}$$

$$+ \frac{H}{s} \frac{H + \sqrt{s/\alpha}}{(H + \sqrt{s/\alpha})^2} [e^{-(3L-x)\sqrt{s/\alpha}} + e^{-(3L+x)\sqrt{s/\alpha}}]_{-\cdots} \tag{7-138b}$$

The first few terms can readily be inverted by the Laplace transform Table 7-1, case 1 and 51; we obtain

$$\frac{T(x,t)}{T_0} = 1 - \left[\text{erfc}\frac{L-x}{\sqrt{4\alpha t}} - e^{H(L-x)+H^2\alpha t}\cdot\text{erfc}\left(H\sqrt{\alpha t} + \frac{L-x}{\sqrt{4\alpha t}}\right)\right]$$

$$- \left[\text{erfc}\frac{L+x}{\sqrt{4\alpha t}} - e^{H(L+x)+H^2\alpha t}\cdot\text{erfc}\left(H\sqrt{\alpha t} + \frac{L+x}{\sqrt{4\alpha t}}\right)\right] + \cdots \tag{7-139}$$

This solution converges fast for small times.

Example 7-21. A solid sphere of radius $r = b$ is initially at a uniform temperature T_0. For times $t > 0$, the boundary surface at $r = b$ is kept at zero temperature. Obtain an expression for the temperature distribution $T(r, t)$ which is useful for small times.

Solution. The mathematical formulation of this problem is given as

$$\frac{1}{r}\frac{\partial^2}{\partial r^2}(rT) = \frac{1}{\alpha}\frac{\partial T(r, t)}{\partial t} \quad \text{in } 0 \le r < b, \ t > 0 \tag{7-140a}$$

$$T(r, t) = 0 \quad \text{at } r = b, \ t > 0 \tag{7-140b}$$

$$T(r, t) = T_0 \quad \text{for } t = 0, \text{ in } 0 \le r \le b \tag{7-140c}$$

The Laplace transform of equation (7-140) gives

$$\frac{1}{r}\frac{d^2}{dr^2}(r\bar{T}) - \frac{s}{\alpha}\bar{T}(r, s) = -\frac{T_0}{\alpha} \quad \text{in } 0 \le r \le b \tag{7-141a}$$

$$\bar{T}(r, s) = 0 \quad \text{at } r = b \tag{7-141b}$$

The solution of equations (7-141) is

$$\frac{\bar{T}(r, s)}{T_0} = \frac{1}{s} - \frac{b}{sr}\frac{\sinh(r\sqrt{s/\alpha})}{\sinh(b\sqrt{s/\alpha})} \tag{7-142}$$

In this transform is inverted by the inversion formula using the contour integration technique, we obtain a solution in the form of infinite series involving trigonometric function and exponentials. Such a solution converges very slowly for small values of time. Therefore, to obtain an alternative solution that converges fast for small times, we expand this transform as an asymptotic series in negative exponentials, and then invert term by term. The procedure is as follows.

$$\frac{\bar{T}(r, s)}{T_0} = \frac{1}{s} - \frac{b}{r}\frac{e^{r\sqrt{s/\alpha}} - e^{-r\sqrt{s/\alpha}}}{s\left[e^{b\sqrt{s/\alpha}} - e^{-b\sqrt{s/\alpha}}\right]}$$

$$= \frac{1}{s} - \frac{b}{r}\frac{1}{s}\left[e^{-(b-r)\sqrt{s/\alpha}} - e^{-(b+r)\sqrt{s/\alpha}}\right]\left[1 - e^{-2b\sqrt{s/\alpha}}\right]^{-1} \tag{7-143}$$

The last term in the bracket is expanded in binomial series; we obtain

$$\frac{\bar{T}(r, s)}{T_0} = \frac{1}{s} - \frac{b}{r}\frac{1}{s}\left[e^{-(b-r)\sqrt{s/\alpha}} - e^{-(b+r)\sqrt{s/\alpha}}\right]\left[\sum_{n=0}^{\infty} e^{-2bn\sqrt{s/\alpha}}\right]$$

$$= \frac{1}{s} - \frac{b}{r}\sum_{n=0}^{\infty}\left\{\frac{1}{s}e^{-[b(1+2n)-r]\sqrt{s/\alpha}} - \frac{1}{s}e^{-[b(1+2n)+r]\sqrt{s/\alpha}}\right\} \tag{7-144}$$

This transform is readily inverted by utilizing the Laplace transform Table 7-1, case 42; we find

$$\frac{T(r,t)}{T_0} = 1 - \frac{b}{r} \sum_{n=0}^{\infty} \left\{ \mathrm{erfc}\frac{b(1+2n)-r}{\sqrt{4\alpha t}} - \mathrm{erfc}\frac{b(1+2n)+r}{\sqrt{4\alpha t}} \right\} \quad (7\text{-}145)$$

This solution converges fast for small values of time.

Example 7-22.   A solid cylinder, $0 \le r \le b$, is initially at zero temperature. For times $t > 0$ the boundary surface at $r = b$ is kept at a constant temperature $T = T_0$. Obtain an expression for the temperature distribution $T(r,t)$ in the solid valid for very small times.

Solution.   The mathematical formulation of this problem is the same as that given by equations (7-108) with $f(t) = T_0$. The Laplace transform of the temperature distribution is therefore obtainable from equations (7-110) by setting $\bar{f}(s) = T_0/s$, which is the Laplace transform of T_0. We obtain

$$\frac{\bar{T}(r,s)}{T_0} = \frac{I_0(rq)}{sI_0(bq)} \quad (7\text{-}146a)$$

where

$$q \equiv \sqrt{\frac{s}{\alpha}} \quad (7\text{-}146b)$$

We expand $I_0(rq)$ and $I_0(bq)$ by the asymptotic expansion of Bessel functions (see Note 4) to obtain

$$\frac{\bar{T}(r,s)}{T_0} = \left(\frac{b}{r}\right)^{1/2} \frac{e^{-(b-r)q}}{s} \frac{1 + (1/8qr) + (9/128q^2r^2) + \cdots}{1 + (1/8qb) + (9/128q^2b^2) + \cdots} \quad (7\text{-}147)$$

Dividing the expansion term we find

$$\frac{\bar{T}(r,s)}{T_0} = \left(\frac{b}{r}\right)^{1/2} \frac{e^{-(b-r)q}}{s} \left[1 + \frac{b-r}{8brq} + \frac{9b^2 - 7r^2 - 2br}{128b^2r^2q^2} + \cdots \right] \quad (7\text{-}148)$$

This transform is now inverted by Table 7-1, cases 42, 44, and 52; we find

$$\frac{T(r,t)}{T_0} = \left(\frac{b}{r}\right)^{1/2} \mathrm{erfc}\left(\frac{b-r}{\sqrt{4\alpha t}}\right) + \frac{b-r}{8b^{1/2}r^{3/2}}\sqrt{4\alpha t}\,\mathrm{ierfc}\left(\frac{b-r}{\sqrt{4\alpha t}}\right)$$

$$+ \frac{9b^2 - 7r^2 - 2br}{128b^{3/2}r^{5/2}}(4\alpha t)i^2\mathrm{erfc}\left(\frac{b-r}{\sqrt{4\alpha t}}\right) + \cdots \quad (7\text{-}149)$$

This solution is valid for small values of time provided that r/b is not too small.

REFERENCES

1. N. W. McLachlan, *Modern Operational Calculus*, MacMillan Co., New York, 1948.
2. R. V. Churchill, *Operational Mathematics*, McGraw-Hill Book Co., Inc., New York, 1958.
3. M. G. Smith, *Laplace Transform Theory*, D. Van Nostrand Company Ltd., New York, 1966.
4. N. W. McLachlan, *Complex Variable Theory and Transform Calculus*, Cambridge University Press, London, 1953.
5. W. Kaplan, *Operational Methods for Linear Systems*, Addison-Wesley, Reading, Mass., 1962.
6. H. S. Carslaw and J. C. Jaeger, *Operational Methods in Applied Mathematics*, Oxford University Press, London, 1948.
7. A. Erde′lyi, *Tables of Integral Transforms I*, McGraw-Hill Book Co., New York, 1954.
8. H. S. Carslaw and J. C. Jaeger, *Conduction of Heat in Solids*, 2 ed., Oxford University Press, London, 1959.
9. Ian N. Sneddon, *Use of Integral Transforms*, McGraw-Hill Book Co., Inc., New York, 1972.
10. J. Irving and N. Mullineaux, *Mathematics in Physics and Engineering*, Academic Press, New York, 1959.
11. V. S. Arpaci, *Conduction Heat Transfer*, Addison-Wesley Publishing Co., Reading, Mass., 1966.
12. A. V. Luikov, *Analytical Heat Diffusion Theory*, Academic Press, New York, 1968.
13. E. C. Titchmarsh, *Fourier Integrals*, 2 ed., Clarendon Press, London, 1962.
14. R. C. Bartels and R. V. Churchill, *Bull. Amer. Math. Soc.* **48**, 276–282, 1942.
15. H. B. Dwight, *Tables of Integrals and Other Mathematical Data*, 4th ed., MacMillan Co., New York, 1961.
16. S. Goldstein, *Proc. London Math. Soc.*, 2nd series, **34**, 51–88, 1932.

PROBLEMS

7-1 A semi-infinite medium, $0 \leq x < \infty$, is initially at uniform temperature T_0. For times $t > 0$ the boundary surface at $x = 0$ is maintained at zero temperature. Obtain an expression for the temperature distribution $T(x, t)$ in the medium for times $t > 0$ by solving this problem with the Laplace transformation.

7-2 A semi-infinite medium, $0 \leq x < \infty$, is initially at a uniform temperature T_0. For times $t > 0$ it is subjected to a prescribed heat flux at the boundary surface $x = 0$, i.e.,

$$-k\frac{\partial T}{\partial x} = f_0 = \text{constant} \qquad \text{at } x = 0$$

Obtain an expression for the temperature distribution $T(x, t)$ in the medium for times $t > 0$.

7-3 A semi-infinite medium, $0 \le x < \infty$, is initially at uniform temperature T_0. For times $t > 0$, the boundary surface at $x = 0$ is kept at zero temperature while heat is generated in the medium at a constant rate of g_0 W/m³ (or Btu/hr ft³). Obtain an expression for the temperature distribution $T(x, t)$ in the medium for times $t > 0$.

7-4 A slab, $0 \le x \le L$, is initially at uniform temperature T_0. For times $t > 0$, the boundary surface at $x = 0$ is kept insulated and the boundary surface at $x = L$ is kept at zero temperature. Obtain an expression for the temperature distribution $T(x, t)$ in the slab for times $t > 0$. Also obtain an expression for $T(x, t)$ valid for very small times.

7-5 A slab, $0 \le x \le L$, is initially at zero temperature. For times $t > 0$, heat is generated in the slab at a constant rate of g_0 W/m³ (or Btu/hr ft³) while the boundary surface at $x = 0$ is kept insulated and the boundary surface at $x = L$ is kept at zero temperature. Obtain an expression for the temperature distribution $T(x, t)$ in the slab for times $t > 0$.

7-6 A slab, $0 \le x \le L$, is initially at zero temperature. For times $t > 0$, the boundary surface at $x = 0$ is kept insulated while the boundary surface at $x = L$ is subjected to a heat flux, that is,

$$k\frac{\partial T}{\partial x} = f_0 \qquad \text{at } x = L$$

Obtain an expression for the temperature distribution $T(x, t)$ in the slab for times $t > 0$.

7-7 A solid cylinder, $0 \le r \le b$, is initially at a uniform temperature T_0. For times $t > 0$, the boundary surface at $r = b$ is kept at zero temperature. Obtain an expression for the temperature distribution $T(r, t)$ in the solid for times $t > 0$. Also obtain a solution valid for very small times.

7-8 A solid cylinder, $0 \le r \le b$, is initially at a uniform temperature T_0. For times $t > 0$, the boundary surface at $r = b$ is subjected to convection boundary condition in the form

$$\frac{\partial T}{\partial r} + HT = 0 \qquad \text{at } r = b$$

Obtain an expression for the temperature distribution $T(r, t)$ in the solid for times $t > 0$.

7-9 A solid sphere, $0 \leq r \leq b$, is initially at a uniform temperature T_0. For times $t > 0$, the boundary surface at $r = b$ is kept at zero temperature. Obtain an expression for the temperature distribution $T(r, t)$ in the solid for times $t > 0$. Also obtain a solution valid for very small times.

NOTES

1. *Analytic Function.* A function $g(s)$ of the complex variable $s = x + iy$ is said to be analytic (regular or holomorphic) at a point s_0 in the complex plane if $g(s)$ is single valued and has a derivative in some neighborhood of the point $s = s_0$. If a function is analytic and therefore continuous at all points in a bounded region of the s-plane, it is said to be analytic throughout that region.

Poles. A pole is regarded as an isolated singularity, because the function is not analytic at the pole. For example, the function $g(s) = 1/s$ has a simple pole (i.e., a pole of unit order) at $s = 0$, irrespective of the direction in which the origin is approached. The function $g(s) = 1/(s - a)$ has a simple pole at $s = a$; the function $g(s) = 1/(s - a)^n$, n is integer and ≥ 1, has a pole of order n at $s = a$.

2. *Branch Point.* The points at which a function $\bar{F}(s)$ is not single valued are called branch points of the function $\bar{F}(s)$. For example, complex logarithmic function $\ln s$ is written as

$$\ln s = \ln |s| + i\theta$$

Here θ is a particular choice of the infinitely many angles differing by integral multiples of 2π. Then, we write

$$\theta = \theta_p + 2\pi k, \qquad k = 0, \pm 1, \pm 2, \pm 3 \ldots$$

and logarithm s becomes

$$\ln s = \ln |s| + i(\theta_p + 2\pi k), \qquad k = 0, \pm 1, \pm 2 \ldots$$

Clearly, "$\ln s$" is infinitely many valued at the origin. That is, if s traverses a closed path surrounding the origin in the positive (counterclockwise) direction and returns to the initial point, the angle θ_p increases by an amount 2π. Thus the point where the function is many valued called a *branch point*. A function having a branch point in the region can be made single valued (i.e., made analytic) by introducing a *branch cut* (i.e., a barrier or cut) from the branch point including the branch point to infinity.

3. Various terms in equation (7-80) are evaluated as

$$\bar{F}(xe^{-i\pi}) = \frac{e^{-a\sqrt{s}}}{s}\Bigg|_{s=xe^{-i\pi}} = \frac{e^{-a\sqrt{x}e^{-i(\pi/2)}}}{xe^{-i\pi}} = \frac{e^{ia\sqrt{x}}}{-x}$$

$$\bar{F}(xe^{i\pi}) = \frac{e^{-a\sqrt{s}}}{s}\Bigg|_{s=xe^{i\pi}} = \frac{e^{-a\sqrt{x}e^{i(\pi/2)}}}{xe^{i\pi}} = \frac{e^{-ia\sqrt{x}}}{-x}$$

$$\bar{F}(\rho e^{i\theta}) = \frac{e^{-a\sqrt{s}}}{s}\Bigg|_{s=\rho e^{i\theta}} = \frac{e^{-a\sqrt{\rho}e^{i(\theta/2/}}}{\rho e^{i\theta}}$$

Since $e^{\pm i(\pi/2)} = \pm i$ and $e^{\pm i\pi} = 1$.

4. The asymptotic expansion of $I_\nu(z)$ for large values of z is given as

$$I_\nu(z) \simeq \frac{e^z}{\sqrt{4\pi z}}\left[1 - \frac{4\nu^2 - 1^2}{1!8z} + \frac{(4\nu^2 - 1^2)(4\nu^2 - 3^2)}{2!(8z)^2} - 0\left(\frac{1}{z^3}\right)\right]$$

CHAPTER 8

ONE-DIMENSIONAL COMPOSITE MEDIUM

The transient temperature distribution in a composite medium consisting of several layers in contact has numerous applications in engineering. In this chapter, the *generalized orthogonal expansion* technique is used to develop solutions for the homogeneous problem of one-dimensional heat conduction in parallel layers of slabs, cylinders, and spheres. The transformation of a problem with nonhomogeneous boundary conditions at the outer surfaces into a problem with homogeneous boundary conditions is discussed. The Green's function approach is used to solve the problems involving heat generation. The Green's function needed for this purpose is obtained from the solution of the homogeneous version of the same problem in a similar manner discussed in Chapter 6 on Green's function for a single-region medium. A section is devoted to illustrate the use of *Laplace transform* technique in the solution of heat conduction in a one-dimensional composite medium. The use of an *integral transform* technique in the solution of heat conduction in composite media will be discussed in a later chapter. The *adjoint solution* technique transforms the partial differential equations of heat conduction into a set of coupled integral equations for the interface temperatures; this method is not considered here.

The reader should consult references [1–13] for the theory and the application of the generalized orthogonal expansion technique and the Green's function approach in the solution of heat-conduction problems of composite media. The application of the Laplace transform technique is given in several references (14–17]. The theory and application of the integral transform technique are given in references [18–26] and of the adjoint solution technique in references [8] and [27].

8-1 SOLUTION OF THE HOMOGENEOUS PROBLEM BY THE GENERALIZED ORTHOGONAL EXPANSION TECHNIQUE

We now consider the solution of the homogeneous problem of heat conduction in a composite medium consisting of M parallel layers of slabs, cylinders, or spheres in contact as illustrated in Fig. 8-1. For generality we assume contact resistance at the interfaces and convection from the outer boundaries. Let h_{i+1} be the arbitrary film coefficient at the interfaces $x = x_{i+1}$, $i = 1$, $2, ..., M - 1$, and h_1 and h_{M+1} the heat transfer coefficients at the outer boundaries $x = x_1$ and $x = x_{M+1}$, respectively. Each layer is homogeneous, isotropic, and has thermal properties (i.e., ρ, C_p, k) that are constant within the layer and different from those of the adjacent layers. Initially each layer is at specified temperature $T_i(x, t) = F_i(x)$, in $x_i < x < x_{i+1}, i = 1, 2, ..., M$ for $t = 0$. For times $t > 0$, heat is dissipated by convection from the two outer boundaries into environments at zero temperature. There is no heat generation in the medium. We are interested in the determination of the temperature distribution $T_i(x, t), i = 1, 2, ..., M$ for times $t > 0$ in the layers. The mathematical formulation of this heat-conduction problem is given as

$$\alpha_i \frac{1}{x^p} \frac{\partial}{\partial x}\left(x^p \frac{\partial T_i}{\partial x}\right) = \frac{\partial T_i(x, t)}{\partial t} \quad \text{in } x_i < x < x_{i+1}, \quad \text{for } t > 0, i = 1, 2, ...,M$$

$$(8-1)$$

where

$$p = \begin{cases} 0 & \text{slab} \\ 1 & \text{cylinder} \\ 2 & \text{sphere} \end{cases}$$

Subject to the boundary conditions

$$-k_1^* \frac{\partial T_1}{\partial x} + h_1 T_1 = 0 \quad \text{at the outer boundary } x = x_1, \text{ for } t > 0$$

$$(8-2a)$$

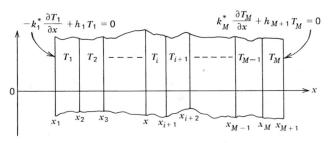

Fig. 8-1 M-layer composite region.

$$-k_i \frac{\partial T_i}{\partial x} = h_{i+1}(T_i - T_{i+1}) \left.\right\} \quad \begin{array}{l} \text{at the interfaces } x = x_{i+1}, \\ i = 1, 2, \ldots, M-1 \end{array} \qquad (8\text{-}2b)$$

$$k_i \frac{\partial T_i}{\partial x} = k_{i+1} \frac{\partial T_{i+1}}{\partial x} \quad \left.\right\} \quad \text{for } t > 0 \qquad (8\text{-}2c)$$

$$k_M^* \frac{\partial T_M}{\partial x} + h_{M+1} T_M = 0 \qquad \text{at the outer boundary } x = x_{M+1}, \; \textit{for } t > 0$$

$$(8\text{-}2d)$$

and the initial conditions

$$T_i(x, t) = F_i(x) \qquad \text{for } t = 0, \qquad \text{in } x_i < x < x_{i+1}, \qquad i = 1, 2, \ldots, M \quad (8\text{-}3)$$

Here, the quantities with asterisk, k_1^* and k_M^* in the boundary conditions (8-2a) and (8-2d) are considered, for generality in the analysis, as boundary condition coefficients rather than the thermal conductivity. Namely, by setting any of the parameters k_1^*, h_1, k_M^*, and h_{M+1} equal to zero, various combinations of boundary conditions of the first, second, or third kind are obtainable at the two outer boundaries.

The finite value of the film coefficient $h_{i+1}, i = 1, 2, \ldots, M - 1$, in the boundary conditions (8-2b) implies the discontinuity of temperature at the interfaces. The boundary conditions (8-2c) state that the heat flux is continuous at the interfaces. When $h_{i+1} \to \infty$, the boundary conditions (8-2b) residue to

$$T_i = T_{i+1} \qquad \text{at } x = x_{i+1}, \qquad i = 1, 2, \ldots, M - 1 \qquad \text{for } t > 0 \quad (8\text{-}2b^*)$$

which implies the continuity of temperature or perfect thermal contact at the interfaces.

To solve the above heat-conduction problem we assume separation of variables in the form

$$T_i(x, t) = \psi_i(x)\Gamma(t) \qquad (8\text{-}4)$$

When equation (8-4) is introduced into (8-1) we obtain

$$\alpha_i \frac{1}{x^p} \frac{1}{\psi_i(x)} \frac{d}{dx}\left(x^p \frac{d\psi_i}{dx}\right) = \frac{1}{\Gamma(t)} \frac{d\Gamma(t)}{dt} \equiv -\beta^2 \qquad (8\text{-}5)$$

where β is the separation constant. We recall that, separating the variables for the problem of heat conduction in a single-region medium we retained the thermal diffusivity α together with the time-variable functions. In the above separation for the multiregion problem we combined α_i with the group involving the space-variable functions for convenience in the subsequent analysis.

The separation as given by equation (8-5) results in the following separated equations for the functions $\Gamma(t)$ and $\psi_i(\beta, x)$:

$$\frac{d\Gamma(t)}{dt} + \beta_n^2 \Gamma(t) = 0 \qquad \text{for } t > 0 \tag{8-6}$$

and

$$\frac{1}{x^p}\frac{d}{dx}\left(x^p \frac{d\psi_{in}}{dx}\right) + \frac{\beta_n^2}{\alpha_i}\psi_{in} = 0 \qquad \text{in } x_i < x < x_{i+1}, \qquad i = 1, 2, \dots, M \tag{8-7}$$

where $\psi_{in} \equiv \psi_i(\beta_n, x)$. The subscript n is included to imply that there are an infinite number of discrete values of the eigenvalues $\beta_1 < \beta_2 < \dots < \beta_n < \dots$ and the corresponding eigenfunctions ψ_{in}.

The boundary conditions for equations (8-7) are obtained by introducing equation (8-4) into the boundary conditions (8-2); we find

$$-k_1^* \frac{d\psi_{1n}}{dx} + h_1 \psi_{1n} = 0 \qquad \text{at the outer boundary } x = x_1 \tag{8-8a}$$

$$\left.\begin{array}{l} -k_i \dfrac{d\psi_{in}}{dx} = h_{i+1}(\psi_{in} - \psi_{i+1,n}) \\[2mm] k_i \dfrac{d\psi_{in}}{dx} = k_{i+1}\dfrac{d\psi_{i+1,n}}{dx} \end{array}\right\} \quad \begin{array}{l} \text{at the interfaces, } x = x_{i+1}, \qquad (8\text{-}8\text{b}) \\ \text{where} \\ i = 1, 2, \dots, M - 1 \qquad (8\text{-}8\text{c}) \end{array}$$

$$k_M^* \frac{d\psi_{Mn}}{dx} + h_{M+1}\psi_{Mn} = 0 \qquad \text{at the outer boundary } x = x_{M+1} \tag{8-8d}$$

Equations (8-7) subject to the boundary conditions (8-8) constitute an eigenvalue problem for the determination of the eigenvalues β_n and the corresponding eigenfunction ψ_{in}.

The eigenfunctions ψ_{in} of the eigenvalue problem defined by equations (8-7) and (8-8) satisfy the following orthogonality relation (see Note 1 for the proof of this orthogonality relation).

$$\sum_{i=1}^{M} \frac{k_i}{\alpha_i} \int_{x=x_i}^{x_{i+1}} x^p \psi_{in}(x)\psi_{ir}(x)\, dx = \begin{cases} 0 & \text{for } n \neq r \\ N_n & \text{for } n = r \end{cases} \tag{8-9a}$$

where the norm N_n is defined as

$$N_n = \sum_{j=1}^{M} \frac{k_j}{\alpha_j} \int_{x_j}^{x_{j+1}} x^p \psi_{jn}^2(x)\, dx \tag{8-9b}$$

and ψ_{in}, ψ_{ir} are the two different eigenfunctions.

The solution for the time-variable function $\Gamma(t)$ is immediately obtained from equation (8-6) as

$$\Gamma(t) = e^{-\beta_n^2 t} \tag{8-10}$$

and the general solution for the temperature $T_i(x, t)$, for any region i, is constructed as

$$T_i(x, t) = \sum_{n=1}^{\infty} c_n e^{-\beta_n^2 t} \psi_{in}(x), \qquad i = 1, 2, \ldots, M \qquad (8\text{-}11)$$

where the summation is over all eigenvalues β_n. This solution satisfies the differential equations (8-1) and the boundary conditions (8-2). We now constrain this solution to satisfy the initial conditions (8-3), and obtain

$$F_i(x) = \sum_{n=1}^{\infty} c_n \psi_{in}(x) \qquad \text{in } x_i < x < x_{i+1}, \qquad i = 1, 2, \ldots, M \qquad (8\text{-}12)$$

The coefficients c_n can be determined by utilizing the above orthogonality relation as now described.

We operate on both sides of equation (8-12) by the operator

$$\frac{k_i}{\alpha_i} \int_{x_i}^{x_{i+1}} x^p \psi_{ir}(x)\, dx$$

and sum up the resulting expressions from $i = 1$ to M (i.e., over all regions) to obtain

$$\sum_{i=1}^{M} \frac{k_i}{\alpha_i} \int_{x_i}^{x_{i+1}} x^p \psi_{ir}(x) F_i(x)\, dx = \sum_{n=1}^{\infty} c_n \left[\sum_{i=1}^{M} \frac{k_i}{\alpha_i} \int_{x_i}^{x_{i+1}} x^p \psi_{ir}(x) \psi_{in}(x)\, dx \right] \qquad (8\text{-}13)$$

In view of the orthogonality relation (8-9), the term inside the bracket on the right-hand side of equation (8-13) vanishes for $n \neq r$ and becomes equal to N_n for $n = r$. Then the coefficients c_n are determined as

$$c_n = \frac{1}{N_n} \sum_{i=1}^{M} \frac{k_i}{\alpha_i} \int_{x_i}^{x_{i+1}} x^p \psi_{in}(x) F_i(x)\, dx \qquad (8\text{-}14)$$

Before introducing this result into equation (8-11), we change the summation indice from i to j, and the dummy integration variable from x to x' in this expression to avoid confusion with the indice i and the space variable x in equation (8-11). Then, the solution for the temperature distribution $T_i(x, t)$, in any region i of the composite medium is obtained as

$$T_i(x, t) = \sum_{n=1}^{\infty} e^{-\beta_n^2 t} \frac{1}{N_n} \psi_{in}(x) \sum_{j=1}^{M} \frac{k_j}{\alpha_j} \int_{x'=x_j}^{x_{j+1}} x'^p \psi_{jn}(x') F_j(x')\, dx'$$

$$\text{in } x_i < x < x_{i+1}, \qquad i = 1, 2, \ldots, M \qquad (8\text{-}15a)$$

where the norm N_n is defined as

$$N_n = \sum_{j=1}^{M} \frac{k_j}{\alpha_j} \int_{x_j}^{x_{j+1}} x'^p \psi_{jn}^2(x')\, dx' \qquad (8\text{-}15b)$$

and

$$p = \begin{cases} 0 & \text{slab} \\ 1 & \text{cylinder} \\ 2 & \text{sphere} \end{cases} \qquad (8\text{-}15c)$$

An examination of this solution reveals that, for $M = 1$, equations (8-15) reduce to the solution for the single-region problem considered in the previous chapters if we set $\beta_n^2 \equiv \alpha \gamma_n^2$ where α is the thermal diffusivity.

The Green's function approach can be used to solve the nonhomogeneous problems of heat conduction in a composite medium. To prepare the necessary background for the application of Green's functions in the solution of nonhomogeneous problems of composite medium, we now rearrange the solution (8-15a) in the form

$$T_i(x,t) = \sum_{j=1}^{M} \int_{x'=x_j}^{x_{j+1}} \frac{k_j}{\alpha_j} \left[\sum_{n=1}^{\infty} e^{-\beta_n^2 t} \frac{1}{N_n} \psi_{in}(x) \psi_{jn}(x') \right] x'^P F_j(x') \, dx'$$

$$\text{in } x_i < x < x_{i+1}, \qquad i = 1, 2, \dots, M \qquad (8\text{-}16)$$

This result is now written more compactly, by introducing the Green's function notation as

$$T_i(x,t) = \sum_{j=1}^{M} \int_{x'=x_j}^{x_{j+1}} x'^P G_{ij}(x,t \,|\, x', \tau) \big|_{\tau=0} F_j(x') \, dx' \qquad (8\text{-}17a)$$

where x'^P is the Sturm-Liouville weight function and

$$G_{ij}(x,t \,|\, x', \tau) \big|_{\tau=0} = \sum_{n=1}^{\infty} e^{-\beta_n^2 t} \frac{1}{N_n} \frac{k_j}{\alpha_j} \psi_{in}(x) \psi_{jn}(x') \qquad (8\text{-}17b)$$

$$p = \begin{cases} 0 & \text{slab} \\ 1 & \text{cylinder} \\ 2 & \text{sphere} \end{cases} \qquad (8\text{-}17c)$$

in the region $x_i < x < x_{i+1}, i = 1, 2, \dots, M$.

Here, $G_{ij}(x,t \,|\, x', \tau)$ is the Green's function for the considered one-dimensional, composite-medium problem. The general procedure is similar to the Green's function approach used for the solution of single-region problems. It will be shown later in this chapter that the Green's function $G_{ij}(x,t \,|\, x', \tau)$ is obtainable from $G_{ij}(x,t \,|\, x', \tau) \big|_{\tau=0}$ by replacing in the latter expression t by $(t - \tau)$. Thus, when the solution of the homogeneous problem is available, we can always rearrange it in the form given by equation (8-17a) and determine the Green's function for that problem. The Green's function obtained in this manner can be used to solve the nonhomogeneous version of the problem as it will be demonstrated later in this chapter.

We now summarize the above results. Equations (8-15) or (8-17) give the temperature distribution $T_i(x, t)$, $i = 1, 2, \ldots, M$, in any layer i of the composite medium provided that the eigenfunctions $\psi_{in}(x)$ and the eigenvalues β_n of the eigenvalue problem defined by equations (8-7) and (8-8) are known. In the following section we examine the determination of these eigenvalues and the eigenfunctions.

8-2 DETERMINATION OF EIGENFUNCTIONS AND EIGENVALUES

The general solution $\psi_{in}(x)$ of the eigenvalue problem given by equations (8-7) and (8-8) can be written as

$$\psi_{in}(x) = A_{in}\phi_{in}(x) + B_{in}\theta_{in}(x) \qquad \text{in } x_i < x < x_{i+1}, \qquad i = 1, 2, \ldots, M \qquad (8-18)$$

where $\phi_{in}(x)$ and $\theta_{in}(x)$ are the two linearly independent solutions of equations (8-7) and A_{in}, B_{in} are the coefficients. Table 8-1 gives the functions $\phi_{in}(x)$ and $\theta_{in}(x)$ for slabs, cyclinders, and spheres. The heat-conduction problem of an M-layer composite medium, in general, involves M solutions in the form given by equation (8-18), hence, there are $2M$ arbitrary coefficients, A_{in} and B_{in}, $i = 1, 2, \ldots, M$ to be determined. The boundary conditions (8-8) provide a system of $2M$, linear, homogeneous equations for the determination of these $2M$ coefficients; but, the resulting system of equations being homogeneous, these coefficients can only be determined in terms of any one of them (i.e., the nonvanishing one) or within a multiple of an arbitrary constant. This arbitrariness does not cause any difficulty, because the arbitrary constant will appear both in the numerator and denominator of equation (8-15a) or equation (8-17a), hence it will cancel out. Therefore, in the process of determining the coefficients A_{in} and B_{in} from the system of $2M$ homogeneous

Table 8-1 Lineary Independent Solutions $\phi_{in}(x)$ and $\theta_{in}(x)$ of Equation (8-7) for Slabs, Cylinders, and Spheres

Geometry	$\phi_{in}(x)$	$\theta_{in}(x)$
Slab	$\sin\left(\dfrac{\beta_n}{\sqrt{\alpha_i}}x\right)$	$\cos\left(\dfrac{\beta_n}{\sqrt{\alpha_i}}x\right)$
Cylinder	$J_0\left(\dfrac{\beta_n}{\sqrt{\alpha_i}}x\right)$	$Y_0\left(\dfrac{\beta_n}{\sqrt{\alpha_i}}x\right)$
Sphere	$\dfrac{1}{x}\sin\left(\dfrac{\beta_n}{\sqrt{\alpha_i}}x\right)$	$\dfrac{1}{x}\cos\left(\dfrac{\beta_n}{\sqrt{\alpha_i}}x\right)$

equations, any one of the nonvanishing coefficients, say A_{in}, can be set equal to unity without loss of generality.

Finally, an additional relationship is needed for the determination of the eigenvalues β_n. This additional relationship is obtained from the requirement that the above system of $2M$ homogeneous equations has a nontrivial solution only if the determinant of the coefficients A_{in} and B_{in} vanishes. This condition leads to a *transcendental equation* for the determination of the eigenvalues

$$\beta_1 < \beta_2 < \beta_3 < \dots < \beta_n < \dots \tag{8-19}$$

Clearly, for each of these eigenvalues there are the corresponding set of values of A_{in} and B_{in}, hence of the eigenfunctions $\psi_{in}(x)$. Once the eigenfunctions $\psi_{in}(x)$ and the eigenvalues β_n are determined by the procedure outlined above, the temperature distribution $T_i(x, t)$ in any region i of the composite medium is determined by equation (8-15a).

To illustrate the above procedure on the determination of the eigenfunctions and the eigenvalues, we now consider the eigenvalue problem for a three-layer region (i.e., $M = 3$) with perfect thermal contact at the interfaces (i.e., $h_{i+1} \to \infty, i = 1, 2$) and convection at the outer boundaries. The appropriate eigenvalue problem is obtained from the general equations (8-7) and (8-8) as

$$\frac{1}{x^p} \frac{d}{dx}\left(x^p \frac{d\psi_{in}}{dx}\right) + \frac{\beta_n^2}{\alpha_i}\,\psi_{in} = 0 \qquad \text{in } x_i < x < x_{i+1}, \qquad i = 1, 2, 3 \tag{8-20}$$

Subject to the boundary conditions

$$-k_1^* \frac{d\psi_{in}}{dx} + h_1\psi_{1n} = 0 \qquad \text{at the outer boundary } x = x_1 \tag{8-21a}$$

$$\left.\begin{aligned} \psi_{in} &= \psi_{i+1,n} \\[2mm] k_i \frac{d\psi_{in}}{dx} &= k_{i+1}\frac{d\psi_{i+1,n}}{dx} \end{aligned}\right\} \quad \begin{aligned} &\text{at the interfaces } x = x_{i+1}, \\[2mm] &i = 1, 2 \end{aligned} \qquad \begin{aligned} &\text{(8-21b)} \\[2mm] &\text{(8-21c)} \end{aligned}$$

$$k_3^* \frac{d\psi_{3n}}{dx} + h_4\psi_{3n} = 0 \qquad \text{at the outer boundary } x = x_4 \tag{8-21d}$$

where the eigenfunctions $\psi_{in}(x)$ are given by

$$\psi_{in}(x) = A_{in}\phi_{in}(x) + B_{in}\theta_{in}(x), \qquad i = 1, 2, 3 \tag{8-22}$$

and $\phi_{in}(x)$ and $\theta_{in}(x)$ are as specified in Table 8-1.

The first step in the analysis is the determination of the six coefficients A_{in}, B_{in} with $i = 1, 2, 3$. Without loss of generality, we set one of the nonvanishing coefficients, say, A_{1n} equal to unity, that is,

$$A_{1n} = 1 \tag{8-23}$$

The eigenfunctions $\psi_{in}(x)$ given by equation (8-22) with $A_{1n} = 1$ are introduced into the boundary conditions (8-21). The resulting system of equations, expressed in the matrix form as

$$
\begin{bmatrix}
X_1 & Y_1 & 0 & 0 & 0 & 0 \\
\phi_{1n} & \theta_{1n} & -\phi_{2n} & -\theta_{2n} & 0 & 0 \\
k_1\phi'_{1n} & k_1\theta'_{1n} & -k_2\phi'_{2n} & -k_2\theta'_{2n} & 0 & 0 \\
0 & 0 & \phi_{2n} & \theta_{2n} & -\phi_{3n} & -\theta_{3n} \\
0 & 0 & k_2\phi'_{2n} & k_2\theta'_{2n} & -k_3\phi'_{3n} & -k_3\theta'_{3n} \\
0 & 0 & 0 & 0 & X_3 & Y_3
\end{bmatrix}
\begin{bmatrix}
1 \\
B_{1n} \\
A_{2n} \\
B_{2n} \\
A_{3n} \\
B_{2n}
\end{bmatrix}
=
\begin{bmatrix}
0 \\
0 \\
0 \\
0 \\
0 \\
0
\end{bmatrix}
\tag{8-24}
$$

where

$$X_1 = -k_1^*\phi'_{1n} + h_1\phi_{1n} \qquad Y_1 = -k_1^*\theta'_{1n} + h_1\theta_{1n} \tag{8-25}$$

$$X_3 = k_3^*\phi'_{3n} + h_4\phi_{3n} \qquad Y_3 = k_3^*\theta'_{3n} + h_4\theta_{3n} \tag{8-26}$$

and the primes denote differentiation with respect to x. Only five of these equations can be used to determine the coefficients. We choose the first five of them; the resulting system of equations for the determination of these five coefficients is given in the matrix form as

$$
\begin{bmatrix}
Y_1 & 0 & 0 & 0 & 0 \\
\theta_{1n} & -\phi_{2n} & -\theta_{2n} & 0 & 0 \\
k_1\theta'_{1n} & -k_2\phi'_{2n} & -k_2\theta'_{2n} & 0 & 0 \\
0 & \phi_{2n} & \theta_{2n} & -\phi_{3n} & \theta_{3n} \\
0 & k_2\phi'_{2n} & k_2\theta'_{2n} & -k_3\phi'_{3n} & -k_3\theta'_{3n}
\end{bmatrix}
\begin{bmatrix}
B_{1n} \\
A_{2n} \\
B_{2n} \\
A_{3n} \\
B_{3n}
\end{bmatrix}
=
\begin{bmatrix}
-X_1 \\
-\phi_{1n} \\
-k_1\phi'_{1n} \\
0 \\
0
\end{bmatrix}
\tag{8-27}
$$

These equations can be solved by the Cramer's rule and the coefficients $B_{1n}, A_{2n}, B_{2n}, \dots$ are determined.

The final step in the analysis is the determination of the transcendental equation for the evaluation of the eigenvalues β_n. The desired relationship is obtained from the requirement that the determinant of the coefficients in the system of equation (8-24) should vanish. This condition leads to the following transcendental equation for the determination of the eigenvalues

$$\beta_1 < \beta_2 < \beta_3 < \ldots < \beta_n < \ldots$$

$$
\begin{vmatrix}
X_1 & Y_1 & 0 & 0 & 0 & 0 \\
\phi_{1n} & \theta_{1n} & -\phi_{2n} & -\theta_{2n} & 0 & 0 \\
k_1\phi'_{1n} & k_1\theta'_{1n} & -k_2\phi'_{2n} & -k_2\theta'_{2n} & 0 & 0 \\
0 & 0 & \phi_{2n} & \theta_{2n} & -\phi_{3n} & -\theta_{3n} \\
0 & 0 & k_2\phi'_{2n} & k_2\theta'_{2n} & -k_3\phi'_{3n} & -k_3\theta'_{3n} \\
0 & 0 & 0 & 0 & X_3 & Y_3
\end{vmatrix} = 0 \qquad (8\text{-}28)
$$

The solution of the considered three-layer problem is now formally complete. The eigenvalues β_n are determined from the solution of the transcendental equation (8-28) and the coefficients $B_{1n}, A_{2n}, B_{2n}, \ldots$, etc. from the solution of equations (8-24). For each of these eigenvalues, there is a set of coefficients. Then, the eigenfunctions $\psi_{in}(x)$ are given by equation (8-22) with the functions $\phi_{in}(x)$ and $\theta_{in}(x)$ as specified in Table 8-1 and the temperature distribution $T_i(x, t)$ in any layer i is computed according to equation (8-15).

We now illustrate the application with specific examples.

Example 8-1. A two-layer solid cylinder as illustrated in Fig. 8-2 contains an inner region $0 \leq r \leq a$ and an outer region $a \leq r \leq b$ which are in perfect thermal contact. k_1 and k_2 are the thermal conductivities, α_1 and α_2 are the thermal diffusivities of the inner and outer regions, respectively. Initially, the inner region is at temperature $T_1(r, t) = f_1(r)$ and the outer region at temperature $T_2(r, t) = f_2(r)$. For times $t > 0$, heat is dissipated by convection

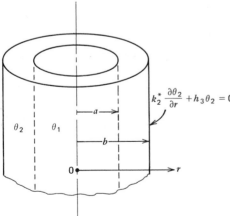

$$k_2^* \frac{\partial \theta_2}{\partial r} + h_3\theta_2 = 0$$

Fig. 8-2 Two-layer cylinder with perfect thermal contact at the interface.

from the outer surface at $r = b$ into an environment at a constant temperature T_∞. Obtain an expression for the temperature distribution in the cylinder for times $t > 0$.

Solution. The boundary condition for this problem is not homogeneous. But it can be made homogeneous by measuring the temperatures in excess of the environment temperature, T_∞. Namely, we define new temperatures for the two regions as

$$\theta_i(r, t) = T_i(r, t) - T_\infty, \qquad i = 1, 2 \tag{8-29}$$

Then, the mathematical formulation of the problem is given as

$$\frac{\alpha_1}{r} \frac{\partial}{\partial r}\left(r \frac{\partial \theta_1}{\partial r} \right) = \frac{\partial \theta_1(r, t)}{\partial t} \qquad \text{in } 0 \leq r < a, \; t > 0 \tag{8-30}$$

$$\frac{\alpha_2}{r} \frac{\partial}{\partial r}\left(r \frac{\partial \theta_2}{\partial r} \right) = \frac{\partial \theta_2(r, t)}{\partial t} \qquad \text{in } a < r < b, \; t > 0 \tag{8-31}$$

Subject to the boundary conditions

$$\theta_1(r, t) = \text{finite} \qquad\quad \text{at } r = 0, \; t > 0 \tag{8-32a}$$

$$\theta_1(r, t) = \theta_2(r, t) \qquad\quad \text{at } r = a, \; t > 0 \tag{8-32b}$$

$$k_1 \frac{\partial \theta_1}{\partial r} = k_2 \frac{\partial \theta_2}{\partial r} \qquad\quad \text{at } r = a, \; t > 0 \tag{8-32c}$$

$$k_2^* \frac{\partial \theta_2}{\partial r} + h_3 \theta_2 = 0 \qquad\quad \text{at } r = b, \; t > 0 \tag{8-32d}$$

and to the initial conditions

$$\theta_1(r, t) = f_1(r) - T_\infty \equiv F_1(r) \qquad \text{for } t = 0, \; 0 < r < a \tag{8-33a}$$

$$\theta_2(r, t) = f_2(r) - T_\infty \equiv F_2(r) \qquad \text{for } t = 0, \; a < r < b \tag{8-33b}$$

The corresponding eigenvalue problem is taken as

$$\frac{1}{r} \frac{d}{dr}\left(r \frac{d\psi_{1n}}{dr} \right) + \frac{\beta_n^2}{\alpha_1} \psi_{1n}(r) = 0 \qquad \text{in } 0 \leq r < a \tag{8-34}$$

$$\frac{1}{r} \frac{d}{dr}\left(r \frac{d\psi_{2n}}{dr} \right) + \frac{\beta_n^2}{\alpha_2} \psi_{2n}(r) = 0 \qquad \text{in } a < r < b \tag{8-35}$$

Subject to the boundary conditions

$$\psi_{1n}(r) = \text{finite} \qquad\quad \text{at } r = 0 \tag{8-36a}$$

$$\psi_{1n}(r) = \psi_{2n}(r) \qquad\quad \text{at } r = a \tag{8-36b}$$

$$k_1 \frac{d\psi_{1n}}{dr} = k_2 \frac{d\psi_{2n}}{dr} \qquad \text{at } r = a \qquad (8\text{-}36\text{c})$$

$$k_2^* \frac{d\psi_{2n}}{dr} + h_3\psi_{2n} = 0 \qquad \text{at } r = b \qquad (8\text{-}36\text{d})$$

The general solution of the above eigenvalue problem, according to Table 8-1, is taken as

$$\psi_{in}(r) = A_{in}J_0\left(\frac{\beta_n}{\sqrt{\alpha_i}}r\right) + B_{in}Y_0\left(\frac{\beta_n}{\sqrt{\alpha_i}}r\right), \qquad i = 1, 2 \qquad (8\text{-}37)$$

The boundary condition (8-36a) requires that $B_{1n} = 0$. Then the solutions $\psi_{in}(r)$ for the two regions become

$$\psi_{1n}(r) = J_0\left(\frac{\beta_n}{\sqrt{\alpha_1}}r\right) \qquad \text{in } 0 \le r < a \quad (8\text{-}38\text{a})$$

$$\psi_{2n}(r) = A_{2n}J_0\left(\frac{\beta_n}{\sqrt{\alpha_2}}r\right) + B_{2n}Y_0\left(\frac{\beta_n}{\sqrt{\alpha_2}}r\right) \qquad \text{in } a < r < b \quad (8\text{-}38\text{b})$$

where we have chosen $A_{1n} = 1$ for the reason stated previously. The requirement that the solutions (8-38) should satisfy the remaining three boundary conditions (8-36b, c, d) leads, respectively, to the following equations for the determinations of these coefficients

$$J_0\left(\frac{\beta_n a}{\sqrt{\alpha_1}}\right) = A_{2n}J_0\left(\frac{\beta_n a}{\sqrt{\alpha_2}}\right) + B_{2n}Y_0\left(\frac{\beta_n a}{\sqrt{\alpha_2}}\right) \qquad (8\text{-}39\text{a})$$

$$\frac{k_1}{k_2}\sqrt{\frac{\alpha_2}{\alpha_1}}J_1\left(\frac{\beta_n a}{\sqrt{\alpha_1}}\right) = A_{2n}J_1\left(\frac{\beta_n a}{\sqrt{\alpha_2}}\right) + B_{2n}Y_1\left(\frac{\beta_n a}{\sqrt{\alpha_2}}\right) \qquad (8\text{-}39\text{b})$$

$$-\left[A_{2n}J_1\left(\frac{\beta_n b}{\sqrt{\alpha_2}}\right) + B_{2n}Y_1\left(\frac{\beta_n b}{\sqrt{\alpha_2}}\right)\right] + \frac{h_3\sqrt{\alpha_2}}{k_2^*\beta_n}\left[A_{2n}J_0\left(\frac{\beta_n b}{\sqrt{\alpha_2}}\right)\right.$$

$$\left. + B_{2n}Y_0\left(\frac{\beta_n b}{\sqrt{\alpha_2}}\right)\right] = 0 \qquad (8\text{-}39\text{c})$$

These equations are now written in the matrix form as

$$\begin{bmatrix} J_0(\gamma) & -J_0\left(\frac{a}{b}\eta\right) & -Y_0\left(\frac{a}{b}\eta\right) \\[2mm] KJ_1(\gamma) & -J_1\left(\frac{a}{b}\eta\right) & -Y_1\left(\frac{a}{b}\eta\right) \\[2mm] 0 & \frac{H}{\eta}J_0(\eta) - J_1(\eta) & \frac{H}{\eta}Y_0(\eta) - Y_1(\eta) \end{bmatrix}\begin{bmatrix} 1 \\[2mm] A_{2n} \\[2mm] B_{2n} \end{bmatrix} = \begin{bmatrix} 0 \\[2mm] 0 \\[2mm] 0 \end{bmatrix} \qquad (8\text{-}40)$$

where we defined

$$\gamma \equiv \frac{a\beta_n}{\sqrt{\alpha_1}} \qquad \eta \equiv \frac{b\beta_n}{\sqrt{\alpha_2}} \qquad H \equiv \frac{bh_3}{k_2^*} \qquad K = \frac{k_1}{k_2}\sqrt{\frac{\alpha_2}{\alpha_1}} \qquad (8\text{-}41)$$

Any of these two equations can be used to determine the coefficients A_{2n} and B_{2n}. We choose the first two and write the resulting equations as

$$\begin{bmatrix} J_0\left(\dfrac{a}{b}\eta\right) & Y_0\left(\dfrac{a}{b}\eta\right) \\[2ex] J_1\left(\dfrac{a}{b}\eta\right) & Y_1\left(\dfrac{a}{b}\eta\right) \end{bmatrix} \begin{bmatrix} A_{2n} \\[2ex] B_{2n} \end{bmatrix} = \begin{bmatrix} J_0(\gamma) \\[2ex] KJ_1(\gamma) \end{bmatrix} \qquad (8\text{-}42)$$

Then, A_{2n} and B_{2n} are obtained as

$$A_{2n} = \frac{1}{\Delta}\left[J_0(\gamma)Y_1\left(\frac{a}{b}\eta\right) - KJ_1(\gamma)Y_0\left(\frac{a}{b}\eta\right) \right] \qquad (8\text{-}43a)$$

$$B_{2n} = \frac{1}{\Delta}\left[KJ_1(\gamma)J_0\left(\frac{a}{b}\eta\right) - J_0(\gamma)J_1\left(\frac{a}{b}\eta\right) \right] \qquad (8\text{-}43b)$$

where

$$\Delta = J_0\left(\frac{a}{b}\eta\right)Y_1\left(\frac{a}{b}\eta\right) - J_1\left(\frac{a}{b}\eta\right)Y_0\left(\frac{a}{b}\eta\right) \qquad (8\text{-}43c)$$

Finally, the equation for the determination of the eigenvalues is obtained from the requirement that in equation (8-40) the determinant of the coefficients should vanish. Then, β_n's are the roots of the following transcendental equation

$$\begin{vmatrix} J_0(\gamma) & -J_0\left(\dfrac{a}{b}\eta\right) & -Y_0\left(\dfrac{a}{b}\eta\right) \\[2ex] KJ_1(\gamma) & -J_1\left(\dfrac{a}{b}\eta\right) & -Y_1\left(\dfrac{a}{b}\eta\right) \\[2ex] 0 & \dfrac{H}{\eta}J_0(\eta) - J_1(\eta) & \dfrac{H}{\eta}Y_0(\eta) - Y_1(\eta) \end{vmatrix} = 0 \qquad (8\text{-}44)$$

Having established the relations for the determination of the coefficients A_{2n}, B_{2n} and the eigenvalues β_n, the eigenfunctions $\psi_{1n}(r)$ and $\psi_{2n}(r)$ are obtained according to equation (8-38). Then, the solution for the temperature $\theta_i(r,t)$, $i = 1, 2$ in any of the regions is given by equation (8-15) as

$$\theta_i(r,t) = \sum_{n=1}^{\infty} \frac{1}{N_n} e^{-\beta_n^2 t} \psi_{in}(r) \left[\frac{k_1}{\alpha_1}\int_0^a r'\psi_{1n}(r')F_1(r')\,dr' \right.$$

$$\left. + \frac{k_2}{\alpha_2}\int_a^b r'\psi_{2n}(r')F_2(r')\,dr' \right], \qquad i = 1, 2 \qquad (8\text{-}45a)$$

where

$$N_n = \frac{k_1}{\alpha_1} \int_0^a r' \psi_{1n}^2(r') \, dr' + \frac{k_2}{\alpha_2} \int_a^b r' \psi_{2n}^2(r') \, dr' \qquad \text{(8-45b)}$$

$$\psi_{1n}(r) = J_0\left(\frac{\beta_n}{\sqrt{\alpha_1}} r\right) \qquad \text{(8-45c)}$$

$$\psi_{2n}(r) = A_{2n} J_0\left(\frac{\beta_n}{\sqrt{\alpha_2}} r\right) + B_{2n} Y_0\left(\frac{\beta_n}{\sqrt{\alpha_2}} r\right) \qquad \text{(8-45d)}$$

This result is now written more compactly in terms of the Green's function as

$$\theta_i(r,t) = \int_0^a r' G_{i1}(r,t|r',\tau)\bigg|_{\tau=0} F_1(r') \, dr' + \int_b^a r' G_{i2}(r,t|r',\tau)\bigg|_{\tau=0} F_2(r') \, dr', \quad i = 1, 2$$

$$\text{(8-46a)}$$

where $G_{ij}(r,t|r',\tau)\big|_{\tau=0}$ is defined as

$$G_{ij}(r,t|r',\tau)\big|_{\tau=0} = \sum_{n=1}^{\infty} e^{-\beta_n^2 t} \frac{1}{N_n} \frac{k_j}{\alpha_j} \psi_{in}(r) \psi_{jn}(r') \qquad \text{(8-46b)}$$

Example 8-2. A two-layer slab consists of the first layer in $0 \le x \le a$ and the second layer in $a \le x \le b$, which are in perfect thermal contact as illustrated in Fig. 8-3. k_1 and k_2 are the thermal conductivities, and α_1 and α_2 are the thermal diffusivities for the first and second layer, respectively. Initially, the first region is at temperature $F_1(x)$ and the second region at $F_2(x)$. For times $t > 0$ the boundary surface at $x = 0$ is kept at zero temperature and the boundary surface at $x = b$ dissipates heat by convection into a medium at zero temperature. Obtain an expression for the temperature distribution in the slab for times $t > 0$.

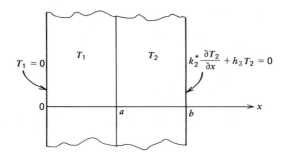

Fig. 8-3 Two-layer slab with perfect thermal contact at the interface.

Solution. The mathematical formulation of this problem is given as

$$\alpha_1 \frac{\partial^2 T_1}{\partial x^2} = \frac{\partial T_1(x,t)}{\partial t} \qquad \text{in } 0 < x < a, \ t > 0 \tag{8-47}$$

$$\alpha_2 \frac{\partial^2 T_2}{\partial x^2} = \frac{\partial T_2(x,t)}{\partial t} \qquad \text{in } a < x < b, \ t > 0 \tag{8-48}$$

subject to the boundary conditions

$$T_1(x,t) = 0 \qquad\qquad \text{at } x = 0, \ t > 0 \tag{8-49a}$$

$$T_1(x,t) = T_2(x,t) \qquad \text{at } x = a, \ t > 0 \tag{8-49b}$$

$$k_1 \frac{\partial T_1}{\partial x} = k_2 \frac{\partial T_2}{\partial x} \qquad \text{at } x = a, \ t > 0 \tag{8-49c}$$

$$k_2^* \frac{\partial T_2}{\partial x} + h_3 T_2 = 0 \qquad \text{at } x = b, \ t > 0 \tag{8-49d}$$

and the initial conditions

$$T_1(x,t) = F_1(x) \qquad \text{for } t = 0, \ 0 < x < a \tag{8-50a}$$

$$T_2(x,t) = F_2(x) \qquad \text{for } t = 0, \ a < x < b \tag{8-50b}$$

The corresponding eigenvalue problem is taken as

$$\frac{d^2 \psi_{1n}}{dx^2} + \frac{\beta_n^2}{\alpha_1} \psi_{1n}(x) = 0 \qquad \text{in } 0 < x < a \tag{8-51}$$

$$\frac{d^2 \psi_{2n}}{dx^2} + \frac{\beta_n^2}{\alpha_2} \psi_{2n}(x) = 0 \qquad \text{in } a < x < b \tag{8-52}$$

subject to the boundary conditions

$$\psi_{1n}(x) = 0 \qquad\qquad \text{at } x = 0 \tag{8-53a}$$

$$\psi_{1n}(x) = \psi_{2n}(x) \qquad \text{at } x = a \tag{8-53b}$$

$$k_1 \frac{d\psi_{1n}}{dx} = k_2 \frac{d\psi_{2n}}{dx} \qquad \text{at } x = a \tag{8-53c}$$

$$k_2^* \frac{d\psi_{2n}}{dx} + h_3 \psi_{2n} = 0 \qquad \text{at } x = b \tag{8-53d}$$

The general solution of the above eigenvalue problem, according to Table 8-1, is taken as

$$\psi_{in}(x) = A_{in} \sin\left(\frac{\beta_n}{\sqrt{\alpha_i}} x\right) + B_{in} \cos\left(\frac{\beta_n}{\sqrt{\alpha_i}} x\right), \qquad i = 1, 2 \tag{8-54}$$

The boundary condition (8-53a) requires that $B_{1n} = 0$. Then, the solutions ψ_{in} for the two regions are reduced to

$$\psi_{1n}(x) = \sin\left(\frac{\beta_n}{\sqrt{\alpha_1}} x\right) \qquad\qquad \text{in } 0 < x < a \quad (8\text{-}55\text{a})$$

$$\psi_{2n}(x) = A_{2n} \sin\left(\frac{\beta_n}{\sqrt{\alpha_2}} x\right) + B_{2n} \cos\left(\frac{\beta_n}{\sqrt{\alpha_2}} x\right) \quad \text{in } a < x < b \quad (8\text{-}55\text{b})$$

where we have chosen $A_{1n} = 1$ for the reason stated previously. The requirement that the solutions (8-55) should satisfy the remaining boundary conditions (8-53b, c, d) yields the following equations for the determination of these coefficients.

$$\sin\left(\frac{\beta_n a}{\sqrt{\alpha_1}}\right) = A_{2n} \sin\left(\frac{\beta_n a}{\sqrt{\alpha_2}}\right) + B_{2n} \cos\left(\frac{\beta_n a}{\sqrt{\alpha_2}}\right) \qquad (8\text{-}56\text{a})$$

$$\frac{k_1}{k_2}\sqrt{\frac{\alpha_2}{\alpha_1}} \cos\left(\frac{\beta_n a}{\sqrt{\alpha_1}}\right) = A_{2n} \cos\left(\frac{\beta_n a}{\sqrt{\alpha_2}}\right) - B_{2n} \sin\left(\frac{\beta_n a}{\sqrt{\alpha_2}}\right) \qquad (8\text{-}56\text{b})$$

$$\left[A_{2n} \cos\left(\frac{\beta_n b}{\sqrt{\alpha_2}}\right) - B_{2n} \sin\left(\frac{\beta_n b}{\sqrt{\alpha_2}}\right)\right] + \frac{h_3 \sqrt{\alpha_2}}{k_2^* \beta_n}\left[A_{2n} \sin\left(\frac{\beta_n b}{\sqrt{\alpha_2}}\right)\right.$$
$$\left. + B_{2n} \cos\left(\frac{\beta_n b}{\sqrt{\alpha_2}}\right)\right] = 0 \quad (8\text{-}56\text{c})$$

These equations are now written in the matrix form as

$$\begin{bmatrix} \sin\gamma & -\sin\left(\dfrac{a}{b}\eta\right) & -\cos\left(\dfrac{a}{b}\eta\right) \\[2mm] K\cos\gamma & -\cos\left(\dfrac{a}{b}\eta\right) & \sin\left(\dfrac{a}{b}\eta\right) \\[2mm] 0 & \dfrac{H}{\eta}\sin\eta + \cos\eta & \dfrac{H}{\eta}\cos\eta - \sin\eta \end{bmatrix} \begin{bmatrix} 1 \\ A_{2n} \\ B_{2n} \end{bmatrix} = \begin{bmatrix} 0 \\ 0 \\ 0 \end{bmatrix} \quad (8\text{-}57)$$

where we defined

$$\gamma \equiv \frac{a\beta_n}{\sqrt{\alpha_1}} \qquad \eta \equiv \frac{b\beta_n}{\sqrt{\alpha_2}} \qquad H \equiv \frac{bh_3}{k_2^*} \qquad K = \frac{k_1}{k_2}\sqrt{\frac{\alpha_2}{\alpha_1}} \qquad (8\text{-}58)$$

We choose the first two of these equations to determine the coefficients A_{2n} and B_{2n}; these two equations are written as

$$\begin{bmatrix} \sin\left(\dfrac{a}{b}\eta\right) & \cos\left(\dfrac{a}{b}\eta\right) \\[2mm] \cos\left(\dfrac{a}{b}\eta\right) & -\sin\left(\dfrac{a}{b}\eta\right) \end{bmatrix} \begin{bmatrix} A_{2n} \\ B_{2n} \end{bmatrix} = \begin{bmatrix} \sin\gamma \\ K\cos\gamma \end{bmatrix} \quad (8\text{-}59)$$

Then, A_{2n} and B_{2n} are determined as

$$A_{2n} = \frac{1}{\Delta}\left[-\sin\gamma\sin\left(\frac{a}{b}\eta\right) - K\cos\gamma\cos\left(\frac{a}{b}\eta\right)\right] \qquad (8\text{-}60a)$$

$$B_{2n} = \frac{1}{\Delta}\left[K\cos\gamma\sin\left(\frac{a}{b}\eta\right) - \sin\gamma\cos\left(\frac{a}{b}\eta\right)\right] \qquad (8\text{-}60b)$$

where

$$\Delta = -\sin^2\left(\frac{a}{b}\eta\right) - \cos^2\left(\frac{a}{b}\eta\right) = -1 \qquad (8\text{-}60c)$$

Finally, the equation for the determination of the eigenvalues β_n is obtained from the requirement that in equation (8-57) the determinant of the coefficients should vanish. This condition yields the following transcendental equation for the determination of the eigenvalues β_n

$$\begin{vmatrix} \sin\gamma & -\sin\left(\frac{a}{b}\eta\right) & -\cos\left(\frac{a}{b}\eta\right) \\[2mm] K\cos\gamma & -\cos\left(\frac{a}{b}\eta\right) & \sin\left(\frac{a}{b}\eta\right) \\[2mm] 0 & \dfrac{H}{\eta}\sin\eta + \cos\eta & \dfrac{H}{\eta}\cos\eta - \sin\eta \end{vmatrix} = 0 \qquad (8\text{-}61)$$

The formal solution of this problem is now complete. That is, the coefficients A_{2n} and B_{2n} are given by equations (8-59), the eigenvalues β_n by equation (8-61). Then, the eigenfunctions $\psi_{1n}(x)$ and $\psi_{2n}(x)$ defined by equations (8-55) are known and the temperature distribution $T_i(x, t)$, $i = 1, 2$ in any one of the two regions is determined according to equation (8-15) as

$$T_i(x, t) = \sum_{n=1}^{\infty} \frac{1}{N_n} e^{-\beta_n^2 t}\psi_{in}(x)\left[\frac{k_1}{\alpha_1}\int_{x'=0}^{a}\psi_{1n}(x')F_1(x')\,dx'\right.$$

$$\left. + \frac{k_2}{\alpha_2}\int_a^b\psi_{2n}(x')F_2(x')\,dx'\right], \qquad i = 1, 2 \qquad (8\text{-}62a)$$

where

$$N_n = \frac{k_1}{\alpha_1}\int_0^a\psi_{1n}^2(x')\,dx' + \frac{k_2}{\alpha_2}\int_a^b\psi_{2n}^2(x')\,dx' \qquad (8\text{-}62b)$$

$$\psi_{1n}(x) = \sin\left(\frac{\beta_n}{\sqrt{\alpha_1}}x\right) \qquad (8\text{-}62c)$$

$$\psi_{2n}(x) = A_{2n}\sin\left(\frac{\beta_n}{\sqrt{\alpha_2}}x\right) + B_{2n}\cos\left(\frac{\beta_n}{\sqrt{\alpha_2}}x\right) \qquad (8\text{-}62d)$$

This result can be written more compactly in the form of a solution in terms of the Green's function as

$$T_i(x, t) = \int_0^a G_{i1}(x, t \,|\, x', \tau)|_{\tau = 0} F_1(x') \, dx'$$

$$+ \int_a^b G_{i2}(x, t \,|\, x', \tau)|_{\tau = 0} F_2(x') \, dx', \qquad i = 1, 2 \qquad (8\text{-}63a)$$

where $G_{ij}(x, t \,|\, x', \tau)|_{\tau = 0}$, the Green's function evaluated at $\tau = 0$, is given by

$$G_{ij}(x, t \,|\, x', \tau)|_{\tau = 0} = \sum_{n = 1}^{\infty} e^{-\beta_n^2 t} \frac{1}{N_n} \frac{k_j}{\alpha_j} \psi_{in}(x) \psi_{jn}(x') \qquad (8\text{-}63b)$$

where $N_n, \psi_{in}(x), i = 1, 2$ are defined by equations (8-62).

8-3 TRANSFORMATION OF NONHOMOGENEOUS OUTER CONDITIONS INTO HOMOGENEOUS ONES

It is more convenient to solve the problems with homogeneous boundary conditions than with nonhomogeneous boundary conditions. The problem of time-dependent heat conduction for a M-layer composite medium with heat generation and nonhomogeneous outer boundary conditions can be transformed into a problem with heat generation but homogeneous boundary conditions as now described.

We consider the following nonhomogeneous problem for a M-layer composite medium

$$\alpha_i \frac{1}{x^p} \frac{\partial}{\partial x} \left(x^p \frac{\partial T_i}{\partial x} \right) + \frac{\alpha_i}{k_i} g_i(x, t) = \frac{\partial T_i(x, t)}{\partial t}$$

$$\text{in } x_i < x < x_{i+1}, \ t > 0, \ i = 1, 2, \ldots, M \qquad (8\text{-}64)$$

where

$$p = \begin{cases} 0 & \text{slab} \\ 1 & \text{cylinder} \\ 2 & \text{sphere} \end{cases}$$

Subject to the boundary conditions

$$-k_1^* \frac{\partial T_1}{\partial x} + h_1 T_1 = h_1 f_1(t) \qquad \text{at the outer boundary } x = x_1, \ t > 0$$

$$(8\text{-}65a)$$

$$-k_i \frac{\partial T_i}{\partial x} = h_{i+1}(T_i - T_{i+1}) \left.\begin{array}{c}\\\\\\\end{array}\right\} \quad \text{at the interfaces} \qquad (8\text{-}65b)$$

where

$$k_i \frac{\partial T_i}{\partial x} = k_{i+1} \frac{\partial T_{i+1}}{\partial x} \qquad x = x_{i+1}, \; i = 1, 2, \ldots, M-1, \; t > 0 \tag{8-65c}$$

$$k_M^* \frac{\partial T_M}{\partial x} + h_{M+1} T_M = h_{M+1} f_M(t) \quad \text{at the outer boundary, } x = x_{M+1}, \; t > 0 \tag{8-65d}$$

and the initial conditions

$$T_i(x, t) = F_i(x) \qquad \text{for } t = 0, \text{ in } x_i < x < x_{i+1}, \; i = 1, 2, \ldots, M \tag{8-66}$$

For generality, in the above formulation, we have taken the temperatures $f_1(t)$ and $f_M(t)$ of the outer environment dependent upon time.

To achieve the desired transformation we now construct the solution $T_i(x, t)$ of the above problem by the superposition of the solutions of three simpler problems in the form

$$T_i(x, t) = \theta_i(x, t) + \phi_i(x) f_1(t) + \psi_i(x) f_M(t)$$
$$\text{in } x_i < x < x_{i+1}, \; i = 1, 2, \ldots, M, \text{ for } t > 0 \tag{8-67}$$

Where the functions $\phi_i(x), \psi_i(x)$, and $\theta_i(x, t)$ are the solutions of the following subproblems.

1. The functions $\phi_i(x)$ are the solutions of the following steady-state problem for the same region, with no heat generation, but with one non-homogeneous boundary condition at $x = x_1$.

$$\frac{d}{dx}\left(x^p \frac{d\phi_i}{dx}\right) = 0 \qquad \text{in } x_i < x < x_{i+1}, \; i = 1, 2, \ldots, M \tag{8-68a}$$

subject to the boundary conditions

$$-k_1^* \frac{d\phi_1(x)}{dx} + h_1 \phi_1(x) = h_1 \qquad \text{at } x = x_1 \tag{8-68b}$$

$$-k_i \frac{d\phi_i}{dx} = h_{i+1}(\phi_i - \phi_{i+1}) \left.\begin{array}{c}\\\\\\\end{array}\right\} \quad \begin{array}{l}\text{at the interfaces} \qquad (8\text{-}68c)\\ x = x_{i+1},\end{array}$$

$$k_i \frac{d\phi_i}{dx} = k_{i+1} \frac{d\phi_{i+1}}{dx} \qquad\qquad i = 1, 2, \ldots, M-1 \tag{8-68d}$$

$$k_M^* \frac{d\phi_M}{dx} + h_{M+1}\phi_M = 0 \qquad \text{at } x = x_{M+1} \tag{8-68e}$$

2. The functions $\psi_i(x)$ are the solutions of the following steady-state problem for the same region, with no heat generation, but with one non-homogeneous boundary condition at $x = x_{M+1}$.

$$\frac{d}{dx}\left(x^p \frac{d\psi_i}{dx}\right) = 0 \quad \text{in } x_i < x < x_{i+1}, \ i = 1, 2, \ldots, M \quad (8\text{-}69a)$$

subject to the boundary conditions

$$-k_1^* \frac{d\psi_1}{dx} + h_1 \psi_1 = 0 \qquad \text{at } x = x_1 \qquad (8\text{-}69b)$$

$$\left. \begin{array}{l} -k_i \dfrac{d\psi_i}{dx} = h_{i+1}(\psi_i - \psi_{i+1}) \\[2mm] k_i \dfrac{d\psi_i}{dx} = k_{i+1}\dfrac{d\psi_{i+1}}{dx} \end{array} \right\} \quad \begin{array}{l} \text{at the interfaces} \qquad\qquad (8\text{-}69c) \\ x = x_{i+1}, \\[1mm] i = 1, 2, \ldots, M-1 \qquad (8\text{-}69d) \end{array}$$

$$k_M^* \frac{d\psi_M}{dx} + h_{M+1}\psi_M = h_{M+1} \qquad \text{at } x = x_{M+1} \qquad (8\text{-}69e)$$

3. The functions $\theta_i(x, t)$ are the solutions of the following time-dependent heat-conduction problem for the same region, with heat generation, but subject to homogeneous boundary conditions

$$\alpha_i \frac{1}{x^p}\frac{\partial}{\partial x}\left(x^p \frac{\partial \theta_i}{\partial x}\right) + g_i^*(x, t) = \frac{\partial \theta_i(x, t)}{\partial t},$$

$$\text{in } x_i < x < x_{i+1}, \ i = 1, 2, \ldots, M, \ \text{for } t > 0 \qquad (8\text{-}70a)$$

where

$$g_i^*(x, t) \equiv \frac{\alpha_i}{k_i} g_i(x, t) - \left[\phi_i(x)\frac{df_1(t)}{dt} + \psi_i(x)\frac{df_M(t)}{dt}\right]$$

Subject to the boundary conditions

$$-k_1^* \frac{\partial \theta_1}{\partial x} + h_1 \theta_1 = 0 \qquad \text{at } x = x_1, \ t > 0 \qquad (8\text{-}70b)$$

$$\left. \begin{array}{l} -k_i \dfrac{\partial \theta_i}{\partial x} = h_{i+1}(\theta_i - \theta_{i+1}) \\[2mm] k_i \dfrac{\partial \theta_i}{\partial x} = k_{i+1}\dfrac{\partial \theta_{i+1}}{\partial x} \end{array} \right\} \quad \begin{array}{l} \text{at the interfaces} \qquad\qquad (8\text{-}70c) \\ x = x_{i+1}, \ i = 1, 2, \ldots, M, \\[1mm] \text{for } t > 0 \qquad\qquad\qquad (8\text{-}70d) \end{array}$$

$$k_M^* \frac{\partial \theta_M}{\partial x} + h_{M+1}\theta_M = 0 \qquad \text{at } x = x_{M+1}, \ t > 0 \qquad (8\text{-}70e)$$

and the initial conditions

$$\theta_i(x, t) = F_i(x) - [\phi_i(x)f_1(0) + \psi_i(x)f_M(0)] \equiv F_i^*(x),$$
$$\text{for } t = 0, \text{ in } x_i < x < x_{i+1}, \ i = 1, 2, \ldots, M \qquad (8\text{-}70\text{f})$$

The validity of the above superposition procedure can readily be verified by introducing equation (8-67) into the general problem given by equations (8-64) to (8-66) and utilizing the above subproblems defined by equations (8-68), (8-69), and (8-70).

The solution of the steady-state problems defined by equations (8-68) or (8-69) is straightforward. For example, if we consider the problem (8-68), the solution of the differential equation (8-68a) is taken in the form

Slab: $\phi_i(x) = A_i + B_i x$

Cylinder: $\phi_i(x) = A_i + B_i \ln x$

Sphere: $\phi_i(x) = A_i + \dfrac{B_i}{x}$

For an M-layer composite medium the problem involves $2M$ coefficients that are determined by the application of $2M$ boundary conditions given by equations (8-68b, c, d, e).

The time-dependent problem defined by equations (8-70) has homogeneous external boundary conditions, but it contains the heat generation term. The solution of problems of this type will be discussed in the next section.

Example 8-3. Solve the two-layer slab problem considered in Example 8-2 for the case when the boundary surface at $x = 0$ is kept at a constant temperature f_1 and the boundary surface at $x = b$ dissipates heat by convection into a medium at a constant temperature f_2.

Solution. The mathematical formulation of this problem is exactly the same as that given by equations (8-47) to (8-50) except the boundary conditions (8-49a) and (8-49d) should be replaced by the following boundary conditions, respectively.

$$T_1(x, t) = f_1 \qquad\qquad \text{at } x = 0, \ t > 0 \qquad (8\text{-}49\text{a}^*)$$

$$k_2^* \frac{\partial T_2}{\partial x} + h_3 T_2 = h_3 f_2 \qquad \text{at } x = b, \ t > 0 \qquad (8\text{-}49\text{d}^*)$$

We split up $T_i(x, t)$, $i = 1, 2$ as

$$T_i(x, t) = \theta_i(x, t) + \phi_i(x)f_1 + \psi_i(x)f_2$$
$$\text{in } x_i < x < x_{i+1}, \ i = 1, 2 \qquad (8\text{-}71)$$

Where the functions $\theta_i(x, t)$, $\phi_i(x)$ and $\psi_i(x)$ are the solutions of the following three subproblems.

1. The functions $\phi_i(x)$, $i = 1, 2$ satisfy the steady-state heat-conduction problem given as

$$\frac{d^2\phi_1(x)}{dx^2} = 0 \qquad \text{in } 0 < x < a \tag{8-72a}$$

$$\frac{d^2\phi_2(x)}{dx^2} = 0 \qquad \text{in } a < x < b \tag{8-72b}$$

Subject to the boundary conditions

$$\phi_1(x) = 1 \qquad\qquad\quad \text{at } x = 0 \tag{8-72c}$$

$$\left.\begin{array}{l} \phi_1(x) = \phi_2(x) \\[2mm] k_1\dfrac{d\phi_1}{dx} = k_2\dfrac{d\phi_2}{dx} \end{array}\right\} \quad \begin{array}{l} \text{at the interface} \\ x = a \end{array} \qquad \begin{array}{l} (8\text{-}72\text{d}) \\[4mm] (8\text{-}72\text{e}) \end{array}$$

$$k_2^*\frac{d\phi_2}{dx} + h_3\phi_2 = 0 \qquad \text{at } x = b \tag{8-72f}$$

2. The functions $\psi_i(x)$, $i = 1, 2$ satisfy the steady-state heat-conduction problem given as

$$\frac{d^2\psi_1(x)}{dx^2} = 0 \qquad \text{in } 0 < x < a \tag{8-73a}$$

$$\frac{d^2\psi_2(x)}{dx^2} = 0 \qquad \text{in } a < x < b \tag{8-73b}$$

Subject to the boundary conditions

$$\psi_1(x) = 0 \qquad\qquad\quad \text{at } x = 0 \tag{8-73c}$$

$$\left.\begin{array}{l} \psi_1(x) = \psi_2(x) \\[2mm] k_1\dfrac{d\psi_1}{dx} = k_2\dfrac{d\psi_2}{dx} \end{array}\right\} \quad \begin{array}{l} \text{at the interface} \\ x = a \end{array} \qquad \begin{array}{l} (8\text{-}73\text{d}) \\[4mm] (8\text{-}73\text{e}) \end{array}$$

$$k_2^*\frac{d\psi_2}{dx} + h_3\psi_2 = h_3 \qquad \text{at } x = b \tag{8-73f}$$

3. The functions $\theta_i(x, t)$, $i = 1, 2$ are the solutions of the following homo-

geneous problem

$$\alpha_1 \frac{\partial^2 \theta_1}{\partial x^2} = \frac{\partial \theta_1(x,t)}{\partial t} \qquad \text{in } 0 < x < a, \ t > 0 \qquad (8\text{-}74a)$$

$$\alpha_2 \frac{\partial^2 \theta_2}{\partial x^2} = \frac{\partial \theta_2(x,t)}{\partial t} \qquad \text{in } a < x < b, \ t > 0 \qquad (8\text{-}74b)$$

subject to the boundary conditions

$$\theta_1(x,t) = 0 \qquad\qquad \text{at } x = 0, \ t > 0 \qquad (8\text{-}75a)$$

$$\left.\begin{array}{l} \theta_1(x,t) = \theta_2(x,t) \\[3mm] k_1 \dfrac{\partial \theta_1}{\partial x} = k_2 \dfrac{\partial \theta_2}{\partial x} \end{array}\right\} \qquad \begin{array}{l} \text{at the interface} \qquad (8\text{-}75b) \\[1mm] x = a, \ t > 0 \\[3mm] \qquad\qquad\qquad\quad (8\text{-}75c) \end{array}$$

$$k_2^* \frac{\partial \theta_2}{\partial x} + h_3 \theta_2 = 0 \qquad \text{at } x = b \qquad (8\text{-}75d)$$

and the initial conditions

$$\theta_1(x,t) = F_1(x) - f_1 \phi_1(x) - f_2 \psi_1(x) \equiv F_1^*(x) \qquad \text{for } t = 0, \text{ in } 0 \le x \le a$$
$$(8\text{-}75e)$$

$$\theta_2(x,t) = F_2(x) - f_1 \phi_2(x) - f_2 \psi_2(x) \equiv F_2^*(x) \qquad \text{for } t = 0, \text{ in } a \le x \le b$$
$$(8\text{-}75f)$$

The steady-state problems given by equations (8-72) and (8-73) can readily be solved. For example, to solve the problem (8-72) for the functions $\phi_i(x), i = 1, 2$, we set

$$\phi_1(x) = A_1 x + B_1 \qquad (8\text{-}76a)$$

$$\phi_2(x) = A_2 x + B_2 \qquad (8\text{-}76b)$$

The four coefficients $A_i, B_i (i = 1, 2)$ are readily determined by the application of the four boundary conditions (8-72c, d, e, f) for the problem. A similar procedure is applicable for the solution of problem (8-73) for the functions $\psi_i(x), i = 1, 2$. When the steady-state temperatures $\phi_i(x)$ and $\psi_i(x), i = 1, 2$ are available, the initial condition functions $F_1^*(x)$ and $F_2^*(x)$ defined by equations (8-75e, f) are known. Then, the homogeneous problem defined by equations (8-74) and (8-75) is exactly the same as that considered in Example 8-2; therefore, its solution is obtainable from the solution given by equation (8-62) if the initial condition functions $F_1(x)$ and $F_2(x)$ in that equation are replaced by $F_1^*(x)$ and $F_2^*(x)$, respectively.

8-4 THE USE OF GREEN'S FUNCTIONS
IN THE SOLUTION OF NONHOMOGENEOUS PROBLEMS

In Chapter 6 we have shown that the nonhomogeneous problems of heat conduction of single-region medium can be solved readily with the Green's function approach. In this section we extend this technique to the solution of one-dimensional, nonhomogeneous problem of heat conduction of one-dimensional composite medium. We assume that the nonhomogeneities associated with the external boundary conditions for the problem are removed with the transformation of the dependent variable as discussed in the previous section so that we need to consider only the solution of the heat-conduction problem in the form

$$\alpha_i \frac{1}{x^p} \frac{\partial}{\partial x}\left(x^p \frac{\partial T_i}{\partial x}\right) + \frac{\alpha_i}{k_i} g_i(x,t) = \frac{\partial T_i(x,t)}{\partial t}$$

$$\text{in } x_i < x < x_{i+1}, \ t > 0, \ i = 1, 2, \dots, M \tag{8-77}$$

where

$$p = \begin{cases} 0 & \text{slab} \\ 1 & \text{cylinder} \\ 2 & \text{sphere} \end{cases}$$

Subject to the boundary conditions

$$-k_1^* \frac{\partial T_1}{\partial x} + h_1 T_1 = 0 \qquad \text{at the outer boundary } x = x_1, \ t > 0 \tag{8-78a}$$

$$\left. \begin{aligned} -k_i \frac{\partial T_i}{\partial x} &= h_{i+1}(T_i - T_{i+1}) \\[2mm] k_i \frac{\partial T_i}{\partial x} &= k_{i+1} \frac{\partial T_{i+1}}{\partial x} \end{aligned} \right\} \quad \begin{aligned} &\text{at the interfaces} \\ &x = x_{i+1}, \ i = 1, 2, \dots, M-1, \\ &\text{for } t > 0 \end{aligned} \qquad \begin{aligned} &(8\text{-}78b) \\[4mm] &(8\text{-}78c) \end{aligned}$$

$$k_M^* \frac{\partial T_M}{\partial x} + h_{M+1} T_M = 0 \qquad \text{at the outer boundary } x = x_{M+1}, \ t > 0 \tag{8-78d}$$

and the initial conditions

$$T_i(x,t) = F_i(x) \qquad \text{for } t = 0, \text{ in } x_i < x < x_{i+1}, \ i = 1, 2, \dots, M \tag{8-79}$$

Appropriate eigenvalue problem for the solution of the above heat-conduction problem is taken as

$$\frac{1}{x^p} \frac{d}{dx}\left(x^p \frac{d\psi_{in}}{dx}\right) + \frac{\beta_n^2}{\alpha_i} \psi_{in}(x) = 0 \qquad \text{in } x_i < x < x_{i+1}, \ i = 1, 2, \dots, M \tag{8-80}$$

Subject to the boundary conditions

$$-k_1^* \frac{d\psi_{1n}}{dx} + h_1\psi_{1n} = 0 \qquad \text{at the outer boundary, } x = x_1 \qquad (8\text{-}81a)$$

$$\left. \begin{array}{l} -k_i \dfrac{d\psi_{in}}{dx} = h_{i+1}(\psi_{in} - \psi_{i+1,n}) \\[3mm] k_i \dfrac{d\psi_{in}}{dx} = k_{i+1} \dfrac{d\psi_{i+1,n}}{dx} \end{array} \right\} \qquad \begin{array}{l} \text{at the interfaces} \\[1mm] x = x_{i+1}, \\[1mm] i = 1, 2, \ldots, M-1 \end{array} \qquad (8\text{-}81b)$$

$$k_M^* \frac{d\psi_{Mn}}{dx} + h_{M+1}\psi_{Mn} = 0 \qquad \text{at the outer boundary, } x = x_{M+1} \quad (8\text{-}81c)$$

We note that this eigenvalue problem is exactly the same as that given by equations (8-7) and (8-8) for the solution of the homogeneous version of the above heat conduction problem.

A general problem of transient heat conduction in three-dimensional composite media, with heat generation and nonhomogeneous outer-boundary condition, is solved in reference [25] by the application of the integral transform technique. Therefore the solution of the nonhomogeneous problem defined by equations (8-77) to (8-79) is readily obtainable from reference [25] as a special case. The solution obtained in this manner is rearranged in terms of the Green's function; the resulting expression for $T_i(x, t)$ is given as [see also equation (14-20)]

$$T_i(x, t) = \sum_{j=1}^{M} \int_{x_j}^{x_{j+1}} x'^P \left| G_{ij}(x, t | x', \tau) \right|_{\tau=0} F_j(x') \, dx'$$

$$+ \int_{\tau=0}^{t} d\tau \int_{x_j}^{x_{j+1}} x'^P G_{ij}(x, t | x', \tau) \left[\frac{\alpha_j}{k_j} g_j(x', \tau) \right] dx'$$

$$\text{in } x_i < x < x_{i+1}, \quad i = 1, 2, \ldots, M \qquad (8\text{-}82a)$$

where the composite medium Green's function $G_{ij}(x, t | x', \tau)$ is defined as

$$G_{ij}(x, t | x', \tau) = \sum_{n=1}^{\infty} e^{-\beta_n^2(t-\tau)} \frac{1}{N_n} \frac{k_j}{\alpha_j} \psi_{in}(x)\psi_{jn}(x') \qquad (8\text{-}28b)$$

and

$$p = \begin{cases} 0 & \text{slab} \\ 1 & \text{cylinder} \\ 2 & \text{sphere} \end{cases}$$

The norm N_n is given by

$$N_n = \sum_{j=1}^{M} \frac{k_j}{\alpha_j} \int_{x_j}^{x_{j+1}} x'^P \psi_{jn}^2(x') \, dx' \qquad (8\text{-}82c)$$

and $\psi_{in}(x)$, $\psi_{jn}(x)$ are the eigenfunctions, β_n's are the eigenvalues of the above eigenvalue problem.

We note that, for the case of no generation in the medium, the solution given by equations (8-82) reduces to that given by equations (8-17) for the homogeneous problem. A comparison of the results given by equations (8-82b) and (8-17b) reveals that the *Green's function* $G(x, t | x', \tau)$ *is obtainable from* $G(x, t | x', \tau)|_{\tau = 0}$ *by replacing in the latter t by* $(t - \tau)$.

We now summarize the basic steps for solving the nonhomogeneous problem of a composite medium. A nonhomogeneous, time-dependent problem with heat generation and nonhomogeneous outer-boundary conditions, such as the one given by equations (8-64) to (8-66), is split up into simpler problems as discussed in the previous section. The resulting steady-state problems can readily be solved; the nonhomogeneous time-dependent problem is in the form given above by equations (8-77) to (8-79). That is, the nonhomogeneous problem involves a heat generation term, but has homogeneous outer-boundary conditions; therefore it can be solved by the Green's function technique and its solution is given by equation (8-82). The desired Green's function for solving the nonhomogeneous problem is obtained from the solution of the homogeneous version of the problem as discussed previously.

The applications of this approach is now illustrated with the examples below. To simplify the analysis we have chosen the examples such that the solutions are available in the previous sections for the homogeneous part of the problem, thus we need not perform additional calculations to determine the Green's function.

Example 8-4. A two-layer solid cylinder contains an inner region $0 \leq r \leq a$ and an outer region $a \leq r \leq b$ that are in perfect thermal contact. Initially, the inner and outer regions are at temperatures $F_1(r)$ and $F_2(r)$, respectively. For times $t > 0$, heat is generated in the inner and outer regions at rates $g_1(r, t)$ and $g_2(r, t)$ W/m³ (or Btu/hr ft³), respectively, whereas the heat is dissipated by convection from the outer boundary surface at $r = b$ into a medium at temperature $f(t)$ that varies with time. Obtain an expression for the temperature distribution in the cylinder for times $t > 0$.

Solution. The mathematical formulation of this problem is given as

$$\alpha_1 \frac{1}{r} \frac{\partial}{\partial r}\left(r \frac{\partial T_1}{\partial r}\right) + \frac{\alpha_1}{k_1} g_1(r, t) = \frac{\partial T_1(r, t)}{\partial t} \qquad \text{in } 0 < r < a, \ t > 0 \quad (8\text{-}83a)$$

$$\alpha_2 \frac{1}{r} \frac{\partial}{\partial r}\left(r \frac{\partial T_2}{\partial r}\right) + \frac{\alpha_2}{k_2} g_2(r, t) = \frac{\partial T_2(r, t)}{\partial t} \qquad \text{in } a < r < b, \ t > 0 \quad (8\text{-}83b)$$

subject to the boundary conditions

$$T_1(r, t) = T_2(r, t) \qquad\qquad \text{at } r = a,\ t > 0 \qquad\qquad (8\text{-}84\text{a})$$

$$k_1 \frac{\partial T_1}{\partial r} = k_2 \frac{\partial T_2}{\partial r} \qquad\qquad \text{at } r = a,\ t > 0 \qquad\qquad (8\text{-}84\text{b})$$

$$k_2^* \frac{\partial T_2}{\partial r} + h_3 T_2 = h_3 f(t) \qquad \text{at } r = b,\ t > 0 \qquad\qquad (8\text{-}84\text{c})$$

and the initial conditions

$$T_1(r, t) = F_1(r) \qquad \text{for } t = 0 \text{ in } 0 \le r < a \qquad\qquad (8\text{-}84\text{d})$$

$$T_2(r, t) = F_2(r) \qquad \text{for } t = 0 \text{ in } a < r < b \qquad\qquad (8\text{-}84\text{e})$$

In this problem, the outer boundary condition at $r = b$ can be made homogeneous if we measure the temperatures in excess of the environment temperature $f(t)$. Namely, we define new temperatures as

$$\theta_i(r, t) = T_i(r, t) - f(t), \qquad i = 1, 2 \qquad\qquad (8\text{-}85)$$

Then, the equations (8-83) and (8-84), respectively, become

$$\alpha_1 \frac{1}{r} \frac{\partial}{\partial r}\left(r \frac{\partial \theta_1}{\partial r} \right) + g_1^*(r, t) = \frac{\partial \theta_1(r, t)}{\partial t} \qquad \text{in } 0 \le r < a,\ t > 0 \qquad (8\text{-}86\text{a})$$

$$\alpha_2 \frac{1}{r} \frac{\partial}{\partial r}\left(r \frac{\partial \theta_2}{\partial r} \right) + g_2^*(r, t) = \frac{\partial \theta_2(r, t)}{\partial t} \qquad \text{in } a < r < b,\ t > 0 \qquad (8\text{-}86\text{b})$$

where

$$g_1^*(r, t) \equiv \frac{\alpha_1}{k_1} g_1(r, t) - \frac{df(t)}{dt} \qquad\qquad (8\text{-}86\text{c})$$

$$g_2^*(r, t) \equiv \frac{\alpha_2}{k_2} g_2(r, t) - \frac{df(t)}{dt} \qquad\qquad (8\text{-}86\text{d})$$

Subject to the boundary conditions

$$\theta_1(r, t) = \theta_2(r, t) \qquad\qquad \text{at } r = a,\ t > 0 \qquad\qquad (8\text{-}87\text{a})$$

$$k_1 \frac{\partial \theta_1}{\partial r} = k_2 \frac{\partial \theta_2}{\partial r} \qquad\qquad \text{at } r = a,\ t > 0 \qquad\qquad (8\text{-}87\text{b})$$

$$k_2^* \frac{\partial \theta_2}{\partial r} + h_3 \theta_2 = 0 \qquad\qquad \text{at } r = b,\ t > 0 \qquad\qquad (8\text{-}87\text{c})$$

and the initial conditions

$$\theta_1(r, t) = F_1(r) - f(0) \equiv F_1^*(r) \qquad \text{for } t = 0, \text{ in } 0 < r < a \qquad (8\text{-}87d)$$

$$\theta_2(r, t) = F_2(r) - f(0) \equiv F_2^*(r) \qquad \text{for } t = 0, \text{ in } a < r < b \qquad (8\text{-}87e)$$

The heat-conduction problem defined by equations (8-86) and (8-87) is a special case of the general problem given by equations (8-77) to (8-79). Therefore, its solution is immediately obtainable in terms of the Green's functions from the general solution (8-82) as

$$\theta_i(r, t) = \int_{r'=0}^{a} r' [G_{i1}(r, t | r', \tau)]_{\tau=0} \cdot F_1^*(r') \, dr' + \int_{r'=a}^{b} r' [G_{i2}(r, t | r', \tau)]_{\tau=0} F_2^*(r') \, dr'$$

$$+ \int_{\tau=0}^{t} d\tau \left[\int_{r'=0}^{a} r' G_{i1}(r, t | r', \tau) \cdot g_1^*(r', \tau) \, dr' \right.$$

$$\left. + \int_{r'=a}^{b} r' G_{i2}(r, t | r', \tau) g_2^*(r', \tau) \, dr' \right], \qquad i = 1, 2 \qquad (8\text{-}88)$$

where the Green's functions $G_{ij}(r, t | r', \tau)$ is obtainable from the solution of the homogeneous version of the problem given by equations (8-86) and (8-87). We note that the homogeneous part of this problem is exactly the same as that considered in Example 8-1, given by equations (8-30) to (8-33). Therefore, the desired Green's function is immediately obtainable from the result (8-46b) worked out in Example 8-1, by replacing t by $(t - \tau)$. We find

$$G_{ij}(r, t | r', \tau) = \sum_{n=1}^{\infty} e^{-\beta_n^2 (t-\tau)} \frac{1}{N_n} \frac{k_j}{\alpha_j} \psi_{in}(r) \psi_{jn}(r') \qquad (8\text{-}89a)$$

$$G_{ij}(r, t | r', \tau) \big|_{\tau=0} = \sum_{n=1}^{\infty} e^{-\beta_n^2 t} \frac{1}{N_n} \frac{k_j}{\alpha_j} \psi_{in}(r) \psi_{jn}(r') \qquad (8\text{-}89b)$$

where the norm N_n is obtained from equation (8-45b) as

$$N_n = \frac{k_1}{\alpha_1} \int_0^a r' \psi_{1n}^2(r') \, dr' + \frac{k_2}{\alpha_2} \int_a^b r' \psi_{2n}^2(r') \, dr' \qquad (8\text{-}89c)$$

The eigenfunctions $\psi_{1n}(r)$ and $\psi_{2n}(r)$ are obtained from equations (8-45c) and (8-45d) as

$$\psi_{1n}(r) = J_0\left(\frac{\beta_n}{\sqrt{\alpha_1}} r\right) \qquad (8\text{-}89d)$$

$$\psi_{2n}(r) = A_{2n} J_0\left(\frac{\beta_n}{\sqrt{\alpha_2}} r\right) + B_{2n} Y_0\left(\frac{\beta_n}{\sqrt{\alpha_2}} r\right) \qquad (8\text{-}89e)$$

The coefficients A_{2n} and B_{2n} are given by equations (8-43a) and (8-43b), respectively. The eigenvalues β_n are the positive roots of the transcendental equation (8-44).

Example 8-5. In a two-layer slab, the first $(0 < x < a)$ and the second $(a < x < b)$ layers are in perfect thermal contact. Initially, the first layer is at temperature $F_1(x)$ and the second layer is at temperature $F_2(x)$. For times $t > 0$, the boundary at $x = 0$ is kept at zero temperature, the boundary at $x = b$ dissipates heat by convection into a medium at zero temperature, while heat is generated in the first layer at a rate of $g_1(x, t)$ W/m^3 (or Btu/hr ft^3). Obtain an expression for the temperature distribution in the medium for times $t > 0$.

Solution. The mathematical formulation of this problem is given as

$$\alpha_1 \frac{\partial^2 T_1}{\partial x^2} + \frac{\alpha_1}{k_1} g_1(x, t) = \frac{\partial T_1(x, t)}{\partial t} \qquad \text{in } 0 < x < a, \ t > 0 \qquad (8\text{-}90a)$$

$$\alpha_2 \frac{\partial^2 T_2}{\partial x^2} = \frac{\partial T_2(x, t)}{\partial t} \qquad \text{in } a < x < b, \ t > 0 \qquad (8\text{-}90b)$$

Subject to the boundary conditions

$$T_1(x, t) = 0 \qquad\qquad \text{at } x = 0, \ t > 0 \qquad (8\text{-}91a)$$

$$T_1(x, t) = T_2(x, t) \qquad \text{at } x = a, \ t > 0 \qquad (8\text{-}91b)$$

$$k_1 \frac{\partial T_1}{\partial x} = k_2 \frac{\partial T_2}{\partial x} \qquad \text{at } x = a, \ t > 0 \qquad (8\text{-}91c)$$

$$k_2^* \frac{\partial T_2}{\partial x} + h_3 T_3 = 0 \qquad \text{at } x = b, \ t > 0 \qquad (8\text{-}91d)$$

and the initial conditions

$$T_1(x, t) = F_1(x) \qquad \text{for } t = 0, \text{ in } 0 < x < a \qquad (8\text{-}91e)$$

$$T_2(x, t) = F_2(x) \qquad \text{for } t = 0, \text{ in } a < x < b \qquad (8\text{-}91f)$$

This heat-conduction problem is a special case of the general problem given by equations (8-77) to (8-79). Therefore, its solution is immediately obtainable in terms of the Green's functions from the general solution (8-82) as

$$T_i(x, t) = \int_{x'=0}^{a} [G_{i1}(x, t | x', \tau)]_{\tau=0} F_1(x') \, dx' + \int_{x'=a}^{b} [G_{i2}(x, t | x', \tau)]_{\tau=0} F_2(x') \, dx'$$

$$+ \int_{\tau=0}^{t} d\tau \int_{x'=0}^{a} G_{i1}(x, t | x', \tau) \frac{\alpha_1}{k_1} g_1(x', \tau) \, dx', \qquad i = 1, 2 \qquad (8\text{-}92a)$$

where the Green's function is obtainable from the solution of the homogeneous version of the heat-conduction problem given by equations (8-90) and (8-91). Actually, the homogeneous version of this problem is exactly the same as that considered in example (8-2), given by equations (8-47) to (8-50). Therefore, the desired Green's function is obtainable from the result given by equation (8-63b) by replacing t by $(t - \tau)$ in this expression. We find

$$G_{ij}(x, t \,|\, x', \tau) = \sum_{n=1}^{\infty} e^{-\beta_n^2(t-\tau)} \frac{1}{N_n} \frac{k_j}{\alpha_j} \psi_{in}(x) \psi_{jn}(x') \qquad (8\text{-}92b)$$

where the norm N_n is obtained from equation (8-62b) as

$$N_n = \frac{k_1}{\alpha_1} \int_0^a \psi_{1n}^2(x') \, dx' + \frac{k_2}{\alpha_2} \int_a^b \psi_{2n}^2(x') \, dx' \qquad (8\text{-}92c)$$

The eigenfunctions $\psi_{1n}(x)$ and $\psi_{2n}(x)$ are obtained from equations (8-62c) and (8-62d), respectively, as

$$\psi_{1n}(x) = \sin\left(\frac{\beta_n}{\sqrt{\alpha_1}} x \right) \qquad (8\text{-}92d)$$

$$\psi_{2n}(x) = A_{2n} \sin\left(\frac{\beta_n}{\sqrt{\alpha_2}} x \right) + B_{2n} \cos\left(\frac{\beta_n}{\sqrt{\alpha_2}} x \right) \qquad (8\text{-}92e)$$

The coefficients A_{2n} and B_{2n} are given by equations (8-60), and the eigenvalues β_n are the positive roots of the transcendental equation (8-61).

8-5 THE USE OF LAPLACE TRANSFORMATION

The Laplace transformation has also been used in the solution of one-dimensional, time-dependent problems of heat conduction in a composite medium. In this method, the partial derivatives with respect to the time variable are removed from the differential equation by the application of the Laplace transform, the resulting system of ordinary differential equations are solved and the transform of the temperature is inverted. The transformation of the differential equations is a straightforward matter, but the solution of the resulting system of ordinary differential equations and the inversion of the transform are quite involved except for simple cases. In this section we illustrate the application of this technique with examples so chosen that the inversions can be performed by the use of Laplace transform table.

Example 8-6. Two semi-infinite regions, $x > 0$ and $x < 0$, illustrated in

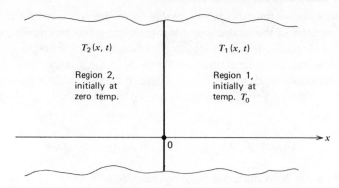

Fig. 8-4 Two semi-infinite regions in perfect thermal contact.

Fig. 8-4 are in perfect thermal contact. Initially, the region 1 (i.e., $x > 0$) is at a uniform temperature T_0, and the region 2 (i.e., $x < 0$) is at zero temperature. Obtain an expression for the temperature distribution in the medium for times $t > 0$.

Solution. For convenience in the analysis, we define a dimensionless temperature $\theta_i(x, t)$ as

$$\theta_i(x, t) = \frac{T_i(x, t)}{T_0} \qquad i = 1, 2 \tag{8-93}$$

Then, the mathematical formulation of the problem, in terms of $\theta_i(x, t)$, is given as

$$\frac{\partial^2 \theta_1}{\partial x^2} = \frac{1}{\alpha_1} \frac{\partial \theta_1(x, t)}{\partial t} \qquad \text{in } x > 0, \ t > 0 \tag{8-94a}$$

$$\frac{\partial^2 \theta_2}{\partial x^2} = \frac{1}{\alpha_2} \frac{\partial \theta_2(x, t)}{\partial t} \qquad \text{in } x < 0, \ t > 0 \tag{8-94b}$$

Subject to the boundary conditions

$$\theta_1(x, t)\big|_{x = 0^+} = \theta_2(x, t)\big|_{x = 0^-} \qquad t > 0 \tag{8-95a}$$

$$-k_1 \frac{\partial \theta_1}{\partial x}\bigg|_{x = 0^+} = k_2 \frac{\partial \theta_2}{\partial x}\bigg|_{x = 0^-} \qquad t > 0 \tag{8-95b}$$

$$\frac{\partial \theta_1}{\partial x}\bigg|_{x \to \infty} = \frac{\partial \theta_2}{\partial x}\bigg|_{x \to -\infty} = 0 \qquad t > 0 \tag{8-95c}$$

and the initial conditions

$$\theta_1(x, t) = 1 \qquad \text{for } t = 0, \ x > 0 \tag{8-95d}$$

$$\theta_2(x, t) = 0 \qquad \text{for } t = 0, \ x < 0 \qquad (8\text{-}95e)$$

The Laplace transform of equations (8-94) is

$$\frac{d^2\bar{\theta}_1(x, s)}{dx^2} = \frac{1}{\alpha_1}[s\bar{\theta}_1(x, s) - 1] \qquad \text{in } x > 0 \qquad (8\text{-}96a)$$

$$\frac{d^2\bar{\theta}_2(x, s)}{dx^2} = \frac{1}{\alpha_2}s\bar{\theta}_2(x, s) \qquad \text{in } x < 0 \qquad (8\text{-}96b)$$

and the Laplace transform of the boundary conditions gives

$$\bar{\theta}_1(0^+, s) = \bar{\theta}_2(0^-, s) \qquad (8\text{-}97a)$$

$$-k_1\frac{d\bar{\theta}_1}{dx}\bigg|_{x=0^+} = k_2\frac{d\bar{\theta}_2}{dx}\bigg|_{x=0^-} \qquad (8\text{-}97b)$$

$$\frac{d\bar{\theta}_1}{dx}\bigg|_{x\to\infty} = \frac{d\bar{\theta}_2}{dx}\bigg|_{x\to-\infty} = 0 \qquad (8\text{-}97c)$$

The solutions of equations (8-96) subject to the boundary conditions (8-97) are

$$\bar{\theta}_1(x, s) = \frac{1}{s} - \frac{1}{1+\beta}\frac{1}{s}e^{-(s/\alpha_1)^{1/2}x} \qquad \text{for } x > 0 \qquad (8\text{-}98a)$$

$$\bar{\theta}_2(x, s) = \frac{\beta}{1+\beta}\frac{1}{s}e^{-(s/\alpha_2)^{1/2}|x|} \qquad \text{for } x < 0 \qquad (8\text{-}98b)$$

where

$$\beta \equiv \frac{k_1}{k_2}\left(\frac{\alpha_2}{\alpha_1}\right)^{1/2} \qquad (8\text{-}98c)$$

These transforms can be inverted using the Laplace transform Table 7-1, cases 1 and 42. The resulting expressions for the temperature distribution in the medium become

$$\theta_1(x, t) \equiv \frac{T_1(x, t)}{T_0} = 1 - \frac{1}{1+\beta}\text{erfc}\left(\frac{x}{2\sqrt{\alpha_1 t}}\right), \qquad \text{for } x > 0 \quad (8\text{-}99a)$$

$$\theta_2(x, t) \equiv \frac{T_2(x, t)}{T_0} = \frac{\beta}{1+\beta}\text{erfc}\left(\frac{|x|}{2\sqrt{\alpha_2 t}}\right), \qquad \text{for } x < 0 \quad (8\text{-}99b)$$

Example 8-7. A two-layer medium illustrated in Fig. 8-5 is composed of region 1, $0 < x < L$, and region 2, $x > L$, which are in perfect thermal contact. Initially, region 1 is at a uniform temperature T_0 and region 2 is at zero temperature. For times $t > 0$, the boundary surface at $x = 0$ is kept insulated.

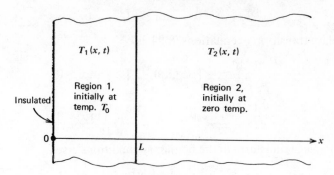

Fig. 8-5 A finite region and a semi-infinite region in perfect thermal contact.

Obtain an expression for the temperature distribution in the medium for times $t > 0$.

Solution.   We define a dimensionless temperature $\theta_i(x, t)$ as

$$\theta_i(x, t) = \frac{T_i(x, t)}{T_0} \qquad i = 1, 2 \tag{8-100}$$

Then, the mathematical formulation of the problem in terms of $\theta_i(x, t)$ is given as

$$\frac{\partial^2 \theta_1}{\partial x^2} = \frac{1}{\alpha_1} \frac{\partial \theta_1(x, t)}{\partial t} \qquad \text{in } 0 < x < L, \ t > 0 \tag{8-101a}$$

$$\frac{\partial^2 \theta_2}{\partial x^2} = \frac{1}{\alpha_2} \frac{\partial \theta_2(x, t)}{\partial t} \qquad \text{in } x > L, \ t > 0 \tag{8-101b}$$

subject to the boundary conditions

$$\frac{\partial \theta_1}{\partial x} = 0 \qquad\qquad \text{at } x = 0, \ t > 0 \tag{8-102a}$$

$$\theta_1(x, t) = \theta_2(x, t) \qquad \text{at } x = L, \ t > 0 \tag{8-102b}$$

$$k_1 \frac{\partial \theta_1}{\partial x} = k_2 \frac{\partial \theta_2}{\partial x} \qquad \text{at } x = L, \ t > 0 \tag{8-102c}$$

$$\theta_2(x, t) \to 0 \qquad\qquad \text{as } x \to \infty, \ t > 0 \tag{8-102d}$$

and the initial conditions

$$\theta_1(x, t) = 1 \qquad \text{for } t = 0, \ \text{in } 0 < x < L \tag{8-102e}$$

$$\theta_1(x, t) = 0 \qquad \text{for } t = 0, \ \text{in } x > L \tag{8-102f}$$

The Laplace transform of equations (8-101) is

$$\frac{d^2\bar{\theta}_1(x,s)}{dx^2} = \frac{1}{\alpha_1}\left[s\bar{\theta}_1(x,s) - 1\right] \quad \text{in } 0 < x < L \quad (8\text{-}103a)$$

$$\frac{d^2\bar{\theta}_2(x,s)}{dx^2} = \frac{1}{\alpha_2}s\bar{\theta}_2(x,s) \quad \text{in } x > L \quad (8\text{-}103b)$$

The Laplace transform of the boundary conditions gives

$$\frac{d\bar{\theta}_1}{dx} = 0 \qquad \text{at } x = 0 \quad (8\text{-}104a)$$

$$\bar{\theta}_1 = \bar{\theta}_2 \qquad \text{at } x = L \quad (8\text{-}104b)$$

$$k_1 \frac{d\bar{\theta}_1}{dx} = k_2 \frac{d\bar{\theta}_2}{dx} \qquad \text{at } x = L \quad (8\text{-}104c)$$

$$\bar{\theta}_2 \to 0 \qquad \text{as } x \to \infty \quad (8\text{-}104d)$$

The solution of equation (8-103a) that satisfies the boundary condition (8-104a) is taken in the form

$$\bar{\theta}_1(x,s) = \frac{1}{s} + A\cosh\left(x\sqrt{\frac{s}{\alpha_1}}\right) \quad \text{in } 0 \le x < L \quad (8\text{-}105a)$$

and the solution of equation (8-103b) satisfying the boundary condition (8-104d) as

$$\bar{\theta}_2(x,s) = Be^{-x(\sqrt{s/\alpha_2})} \quad \text{in } x > L \quad (8\text{-}105b)$$

The constants A and B are determined by the application of the remaining boundary conditions (8-104b, c); we find

$$A = -\frac{1-\gamma}{s}\frac{e^{-\sigma L}}{1 - \gamma e^{-2\sigma L}} \quad (8\text{-}106a)$$

$$B = \frac{1+\gamma}{2s}e^{\sigma\mu L}\frac{1 - e^{-2\sigma L}}{1 - \gamma e^{-2\sigma L}} \quad (8\text{-}106b)$$

where

$$\sigma \equiv \sqrt{\frac{s}{\alpha_1}}, \qquad \mu \equiv \sqrt{\frac{\alpha_1}{\alpha_2}} \quad (8\text{-}106c)$$

$$\gamma \equiv \frac{\beta - 1}{\beta + 1}, \qquad \beta \equiv \frac{k_1}{k_2}\frac{1}{\mu} \quad (8\text{-}106d)$$

Introducing equations (8-106) into (8-105) we obtain

$$\bar{\theta}_1(x,s) = \frac{1}{s} - \frac{1-\gamma}{2s} \frac{e^{-\sigma(L-x)} + e^{-\sigma(L+x)}}{1 - \gamma e^{-2\sigma L}}, \qquad \text{in } 0 < x < L \quad (8\text{-}107a)$$

$$\bar{\theta}_2(x,s) = \frac{1+\gamma}{2s} \frac{e^{-\sigma\mu(x-L)} - e^{-\sigma(2L+\mu x - \mu L)}}{1 - \gamma e^{-2\sigma L}}, \qquad x > L \quad (8\text{-}107b)$$

Here we note that $|\gamma| < 1$. Therefore, the term $[1 - \gamma \exp(-2\sigma L)]^{-1}$ can be expanded as a binomial series, and equations (8-107) become

$$\bar{\theta}_1(x,s) = \frac{1}{s} - \frac{1-\gamma}{2} \sum_{n=0}^{\infty} \gamma^n \left[\frac{e^{-\sigma[(2n+1)L-x]}}{s} + \frac{e^{-\sigma[(2n+1)L+x]}}{s} \right],$$

$$\text{in } 0 < x < L \quad (8\text{-}108a)$$

$$\bar{\theta}_2(x,s) = \frac{1+\gamma}{2} \sum_{n=0}^{\infty} \gamma^n \left[\frac{e^{-\sigma[2nL+\mu(x-L)]}}{s} - \frac{e^{-\sigma[(2n+2)L+\mu(x-L)]}}{s} \right],$$

$$\text{in } x > L \quad (8\text{-}108b)$$

The inversion of these transforms are available in the Laplace transform Table 7-1 as cases 1 and 42. After the inversion, the temperature distribution in the medium becomes

$$\theta_1(x,t) \equiv \frac{T_1(x,t)}{T_0} = 1 - \frac{1-\gamma}{2} \sum_{n=0}^{\infty} \gamma^n \left\{ \text{erfc}\left[\frac{(2n+1)L-x}{2\sqrt{\alpha_1 t}} \right] \right.$$

$$\left. + \text{erfc}\left[\frac{(2n+1)L-x}{2\sqrt{\alpha_1 t}} \right] \right\}, \quad \text{in } 0 < x < L \ (8\text{-}109a)$$

$$\theta_2(x,t) \equiv \frac{T_2(x,t)}{T_0} = \frac{1+\gamma}{2} \sum_{n=0}^{\infty} \gamma^n \left\{ \text{erfc}\left[\frac{2nL+\mu(x-L)}{2\sqrt{\alpha_1 t}} \right] \right.$$

$$\left. - \text{erfc}\left[\frac{(2n+2)L+\mu(x-L)}{2\sqrt{\alpha_1 t}} \right] \right\}, \qquad \text{in } x > L$$

$$(8\text{-}109b)$$

where γ and μ are defined by equations (8-106).

REFERENCES

1. V. Vodicka, *Schweizer Arch.* **10**, 297–304, 1950.
2. V. Vodicka, *Math. Nach.* **14**, 47–55, 1955.
3. P. E. Bulavin and V. M. Kascheev, *Int. Chem. Eng.* **1**, 112–115, 1965.
4. C. W. Tittle, *J. Appl. Phys.* **36**, 1486–1488, 1965.
5. C. W. Tittle and V. L. Robinson, Analytical Solution of Conduction Problems in Composite Media, ASME Paper 65-WA-HT-52, 1965.

6. H. L. Beach, The Application of the Orthogonal Expansion Technique to Conduction Heat Transfer Problems in Multilayer Cylinders, M. S. Thesis, Mech. and Aerospace Eng. Dept., N. C. State University, Releigh, N.C. 27607, 1967.

7. C. J. Moore, Heat Transfer Across Surfaces in Contact: Studies of Transients in One-Dimensional Composite Systems, Ph.D. Dissertation, Mechanical Eng. Dept., Southern Methodist University, Dallas, Texas, 1967.

8. M. N. Özışık, *Boundary Value Problems of Heat Conduction*, International Textbook Co., Scranton, Pa., 1968.

9. M. H. Cobble, *J. Franklin Inst.* **290** (5), 453–465, 1970.

10. G. P. Mulholland and M. N. Cobble, *Int. J. Heat Mass Transfer* **15**, 147–160, 1972.

11. C. A. Chase, D. Gidaspow, and R. E. Peck, Diffusion of Heat and Mass in Porous Medium with Bulk Flow: Part I. Solution by Green's Functions, Chem. Eng. Progr. Symposium Ser. No. 92 Vol. 65, 91–109, 1969.

12. B. S. Baker, D. Gidaspow, and D. Wasan, in *Advances in Electrochemistry and Electrochemical Engineering*, Wiley-Interscience, New York, 1971, pp. 63–156.

13. S. S. Sareen and D. Gidaspow, *Energy Conversion* **15**, 113–120, 1976.

14. J. Crank, *The Mathematics of Diffusion*, 2nd ed., Clarendon Press, London, 1975.

15. H. S. Carslaw and J. C. Jaeger, *Conduction of Heat in Solids*, Clarendon Press, London, 1959.

16. V. S. Arpaci, *Conduction Heat Transfer*, Addison-Wesley Publishing Co., Reading, Mass., 1966.

17. A. V. Luikov, *Analytical Heat Diffusion Theory*, Academic Press, New York, 1968.

18. N. Y. Ölçer, *Ingenieur-Arch.* **36**, 285–293, 1968.

19. N. Y. Ölçer, *Quart. Appl. Math.* **26**, 355–371, 1968.

20. N. Y. Ölçer, *Nucl. Eng. Design* **7**, 97–112, 1968.

21. Kanae Senda, A Family of Integral Transforms and Some Applications to Physical Problems, Technology Reports of the Osaka University, Osaka, Japan, No. 823, Vol. 18, 261–286, 1968.

22. J. D. Lockwood and G. P. Mulholland, *J. Heat Transfer* **95c**, 487–491, 1973.

23. M. D. Mikhailov, *Int. J. Eng. Sci.* **11**, 235–241, 1973.

24. M. D. Mikhailov, *Int. J. Heat Mass Transfer* **16**, 2155–2164, 1973.

25. Y. Yener and M. N. Özışık, *Proceedings of the 5th International Heat Transfer Conference*, Tokyo, Sept. 1974.

26. J. Padovan, *AIAA J.* **12**, 1158–1160, 1974.

27. T. R. Goodman, The Adjoint Heat-Conduction Problems for Solids, ASTIA-AD 254-769, (AFOSR-520), April 1961.

PROBLEMS

8-1 A two-layer solid cylinder contains the inner region, $0 \leq r \leq a$, and the outer region, $a \leq r \leq b$, which are in perfect thermal contact. Initially, the inner region is at temperature $F_1(r)$ and the outer region at temperature $F_2(r)$. For times $t > 0$, the boundary surface at $r = b$ is kept at zero temperature. Obtain an expression for the temperature distribution in the medium. Also, express the solution in terms of Green's function and determine the Green's function for this problem.

8-2   A two-layer slab consists of the first layer $0 \leq x \leq a$ and the second layer $a \leq x \leq b$, which are in perfect thermal contact. Initially, the first region is at temperature $F_1(x)$ and the second region is at temperature $F_2(x)$. For times $t > 0$, the outer boundaries at $x = 0$ and $x = b$ are kept at zero temperatures. Obtain an expression for the temperature distribution in the medium. Also determine the Green's function for this problem.

8-3   A two-layer hollow sphere consists of the first layer $a \leq r \leq b$ and the second layer $b \leq r \leq c$, which are in perfect thermal contact. Initially the first region is at temperature $F_1(r)$ and the second region at temperature $F_2(r)$. For times $t > 0$, the outer boundaries at $r = a$ and $r = c$ are kept at zero temperature. Obtain an expression for the temperature distribution in the medium. Also, determine the Green's function for this problem.

8-4   Repeat Problem (8-2) for the case when boundary surface at $x = 0$ is kept insulated and the boundary surface at $x = b$ dissipates heat by convection into an environment at zero temperature. Also determine the Green's function for this problem.

8-5   Repeat Problem (8-3) for the case when the boundary surface at $r = a$ is kept insulated and the boundary surface at $r = c$ dissipates heat by convection into an environment at zero temperature. Also determine the Green's function for this problem.

8-6   A two-layer solid cylinder contains the inner region, $0 \leq r \leq a$, and the outer region, $a \leq r \leq b$, which are in perfect thermal contact. Initially the inner region is at temperature $F_1(r)$, the outer region at temperature $F_2(r)$. For times $t > 0$, heat is generated in the inner region at a rate of $g_1(r, t)$ W/m^3 while the boundary surface at $r = b$ is kept at temperature $f(t)$. By following an approach discussed in Example 8-4, transform this problem into a one with homogeneous boundary condition at $r = b$.

8-7   A two-layer slab consists of the first layer $0 \leq x \leq a$ and the second layer $a \leq x \leq b$, which are in perfect thermal contact. Initially the first region is at temperature $F_1(x)$ and the second region at temperature $F_2(x)$. For times $t > 0$, heat is generated in the first region at a rate of $g_1(x, t)$, W/m^3, and in the second region at a rate of $g_2(x, t)$, W/m^3, while the outer boundary surfaces at $x = 0$ and $x = b$ are kept at temperatures $f_1(t)$ and $f_2(t)$ respectively. Split up this problem into a steady-state problem and a time dependent problem with heat generation, subject to homogeneous boundary conditions by following the procedure discussed in Section 8-3.

8-8   Solve Problem (8-1) with the additional condition that heat is generated in the inner region, $0 \leq r \leq a$, at a rate of $g_1(r, t)$, W/m^3. Utilize the Green's function constructed in Problem (8-1) to solve this nonhomogeneous problem.

8-9   Solve Problem (8-2) with the additional condition that heat is generated in the first and second layers at a rate of $g_1(x, t)$ and $g_2(x, t)$, W/m^3

respectively. Utilize the Green's function constructed in Problem (8-2) to solve this problem.

8-10 Solve Problem (8-3) with the additional condition that heat is generated in the first and second regions at a rate of $g_1(r, t)$ and $g_2(r, t)$, W/m^3, respectively.

NOTES

1. A proof of the orthogonality relation given by equations (8-9) is as follows: Equations (8-7) are written for two different eigenfunctions ψ_{in} and ψ_{ir} as

$$\frac{1}{x^p}\frac{d}{dx}\left(x^p\frac{d\psi_{in}}{dx}\right) + \frac{\beta_n^2}{\alpha_i}\psi_{in} = 0 \qquad \text{in } x_i < x < x_{i+1} \tag{1}$$

$$\frac{1}{x^p}\frac{d}{dx}\left(x^p\frac{d\psi_{ir}}{dx}\right) + \frac{\beta_r^2}{\alpha_i}\psi_{ir} = 0 \qquad \begin{array}{l}\text{in } x_i < x < x_{i+1} \\ \text{for } i = 1, 2, \ldots, M\end{array} \tag{2}$$

The first equation is multiplied by ψ_{ir}, the second by ψ_{in} and the results are subtracted

$$\frac{1}{\alpha_i}(\beta_n^2 - \beta_r^2)\psi_{in}\psi_{ir} = \frac{1}{x^p}\left[\psi_{in}\frac{d}{dx}\left(x^p\frac{d\psi_{ir}}{dx}\right) - \psi_{ir}\frac{d}{dx}\left(x^p\frac{d\psi_{in}}{dx}\right)\right] \tag{3}$$

Both sides of this equation are multiplied by x^p and the result is integrated from $x = x_i$ to $x = x_{i+1}$ (i.e., over the region i)

$$\frac{1}{\alpha_i}(\beta_n^2 - \beta_r^2)\int_{x_i}^{x_{i+1}} x^p\psi_{in}\psi_{ir}\,dx = \int_{x_i}^{x_{i+1}}\left[\psi_{in}\frac{d}{dx}\left(x^p\frac{d\psi_{ir}}{dx}\right) - \psi_{ir}\frac{d}{dx}\left(x^p\frac{d\psi_{in}}{dx}\right)\right]dx \tag{4}$$

To evaluate the integral on the right-hand side we consider the following identity

$$\psi_{in}\frac{d}{dx}\left(x^p\frac{d\psi_{ir}}{dx}\right) - \psi_{ir}\frac{d}{dx}\left(x^p\frac{d\psi_{in}}{dx}\right) = \frac{d}{dx}\left[\psi_{in}x^p\frac{d\psi_{ir}}{dx} - \psi_{ir}x^p\frac{d\psi_{in}}{dx}\right] \tag{5}$$

The validity of this identity can readily be verified by differentiating the right-hand side of equation (5).

Clearly, the left-hand side of equation (5) is exactly the same as the integrand on the right-hand side of equation (4). When equation (5) is introduced into equation (4) and the integration is performed we obtain

$$\frac{1}{\alpha_i}(\beta_n^2 - \beta_r^2)\int_{x_i}^{x_{i+1}} x^p\psi_{in}\psi_{ir}\,dx = \left[x^p\left(\psi_{in}\frac{d\psi_{ir}}{dx} - \psi_{ir}\frac{d\psi_{in}}{dx}\right)\right]\Big|_{x=x_i}^{x=x_{i+1}} \tag{6}$$

Both sides of this equation are multiplied by k_i and the result is summed up over $i = 1$ to $i = M$ (i.e., over all regions). We obtain

$$(\beta_n^2 - \beta_r^2) \sum_{i=1}^{M} \frac{k_i}{\alpha_i} \int_{x_i}^{x_{i+1}} x^p \psi_{in} \psi_{ir}\, dx = \sum_{i=1}^{M} [x^p B_i]_{x=x_i}^{x_{i+1}} \equiv J \tag{7a}$$

where

$$B_i \equiv k_i \left(\psi_{in} \frac{d\psi_{ir}}{dx} - \psi_{ir} \frac{d\psi_{in}}{dx} \right) \tag{7b}$$

It will now be shown that the summation term on the right-hand side of equation (7a) vanishes. To prove this, we consider the boundary conditions at the interfaces given by equations (8-8b) and (8-8c) as

$$\left. \begin{aligned} -k_i \frac{d\psi_{in}}{dx} &= h_{i+1}(\psi_{in} - \psi_{i+1,n}) \\[2mm] k_i \frac{d\psi_{in}}{dx} &= k_{i+1} \frac{d\psi_{i+1,n}}{dx} \end{aligned} \right\} \quad \begin{aligned} &\text{at the interfaces} \tag{8a} \\[4mm] &x = x_{i+1}, \\ &i = 1, 2, \ldots, M-1 \tag{8b} \end{aligned}$$

We also write these equations for the different eigenfunctions as

$$\left. \begin{aligned} -k_i \frac{d\psi_{ir}}{dx} &= h_{i+1}(\psi_{ir} - \psi_{i+1,r}) \\[2mm] k_i \frac{d\psi_{ir}}{dx} &= k_{i+1} \frac{d\psi_{i+1,r}}{dx} \end{aligned} \right\} \quad \begin{aligned} &\text{at the interfaces} \tag{9a} \\[4mm] &x = x_i + 1, \\ &i = 1, 2, \ldots, M-1 \tag{9b} \end{aligned}$$

Equation (8b) is multiplied by ψ_{ir}, equation (9b) by ψ_{in} and the results are subtracted. We obtain

$$k_i \left(\psi_{in} \frac{d\psi_{ir}}{dx} - \psi_{ir} \frac{d\psi_{in}}{dx} \right) = k_{i+1} \left(\psi_{in} \frac{d\psi_{i+1,r}}{dx} - \psi_{ir} \frac{d\psi_{i+1,n}}{dx} \right)$$
$$\text{at } x = x_{i+1}, \quad i = 1, 2, \ldots, M-1 \tag{10}$$

From the boundary conditions (8a) and (8b) we write

$$\psi_{in} = \psi_{i+1,n} - \frac{k_{i+1}}{h_{i+1}} \frac{d\psi_{i+1,n}}{dx} \tag{11a}$$

and from the boundary conditions (9a) and (9b) we obtain

$$\psi_{ir} = \psi_{i+1,r} - \frac{k_{i+1}}{h_{i+1}} \frac{d\psi_{i+1,r}}{dx} \tag{11b}$$

We now introduce ψ_{in} and ψ_{ir} from equations (11) into the right-hand side of equation (10) and obtain

$$k_i\left(\psi_{in}\frac{d\psi_{ir}}{dx} - \psi_{ir}\frac{d\psi_{in}}{dx}\right) = k_{i+1}\left(\psi_{i+1,n}\frac{d\psi_{i+1,r}}{dx} - \psi_{i+1,r}\frac{d\psi_{i+1,n}}{dx}\right)$$

at $x = x_{i+1}$, $i = 1, 2, ..., M - 1$ (12)

In view of the definition of B_i given by equation (7b), equation (12) is written more compactly as

$$B_i = B_{i+1} \qquad \text{at } x = x_{i+1}, \; i = 1, 2, ..., M - 1 \qquad (13)$$

We now consider the summation on the right-hand side of equation (7a) as

$$J \equiv \sum_{i=1}^{M} [x^p B_i]_{x=x_i}^{x_{i+1}} \qquad (14a)$$

When this summation is expanded and the result given by equation (13) is utilized we note that all the intermediate terms cancel out and the summation reduces to

$$J \equiv -x_1^p [B_1]_{x_1} + x_{M+1}^p [B_M]_{x_{M+1}} \qquad (14b)$$

or

$$J \equiv -x_1^p k_1\left(\psi_{1n}\frac{d\psi_{1r}}{dx} - \psi_{1r}\frac{d\psi_{1n}}{dx}\right) + x_{M+1}^p k_M\left(\psi_{Mn}\frac{d\psi_{Mr}}{dx} - \psi_{Mr}\frac{d\psi_{Mn}}{dx}\right) \qquad (14c)$$

To show that J vanishes, we consider the boundary conditions at the outer surfaces given by equations (8-8a) and (8-8d)

$$-k_1^*\frac{d\psi_{1n}}{dx} + h_1\psi_{1n} = 0 \qquad \text{at } x = x_1 \qquad (15a)$$

$$k_M^*\frac{d\psi_{Mn}}{dx} + h_{M+1}\psi_{Mn} = 0 \qquad \text{at } x = x_M \qquad (15b)$$

we write these equations for ψ_{1r} and ψ_{Mr} as

$$-k_1^*\frac{d\psi_{1r}}{dx} + h_1\psi_{1r} = 0 \qquad \text{at } x = x_1 \qquad (16a)$$

$$k_M^*\frac{d\psi_{Mr}}{dx} + h_{M+1}\psi_{Mr} = 0 \qquad \text{at } x = x_M \qquad (16b)$$

We multiply (15a) by ψ_{1r} and (16a) by ψ_{1n} and subtract

$$k_1^*\left[\psi_{1n}\frac{d\psi_{1r}}{dx} - \psi_{1r}\frac{d\psi_{1n}}{dx}\right] = 0 \qquad (17a)$$

Similarly, we multiply (15b) by ψ_{Mr} and (16b) by ψ_{Mn} and subtract

$$k_M^* \left[\psi_{Mn} \frac{d\psi_{Mr}}{dx} - \psi_{Mr} \frac{d\psi_{Mn}}{dx} \right] = 0 \tag{17b}$$

In view of equations (17) we conclude that the right-hand side of (14b) vanishes, that is

$$J = 0 \tag{18}$$

Then equation (7a) reduces to

$$(\beta_n^2 - \beta_r^2) \sum_{i=1}^{M} \frac{k_i}{\alpha_i} \int_{x_i}^{x_{i+1}} x^p \psi_{in} \psi_{ir}\, dx = 0 \tag{19}$$

or this result leads to the orthogonality relation given by equations (8-9), that is

$$\sum_{i=1}^{M} \frac{k_i}{\alpha_i} \int_{x_i}^{x_{i+1}} x^p \psi_{in} \psi_{ir}\, dx = \begin{cases} 0 & \text{for } n \neq r \\ N_n & \text{for } n = r \end{cases} \tag{20a}$$

where

$$N_n \equiv \sum_{i=1}^{M} \frac{k_i}{\alpha_i} \int_{x_i}^{x_{i+1}} x^p \psi_{in}^2\, dx \tag{20b}$$

CHAPTER 9

APPROXIMATE ANALYTIC METHODS

In the previous chapters we examined various analytic methods of solution of heat-conduction problems for simple geometries where the differential equation and the boundary conditions were linear. The nonlinear problems can be solved exactly only for a limited number of special cases. Also, when the geometries are complicated the exact analysis is not applicable. Therefore, approximate analytic solutions are useful when exact analytic solutions are too difficult or impossible to obtain or when the numerical solution of the problem cannot be justified. Furthermore, an analytic solution provides a better insight to the physical significance of various parameters effecting a given problem than a purely numerical solution. Therefore, various approximate methods of analysis have been developed to solve heat-conduction problems. In this chapter we present the *integral method*, the variational formulation leading to the *Rayleigh-Ritz method*, the *Galerkin method*, and the method of *partial integration*. The accuracy of an approximate solution cannot be assessed unless the results are compared with the exact solution. Therefore, in order to give some idea of the accuracy of the approximate analysis, simple problems for which exact solutions are available are first solved with the approximate methods and the results are compared with the exact solutions. The applications to the solution of more complicated, nonlinear problems are then considered.

9-1 THE INTEGRAL METHOD—BASIC CONCEPTS

The use of integral method for the solution of partial differential equations dates back to von Kármán and Pohlhausen, who applied the method for the approximate analysis of boundary-layer momentum and energy equations of fluid mechanics [1]. Landahl [2] used it in the field of biophysics to solve the diffusion equation in connection with the spread of a concentrate.

Merk [3] applied this approach to solve a two-dimensional steady-state melting problem and Goodman [4–5] used it for the solution of a one-dimensional transient melting problem. Since then, this method has been applied in the solution of various types of one-dimensional transient heat-conduction problems [6–16], melting and solidification problems [16–25], and heat and momentum transfer problems involving melting of ice in seawater, melting and extrusion of polymers [26–29].

The method is simple, straightforward and easily applicable to both linear and nonlinear one-dimensional transient boundary value problems of heat conduction for certain boundary conditions. The results are approximate, but several solutions obtained with this method when compared with the exact solutions have confirmed that the accuracy is generally acceptable for many engineering applications. In this section we first present the basic concepts involved in the application of this method by solving a simple transient heat-conduction problem for a semi-infinite medium. The method is then applied to the solution of various one-dimensional, time-dependent heat-conduction problems. The application to the solution of melting, solidification, and ablation problems is considered in a later chapter on moving boundary problems.

When the differential equation of heat conduction is solved exactly in a given region subject to specified boundary and initial conditions, the resulting solution is satisfied at each point over the considered region; but with the integral method the solution is satisfied only on the average over the region. We now summarize the basic steps in the analysis with the integral method when it is applied to the solution of one-dimensional, transient heat-conduction problem in a semi-infinite medium subject to some prescribed boundary and uniform initial conditions but no heat generation.

1. The differential equation of heat conduction is integrated over a phenomenologic distance $\delta(t)$, called the *thermal layer*, to remove from the differential equation the derivative with respect to the space variable. The thermal layer is defined as the distance beyond which, for practical purposes, there is no heat flow; hence the initial temperature distribution remains uneffected beyond $\delta(t)$. The resulting equation is called the *energy integral equation* (i.e., it is also called the *heat-balance integral*).

2. A suitable profile is chosen for the temperature distribution over the thermal layer. A polynomial profile is generally preferred for this purpose; experience has shown that there is no significant improvement in the accuracy of the solution to choose a polynomial greater than the fourth degree. The coefficients in the polynomial are determined in terms of the thermal layer thickness $\delta(t)$ by utilizing the actual (if necessary some derived) boundary conditions.

3. When the temperature profile thus obtained is introduced into the energy integral equation and the indicated operations are performed, an ordinary differential equation is obtained for the thermal layer thickness $\delta(t)$ with time as the independent variable. The solution of this differential equation subject to the appropriate initial condition [i.e., in this case $\delta(t) = 0$ for $t = 0$] gives $\delta(t)$ as a function of time.

4. Once $\delta(t)$ is known from step 3, the temperature distribution $T(x,t)$ is known as a function of time and position in the medium.

To illustrate the application of the above procedure, we consider a transient heat-conduction problem in a semi-infinite medium $x > 0$, initially at a uniform temperature T_i and for times $t > 0$ the boundary surface is kept at constant temperature T_0 as illustrated in Fig. 9-1. The mathematical formulation of this problem is given as

$$\frac{\partial^2 T(x,t)}{\partial x^2} = \frac{1}{\alpha}\frac{\partial T(x,t)}{\partial t} \qquad \text{in } x > 0,\ t > 0 \tag{9-1a}$$

$$T(x,t) = T_0 \qquad \text{at } x = 0,\ t > 0 \tag{9-1b}$$

$$T(x,t) = T_i \qquad \text{for } t = 0,\ \text{in } x \geq 0 \tag{9-1c}$$

We now solve this problem with the integral method by following the basic steps discussed above.

1. We integrate equation (9-1a) with respect to the space variable from $x = 0$ to $x = \delta(t)$.

$$\left.\frac{\partial T}{\partial x}\right|_{x=\delta(t)} - \left.\frac{\partial T}{\partial x}\right|_{x=0} = \frac{1}{\alpha}\int_{x=0}^{\delta(t)}\frac{\partial T}{\partial t}\,dx \tag{9-2a}$$

when the integral on the right-hand side is performed by the rule of differen-

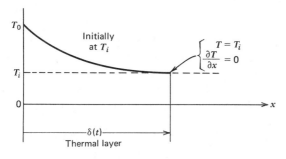

Fig. 9-1 Definition of thermal layer for heat conduction in a semi-infinite region.

tiation under the integral sign we obtain

$$\left.\frac{\partial T}{\partial x}\right|_{x=\delta} - \left.\frac{\partial T}{\partial x}\right|_{x=0} = \frac{1}{\alpha}\left[\frac{d}{dt}\left(\int_{x=0}^{\delta} T\,dx\right) - T\left.\right|_{x=\delta}\frac{d\delta}{dt}\right] \tag{9-2b}$$

By the definition of thermal layer as illustrated in Fig. 9-1 we have

$$\left.\frac{\partial T}{\partial x}\right|_{x=\delta} = 0 \quad \text{and} \quad T\left.\right|_{x=\delta} = T_i \tag{9-3a}$$

and for convenience in the analysis we define

$$\theta \equiv \int_{x=0}^{\delta(t)} T(x,t)\,dx \tag{9-3b}$$

Introducing equations (9-3) into (9-2b) we obtain

$$-\alpha\left.\frac{\partial T}{\partial x}\right|_{x=0} = \frac{d}{dt}(\theta - T_i\delta) \tag{9-4}$$

which is called the *energy integral equation* for the problem considered here.

2. We choose a cubic-polynomial representation for $T(x,t)$ in the form

$$T(x,t) = a + bx + cx^2 + dx^3 \quad \text{in } 0 \le x \le \delta(t) \tag{9-5}$$

where the coefficients are in general functions of time. Four conditions are needed to determine these four coefficients in terms of $\delta(t)$. Three of these conditions are obtained from the boundary conditions at $x = 0$ and at the edge of the thermal layer $x = \delta(t)$, as

$$T\left.\right|_{x=0} = T_0, \quad T\left.\right|_{x=\delta} = T_i, \quad \left.\frac{\partial T}{\partial x}\right|_{x=\delta} = 0 \tag{9-6a}$$

The fourth condition may be derived by evaluating the differential equation (9-1a) at $x = 0$ and by making use of the fact that $T = T_0 = $ constant at $x = 0$; then the derivative of temperature with respect to the time vanishes at $x = 0$ and we obtain

$$\left.\frac{\partial^2 T}{\partial x^2}\right|_{x=0} = 0 \tag{9-6b}$$

Clearly, the fourth condition could also be derived by evaluating the differential equation (9-1a) at $x = \delta(t)$ and utilizing the fact that $T = T_i = $ constant, by definition, at $x = \delta$. This matter will be discussed later in the analysis.

The application of the four conditions (9-6) to equation (9-5) yields the temperature profile in the form

$$\frac{T(x,t) - T_i}{T_0 - T_i} = 1 - \frac{3}{2}\frac{x}{\delta} + \frac{1}{2}\left(\frac{x}{\delta}\right)^3 \tag{9-7}$$

3. When the temperature profile (9-7) is introduced into the energy integral equation (9-4) and the indicated operations are performed, we obtain the following ordinary differential equation for $\delta(t)$

$$4\alpha = \delta \frac{d\delta}{dt} \qquad \text{for } t > 0 \qquad (9\text{-}8a)$$

subject to

$$\delta = 0 \qquad \text{for } t = 0 \qquad (9\text{-}8b)$$

The solution of equations (9-8) gives

$$\delta = \sqrt{8\alpha t} \qquad (9\text{-}9)$$

4. Knowing $\delta(t)$, the temperature distribution $T(x, t)$ is determined according to equation (9-7) and we obtain

$$\frac{T(x, t) - T_i}{T_0 - T_i} = 1 - \frac{3}{2}\frac{x}{\delta} + \frac{1}{2}\left(\frac{x}{\delta}\right)^3 \qquad (9\text{-}10a)$$

where

$$\delta = \sqrt{8\alpha t} \qquad (9\text{-}10b)$$

Solution With Other Profiles

In the foregoing analysis we used a cubic polynomial representation for $T(x, t)$ and utilized the condition at $x = 0$ to obtain the fourth condition (9-6b). If we utilize fact that $T = T_i = $ constant at $x = \delta$, the fourth condition is derived from the differential equation (9-1a) as

$$\left. \frac{\partial^2 T}{\partial x^2} \right|_{x = \delta} = 0 \qquad (9\text{-}6b^*)$$

If the conditions (9-6a) are used together with the condition (9-6b*) in the cubic profile (9-5) and the problem is solved by the same procedure discussed above, the resulting temperature profile becomes

$$\frac{T(x, t) - T_i}{T_0 - T_i} = \left(1 - \frac{x}{\delta}\right)^3 \qquad (9\text{-}11a)$$

where

$$\delta = \sqrt{24\alpha t} \qquad (9\text{-}11b)$$

If a fourth-degree polynomial representation is used for $T(x, t)$, the resulting five coefficients are determined by the application of the five conditions given by equations (9-6a), (9-6b), and (9-6b*), and the problem is solved in in a similar manner, the following temperature profile is obtained

$$\frac{T(x,t) - T_i}{T_0 - T_i} = 1 - 2\left(\frac{x}{\delta}\right) + 2\left(\frac{x}{\delta}\right)^3 - \left(\frac{x}{\delta}\right)^4 \qquad (9\text{-}12\text{a})$$

where

$$\delta = \sqrt{\frac{40}{3}\alpha t} \qquad (9\text{-}12\text{b})$$

Comparison With Exact Solution

Three different approximate solutions, given by equations (9-10) to (9-12) are obtained for the heat-conduction problem defined by equations (9-1). One can also obtain another approximate solution by utilizing a second-degree polynomial representation. The question regarding which one of these approximate solutions is more accurate cannot be answered until each of these solutions are compared with the exact solution of the same problem given by

$$\frac{T(x,t) - T_i}{T_0 - T_i} = 1 - \operatorname{erf}\frac{x}{\sqrt{4\alpha t}} \qquad (9\text{-}13)$$

Figure 9-2 shows a comparison of these approximate temperature distri-

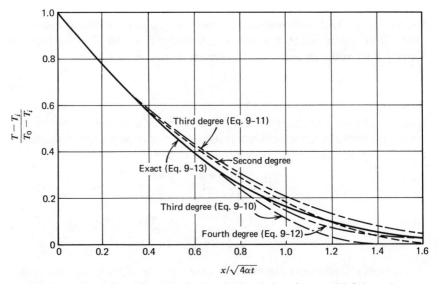

Fig. 9-2 Comparison of exact and approximate solutions for a semi-infinite region.

Table 9-1 Error Involved in the Surface Heat Flux

Temperature Profile	C as Defined by Eq. (9-14)	Percent Error Involved
Exact (Eq. 9-13)	$\dfrac{1}{\sqrt{\pi}} = 0.565$	0
Cubic approximation (Eq. 9-10)	$\dfrac{3}{2\sqrt{8}} = 0.530$	6
Cubic approximation (Eq. 9-11)	$\dfrac{3}{\sqrt{24}} = 0.612$	8
Fourth-degree approximation (Eq. 9-12)	$\dfrac{2}{\sqrt{\dfrac{40}{3}}} = 0.548$	3

butions with the exact solution. The agreement is better for small values of the parameter $x/\sqrt{4\alpha t}$. The fourth-degree polynomial approximation agrees better with the exact solution. The cubic polynomial representation utilizing the condition at $x = 0$ seems to agree with the exact solution better than the one utilizing the condition at $x = \delta$.

The heat flux at the boundary surface $x = 0$ is a quantity of practical interest and for the various temperature profiles considered above it may be expressed in the form

$$q(t) = -k\frac{\partial T}{\partial x}\bigg|_{x=0} = C\frac{k(T_0 - T_i)}{\sqrt{\alpha t}} \qquad (9\text{-}14)$$

Table 9-1 gives the values of the constant C as calculated from the above exact and approximate solutions. The fourth-degree polynomial approxima- tion represents the heat flux with an error of approximately 3%, which is acceptable for most engineering applications.

9-2 THE INTEGRAL METHOD—VARIOUS APPLICATIONS

Having presented the basic steps involved in the solution of transient heat- conduction problem with the integral method and given some idea about its accuracy, we now discuss its application in the solution of different types of problems.

Cylindrical and Spherical Symmetry

The use of polynomial representation for temperature, although it gives reasonably good results in the rectangular coordinate system, will yield significant error in the problems of cylindrical and spherical symmetry [11]. This is to be expected since the volume into which the heat diffuses does not remain the same for equal increments of r in the cylindrical and spherical coordinate systems. This situation may be remedied by modifying the temperature profiles as

$$\text{Cylindrical Symmetry:} \qquad T(r,t) = (\text{Polynomial in } r)(\ln r) \qquad (9\text{-}15a)$$

$$\text{Spherical Symmetry:} \qquad T(r,t) = \frac{\text{Polynomial in } r}{r} \qquad (9\text{-}15b)$$

Since the problems with spherical symmetry can always be transformed into a problem in the rectangular coordinate system as discussed in Chapter 4, one needs to be concerned with such a modification only for the cylindrical symmetry. The importance of this matter is illustrated with the following example.

Example 9-1. A region exterior to a cylindrical hole of radius $r = b$ is initially at zero temperature. For times $t > 0$, the boundary surface at $r = b$ exposed to a constant heat flux. Obtain an expression for the temperature distribution $T(r,t)$ in the region for times $t > 0$ using the integral method.

Solution. The mathematical formulation of this problem is given as

$$\frac{1}{r}\frac{\partial}{\partial r}\left(r\frac{\partial T}{\partial r}\right) = \frac{1}{\alpha}\frac{\partial T}{\partial t} \qquad \text{in } b < r < \infty, \ t > 0 \qquad (9\text{-}16a)$$

$$-k\frac{\partial T}{\partial r} = f \qquad \text{at } r = b, \ t > 0 \qquad (9\text{-}16b)$$

$$T = 0 \qquad \text{for } t = 0, \ r \geq b \qquad (9\text{-}16c)$$

Figure 9-3 shows the geometry and the thermal-layer thickness $\delta(t)$. The integration of equation (9-16a) over the thermal layer $\delta(t)$ is equivalent to operating on both sides of this equation by the operator

$$\int_{b}^{b+\delta} r\, dr$$

After performing this integration and applying the conditions

$$\frac{\partial T}{\partial r} = 0 \qquad \text{and} \qquad T = 0 \qquad \text{at } r = b + \delta \qquad (9\text{-}17)$$

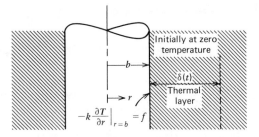

Fig. 9-3   Thermal layer $\delta(t)$ for the region exterior to a cylindrical hole of radius $r = b$.

the following energy-integral equation is obtained

$$-\left[r\frac{\partial T}{\partial r} \right]_{r=b} = \frac{1}{\alpha}\frac{\partial \theta}{\partial t} \tag{9-18a}$$

where

$$\theta \equiv \int_{b}^{b+\delta(t)} rT\,dr \tag{9-18b}$$

The next step in the analysis is to choose a suitable profile for the temperature $T(r,t)$ within the thermal layer. A second degree polynomial in r multiplied by $\ln r$ is taken as

$$T(r,t) = (a_1 + a_2 r + a_3 r^2)\cdot\ln r \qquad \text{in } b \le r \le (b + \delta) \tag{9-19}$$

The coefficients $a_1, a_2,$ and a_3 are determined by the application of the conditions (9-16b) and (9-17); then the following temperature profile is obtained

$$T(r,t) = -\frac{\dfrac{fb}{k}}{\dfrac{\delta}{b}}\left(1 + \frac{\delta}{b} - \frac{r}{b} \right)^2 \frac{1}{\dfrac{\delta}{b} + 2\ln\left(1 + \dfrac{\delta}{b} \right)}\ln\left(\dfrac{\dfrac{r}{b}}{1 + \dfrac{\delta}{b}} \right) \tag{9-20}$$

The substitution of this expression into the energy-integral equation (9-18) and solving the resulting differential equation gives the thermal layer thickness $\delta(t)$

$$\frac{\alpha t}{b^2} = -\frac{(72\eta^2 - 96\eta + 36)\ln\eta - 13\eta^4 + 36\eta^2 - 32\eta + 9}{144(\eta - 1)\cdot(2\ln\eta + \eta - 1)} \tag{9-21a}$$

where

$$\eta = 1 + \frac{\delta}{b} \tag{9-21b}$$

The surface temperature at $r = b$ is obtained by setting $r = b$ in equation (9-20)

$$T(r,t)\bigg|_{r=b} = \frac{fb}{k}\left(\frac{\delta}{b}\right)\frac{1}{\dfrac{\delta}{b} + 2\ln\left(1 + \dfrac{\delta}{b}\right)}\ln\left(1 + \frac{\delta}{b}\right) \qquad (9\text{-}22)$$

Thus, equation (9-20) together with equation (9-21) gives the temperature distribution in the medium; and equation (9-22) together with (9-21) gives the surface temperature at $r = b$.

If a second-degree polynomial representation without a logarithmic term is used, i.e.,

$$T(r,t) = a_1 + a_2 r + a_3 r^2 \qquad \text{in } b \le r \le (b + \delta) \qquad (9\text{-}23)$$

the application of the conditions (9-16b) and (9-17) yields the temperature profile as

$$T(r,t) = \frac{1}{2}\frac{fb/k}{\delta/b}\left(1 + \frac{\delta}{b} - \frac{r}{b}\right)^2 \qquad \text{in } b \le r \le (b + \delta) \qquad (9\text{-}24)$$

The substitution of this profile into the energy-integral equation (9-18) gives the following differential equation for $\delta(t)$

$$\frac{d}{dt}(\delta^3 + 4b\delta^2) = 24\alpha b \qquad \text{for } t > 0 \qquad (9\text{-}25a)$$

subject to

$$\delta = 0 \qquad \text{for } t = 0 \qquad (9\text{-}25b)$$

The solution of this equation results in the following relation for the thickness of the thermal layer

$$\left(\frac{\delta}{b}\right)^3 + 4\left(\frac{\delta}{b}\right)^2 = \frac{24\alpha}{b^2}t \qquad (9\text{-}26)$$

The surface temperature at $r = b$ is obtained by setting $r = b$ in equation (9-24)

$$T(r,t)\bigg|_{r=b} = \frac{f}{2k}\delta \qquad (9\text{-}27)$$

where δ is given by equation (9-26).

Figure 9-4 shows a comparison of the surface temperature $T(r,t)\big|_{r=b} \equiv T_s$ obtained from equations (9-22) and (9-27) with the exact solution of the same problem. Clearly, the solution based on the simple polynomial representation of temperature is in poor agreement with the exact solution, whereas the one base on the polynomial representation modified by the logarithmic term is in good agreement.

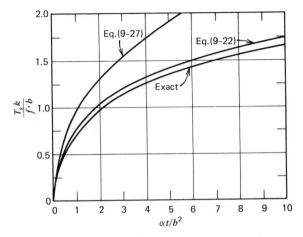

Fig. 9-4 A comparison of exact and approximate solutions for the surface temperature for the region exterior to a cylindrical hole of radius $r = b$. (From Lardner and Pohle [11].)

Problems with Heat Generation

The integral method is also applicable to the solution one-dimensional transient heat conduction in a semi-infinite medium subject to some prescribed boundary and uniform initial condition, with uniform or time-dependent heat generation in the medium. We illustrate the application with the following example.

Example 9-2. A semi-infinite region, $x > 0$, is initially at a constant temperature T_i. For times $t > 0$ heat is generated within the solid at a rate of $g(t)$ W/m³ (i.e., Btu/hr ft³) while the boundary at $x = 0$ is kept at a constant temperature T_0. Obtain an expression for the temperature distribution $T(x, t)$ in the medium using the integral method.

Solution. The mathematical formulation of this problem is given as

$$\alpha \frac{\partial^2 T}{\partial x^2} + \frac{\alpha}{k} g(t) = \frac{\partial T}{\partial t} \qquad \text{in } x > 0, \ t > 0 \qquad (9\text{-}28\text{a})$$

$$T = T_0 \qquad \text{at } x = 0, \ t > 0 \qquad (9\text{-}28\text{b})$$

$$T = T_i \qquad \text{for } t = 0, \ x \geq 0 \qquad (9\text{-}28\text{c})$$

The integration of equation (9-28a) from $x = 0$ to $x = \delta(t)$ gives

$$-\alpha \frac{\partial T}{\partial x}\bigg|_{x=0} + \frac{\alpha}{k} g(t)\delta(t) = \frac{d\theta}{dt} - T\bigg|_{x=\delta} \frac{d\delta}{dt} \qquad (9\text{-}29)$$

where we utilized the condition $dT/dx = 0$ at $x = \delta$, and defined

$$\theta \equiv \int\limits_{x=0}^{\delta(t)} T(x,t)\,dx \qquad (9\text{-}30)$$

We note that equation (9-29) is similar to equation (9-2b) except for the generation term. The term $T\big|_{x=\delta}$ is now determined by evaluating the differential equation (9-28a) at $x = \delta(t)$ where $\partial T/\partial x = 0$, and then integrating the resulting ordinary differential equation from $t = 0$ to t subject to the condition $T = T_i$ for $t = 0$. We find

$$T\big|_{x=\delta} = T_i + \frac{\alpha}{k}G(t) \qquad (9\text{-}31\text{a})$$

where we defined

$$G(t) \equiv \int\limits_0^t g(t')\,dt' \qquad (9\text{-}31\text{b})$$

We also note that the term $g(t)\,\delta(t)$ on the left-hand side equation (9-29) can be written as

$$g(t)\,\delta(t) = \delta(t)\frac{dG(t)}{dt} \qquad (9\text{-}32)$$

Equations (9-31) and (9-32) are introduced into equation (9-29)

$$-\alpha\frac{\partial T}{\partial x}\bigg|_{x=0} = \frac{d\theta}{dt} - \frac{\alpha}{k}\left(G\frac{d\delta}{dt} + \delta\frac{dG}{dt}\right) - T_i\frac{d\delta}{dt}$$

or

$$-\alpha\frac{\partial T}{\partial x}\bigg|_{x=0} = \frac{d}{dt}\left[\theta - \frac{\alpha}{k}G\delta - T_i\delta\right] \qquad (9\text{-}33)$$

which is the energy integral equation for the considered problem. To solve this equation we assume a cubic polynomial representation for $T(x,t)$ in the form

$$T(x,t) = a_1 + a_2 x + a_3 x^2 + a_4 x^3 \qquad (9\text{-}34)$$

and choose the four conditions needed to evaluate these four coefficients as

$$T\bigg|_{x=0} = T_0, \qquad \frac{\partial T}{\partial x}\bigg|_{x=\delta} = 0, \qquad \frac{\partial^2 T}{\partial x^2}\bigg|_{x=\delta} = 0 \qquad (9\text{-}35\text{a})$$

$$T\bigg|_{x=\delta} = T_i + \frac{\alpha}{k}G(t) \qquad (9\text{-}35\text{b})$$

Then, the temperature profile is determined as

$$T(x,t) = T_0 + \left[1 - \left(1 - \frac{x}{\delta} \right)^3 \right] F \qquad \text{in } 0 \le x \le \delta \qquad (9\text{-}36\text{a})$$

where

$$F \equiv (T_i - T_0) + \frac{\alpha}{k} G \qquad (9\text{-}36\text{b})$$

Introducing equation (9-36) into equation (9-33) and performing the indicated operations, we obtain the following differential equations for the determination of δ:

$$12\alpha F^2 = (F\delta)\frac{d(F\delta)}{dt} \qquad \text{for } t > 0 \qquad (9\text{-}37\text{a})$$

subject to the condition

$$\delta = 0 \qquad \text{for } t = 0 \qquad (9\text{-}37\text{b})$$

The solution of equation (9-37) gives

$$\delta^2 = 24\alpha \frac{\int_0^t F^2\, dt}{F^2} \qquad (9\text{-}38)$$

Equation (9-36) together with equation (9-38) gives the temperature distribution in the medium as a function of time and position. For the special case of no heat generation, equations (9-36) and (9-38), respectively, reduce to

$$\frac{T(x,t) - T_i}{T_0 - T_i} = \left(1 - \frac{x}{\delta} \right)^3 \qquad (9\text{-}39\text{a})$$

$$\delta = \sqrt{24\alpha t} \qquad (9\text{-}39\text{b})$$

which are exactly the same as equations (9-11a, b).

Nonlinear Problems

In the foregoing examples we examined the solution of one-dimensional, time-dependent linear problems of heat conduction in a semi-infinite medium and demonstrated that the approximate solutions obtained by the integral method closely agree with the exact solutions. The advantage of the integral method is that it can also handle the nonlinear problems quite readily. In the following two examples we illustrate the application of the integral method to the solution of a nonlinear heat-conduction problem. In the first example the nonlinearity is due to the boundary condition, in the second due to the differential equation.

Example 9-3. A semi-infinite medium is initially at uniform temperature T_i. For times $t > 0$, the boundary surface at $x = 0$ is subjected to a heat flux that is a prescribed function of time and surface temperature. Obtain an expression for the surface temperature $T_s(t)$ for times $t > 0$.

Solution. The mathematical formulation of this problem is given as

$$\frac{\partial^2 T}{\partial x^2} = \frac{1}{\alpha} \frac{\partial T}{\partial t} \qquad \text{in } x > 0, \text{ for } t > 0 \tag{9-40a}$$

$$-\frac{\partial T}{\partial x} = f(T_s, t) \qquad \text{at } x = 0, \text{ for } t > 0 \tag{9-40b}$$

$$T = T_i \qquad \text{for } t = 0, \text{ in } x \geq 0 \tag{9-40c}$$

Here the boundary condition function $f(T_s, t)$ is a function of time t and the boundary surface temperature $T_s(t) \equiv T_s$ at $x = 0$.

The integration of the differential equation (9-40a) over the thermal layer $\delta(t)$ gives

$$\left.\frac{\partial T}{\partial x}\right|_{x=\delta} - \left.\frac{\partial T}{\partial x}\right|_{x=0} = \frac{1}{\alpha}\left[\frac{d}{dt}\left(\int_0^\delta T\,dx\right) - T\bigg|_{x=\delta} \cdot \frac{d\delta}{dt}\right] \tag{9-41}$$

In view of the conditions

$$\left.\frac{\partial T}{\partial x}\right|_{x=\delta} = 0, \qquad T\bigg|_{x=\delta} = T_i, \qquad -\left.\frac{\partial T}{\partial x}\right|_{x=0} = f(T_s, t) \tag{9-42}$$

Equation (9-41) becomes

$$\alpha f(T_s, t) = \frac{d}{dt}(\theta - T_i \delta) \tag{9-43a}$$

where

$$\theta \equiv \int_{x=0}^{\delta} T\,dx \tag{9-43b}$$

which is the energy integral equation for the considered problem. To solve this equation we choose a cubic polynomial representation for $T(x, t)$ as

$$T(x, t) = a_1 + a_2 x + a_3 x^2 + a_4 x^3 \tag{9-44}$$

These four coefficients are determined by utilizing the three conditions (9-42) together with the derived condition

$$\left.\frac{\partial^2 T}{\partial x^2}\right|_{x=\delta} = 0 \tag{9-45}$$

The resulting temperature profile becomes

$$T(x,t) - T_i = \frac{\delta f(T_s, t)}{3}\left(1 - \frac{x}{\delta}\right)^3 \quad \text{in } 0 \leq x \leq \delta \tag{9-46}$$

and for $x = 0$, this relation gives

$$T_s(t) - T_i = \frac{\delta f(T_s, t)}{3} \tag{9-47}$$

From equations (9-46) and (9-47) we write

$$\frac{T(x,t) - T_i}{T_s(t) - T_i} = \left(1 - \frac{x}{\delta}\right)^3 \tag{9-48}$$

Introducing equation (9-48) into equation (9-43), performing the indicated operations, and eliminating δ from the resulting expression by means of equation (9-47) we obtain the following first-order ordinary differential equation for the determination of the surface temperature T_s.

$$\tfrac{4}{3}\alpha f(T_s, t) = \frac{d}{dt}\left[\frac{(T_s - T_i)^2}{f(T_s, t)}\right] \quad \text{for } t > 0 \tag{9-49a}$$

with

$$T_s = T_i \quad \text{for } t = 0 \tag{9-49b}$$

Equation (9-49) can be integrated numerically if the boundary condition function $f(T_s, t)$ depends on both the surface temperature and the time.

For the special case of $f(T_s, t)$ is a function of surface temperature only, namely,

$$f(T_s, t) = f(T_s) \tag{9-50}$$

equation (9-49) is written as

$$\tfrac{4}{3}\alpha f(T_s) = \frac{d}{dT_s}\left[\frac{(T_s - T_i)^2}{f(T_s)}\right]\cdot\frac{dT_s}{dt}$$

or

$$\tfrac{4}{3}\alpha = \frac{2(T_s - T_i)f(T_s) - f'(T_s)\cdot(T_s - T_i)^2}{f^3(T_s)}\frac{dT_s}{dt} \quad \text{for } t > 0 \tag{9-51a}$$

with

$$T_s = T_i \quad \text{for } t = 0 \tag{9-51b}$$

The integration of equation (9-51) establishes the relation between the surface temperature $T_s(t)$ and the time t as

$$\tfrac{4}{3}\alpha t = \int_{T_i}^{T_s} \frac{2(T_s - T_i)f(T_s) - f'(T_s) \cdot (T_s - T_i)^2}{f^3(T_s)} dT_s \tag{9-52}$$

Example 9-4. A semi-infinite medium, $x > 0$, is initially at zero temperature. For times $t > 0$, the boundary surface is subjected to a prescribed heat flux that varies with time. The thermal properties $k(T)$, $C_p(T)$, and $\rho(T)$ are all assumed depend on temperature. Obtain an expression for the temperature distribution in the medium.

Solution. The mathematical formulation of this problem is given as

$$\frac{\partial}{\partial x}\left(k \frac{\partial T}{\partial x} \right) = \rho C_p \frac{\partial T}{\partial t} \quad \text{in } x > 0, \ t > 0 \tag{9-53a}$$

$$-k \frac{\partial T}{\partial x} = f(t) \quad \text{at } x = 0, \ t > 0 \tag{9-53b}$$

$$T = 0 \quad \text{for } t = 0, \ x \geq 0 \tag{9-53c}$$

where $k \equiv k(T)$, $C_p \equiv C_p(T)$, and $\rho \equiv \rho(T)$. By applying the transformation

$$U = \int_0^T \rho C_p \, dT \tag{9-54}$$

The system (9-53) is transformed into

$$\frac{\partial}{\partial x}\left(\alpha \frac{\partial U}{\partial x} \right) = \frac{\partial U}{\partial t} \quad \text{in } x > 0, \ t > 0 \tag{9-55a}$$

$$-\frac{\partial U}{\partial x} = \frac{1}{\alpha_s} f(t) \quad \text{at } x = 0, \ t > 0 \tag{9-55b}$$

$$U = 0 \quad \text{for } t = 0, \ x \geq 0 \tag{9-55c}$$

where $\alpha \equiv \alpha(U)$ and α_s refers to the value of α at the boundary surface $x = 0$. Equation (9-55a) is integrated over the thermal layer $\delta(t)$

$$\left[\alpha \frac{\partial U}{\partial x} \right]_{x=0}^{\delta} = \frac{d}{dt}\left[\int_0^{\delta} U \, dx - U \Big|_{\delta} \cdot \delta \right] \tag{9-56}$$

In view of the conditions

$$\frac{\partial U}{\partial x}\bigg|_{x=\delta} = 0, \qquad U\bigg|_{x=\delta} = 0, \qquad \left[\alpha\frac{\partial U}{\partial x}\right]_{x=0} = -f(t) \qquad (9\text{-}57)$$

Equation (9-56) becomes

$$\frac{d\theta}{dt} = f(t) \qquad (9\text{-}58a)$$

where

$$\theta \equiv \int_0^\delta U\,dx \qquad (9\text{-}58b)$$

which is the energy integral equation for the considered problem. To solve this equation we choose a cubic polynomial representation for $U(x, t)$ as

$$U(x, t) = a_1 + a_2 x + a_3 x^2 + a_4 x^3 \qquad (9\text{-}59)$$

The four coefficients are determined by utilizing the following four conditions

$$U\bigg|_{x=\delta} = 0, \qquad \frac{\partial U}{\partial x}\bigg|_{x=\delta} = 0, \qquad \frac{\partial U}{\partial x}\bigg|_{x=0} = -\frac{f(t)}{\alpha_s}, \qquad \frac{\partial^2 U}{\partial x^2}\bigg|_{x=\delta} = 0 \quad (9\text{-}60)$$

Then, the corresponding profile becomes

$$U(x, t) = \frac{\delta f(t)}{3\alpha_s}\left(1 - \frac{x}{\delta}\right)^3 \qquad \text{in } 0 \le x \le \delta \qquad (9\text{-}61)$$

The substitution of equation (9-61) into equation (9-58) and performing the indicated operations we obtain the following differential equation for the determination of the thermal-layer thickness $\delta(t)$:

$$\frac{d}{dt}\left[\frac{\delta^2 f(t)}{12\alpha_s}\right] = f(t) \qquad \text{for } t > 0 \qquad (9\text{-}62a)$$

with

$$\delta = 0 \qquad \qquad \text{for } t = 0 \qquad (9\text{-}62b)$$

The solution of equation (9-62) is

$$\delta = \left[\frac{12\alpha_s}{f(t)}\int_0^t f(t')\,dt'\right]^{1/2} \qquad (9\text{-}63)$$

This equation cannot yet be used to calculate the thermal layer thickness δ directly, because it involves α_s, the thermal diffusivity evaluated at the surface temperature, U_s, which is still unknown. To circumvent this difficulty an additional relationship is needed between α_s and U_s; such a relationship is obtained as now described.

For $x = 0$ equation (9-61) gives

$$U_s = \frac{\delta f(t)}{3\alpha_s} \tag{9-64}$$

Eliminating δ between equations (9-63) and (9-64), we obtain

$$U_s\sqrt{\alpha_s} = \left[\frac{4}{3} f(t) \int_0^t f(t')\, dt' \right]^{1/2} \tag{9-65}$$

Then the calculational procedure is as follows: Knowing α_s as a function of T_s or U_s, equation (9-65) enables us to compute α_s as a function of time. Knowing α_s for each given time, δ is calculated from equation (9-63). Knowing δ, the transformed temperature $U(x,t)$ is determined from equation (9-61) and the actual temperature $T(x,t)$ is obtained through the transformation (9-54).

Phase Change Problems

The integral method is applicable to the solution of phase change problems involving melting, solidification, and ablation. The solution of the problems belonging to this class will be discussed in the next chapter on phase change problems.

One-Dimensional Finite Region

In the foregoing examples the application of the integral method to the solution of heat-conduction problems for the semi-infinite region was examined in which the thermal layer $\delta(t)$ could increase indefinitely in the region $x > 0$. For the problem of heat conduction in a finite region, say, a slab in $0 \le x \le L$, provided that the thermal layer thickness $\delta(t)$ is less than the slab thickness L and the boundary surface at $x = L$ is insulated the analysis is exactly the same as that described for the semi-infinite region. As soon as $\delta(t) = L$, the thermal layer has no physical significance and a different type of analysis is required for this stage. We illustrate the procedure with the following example.

Example 9-5. A slab, $0 \le x \le L$, is initially at a uniform temperature T_i. For times $t > 0$, the boundary surface at $x = 0$ is kept at a constant temperature T_0 and the boundary at $x = L$ is kept insulated. Obtain an expression for the temperature distribution in the slab for times $t > 0$ by using the integral method.

Solution.   The mathematical formulation of this problem is given as

$$\frac{\partial^2 T}{\partial x^2} = \frac{1}{\alpha}\frac{\partial T}{\partial t} \qquad \text{in } 0 < x < L, \; t > 0 \tag{9-66a}$$

$$T(x,t) = T_0 \qquad \text{at } x = 0, \; t > 0 \tag{9-66b}$$

$$\frac{\partial T}{\partial x} = 0 \qquad \text{at } x = L, \; t > 0 \tag{9-66c}$$

$$T(x,t) = T_i \qquad \text{for } t = 0, \text{ in } 0 \le x \le L \tag{9-66d}$$

For the reasons discussed above the analysis is now performed in *two stages*:

1.   The *first stage*, during which the thermal layer thickness is less than the slab thickness (i.e., $\delta \le L$).
2.   The *second stage*, during which δ exceeds the slab thickness L.

The First stage.   For the case $\delta(t) < L$, we integrate equation (9-66a) over the thermal layer thickness and obtain

$$-\alpha\frac{\partial T}{\partial x}\bigg|_{x=0} = \frac{d}{dt}(\theta - T_i\delta) \tag{9-67a}$$

where

$$\theta \equiv \int_{x=0}^{\delta} T(x,t)\,dx \tag{9-67b}$$

The energy integral equation thus obtained is exactly the same as that given by equation (9-4) for the semi-infinite region.

We choose a cubic profile for the temperature as given by equation (9-5), apply the conditions given by equations (9-6) to determine the coefficients, and utilize equation (9-67) to determine the thermal layer thickness as discussed for the semi-infinite region. The resulting temperature profile becomes

$$\frac{T(x,t) - T_i}{T_0 - T_i} = 1 - \frac{3}{2}\left(\frac{x}{\delta}\right) + \frac{1}{2}\left(\frac{x}{\delta}\right)^3 \tag{9-68a}$$

where

$$\delta = \sqrt{8\alpha t} \tag{9-68b}$$

This solution is valid for $0 \leq x \leq \delta$, so long as $\delta \leq L$. The time t_L when $\delta = L$ is obtained from equation (9-68b) by setting $\delta = L$, that is

$$t_L = \frac{L^2}{8\alpha} \tag{9-69}$$

Clearly, the solution (9-68) is not applicable for times $t > t_L$.

The Second Stage. For times $t > t_L$, the concept of thermal layer has no physical significance. The analysis for the second stage may be performed in the following manner: The temperature $T(x, t)$ is again expressed by a polynomial. Suppose we choose a cubic polynomial representation in the form

$$T(x, t) = a + bx + cx^2 + dx^3 \quad \text{in } 0 < x < L, \ t > t_L \tag{9-70}$$

where the coefficients are generally function of time. In this case we have no thermal layer; therefore, we need four independent relations to determine the four coefficients in equation (8-70). Two of these relations are obtained from the boundary conditions at $x = 0$ and $x = L$ as

$$T\Big|_{x=0} = T_0, \qquad \frac{\partial T}{\partial x}\Big|_{x=L} = 0 \tag{9-71a}$$

The third relation can be derived by evaluating the differential equation (9-66a) at $x = 0$, to give

$$\frac{\partial^2 T}{\partial x^2}\Big|_{x=0} = 0 \tag{9-71b}$$

and the fourth relation is obtained by integrating the differential equation (9-66a) from $x = 0$ to $x = L$; we find

$$-\alpha \frac{\partial T}{\partial x}\Big|_{x=0} = \frac{d}{dt}(\theta - T_i L) \tag{9-71c}$$

where

$$\theta \equiv \int_0^L T(x, t)\, dx$$

By the application of three conditions (9-71a) and (9-71b), three of the coefficients in equation (9-70) are expressed in terms of one of them, say b; the resulting profile is given in the form

$$T(x, t) = T_0 + bL\left[\frac{x}{L} - \frac{1}{3}\left(\frac{x}{L}\right)^3\right] \quad \text{in } 0 \leq x \leq L, \text{ for } t \geq t_L \tag{9-72}$$

where $b \equiv b(t)$. Equation (9-72) can be expressed in the form

$$\frac{T(x,t) - T_i}{T_0 - T_i} = 1 + \eta(t)\left[\frac{x}{L} - \frac{1}{3}\left(\frac{x}{L}\right)^3\right] \quad \text{in } 0 \leq x \leq L, \quad (9\text{-}73)$$

where

$$\eta(t) \equiv \frac{Lb(t)}{T_0 - T_i}$$

When the profile (9-73) is introduced into equation (9-71c) and the indicated operations are performed, the following ordinary differential equation is obtained for the determination of $\eta(t)$:

$$\frac{d\eta(t)}{dt} + \frac{12\alpha}{5L^2}\eta(t) = 0 \quad \text{for } t \geq t_L \quad (9\text{-}74)$$

The initial condition needed to solve this differential equation is determined from the requirement that the temperature defined by equation (9-73) at $x = L$ at the time $t = t_L = L^2/8\alpha$ should be equal to the initial condition $T = T_i$; we find

$$\eta(t) = -\frac{3}{2} \quad \text{for } t = t_L = \frac{L^2}{8\alpha} \quad (9\text{-}75)$$

The solution of the differential equation (9-74) subject to the initial condition (9-75) gives

$$\eta(t) = -\frac{3}{2}\exp\left[-\left(\frac{12\alpha}{5L^2}t - \frac{3}{10}\right)\right] \quad (9\text{-}76)$$

Thus equation (9-73) with $\eta(t)$ as given by equation (9-76) represents the temperature distribution in the slab for times $t > t_L \equiv L^2/8\alpha$. Figure 9-5 shows a comparison of the exact and approximate solutions.

Nonuniform Initial Condition

A uniform initial temperature was assumed for all the applications considered above. The problems involving nonuniform initial condition can also be solved approximately [12, 14, 15]. The method is based on the concept of taking various moments of the differential equation of heat conduction with respect to a suitable weight function over the finite region for the problem. For example, equation (9-71c), which is obtained by integrating the differential equation over the region $0 \leq x \leq L$ is the zeroth moment with respect to the weight function of unity. This approach, which is called the *moment method* is now illustrated with the example given below.

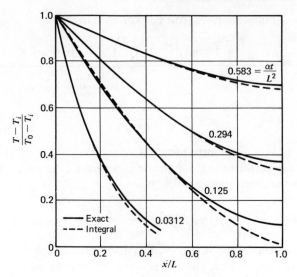

Fig. 9-5 Comparison of exact and approximate temperature profiles for a slab of thickness L. (From Reynolds and Dolton [7].)

Consider a slab, in $0 \leq x \leq L$, initially at a nonuniform temperature $F(x)$. For times $t > 0$, the boundaries at $x = 0$ and $x = L$ are both kept insulated. The mathematical formulation of this problem is given in terms of dimensionless variables as

$$\frac{\partial^2 T}{\partial \eta^2} = \frac{\partial T}{\partial \tau} \qquad \text{in } 0 < \eta < 1, \ \tau > 0 \tag{9-77a}$$

$$\frac{\partial T}{\partial \eta} = 0 \qquad \text{at } \eta = 0 \text{ and } \eta = 1, \ \tau > 0 \tag{9-77b}$$

$$T = F(\eta) \qquad \text{for } \tau = 0, \text{ in } 0 \leq \eta \leq 1 \tag{9-77c}$$

where we defined various dimensionless quantities as

$$\eta = \frac{x}{L} \qquad \text{and} \qquad \tau = \frac{\alpha t}{L^2}$$

To solve this problem approximately by the *moment method* we assume that the temperature $T(\eta, \tau)$ can be expressed by a polynomial in the form

$$T(\eta, \tau) = \sum_{k=0}^{n} a_k(\tau)\eta^k \qquad \text{in } 0 < \eta < 1 \tag{9-78}$$

Clearly, $(n + 1)$ relations are needed to determine the $(n + 1)$ unknown coefficients $a_k(\tau), k = 0, 1, \ldots, n$. The two boundary conditions given by equations (9-77b) provide two relations. The remaining $(n-1)$ relations may be obtained by taking $(n-1)$ moments of the differential equation (9-77a). Namely, we operate on both sides of equation (9-77a) by the operators

$$\int_{\eta=0}^{1} w_i(\eta)\, d\eta \qquad i = 1, 2, \ldots, n-1 \tag{9-79}$$

where $w_i(\eta), i = 1, 2, \ldots, n-1$ are suitable weight functions. We obtain

$$\int_{\eta=0}^{1} w_i(\eta) \frac{\partial^2 T}{\partial \eta^2}\, d\eta = \frac{d}{d\tau}\left(\int_{\eta=0}^{1} w_i(\eta) T(\eta, \tau)\, d\eta \right), \qquad i = 1, 2, \ldots, (n-1) \tag{9-80}$$

Now, introducing equation (9-78) into equation (9-80) we obtain

$$\sum_{k=2}^{n} \left[k(k-1) \int_{\eta=0}^{1} w_i(\eta)\eta^{k-2}\, d\eta \right] a_k(\tau) = \sum_{k=0}^{n} \left(\int_{\eta=0}^{1} w_i(\eta)\eta^{k}\, d\eta \right) \frac{da_k(\tau)}{d\tau}$$
$$i = 1, 2, \ldots, (n-1) \tag{9-81}$$

Thus equations (9-81) provide a system of $(n-1)$ linearly independent ordinary differential equations for the determination of the remaining $(n-1)$ coefficients. To solve these $(n-1)$ equations $(n-1)$ initial conditions are needed. These initial conditions are obtained by introducing equation (9-78) into the initial condition (9-77c) and operating on both sides of the resulting expression by the operator (9-79). We find

$$\sum_{k=0}^{n} \left[\int_{\eta=0}^{1} w_i(\eta)\eta^{k}\, d\eta \right] a_k(0) = \int_{\eta=0}^{1} w_i(\eta) F(\eta)\, d\eta, \qquad i = 1, 2, \ldots, (n-1) \tag{9-82}$$

which formally completes the analysis of this problem. We now summarize the above procedure: The solution (9-78) contains $(n+1)$ unknown coefficients $a_k(\tau), k = 0, 1, 2, \ldots, n$. Two of these are determined by utilizing the two boundary conditions (9-77b). The remaining $(n-1)$ coefficients are determined from the solution of the $(n-1)$ ordinary differential equations (9-81) subject to the $(n-1)$ initial conditions (9-82). The simplest weight function $w_i(\eta)$ to be used in the above equations may be taken as

$$w_i(\eta) = \eta^{i-1} \tag{9-83}$$

The use of orthogonal polynomials, such as the Legendre polynomials, $P_i(\eta)$, instead of η^{i-1} may be advantageous [30, pp. 243–262; 31, pp. 184–196]; but the amount of computation increases when such polynomials are used.

The limitations to the above method should also be recognized. Since two of the boundary conditions are used to determine two of the coefficients $a_k(t)$ at all times, difficulty may be experienced in satisfying the initial condition for very short times. Therefore, the solutions obtained with this method may not be accurate for very short times. When the initial temperature varies, say, linearly with position, a cubic profile may yield solutions sufficiently accurate for times $\tau = \alpha t/L^2 > 0.05$; but higher order polynomial representations may be needed for more complicated distributions. For example, the solution of the heat conduction problem (9-77) for an initial distribution in the form

$$F(\eta) = T_0 \eta \qquad (9\text{-}84)$$

has been solved using a cubic profile by the moment method described above and the resulting solution is obtained as [12]

$$\frac{T(\eta, \tau)}{T_0} = \frac{1}{2} - 5\left(\frac{1}{12} - \frac{1}{2}\eta^2 + \frac{1}{3}\eta^3\right)\exp(-10\tau) \qquad (9\text{-}85)$$

which agrees reasonably well with the exact solution for $\tau \geq 0.05$.

9-3 THE VARIATIONAL PRINCIPLES

In the past 50 years the variational methods have been applied to the analysis of numerous problems in mathematical physics and engineering, and have been extensively used in classical and quantum mechanics. This section is devoted to the discussion of basic principles leading to the variational formulation of the heat-conduction equation in order to provide the necessary background needed in the next section on *the Ritz method* for approximate solution of heat-conduction problems. The principles of variational calculus are discussed in several texts [32–36] and its application to the solution of heat-conduction problems can be found in various references [37–50].

Basic Concepts

Consider an integral I of a single independent variable x defined as

$$I = \int_{x=x_1}^{x_2} F(x, T, T_x)\, dx \qquad (9\text{-}86)$$

where the integrand F is, in general, an implicit and explicit function of the coordinate x, the function $T \equiv T(x)$ and its derivative with respect to x, namely, $T_x \equiv dT/dx$. The integral I is called a *functional* because its value depends on the choice of the function $T(x)$. Clearly, in the more general cases, the function T may depend on more than one independent variable. For the one dimensional case considered above let the function $T(x)$ be defined in the interval $x_1 < x < x_2$ and let the boundary conditions be given, say, in the form

$$T(x) = f_1 \qquad \text{at } x = x_1 \qquad (9\text{-}87a)$$

$$T(x) = f_2 \qquad \text{at } x = x_2 \qquad (9\text{-}87b)$$

In general, these boundary conditions can be any combination of the boundary conditions of the first, second, and third kind.

The variational calculus is concerned with the determination of function $T(x)$ such that it will produce an extremum (i.e., maximum or minimum) in the value of the integral I defined by equation (9-86), while it satisfies the boundary conditions (9-87). We now illustrate the basic steps involved in performing the variational calculus for the simple case considered above.

Let $T(x)$ be the desired function that produces *extremum* (or render *stationary*) the integral I given by equation (9-86) subject to the boundary conditions (9-87). Suppose this function is perturbed by an infinitesimal amount to a new value $\tilde{T}(x)$ as illustrated in Fig. 9-6. Let δT be the magnitude of this perturbation at the location x. We write

$$\tilde{T}(x) - T(x) = \delta T \equiv \varepsilon \eta(x) \qquad (9\text{-}88)$$

where $\tilde{T}(x)$ is called a *trial function* and the operator δ is called the *variation operator*. Here δT represents the *variation* of the function $T(x)$ and ε is a perturbation parameter. The function $\eta(x)$ is a continuous and differentiable function of x, arbitrary except for the requirement that the function $T(x)$ satisfies the boundary conditions at $x = x_1$ and x_2. For this particular example, as illustrated in Fig. 9-6, the value of $T(x)$ remain unchanged at the boundaries x_1 and x_2 as specified by equations (9-87). This requirement

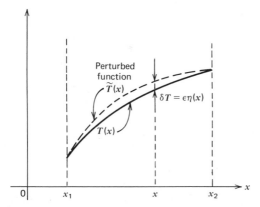

Fig. 9-6 Function $T(x)$ and the perturbed function $\tilde{T}(x)$.

is satisfied if $\eta(x)$, while being arbitrary, vanishes at the boundaries, namely

$$\eta(x) = 0 \qquad \text{at } x = x_1 \qquad (9\text{-}89a)$$

$$\eta(x) = 0 \qquad \text{at } x = x_2 \qquad (9\text{-}89b)$$

A change in the value of $T(x)$ by an amount $\delta T \equiv \varepsilon\eta(x)$ causes a change in the value of the integral I by an amount δI given by

$$\delta I = \delta\left[\int_{x_1}^{x_2} F\,dx\right] = \int_{x_1}^{x_2} \delta F\,dx \qquad (9\text{-}90)$$

Here the variation operator δ is moved under the integral sign because *the integration and the variation operators commute.* The quantity δF in equation (9-90) represents the variation of F resulting from a change in the value of T by an amount δT; thus it is defined as

$$\delta F = F(x, T + \delta T, T_x + \delta T_x) - F(x, T, T_x) \qquad (9\text{-}91)$$

A Taylor series expansion is now applied to evaluate δF. Since F depends on both T and T_x, we take derivatives of F with respect to T and T_x in the Taylor series expansion, and obtain

$$\delta F = \frac{\partial F}{\partial T}\delta T + \frac{\partial F}{\partial T_x}\delta T_x \qquad (9\text{-}92a)$$

or

$$\delta F = \frac{\partial F}{\partial T}\varepsilon\eta + \frac{\partial F}{\partial T_x}\varepsilon\eta_x \qquad (9\text{-}92b)$$

since $\delta T \equiv \varepsilon\eta$. Here the term $\partial F/\partial T_x$ represents the derivative of F with respect to $T_x \equiv dT/dx$.

Equation (9-92a) is introduced into equation (9-90)

$$\delta I = \int_{x_1}^{x_2}\left(\frac{\partial F}{\partial T}\delta T + \frac{\partial F}{\partial T_x}\delta T_x\right)dx \qquad (9\text{-}93)$$

If $T(x)$ is the desired function that produces an extremum in the integral I, then the variation δI of this integral should vanish, namely

$$\delta I = 0 \qquad (9\text{-}94)$$

With this consideration we write equation (9-93) as

$$\delta I = \int_{x_1}^{x_2}\left(\frac{\partial F}{\partial T}\delta T + \frac{\partial F}{\partial T_x}\delta T_x\right)dx = 0 \qquad (9\text{-}95)$$

Then the function $T(x)$ satisfying this condition together with the boundary conditions (9-87) is the desired function that produces an extremum (or render stationary) the integral I defined by equation (9-86). The extrenum problem as defined by equation (9-95) is not suitable for the determination of $T(x)$; further manipulation of this equation is performed as now described.

The second term on the right-hand side of equation (9-95) is arranged as (see Note 1 for details)

$$\frac{\partial F}{\partial T_x}\delta T_x = \frac{d}{dx}\left(\frac{\partial F}{\partial T_x}\delta T\right) - \frac{d}{dx}\left(\frac{\partial F}{\partial T_x}\right)\delta T \qquad (9\text{-}96)$$

When this result is introduced into equation (9-95), we obtain

$$\delta I = \int_{x_1}^{x_2}\left[\frac{d}{dx}\left(\frac{\partial F}{\partial T_x}\delta T\right) + \frac{\partial F}{\partial T}\delta T - \frac{d}{dx}\left(\frac{\partial F}{\partial T_x}\right)\delta T\right]dx = 0 \qquad (9\text{-}97a)$$

Here the first term is integrated

$$\delta I = \left[\delta T\frac{\partial F}{\partial T_x}\right]_{x=x_1}^{x_2} + \int_{x_1}^{x_2}\left[\frac{\partial F}{\partial T} - \frac{d}{dx}\left(\frac{\partial F}{\partial T_x}\right)\right]\delta T\,dx = 0 \qquad (9\text{-}97b)$$

Thus, the transformation from equation (9-95) to (9-97b) is equivalent to integrating the second term in equation (9-95) by parts.

We note that the first term on the right-hand side of equation (9-97b) takes into account the effects of the boundary conditions on the function $T(x)$, whereas the integral term will produce the desired expression for the determination of $T(x)$ as it will soon be apparent.

In the present problem the boundary conditions (9-87) requires that no variation is allowed for $T(x)$ at the boundaries. This condition implies that $\delta T \equiv \varepsilon\eta(x) = 0$ at x_1 and x_2, which is equivalent to the conditions (9-89). Then, the first term in equation (9-97b) vanishes; and by setting $\delta T \equiv \varepsilon\eta(x)$, we obtain

$$\delta I = \int_{x_1}^{x_2}\left[\frac{\partial F}{\partial T} - \frac{d}{dx}\left(\frac{\partial F}{\partial T_x}\right)\right]\varepsilon\eta(x)\,dx = 0 \qquad (9\text{-}99)$$

In this integral $\eta(x)$ is an arbitrary function except for the restriction imposed by equations (9-89) at the boundaries; then, equation (9-99) is satisfied for all values of $\eta(x)$ if the integrand in the bracket vanishes, that is

$$\frac{\partial F}{\partial T} - \frac{d}{dx}\left(\frac{\partial F}{\partial T_x}\right) = 0 \qquad (9\text{-}100)$$

This equation is called the *Euler-Lagrange* equation for the particular variational problem considered here. The boundary conditions for this equation are given by equations (9-87), namely

$$T(x) = f_1 \qquad \text{at } x = x_1 \qquad (9\text{-}101a)$$

$$T(x) = f_2 \qquad \text{at } x = x_2 \qquad (9\text{-}101b)$$

We now summarize the above variational procedure: The variational problem of determining the function $T(x)$ that will produce an extremum in the variational expression defined by equation (9-86) subject to the boundary conditions (9-87) is transformed to the solution of the differential equation (9-100) subject to the same boundary conditions.

The implications of the variational approach to obtain approximate solutions to the heat-conduction problems will be apparent in the next section on the Ritz method.

Example 9-6. Consider the variational problem defined by the integral

$$I = \int_0^L \left[p(x)T_x^2 - q(x)T^2 - 2g(x)T \right] dx \qquad (9\text{-}101)$$

with boundary conditions on $T(x)$ given as

$$T(x) = T_1 \qquad \text{at } x = 0 \qquad (9\text{-}102a)$$

$$T(x) = T_2 \qquad \text{at } x = L \qquad (9\text{-}102b)$$

Determine the corresponding Euler-Lagrange equation.

Solution. By comparing equation (9-101) with the general form given by equation (9-86) we find

$$F(x, T, T_x) = p(x)T_x^2 - q(x)T^2 - 2g(x)T \qquad (9\text{-}103)$$

where $T_x \equiv dT/dx$. The integral I given by equation (9-101) becomes stationary if its variation δI vanishes; then the expression for δI is obtained from equation (9-97b) as

$$\delta I = \left[\delta T \frac{\partial F}{\partial T_x} \right]_{x=0}^{L} + \int_0^L \left[\frac{\partial F}{\partial T} - \frac{d}{dx}\left(\frac{\partial F}{\partial T_x} \right) \right] \delta T\, dx = 0 \qquad (9\text{-}104)$$

For the function F as defined by equation (9-103) various terms in this expression are evaluated as

$$\frac{\partial F}{\partial T} = -2q(x)T - 2g(x) \qquad (9\text{-}105a)$$

$$\frac{\partial F}{\partial T_x} = +2p(x)T_x \qquad (9\text{-}105b)$$

Introducing equations (9-105) into equation (9-104) we obtain

$$\delta I = 2\left[p(x)T_x \delta T \right]_{x=0}^{L} - 2\int_0^L \left[\frac{d}{dx}\left(p(x)\frac{dT}{dx} \right) + q(x)T + g(x) \right] \delta T\, dx = 0$$

$$(9\text{-}106a)$$

Here the first term on the right-hand side vanishes because $\delta T = 0$ at the boundaries where the value of the function is prescribed. Then,

$$\delta I = -2\int_0^L \left[\frac{d}{dx}\left(p(x)\frac{dT}{dx}\right) + q(x)T + g(x) \right]\delta T\,dx = 0 \qquad (9\text{-}106\text{b})$$

where δT being arbitrary this equation is satisfied if the integrand in the bracket vanishes. Then we obtain the following Euler-Lagrange equation for $T(x)$

$$\frac{d}{dx}\left[p(x)\frac{dT}{dx}\right] + q(x)T + g(x) = 0 \qquad \text{in } 0 < x < L \qquad (9\text{-}107\text{a})$$

subject to the boundary conditions

$$T(x) = T_1 \qquad \text{at } x = 0 \qquad\qquad (9\text{-}107\text{b})$$

$$T(x) = T_2 \qquad \text{at } x = L \qquad\qquad (9\text{-}107\text{c})$$

We note that the Euler-Lagrange equations (9-107) obtained above define a steady-state heat-conduction problem with generation and space-dependent thermal conductivity. Thus, function $T(x)$ satisfying this heat-conduction problem renders stationary the variational problem given by equation (9-101).

The variational problem (9-101) is considered above for a boundary condition of the first kind at both boundaries as given by equations (9-102). If the boundary conditions (9-102) were both of the type $\partial T/\partial x = 0$ or any combination of $\partial T/\partial x = 0$ and the boundary condition of the first kind, the above Euler-Lagrange equation (9-107a) would still be applicable with appropriate change in the boundary condition. This result is apparent from the fact that the first term on the right-hand side of equation (9-106a) vanishes when the value of the function is specified or $\partial T/\partial x = 0$ at the boundaries.

Variational Form of One-Dimensional Steady-State Heat Conduction Equation

In the above example we determined the Euler-Lagrange equation for a given variational problem. In the following example we perform such analysis in the reverse order; namely, we determine the variational form of a given Euler-Lagrange equation subject to some prescribed boundary conditions. The analysis of this type will be needed in the approximate solution of the heat-conduction problem by the Rayleigh-Ritz method in the next section.

Example 9-7. Consider the following steady-state heat-conduction problem

$$\frac{d}{dx}\left(k\frac{dT}{dx}\right) + g(x) = 0 \qquad \text{in } 0 < x < L \tag{9-108a}$$

$$-k\frac{dT}{dx} + h_1 T = f_1 \qquad \text{at } x = 0 \tag{9-108b}$$

$$k\frac{dT}{dx} + h_2 T = f_2 \qquad \text{at } x = L \tag{9-108c}$$

Treating this problem as the Euler-Lagrange equations, determine the corresponding variational form.

Solution. We consider equation (9-108a) as the Euler-Lagrange equation and carry out the analysis in the reverse order to the one considered in the previous example. Then, analogous to equation (9-106) we write

$$\delta I = \int_0^L \left[\frac{d}{dx}\left(k\frac{dT}{dx}\right) + g\right]\delta T\,dx = 0 \tag{9-109}$$

The objective of the following analysis is to manipulate this integral into a form that will allow the variational operator, δ, to be moved outside the integral sign. When this is accomplished, the variational form is recovered. The integration by parts must be applied to invoke the boundary conditions; the procedure is as follows:

The first term on the right-hand side is integrated by parts

$$\int_0^L \left[\frac{d}{dx}(kT_x)\right]\delta T\,dx = [(kT_x)\delta T]_0^L - \int_0^L (kT_x)\frac{d}{dx}(\delta T)\,dx$$

$$= [(kT_x)\delta T]_0^L - \int_0^L (kT_x)\delta(T_x)\,dx$$

$$= [kT_x\delta T]_0^L - \frac{1}{2}\int_0^L k\delta(T_x^2)\,dx \tag{9-110}$$

since $d/dx(\delta T) = \delta T_x$ and $T_x\delta(T_x) = \frac{1}{2}\delta(T_x^2)$. Equation (9-110) is introduced into equation (9-109).

$$\delta I = [kT_x\delta T]_0^L - \frac{1}{2}\int_0^L \delta(kT_x^2 - 2gT)\,dx = 0 \tag{9-111}$$

The first term on the right is evaluated by utilizing the boundary conditions (9-108b, c).

$$[kT_x\delta T]_0^L = [f_2\delta T - h_2 T\delta T]_{x=L} + [f_1\delta T - h_1 T\delta T]_{x=0}$$

$$= [f_2\delta T - \tfrac{1}{2}h_2\delta(T^2)]_{x=L} + [f_1\delta T - \tfrac{1}{2}h_1\delta(T^2)]_{x=0}$$

$$= \tfrac{1}{2}\delta[2f_2 T - h_2 T^2]_{x=L} + \tfrac{1}{2}\delta[f_1 T - h_1 T^2]_{x=0} \tag{9-112}$$

Equation (9-112) is introduced into equation (9-111).

$$\delta I = -\tfrac{1}{2}\delta\left\{\int_0^L (kT_x^2 - 2gT)\,dx + [h_1 T^2 - 2f_1 T]_{x=0} + [h_2 T^2 - 2f_2 T]_{x=L}\right\} = 0$$

or

$$\delta\left\{\int_0^L (kT_x^2 - 2gT)\,dx + [h_1 T^2 - 2f_1 T]_{x=0} + [h_2 T^2 - 2f_2 T]_{x=L}\right\} = 0 \quad (9\text{-}113)$$

Then, the desired variational form becomes

$$I = \int_0^L [kT_x^2 - 2gT]\,dx + [h_1 T^2 - 2f_1 T]_{x=0} + [h_2 T^2 - 2f_2 T]_{x=L} \quad (9\text{-}114)$$

We note that, the variational form as given above includes the boundary conditions for the problem.

Generalization to Three Dimensional Problems

The variational procedure discussed above can readily be generalized to problems involving more than one independent variable. Our interest being in the reverse variational procedure, in the following analysis we start with the three-dimensional Euler-Lagrange equation subject to a general boundary condition and determine the equivalent variational expression.

We consider the following three-dimensional steady-state heat-conduction problem

$$\nabla^2 T(\mathbf{r}) + A(\mathbf{r})T(\mathbf{r}) + \frac{1}{k}g(\mathbf{r}) = 0 \qquad \text{in region } R \qquad (9\text{-}115a)$$

$$\frac{\partial T}{\partial n} + HT = f(\mathbf{r}_s) \qquad \text{on the boundary } S \qquad (9\text{-}115b)$$

where $\partial/\partial n$ is the derivative along the outward drawn normal to the boundary surface S.

To determine the corresponding variational expression we treat equation (9-115a) as the Euler-Lagrange equation and follow a procedure similar to the one discussed in example 9-7, but by generalizing it to the three-dimensional case. We write the variation δI of the functional I as

$$\delta I = \int_R \left[\nabla^2 T + AT + \frac{1}{k}g\right]\delta T\,dv = 0 \qquad (9\text{-}116)$$

The term $\delta T \nabla^2 T$ can be written as (see Note 2)

$$\delta T \nabla^2 T = \nabla\cdot(\delta T \nabla T) - \nabla(\delta T)\cdot\nabla T \qquad (9\text{-}117)$$

Introducing this into equation (9-116) we obtain

$$\delta I = \int_R \nabla \cdot (\delta T \nabla T)\, dv - \int_R \nabla T \cdot \nabla(\delta T)\, dv + \int_R A T \delta T\, dv + \frac{1}{k}\int_R g\delta T\, dv \quad (9\text{-}118)$$

The first term in this expression are written in alternative forms as

$$\int_R \nabla \cdot (\delta T \nabla T)\, dv = \int_S \delta T \nabla T \cdot \mathbf{n}\, ds = \int_S \delta T \frac{\partial T}{\partial n}\, ds$$
$$= \int_S \delta T(f - HT)\, ds = -\tfrac{1}{2}\delta\int_S (HT^2 - 2fT)\, ds \quad (9\text{-}119a)$$

where we utilized the boundary condition (9-115b). The remaining terms become

$$\int_R \nabla T \cdot \nabla(\delta T)\, dv = \tfrac{1}{2}\int_R \delta(\nabla T)^2\, dv = \tfrac{1}{2}\delta\int_R (\nabla T)^2\, dv \quad (9\text{-}119b)$$

$$\int_R A T \delta T\, dv = \tfrac{1}{2}\int_R A\delta T^2\, dv = \tfrac{1}{2}\delta\int_R A T^2\, dv \quad (9\text{-}119c)$$

$$\frac{1}{k}\int_R g\delta T\, dv = \frac{1}{k}\delta\int_R gT\, dv \quad (9\text{-}119d)$$

Introducing equations (9-119) into (9-118) we obtain

$$\delta I = -\tfrac{1}{2}\delta\left\{ \int_S (HT^2 - 2fT)\, ds + \int_R \left[(\nabla T)^2 - AT^2 - \frac{2}{k}gT \right] dv \right\} = 0 \quad (9\text{-}120)$$

or

$$\delta\left\{ \int_R \left[(\nabla T)^2 - AT^2 - \frac{2}{k}gT \right] dv + \int_S (HT^2 - 2fT)\, ds \right\} = 0 \quad (9\text{-}121)$$

Then, the desired variational expression is obtained as

$$I = \int_R \left[(\nabla T)^2 - AT^2 - \frac{2}{k}gT \right] dv + \int_S (HT^2 - 2fT)\, ds \quad (9\text{-}122)$$

where $(\nabla T)^2$ is given in different coordinate systems as

$$(\nabla T)^2 \equiv \left(\mathbf{i}\frac{\partial T}{\partial x} + \mathbf{j}\frac{\partial T}{\partial y} + \mathbf{k}\frac{\partial T}{\partial z} \right)^2$$
$$= \left(\frac{\partial T}{\partial x}\right)^2 + \left(\frac{\partial T}{\partial y}\right)^2 + \left(\frac{\partial T}{\partial z}\right) \qquad \text{in the rectangular coord.}$$
$$(9\text{-}123a)$$

$$(\nabla T)^2 \equiv \left(\frac{\partial T}{\partial r}\right)^2 + \frac{1}{r^2}\left(\frac{\partial T}{\partial \phi}\right)^2 + \left(\frac{\partial T}{\partial z}\right) \qquad \text{in the cylindrical coord.}$$
$$(9\text{-}123b)$$

$$(\nabla T)^2 \equiv \left(\frac{\partial T}{\partial r}\right)^2 + \frac{1}{r^2 \sin^2\theta}\left(\frac{\partial T}{\partial \phi}\right)^2 + \frac{1}{r^2}\left(\frac{\partial T}{\partial \theta}\right)^2 \qquad \text{in the spherical coord.}$$

$$(9\text{-}123\text{c})$$

We note that the variational expression (9-122) contains the boundary conditions for the problem.

9-4 THE RITZ METHOD

When the equivalent variational form of the steady-state heat-conduction equation is available, the problem can be solved approximately by a simple and efficient method originally proposed by Ritz [51]. The reader should consult references [52–56] for further discussion of the theory and application of the Ritz method. In this section we discuss the method of solving the steady-state heat-conduction problems in finite regions by the Ritz method and illustrate its application with specific examples.

Consider the steady-state problem for a finite region given in the form

$$\nabla^2 T(\mathbf{r}) + A(\mathbf{r})T(\mathbf{r}) + \frac{1}{k}g(\mathbf{r}) = 0 \qquad \text{in region } R \qquad (9\text{-}124\text{a})$$

$$\frac{\partial T}{\partial n_i} + H_i T = f_i(\mathbf{r}_s) \qquad \text{on boundary } s_i \qquad (9\text{-}124\text{b})$$

where $i = 1, 2, \ldots, s$ and s is the number of continuous boundary surfaces of the region R, $\partial/\partial n_i$ is the derivative along the outward-drawn normal to the surface s_i of the region R.

We have already determined the equivalent variational form of the problem (9-124). Therefore, from equation (9-122) we obtain the corresponding variational expression as

$$I = \int_R \left[(\nabla T)^2 - AT^2 - \frac{2}{k}gT \right] dv + \sum_{i=1}^{s} \int_{s_i} (H_i T^2 - 2f_i T)\, ds_i \qquad (9\text{-}125)$$

since

$$\int_s \equiv \sum_{i=1}^{s} \int_{s_i}$$

which contains the boundary conditions for the problem. The exact solution of this variational expression is very difficult. On the other hand, it can readily be solved approximately by the method proposed by Ritz. The first step in this method of analysis is the selection of a *trial solution* containing a number of adjustable parameters. The trial solution should be so chosen that it should satisfy the boundary conditions (9-124b) for the problem but not necessarily the differential equation (9-124a). With this consideration we choose the trial solution $\tilde{T}_n(\mathbf{r})$ as

$$\tilde{T}_n(\mathbf{r}) = \psi_0(\mathbf{r}) + \sum_{j=1}^{n} c_j \phi_j(\mathbf{r}) \qquad \text{in region } R \qquad (9\text{-}126)$$

where the function ψ_0 satisfies the nonhomogeneous part of the boundary conditions (9-124b), namely

$$\frac{\partial \psi_0}{\partial n_i} + H_i \psi_0 = f_i \qquad (9\text{-}127a)$$

and ϕ_j's, $j = 1, 2, \ldots, n$ are linearly independent, known, suitably chosen functions in region R which satisfy the homogeneous part of the boundary conditions (9-124b), namely,

$$\frac{\partial \phi_j}{\partial n_i} + H_i \phi_j = 0 \qquad (9\text{-}127b)$$

Then, the trial solution (9-126) satisfies the boundary conditions (9-124b) for arbitrary values of c_j's. If the boundary conditions for the problem are all homogeneous, then the function ψ_0 is not needed, only the functions ϕ_j's should be chosen. Here we assume that the functions ϕ_j's have continuous first- and second-order derivatives with respect to the space variables.

Once the trial solution $\tilde{T}_n(\mathbf{r})$ is established, the Ritz approach to the determination of the coefficients c_j's consists of inserting the trial solution $\tilde{T}_n(\mathbf{r})$ into the variational expression (9-125) and requiring that

$$\frac{\partial I(c_1, \ldots, c_n)}{\partial c_j} = 0 \qquad \text{for } j = 1, 2, \ldots, n \qquad (9\text{-}128)$$

This procedure results in n algebraic equations for the determination of n unknown coefficients c_j's and represents an approximate solution to the extremum problem or to the heat-conduction problem (9-124). The solution is approximate because it renders stationary the integral $I(c_1, \ldots, c_n)$ only for those values of c_j's which are contained in the trial solution. A discussion of the error estimation in the Ritz method can be found in reference [52].

The selection of the family of functions ϕ_j's is the most important step in this approach. The functions ϕ_j's, $j = 1, 2, \ldots, n, \ldots$ if possible, should belong to a class of functions that are *complete* in the given region. That is, a function is called *complete* in a sense that any arbitrary function that is continuous, together with its partial derivatives in the considered region, can be represented in the form of infinite series by these functions in the considered region. The functions ϕ_j's can be polynomials, trigonometric functions, cylindrical, or spherical functions depending on the nature of the problem. Good approximation to the solution cannot be obtained unless good approximation is included in the selection of functions ϕ_j's. A discussion of the construction of ϕ_j functions will be given in the next section.

When the original differential equation [i.e., equation (9-124)] is linear the resulting system of n algebraic equations for n unknown c_j's is linear. If the original problem is nonlinear, the resulting system of n equations is nonlinear.

Example 9-8. Consider the following one-dimensional steady-state heat-conduction problem

$$\frac{d^2 T}{dx^2} + AT + Bx = 0 \qquad \text{in } 0 < x < 1 \tag{9-129a}$$

$$T = 0 \qquad \text{at } x = 0 \text{ and } x = 1 \tag{9-129b}$$

where A and B are constants. Solve this problem by the Ritz method and compare the exact and approximate results for $A = B = 1$.

Solution. This problem is a special case of the general problem (9-115). Therefore, the equivalent variational form is immediately obtainable from equation (9-122) as

$$I = \int_{x=0}^{1} \left[\left(\frac{dT}{dx} \right)^2 - AT^2 - 2BxT \right] dx \tag{9-130}$$

To illustrate the accuracy of various order approximations we solve this problem using both one-term and two-term trial solutions.

1. *One-term trial solution.* We choose the trial solution as

$$\tilde{T}_1(x) = c_1 \phi_1(x) \tag{9-131a}$$

where

$$\phi_1(x) = x(1 - x) \tag{9-131b}$$

Clearly, function $\phi_1(x)$ satisfies both boundary conditions (9-129b). Introducing this trial solution into equation (9-130) we obtain (see note 3 for the evaluation of some of the integrals)

$$I(c_1) = \frac{1}{3}\left(1 - \frac{A}{10} \right) c_1^2 - \frac{B}{6} c_1 \tag{9-132}$$

The coefficient c_1 is determined according to equation (9-128) as

$$\frac{dI(c_1)}{dc_1} = \frac{2}{3}\left(1 - \frac{A}{10}\right)c_1 - \frac{B}{6} = 0 \qquad (9\text{-}133a)$$

hence

$$c_1 = \frac{B}{4(1 - A/10)} \qquad (9\text{-}133b)$$

Then the one-term trial solution becomes

$$\tilde{T}_1(x) = \frac{B}{4(1 - A/10)}x(1 - x) \qquad (9\text{-}134)$$

2. *Two-term trial solution.*   We choose the trial solution as

$$\tilde{T}_2(x) = c_1\phi_1(x) + c_2\phi_2(x) \qquad (9\text{-}135a)$$

where

$$\phi_1(x) = x(1 - x) \qquad \text{and} \qquad \phi_2(x) = x^2(1 - x) \qquad (9\text{-}135b)$$

Both $\phi_1(x)$ and $\phi_2(x)$ satisfy the boundary conditions (9-129b). Introducing these trial solutions into equation (9-130) we obtain $I(c_1, c_2)$. Then, setting

$$\frac{dI(c_1, c_2)}{dc_j} = 0 \qquad j = 1, 2 \qquad (9\text{-}136)$$

we obtain two algebraic equations for the determination of the coefficients c_1 and c_2. We find, for $A = B = 1$, $c_1 = 71/369$ and $c_2 = 7/41$; then the two-term trial solution becomes

$$\tilde{T}_2(x) = x(1 - x)\left(\frac{71}{369} + \frac{7}{41}x\right) \qquad (9\text{-}137)$$

Table 9-2   A Comparison of Approximate and Exact Solutions of Example 9-8 for $A = B = 1$

x	T Exact	T_1 Approx	% Error	T_2 Approx	% Error
0.25	0.04400	0.0521	+ 18.4	0.04408	+ 0.18
0.50	0.06974	0.0694	− 0.48	0.06944	− 0.43
0.75	0.06005	0.0521	− 13.2	0.06009	+ 0.06
0.85	0.04282	0.0354	− 17.3	0.04302	+ 0·46

The exact solution of this problem is given as

$$T(x) = \frac{B}{A}\left[\frac{\sin A^{1/2}x}{\sin A^{1/2}} - x\right] \tag{9-138}$$

We present in Table 9-2 a comparison of the one- and two-term approximate solutions with the exact result. Clearly, the accuracy is significantly improved using a two-term solution.

Example 9-9. Consider the following steady-state heat-conduction problem for a solid cylinder

$$\frac{1}{r}\frac{d}{dr}\left(r\frac{dT}{dr}\right) + \left(1 - \frac{1}{r^2}\right)T = 0 \qquad \text{in } 1 < r < 2 \tag{9-139a}$$

$$T = 4 \qquad \text{at } r = 1 \tag{9-139b}$$

$$T = 8 \qquad \text{at } r = 2 \tag{9-139c}$$

Solve this problem with the Ritz method.

Solution. This problem is a special case of the general problem (9-115). Therefore, the equivalent variational form is immediately obtainable from equations (9-122) and (9-123b); for the value of function fixed at the boundaries, we find

$$I = \int_{r=1}^{2}\left[\left(\frac{dT}{dr}\right)^2 - \left(1 - \frac{1}{r^2}\right)T^2\right]r\,dr \tag{9-140}$$

We choose a one-term trial solution $\tilde{T}_1(r)$ as

$$\tilde{T}_1(t) = c_1\phi_1(r) + \psi_0(r) \tag{9-141a}$$

where

$$\phi_1(r) = (r-1)(r-2) \qquad \text{and} \qquad \psi_0(r) = 4r \tag{9-141b}$$

This solution satisfies the boundary conditions (9-139b,c). Substituting this solution into the variational form, (9-140), differentiating the resulting expression with respect to c_1 and equating it to zero we obtain

$$\frac{dI}{dc_1} = 2c_1\int_{1}^{2}\left(-r^5 + 6r^4 - 8r^3 - 6r^2 + 18r - 12 + \frac{4}{r}\right)dr$$

$$+ 8\int_{1}^{2}(-r^4 + 3r^3 + r^2 - 6r + 2)\,dr = 0 \tag{9-142}$$

After performing the integration, c_1 is determined as

$$c_1 = -3.245$$

Then, the one-term approximate solution becomes

$$\tilde{T}_1(r) = 3.245(r - 1)(2 - r) + 4r \tag{9-143}$$

The exact solution of this problem is

$$T(r) = 14.43 J_1(r) + 3.008 Y_1(r) \tag{9-144}$$

A comparison of the approximate and exact solutions at the locations $r = 1.2, 1.5$, and 1.8 shows that the agreement is within 0.03%. Therefore, in this example even the one-term approximation gives very good results.

9-5 THE GALERKIN METHOD

In the previous section we presented the Ritz method, which requires that the equivalent variational form of the governing differential equations should be available for this method to be applicable. In 1915 Galerkin [57] proposed an approximate method of solving boundary-value problems that does not require the variational formulation of the problem; therefore, it provides a more general and straightforward approach to the solution of boundary-value problems. It is applicable to the solution of elliptic, hyperbolic, and parabolic types of equations as well as to both linear and nonlinear problems. When the variational form of a boundary-value problem exists, it can be shown that the Ritz and Galerkin methods are equivalent and produce identical results. Therefore, instead of trying to develop the equivalent variational form of a given boundary-value problem and then apply the Ritz method, one can apply the Galerkin method directly to the boundary-value problem. We present below the basic theory and application of the Galerkin method to the solution of steady-state heat-conduction problems in finite domains. The reader should consult to references [16, 37, 53–55] for a discussion of the theory and application of the Galerkin method and to references [58–64] for its application in the solution of various types of boundary-value problems.

The basic idea in Galerkin's method can be illustrated by referring to the boundary-value problem given by equations (9-124) considered in connection with the Ritz method. We write this problem more compactly in the form

$$L[T(\mathbf{r})] = 0 \qquad \text{in region } R \tag{9-145a}$$

$$B[T(\mathbf{r}_s)] = f(\mathbf{r}_s) \qquad \text{on boundary } S \tag{9-145b}$$

where L is a linear differential operator [i.e., $L[T] \equiv \nabla^2 T + AT + (1/k)g$] and B is a linear boundary condition operator [i.e., $B[T] \equiv k(\partial T/\partial n) + hT$].

Clearly, the problem defined by equation (9-145) covers a wide range of heat-conduction problems of practical interest. We choose a trial solution $\tilde{T}_n(\mathbf{r})$ in the form

$$\tilde{T}_n(\mathbf{r}) = \psi_0(\mathbf{r}) + \sum_{j=1}^{n} c_j \phi_j(\mathbf{r}) \qquad \text{in region } R \qquad (9\text{-}146)$$

where the function $\psi_0(\mathbf{r})$ satisfies the nonhomogeneous part of boundary conditions (9-145b) and the functions $\phi_j(\mathbf{r})$ satisfy the homogeneous part; namely

$$B[\psi_0] = f(\mathbf{r}_s) \qquad (9\text{-}147a)$$

$$B[\phi_j] = 0 \qquad j = 1, 2, \ldots, n \qquad (9\text{-}147b)$$

If the boundary conditions for the problem are all homogeneous, the function ψ_0 is not needed. It is also possible to transform the nonhomogeneous boundary conditions into homogeneous ones. For example, in the case of a two-dimensional problem, one can define a new dependent variable $T^*(x, y)$ such that

$$T^*(x, y) = T(x, y) + p(x, y) \qquad (9\text{-}148)$$

where the function $p(x, y)$ is so chosen that for each boundary surface the left-hand side of equation (9-147a) produces a term that cancels out the nonhomogeneous term f on the right-hand side.

Suppose proper functions $\psi_0(\mathbf{r})$ and $\phi_j(\mathbf{r})$, $j = 1, 2, \ldots, n$, are found and the trial solution $\tilde{T}_n(\mathbf{r})$ is constructed as given by equation (9-146). Clearly, such a trial function satisfies all the boundary conditions for the problem but not the differential equation (9-145a). If it is inserted into the differential equation (9-145a) a residual will be left because it is only with the exact solution that the residual is identically zero and the differential equation is satisfied at every point in the medium. For a selected trial function consisting of a number of adjustable parameters as the one given above, a *good approximation* to the exact solution may be considered to be the one for which the coefficients c_j's are so adjusted as to maintain the residuals as small as possible. Galerkin's method for determining the unknown coefficients c_j's consists of requiring that the weighted averages of the residuals over the considered region should vanish. The weighting functions are taken to be the same functions ϕ_j's, which are used to construct the trial solution given by equation (9-146). Then, the Galerkin method for the determination of the coefficients c_j's is stated as

$$\int_R L[\tilde{T}_n(\mathbf{r})] \phi_i(\mathbf{r}) \, dv = 0 \qquad (9\text{-}149a)$$

or

$$\int_R L[\psi_0(\mathbf{r}) + \sum_{j=1}^n c_j\phi_j(\mathbf{r})]\phi_i(\mathbf{r})\, dv = 0 \qquad i = 1, 2, \ldots, n \qquad (9\text{-}149\text{b})$$

This relation yields a system of algebraic equations for the determination of n coefficients $c_1, c_2, \ldots, c_n$. The expression given by equation (9-149) may be interpreted as being equivalent to the orthogonality of the expression $L[\tilde{T}_n]$ to all functions of the system $\phi_i(\mathbf{r})$. The function $\phi_i(\mathbf{r})$, $i = 1, 2, \ldots, n, \ldots$ are considered *complete* in the considered region R. Therefore, if all the functions $\phi_i(\mathbf{r})$ belonging to this complete set are included, the requirement given by equation (9-149) corresponds to the exact solution of the problem. However, in the Galerkin method only a finite number of these functions are considered in equation (9-149), therefore the resulting solution will be an approximate one.

The Galerkin method as described above provides a simple and straightforward approach to the solution of steady-state heat-conduction problems. When the boundary-value problem has the variational form, the solutions obtained by the Galerkin method as defined by equations (9-149) and the Ritz method defined by equations (9-128), using the same trial solution (9-146) give identical results. A discussion of the equivalence of these two methods, when the variational form of the problem exists, is given in reference [53, pp. 279–281]. Therefore, the Galerkin method is preferable to the Ritz method, because it does not require the variational form of the problem, in addition it is applicable to problems for which no variational form is available.

An important step in the solution of boundary value problems by the Ritz or the Galerkin methods is the construction of $\phi_j(\mathbf{r})$ functions that will satisfy the homogeneous part of the boundary conditions for the problem. We now present a discussion of the construction of ϕ_j functions.

Construction of ϕ_j Functions

The functions $\phi_j(\mathbf{r})$, $j = 1, 2, \ldots, n, \ldots$, if possible, should belong to a class of functions which are *complete* in the considered region. They should be continuous in the region and should have continuous first and second derivatives. They may be polynomials, trigonometric, circular, or spherical functions, but, they should satisfy the homogeneous part of the boundary conditions for the problem. A problem for a finite region may be subjected to boundary conditions of the first, second, or third kind or their combinations. In the following discussion we present some useful guidelines which can be helpful in the construction of ϕ_j, $j = 1, 2, \ldots, n$ functions that satisfy the homogeneous part of the boundary conditions for the problem.

For geometries such as a slab, cylinder, hollow cylinder, rectangle, etc., for which the coordinate surfaces coincide with the boundary surfaces, the elementary solutions listed in Tables 2-1, 3-1, and 3-2 can be taken as the ϕ_j functions. For example, for a slab in $0 \le x \le L$, the functions ϕ_j, $j = 1, 2, \ldots, n$ depending on the combination of the boundary conditions at $x = 0$ and $x = L$, can be obtained from the elementary solutions listed in Table 2-1 by taking only the first n of the eigenfunctions. Similarly, for the problems of a solid cylinder and hollow cylinder with cylindrical symmetry, the functions $\phi_j, j = 1, 2, \ldots, n$ can be obtained from Tables 3-1 and 3-2, respectively.

There are many situations in which the boundaries of the region are irregular, as a result the trial solution cannot be constructed by the elementary solutions listed in Tables 2-1, 3-1, and 3-3 as discussed above. We now describe other methods of constructing ϕ_j functions that are applicable for both regular and irregular boundaries.

Boundary Conditions of the First Kind. We assume that the boundary conditions for the problem are all of the first kind at all boundaries. Let, a function $\omega(x, y)$ be a continuous function, and within the region R have continuous derivatives with respect to x and y, and in addition satisfies the conditions

$$\omega(x, y) > 0 \quad \text{within } R \quad \text{and} \quad \omega(x, y) = 0 \quad \text{on boundary } S \quad (9\text{-}150)$$

Clearly, the function $\omega(x, y)$ satisfies the homogeneous part of the boundary conditions of the first kind for the problem since it vanishes at the boundaries. Then, the functions $\phi_j(x, y)$ for such problems can be constructed by the products of $\omega(x, y)$ and various powers of x and y in the form

$$\phi_1 = \omega, \quad \phi_2 = \omega x, \quad \phi_3 = \omega y, \quad \phi_4 = \omega x^2, \quad \phi_5 = \omega xy, \ldots \quad (9\text{-}151)$$

The functions $\phi_j(x, y), j = 1, 2, \ldots, n$ constructed in this manner satisfy the homogeneous part of the boundary conditions for the problem, have continuous derivatives in x and y, and it is proved in reference [53, p. 276] that they constitute a *complete* system of functions. Then, the problem becomes one of determining the auxiliary functions $\omega(x, y)$. These functions can be determined by utilizing the equations for the contour of the boundary as now described.

1. *For regions having a single continuous contour,* such as the circle, let

$$F(x, y) = 0 \quad (9\text{-}152a)$$

be the equation of the contour. Clearly, the function $F(x, y)$ is continuous and has partial derivatives with respect to x and y. Then, the function

$\omega(x, y)$ can be chosen as

$$\omega(x, y) = \pm F(x, y) \qquad (9\text{-}152b)$$

For example, for a circular region of radius R with center at the origin, the equation for the contour satisfies the equation

$$F(x, y) = R^2 - x^2 - y^2 = 0 \qquad (9\text{-}153a)$$

and the function $\omega(x, y)$ is taken as

$$\omega(x, y) = R^2 - x^2 - y^2 \qquad (9\text{-}153b)$$

2. *For regions having boundary contour in the form of a convex polynomial,* let the equations for its sides be given in the form

$$F_1 \equiv a_1 x + b_1 y + d_1 = 0, \qquad F_2 \equiv a_2 x + b_2 y + d_2 = 0, \dots,$$
$$F_n \equiv a_n x + b_n y + d_n = 0 \qquad (9\text{-}154a)$$

Then, the function $\omega(x, y)$ chosen in the form

$$\omega(x, y) = \pm F_1(x, y) F_2(x, y), \dots F_n(x, y) \qquad (9\text{-}154b)$$

vanishes at every point on the boundary and satisfies the homogeneous part of the boundary conditions of the first kind for the region.

For nonconvex geometries the problem is more involved; a discussion of this matter is given in reference [53, p. 278].

Example 9-10. Construct the functions $\omega(x, y)$ as discussed above for the four different geometries shown in Fig. 9-7.

Solution. The equations of the contours for each of the four geometries shown in Figs. 9-7a, b, c, d are given respectively as

$$a - x = 0, \ a + x = 0, \ b - y = 0, \ b + y = 0. \qquad (9\text{-}155a)$$

$$y - \alpha x = 0, \ y + \beta x = 0, \ L - x = 0. \qquad (9\text{-}155b)$$

$$x = 0, \ y = 0, \ 1 - \frac{x}{a} - \frac{y}{b} = 0. \qquad (9\text{-}155c)$$

$$R_1^2 - x^2 - y^2 = 0, \ R_2^2 - (x - L)^2 - y^2 = 0. \qquad (9\text{-}155d)$$

Then the corresponding function $\omega(x, y)$ for each of these geometries shown in Figs. 9-7a, b, c, d are given respectively as

$$\omega(x, y) = (a^2 - x^2)(b^2 - y^2) \qquad (9\text{-}156a)$$

$$\omega(x, y) = (y - \alpha x)(y + \beta x)(L - x) \qquad (9\text{-}156b)$$

$$\omega(x, y) = xy\left(1 - \frac{x}{a} - \frac{y}{b}\right) \qquad (9\text{-}156c)$$

$$\omega(x, y) = (R_1^2 - x^2 - y^2)[R_2^2 - (x - L)^2 - y^2] \qquad (9\text{-}156d)$$

Other Boundary Conditions. No general rule can be set for situations involving different combinations of boundary conditions of the first, second, or third kind. The functions ϕ_j must be so selected that they are continuous together with their derivative and satisfy the boundary conditions for the problem. Then, the trial solution is constructed by means of linear combination of ϕ_j functions. We illustrate this matter with specific examples.

Consider a one-dimensional steady-state heat-conduction problem subject

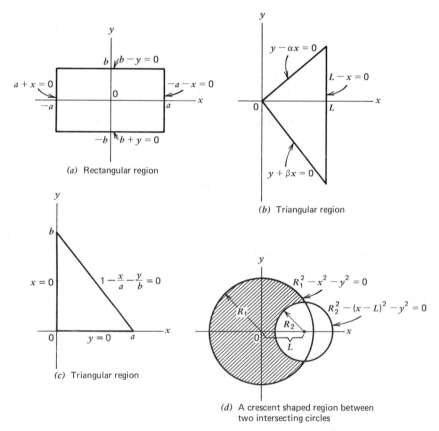

(a) Rectangular region

(b) Triangular region

(c) Triangular region

(d) A crescent shaped region between
two intersecting circles

Fig. 9-7   Regions having boundary contour in the form of a convex polygon and a region bounded by two circles: (a) rectangular region; (b) triangular region; (c) triangular region; (d) a cresent shaped region between two intersecting circles.

to the boundary conditions

$$\left[-\frac{dT}{dx} + h_1 T \right]_{x=0} = 0 \quad \text{and} \quad \left[\frac{dT}{dx} + h_2 T \right]_{x=L} = 0 \quad (9\text{-}157a)$$

The functions ϕ_j may be chosen as

$$\left. \phi_1 = x^2 \left(x - L - \frac{L}{2 + h_2 L} \right), \ \phi_2 = (L - x)^2 \left(x + \frac{L}{2 + h_1 L} \right) \right\}$$

and

$$\phi_j = x^j (L - x)^2, \qquad j = 3, 4, 5 \ldots \left. \right\} \quad (9\text{-}157b)$$

Then, the trial solution constructed as

$$\tilde{T}_n(x) = \phi_1 + \phi_2 + \sum_{j=3}^{n} c_j \phi_j \qquad \text{in } 0 \le x \le L \qquad (9\text{-}157c)$$

satisfies the boundary conditions (9-157a). The coefficients c_j are determined by the Galerkin method.

We now illustrate the application of the Galerkin method with examples.

Example 9-11. Solve Example 9-8 by the Galerkin method by using the one-term trial solution given by equation (9-131).

Solution. The Galerkin method defined by equation (9-149) is applied to the solution of the problem given by equations (9-129); we obtain

$$\int_{x=0}^{1} \left[\frac{d^2 \tilde{T}}{dx^2} + A\tilde{T} + Bx \right] \phi_i(x)\, dx = 0 \qquad (9\text{-}158a)$$

and the one-term trial solution is taken as

$$\tilde{T}_1(x) = c_1 x (1 - x) \qquad (9\text{-}158b)$$

The solution of equation (9-158) yields

$$\tilde{T}_1(x) = \frac{B}{4(1 - A/10)} x(1 - x) \qquad (9\text{-}159)$$

which is exactly the same as that given by equation (9-134) obtained by the Ritz method.

Example 9-12. Solve Example 9-9 by the Galerkin method by using the trial solution given by equation (9-141).

Solution. The Galerkin method when applied to the solution of the problem given by equations (9-139), yields

$$\sum_{r=1}^{2} \int \left[\frac{1}{r} \frac{d}{dr}\left(r \frac{d\tilde{T}}{dr} \right) + \left(1 - \frac{1}{r^2} \right) \tilde{T} \right] \phi_i(r)\, dr = 0 \qquad (9\text{-}160a)$$

where

$$\tilde{T}_1(r) = c_1 \phi_1(r) + \psi_0(r) \qquad (9\text{-}160b)$$

$$\phi_1(r) = (r-1)(r-2), \quad \psi_0(r) = 4r \qquad (9\text{-}160c)$$

After performing the indicated operation we find

$$c_1 = -3.245$$

or

$$\tilde{T}_1(r) = 3.245(r-1)(2-r) + 4r \qquad (9\text{-}161)$$

which is exactly the same as that given by equation (9-143) obtained by the Ritz method.

Example 9-13. Solve the steady-state heat-conduction problem in a rectangular region $(-a, a; -b, b)$ with heat generation at a constant rate of g W/m^3 and the boundaries kept at zero temperature using the Galerkin method and compare the result with the exact solution.

Solution. The mathematical formulation of the problem is

$$\frac{\partial^2 T}{\partial x^2} + \frac{\partial^2 T}{\partial y^2} + \frac{1}{k} g = 0 \qquad \text{in } -a < x < a, \ -b < y < b \qquad (9\text{-}162a)$$

$$T = 0 \qquad \text{at } x = \pm a \ \text{and} \ y = \pm b \qquad (9\text{-}162b)$$

The solution of this problem by the Galerkin method, according to equation (9-149), is written as

$$\int_{x=-a}^{a} \int_{y=-b}^{b} \left[\frac{d^2 \tilde{T}}{dx^2} + \frac{d^2 \tilde{T}}{dy^2} + \frac{1}{k} g \right] \phi_i(x, y)\, dx\, dy = 0 \qquad (9\text{-}163a)$$

We consider one-term trial solution taken as

$$\tilde{T}_1(x, y) = c_1 \phi_1(x, y) \qquad (9\text{-}163b)$$

where the function ϕ_1 is obtained from equation (9-156a) as

$$\phi_1(x, y) = (a^2 - x^2)(b^2 - y^2) \qquad (9\text{-}163c)$$

Introducing this trial solution into equation (9-163a) and performing the integrations we obtain

$$c_1 = \frac{5}{8} \frac{g/k}{a^2 + b^2}$$

Hence, the one-term approximate solution becomes

$$T_1(x, y) = \frac{5}{8} \frac{g/k}{a^2 + b^2}(a^2 - x^2)(b^2 - y^2) \tag{9-164}$$

The exact solution of this problem is

$$T(x, y) = \frac{g}{k}\left[\frac{a^2 - x^2}{2}\right] - 2a^2 \sum_{n=0}^{\infty} \frac{(-1)^n}{\beta_n^3} \frac{\cosh\left(\beta_n \frac{y}{b}\right) \cdot \cos\left(\beta_n \frac{x}{a}\right)}{\cosh\left(\beta_n \frac{b}{a}\right)} \tag{9-165}$$

where

$$\beta_n = \frac{(2n + 1)\pi}{2}$$

To compare these two results we consider the center temperature (i.e., $x = 0$, $y = 0$) for the case $a = b$, and obtain

Approximate : $$T_1(0, 0) = \frac{5}{16} \frac{ga^2}{k} = 0.3125 \frac{ga^2}{k} \tag{9-166a}$$

Exact : $$T(0, 0) = \frac{ga^2}{k}\left[\frac{1}{2} - 2 \sum_{n=0}^{\infty} \frac{(-1)^n}{\beta_n^3 \cdot \cosh \beta_n}\right] = 0.293 \frac{ga^2}{k} \tag{9-166b}$$

The error involved with one-term solution is about 6.7%.

For a two-term trial solution, the temperature distribution may be taken in the form

$$T_2(x, y) = (c_1 + c_2 x^2)(a^2 - x^2)(b^2 - y^2) \tag{9-167}$$

and the calculations are performed in a similar manner to determine the coefficients c_1 and c_2.

9-6 PARTIAL INTEGRATION

In the previous section the Galerkin method has been applied for the solution of the two-dimensional steady-state heat-conduction problem by using a trial solution $\tilde{T}(x, y)$ constructed by specifying the functional form of $\phi(x, y)$ in the x and y variables. A better approximation can be obtained for the solution, if the trial solution $\tilde{T}(x, y)$ is constructed by specifying the functional form of the profile in one of the variables, say y, and leaving it in the form of an unspecified function, say, $X(x)$ in the x variable. Then, for the two dimensional problem in the x, y variables, the application of the Galerkin method in the y variable will result in an ordinary differential equation for the function $X(x)$. One advantage of this method is that, in situations when the functional form of the temperature profile cannot be chosen *a priori* in one direction, it is left to be determined according to the character of the problem from the solution of the resulting ordinary differential equation. We illustrate this procedure with simple examples.

Example 9-14. Solve the steady-state heat-conduction problem considered in Example 9-13 with the Galerkin method using partial integration with respect to the y variable and solving the resulting ordinary differential equation in the x variable.

Solution. The Galerkin method when applied to the differential equation (9-162a) by partial integration with respect to the y variable, gives

$$\int_{y=-b}^{b}\left[\frac{\partial^2 \tilde{T}}{\partial x^2} + \frac{\partial^2 \tilde{T}}{\partial y^2} + \frac{g}{k}\right]\phi_i(y)\,dy = 0 \qquad \text{in } -a < x < a \qquad (9\text{-}168)$$

We consider only a one-term trial solution $\tilde{T}_1(x, y)$ choosen as

$$\tilde{T}_1(x, y) = \phi_1(y)X(x) \qquad (9\text{-}169\text{a})$$

where

$$\phi_1(y) = b^2 - y^2 \qquad (9\text{-}169\text{b})$$

This trial solution satisfies the boundary conditions at $y = \pm b$; the function $X(x)$ is yet to be determined. Introducing the trial solution (9-169) into equation (9-168) and performing the indicated operations we obtain

$$X''(x) - \frac{5}{2b^2}X(x) = -\frac{5g}{4b^2k} \qquad \text{in } -a < x < a \qquad (9\text{-}170\text{a})$$

Subject to the boundary conditions

$$X(x) = 0 \qquad \text{at } x = \pm a \qquad (9\text{-}170\text{b})$$

where the prime shows differentiation with respect to x. The solution of the ordinary differential equation (9-170) is

$$X(x) = \frac{g}{2k}\left[1 - \frac{\cosh\left(\sqrt{2.5}\dfrac{x}{b}\right)}{\cosh\left(\sqrt{2.5}\dfrac{a}{b}\right)}\right] \qquad (9\text{-}171)$$

Then the one-term trial solution becomes

$$\tilde{T}_1(x, y) = \frac{g}{2k}(b^2 - y^2)\left[1 - \frac{\cosh\left(\sqrt{2.5}\dfrac{x}{b}\right)}{\cosh\left(\sqrt{2.5}\dfrac{a}{b}\right)}\right] \qquad (9\text{-}172)$$

and the temperature at the center (i.e., $x = y = 0$) for $a = b$ becomes

$$\tilde{T}_1(x, y) = 0.3026\frac{ga^2}{k} \qquad (9\text{-}173)$$

This result involves an error of only approximately 3.6%, whereas the one-term approximation obtained in the previous example by the application of the Galerkin method for both x and y variables involves an error of approximately 6.7%. Thus the solution by partial integration improves the accuracy.

Example 9-15. Consider the following steady-state heat-conduction problem for a segment of a cylinder, $0 \le r \le 1, 0 \le \theta \le \theta_0$, in which heat is generated at a constant rate of g W/m^3 and all the boundary surfaces are kept at zero temperature.

$$\frac{1}{r}\frac{\partial}{\partial r}\left(r\frac{\partial T}{\partial r}\right) + \frac{1}{r^2}\frac{\partial^2 T}{\partial \theta^2} + \frac{g}{k} = 0 \qquad \text{in } 0 \le r < 1, \ 0 < \theta < \theta_0 \quad (9\text{-}174\text{a})$$

$$T = 0 \qquad \text{at } r = 1, \ \theta = 0, \ \theta = \theta_0 \quad (9\text{-}174\text{b})$$

Solve this problem using the Galerkin method by partial integration with respect to the θ variable. Compare the approximate result with the exact solution.

Solution. The Galerkin method is now applied to the differential equation (9-174a) by partial integration with respect to the variable θ.

$$\int_{\theta=0}^{\theta_0}\left[\frac{1}{r}\frac{\partial}{\partial r}\left(r\frac{\partial \tilde{T}}{\partial r}\right) + \frac{1}{r^2}\frac{\partial^2 \tilde{T}}{\partial \theta^2} + \frac{g}{k}\right]\phi_1(\theta)\, d\theta = 0 \qquad \text{in } 0 \le r < 1 \quad (9\text{-}175)$$

we consider a one-term trial solution taken as

$$\tilde{T}(r, \theta) = F(r)\phi_1(\theta) \qquad (9\text{-}176\text{a})$$

where

$$\phi_1(\theta) = \sin\left(\frac{\pi\theta}{\theta_0}\right) \qquad (9\text{-}176\text{b})$$

The trial solution thus chosen satisfies the boundary conditions at $\theta = 0$

and $\theta = \theta_0$; but the function $F(r)$ is yet to be determined. Introducing the trial solution (9-176) into (9-175) and performing the integration we obtain

$$\frac{1}{r}\frac{d}{dr}\left(r\frac{dF}{dr}\right) - \frac{\beta^2}{r^2}F(r) = -\frac{4g}{k\pi} \qquad \text{in } 0 \le r < 1 \qquad (9\text{-}177a)$$

$$F(r) = 0 \qquad\qquad\qquad\qquad \text{at } r = 1 \qquad (9\text{-}177b)$$

where

$$\beta \equiv \frac{\pi}{\theta_0} \qquad (9\text{-}177c)$$

A particular solution of equation (9-177a) is

$$F_p = \frac{4g}{\pi k}\frac{r^2}{\beta^2 - 4}$$

and the complete solution for $F(r)$ is constructed as

$$F(r) = c_1 r^\beta + c_2 r^{-\beta} + \frac{4g}{\pi k}\frac{r^2}{\beta^2 - 4} \qquad (9\text{-}178)$$

Here, $c_2 = 0$ from the requirement that the solution should remain finite at $r = 0$; c_1 is determined by the application of the boundary condition at $r = 1$ to give

$$c_1 = -\frac{4g}{\pi k}\frac{1}{\beta^2 - 4}$$

Then the solution for $F(r)$ is obtained as

$$F(r) = \frac{4g}{\pi k}\frac{r^2 - r^\beta}{\beta^2 - 4} \qquad (9\text{-}179)$$

and the one-term trial solution $\tilde{T}(r, \theta)$ becomes

$$\tilde{T}(r, \theta) = \frac{4g}{\pi k}\frac{r^2 - r^{(\pi/\theta_0)}}{(\pi/\theta_0)^2 - 4}\sin\left(\frac{\pi\theta}{\theta_0}\right) \qquad (9\text{-}180)$$

The exact solution of the problem (9-174) is

$$T(r, \theta) = \frac{4g}{\pi k}\sum_{n=1,3,5\ldots}\frac{r^2 - r^{(n\pi/\theta_0)}}{(n\pi/\theta_0)^2 - 4}\sin\left(\frac{n\pi\theta}{\theta_0}\right) \qquad (9\text{-}181)$$

The one-term approximate solution obtained above represents the first term in the series of the exact solution.

Example 9-16. Solve the steady-state heat-conduction problem with constant rate of heat generation for a region bounded by $x = 0$, $x = a$, $y = 0$,

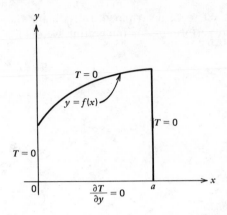

Fig. 9-8   Region considered in Example 9-16.

and $y = f(x)$ for the boundary conditions as shown in Fig. 9-8, using the Galerkin method by partial integration with respect to the y variable.

Solution. The mathematical formulation of this problem is given as

$$\frac{\partial^2 T}{\partial x^2} + \frac{\partial^2 T}{\partial y^2} + \frac{g}{k} = 0 \qquad \text{in } 0 < x < a, \ 0 < y < f(x) \qquad (9\text{-}182a)$$

$$T = 0 \qquad \qquad \text{at } x = 0, \ x = a, \text{ and } y = f(x) \qquad (9\text{-}182b)$$

$$\frac{\partial T}{\partial y} = 0 \qquad \qquad \text{at } y = 0 \qquad (9\text{-}182c)$$

The Galerkin method is now applied to the differential equation (9-182a) by partial integration with respect to the y variable. We obtain

$$\int_{y=0}^{f(x)} \left[\frac{\partial^2 \tilde{T}}{\partial x^2} + \frac{\partial^2 \tilde{T}}{\partial y^2} + \frac{g}{k} \right] \phi_i(y)\, dy = 0 \qquad (9\text{-}183)$$

We consider one-term trial solution taken as

$$\tilde{T}_1(x, y) = X(x) \cdot \phi_1(y) \qquad (9\text{-}184a)$$

where

$$\phi_1(y) = \left[y^2 - f^2(x) \right] \qquad (9\text{-}184b)$$

Clearly, this trial solution satisfies the boundary conditions at $y = 0$ and $y = f(x)$; but the function $X(x)$ is yet to be determined. Introducing the trial solution (9-184) into equation (9-183) and performing the indicated operations we obtain the following ordinary differential equation for the determination of the function $X(x)$.

$$\tfrac{2}{5}f^2 X'' + 2ff'X' + (ff'' + f'^2 - 1)X = -\frac{g}{2k} \qquad \text{in } 0 < x < a \quad \text{(9-185a)}$$

subject to

$$X = 0 \qquad \text{at } x = 0 \qquad \text{and} \qquad x = a \qquad \qquad \text{(9-185b)}$$

Once the function $f(x)$ defining the form of the boundary arc is specified, this equation can be solved and the function $X(x)$ can be determined. We consider the following special cases.

1. $y = f(x) = b$: The region is rectangular and equations (9-185) reduce to

$$X'' - \frac{5}{2b^2}X = -\frac{5g}{4b^2 k} \qquad \text{in } 0 < x < a \qquad \qquad \text{(9-186a)}$$

$$X = 0 \qquad\qquad\qquad \text{at } x = 0 \text{ and } x = a \qquad \text{(9-186b)}$$

Which is the same as that given by equations (9-170); the one term approximate solution becomes

$$\tilde{T}_1(x, y) = (y^2 - b^2)X(x) \qquad\qquad\qquad\qquad \text{(9-187)}$$

where $X(x)$ is as given by equation (9-171).

2. $y = f(x) = \beta x$:   For this case equations (9-185) reduce to

$$x^2 X'' + 5xX' + \frac{5(\beta^2 - 1)}{2\beta^2}X = \frac{5g}{4\beta^2 k} \qquad \text{in } 0 < x < a \qquad \text{(9-188a)}$$

$$X = 0 \qquad\qquad\qquad\qquad \text{at } x = 0 \text{ and } x = a \qquad \text{(9-188b)}$$

This is an Euler type equation that can be solved by seeking a solution for $X(x)$ in the form x^n. The substitution of $X = x^n$ into the homogeneous part of equation (9-188a) yields the following expression for the determination of n:

$$n^2 + 4n + \frac{5(\beta^2 - 1)}{2\beta^2} = 0 \qquad\qquad\qquad \text{(9-189a)}$$

Hence

$$n_1, n_2 = -2 \pm \sqrt{4 - B} \qquad\qquad\qquad\qquad \text{(9-189b)}$$

where

$$B \equiv \frac{5(\beta^2 - 1)}{2\beta^2} \qquad\qquad\qquad\qquad\qquad \text{(9-189c)}$$

Then the complete solution for $X(x)$ is written as

$$X(x) = c_1 x^{n_1} + c_2 x^{n_2} - P(x) \qquad (9\text{-}189d)$$

where $P(x)$ is a particular solution of equation (9-188a), which is given as $P(x) = g/2k(\beta^2 - 1)$. Then, the two coefficients c_1 and c_2 are readily determined by the application of the boundary conditions (9-188b). Knowing the function $X(x)$, the one-term approximate solution is determined from

$$\tilde{T}_1(x, y) = (y^2 - \beta^2 x^2) X(x) \qquad (9\text{-}189e)$$

9-7 TIME DEPENDENT PROBLEMS

A one-dimensional, simple time-dependent heat-conduction problem can readily be solved by the Galerkin or Ritz method as illustrated with examples later in this section. Another approach for the handling of time-dependent problems with the Galerkin or Ritz method is the removal of the time derivative from the differential equation of heat conduction by the Laplace transformation. Then, by treating the resulting system as a steady-state problem, it is solved by the Galerkin or Ritz method in the transformed domain and the desired solution is obtained after the transform is inverted. To illustrate this approach formally, we consider the following time-dependent heat-conduction problem

$$\nabla^2 T(\mathbf{r}, t) + A(\mathbf{r})T(\mathbf{r}, t) + \frac{1}{k}g(\mathbf{r}, t) = \frac{1}{\alpha}\frac{\partial T}{\partial t} \qquad \text{in } R, \ t > 0 \qquad (9\text{-}190a)$$

$$\frac{\partial T}{\partial n} + HT(\mathbf{r}_s, t) = f(\mathbf{r}_s, t) \qquad \text{on } S, \ t > 0 \qquad (9\text{-}190b)$$

$$T = F(\mathbf{r}) \qquad \text{for } t = 0, \text{ in } R \quad (9\text{-}190c)$$

Taking the Laplace transform of this system, we obtain

$$L[\bar{T}] \equiv \nabla^2 \bar{T} + \left(A - \frac{s}{\alpha}\right)\bar{T} + \left(\frac{\bar{g}}{k} + \frac{F}{\alpha}\right) = 0 \qquad \text{in } R \qquad (9\text{-}191a)$$

$$B[\bar{T}] \equiv \frac{\partial \bar{T}}{\partial n} + H\bar{T} = \bar{f}(\mathbf{r}, s) \qquad \text{on } S \qquad (9\text{-}191b)$$

where $\bar{T} \equiv \bar{T}(\mathbf{r}, s)$ and $\bar{g} \equiv \bar{g}(\mathbf{r}, s)$ are the Laplace transform of the function $T(\mathbf{r}, t)$ and $g(\mathbf{r}, t)$, respectively, and s is the Laplace transform variable.

Clearly, the system (9-191) is exactly of the same form as that given by equations (9-124) in the analysis by the Ritz method or given by equations (9-145) in the analysis by the Galerkin method. Therefore, if the system (9-191) is to be solved by the Ritz method, the corresponding variational form is obtained according to equation (9-125) as

$$I = \int_R \left[(\nabla \bar{T})^2 - \left(A - \frac{s}{\alpha} \right) \bar{T}^2 - 2 \left(\frac{\bar{g}}{k} + \frac{F}{\alpha} \right) \bar{T} \right] dv + \int_s (H\bar{T}^2 - 2\bar{f}\bar{T}) ds \quad (9\text{-}192)$$

If the system (9-191) is to be solved by the Galerkin method, the resulting equation is obtained according to equation (9-149) as

$$\int_R L[\tilde{\bar{T}}_n(\mathbf{r}, s)] \phi_i(\mathbf{r}) \, dv = 0 \quad (9\text{-}193a)$$

where $\tilde{\bar{T}}_n(\mathbf{r}, s)$ denote the n-term approximate solution chosen in the form

$$\tilde{\bar{T}}_n(\mathbf{r}, s) = \psi_0(\mathbf{r}) + \sum_{j=1}^{n} c_j \phi_j(\mathbf{r}) \quad (9\text{-}193b)$$

and the functions $\psi_0(\mathbf{r})$ and $\phi_j(\mathbf{r})$ are defined in equations (9-146).

Example 9-17. A slab in $0 \le x \le 1$ is initially at a temperature $T(x, t) = T_0(1 - x^2)$. For times $t > 0$, the boundary at $x = 0$ is kept insulated and the boundary at $x = 1$ is kept at zero temperature. Using the Galerkin method obtain an approximate solution for the temperature distribution $\tilde{T}(x, t)$ in the slab and compare it with the exact solution $T(x, t)$.

Solution. The mathematical formulation of this problem is given as

$$\frac{\partial^2 T}{\partial x^2} = \frac{1}{\alpha} \frac{\partial T(x, t)}{\partial t} \qquad \text{in } 0 < x < 1, \ t > 0 \quad (9\text{-}194a)$$

$$\frac{\partial T}{\partial x} = 0 \qquad \text{at } x = 0, \ t > 0 \quad (9\text{-}194b)$$

$$T = 0 \qquad \text{at } x = 1, \ t > 0 \quad (9\text{-}194c)$$

$$T = T_0(1 - x^2) \qquad \text{for } t = 0, \text{ in } 0 \le x \le 1 \quad (9\text{-}194d)$$

We apply the Galerkin method to equation (9-194a) with partial integration with respect to x and obtain

$$\int_{x=0}^{1} \left[\frac{\partial^2 \tilde{T}}{\partial x^2} - \frac{1}{\alpha} \frac{\partial \tilde{T}}{\partial t} \right] \phi_i(x) \, dx = 0 \quad (9\text{-}195)$$

and choose a one-term trial solution $\tilde{T}_1(x, t)$ as

$$\tilde{T}_1(x, t) = T_0 f(t) \phi_1(x) \quad (9\text{-}196a)$$

where

$$\phi_1(x) = 1 - x^2 \quad (9\text{-}196b)$$

$$f(t) = 1 \qquad \text{for } t = 0 \quad (9\text{-}196c)$$

and the function $f(t)$ is yet to be determined. Clearly, the trial solution chosen as above satisfies the initial condition and the two boundary conditions for the problem. Substituting the trial solution (9-196) into equation (9-195) and performing the indicated operations we obtain the differential equation for $f(t)$ as

$$\frac{df(t)}{dt} + \frac{5\alpha}{2} f(t) = 0 \qquad \text{for } t > 0 \qquad (9\text{-}197a)$$

$$f(t) = 1 \qquad \text{for } t = 0 \qquad (9\text{-}197b)$$

The solution for $f(t)$ is

$$f(t) = e^{-(5\alpha/2)t} \qquad (9\text{-}198)$$

and the one-term approximate solution $\tilde{T}_1(x, t)$ becomes

$$\frac{\tilde{T}(x, t)}{T_0} = (1 - x^2) e^{-(5\alpha/2)t} \qquad (9\text{-}199)$$

The exact solution of the problem (9-194) is obtained as

$$\frac{T(x, t)}{T_0} = 4 \sum_{n=0}^{\infty} (-1)^n \frac{1}{\beta_n^3} e^{-\alpha \beta_n^2 t} \cos \beta_n x \qquad (9\text{-}200a)$$

where

$$\beta_n = \frac{(2n + 1)\pi}{2} \qquad (9\text{-}200b)$$

We list in Table 9-3 a comparison of this approximate solution with the exact solution. Even the one-term approximate solution is in reasonably good agreement with the exact solution.

Improved approximations can be obtained by choosing a higher order trial solution in the form

$$\tilde{T}_n(x, t) = T_0 \sum_{i=1}^{n} f_i(t)\phi_i(x)$$

where the functions $\phi_i(x)$ satisfy the boundary conditions for the problem and the function $f_i(t)$ with $f_i(0) = 1$ are determined from the resulting ordinary differential equations obtained after the application of the Galerkin method with partial integration with respect to the x variable.

Example 9-18. The transient heat-conduction problem for a solid cylinder, $0 \le r \le 1$, with heat generation within the medium is given in the dimension-

Table 9-3 A Comparison of Approximate and Exact Solutions of Example 9-17

	$[(\tilde{T}_1 - T)/T] \times 100$		
x	$\alpha t = 0.01$	$\alpha t = 0.1$	$\alpha t = 1$
0.2	$+1$	-1	$+4.4$
0.6	$+2$	$+5.5$	$+3.1$

less form as

$$\frac{1}{r}\frac{\partial}{\partial r}\left(r\frac{\partial T}{\partial r}\right) + G(r) = \frac{\partial T(r,t)}{\partial t} \quad \text{in } 0 < r < 1, \ t > 0 \quad (9\text{-}202\text{a})$$

$$T = \text{finite} \quad \text{at } r = 0, \ t > 0 \quad (9\text{-}202\text{b})$$

$$T = 0 \quad \text{at } r = 1, \ t > 0 \quad (9\text{-}202\text{c})$$

$$T = 0 \quad \text{for } t = 0, \ 0 \le r \le 1 \quad (9\text{-}202\text{d})$$

Solve this problem by the combined application of the Laplace transform and the Galerkin method.

Solution. The Laplace transform of this problem with respect to the time variable is

$$L(\bar{T}) \equiv \frac{d}{dr}\left(r\frac{d\bar{T}}{dr}\right) - sr\bar{T} + \frac{1}{s}rG(r) = 0 \quad \text{in } 0 < r < 1 \quad (9\text{-}203\text{a})$$

$$\bar{T}(r,s) = \text{finite} \quad \text{at } r = 0 \quad (9\text{-}203\text{b})$$

$$\bar{T}(r,s) = 0 \quad \text{at } r = 1 \quad (9\text{-}203\text{c})$$

where $\bar{T}(r,s)$ is the Laplace transform of $T(r,t)$ and s is the Laplace transform variable.

The application of the Galerkin method to equation (9-203a) is written as

$$\int_{r=0}^{1} L[\tilde{\bar{T}}(r,s)]\phi_i(r)\,dr = 0 \quad (9\text{-}204)$$

where $\tilde{\bar{T}}(r,s)$ is the trial solution for $\bar{T}(r,s)$ and $\phi_i(r)$ are the functions that satisfy the boundary conditions for the problem and from which the trial solution is constructed. In this example we show that if the proper function is chosen for $\phi_i(r)$ and sufficient number of $\phi_i(r)$ are included to construct the trial solution, it is possible to obtain the exact solution for the problem.

We choose $\phi_i(r)$ as

$$\phi_i(r) = J_0(\beta_i r) \qquad (9\text{-}205a)$$

and β_i's are the roots of

$$J_0(\beta_i) = 0 \qquad (9\text{-}205b)$$

Then, each of the functions $\phi_i(r)$ satisfy the boundary conditions (9-203b, c) for the problem. We construct the trial solution $\tilde{\tilde{T}}(r, s)$ in terms of the $\phi_i(r)$ functions as

$$\tilde{\tilde{T}} = \sum_j c_j \phi_j(r) = \sum_j c_j J_0(\beta_j r) \qquad (9\text{-}206)$$

where the summation is taken over the permissible values of β_j as defined by equation (9-205b). Introducing equations (9-206) and (9-205a) into equation (9-204) we obtain

$$\int_{r=0}^{1} L\left[\sum_j c_j J_0(\beta_j r)\right] \cdot J_0(\beta_i r)\,dr = 0, \qquad i = 1, 2, \dots \qquad (9\text{-}207a)$$

or

$$\sum_j c_j \int_{r=0}^{1} \left[\frac{d}{dr}\left(r\frac{dJ_0(\beta_j r)}{dr}\right) - srJ_0(\beta_j r)\right] J_0(\beta_i r)\,dr + \frac{1}{s}\int_{r=0}^{1} rG(r)J_0(\beta_i r)\,dr = 0$$
$$(9\text{-}207b)$$

or

$$-\sum_j c_j(\beta_j^2 + s) \int_{r=0}^{1} rJ_0(\beta_j r)J_0(\beta_i r)\,dr + \frac{1}{s}\int_{r=0}^{1} rG(r)J_0(\beta_i r)\,dr = 0 \qquad (9\text{-}207c)$$

The first integral is evaluated as

$$\int_{r=0}^{1} rJ_0(\beta_j r)J_0(\beta_i r)\,dr = \begin{cases} 0 & i \neq j \\ \frac{1}{2}J_1^2(\beta_i) & i = j \end{cases} \qquad (9\text{-}208)$$

Introducing (9-208) into (9-207c), the summation drops out and we obtain

$$c_i = \frac{2}{s(s + \beta_i^2)} \frac{1}{J_1^2(\beta_i)} \int_{r=0}^{1} rG(r)J_0(\beta_i r)\,dr \qquad (9\text{-}209)$$

We introduce equation (9-209) into (9-206) after changing i to j and r to r' to obtain

$$\tilde{\tilde{T}}(r, s) = 2\sum_j \frac{1}{s(s + \beta_j^2)} \frac{J_0(\beta_j r)}{J_1^2(\beta_j)} \int_{r'=0}^{1} r'G(r')J_0(\beta_j r')\,dr' \qquad (9\text{-}210a)$$

or

$$\tilde{\tilde{T}}(r,s) = 2\sum_{j}\frac{1}{\beta_j^2}\left(\frac{1}{s} - \frac{1}{s+\beta_j^2}\right)\frac{J_0(\beta_j r)}{J_1^2(\beta_j)}\int_{r'=0}^{1} r'G(r')J_0(\beta_j r')\,dr' \quad (9\text{-}210b)$$

The Laplace transform can be inverted by means of the Laplace transform Table 7-1, cases 1 and 8; we obtain

$$\tilde{T}(r,t) = 2\sum_{j}\frac{1}{\beta_j^2}\left(1 - e^{-\beta_j^2 t}\right)\frac{J_0(\beta_j r)}{J_1^2(\beta_j)}\int_{r'=0}^{1} r'G(r')J_0(\beta_j r')\,dr' \quad (9\text{-}211a)$$

where the summation is over all eigenvalues β_j's which are the positive roots of

$$J_0(\beta_j) = 0 \quad (9\text{-}211b)$$

We note that, the solution obtained in this manner is in fact the exact solution of this problem.

REFERENCES

1. H. Schlichting, *Boundary Layer, Theory*, 6th ed., McGraw-Hill Book Co., Inc., New York, 1968, Chapter 13.

2. H. D. Landahl, *Bull. Math. Biophys.* **15**, 49–61, 1953.

3. H. J. Merk, *Appl. Sci. Res.* **4**, Section A, 435–452, 1954.

4. T. R. Goodman, *Trans. ASME* **80**, 335–342, 1958.

5. T. R. Goodman, *J. Heat Transfer* **83c**, 83–86, 1961.

6. T. R. Goodman, in T. F. Irvine and J. P. Hartnett, eds., *Advances in Heat Transfer*, Vol. 1, Academic Press, New York, 1964, pp. 52–120.

7. W. C. Reynolds and T. A. Dolton, The Use of Integral Methods in Transient Heat Transfer Analysis, Department of Mechanical Engineering, Report No. 36, Stanford University, Stanford, Calif., Sept. 1, 1958.

8. K. T. Yang, *Trans. ASME* **80**, 146–147, 1958.

9. K. T. Yang, *International Developments in Heat Transfer*, Vol. 1, ASME, New York, 1963, pp. 18–27.

10. P. J. Schneider, *J. Aerospace Sci.* **27**, 546–549, 1960.

11. T. J. Lardner and F. B. Pohle, *J. Appl. Mech.* 310–312, June 1961.

12. R. Thorsen and F. Landis, *Int. J. Heat Mass Transfer* **8**, 189–192, 1965.

13. B. Persson and L. Persson, Calculation of the Transient Temperature Distribution in Convectively Heated Bodies With Integral Method, ASME Paper No. 64-HT-19, 1964.

14. F. A. Castello, An Evaluation of Several Methods of Approximating Solutions to the Heat Conduction Equation, ASME Paper No. 63-HT-44, 1963.

15. H. H. Bengston and F. Kreith, *J. Heat Transfer* **92c**, 182–184, 1970.

16. M. N. Özışık, *Boundary Value Problems of Heat Conduction*, International Textbook Co., Scranton, P., 1968.

17. M. Altman, *Chem. Eng. Prog. Symp. Series*, **57**, 16–23, Buffalo, 1961.

18. G. Poots, *Int. J. Heat Mass Transfer* **5**, 339–348, 1962.

19. G. Poots, *Int. J. Heat Mass Transfer* **5**, 525, 1962.

20. R. H. Tien and G. E. Geiger, *J. Heat Transfer* **89c**, 230–234, 1967.

21. R. H. Tien and G. E. Geiger, *J. Heat Transfer* **90c**, 27–31, 1968.

22. J. C. Muehlbauer J. D. Hatcher, D. W. Lyons, and J. E. Sunderland, *J. Heat Transfer* **95c**, 324–331, 1973.

23. S. Cho and J. E. Sunderland, Melting or Freezing of Finite Slabs, ASME Paper 68-WA/HT-37, Dec. 1968.

24. S. H. Cho and J. E. Sunderland, *J. Heat Transfer* **91c**, 421–426, 1969.

25. K. Mody and M. N. Özışık, *Lett. Heat Mass Transfer* **2**, 487–493, 1975.

26. O. M. Griffin, *J. Heat Transfer* **95c**, 317–322, 1973.

27. O. M. Griffin, *Poly. Eng. Sci.* **12**, 140–149, 1972.

28. O. M. Griffin, *Proceedings of the 5th International Heat Transfer Conference*, Vol. 1, Tokyo, 1974, pp. 211–215.

29. O. M. Griffin, *Int. J. Heat Mass Transfer* **20**, 675–683, 1977.

30. W. F. Ames, *Nonlinear Partial Differential Equations in Engineering*, Academic Press, New York, 1965.

31. W. F. Ames, *Nonlinear Ordinary Differential Equations in Transport Process*, Academic Press, New York, 1968.

32. R. Weinstock, *Calculus of Variations*, McGraw-Hill Book Co., Inc., New York, 1952.

33. I. M. Gelfand and S. V. Fomin, *Calculus of Variations*, Prentice-Hall, New Jersey, 1963.

34. P. M. Morse and H. Feshbach, *Methods of Theoretical Physics*, McGraw-Hill Book Co., Inc., New York, 1953.

35. A. R. Forsythe, *Calculus of Variations*, Dover Publications, New York, 1960.

36. S. G. Mikhlin, *Variational Methods in Mathematical Physics*, Macmillan Company, New York, 1964.

37. R. S. Schechter, *The Variational Method in Engineering*, McGraw-Hill Book Co., Inc., New York, 1967.

38. M. A. Biot, *J. Aeronaut. Sci.* **24**, 857–873, 1957.

39. M. A. Biot, *J. Aeronaut. Sci.* **26**, 367–381, 1959.

40. P. D. Richardson, *J. Heat Transfer* **86c**, 298–299, 1964.

41. V. S. Arpaci and C. M. Vest, Variational Formulation of Transformed Diffusion Problems, ASME Paper No. 67-HT-77.

42. T. J. Lardner, *AIAA J.* **1**, 196–206, 1963.

43. M. E. Gurtin, *Quart. Appl. Math.* **22**, 252–256, 1964.

44. B. A. Finlayson and L. E. Scriven, *Int. J. Heat Mass Transfer* **10**, 799–821, 1967.

45. D. F. Hays and H. N. Curd, *Int. J. Heat Mass Transfer* **11**, 285–295, 1968.

46. P. Rafalski and W. Zyszkowski, *AIAA J.* **6**, 1606, 1968.

47. W. Zyszkowski, *J. Heat Transfer* **91c**, 77–82, 1969.

48. D. Djukic and B. Vujanovic, *Z. Angew. Math. Mech.* **51**, 611–616, 1971.

49. B. Vujanovic and A. M. Straus, *AIAA J.* **9**, 327–330, 1971.

50. B. Krajewski, *Int. J. Heat Mass Transfer* **18**, 495–502, 1975.

51. W. Ritz, *J. Reine Angewandte Math.* **135**, 1–61, 1908.

52. N. Kryloff, *Memorial Sci. Math. Paris* **49**, 1931.

53. L. V. Kantorovich and V. I. Krylov, *Approximate Methods of Higher Analysis*, John Wiley and Sons, Inc., New York, 1964.

54. L. Collatz, *The Numerical Treatment of Differential Equations*, (English Translation), Springer-Verlag, Heidelberg, 1960.

55. S. H. Crandall, *Engineering Analysis*, McGraw-Hill Book Co., Inc., New York, 1956.

56. V. S. Arpaci, *Conduction Heat Transfer*, Addison-Wesley Publishing Company, Reading, Mass., 1966.

57. G. B. Galerkin, *Vestnik Inzhenerov Teckhnikov*, p. 879, 1915.

58. N. W. McLachlan, *Phil. Mag.* **36**, 600, 1945.

59. D, Dicker and M. B. Friedman, *J. Appl. Mech.* **30**, 493–499, 1963.
60. F. Erdogan, *J. Heat Transfer* **85c**, 203–208, 1963.
61. L. J. Snyder, T. W. Spiggs, and W. E. Stewart, *AICHE J.*, **10**, 535–540, 1964.
62. B. A. Finlayson and L. E. Scriven, *Chem. Eng. Sci.* **20**, 395–404, 1965.
63. P. A. Laura and A. J. Faulstich, *Int. J. Heat Mass Transfer* **11**, 297–303, 1968.
64. A. H. Eraslan, *J. Heat Transfer* **91c**, 212–220, 1969.
65. A. H. Eraslan, *AIAA J.* **10**, 1759–1766, 1966.
66. A. H. Eraslan and W. Frost, B. G. Galerkin Method for Heat Transfer Solution in Longitudinal Convection Fins of Arbitrary Shape with Nonuniform Surface Film Coefficients, ASME, Paper No. 68-HT-5, 1968.

PROBLEMS

9-1   A semi-infinite region $x > 0$ is initially at zero temperature. For times $t > 0$, the convection boundary condition at the surface $x = 0$ is given as $- k(\partial T/\partial x) + hT = f_1$, where $f_1 = $ constant. Obtain an expression for the temperature distribution $T(x,t)$ in the medium using the integral method with a cubic polynomial representation for temperature.

9-2   A semi-infinite medium $x > 0$ is initially at a uniform temperature T_i. For times $t > 0$, the boundary surface at $x = 0$ is subjected to a prescribed heat flux, that is, $- k(\partial T/\partial x) = f(t)$ at $x = 0$, where $f(t)$ varies with time. Obtain an expression for the temperature distribution $T(x,t)$ in the medium using the integral method and a cubic polynomial representation for $T(x,t)$.

9-3   A region exterior to a cylindrical hole of radius $r = b$ (i.e., $r > b$) is initially at zero temperature. For times $t > 0$ the boundary surface at $r = b$ is kept at a constant temperature T_0. Obtain an expression for the temperature distribution in the medium using the integral method with a second-degree polynomial representation modified by $\ln r$ for $T(x,t)$.

9-4   A semi-infinite medium $x > 0$ is initially at zero temperature. For times $t > 0$ heat is generated in the medium at a constant rate of g W/m^3, while heat is removed from the boundary surface at $x = 0$ as $k(\partial T/\partial x) = f = $ constant. Obtain an expression for the temperature distribution $T(x,t)$ in the medium for times $t > 0$, using the integral method and a cubic polynomial representation for $T(x,t)$.

9-5   Consider a heat-conduction problem for a semi-infinite medium $x > 0$ with the fourth-power radiative heat transfer at the boundary surface $x = 0$ defined as

$$\frac{\partial^2 T}{\partial x^2} = \frac{1}{\alpha}\frac{\partial T}{\partial t} \qquad \text{in } x > 0,\ t > 0$$

$$k\frac{\partial T}{\partial x} = \sigma\varepsilon(T_s^4 - T_\infty^4) \qquad \text{at } x = 0,\ t > 0$$

$$T = T_i \qquad \text{for } t = 0,\ x \geq 0$$

where T_s is the surface temperature. Apply the formal solution given by equation (9-52) for the solution of this problem. For the case of $T_\infty = 0$, by performing the resulting integration analytically obtain an expression for the surface temperature T_s as a function of the time.

9-6 A slab, in $0 \le x \le 1$, is initially at a nonuniform temperature $T(x, t) = \beta x$. For times $t > 0$, the boundary at $x = 0$ is kept insulated and the boundary at $x = 1$ is kept at zero temperature. Using the moment method obtain an expression for the temperature distribution $T(x, t)$ in the slab for times $t > 0$ by choosing (1) a second-degree polynomial and (2) a cubic polynomial representation for $T(x, t)$.

9-7 In Section 9-3 we considered the one-dimensional variational problem given by equation (9-86) and derived the equivalent Euler-Lagrange equation given by equation (9-100). Now consider the two-dimensional variational form given as

$$I = \int_{x_1}^{x_2} \int_{y_1}^{y_2} F(x, y; T; T_x, T_y) \, dx \, dy$$

subject to prescribed temperatures at the boundaries. Following a procedure similar to the one described in Section 9-3, obtain the equivalent Euler-Lagrange equation.

9-8 Starting with the following Euler-Lagrange equation

$$\frac{\partial}{\partial x}\left(k_1 \frac{\partial T}{\partial x}\right) + \frac{\partial}{\partial y}\left(k_2 \frac{\partial T}{\partial y}\right) + g = 0 \qquad \text{in } R$$

$$T = f(x, y) \qquad\qquad\qquad\qquad \text{on } S \text{ of region } R$$

show that the equivalent variational form is given by

$$I = \int\int_R \left[k_1 \left(\frac{\partial T}{\partial x}\right)^2 + k_2 \left(\frac{\partial T}{\partial y}\right)^2 - 2gT \right] dx \, dy$$

9-9 Consider the following steady-state heat-conduction problem

$$\frac{d^2 T}{dx^2} + \frac{1}{k} g(x) = 0 \qquad \text{in } 0 < x < L$$

$$-\frac{dT}{dx} + h_1 T = f_1 \qquad \text{at } x = 0$$

$$\frac{dT}{dx} + h_2 T = f_2 \qquad \text{at } x = L$$

Obtain the equivalent variational form of this heat-conduction problem.

9-10 Consider the following steady-state heat-conduction problem for a rectangular region $0 < x < a, 0 < y < b$

$$\frac{\partial^2 T}{\partial x^2} + \frac{\partial^2 T}{\partial y^2} = 0 \qquad \text{in } 0 < x < a, \ 0 < y < b$$

$$T = 0 \qquad \text{at } y = 0, \ y = b$$

$$\frac{\partial T}{\partial x} = 0 \qquad \text{at } x = 0$$

$$T = T_0 \sin\left(\frac{3\pi y}{b}\right) \qquad \text{at } x = a$$

Solve this problem by the Galerkin method using partial integration with respect to the y variable for a trial function chosen in the form $\tilde{T}_1(x, y) = f(x) \sin(3\pi y/b)$ and compare this result with the exact solution.

9-11   Solve the following steady-state heat-conduction problem

$$\frac{\partial^2 T}{\partial x^2} + \frac{\partial^2 T}{\partial y^2} + \frac{1}{k}g = 0 \qquad \text{in the region shown in Fig. (9-7b)}$$

$$T = 0 \qquad \text{on the boundaries}$$

using the Galerkin method and a one-term trial solution chosen in the form

$$\tilde{T}_1(x, y) = c_1(y - \alpha x)(y + \beta x)(L - x)$$

9-12   Solve the following steady-state heat-conduction problem

$$\frac{\partial^2 T}{\partial x^2} + \frac{\partial^2 T}{\partial y^2} + \frac{1}{k}g = 0 \qquad \text{in the region shown in Fig. (9-7c) for } a = b = 1.$$

$$T = 0 \qquad \text{on the boundaries}$$

using the Galerkin method and a one-term trial solution.

9-13   Repeat the solution of Example 9-8 listed in Table 9-2 for the case $A = B = 2$.

NOTES

1.   The result in equation (9-96) is derived as

$$\frac{d}{dx}\left(\frac{\partial F}{\partial T_x}\delta T\right) = \frac{d}{dx}\left(\frac{\partial F}{\partial T_x}\right)\delta T + \frac{\partial F}{\partial T_x}\frac{d}{dx}(\delta T)$$

$$= \frac{d}{dx}\left(\frac{\partial F}{\partial T_x}\right)\delta T + \frac{\partial F}{\partial T_x}\delta\left(\frac{dT}{dx}\right)$$

$$= \frac{d}{dx}\left(\frac{\partial F}{\partial T_x}\right)\delta T + \frac{\partial F}{\partial T_x}\delta T_x \tag{1}$$

where we utilized the property that the differentiation and the variation operators commute, that is, $(d/dx)\delta T = \delta(dT/dx)$. Rearranging this result we obtain

$$\frac{\partial F}{\partial T_x}\delta T_x = \frac{d}{dx}\left(\frac{\partial F}{\partial T_x}\delta T\right) - \frac{d}{dx}\left(\frac{\partial F}{\partial T_x}\right)\delta T \tag{2}$$

which is the result given by equation (9-96).

2. Consider the following vector identity

$$\nabla\cdot(u\mathbf{V}) = \nabla u\cdot\mathbf{V} + u\nabla\cdot\mathbf{V} \tag{1}$$

Let

$$u \equiv \delta T \quad \text{and} \quad \mathbf{V} \equiv \nabla T \tag{2}$$

Then

$$\begin{aligned}
\nabla\cdot(\delta T\nabla T) &= \nabla(\delta T)\cdot\nabla T + \delta T\nabla\cdot\nabla T \\
&= \nabla(\delta T)\cdot\nabla T + \delta T\nabla^2 T
\end{aligned} \tag{3}$$

or

$$\delta T\nabla^2 T = \nabla\cdot(\delta T\nabla T) - \nabla(\delta T)\cdot\nabla T \tag{4}$$

3. The following integral is useful to perform computations of this type

$$\int_0^L x^k(L-x)^m\,dx = \frac{k!m!}{(k+m+1)!}L^{k+m+1}$$

CHAPTER 10

PHASE-CHANGE PROBLEMS

Transient heat-transfer problems involving melting or soldification generally referred to as "phase-change" or "moving-boundary" problems are important in many engineering applications such as in the making of ice, the freezing of food, the solidification of metals in the casting, and the cooling of large masses of igneous rock. The solution of such problems is inherently difficult because the interface between the solid and liquid phases is moving as the latent heat is absorbed or released at the interface; as a result the location of the solid-liquid interface is not known a priori and must follow as a part of the solution. In the solidification of pure substances, like water, the solidification takes place at a discrete temperature, and the solid and liquid phases are separated by a *sharp moving interface*. On the other hand, in the solidification of mixtures, alloys, and impure materials the solidification takes place over an extended temperature range, and as a result the solid and liquid phases are separated by a *two-phase moving* region.

Early analytic work on the solution of phase change problems include those by Lamé and Clapeyron [1] in 1831 and by Stefan [2] in 1891 in relation to the ice formation. The fundamental feature of this type of problems is that the boundary is both unknown and moving, and that the parabolic heat-conduction equation is to be solved in a region whose boundary is also to be determined. Although the references [1, 2] are the early published work on this subject, the exact solution of a more general phase-change problem was discussed by F. Neumann in his lectures in the 1860's, but his lecture notes containing these solutions were not published until 1912. Since then, many phase-change problems have appeared in the literature, but the exact solutions are limited to a number of idealized situations involving semi-infinite or infinite regions and subject to simple boundary and initial conditions [3]. Because of the nonlinearity of such problems, the superposition principle is not applicable and each case must be treated separately. When exact solutions are not available, approximate, semi-analytic, and numerical methods can be used to solve the phase-change problems. We now present a brief discussion of various methods of solution of phase-change problems.

The *integral method*, which dates back to von Kármán and Pohlhausen who used it for the approximate analysis of boundary layer equations, was applied by Goodman [4, 5] to solve a one-dimensional transient melting problem, and subsequently by many other investigators [6–15] to solve various types of one-dimensional transient phase-change problems. This method provides a relatively straightforward and simple approach for approximate analysis of one-dimensional transient phase-change problems. The *Variational Formulation* derived by Biot [16] on the basis of an irreversible thermodynamic argument, was used in the solution of one-dimensional, transient phase-change problems [17–21]. The *moving heat source* (or the *integral equation*) *method*, originally applied by Lightfoot [22] to solve Neuman's problem, is based on the concept of representing the liberation (or absorption) of latent heat by a moving plane heat source (or sink) located at the solid-liquid interface. In this method, the analysis of the phase-change problem is transformed to the solution of an integral equation for the location of the solid-liquid interface. The Green's function approach used by some investigators [23–26] is the same as the moving heat source method. Further applications of reducing phase-change problems to an integral equation for the location of solid-liquid interface are discussed by Rubenstein [27]. The *perturbation method* has been used by several investigators [28–34]; however, the analysis becomes very complicated if higher order solutions are to be determined; also it is difficult to use this method for problems involving more than one dimension. The *embedding technique*, first introduced by Boley [35] to solve the problem of melting of a slab, has been applied to solve various phase-change problems [36–41]. The method appears to be versatile to obtain solutions for one, two, or three dimensions and to develop general starting solutions. A *variable eigenvalue approach* developed in connection with the solution of heat-conduction problems involving time-dependent boundary condition parameters [42, 43] has been applied to solve one dimensional transient phase-change problems [44]. The method is applicable to solve similar problems in the cylindrical or spherical symmetry. The *electrical network analog method* often used in early applications [45–49] has now been replaced by purely numerical methods of solution because of the availability of high-speed digital computers. A large number of purely numerical solutions of phase-change problems has been reported [50–73]. However, only few of these solutions may be generalized to handle phase-change problems in several dimensions or in situations in which the phase change takes place over a temperature range rather than at a discrete melting point. The writing down of the finite-difference or the finite-element equations and solving them numerically in the main part of the solid and liquid regions poses no problem; but the difficulty arises at the solid-liquid interface where the temperature gradient is discontinuous and the location of the interface is not known a priori.

Experimental investigation of phase-change problems is important in order to check the validity of various analytic models; but, only a limited number of experimental studies are available in the literature [74–78].

Additional reviews of phase-change problems and discussion of various other developments in this field may be found in references [79–83].

10-1 BOUNDARY CONDITIONS AT THE MOVING INTERFACE

We now present a discussion of the boundary conditions at the solid-liquid interface for the phase-change problems. We focus our attention on situations in which melting (or solidification) takes place at a discrete melting-point temperature and as a result the solid and liquid phases are separated by a *sharp interface*. The fundamental relations to be satisfied at such an interface should express the facts that (1) the temperatures of the adjacent phases should be equal to the same prescribed constant temperature, T_m, which is normally the melting (or the solidification) temperature of the material, and (2) an energy balance must be satisfied at the interface. The mathematical expressions defining these requirements are now derived with reference to the one-dimensional, transient *solidification* process illustrated in Fig. 10-1a. In general the solid and liquid densities are not the same, therefore some motion of liquid resulting from the density change is expected in actual situation. Usually the solid density ρ_s is greater than the liquid density ρ_l (except for water, bismuth, and antimony) at the melting point and, as a result, some liquid motion is expected toward the interface during solidification. In the following analysis we assume the density ρ to be the same for both phases so that the convective velocity resulting from the volumetric effects can be neglected.

The requirement on the continuity of temperature at the solid-liquid interface $x = s(t)$ is given as

$$T_s(x, t) = T_l(x, t) = T_m \qquad \text{at } x = \overset{\cdot}{s}(t) \qquad (10\text{-}1)$$

where $T_s(x, t)$ and $T_l(x, t)$ are the temperatures of the solid and the liquid phases, respectively, and T_m is the melting (or solidification) temperature which is constant for a given substance.

The energy equation at the solid-liquid interface for the solidification

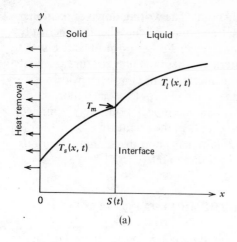

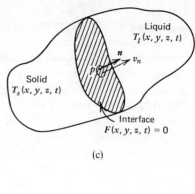

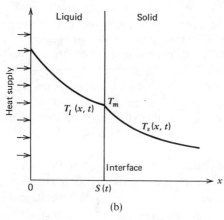

Fig. 10-1 Nomenclature and coordinates for the derivation of the boundary condition at the solid-liquid interface. (a) Solidification: interface moving in the positive x-direction (b) Melting: interface moving in the positive x-direction (c) Solidification in three dimensions: interface moving in the n direction.

problem illustrated in Fig. 10-1a can be stated as

$$\begin{bmatrix} \text{the heat flux in} \\ \text{the negative } x \\ \text{direction through} \\ \text{the solid phase} \end{bmatrix} - \begin{bmatrix} \text{the heat flux} \\ \text{in the negative } x \\ \text{direction through} \\ \text{the liquid phase} \end{bmatrix} = \begin{bmatrix} \text{rate of heat} \\ \text{liberated during} \\ \text{solidification} \\ \text{per unit area of} \\ \text{interface} \end{bmatrix} \quad (10\text{-}2a)$$

or

$$-(q_s - q_l) = \rho L \frac{ds(t)}{dt} \qquad \text{at } x = s(t) \qquad (10\text{-}2b)$$

where q_l and q_s are the heat fluxes (in W/m^2 or Btu/hr ft^2) in the positive x direction in the liquid and the solid phases, respectively, and the minus sign on the left-hand side is included to ensure that the heat flow is in the negative x direction. Here, L is the latent heat of melting (or solidification) per unit mass of the material (in Ws/kg or Btu/lb), ρ is the density (in kg/m^3 or 1b/ft^3) and $s(t)$ is the location of the solid-liquid interface. When the heat transfer on both phases is by pure conduction, we have

$$q_l = -k_l \frac{\partial T_l}{\partial x} \quad \text{and} \quad q_s = -k_s \frac{\partial T_s}{\partial x} \tag{10-3}$$

Then the interface energy-balance equation (10-2b) takes the form

$$k_s \frac{\partial T_s}{\partial x} - k_l \frac{\partial T_l}{\partial x} = \rho L \frac{ds(t)}{dt} \quad \text{at } x = s(t) \tag{10-4a}$$

This equation is derived for the solidification process shown in Fig. 10-1a in which the solid-liquid interface is moving in the positive x direction. It can readily be verified that equation (10-4a) is also valid for the melting problem illustrated in Fig. 10-1b in which the solid-liquid interface is also moving in the positive x direction.

We note that in equation (10-4a) the quantity $ds(t)/dt$ is the velocity of the interface in the positive x direction. If we denote this velocity by v_x, we write

$$\frac{ds(t)}{dt} \equiv v_x \tag{10-4b}$$

Then equation (10-4a) is written as

$$k_s \frac{\partial T_s}{\partial x} - k_l \frac{\partial T_l}{\partial x} = \rho L v_x \quad \text{at } x = s(t) \tag{10-4c}$$

Equations (10-4) are derived by assuming that the heat transfer in both phases is by pure conduction. If the heat transfer on the liquid side is controlled by *convection* characterized by a heat transfer coefficient h rather than conduction, equation (10-4a) should be modified by replacing the conductive heat flux term for the liquid phase by the convective heat flux term. For example, for the solidification problem illustrated in Fig. 10-1a, if the heat transfer on the liquid phase is by convection, the interface equation (10-4a) takes the form

$$k_s \frac{\partial T_s}{\partial x} - h(T_\infty - T_m) = \rho L \frac{ds(t)}{dt} \quad \text{at } x = s(t) \tag{10-5}$$

where h is the heat transfer coefficient for the liquid side, T_∞ is the bulk temperature of the liquid phase, and T_m is the melting point temperature at the interface.

It is to be noted that, for the melting problem shown in Fig. 10-1b, if heat transfer on the liquid side is by convection, equation (10-5) is applicable by changing the minus sign before h to positive.

The interface boundary conditions given by equations (10-4a) and (10-5) are nonlinear. To show the nonlinearity of these equations we need to relate $ds(t)/dt$ to the derivative of temperatures. This is done by taking the total derivative of the interface equation (10-1).

$$\left[\frac{\partial T_s}{\partial x}dx + \frac{\partial T_s}{\partial t}dt\right]_{x=s(t)} = \left[\frac{\partial T_l}{\partial x}dx + \frac{\partial T_l}{\partial t}dt\right]_{x=s(t)} = 0 \qquad (10\text{-}6a)$$

or

$$\frac{\partial T_s}{\partial x}\frac{ds(t)}{dt} + \frac{\partial T_s}{\partial t} = \frac{\partial T_l}{\partial x}\frac{ds(t)}{dt} + \frac{\partial T_l}{\partial t} = 0 \qquad \text{at } x = s(t) \qquad (10\text{-}6b)$$

which can be rearranged as

$$\frac{ds(t)}{dt} = -\frac{\partial T_s/\partial t}{\partial T_s/\partial x} \qquad \text{and} \qquad \frac{ds(t)}{dt} = -\frac{\partial T_l/\partial t}{\partial T_l/\partial x} \qquad (10\text{-}6c)$$

Introducing these results, for example, into equation (10-4a) we obtain

$$k_s\frac{\partial T_s}{\partial x} - k_l\frac{\partial T_l}{\partial x} = -\rho L\frac{\partial T_s/\partial t}{\partial T_s/\partial x} = -\rho L\frac{\partial T_l/\partial t}{\partial T_s/\partial x} \qquad (10\text{-}7)$$

The nonlinearity of this equation is now apparent.

Effects of Density Variation

To illustrate the effects of different density for the liquid and solid phases (i.e., $\rho_s \neq \rho_l$) on the energy-balance equation at the interface, we refer to the solidification problem illustrated in Fig. 10-1a. We assume $\rho_s > \rho_l$ and denote the speeds in the positive x direction for the motion of the interface by v_x and for the motion of the liquid resulting from the volumetric effects by v_l. Let, H_s and H_l denote the enthalpies (i.e., the sum of the sensible and the latent heat content per unit mass of the material) for the solid and liquid phases, respectively. Then, by noting that the actual motion of the interface is in the positive x direction while the convective motion is in the opposite direction, the interface energy-balance equation (10-4c) is modified as

$$k_s\frac{\partial T_s}{\partial x} - k_l\frac{\partial T_l}{\partial x} = (\rho_l H_l - \rho_s H_s)v_x - \rho_l H_l v_l \qquad \text{at } x = s(t) \qquad (10\text{-}8)$$

The mass-conservation equation at the interface may be written as

$$(\rho_l - \rho_s)v_x = \rho_l v_l \qquad (10\text{-}9a)$$

or

$$v_l = -\frac{\rho_s - \rho_l}{\rho_l} v_x \qquad (10\text{-}9b)$$

Eliminating v_l from equation (10-8) by means of equation (10-9b) we obtain

$$k_s \frac{\partial T_s}{\partial x} - k_l \frac{\partial T_l}{\partial x} = \rho_s L v_x \qquad (10\text{-}10a)$$

since

$$H_l - H_s = L = \text{the latent heat} \qquad (10\text{-}10b)$$

which is similar to equation (10-4c) except ρ is now replaced by ρ_s.

If the effects of different density for the liquid and solid phases are to be included in the analysis, then the energy equation for the liquid phase should include the convection term and the analysis becomes more involved.

Generalization to Three-Dimension

We now generalize the interface boundary conditions given above by equations (10-1) and (10-4) for the case of three-dimensional solidification illustrated in Fig. 10-1c. In this figure, the solid and liquid phases are separated by a sharp interface defined by the equation

$$F(x, y, z, t) = 0 \qquad (10\text{-}11)$$

Let, $\mathbf{n}$ denote the unit vector normal to this interface at any location P on the interface and pointing toward the liquid region and v_n be the velocity of this interface in the $\mathbf{n}$ direction at the same location P. We assume that the densities of the solid and liquid phases are the same. Then, the boundary conditions at the interface corresponding to the equations (10-1) and (10-4c) are given, respectively, as

$$T_s(x, y, z, t) = T_l(x, y, z, t) = T_m \qquad \text{at } F(x, y, z, t) = 0 \qquad (10\text{-}12)$$

$$k_s \frac{\partial T_s}{\partial n} - k_l \frac{\partial T_l}{\partial n} = \rho L v_n \qquad \text{at } F(x, y, z, t) = 0 \qquad (10\text{-}13)$$

where $\partial/\partial n$ denotes the derivative at the interface along the normal direction vector $\mathbf{n}$. The interface energy balance equation (10-13) is not in a form suitable for developments of analytic or numerical solutions of the phase-change problems. An alternative form of equation (10-13) resembling equation (10-4a) can be derived as now described.

Equation (10-13) can also be written as (see Note 1 for the derivation of this expression)

$$k_s \nabla T_s \cdot \nabla F - k_l \nabla T_l \cdot \nabla F = -\rho L \frac{\partial F}{\partial t} \qquad (10\text{-}14\text{a})$$

where

$$\nabla T_i \cdot \nabla F \equiv \frac{\partial T_i}{\partial x} \frac{\partial F}{\partial x} + \frac{\partial T_i}{\partial y} \frac{\partial F}{\partial y} + \frac{\partial T_i}{\partial z} \frac{\partial F}{\partial z}, \qquad i = s \text{ or } l \qquad (10\text{-}14\text{b})$$

The temperature gradients $\partial T_i / \partial x$ and $\partial T_i / \partial y$, $i = s$ or l, at the interface can be related to $\partial T_i / \partial z$ by noting that $\nabla T_i = c \nabla F$ according to equation (4) of Note 1. We find

$$\frac{\partial T_i}{\partial x} = \frac{\partial F / \partial x}{\partial F / \partial z} \frac{\partial T_i}{\partial z} \qquad i = s \text{ or } l \qquad (10\text{-}15\text{a})$$

$$\frac{\partial T_i}{\partial y} = \frac{\partial F / \partial y}{\partial F / \partial z} \frac{\partial T_i}{\partial z} \qquad i = s \text{ or } l \qquad (10\text{-}15\text{b})$$

Introducing equations (10-15) into equation (10-14b) we obtain

$$\nabla T_i \cdot \nabla F = \frac{\partial T_i}{\partial z} \frac{\partial F}{\partial z} \left[1 + \left(\frac{\partial F / \partial x}{\partial F / \partial z} \right)^2 + \left(\frac{\partial F / \partial y}{\partial F / \partial z} \right)^2 \right], \qquad i = s \text{ or } l \qquad (10\text{-}16)$$

substituting equation (10-16) into equation (10-14a) we find

$$\frac{\partial F}{\partial z} \left[1 + \left(\frac{\partial F / \partial x}{\partial F / \partial z} \right)^2 + \left(\frac{\partial F / \partial y}{\partial F / \partial z} \right)^2 \right] \left[k_s \frac{\partial T_s}{\partial z} - k_l \frac{\partial T_l}{\partial z} \right] = -\rho L \frac{\partial F}{\partial t}$$

$$\text{on the interface} \qquad (10\text{-}17)$$

If the equation of the interface is expressed in the form

$$F(x, y, z, t) \equiv z - s(x, y, t) = 0 \qquad (10\text{-}18\text{a})$$

Then,

$$\frac{\partial F}{\partial x} = -\frac{\partial s}{\partial x}, \qquad \frac{\partial F}{\partial y} = -\frac{\partial s}{\partial y}, \qquad \frac{\partial F}{\partial z} = 1, \qquad \text{and} \qquad \frac{\partial F}{\partial t} = -\frac{\partial s}{\partial t} \quad (10\text{-}18\text{b})$$

Introducing equations (10-18b) into equation (10-17) we obtain

$$\left[1 + \left(\frac{\partial s}{\partial x} \right)^2 + \left(\frac{\partial s}{\partial y} \right)^2 \right] \left[k_s \frac{\partial T_s}{\partial z} - k_l \frac{\partial T_l}{\partial z} \right] = \rho L \frac{\partial s}{\partial t} \qquad \text{at } z = s(x, y, t) \quad (10\text{-}19)$$

This form of the interface energy balance equation is analogous to the form given by Eq. (10-4a) for the one-dimensional case; therefore, it is more suitable for numerical or analytic purposes. We now examine some special cases of the result given by equation (10-19).

For the two-dimensional problem involving (x, z, t) variables, if the location of the solid-liquid interface is specified by the relation $F(x, z, t) = z - s(x, t) = 0$, then equation (10-19) reduces to

$$\left[1 + \left(\frac{\partial s}{\partial x}\right)^2\right]\left[k_s \frac{\partial T_s}{\partial z} - k_l \frac{\partial T_l}{\partial z}\right] = \rho L \frac{\partial s}{\partial t} \qquad \text{at } z = s(x, t) \quad (10\text{-}20a)$$

where $T_i \equiv T_i(x, z, t)$, $i = s$ or l. This equation is the same as that used in references [24], [38], and [39] for interface boundary condition in the analysis of two-dimensional phase-change problems.

For the one-dimensional problem involving (z, t) variables, if the location of the solid-liquid interface is given by $F(z, t) = z - s(t) = 0$, equation (10-19) reduces to

$$k_s \frac{\partial T_s}{\partial z} - k_l \frac{\partial T_l}{\partial z} = \rho L \frac{ds}{dt} \qquad \text{at } z = s(t) \qquad (10\text{-}20b)$$

which is identical to equation (10-4a) if z is replaced by x.

In the cylindrical coordinate system involving (r, ϕ, t) variables, if the location of the solid-liquid interface is given by $F(r, \phi, t) = r - s(\phi, t) = 0$, then the corresponding form of equation (10-19) becomes

$$\left[1 + \frac{1}{s^2}\left(\frac{\partial s}{\partial \phi}\right)^2\right]\left[k_s \frac{\partial T_s}{\partial r} - k_l \frac{\partial T_l}{\partial r}\right] = \rho L \frac{\partial s}{\partial t} \qquad \text{at } r = s(\phi, t) \quad (10\text{-}20c)$$

where $T_i \equiv T_i(r, \phi, t)$, $i = s$ or l.

In the cylindrical coordinate system involving (r, z, t) variables, if the location of the solid-liquid interface is given as $F(r, z, t) = z - s(r, t) = 0$, the interface equation takes the form

$$\left[1 + \left(\frac{\partial s}{\partial r}\right)^2\right]\left[k_s \frac{\partial T_s}{\partial z} - k_l \frac{\partial T_l}{\partial z}\right] = \rho L \frac{\partial s}{\partial t} \qquad \text{at } z = s(r, t) \quad (10\text{-}20d)$$

where $T_i \equiv T_i(r, z, t)$, $i = s$ or l.

Dimensionless Variables of Phase-Change Problem

The role of dimensionless variables in phase-change problems is envisioned better if the interface energy-balance equation (10-4a) is expressed in the dimensionless form as

$$\frac{\partial \theta_s}{\partial \eta} - \frac{k_l}{k_s} \frac{\partial \theta_l}{\partial \eta} = \frac{1}{Ste} \frac{d\delta(\tau)}{d\tau} \qquad (10\text{-}21a)$$

where various dimensionless quantities are defined as

$$\theta_i(\tau, \eta) = \frac{T_i(x, t) - T_m}{T_m - T_0}, \quad i = s \text{ or } l; \quad \eta = x/b;$$

$$\delta(\tau) = \frac{s(t)}{b}; \quad \tau = \frac{\alpha_s t}{b^2}; \quad Ste = \frac{C_{ps}(T_m - T_0)}{L} \quad (10\text{-}21b)$$

Here, b is a reference length, L is the latent heat, C_{ps} is the specific heat, T_m is the melting temperature, T_0 is a reference temperature, $s(t)$ is the location of the solid-liquid interface and Ste is the *Stefan number*, named after J. Stefan. The above dimensionless variables, other than the Stefan number, are similar to those frequently used in the standard heat-conduction problems; the Stefan number is associated with the phase-change process.

The above definition of the Stefan number implies that it signifies the importance of sensible heat relative to the latent heat. If the Stefan number is small, say less than approximately 0.1, the heat released or absorbed by the interface during phase change is affected very little as a result of the variation of the sensible heat content of the material during the propagation of heat through the medium. For materials such as aluminum, copper, iron, lead, nickel, tin, etc., the Stefan number based on a temperature difference between the melting temperature and the room temperature varies from 1 to 3. For melting or solidification processes taking place with much smaller temperature differences, the Stefan number is much smaller. For example, in phase-change problems associated with thermal energy storage, the temperature differences are small; as a result the Stefan number is generally smaller than 0.1.

10-2 EXACT SOLUTION OF PHASE-CHANGE PROBLEMS

The exact solution of phase-change problems is limited to few idealized situations [3, 86, 94] for the reasons stated previously. To illustrate the implications of the exact methods of analysis we present in this section some of these exact solutions.

Example 10-1. *Solidification of a Supercooled Liquid in a Half-Space (One-Region Problem).* A Supercooled liquid at a uniform temperature T_i which is lower than the solidification (or melting) temperature T_m of the solid phase is confined to a half-space $x > 0$. It is assumed that the solidification starts at the surface $x = 0$ at time $t = 0$ and the solid-liquid interface moves in the positive x direction. Figure 10-2 illustrates the geometry, the coordinates, and the temperature profiles. The solid phase being at the

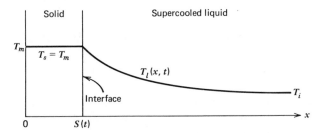

Fig. 10-2 Solidification of supercooled liquid in a half-space. One-region problem.

uniform temperature T_m throughout, there is no heat transfer through it; the heat released during the solidification process is transferred into the supercooled liquid and raises its temperature. The temperature distribution is unknown only in the liquid phase, hence the problem is a one-region problem. In the following analysis we determine the temperature distribution in the liquid phase and the location of the solid-liquid interface as a function of time.

Solution. Before presenting the analysis for the solution of this problem we discuss the implications of the supercooling of a liquid. If a liquid is cooled very slowly, the bulk temperature may be lowered below the solidification temperature and the liquid in such a state is called a supercooled liquid. After supercooling reaches some critical temperature, the solidification starts, and heat released during freezing raises the temperature of the supercooled liquid. Little is known about the actual condition of the solid-liquid interface during the solidification of a supercooled liquid. Recent work [87, 88] on this subject has shown that during the solidification of supercooled water the interface may grow as a dentritic surface consisting of thin, plate-like crystals of ice interspersed in water rather than moving as a sharp interface. As a result, it is a very complicated matter to include in the analysis the effects of irregular surface conditions. Therefore, in the following solution only an idealized situation is considered. Namely, it is assumed that the solid-liquid interface is a sharp surface whose motion is similar to that encountered in the normal solidification process.

The mathematical formulation for the liquid-phase is given as

$$\frac{\partial^2 T_l}{\partial x^2} = \frac{1}{\alpha_l}\frac{\partial T_l(x,t)}{\partial t} \quad \text{in } s(t) < x < \infty, \ t > 0 \qquad (10\text{-}22a)$$

$$T_l(x,t) \to T_i \quad \text{as } x \to \infty, \ t > 0 \qquad (10\text{-}22b)$$

$$T_l(x,t) = T_i \quad \text{for } t = 0, \text{ in } x > 0 \qquad (10\text{-}22c)$$

and for the interface as

$$T_l(x, t) = T_m \qquad\qquad \text{at } x = s(t),\ t > 0 \qquad (10\text{-}23a)$$

$$-k_l \frac{\partial T_l(x, t)}{\partial x} = \rho L \frac{ds(t)}{dt} \qquad \text{at } x = s(t),\ t > 0 \qquad (10\text{-}23b)$$

The interface equation (10-23b) states that the heat liberated at the interface as a result of solidification is equal to the heat conducted into the super-cooled liquid. No equations are needed for the solid-phase because it is at uniform temperature T_m.

Recalling that $\text{erfc}[x/2(\alpha_l t)^{1/2}]$ is a solution of the heat-conduction equation (10-22a), we choose a solution for $T_l(x, t)$ in the form

$$T_l(x, t) = T_i + B \,\text{erfc}[x/2(\alpha_l t)^{1/2}] \qquad (10\text{-}24)$$

where B is an arbitrary constant. This solution satisfies the differential equation (10-22a), the boundary condition (10-22b), and the initial condition (10-22c) since $\text{erfc}(\infty) = 0$. If we require that the solution (10-24) should also satisfy the interface condition (10-23a), we find

$$T_m = T_i + B \,\text{erfc}(\lambda) \qquad (10\text{-}25a)$$

where

$$\lambda = \frac{s(t)}{2(\alpha_l t)^{1/2}} \qquad (10\text{-}25b)$$

Since equation (10-25a) should be satisfied for all times, the *parameter* λ must be a constant. Equation (10-25a) is solved for the coefficient B

$$B = \frac{T_m - T_i}{\text{erfc}(\lambda)} \qquad (10\text{-}26)$$

and this result is introduced into equation (10-24). We obtain

$$\frac{T_l(x, t) - T_i}{T_m - T_i} = \frac{\text{erfc}[x/2(\alpha_l t)^{1/2}]}{\text{erfc}(\lambda)} \qquad (10\text{-}27)$$

Finally, the interface energy-balance equation (10-23b) provides the additional relationship for the determination of the parameter λ. Namely, substituting $s(t)$ and $T_l(x, t)$ from equations (10-25b) and (10-27), respectively, into equation (10-23b) and after performing the indicated operations we obtain the following transcendental equation for the determination of λ

$$\lambda e^{\lambda^2} \text{erfc}(\lambda) = \frac{C_p(T_m - T_i)}{L\sqrt{\pi}} \qquad (10\text{-}28)$$

and λ is the root of this equation. Knowing λ, the location of the solid-liquid

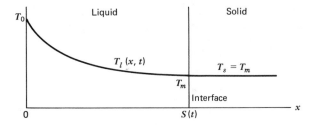

Fig. 10-3 Melting in a half-space. One-region problem.

interface $s(t)$ is determined from equation (10-25b) and the temperature distribution $T_l(x, t)$ in the liquid phase from equation (10-27).

Example 10-2. *Melting in a Half-Space (One-Region Problem).* A solid at the solidification (or melting) temperature T_m is confined to a half-space $x > 0$. At time $t = 0$, the temperature of the boundary surface at $x = 0$ is raised to T_0, which is higher than T_m and maintained at that temperature for times $t > 0$. As a result melting starts at the surface $x = 0$ and the solid-liquid interface moves in the positive x direction. Figure 10-3 shows the coordinates and the temperature profiles. The solid phase being at a constant temperature T_m throughout, the temperature is unknown only in the liquid phase, hence the problem is a one-region problem. In the following analysis the temperature distribution in the liquid phase and the location of the solid-liquid interface as a function of time are determined.

Solution. The mathematical formulation for the liquid-phase is given as

$$\frac{\partial^2 T_l(x,t)}{\partial x^2} = \frac{1}{\alpha_l} \frac{\partial T_l(x,t)}{\partial t} \qquad \text{in } 0 < x < s(t), \ t > 0 \qquad (102\text{-}29a)$$

$$T_l(x,t) = T_0 \qquad \text{at } x = 0, \ t > 0 \qquad (10\text{-}29b)$$

and for the interface as

$$T_l(x,t) = T_m \qquad \text{at } x = s(t), \ t > 0 \qquad (10\text{-}30a)$$

$$-k_l \frac{\partial T_l}{\partial x} = \rho L \frac{ds(t)}{dt} \qquad \text{at } x = s(t), \ t > 0 \qquad (10\text{-}30b)$$

No equations are needed for the solid phase because it is at the melting temperature T_m throughout.

If we assume a solution in the form

$$T_l(x,t) = T_0 + B \, \text{erf}\left[x/2(\alpha_l t)^{1/2}\right] \qquad (10\text{-}31)$$

where B is an arbitrary constant, the differential equation (10-29a) and the boundary condition (10-29b) are satisfied since erf(0) = 0. If we impose the condition that this solution should also satisfy the boundary condition (10-30a) at $x = s(t)$ we obtain

$$T_m = T_0 + B \operatorname{erf}(\lambda) \tag{10-32a}$$

where

$$\lambda = \frac{s(t)}{2(\alpha_l t)^{1/2}} \quad \text{or} \quad s(t) = 2\lambda(\alpha_l t)^{1/2} \tag{10-32b}$$

Equation (10-32a) implies that λ should be a constant. Then the coefficient B is determined from equation (10-32a) as

$$B = \frac{T_m - T_0}{\operatorname{erf}(\lambda)} \tag{10-33}$$

Introducing equation (10-33) into (10-31) we obtain

$$\frac{T_l(x, t) - T_0}{T_m - T_0} = \frac{\operatorname{erf}\left[x/2(\alpha_l t)^{1/2}\right]}{\operatorname{erf}(\lambda)} \tag{10-34}$$

Finally, we utilize the interface condition (10-30b) to obtain an additional relationship for the determination of the parameter λ. When $s(t)$ and $T_l(x,t)$ from equations (10-32b) and (10-34), respectively, are introduced into equation (10-30b), the following transcendental equation, similar to equation (10-28), is obtained for the determination of λ

$$\lambda e^{\lambda^2} \operatorname{erf}(\lambda) = \frac{C_p(T_0 - T_m)}{L\sqrt{\pi}} \tag{10-35}$$

and λ is the root of this equation. Knowing λ, $s(t)$ is determined from equation (10-32b) and $T_l(x, t)$ from equation (10-34).

Example 10-3. *Solidification in a Half-Space (Two-Region Problem).* A liquid at a uniform temperature T_i that is higher than the melting temperature T_m of the solid phase is confined to a half-space $x > 0$. At time $t = 0$ the boundary surface at $x = 0$ is lowered to a temperature T_0 below T_m and maintained at that temperature for times $t > 0$. As a result the solidification starts at the surface $x = 0$ and the solid-liquid interface moves in the positive x direction. Figure 10-4 illustrates the coordinates and the temperatures. This problem is a two-region problem because the temperatures are unknown in both the solid and liquid phases. In the following analysis we determine the temperature distributions in both phases and the location of the solid-liquid interface. This problem is more general than the ones considered in the previous examples; its solution is known as Neumann's Solution.

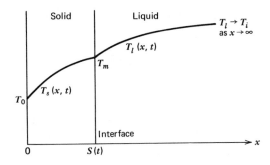

Fig. 10-4 Solidification in a half-space. Two region problem.

Solution. The mathematical formulation of this problem for the solid phase is given as

$$\frac{\partial^2 T_s}{\partial x^2} = \frac{1}{\alpha_s} \frac{\partial T_s(x,t)}{\partial t} \qquad \text{in } 0 < x < s(t),\ t > 0 \qquad (10\text{-}36\text{a})$$

$$T_s(x,t) = T_0 \qquad \text{at } x = 0,\ t > 0 \qquad (10\text{-}36\text{b})$$

for the liquid phase as

$$\frac{\partial^2 T_l}{\partial x^2} = \frac{1}{\alpha_l} \frac{\partial T_l(x,t)}{\partial t} \qquad \text{in } s(t) < x < \infty,\ t > 0 \qquad (10\text{-}37\text{a})$$

$$T_l(x,t) \to T_i \qquad \text{as } x \to \infty,\ t > 0 \qquad (10\text{-}37\text{b})$$

$$T_l(x,t) = T_i \qquad \text{for } t = 0,\ \text{in } x > 0 \qquad (10\text{-}37\text{c})$$

and the coupling conditions at the interface $x = s(t)$ as

$$T_s(x,t) = T_l(x,t) = T_m \qquad \text{at } x = s(t),\ t > 0 \qquad (10\text{-}38\text{a})$$

$$k_s \frac{\partial T_s}{\partial x} - k_l \frac{\partial T_l}{\partial x} = \rho L \frac{ds(t)}{dt} \qquad \text{at } x = s(t),\ t > 0 \qquad (10\text{-}38\text{b})$$

If we choose a solution for $T_s(x,t)$ in the form

$$T_s(x,t) = T_0 + A\, \mathrm{erf}\big[x/2(\alpha_s t)^{1/2}\big] \qquad (10\text{-}39)$$

the differential equation (10-36a) and the boundary condition (10-36b) are satisfied.

If we choose a solution for $T_l(x,t)$ in the form

$$T_l(x,t) = T_i + B\, \mathrm{erfc}\big[x/2(\alpha_l t)^{1/2}\big] \qquad (10\text{-}40)$$

the differential equation (10-37a), the boundary condition (10-37b), and the initial condition (10-37c) are satisfied. The constants A and B are yet to be determined.

Equations (10-39) and (10-40) are introduced into the interface condition (10-38a); we find

$$T_0 + A\,\text{erf}(\lambda) = T_i + B\,\text{erfc}\left[\lambda\left(\frac{\alpha_s}{\alpha_l}\right)^{1/2}\right] = T_m \qquad (10\text{-}41a)$$

where

$$\lambda = \frac{s(t)}{2(\alpha_s t)^{1/2}} \quad \text{or} \quad s(t) = 2\lambda(\alpha_s t)^{1/2} \qquad (10\text{-}41b)$$

Equations (10-41a) implies that λ should be a constant. The coefficients A and B are determined from equations (10-41a) as

$$A = \frac{T_m - T_0}{\text{erf}(\lambda)}, \qquad B = \frac{T_m - T_i}{\text{erfc}\left[\lambda(\alpha_s/\alpha_l)^{1/2}\right]} \qquad (10\text{-}42)$$

Introducing the coefficients A and B into equations (10-39) and (10-40) we obtain the temperatures for the solid and liquid phases as

$$\frac{T_s(x,t) - T_0}{T_m - T_0} = \frac{\text{erf}\left[x/2(\alpha_s t)^{1/2}\right]}{\text{erf}(\lambda)} \qquad (10\text{-}43a)$$

$$\frac{T_l(x,t) - T_i}{T_m - T_i} = \frac{\text{erfc}\left[x/2(\alpha_l t)^{1/2}\right]}{\text{erfc}\left[\lambda(\alpha_s/\alpha_l)^{1/2}\right]} \qquad (10\text{-}43b)$$

The interface energy balance equation (10-38b) is now used to determine the relation for the evaluation of the parameter λ. That is, when $s(t)$, $T_s(x,t)$ and $T_l(x,t)$ from equations (10-41b), (10-43a), and (10-43b), respectively, are substituted into equation (10-38b) we obtain the following transcendental equation for the determination of λ

$$\frac{e^{-\lambda^2}}{\text{erf}(\lambda)} + \frac{k_l}{k_s}\left(\frac{\alpha_s}{\alpha_l}\right)^{1/2}\frac{T_m - T_i}{T_m - T_0}\frac{e^{-\lambda(\alpha_s/\alpha_l)}}{\text{erfc}\left[\lambda(\alpha_s/\alpha_l)^{1/2}\right]} = \frac{\lambda L\sqrt{\pi}}{C_{ps}(T_m - T_0)} \qquad (10\text{-}44)$$

Once λ is known from the solution of this equation, $s(t)$ is determined from equation (10-41b), $T_s(x,t)$ from equation (10-43a) and $T_l(x,t)$ from equation (10-43b).

Example 10-4. *Solidification by a Line Heat Sink in an Infinite Medium with Cyclindrical Symmetry (Two-Region Problem).* A line heat sink of strength Q W/m (or Btu/hr ft) is located at $r = 0$ in a large body of liquid at a uniform temperature T_i higher than the melting (or solidification) temperature T_m of the medium. The heat sink is activated at time $t = 0$ to absorb heat continuously for times $t > 0$. As a result the solidification starts at the origin $r \to 0$ and the solid-liquid interface moves in the positive r direction. Figure 10-5 shows the coordinates and the temperature profiles. The problem

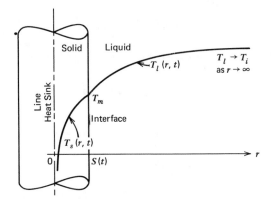

Fig. 10.5 Solidification by a line heat sink in an infinite medium with cylindrical symmetry. Two-region problem.

has cylindrical symmetry, and the temperatures being unknown in both regions, it is a two-region problem. In this example, the temperature distributions in the solid and liquid phases, and the location of the solid-liquid interface as a function of time will be determined.

Solution. Paterson [89] has shown that the exact solution to the above problem is obtainable if the solution of the heat conduction equation is chosen as an *exponential integral function* in the form $Ei(-r^2/4\alpha t)$. A brief discussion of the exponential integral function is given in Note 2; the reader should consult reference [90] for further details of the properties of exponential integral function and references [91] and [92] for its tabulation. The function $-Ei(-x)$ is also denoted by $E_1(x)$.

The mathematical formulation of this problem is given for the solid phase as

$$\frac{1}{r}\frac{\partial}{\partial r}\left(r\frac{\partial T_s}{\partial r}\right) = \frac{1}{\alpha_s}\frac{\partial T_s(r,t)}{\partial t} \qquad \text{in } 0 < r < s(t),\ t > 0 \qquad (10\text{-}45)$$

for the liquid phase as

$$\frac{1}{r}\frac{\partial}{\partial r}\left(r\frac{\partial T_l}{\partial r}\right) = \frac{1}{\alpha_l}\frac{\partial T_l(r,t)}{\partial t} \qquad \text{in } s(t) < r < \infty,\ t > 0 \qquad (10\text{-}46)$$

$$T_l(r,t) \rightarrow T_i \qquad \text{as } r \rightarrow \infty,\ t > 0 \qquad (10\text{-}47a)$$

$$T_l(r,t) = T_i \qquad \text{for } t = 0,\ \text{in } r > 0 \qquad (10\text{-}47b)$$

and for the solid-liquid interface as

$$T_s(r,t) = T_l(r,t) = T_m \qquad \text{at } r = s(t),\ t > 0 \qquad (10\text{-}48a)$$

$$k_s \frac{\partial T_s}{\partial r} - k_l \frac{\partial T_l}{\partial r} = \rho L \frac{ds(t)}{dt} \qquad \text{at } r = s(t), \ t > 0 \qquad (10\text{-}48\text{b})$$

We now choose the solutions for the solid and liquid phases in the forms

$$T_s(r,t) = A - BEi\left(\frac{-r^2}{4\alpha_s t}\right) \qquad \text{in } 0 < r < s(t) \qquad (10\text{-}49\text{a})$$

$$T_l(r,t) = T_i - CEi\left(\frac{-r^2}{4\alpha_l t}\right) \qquad \text{in } s(t) < r < \infty \qquad (10\text{-}49\text{b})$$

and the derivatives of these solutions with respect to r are given as

$$\frac{\partial T_s(r,t)}{\partial r} = -\frac{2B}{r} e^{-r^2/4\alpha_s t} \qquad (10\text{-}49\text{c})$$

$$\frac{\partial T_l(r,t)}{\partial r} = -\frac{2C}{r} e^{-r^2/4\alpha_l t} \qquad (10\text{-}49\text{d})$$

The solution (10-49a) for $T_s(\mathbf{r},t)$ satisfies the differential equation (10-45), while the solution (10-49b) for $T_l(\mathbf{r},t)$ satisfies the differential equation (10-46), the boundary condition (10-47a), and the initial condition (10-47b) since $Ei(-\infty) = 0$. The remaining conditions are used to determine the coefficients A, B, and C as now described.

The energy balance around the line heat sink is written as

$$\lim_{r \to 0} \left[2\pi r k_s \frac{\partial T_s}{\partial r} \right] = Q \qquad (10\text{-}50\text{a})$$

Introducing equation (10-49c) into (10-50a) we find

$$B = -Q/4\pi k_s \qquad (10\text{-}50\text{b})$$

Equations (10-49a), (10-49b), and (10-50b) are introduced into the interface condition (10-48a)

$$A + \frac{Q}{4\pi k_s} Ei(-\lambda^2) = T_i - CEi\left(\frac{-\lambda^2 \alpha_s}{\alpha_l}\right) = T_m \qquad (10\text{-}51\text{a})$$

where

$$\lambda = \frac{s(t)}{2(\alpha_s t)^{1/2}} \qquad (10\text{-}51\text{b})$$

Since equation (10-51a) should be valid for all values of time, we conclude that λ *must be a constant.* The coefficients A and C are solved for from equations (10-51a); we find

$$A = T_m - \frac{Q}{4\pi k_s} Ei(-\lambda^2) \qquad (10\text{-}52a)$$

$$C = \frac{T_i - T_m}{Ei(-\lambda^2 \alpha_s/\alpha_l)} \qquad (10\text{-}52b)$$

The derivative of $s(t)$ is obtained from equation (10-51b) as

$$\frac{ds(t)}{dt} = \frac{2\alpha_s \lambda^2}{s} \qquad (10\text{-}52c)$$

Introducing equations (10-52a) and (10-52b) into equations (10-49a, b) the solutions for the temperatures in the solid and liquid phases become

$$T_s(r,t) = T_m + \frac{Q_s}{4\pi k_s}\left[Ei\left(-\frac{r^2}{4\alpha_s t}\right) - Ei(-\lambda^2)\right] \qquad \text{in } 0 < r < s(t) \qquad (10\text{-}53a)$$

$$T_l(r,t) = T_i - \frac{T_i - T_m}{Ei(-\lambda^2 \alpha_s/\alpha_l)} Ei\left(-\frac{r^2}{4\alpha_l t}\right), \qquad \text{in } s(t) < r < \infty \qquad (10\text{-}53b)$$

Finally, when equations (10-52c) and (10-53) are introduced into the interface energy-balance equation (10-48b) the following transcendental equation is obtained for the determination of λ

$$\frac{Q}{4\pi} e^{-\lambda^2} + \frac{k_l(T_i - T_m)}{Ei(-\lambda^2 \alpha_s/\alpha_l)} e^{-\lambda^2 \alpha_s/\alpha_l} = \lambda^2 \alpha_s \rho L \qquad (10\text{-}54)$$

and λ is the root of this equation. Once λ is known, the location of the solid-liquid interface is determined from equation (10-51b), the temperatures in the solid and liquid phases from equations (10-53a) and (10-53b), respectively.

A scrutiny of the foregoing exact analyses reveals that in the rectangular coordinate system exact solutions are obtained for some half-space problems when the solution of the heat-conduction equation is chosen as a function of $xt^{-1/2}$, namely as $\text{erf}[x/2(\alpha t)^{1/2}]$ or $\text{erfc}[x/2(\alpha t)^{1/2}]$. In the cylindrical symmetry the corresponding solutions are in the form

$$- Ei(-r^2/4\alpha t)$$

which is again a function of $rt^{-1/2}$. Paterson [89] has shown that the corresponding solution of the heat-conduction equation in spherical symmetry is given in the form

$$\frac{(\alpha t)^{1/2}}{r} e^{-r^2/4\alpha t} - \tfrac{1}{2}\pi^{1/2} \, \text{erfc}\left(\frac{r}{2(\alpha t)^{1/2}}\right)$$

10-3 INTEGRAL METHOD OF SOLUTION
OF PHASE-CHANGE PROBLEMS

The integral method provides a relatively simple and straightforward approach for the solution of one-dimensional transient phase-change problems and has been used for this purpose by several investigators [4–15]. The basic theory of this method has already been described in the chapter on approximate solution of heat-conduction problems. When it is applied to the solution of phase-change problems, the fundamental steps in the analysis remain essentially the same, except some modifications are needed in the construction of the temperature profile. In this section we illustrate the use of the integral method in the solution of phase-change problems with simple examples.

Example 10-5. *Melting in a Half-Space (One-Region Problem).* To give some idea on the accuracy of the integral method of solution of one-dimensional, time-dependent phase-change problems, we consider the one-region melting problem for which exact solution is available in Example 10-2. The problem considered is the melting of a solid confined to a half-space $x > 0$, initially at the melting temperature T_m. For times $t > 0$ the boundary surface at $x = 0$ is kept at a constant temperature T_0, which is higher than the melting temperature T_m of the solid. The melting starts at the surface $x = 0$ and the solid-liquid interface moves in the positive x direction as illustrated in Fig. 10-3. In the following analysis we determine the location of the solid-liquid interface as a function of time.

Solution. The mathematical formulation of this problem is exactly the same as those given by equations (10-29) and (10-30). Namely, for the liquid phase the equations are given as

$$\frac{\partial^2 T_l}{\partial x^2} = \frac{1}{\alpha_l} \frac{\partial T_l(x,t)}{\partial t} \qquad \text{in } 0 < x < s(t), \ t > 0 \qquad (10\text{-}55a)$$

$$T_l(x,t) = T_0 \qquad \text{at } x = 0, \ t > 0 \qquad (10\text{-}55b)$$

and for the interface as

$$T_l(x,t) = T_m \qquad \text{at } x = s(t), \ t > 0 \qquad (10\text{-}56a)$$

$$-k_l \frac{\partial T_l}{\partial x} = \rho L \frac{ds(t)}{dt} \qquad \text{at } x = s(t), \ t > 0 \qquad (10\text{-}56b)$$

We recall that the first step in the analysis with the integral method is to define a thermal layer thickness beyond which the temperature gradient is considered zero for practical purposes. Referring to Fig. 10-3 we note that the location of the solid-liquid interface $x = s(t)$ is identical to the definition of the thermal layer, since the temperature gradient in the solid phase is zero for $x > s(t)$. Hence, we choose the region $0 \le x \le s(t)$ as the thermal layer appropriate for this problem and integrate the heat-conduction equation from $x = 0$ to $x = s(t)$ to obtain

$$\frac{\partial T}{\partial x}\bigg|_{x=s(t)} - \frac{\partial T}{\partial x}\bigg|_{x=0} = \frac{1}{\alpha}\frac{d}{dt}\left[\int_{x=0}^{s(t)} T\,dx - T\bigg|_{x=s(t)} \cdot s(t)\right] \qquad (10\text{-}57)$$

For simplicity we omitted the subscript l and it will be done so in the following analysis. We note that equation (10-57) is similar to equation (9-2b) considered in Chapter 9. In view of the boundary conditions (10-56a) and (10-56b) the equation (10-57) reduces to

$$-\frac{\rho L}{k}\frac{ds(t)}{dt} - \frac{\partial T}{\partial x}\bigg|_{x=0} = \frac{1}{\alpha}\frac{d}{dt}[\theta - T_m s(t)] \qquad (10\text{-}58\text{a})$$

where

$$\theta \equiv \int_0^{s(t)} T(x,t)\,dx \qquad (10\text{-}58\text{b})$$

Equation (10-58) is the *energy-integral equation* for this problem. To solve this equation we choose a second-degree polynomial approximation for the temperature in the form

$$T(x,t) = a + b(x - s) + c(x - s)^2 \qquad (10\text{-}59)$$

where $s \equiv s(t)$. Three conditions are needed to determine these three coefficients. Equations (10-55b) and (10-56a) provide two conditions; but, the relation given by equation (10-56b) is not suitable for this purpose, because if it is used, the resulting temperature profile will involve the $ds(t)/dt$ term. When such a profile is substituted into the energy integral equation, a second-order ordinary differential equation will result for $s(t)$ instead of the usual first-order equation. To alleviate this difficulty an alternative relation is now developed [4]. The boundary condition (10-56a) is differentiated

$$dT \equiv \left[\frac{\partial T}{\partial x}dx + \frac{\partial T}{\partial t}dt\right]_{x=s(t)} = 0 \qquad (10\text{-}60\text{a})$$

or

$$\frac{\partial T}{\partial x}\frac{ds(t)}{dt} + \frac{\partial T}{\partial t} = 0 \qquad (10\text{-}60\text{b})$$

where we omitted the subscript l for simplicity. The term $ds(t)/dt$ is eliminated between equations (10-56b) and (10-60b)

$$\left(\frac{\partial T}{\partial x}\right)^2 = \frac{\rho L}{k}\frac{\partial T}{\partial t} \qquad \text{at } x = s(t) \qquad (10\text{-}61)$$

and eliminating $\partial T/\partial t$ between equations (10-55a) and (10-61) we obtain

$$\left(\frac{\partial T}{\partial x}\right)^2 = \frac{\alpha\rho L}{k}\frac{\partial^2 T}{\partial x^2} \qquad \text{at } x = s(t) \qquad (10\text{-}62)$$

This relation, together with the boundary conditions at $x = 0$ and $x = s(t)$, i.e.,

$$T = T_0 \qquad \text{at } x = 0 \qquad\qquad (10\text{-}63a)$$

$$T = T_m \qquad \text{at } x = s(t) \qquad\qquad (0\text{-}63b)$$

provide three independent relations for the determination of three unknown coefficients in equation (10-59); the resulting temperature profile becomes

$$T(x,t) = T_m + b(x - s) + c(x - s)^2 \qquad (10\text{-}64a)$$

where

$$b = \frac{\alpha\rho L}{ks}[1 - (1 + \mu)^{1/2}] \qquad (10\text{-}64b)$$

$$c = \frac{bs + (T_0 - T_m)}{s^2} \qquad (10\text{-}64c)$$

$$\mu = \frac{2k}{\alpha\rho L}(T_0 - T_m) = \frac{2C_p(T_0 - T_m)}{L} \qquad (10\text{-}64d)$$

Substituting the temperature profile (10-64) into the energy-integral equation (10-58) and performing the indicated operations we obtain the following ordinary differential equation for the determination of the location of the solid-liquid interface $s(t)$

$$s\frac{ds}{dt} = 6\alpha\frac{1 - (1 + \mu)^{1/2} + \mu}{5 + (1 + \mu)^{1/2} + \mu} \qquad (10\text{-}65a)$$

with

$$s = 0 \qquad \text{for } t = 0 \qquad (10\text{-}65b)$$

The solution of equation (10-65) is

$$s(t) = 2\lambda\sqrt{\alpha t} \qquad (10\text{-}66a)$$

where

$$\lambda \equiv \left[3\frac{1 - (1 + \mu)^{1/2} + \mu}{5 + (1 + \mu)^{1/2} + \mu}\right]^{1/2} \qquad (10\text{-}66b)$$

We note that the approximate solution (10-66a) for $s(t)$ is of the same form as the exact solution of the same problem given previously by equation (10-32b); but the parameter λ is given by equation (10-66b) for the approximate solution, whereas it is the root of the transcendental equation (10-35), that is,

$$\lambda e^{\lambda^2} \operatorname{erf}(\lambda) = \frac{C_p(T_0 - T_m)}{L\sqrt{\pi}} = \frac{\mu}{2\sqrt{\pi}} \tag{10-67}$$

for the exact solution. Therefore, the accuracy of the approximate analysis can be determined by comparing the exact and approximate values of λ as a function of the quantity μ. Now, recalling the definition of the Stefan number given by equation (10-21b) we note that the parameter μ is actually twice the Stefan number. Figure 10-6 shows a comparison of the exact and approximate values of λ as a function of the parameter μ. The agreement between the exact and approximate analysis is reasonably good for the second-degree profile used here. If a cubic polynomial approximation were used, the agreement would be much closer [4].

Example 10-6. *Solidification of a Slab (Two-Region Problem).* A liquid at a temperature T_i which is higher than the melting (or solidification) temperature T_m is confined in a space of finite thickness, $0 \le x \le b$. For times $t > 0$ the boundary surface at $x = 0$ is maintained at a constant tempera-

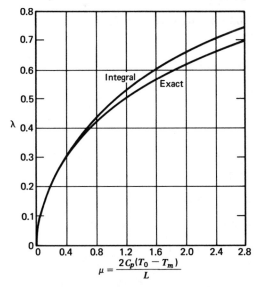

Fig. 10-6 A comparison of exact and approximate solutions of the melting problem in half-space. (From T. R. Goodman [4].)

ture T_0 below T_m and the boundary at $x = b$ is kept insulated. The solidification starts at the surface $x = 0$ and the solid-liquid interface moves
in the positive x direction. The location $s(t)$ of the solid-liquid interface
is to be determined as a function of time.

Solution. No exact solution is available for the melting or solidification
of a slab of finite thickness. Therefore, the integral method can be used to
obtain an approximate solution for this problem as discussed in references [6]
and [13]. The former reference analyzes the problem completely with the
integral method, the latter by a combination of the exact and the integral
methods. In the following analysis we solve the problem by a combination
of exact and integral methods.

The mathematical formulation of this problem is similar to the Neumann's
problem considered in Example 10-3, except for the present problem the
extent of the region is finite. The mathematical formulation is now given in
the dimensionless form.

The equations for the solid phase are taken as

$$\frac{\partial^2 \theta_s}{\partial X^2} = \frac{\partial \theta_s(X, \tau)}{\partial \tau} \qquad \text{in } 0 < X < S(t),\ \tau > 0 \tag{10-68a}$$

$$\theta_s(X, \tau) = 0 \qquad \text{at } X = 0,\ \tau > 0 \tag{10-68b}$$

for the liquid phase as

$$\frac{\partial^2 \theta_l}{\partial X^2} = \frac{\alpha_s}{\alpha_l} \frac{\partial \theta_l(X, \tau)}{\partial \tau} \qquad \text{in } S(\tau) < X < 1,\ \tau > 0 \tag{10-69a}$$

$$\frac{\partial \theta_l}{\partial X} = 0 \qquad \text{at } X = 1,\ \tau > 0 \tag{10-69b}$$

$$\theta_l = 1 \qquad \text{for } \tau = 0 \text{ in } 0 < X < 1 \tag{10-69c}$$

and for the solid-liquid interface as

$$\theta_s(X, \tau) = \theta_l(X, \tau) = \theta_m \qquad \text{at } X = S(\tau),\ \tau > 0 \tag{10-70a}$$

$$\frac{\partial \theta_s}{\partial X} - \frac{k_l}{k_s} \frac{\partial \theta_l}{\partial X} = \frac{L}{C_{ps}(T_i - T_0)} \frac{dS(\tau)}{d\tau} \qquad \text{at } X = S(\tau),\ \tau > 0 \tag{10-70b}$$

where various dimensionless quantities are defined as

$$\theta_j \equiv \frac{T_j - T_0}{T_i - T_0} \qquad \text{with } j = s,\ l, \text{ or } m,$$

$$X = \frac{x}{b},\ S = \frac{s}{b},\ \tau = \frac{\alpha_s t}{b^2} \tag{10-71}$$

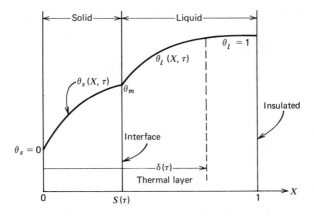

Fig. 10-7 Solidification of a slab. Two-region problem.

and the subscripts l, s, and m refer to the liquid phase, solid phase, and melting temperature, respectively. Figure 10-7 shows the geometry and the temperature profiles.

To determine the temperature profile for the solid phase, we make use of the exact solution of the solidification problem for the half-space considered previosuly. That is, we choose the temperature distribution $\theta_s(X, \tau)$ for the solid phase in the form given by equation (10-43a) as

$$\frac{\theta_s(X, \tau)}{\theta_m} = \frac{\text{erf}\left[X/2\sqrt{\tau}\right]}{\text{erf}(\lambda)}, \qquad \tau > 0 \tag{10-72}$$

and assume that the location of the solid-liquid interface $S(\tau)$ is given by [see equation (10-41b)]

$$S(\tau) = 2\lambda\sqrt{\tau} \tag{10-73}$$

where the *parameter λ is yet to be determined*. Clearly, the solution (10-72) satisfies the differential equation (10-68a) and the boundary condition (10-68b).

The integral method is now used to determine the temperature distribution $\theta_l(X, \tau)$ for the liquid phase. To apply the integral method, a thermal layer $\delta(\tau)$ is chosen as illustrated in Fig. 10-7. For the finite region considered here the thermal layer concept is valid so long as $\delta(\tau) \leq 1$; it looses its physical significance for $\delta(\tau) > 1$. By the definition of the thermal layer the boundary conditions at $X = \delta(\tau)$ are taken as

$$\theta_l(X, \tau) = 1 \qquad \text{at } X = \delta(\tau) \tag{10-74a}$$

$$\frac{\partial \theta_l}{\partial X} = 0 \qquad \text{at } X = \delta(\tau) \tag{10-74b}$$

The heat-conduction equation (10-68b) for the liquid phase is integrated from $X = S(\tau)$ to $X = \delta(\tau)$ and the boundary conditions (10-70a) and (10-74) are utilized. We obtain

$$-\frac{\alpha_l}{\alpha_s}\frac{\partial \theta_l}{\partial X}\bigg|_{X=S(\tau)} + \frac{d\delta}{d\tau} - \theta_m\frac{dS}{d\tau} = \frac{d}{d\tau}\left[\int_{S(\tau)}^{\delta(\tau)} \theta_l(X,\tau)\,dX\right] \qquad (10\text{-}75)$$

which is the *energy-integral equation* for the considered problem. To solve this equation a suitable profile is needed for $\theta_l(X,\tau)$. If the profile for $\theta_l(X,\tau)$ is chosen in the form

$$\theta_l(X,\tau) = 1 - (1 - \theta_m)\left(\frac{\delta - X}{\delta - S}\right)^n, \quad n \geq 2 \qquad (10\text{-}76)$$

where n is a dimensionless index to be specified, then this profile satisfies the boundary conditions (10-70a) and (10-74). In addition we assume that $\delta(\tau)$ is related to τ in the form

$$\delta(\tau) = 2\beta\sqrt{\tau} \qquad (10\text{-}77)$$

where β is yet to be determined.

Substituting the temperature profile (10-76) into the energy-integral equation (10-75), performing the indicated operations, and utilizing equation (10-77) we obtain

$$\beta - \lambda = \frac{n+1}{2}\left[-\lambda + \sqrt{\lambda^2 + \frac{2n}{n+1}\frac{\alpha_l}{\alpha_s}}\right] \qquad (10\text{-}78)$$

Finally, introducing $\theta_s(X,\tau)$ and $\theta_l(X,\tau)$ given by equation (10-72) and (10-76) into the interface condition (10-70b) and after performing the indicated operations, the following transcendental equation is obtained for the determination of λ

$$\frac{e^{-\lambda^2}}{\operatorname{erf}(\lambda)} + \frac{k_l}{k_s}\left(\frac{\alpha_s}{\alpha_l}\right)^{1/2}\frac{\theta_m - 1}{\theta_m}\frac{1}{Z_n} = \frac{\lambda L\sqrt{\pi}}{C_{ps}(T_m - T_0)} \qquad (10\text{-}79a)$$

where

$$Z_n \equiv \frac{n+1}{n\sqrt{\pi}}\left[-\gamma + \sqrt{\gamma^2 + \frac{2n}{n+1}}\right] \qquad (10\text{-}79b)$$

$$\gamma = \lambda\left(\frac{\alpha_s}{\alpha_l}\right)^{1/2} \qquad (10\text{-}79c)$$

$$\frac{\theta_m - 1}{\theta_m} = \frac{T_m - T_i}{T_m - T_0} \qquad (10\text{-}79d)$$

Once λ is determined from the solution of equation (10-79), β is evaluated from equation (10-78). Knowing λ and β, the dimensionless location of the solid-liquid interface $S(\tau)$ and the thermal layer thickness $\delta(\tau)$ are obtained from equations (10-73) and (10-77), respectively. The temperature distributions in the solid-liquid phases are determined from equations (10-72) and (10-76), respectively.

The foregoing analysis is valid for $\delta(\tau) \leq 1$, that is until the thermal layer reaches the back wall. The times τ_1 and τ_2 when $\delta(\tau_1) = 1$ and $S(\tau_2) = 1$ are determined from equations (10-77) and (10-73), respectively, as

$$\tau_1 = \frac{1}{4\beta^2} \quad \text{and} \quad \tau_2 = \frac{1}{4\lambda^2} \tag{10-80}$$

For times $\tau > \tau_2$, the liquid region no longer exists.

It is interesting to compare the transcendental equation (10-79a) for the above slab problem with the transcendental equation (10-44) for the Neumann problem in a half-space. They are of the same form except the term Z_n for the slab problem is given by equation (10-79b) and for the Neumann problem in half-space is given by the expression

$$Z_\infty = e^{\gamma^2} \operatorname{erfc}(\gamma) \tag{10-81a}$$

with

$$\gamma = \lambda \left(\frac{\alpha_s}{\alpha_l}\right)^{1/2} \tag{10-81b}$$

A comparison of the above results reveals that, except for small values of λ, the value of Z_n is greater than Z_∞, which implies a larger value of λ for the slab problem. As a result the slab is expected to freeze (or melt) faster than a half-space with the same boundary condition at $X = 0$.

10-4 MOVING HEAT SOURCE METHOD FOR THE SOLUTION OF PHASE-CHANGING PROBLEMS

The liberation (or absorption) of heat during solidification (or melting) can be treated as a moving-plane heat source (or sink) located at the solid-liquid interface. With this consideration it may be possible to recast the transient phase-change problem in the form of a transient heat-conduction problem with a moving plane heat source. This approach originally applied by Lightfoot [22] for the solution of one-dimensional transient phase-change problems, was later used by several investigators [23–27].

The basic steps in the solution of phase-change problem with this approach may be summarized as follows: The phase-change problem is replaced by an equivalent transient heat-conduction problem with a moving-plane heat source (or sink) located at the solid-liquid interface. The resulting heat-conduction problem is solved formally for the temperature; then, it is required that this temperature, when evaluated at the solid-liquid interface, should be equal to the melting temperature T_m of the phase-change material. This requirement yields in an integral equation for the location of the solid-liquid interface. When this integral equation is solved, the location of the solid-liquid interface is determined. The method is straightforward in that it transforms the analysis of the phase-change problem into the solution of an integral equation for the location of the solid-liquid interface. The resulting integral equation may not be solved analytically, but it can be solved approximately or numerically. For simpler problems, it may even be solved exactly as in the case of the problem considered by Lightfoot. We illustrate this approach with the example considered below.

Example 10-7. *Solidification in a Half-Space (Two-Region Problem).* A liquid contained in a half-space $x > 0$ is at a uniform temperature T_i higher than the melting temperature T_m of the phase-change material. For times $t > 0$ the boundary surface is kept at a temperature $T_0 = 0$ lower than T_m. The solidification starts at the surface $x = 0$ and the solid front moves in the positive x direction. This problem is essentially the same as the Neumann problem solved in Example 10-3. In the following analysis we assume that the thermal properties for the liquid and solid phases are the same in order to transform this phase-change problem into a transient heat-conduction problem with a moving source. However, as will be illustrated later in this section, this restriction on thermal properties may be relaxed by the proper choice of the dimensionless temperatures.

Solution. The mathematical formulation of this problem is given as for the solid phase,

$$\frac{\partial^2 T_s}{\partial x^2} = \frac{1}{\alpha} \frac{\partial T_s(x,t)}{\partial t} \qquad \text{in } 0 < x < s(t), \ t > 0 \qquad (10\text{-}82\text{a})$$

$$T_s(x,t) = T_0 = 0 \qquad \text{at } x = 0, \ t > 0 \qquad (10\text{-}82\text{b})$$

for the liquid phase,

$$\frac{\partial^2 T_l}{\partial x^2} = \frac{1}{\alpha} \frac{\partial T_l(x,t)}{\partial t} \qquad \text{in } s(t) < x < \infty, \ t > 0 \qquad (10\text{-}83\text{a})$$

$$T_l(x,t) \to T_i \qquad \text{as } x \to \infty, t > 0 \qquad (10\text{-}83\text{b})$$

$$T_l(x,t) = T_i \qquad \text{for } t = 0, \text{ in } x > 0 \qquad (10\text{-}83\text{c})$$

and for the solid-liquid interface

$$T_s(x,t) = T_l(x,t) = T_m \qquad \text{at } x = s(t), \ t > 0 \qquad (10\text{-}84a)$$

$$\frac{\partial T_s}{\partial x} - \frac{\partial T_l}{\partial x} = \frac{\rho L}{k}\frac{ds(t)}{dt} \qquad \text{at } x = s(t), \ t > 0 \qquad (10\text{-}84b)$$

The above phase-change problem is equivalent to the solution of the following transient heat-conduction problem with a moving-plane heat source located at $x = s(t)$ in the region $x > \infty$

$$\frac{\partial^2 T(x,t)}{\partial x^2} + \frac{1}{k}\rho L\frac{ds(t)}{dt}\delta[x - s(t)] = \frac{1}{\alpha}\frac{\partial T(x,t)}{\partial t} \qquad \text{in } 0 < x < \infty, \ t > 0 \ (10\text{-}85a)$$

$$T(x,t) = T_0 = 0 \qquad\qquad \text{at } x = 0, \ t > 0 \qquad (10\text{-}85b)$$

$$T(x,t) \to T_i \qquad\qquad \text{as } x \to \infty, \ t > 0 \qquad (10\text{-}85c)$$

$$T(x,t) = T_i \qquad\qquad \text{for } t = 0, \ \text{in } x > 0 \qquad (10\text{-}85d)$$

with the additional requirement that

$$T(x,t) = T_m \qquad \text{at } x = s(t) \qquad (10\text{-}85e)$$

where $\delta[x - s(t)]$ is the Dirac delta function. The equivalence of these two problems is shown below.

Clearly, the differential equation of heat conduction (10-85a) reduces to equation (10-82a) for $x < s(t)$ and to equation (10-83a) for $x > s(t)$ because of the delta function heat source. The boundary and initial conditions (10-85b), (10-85c), and (10-85d) are, respectively, the same as those given by equations (10-82b), (10-83b), and (10-83c) for the phase-change problem. The constraint (10-85e) is equivalent to the interface condition (10-84a). Finally, we need to show that equation (10-85a) yields the interface jump condition (10-84b). To show this, we integrate equation (10-85a) across the interface from $x = s(t) - \varepsilon$ to $x = s(t) + \varepsilon$ and then let $\varepsilon \to 0$. The right-hand side of equation (10-85a) vanishes because $\partial T/\partial t$ is a continuous function across the interface; we obtain

$$\frac{\partial T_l}{\partial x} - \frac{\partial T_s}{\partial x} + \frac{1}{k}\rho L\frac{ds(t)}{dt} = 0 \qquad \text{at } x = s(t) \qquad (10\text{-}86a)$$

or

$$\frac{\partial T_s}{\partial x} - \frac{\partial T_l}{\partial x} = \frac{\rho L}{k}\frac{ds(t)}{dt} \qquad \text{at } x = s(t) \qquad (10\text{-}86b)$$

which is identical to the interface equation (10-84b). Therefore, the solution of the transient heat-conduction problem defined by equations (10-85) is equivalent to the solution of the above phase-change problem.

To solve the heat-conduction problem defined by equations (10-85a) to (10-85d) it is convenient to split it into two simpler problems as

$$T(x,t) = T_1(x,t) + T_2(x,t) \tag{10-87}$$

where $T_1(x,t)$ is the solution of

$$\frac{\partial^2 T_1(x,t)}{\partial x^2} = \frac{1}{\alpha}\frac{\partial T_1(x,t)}{\partial t} \qquad \text{in } 0 < x < \infty, \ t > 0 \tag{10-88a}$$

$$T_1(x,t) = 0 \qquad \text{at } x = 0, \ t > 0 \tag{10-88b}$$

$$T_1(x,t) = T_i \qquad \text{for } t = 0, \ \text{in } x > 0 \tag{10-88c}$$

and $T_2(x,t)$ is the solution of

$$\frac{\partial^2 T_2(x,t)}{\partial x^2} + \frac{\rho L}{k}\frac{ds(t)}{dt}\delta[x - s(t)] = \frac{1}{\alpha}\frac{\partial T_2(x,t)}{\partial t} \qquad \text{in } 0 < x < \infty, \ t > 0 \tag{10-89a}$$

$$T_2(x,t) = 0 \qquad \text{at } x = 0, \ t > 0 \tag{10-89b}$$

$$T_2(x,t) = 0 \qquad \text{for } t = 0, \ \text{in } x > 0 \tag{10-89c}$$

The solution for $T_1(x,t)$ is given as [see equation (2-62)]

$$T_1(x,t) = T_i \operatorname{erf}\left(\frac{x}{2\sqrt{\alpha t}}\right) \tag{10-90}$$

and the solution for $T_2(x,t)$ is given in terms of the Green's function as [see equation (6-19)]

$$T_2(x,t) = \frac{\alpha}{k}\int_{\tau=0}^{t} d\tau \int_{x'=0}^{\infty} G(x,t|x',\tau)g(x',\tau)\,dx' \tag{10-91a}$$

where

$$g(x',\tau) = \rho L\frac{ds(t)}{dt}\delta[x' - s(t)] \tag{10-91b}$$

$$G(x,t|x',\tau) = \frac{1}{2\sqrt{\pi\alpha(t-\tau)}}\left[\exp\left(-\frac{(x-x')^2}{4\alpha(t-\tau)}\right) - \exp\left(-\frac{(x+x')^2}{4\alpha(t-\tau)}\right)\right] \tag{10-91c}$$

The integration with respect to x' can be performed; then the solution for $T_2(x,t)$ becomes

$$T_2(x,t) = \frac{L}{2C_p(\pi\alpha)^{1/2}}\int_{\tau=0}^{t}\frac{ds(t)}{dt}\frac{1}{(t-\tau)^{1/2}}$$
$$\cdot\left[\exp\left(-\frac{(x-s)^2}{4\alpha(t-\tau)}\right) - \exp\left(-\frac{(x+s)^2}{4\alpha(t-\tau)}\right)\right] \tag{10-92}$$

When the solutions (10-90) and (10-92) are introduced into equation (10-87) and the requirement (10-85e) is imposed, we obtain

$$T_m = T_1[s(t), t] + T_2[s(t), t] \qquad (10\text{-}93)$$

which is now an integral equation for the location of the solid-liquid interface $s(t)$. When this integral equation is solved, $s(t)$ is determined. Lightfoot solved this integral equation on the assumption that $s(t)$ can be expressed in the form

$$s(t) = 2\lambda \sqrt{\alpha t} \qquad (10\text{-}94)$$

where λ is yet to be determined. With this value of $s(t)$ the integral equation (10-93) could be expressed in terms of error functions. After some transformation of variables, the integral equation (10-93) is reduced to the following transcendental equation for the determination of λ

$$T_m = T_i \operatorname{erf}(\lambda) + \frac{\lambda L \sqrt{\pi}}{C_p} e^{\lambda^2} \operatorname{erf}(\lambda) \operatorname{erfc}(\lambda) \qquad (10\text{-}95\text{a})$$

which can be rearranged as

$$\frac{e^{-\lambda^2}}{\operatorname{erf}(\lambda)} + \frac{T_m - T_i}{T_m} \frac{e^{-\lambda^2}}{\operatorname{erfc}(\lambda)} = \frac{\lambda L \sqrt{\pi}}{C_p T_m} \qquad (10\text{-}95\text{b})$$

We note that equation (10-95b) is a special case of equation (10-44) for the Neumann problem (i.e., for $k_l = k_s$, $\alpha_s = \alpha_l$, and $T_0 = 0$). Thus, the solution obtained with the moving heat-source approach yielded the exact result for the considered problem.

Generalization to Three-Dimension

The moving heat-source approach described above for the one-dimensional case is now generalized to a three-dimensional case [93]. We consider the following three-dimensional phase-change problem

$$\nabla^2 \theta_s(\mathbf{r}, t) = \frac{1}{\alpha} \frac{\partial \theta_s(\mathbf{r}, t)}{\partial t} \qquad \text{in region } R_s, \ t > 0 \qquad (10\text{-}96\text{a})$$

$$\nabla^2 \theta_l(\mathbf{r}, t) = \frac{1}{\alpha} \frac{\partial \theta_l(\mathbf{r}, t)}{\partial t} \qquad \text{in region } R_l, \ t > 0 \qquad (10\text{-}96\text{b})$$

where we defined

$$\theta_s(\mathbf{r}, t) \equiv \frac{T_s(\mathbf{r}, t) - T_m}{\Delta T}, \qquad \theta_l(\mathbf{r}, t) \equiv \frac{k_l}{k_s} \frac{T_l(\mathbf{r}, t) - T_m}{\Delta T} \qquad (10\text{-}96\text{c})$$

Here, T_m is the melting point temperature, ΔT is a reference temperature difference, k_l and k_s are the thermal conductivities of the liquid and solid phases, and subscripts l and s refer to the liquid and solid phases, respectively.

Let the location of the solid-liquid interface be defined by the equation $F(\mathbf{r}, t) = 0$. The boundary conditions at the solid-liquid interface are given as

$$\theta_s(\mathbf{r}, t) = \theta_l(\mathbf{r}, t) = 0 \qquad \text{on } F(\mathbf{r}, t) = 0, \ t > 0 \qquad (10\text{-}97\text{a})$$

$$\frac{\partial \theta_s(\mathbf{r}, t)}{\partial n} - \frac{\partial \theta_l(\mathbf{r}, t)}{\partial n} = \frac{\rho L}{k_s \Delta T} v_n(t) \qquad \text{on } F(\mathbf{r}, t) = 0, \ t > 0 \qquad (10\text{-}97\text{b})$$

Here ρ is the density, L is the latent heat per unit mass, $v_n(t)$ is the normal velocity of the solid-liquid interface at any point P in the direction of a vector $\mathbf{n}$ that is normal to the interface at the point P and pointing into the liquid phase, and $\partial/\partial n$ is the derivative along the normal vector $\mathbf{n}$ as illustrated in Fig. 10-1c. The solid-liquid interface is moving in the positive $\mathbf{n}$ direction for the solidification problem. Finally we assume that:

$$\left(\begin{array}{l}\text{Appropriate linear boundary conditions are specified at the} \\ \text{outer boundaries of the regions } R_s \text{ and } R_l, \text{ for } t > 0\end{array}\right) \qquad (10\text{-}98\text{a})$$

and

(The initial conditions are specified for the regions R_s and R_l)   (10-98b)

Equations (10-96) to (10-98) describe the complete mathematical formulation of the considered three-dimensional solidification problem.

The above solidification problem is equivalent to the following transient heat-conduction problem in the same region $R_s + R_l$ with a moving heat source located at the solid-liquid interface

$$\nabla^2 \theta(\mathbf{r}, t) + \frac{1}{k_s} \frac{\rho L}{\Delta T} v_n(t) \delta(n - n_0) = \frac{1}{\alpha} \frac{\partial \theta(\mathbf{r}, t)}{\partial t} \qquad \text{in } R_s + R_l, \ t > 0 \qquad (10\text{-}99)$$

where $\delta(n - n_0)$ is the Dirac delta function with n denoting the distance measured along the normal vector $\mathbf{n}$ at the point P to the solid-liquid interface $F(\mathbf{r}, t) = 0$ and n_0 is the location of the point P. Clearly, the term $(\rho L/\Delta T) v_n(t) \delta(n - n_0)$ represents a moving-surface heat source. The boundary and initial conditions for this problem are taken the same as those given by equations (10-98). In addition we impose the requirement that the temperature $\theta(\mathbf{r}, t)$ should be zero over the surface $F(\mathbf{r}, t) = 0$, that is

$$\theta(\mathbf{r}, t) = 0 \qquad \text{at } F(\mathbf{r}, t) = 0 \text{ within } R_s + R_l, \text{ for } t > 0 \qquad (10\text{-}100)$$

We now show that the solution of the above transient heat-conduction problem is equivalent to the solution of the transient phase-change problem discussed above. The heat-conduction equation (10-99) reduces to equation (10-96a) in the region R_s and to (10-96b) in the region R_l because of the delta-function-type heat source. The requirement given by equation (10-100) is equivalent to the interface boundary condition (10-97a) of the phase-change problem. The boundary and the initial conditions for both the phase-change and the transient heat-conduction problems are taken to be the same. Therefore, all we need to prove is that the heat-conduction equation (10-99) also satisfies the interface boundary condition (10-97b) of the phase-change problem. This can be proved by integrating equation (10-99) over a small volume element across the interface, changing the volume integral to the surface integral and letting the thickness ε of this volume element across the interface to become zero so that in the limit as $\varepsilon \to 0$ this volume element coincides with the interface $F(\mathbf{r}, t) = 0$. Such an analysis shows that equation (10-99) indeed reduces to equation (10-97b) at the interface. Thus the two problems are identical.

The moving surface heat-source term in equation (10-99) given in the form

$$g(\mathbf{r}, t) \equiv \frac{\rho L}{\nabla T} v_n(t) \delta(n - n_0) \tag{10-101}$$

is not so convenient for the purposes of numerical or analytic computations. Depending on the type of the coordinate system used and the functional form selected for the interface equation $F(\mathbf{r}, t) = 0$, the expression for the generation term given by equation (10-101) can be expressed in the alternative form as described below.

We consider a three-dimensional problem in the rectangular coordinate system and assume that the interface equation is given in the form

$$F(\mathbf{r}, t) = z - s(x, y, t) = 0 \tag{10-102}$$

The distance n measured along the normal $\mathbf{n}$ to the interface is related to the distance along the z axis by the relation

$$n = \frac{z}{\mathbf{n} \cdot \mathbf{k}} \tag{10-103}$$

where $\mathbf{k}$ is the unit direction vector along the z axis. Then

$$\delta(n - n_0) = \frac{1}{\mathbf{n} \cdot \mathbf{k}} \delta(z - z_0) \tag{10-104}$$

here, z_0 is the z coordinate of the point n_0 on the surface $F(\mathbf{r}, t) = 0$. We also have the relations (see Note 1)

$$\mathbf{n} \cdot \mathbf{k} = \frac{\partial F / \partial z}{|\nabla F|} \tag{10-105a}$$

$$v_n(t) = -\frac{\partial F / \partial t}{|\nabla F|} \tag{10-105b}$$

Introducing equations (10-104) and (10-105) into (10-101) we find

$$g(\mathbf{r}, t) = -\frac{\rho L}{\Delta T} \frac{\partial F/\partial t}{\partial F/\partial z} \delta(z - z_0)$$ (10-106)

In view of the expression (10-102), equation (10-106) becomes

$$g(\mathbf{r}, t) = \frac{\rho L}{\Delta T} \frac{\partial s(x, y, t)}{\partial t} \delta(z - z_0)$$ (10-107)

Then, the heat-conduction equation (10-99) takes the form

$$\nabla^2 \theta(\mathbf{r}, t) + \frac{1}{k_s} \frac{\rho L}{\Delta T} \frac{\partial s(x, y, t)}{\partial t} \delta(z - z_0) = \frac{1}{\alpha} \frac{\partial \theta(\mathbf{r}, t)}{\partial t}, \quad \text{in } R_s + R_l, \ t > 0$$

(10-108)

An equation given in this form is better suited for analysis. Similar expression can be obtained for other coordinate systems.

10-5 PHASE CHANGE OVER A TEMPERATURE RANGE

The solidification (or melting) of a pure substance takes place at a discrete melting-point temperature, as a result, during a phase-change process, the solid and liquid phases are separated by a sharp interface that is at the melting-point temperature of the material. All the phase-change problems considered in the previous sections belong to this type of melting or solidification process. In the case of a binary system, such as an aluminum-copper alloy or a lead-tin alloy, there may exist a two-phase region (also called a mushy region) consisting of liquid and solid, between the purely solid and purely liquid phases. Here, the two-phase region is bounded by the two isothermal interfaces, one at the *solidus temperature* T_1 and the other at the

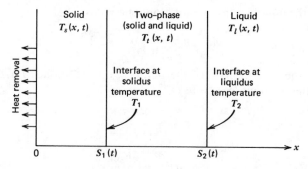

Fig. 10-8   Various phases during the solidification of a binary system.

liquidus temperature T_2 as illustrated in Fig. 10-8. The analysis of phase-change problems of this type may involve the determination of temperature distribution in the solid, the two-phase, and the liquid regions, hence the problem is a three-region problem. In addition, the location of the two interfaces are to be determined as a function of time. An exact analysis of a three-region problem of this type for a half-space is given in references [13] and [94], and approximate analysis of related problems is reported in several references [10–14]. The reader should consult the original references for the details of the methods of solution.

In the case of impure materials such as waxes, various hydrocarbons, paraffin, and many others that are composed of the combinations of several different substances, the phase change from the solid to the liquid state (or vice versa) takes place with gradual transition so that there is no apparent sharp interface. In the analysis of phase-change problems of this type, it may be convenient to consider the enthalpy form of the energy equation given as

$$\nabla \cdot (k \nabla T) + g = \rho \frac{\partial H}{\partial t} \qquad (10\text{-}109)$$

where H is the heat content of the material per unit mass (i.e., the sum of the sensible heat and the latent heat content per unit mass). The energy equation given in this form apparently does not reveal the presence or absence of phase change; but, when the specific heat content H is specified as a function of temperature in the form

$$H \equiv f(T) \qquad (10\text{-}110)$$

the phase change effects are automatically included in the above energy equation since H includes the latent heat.

If $k(T)$ and $H(T)$ are smooth functions of T, that is when the transition from the solid to the liquid phase (or vice versa) is gradual with no sharp interface, then equation (10-109) is applicable over the entire three regions. As a result, the phase-change problem defined by the above two equations is equivalent to the solution of a nonlinear heat-conduction equation subject to some specified boundary and initial conditions. It is highly unlikely that analytic solutions can be obtained for such problems when H is a complicated function of temperature. However, the problem can be solved by a suitable numerical scheme such as the finite-difference or the finite-element method.

The use of the enthalpy form of the energy equation for the solution of phase-change problems has been qualitatively described in reference [58]; the method, since then, has been applied to the solution of various types of phase-change problems [59, 60, 70–73]. The reader should consult the original references for details of various numerical schemes used in the solution of the enthalpy form of the energy equation.

REFERENCES

1. G. Lamé and B. P. Clapeyron, *Ann, Chem. Phys.*, **47**, 250–256, 1831
2. J Stefan, *Ann. Phys. Chemie (Wiedemannsche Annalen)* **42**, 269–286, 1891.
3. H. S. Carslaw and J. C. Jaeger, *Conduction of Heat in Solids*, 2nd ed., Clarendon Press, London, 1959.
4. T. R. Goodman, *Trans. Am. Soc. Mech. Eng.* **80**, 335–342, 1958.
5. T. R. Goodman, *J. Heat Transfer* **83c**, 83–86, 1961.
6. T. R. Goodman and J. Shea, *J. Appl. Mech.* **32**, 16–24, 1960.
7. G. Poots, *Int. J. Heat Mass Transfer* **5**, 339–348, 1962.
8. G. Poots, *Int. J. Heat Mass Transfer* **5**, 525, 1962.
9. R. H. Tien, *Trans. Metall. Soc. AIME* **233**, 1887–1891, 1965.
10. R. H. Tien and G. E. Geiger, *J. Heat Transfer* **89c**, 230–234, 1967.
11. R. H. Tien and G. E. Geiger, *J. Heat Transfer* **90c**, 27–31, 1968.
12. S. Cho and J. E. Sunderland, Melting or Freezing of Finite Slabs, ASME Paper 68-WA/HT-37, Dec. 1968.
13. S. H. Cho and J. E. Sunderland, *J. Heat Transfer* **91c**, 421–426, 1969.
14. J. C. Muehlbauer J. D. Hatcher, D. W. Lyons, and J. E. Sunderland, *J. Heat Transfer* **95c**, 324–331, 1973.
15. K. Mody and M. N. Özışık, *Lett. Heat Mass Transfer* **2**, 487–493, 1975.
16. M. A. Biot, *J. Aeronaut. Sci.* **24**, 857–873, 1957.
17. T. J. Lardner, *AIAA J.* **1**, 196–206, 1963.
18. W. Zyszkowski, The Transient Temperature Distribution in One-Dimensional Heat-Conduction Problems with Nonlinear Boundary Conditions, ASME Paper No. 68-HT-6, 1968.
19. M. A. Biot and H. Daughaday, *J. Aerospace Sci.* **29**, 227–229, 1962.
20. M. A. Biot, *Variational Principles in Heat Transfer*, Oxford University Press, London, 1970.
21. A. Prasad and H. C. Agrawal, *AIAA J.* **12**, 250–252, 1974.
22. N. M. H. Lightfoot, *Proc. London Math. Soc.* **31**, 97–116, 1929.
23. Y. K. Chuang and J. Szekely, *Int. J. Heat Mass Transfer* **14**, 1285–1295, 1971.
24. K. A. Rathjen and L. M. Jiji, *J. Heat Transfer* **93c**, 101–109, 1971.
25. Y. K. Chuang and J. Szekely, *Int. J. Heat Mass Transfer* **15**, 1171–1175, 1972.
26. H. Budhia and F. Kreith, *Int. J. Heat Mass Transfer* **16**, 195–211, 1973.
27. L. T. Rubenstein, *The Stefan Problem*, Trans. Math. Monographs Vol. 27, Am. Math. Soc., Providence, R.I., 1971, pp. 94–181.
28. L. M. Jiji, *J. Franklin Inst.* **289**, 281, 1970.
29. K. A. Rathjen and L. M. Jiji, Transient Heat Transfer in Fins Undergoing Phase Transformation, *Fourth International Heat Transfer Conference, Paris-Versailles*, **2**, 1970.
30. R. I. Pedroso and G. A. Domoto, *J. Heat Transfer* **95**, 42, 1973.
31. R. I. Pedroso and G. A. Domoto, *Int. J. Heat Mass Transfer* **16**, 1037, 1973.
32. L. M. Jiji and S. Weimbaum, A Nonlinear Singular Perturbation Theory for Non-Similar Melting or Freezing Problems, Conduction Cu-3, 5th International Heat Transfer Conference, Tokyo, 1974.
33. D. S. Riley, F. T. Smith and G. Poots, *Int. J. Heat Mass Transfer* **17**, 1507, 1974.
34. C. L. Hwang and Y. P. Shih, *Int. J. Heat Mass Transfer*, **18**, 689–695, 1975.
35. B. A. Boley, *J. Math. Phys.* **40**, 300–313, 1961.
36. B. A. Boley, *Int. J. Eng. Sci.* **6**, 89–111, 1968.
37. J. M. Lederman and B. A. Boley, *Int. J. Heat Mass Transfer* **13**, 413–427, 1970.
38. D. L. Sikarshie and B. A. Boley, *Int. J. Solids and Structures* **1**, 207–234, 1965.
39. B. A. Boley and H. P. Yagoda, *Quart. Appl. Math.* **27**, 223–246, 1969.

40. Y. F. Lee and B. A. Boley, *Int. J. Eng. Sci.* **11**, 1277, 1973.

41. A. N. Güzelsu and A. S. Çakmak, *Int. J. Solids and Structures* **6**, 1087, 1970.

42. M. N. Özışık and R. L. Murray, *J. Heat Transfer* **96c**, 48–51, 1974.

43. Y. Yener and M. N. Özışık, On the Solution of Unsteady Heat Conduction in Multi-Region Finite Media with Time Dependent Heat Transfer Coefficient, Proceeding of 5th International Heat Transfer Conference, Tokyo, September 3–7, 1974.

44. M. N. Özışık and S. Güçeri, *Ca. J. Chem. Eng.* **55**, 145–148, 1977.

45. F. Kreith and F. E. Romie, *Proc. Phys. Soc. Lond.* **68(B)**, 283, 1955.

46. D. R. Otis, Solving the Melting Problem Using the Electric Analog to Heat Conduction, *Heat Transfer and Fluid Mechanics Institute*, Stanford Univ., 1956.

47. G. Liebmann, *ASME Trans.* **78**, 1267, 1956.

48. D. C. Baxter, The Fusion Times of Slabs and Cylinders, ASME Paper No. 61-WA-179, 1961.

49. C. F. Bonilla and A. L. Strupczewski, *Nucl. Struc. Eng.* **2**, 40–47, 1965.

50. J. Douglas and T. M. Gallie, *Duke Math. J.* **22**, 557, 1955.

51. J. Crank, *Quart. J. Mech. Appl. Math.* **10**, 220, 1957.

52. W. D. Murray and F. Landis, *Trans. Am. Soc. Mech. Eng.* **81**, 106, 1959.

53. G. S. Springer and D. R. Olson, Method of Solution of Axisymmetric Solidification and Melting Problems, ASME Paper No. 62-WA-246, 1962.

54. G. S. Springer and D. R. Olson, Axisymmetric Solidification and Melting of Materials, ASME Paper No. 63-WA-185, 1963.

55. D. N. de G. Allen and R. T. Severn, *Quart. J. Mech. Appl. Math.* **15**, 53, 1962.

56. W. D. Seider and S. W. Churchill, The Effect of Insulation on Freezing Motion, 7th National Heat Transfer Conference, Cleveland, 1964.

57. C. Bonacina G. Comini, A. Fasano, and M. Primicerio, *Int. J. Heat Mass Transfer* **16**, 1825–1832, 1973.

58. G. M. Dusinberre, A Note on Latent Heat in Digital Computer Calculations, ASME Paper No. 58-HT-7.

59. N. R. Eyres, D. R. Hartree, J. Ingham, R. Jackson, R. J. Jarjant, and J. B. Wagstaff, *Phil. Trans. Roy. Soc.* **A240**, 1–57, 1948.

60. D. C. Baxter, *J. Heat Transfer* **84c**, 317–326, 1962.

61. L. C. Tao, *AIChE J.* **13**, 165, 1967.

62. L. C. Tao, *AIChE J.* **14**, 720, 1968.

63. G. S. Springer, *Int. J. Heat Mass Transfer* **12**, 521, 1969.

64. S. H. Cho and J. E. Sunderland, *Int. J. Heat Mass Transfer* **13**, 123, 1970.

65. A. Lazaridis, *Int. J. Heat Mass Transfer* **13**, 1459–1477, 1970.

66. J. Crank and R. S. Gupta, *J. Int. Maths. Appl.* **10**, 296–304, 1972.

67. G. G. Sackett, *SIAM J. Numer. Anal.* **8**, 80–96, 1971.

68. G. H. Meyer, *Num. Math.* **16**, 248–267, 1970.

69. J. Crank and R. D. Phahle, *Bull. Inst. Maths. Appl.* **9**, 12–14, 1973.

70. J. Szekely and M. J. Themelis, *Rate Phenomena in Process Metallurgy*, Wiley-Interscience, New York, 1971, Chapter 10.

71. R. D. Atthey, *J. Inst. Math. Appl.* **13**, 353–366, 1974.

72. G. H. Meyer, *SIAM J. Numer. Anal.* **10**, 522–538, 1973.

73. N. Shamsunder and E. M. Sparrow, *J. Heat Transfer* **97c**, 333–340, 1975.

74. L. T. Thomas and J. W. Westwater, *Chem. Eng. Prog. Symp.* **59**, 155–164, 1963.

75. D. V. Boger and J. E. Westwater, *J. Heat Transfer* **89c**, 81–89, 1967.

76. L. M. Jiji, K. A. Rathjen, and T. Drezewiecki, *Int. J. Heat Mass Transfer* **13**, 215–218, 1970.

77. J. A. Bailey and J. R. Davila, *Appl. Sci. Res.* **25**, 245–261, 1971.

78. B. W. Grange, R. Viskanta, and W. H. Stevenson, Solute and Thermal Redistribution During Freezing of Salt Solutions, *Fifth International Heat Transfer Conference, Cu 3.4, Tokyo,* 1974.

79. B. A. Boley, in *Proceedings of the 3rd Symposium on Naval Structural Mechanics,* Pergamon Press, New York, 1963.

80. S. B. Bankoff, in *Advances in Chemical Engineering,* Vol 5, Academic Press, New York, 1964.

81. J. C. Muehlbauer and J. E. Sunderland, *Appl. Mech. Rev.* **18.**, 951–959, 1965.

82. J. R. Ockendon and W. R. Hodgkins, eds., *Moving Boundary Problems in Heat Flow and Diffusion,* Clarendon Press—Oxford, London, 1975.

83. D. G. Wilson, Allen D. Solomon and Paul T. Boggs, eds. *Moving Boundary Problems,* Academic Press, New York, 1978.

84. P. D. Patel, *AIAA J.* **6**, 2454, 1968.

85. F. B. Hildebrand, *Advanced Calculus for Engineers,* Prentice-Hall, New York, 1954.

86. M. D. Mikhailov, *Int. J. Heat Mass Transfer* **19**, 651–655, 1976.

87. C. A. Knight, *The Freezing of Supercooled Liquids,* Van Nostrand, Princeton, N.J., 1967.

88. R. R. Gilpin, *Int. J. Heat Mass Transfer* **20**, 693–699, 1977.

89. S. Paterson, *Proc. Glasgow Math. Assoc.* **1**, 42–47, 1952–53.

90. N. N. Levedev, *Special Functions and Their Applications,* Prentice-Hall, Inc., Englewood Cliffs, N.J., 1965.

91. M. Abramowitz and I. A. Stegun, *Handbook of Mathematical Functions,* NBS Applied Mathematics series 55, U.S. Government Printing Office, Washingon, D.C., 1964, p. 239.

92. S. M. Selby, *Standard Mathematical Tables,* The Chemical Rubber Company, Ohio, 1971, p. 515

93. M. N. Özışık, *J. Heat Transfer,* **100C**, 370–371, 1978.

94. M. N. Özışık and J. C. Uzzell, *J. Heat Transfer,* **101C**, 331–334, 1979.

PROBLEMS

10-1   Verify that the interface energy-balance equation (10-4a) is also applicable for the melting problem illustrated in Fig. 10-1b.

10-2   In the melting problem illustrated in Fig. 10-1b, if the heat transfer on the liquid side is by convection and on the solid phase is by pure conduction, derive the interface energy-balance equation Take the bulk temperature of the liquid side as T_∞ and the heat-transfer coefficient as h.

10-3   Solve exactly the phase-change problem considered in Example 10-2 for the case of solidification in a half-space $x > 0$. That is, a liquid at the melting temperature T_m is confined to a half-space $x > 0$. At time $t = 0$ the boundary at $x = 0$ is lowered to a temperature T_0 below T_m and maintained at that temperature for times $t > 0$. Determine the temperature distribution in the solid phase and the location of the solid-liquid interface as a function of time.

10-4   Solve exactly the problem considered in Example 10-3 for the case of melting. That is a solid in $x > 0$ is initially at a uniform temperature T_i lower than the melting temperature T_m. For times $t > 0$ the boundary surface at $x = 0$ is kept at a constant temperature T_0, which is higher than the melting temperature T_m. Determine the temperature distribution in the liquid and solid phases, and the location of the solid-liquid interface as a function of time.

10-5   Solve exactly the problem considered in Example 10-4 for the case of melting. That is, a line heat source of strength Q W/cm (or Btu/hr ft) is situated at $r = 0$ in an infinite medium that is at a uniform temperature T_i lower than the melting temperature T_m. The melting will start at $r \to 0$ and the solid-liquid interface will move in the positive r direction. Determine the temperature distribution in the solid and liquid phases, and the location of the solid-liquid interface as a function of time.

10-6   Using the integral method of solution, solve the solidification Problem 10-3 and obtain an expression for the location of the solid-liquid interface. Compare this result with that obtained in Example 10-5 for the case of melting.

10-7   Using the integral method of solution, solve the problem considered in Example 10-6 for the case of melting. That is, a solid in the finite region $0 \leq x \leq b$ is initially at a uniform temperature T_i that is lower than the melting temperature T_m. For times $t > 0$, the boundary surface at $x = 0$ is kept at a constant temperature T_0 higher than the melting temperature T_m and the other boundary at $x = b$ is kept insulated. Obtain an expression for the location of the solid-liquid interface by following an approach used in Example 10-6.

10-8   A solid confined in a half-space $x > 0$ is initially at the melting temperature T_m. For times $t > 0$ the boundary surface at $x = 0$ is subjected to a heat flux in the form

$$-k\frac{\partial T}{\partial x}\bigg|_{x=0} = H \equiv \text{constant}$$

Using the integral method of solution and a second-degree polynomial approximation for the temperature, obtain an expression for the location of the solid-liquid interface as a function of time.

NOTES

1.   We consider the energy balance equation at the solid-liquid interface given by equation (10-13) as

$$k_s\frac{\partial T_s}{\partial n} - k_l\frac{\partial T_l}{\partial n} = \rho L v_n \tag{1}$$

valid on the solid-liquid interface

$$F(x, y, z, t) = 0 \tag{2}$$

An alternative form of equation (1) can be derived by an approach discussed in reference [84].

At any point of the interface defined by equation (2) the vector ∇F is normal to this interface. Then a unit vector $\mathbf{n}$ normal to this interface is given by

$$\mathbf{n} = \frac{\nabla F}{|\nabla F|} \tag{3a}$$

where

$$\nabla F \equiv \mathbf{i}\frac{\partial F}{\partial x} + \mathbf{j}\frac{\partial F}{\partial y} + \mathbf{k}\frac{\partial F}{\partial z} \tag{3b}$$

here $\mathbf{i}, \mathbf{j}$, and $\mathbf{k}$ are unit vectors in the x, y, and z directions, respectively. In the present analysis we assume that $\mathbf{n}$ is pointing into the liquid phase. We note the solid-liquid interface is at the melting temperature T_m; therefore the surface $F = 0$ is an isothermal surface, hence ∇T is normal to the interface. With this consideration $\mathbf{n}$ is given by

$$\mathbf{n} = \frac{\nabla F}{|\nabla F|} = \frac{\nabla T_i}{|\nabla T_i|}, \qquad i = s \text{ or } l \tag{4}$$

The terms $\partial T_i/\partial n$, $i = s$ or l, and v_n appearing in equation (1) can be written as

$$\frac{\partial T_i}{\partial n} = \nabla T_i \cdot \mathbf{n} = \frac{\nabla T_i \cdot \nabla F}{|\nabla F|}, \qquad i = s \text{ or } l \tag{5}$$

$$v_n = \mathbf{v} \cdot \mathbf{n} = \frac{\mathbf{v} \cdot \nabla F}{|\nabla F|} \tag{6}$$

The total derivative of equation (2) gives

$$\left[\frac{\partial F}{\partial t}dt + \frac{\partial F}{\partial x}dx + \frac{\partial F}{\partial y}dy + \frac{\partial F}{\partial z}dz \right]_{\text{at interface}} = 0 \tag{7a}$$

or

$$\left[\frac{\partial F}{\partial x}\dot{x} + \frac{\partial F}{\partial y}\dot{y} + \frac{\partial F}{\partial z}\dot{z} \right] = -\frac{\partial F}{\partial t} \tag{7b}$$

at the interface where dots denote derivative with respect to t. The velocity vector $\mathbf{v}$ is written as

$$\mathbf{v} = \mathbf{i}\dot{x} + \mathbf{j}\dot{y} + \mathbf{k}\dot{z} \tag{8}$$

Then,

$$\mathbf{v} \cdot \nabla F = \dot{x} \frac{\partial F}{\partial x} + \dot{y} \frac{\partial F}{\partial y} + \dot{z} \frac{\partial F}{\partial z} = -\frac{\partial F}{\partial t} \tag{9}$$

Introducing equation (9) into (6) we obtain

$$v_n = -\frac{\partial F/\partial t}{|\nabla F|} \tag{10}$$

Table 10-1 $E_1(x)$ or $-Ei(-x)$ Function

x	$E_1(x)$	x	$E_1(x)$	x	$E_1(x)$	x	$E_1(x)$
0.00	∞	0.25	1.0442826	0.50	0.5597736	1.60	0.0863083
0.01	4.0379296	0.26	0.0138887	0.55	0.5033641	1.65	0.0802476
0.02	3.3547078	0.27	0.9849331				
0.03	2.9591187	0.28	0.9573083	0.60	0.4543795	1.70	0.0746546
0.04	2.6812637	0.29	0.9309182	0.65	0.4115170	1.75	0.0694887
0.05	2.4678985	0.30	0.9056767	0.70	0.3737688	1.80	0.0647131
0.06	2.2953069	0.31	0.8815057	0.75	0.3403408	1.85	0.0602950
0.07	2.1508382	0.32	0.8583352				
0.08	2.0269410	0.33	0.8361012	0.80	0.3105966	1.90	0.0562044
0.09	1.9187448	0.34	0.8147456	0.85	0.2840193	1.95	0.0524144
0.10	1.8229240	0.35	0.7942154	0.90	0.2601839	2.0	$4.89005(-2)$
0.11	1.7371067	0.36	0.7744622	0.95	0.2387375	2.1	4.26143
0.12	1.6595418	0.37	0.7554414				
0.13	1.5888993	0.38	0.7371121	1.00	0.2193839	2.2	3.71911
0.14	1.4241457	0.39	0.7194367	1.05	0.2018728	2.3	3.25023
0.15	1.4644617	0.40	0.7023801	1.10	0.1859909	2.4	2.84403
0.16	1.4091867	0.41	0.6859103	1.15	0.1715554	2.6	2.18502
0.17	1.3577806	0.42	0.6699973				
0.18	1.3097961	0.43	0.6546134	1.20	0.1584084	2.8	1.68553
0.19	1.2648584	0.44	0.6397328	1.25	0.1464134	3.0	1.30484
0.20	1.2226505	0.45	0.6253313	1.30	0.1354510	3.5	$6.97014(-3)$
0.21	1.1829020	0.46	0.6113865	1.35	0.1254168	4.0	3.77935
0.22	1.1453801	0.47	0.5978774	1.40	0.1162193	4.5	2.07340
0.23	1.1098831	0.48	0.5847843	1.45	0.1077774	5.0	1.14830
0.24	1.0762354	0.49	0.5720888	1.50	0.1000196	∞	0

(The figures in parenthesis indicate the power of 10 by which the numbers to the left, and those below in the same column, are to be multiplied).

substituting equations (5) and (10) into equation (1) we find

$$k_s \nabla T_s \cdot \nabla F - k_l \nabla T_l \cdot \nabla F = - \rho L \frac{\partial F}{\partial t} \tag{11}$$

which is the relation given by equation (10-14).

2. The exponential-integral function $- Ei(- x)$ or $E_1(x)$ is defined as

$$- Ei(- x) \equiv E_1(x) = \int_x^\infty \frac{e^{-u}}{u} du = \int_1^\infty \frac{e^{-xt}}{t} dt \qquad \text{for } x > 0 \tag{1}$$

The function $- Ei(- x)$ which is also denoted by $E_1(x)$ decreases monotonically from the value $E_1(0) = \infty$ to $E_1(\infty) = 0$ as x is varied from $x = 0$ to $x \to \infty$ as shown in Table 10-1. The derivative of $- Ei(- x)$ with respect to x is given as

$$\frac{d}{dx} \left[- Ei(- x) \right] = \frac{d}{dx} \left[+ \int_x^\infty \frac{e^{-u}}{u} du \right] = - \frac{e^{-x}}{x} \tag{2}$$

The notation $E_1(x)$ has been used for $- Ei(- x)$ function in reference [91, p. 228] and its polynomial approximations are given for $0 \leq x \leq 1$ and $1 \leq x < \infty$ [91, p. 231]. A tabulation of $E_1(x)$ function is given in references [91, p. 239] and [92, p. 515].

CHAPTER 11 $\mathbf{N}$ONLINEAR
PROBLEMS

In the analysis of heat-conduction problems the assumption of linearity
is frequently made to take advantage of the powerful superposition principles
of linear theory of mathematics to obtain analytic solutions. However, most
realistic problems encountered in engineering applications are nonlinear
in nature. For example, when temperature variations are large or the
transport properties vary rapidly with temperature, a valid description of
the heat-conduction problem must take into account the variation of the
transport coefficients with temperature. Then the differential equation of
heat conduction becomes nonlinear. When heat transfer takes place at high
temperatures, it may be necessary to include the effects of thermal radiation
according to the fourth power law at the boundaries. Then the boundary
condition becomes nonlinear. Therefore, a heat-conduction problem becomes
nonlinear either due to the nonlinearity of the differential equation or the
boundary conditions or both. The difficulty in the analysis of nonlinear
problems is due to the fact that no general theory is yet available for the
solution of nonlinear partial differential equations; each problem should be
treated individually and the principle of superposition being not applicable,
the analytic solution of nonlinear problems are often ad hoc and approximate.
Various techniques applied for the solution of nonlinear boundary value
problems of heat conduction are discussed in several texts [1–7] and
references [8–34]. The approximate methods used for their solution include
the *integral method* [35, 36], the *variational method* [37–43], *linearization*
[44], and the *perturbation technique* [45]. *Similarity analysis* has been
applied for the solution of nonlinear problems [46–56]; the similarity
analysis via *group theory method* has been discussed in several references
[4, 52–58].

In this chapter we present some of the analytic methods of solution of
nonlinear heat-conduction problems.

11-1 TRANSFORMATION OF A DEPENDENT VARIABLE—
THE KIRCHHOFF TRANSFORMATION

When the thermal conductivity of the solid varies with temperature, then a change of the dependent variable by means of the *Kirchhoff transformation* [9] will remove the thermal conductivity $k(T)$ outside the differential operator as now described.

Consider the differential equation of heat conduction given in the form

$$\nabla \cdot [k(T)\nabla T] + g(\mathbf{r}, t) = \rho(T)C_p(T)\frac{\partial T}{\partial t} \tag{11-1}$$

where C_p, ρ, k are assumed to depend on temperature, but the heat generation term $g(\mathbf{r}, t)$ is independent of temperature.

A new dependent variable U is defined according to *Kirchhoff transformation* as

$$U = \int_{T_0}^{T} \frac{k(T')}{k_0} dT' \tag{11-2}$$

where T_0 is a reference temperature and k_0 is the value of $k(T)$ at T_0.

Equation (11-1) is rearranged as

$$\nabla \cdot \left[k(T)\frac{\partial T}{\partial U}\nabla U \right] + g(\mathbf{r}, t) = \rho C_p \frac{\partial T}{\partial U}\frac{\partial U}{\partial t} \tag{11-3}$$

From equation (11-2) we have

$$\frac{\partial U}{\partial T} = \frac{k(T)}{k_0} \quad \text{or} \quad \frac{\partial T}{\partial U} = \frac{k_0}{k(T)} \tag{11-4}$$

Introducing equation (11-4) into equation (11-3) we obtain

$$\nabla^2 U(\mathbf{r}, t) + \frac{1}{k_0}g(\mathbf{r}, t) = \frac{1}{\alpha}\frac{\partial U(\mathbf{r}, t)}{\partial t} \tag{11-5}$$

where $\alpha \equiv \alpha(T)$ is a function of temperature. Equation (11-5) is still nonlinear because α depends on temperature, but it is in a form that is more suitable for analysis than equation (11-1). If $\alpha(T)$ varies little with temperature, then it can be assumed constant and equation (11-5) becomes linear.

In the case of steady-state problems, the nonlinear differential equation of heat conduction is transformed to a linear equation by the Kirchhoff transformation, since the right-hand side of equation (11-5) vanishes for the steady state.

We now examine the transformation of the boundary conditions by the Kirchhoff transformation.

Boundary Condition of the First Kind

Let the temperature at the boundary be prescribed as

$$T = f_i(\mathbf{r}, t) \qquad \text{on } S_i \tag{11-6}$$

The transformation of this boundary condition by the transformation (11-2) is also a boundary condition of the first kind. To illustrate this, consider $k(T)$ to depend on temperature in the form

$$k(T) = k_0(1 + \beta T) \tag{11-7}$$

Then, the transformation (11-2) becomes

$$U = \int_{T_0}^{T} (1 + \beta T') dT' = (T - T_0) + \frac{\beta}{2}(T^2 - T_0^2) \tag{11-8}$$

and the transformation of the boundary condition (11-6) gives

$$U = (f_i - T_0) + \frac{\beta}{2}(f_i^2 - T_0^2) \equiv f_i^*(\mathbf{r}, t) \tag{11-9}$$

which is again a boundary condition of the first kind.

Boundary Condition of the Second Kind

The boundary condition is of the second kind in the form

$$k(T) \frac{\partial T}{\partial n_i} = f_i(\mathbf{r}, t) \qquad \text{on } S_i \tag{11-10}$$

Then, the transformation of this boundary condition by means of the transformation (11-2) is a linear boundary condition of the second kind since

$$\frac{\partial T}{\partial n_i} = \frac{\partial T}{\partial U} \cdot \frac{\partial U}{\partial n_i} = \frac{k_0}{k(T)} \frac{\partial U}{\partial n_i} \tag{11-11}$$

That is, introducing this expression into (11-10) we obtain

$$k_0 \frac{\partial U}{\partial n_i} = f_i(\mathbf{r}, t) \qquad \text{on } S_i \tag{11-12}$$

which is a linear boundary condition of the second kind.

Boundary Condition of the Third Kind

We now consider a boundary condition of the third kind given in the form

$$k(T) \frac{\partial T}{\partial n_i} + h_i(T) \cdot T = f_i(\mathbf{r}, t) \qquad \text{on } S_i \tag{11-13}$$

The transformation of this boundary condition to a linear boundary condition of the third kind, using the transformation (11-2), is possible only under certain restrictions on the heat-transfer coefficient $h(T)$ as illustrated below.

Suppose we wish to transform (11-13) into a linear boundary condition in the variable U as

$$k_0 \frac{\partial U}{\partial n_i} + h_{0,i} U = f_i(\mathbf{r}, t) \qquad \text{on } S_i \qquad (11\text{-}14a)$$

where k_0 and $h_{0,i}$ are constants. Introducing equations (11-2) and (11-11) into (11-14a) we obtain

$$k(T)\frac{\partial T}{\partial n_i} + h_{0,i} \int_{T_0}^{T} \frac{k(T')}{k_0} dT' = f_i(\mathbf{r}, t) \qquad \text{on } S_i \qquad (11\text{-}15)$$

A comparison of equations (11-13) and (11-15) reveals that

$$h_i(T) = h_{0,i} \frac{1}{T} \int_{T_0}^{T} \frac{k(T')}{k_0} dT' \qquad (11\text{-}16)$$

Thus, when $h_i(T)$ satisfies the restriction imposed on by equation (11-16), the nonlinear boundary condition (11-13) is transformed into a linear boundary condition in U given by equation (11-14a) under the transformation (11-2).

Example 1-1. Consider the following nonlinear heat-conduction problem for a slab

$$\frac{\partial}{\partial x}\left(k \frac{\partial T}{\partial x} \right) + g(x, t) = \rho C_p \frac{\partial T}{\partial t} \qquad \text{in } 0 < x < L, \ t > 0 \qquad (11\text{-}17a)$$

$$k \frac{\partial T}{\partial x} = f_1(t) \qquad \text{at } x = 0, \ t > 0 \qquad (11\text{-}17b)$$

$$T = f_2(t) \qquad \text{at } x = L, \ t > 0 \qquad (11\text{-}17c)$$

$$T = F(x) \qquad \text{for } t = 0, \ \text{in } 0 \le x \le L, \quad (11\text{-}17d)$$

where the thermal conductivity $k(T)$ is assumed to depend on temperature in the form

$$k(T) = k_0(1 + \beta T) \qquad (11\text{-}18)$$

Transform this problem with the Kirchhoff transformation.

Solution. The Kirchhoff transformation equation (11-2), when $k(T)$ is given by equation (11-18), becomes

$$U = \int_{T_0}^{T} \frac{k(T')}{k_0} dT' = \int_{T_0}^{T} (1 + \beta T') dT' = (T - T_0) + \frac{\beta}{2}(T^2 - T_0^2) \quad (11\text{-}19)$$

Then, the problem (11-17) is transformed by utilizing the results given by equations (11-5), (11-9), and (11-10). We obtain

$$\frac{\partial^2 U}{\partial x^2} + \frac{1}{k_0} g(x, t) = \frac{1}{\alpha} \frac{\partial U}{\partial t} \qquad \text{in } 0 < x < L, \ t > 0 \quad (11\text{-}20a)$$

$$k_0 \frac{\partial U}{\partial x} = f_1(t) \qquad \text{at } x = 0 \quad (11\text{-}20b)$$

$$U = [f_2(t) - T_0] + \frac{\beta}{2}[f_2^2(t) - T_0^2] \equiv f_2^*(t) \qquad \text{at } x = L \quad (11\text{-}20c)$$

$$U = [F(x) - T_0] + \frac{\beta}{2}[F^2(x) - T_0^2] \equiv F^*(x) \qquad \text{for } t = 0 \quad (11\text{-}20d)$$

where $\alpha \equiv \alpha(t) = k/\rho C_p$. Clearly, the transformed problem (11-20) becomes linear if we assume α constant; then it can readily be solved for U.

If the reference temperature T_0 is taken as zero, the transformation equation (11-19) reduces to

$$U = T + \tfrac{1}{2}\beta T^2 \qquad (11\text{-}21a)$$

and the inverse transformation from U to T becomes

$$T(x, t) = \frac{1}{\beta}[\sqrt{1 + 2\beta U(x, t)} - 1] \qquad (11\text{-}21b)$$

11-2 LINEARIZATION OF A ONE-DIMENSIONAL NONLINEAR HEAT-CONDUCTION PROBLEM

In the previous section we transformed the three-dimensional nonlinear heat-conduction equation by Kirchhoff transformation into the form given by equation (11-5), which becomes linear if $\alpha(T)$ can be assumed constant. A method of linearization of the one-dimensional nonlinear heat diffusion equation by successive transformation of the dependent and independent variables has been discussed in references [11] and [32]. It is shown that when the thermal properties depend on temperature in a certain way the linearization is possible for a prescribed heat flux (i.e., constant or a function of time) boundary condition at $x = 0$. This linearization procedure developed by Storm [11] is based on the requirements that $k(T)$ and the product $\rho(T)C_p(T)$ should depend on temperature in the form

$$k(T) = k_0\phi(T)\exp\left[-A(k_0\rho_0C_{p0})^{1/2}\int_{T_0}^{T}\phi(T')\,dT'\right] \quad (11\text{-}22a)$$

$$\rho(T)C_p(T) = \rho_0 C_{p0}\phi(T)\exp\left[A(k_0\rho_0C_{p0})^{1/2}\int_{T_0}^{T}\phi(T')\,dT'\right] \quad (11\text{-}22b)$$

where the subscript zero denotes that the function is evaluated at the reference temperature T_0; here the function $\phi(T)$ is an arbitrary function, except it satisfies the condition $\phi(T_0) = 1$.

Equations (11-22) can be simplified if the product

$$k\rho C_p = \text{constant} \quad (11\text{-}23a)$$

Then introducing this condition to the above expressions it is seen that $\phi(T) = 1$. For such a case, the variation of k and ρC_p with temperature is given by

$$k(T) = k_0 \exp\left[-A(k_0\rho_0C_{p0})^{1/2}(T - T_0)\right] \quad (11\text{-}23b)$$

$$\rho(T)C_p(T) = \rho_0 C_{p0}\exp\left[A(k_0\rho_0C_{p0})^{1/2}(T - T_0)\right] \quad (11\text{-}23c)$$

If the exponentials in these expressions can be linearized, equations (11-23b) and (11-23c) reduce to

$$k(T) = k_0\left[1 - A(k_0\rho_0C_{p0})^{1/2}(T - T_0)\right] \quad (11\text{-}24a)$$

$$\rho(T)C_p(T) = \rho_0 C_{p0}\left[1 + A(k_0\rho_0C_{p0})^{1/2}(T - T_0)\right] \quad (11\text{-}24b)$$

We now present a discussion of the linearization process.

Consider the one-dimensional, nonlinear heat-conduction equation given in the form

$$\frac{\partial}{\partial x}\left(k\frac{\partial T}{\partial x}\right) = \rho C_p\frac{\partial T}{\partial t} \quad \text{in } x > 0,\ t > 0 \quad (11\text{-}25a)$$

where k, ρ, and C_p depend on temperature. It is assumed that the heat flux at the boundary surface $x = 0$ is prescribed

$$-k\frac{\partial T}{\partial x} = f(t) \quad (11\text{-}25b)$$

A new dependent variable $U(x, t)$ is defined as

$$U = \int_{T_0}^{T}\left[k(T')C_p(T')\rho(T')\right]^{1/2}dT' \quad (11\text{-}26a)$$

then we have

$$\frac{\partial U}{\partial T} = (kC_p\rho)^{1/2} \quad \text{or} \quad \frac{\partial T}{\partial U} = (kC_p\rho)^{-1/2} \tag{11-26b}$$

Equation (11-25a) is rearranged as

$$\frac{\partial}{\partial x}\left(k\frac{\partial T}{\partial U}\frac{\partial U}{\partial x}\right) = \rho C_p \frac{\partial T}{\partial U}\frac{\partial U}{\partial t} \tag{11-27a}$$

and in view of the expression (11-26b), equation (11-27a) becomes

$$\alpha^{1/2}\frac{\partial}{\partial x}\left(\alpha^{1/2}\frac{\partial U}{\partial x}\right) = \frac{\partial U}{\partial t} \tag{11-27b}$$

where $\alpha \equiv k/\rho C_p$.

A new independent variable $X(x, t)$ is defined as

$$X(x, t) = \int_0^x \alpha^{-1/2}\, dx' \tag{11-28a}$$

and we let

$$U(x, t) = U^*[X(x, t), t] \tag{11-28b}$$

The application of the transformation (11-28) transforms equation (11-27b) into (see Note-1 for the details of this transformation)

$$\frac{\partial^2 U^*}{\partial X^2} = \frac{\partial U^*}{\partial t} + \frac{\partial U^*}{\partial X}\left\{\int_0^X\left[\frac{d}{dU}(\ln \alpha^{-1/2})\right]\frac{\partial^2 U^*}{\partial X^2}\, dX\right\} \tag{11-29a}$$

If we assume (the significance of this assumption is discussed later)

$$\frac{d}{dU}(\ln \alpha^{-1/2}) = (k\rho C_p)^{-1/2}\frac{d}{dT}(\ln \alpha^{-1/2}) \equiv A = \text{constant} \tag{11-29b}$$

Equation (11-29a) reduces to

$$\frac{\partial^2 U^*}{\partial X^2} = \frac{\partial U^*}{\partial t} + A\frac{\partial U^*}{\partial X}\int_0^X \frac{\partial^2 U^*}{\partial X^2}\, dX \tag{11-30a}$$

or

$$\frac{\partial^2 U^*}{\partial X^2} = \frac{\partial U^*}{\partial t} + A\left(\frac{\partial U^*}{\partial X}\right)^2 - A\frac{\partial U^*}{\partial X}\left[\frac{\partial U^*}{\partial X}\right]_{X=0} \tag{11-30b}$$

Clearly, the transformation into the form (11-30b) is valid if the assumption (11-29b) is satisfied. The assumption (11-29b) is valid if k and ρC_p satisfies the conditions given by equations (11-22). The validity of this condition is readily verified by introducing equations (11-22) into (11-29b).

We note that equation (11-30b) involves a term $[\partial U^*/\partial X]_{X=0}$; this can be evaluated from the prescribed heat flux boundary condition (11-25b) as

$$-k\frac{\partial T}{\partial U}\left[\frac{\partial U}{\partial x}\right]_{x=0} = -k\frac{\partial T}{\partial U}\left[\frac{\partial U^*}{\partial X}\right]_{X=0}\frac{\partial X}{\partial x} = f(t) \qquad (11\text{-}31a)$$

From equations (11-26b) and (11-28a) we have, respectively,

$$\frac{\partial T}{\partial U} = (k\rho C_p)^{-1/2} \quad \text{and} \quad \frac{\partial X}{\partial x} = \left(\frac{k}{\rho C_p}\right)^{-1/2} \qquad (11\text{-}31b)$$

Introducing equation (11-31b) into equation (11-31a) we obtain

$$-\left[\frac{\partial U^*}{\partial X}\right]_{X=0} = f(t) \qquad (11\text{-}32)$$

Substituting equation (11-32) into equation (11-30b) we find

$$\frac{\partial^2 U^*}{\partial X^2} = \frac{\partial U^*}{\partial t} + A\left(\frac{\partial U^*}{\partial X}\right)^2 + Af(t)\frac{\partial U^*}{\partial X} \qquad (11\text{-}33)$$

This equation is still nonlinear; but it can be linearized by defining a new dependent variable W as

$$U^*(X,t) = -\frac{1}{A}\ln W(X,t) \qquad (11\text{-}34)$$

Then equation (11-33) becomes [see Note-2 for the details of this transformation]

$$\frac{\partial^2 W}{\partial X^2} = \frac{\partial W}{\partial t} + Af(t)\frac{\partial W}{\partial X} \qquad (11\text{-}35)$$

which is now a linear partial differential equation for the variable $W(X,t)$.

We now summarize the results of the above analysis: The nonlinear heat-conduction equation (11-25a) subject to the prescribed heat-flux boundary condition (11-25b) is transformed into the linear equation (11-35) on the assumption that the physical properties k and ρC_p depend on temperature in the form specified by equations (11-22), (11-23), or (11-24). The physical properties for metals such as aluminum, copper, lead, 0.8% carbon steel, iron, silver, and zinc satisfy the condition imposed in the present analysis [11].

Example 11-2. A semi-infinite medium $x \geq 0$ is initially at zero temperature. For times $t > 0$, a constant heat flux is applied at the boundary surface $x = 0$. The properties k and ρC_p vary with temperature according to the expressions given by equations (11-22), (11-23), or (11-24). By utilizing the transformation described above, transform this nonlinear problem into a linear one.

Solution. The mathematical formulation of this problem is given as

$$\frac{\partial}{\partial x}\left(k\frac{\partial T}{\partial x}\right) = \rho C_p \frac{\partial T}{\partial t} \qquad \text{in } x > 0,\ t > 0 \qquad (11\text{-}36\text{a})$$

$$-k\frac{\partial T}{\partial x} = f \qquad \text{at } x = 0,\ t > 0 \qquad (11\text{-}36\text{b})$$

$$T \to 0 \qquad \text{as } x \to \infty,\ t > 0 \qquad (11\text{-}36\text{c})$$

$$T = 0 \qquad \text{for } t = 0,\ x > 0 \qquad (11\text{-}36\text{d})$$

where k and ρC_p are functions of temperature.

We define a new dependent variable $U(x, t)$ according to the transformation (11-26a) as

$$U(x,t) = \int_0^T \left[k(T')C_p(T')\rho(T')\right]^{1/2} dT' \qquad (11\text{-}37)$$

where the lower limit T_0 is chosen as zero without loss of generality since the medium is at zero temperature initially.

A new independent variable $X(x, t)$ is defined according to the transformation (11-28a) as

$$X(x,t) = \int_0^x \alpha^{-1/2} dx' \qquad (11\text{-}38\text{a})$$

and the corresponding dependent variable is denoted by

$$U(x,t) = U^*[X(x,t), t] \qquad (11\text{-}38\text{b})$$

Finally, a new dependent variable $W(X, t)$ is introduced according to the transformation (11-34) as

$$U^*(X,t) = -\frac{1}{A}\ln W \qquad (11\text{-}39)$$

The transformations (11-37) to (11-39) are successively applied to the equations (11-36) as discussed above. The resulting transformed problem in the W variable becomes

$$\frac{\partial^2 W}{\partial X^2} = \frac{\partial W}{\partial t} + Af\frac{\partial W}{\partial X} \qquad X > 0,\ t > 0 \qquad (11\text{-}40\text{a})$$

$$\frac{\partial W}{\partial X} - AfW = 0 \qquad X = 0,\ t > 0 \qquad (11\text{-}40\text{b})$$

$$W \to 1 \qquad X \to \infty,\ t > 0 \qquad (11\text{-}40\text{c})$$

$$W = 1 \qquad t = 0,\ X > 0 \qquad (11\text{-}40\text{d})$$

which is now a linear problem and the coefficient A is associated with the constant A appearing in equations (11-22), (11-23), or (11-24) giving the functional form of the dependence of physical properties on temperature.

This problem can be transformed into a more convenient form by defining a new dependent variable $V(X,t)$ as

$$W(X,t) = V(X,t)e^{(Af/2)X} \tag{11-41}$$

Then, equations (11-40) become

$$\frac{\partial^2 V}{\partial X^2} - \left(\frac{Af}{2}\right)^2 V = \frac{\partial V}{\partial t} \qquad X > 0,\ t > 0 \tag{11-42a}$$

$$\frac{\partial V}{\partial X} - \frac{Af}{2} V = 0 \qquad X = 0,\ t > 0 \tag{11-42b}$$

$$V \to 0 \qquad X \to \infty,\ t > 0 \tag{11-42c}$$

$$V = e^{-(Af/2)X} \qquad t = 0,\ X > 0 \tag{11-42d}$$

This problem can now be solved for V by the standard techniques of the linear theory discussed in the previous chapters.

11-3 TRANSFORMATION OF AN INDEPENDENT VARIABLE— THE BOLTZMANN TRANSFORMATION

In this section we discuss the transformation of the one-dimensional, nonlinear, time-dependent heat-conduction equation by the application of the *Boltzmann transformation* into a nonlinear ordinary differential equation. It is easier to solve a nonlinear ordinary differential equation than a nonlinear partial differential equation. The limitations of this technique is that it is applicable only under very restrictive conditions. The Boltzmann transformation considered here is, in fact, a special case of the more general *similarity transformation* of partial differential equations that will be discussed in the next section.

Consider the following nonlinear, time-dependent heat-conduction equation

$$\frac{\partial}{\partial x}\left(k\frac{\partial T}{\partial x}\right) = \rho C_p \frac{\partial T}{\partial t} \tag{11-43}$$

where $k \equiv k(T)$, but $\rho C_p = $ constant.

The Boltzmann transformation that transforms the two independent variables x and t into a single independent variable $\eta \equiv \eta(x,t)$ is defined as [8]

$$\eta = \frac{x}{\sqrt{t}} \qquad (11\text{-}44)$$

Then, the partial differential equation (11-43) is transformed into the following nonlinear ordinary differential equation in the independent variable η (see Note 3 for the details of this transformation)

$$\frac{d}{d\eta}\left(k\frac{dT}{d\eta}\right) + \tfrac{1}{2}\rho C_p \eta \frac{dT}{d\eta} = 0 \qquad (11\text{-}45)$$

where $T \equiv T(\eta)$ and $\eta \equiv \eta(x,t)$.

This transformation is useful in the solution of nonlinear heat-conduction problems provided that the boundary and initial conditions for the problem are also transformed appropriately under the transformation. This is *possible only under very restrictive conditions* and the reason for this can be explained as follows: To solve the partial differential equation (11-43), one initial and two boundary conditions are needed, whereas, to solve the transformed equation (11-45) only two boundary conditions are needed. This reduction in the auxiliary conditions from three to two requires that two of the original conditions should coalesce under the transformation. This requirement imposes severe restrictions on the choice of boundary and initial conditions that permit the transformation of the entire problem. Generally, if the x variable extends from $x = 0$ to infinity and the medium is initially at a uniform temperature, then with some restriction on the choise of the boundary condition at $x = 0$, the transformation of the problem under this transformation is possible. The reason for this is that the initial condition and the condition at infinity coalesce into one condition after the transformation. This matter is illustrated with the following example.

Example 11-3. A semi-infinite medium $x \geq 0$ is initially at a uniform temperature T_0. For times $t > 0$ the boundary surface at $x = 0$ is kept at a constant temperature T_0. The thermal conductivity of the medium varies with temperature. Transform this problem by the application of Boltzmann transformation.

Solution. The mathematical formulation of this problem is given as

$$\frac{\partial}{\partial x}\left(k\frac{\partial T}{\partial x}\right) = \rho C_p \frac{\partial T(x,t)}{\partial t} \qquad x > 0,\ t > 0 \qquad (11\text{-}46a)$$

$$T = T_0 \qquad\qquad x = 0,\ t > 0 \qquad (11\text{-}46b)$$

$$T \to T_i \qquad\qquad\qquad x \to \infty, \; t > 0 \qquad\qquad (11\text{-}46\text{c})$$

$$T = T_i \qquad\qquad\qquad t = 0, \; x \geq 0 \qquad\qquad (11\text{-}46\text{d})$$

where $k \equiv k(T)$ and $\rho C_p = $ constant. A new independent variable η is defined as

$$\eta = \frac{x}{\sqrt{t}} \qquad\qquad (11\text{-}47)$$

Under this transformation the system (11-46) is transformed into

$$\frac{d}{d\eta}\left(k\frac{dT}{d\eta} \right) + \tfrac{1}{2}\rho C_p \eta \frac{dT(\eta)}{d\eta} = 0 \qquad \eta > 0 \qquad (11\text{-}48\text{a})$$

$$T = T_0 \qquad\qquad\qquad\qquad \eta = 0 \qquad\qquad (11\text{-}48\text{b})$$

$$T \to T_i \qquad\qquad\qquad\qquad \eta \to \infty \qquad\qquad (11\text{-}48\text{c})$$

It is apparent from this result that the initial condition (11-46d) and the condition at infinity (11-46c) coalesced into a single condition (11-48c) in the transformed problem. Once the functional form of $k(T)$ is specified, the problem defined by equations (11-48) can be solved. For example, Fujita [17] obtained *formal solutions* to the problem (11-48) for the cases of $k(T)$ depending on temperature in the forms

$$k(T) = \frac{k_0}{1 - \lambda T}$$

$$k(T) = \frac{k_0}{(1 - \lambda T)^2}$$

$$k(T) = \frac{k_0}{1 + 2aT + bT^2}$$

where k_0, λ, a, and b are constant. Reader should consult to the original reference [17] for a discussion of the details of such solutions.

The problem defined by equations (11-48) can be solved numerically by the method of *successive approximations* as now described. For convenience in the analysis new variables are defined as

$$\theta(\eta) = \frac{T(\eta) - T_i}{T_0 - T_i}, \qquad \alpha(T) \equiv \alpha = \frac{k(T)}{\rho C_p} \qquad (11\text{-}49)$$

Then, the differential equation (11-48a) takes the form

$$\frac{d}{d\eta}\left(\alpha \frac{d\theta}{d\eta} \right) + \tfrac{1}{2}\eta \frac{d\theta(\eta)}{d\eta} = 0 \qquad (11\text{-}50)$$

or the problem (11-48) can be written in the form

$$\frac{d^2\theta}{d\eta^2} = -f(\eta)\frac{d\theta(\eta)}{d\eta} \qquad \eta > 0 \qquad (11\text{-}51a)$$

$$\theta = 1 \qquad \eta = 0 \qquad (11\text{-}51b)$$

$$\theta \to 0 \qquad \eta \to \infty \qquad (11\text{-}51c)$$

where

$$f(\eta) \equiv \frac{1}{\alpha}\frac{d\alpha}{d\theta}\frac{d\theta}{d\eta} + \frac{1}{2\alpha}\eta \qquad (11\text{-}51d)$$

If the function $f(\eta)$ is computed for an initial guess value of $\theta(\eta)$ and a specified α, equation (11-51a) is integrated as

$$\frac{d\theta}{d\eta} = c\exp\left[-\int_0^\eta f(\eta')\,d\eta'\right] \qquad (11\text{-}52)$$

where c is the integration constant. A further integration from $\eta = 0$ to η and the application of the boundary condition (11-51b) yields

$$\theta(\eta) = 1 + c\int_0^\eta \exp\left[-\int_0^{\eta'} f(\eta'')\,d\eta''\right]d\eta' \qquad (11\text{-}53)$$

The constant c is determined by the application of the boundary condition (11-51c); then the expression for $\theta(\eta)$ becomes

$$\theta(\eta) = 1 - \frac{\displaystyle\int_0^\eta \exp\left[-\int_0^{\eta'} f(\eta'')\,d\eta''\right]d\eta'}{\displaystyle\int_0^\infty \exp\left[-\int_0^{\eta'} f(\eta'')\,d\eta''\right]d\eta'} \qquad (11\text{-}54)$$

The solution given in this form is suitable for numerical calculation by iteration. The initial guess for $\theta^{(0)}(\eta)$ needed to start the calculations can be taken as the solution of the problem (11-51) for $\alpha = \alpha_0 = $ constant; that is

$$\theta^{(0)}(\eta) = 1 - \text{erf}\left(\frac{\eta}{2\sqrt{\alpha_0}}\right) \qquad (11\text{-}55)$$

Using this value of $\theta^{(0)}(\eta)$, the corresponding $f^{(0)}(\eta)$ is calculated and the first approximation for the temperature $\theta^{(1)}(\eta)$ is determined from equation (11-54). Using this first approximation, a second approximation for the temperature $\theta^{(2)}(\eta)$ is determined. The procedure is repeated until desired convergence is achieved.

11-4   SIMILARITY TRANSFORMATION VIA
ONE-PARAMETER GROUP THEORY

The transformation of independent variables of a partial differential equation in such a manner as to achieve a reduction in the number of independent variables is called the *similarity transformation*. The transformation variables that will achieve such a reduction in the number of independent variables are called *similarity variables*. The Boltzmann transformation discussed in the previous section is a similarity transformation because it transforms the nonlinear partial differential equation of heat conduction into a nonlinear ordinary differential equation. It is always easier to solve a nonlinear ordinary differential equation than a nonlinear partial differential equation. Such transformations are applicable only under certain conditions. There are several methods of developing similarity variables. They include the *free parameter method* [46–50], the *separation of variables* [51], and the *group-theory method* [4, 52–58]. In the free parameter method, the boundary and initial conditions are examined at the beginning of the analysis and then the attempt is made to construct the transformation function for the dependent variables in such a manner that the boundary and initial conditions are also transformed together with the differential equation under the transformation. Therefore, the procedure is not routine, it requires a considerable amount of insight into the nature of the problem. The method of separation of variables involves the classical separation of variables and in many respects it is similar to the free parameter method in that the transformation of the boundary conditions are examined at the onset of the analysis. The group-theory method on the other hand is the mathematically most sophisticated in its development, but most straightforward and simple in its application. That is, the similarity transformation is readily developed according to the rules established with this theory and the differential equation is transformed under the transformation with no concern about the boundary and initial conditions. Proceeding in this manner, a partial differential equation of several independent variables can be transformed into an ordinary differential equation. On the other hand, there is no way of knowing whether the boundary and initial conditions will also be transformed under the transformation developed in this manner, because they are not taken into account at the onset of the problem. Therefore, after the similarity variables are developed, the transformation of boundary conditions are examined. Here we present the results of one-parameter group theory for the development of the similarity variables; the reader should consult the original reference [54] for the details and the proof of the results presented here.

Consider a system of partial differential equations in the independent variables $x_i, i = 1, 2, \ldots, m$, the dependent variables $T_j, j = 1, 2, \ldots, n$ and its various partial derivatives, represented compactly in the form

$$F_j(x_i, T_j) = 0 \qquad i = 1, 2, \ldots, m \qquad \text{and} \qquad j = 1, 2, \ldots, n \ (11\text{-}56)$$

The procedure for the determination of the *one-parameter group transformation* and the corresponding *similarity* variables is as follows.

A one-parameter group transformation consisting of a set of new independent variables $\bar{x}_i$ and dependent variables $\bar{T}_j$ is defined as

$$\bar{x}_i = a^{\beta_i} x_i \qquad i = 1, 2, \ldots, m \qquad (11\text{-}57a)$$

$$\bar{T}_j = a^{\gamma_j} T_j \qquad j = 1, 2, \ldots, n \qquad (11\text{-}57b)$$

where the parameter $a \neq 0$ is real and the exponents β_i and γ_j are to be determined from the requirement that the system of partial differential equations (11-56) remains *absolutely constant conformally invariant* (or *absolutely invariant*) under the transformation (11-57); that is

$$F_j(x_i, T_j) = F_j(\bar{x}_i, \bar{T}_j) \qquad (11\text{-}58)$$

This requirement of absolute invariance leads to a set of algebraic relations for the determination of the exponents β_i and γ_j as will be illustrated with examples later in this section.

Having defined the one-parameter group transformation as given by equations (11-57) we now present the results for the determination of the similarity variables. Suppose the independent variable x_1 is to be eliminated from the system of partial differential equations (11-56). The procedure for the determination of the similarity variables is as follows. We consider two possibilities: $\beta_1 \neq 0$ and $\beta_1 = 0$.

1. If $\beta_1 \neq 0$, the similarity variables that will remove the independent variable x_1 from the system (11-56) are given as [54; 4, p. 137]

$$\eta_i = \frac{x_i}{x_1^{\beta_i/\beta_1}} \qquad i = 2, 3, \ldots, m \quad (11\text{-}59a)$$

$$g_j(\eta_2, \eta_3, \ldots, \eta_m) = \frac{T_j(x_1, x_2, \ldots, x_m)}{x_1^{\gamma_j/\beta_1}} \qquad j = 1, 2, \ldots, n \quad (11\text{-}59b)$$

2. If $\beta_1 = 0$, then the one-parameter group transformation (11-57) is modified as

$$\bar{x}_1 = x_1 + \ln a \qquad \text{and} \qquad \bar{x}_i = a^{\beta_i} x_i, \qquad i = 2, 3, \ldots, m \quad (11\text{-}60a)$$

$$\bar{T}_j = a^{\gamma_j} T_j \qquad\qquad j = 1, 2, \ldots, n \qquad (11\text{-}60b)$$

Then, the corresponding similarity variables are given by

$$\eta_i = \frac{x_i}{\exp(\beta_i x_1)} \qquad\qquad i = 2, 3, \ldots, m \quad (11\text{-}61a)$$

$$g_j(\eta_2, \eta_3, \ldots, \eta_m) = \frac{T_j(x_1, x_2, \ldots, x_m)}{\exp(\gamma_j x_1)} \qquad\qquad j = 1, 2, \ldots, n \quad (11\text{-}61b)$$

When the similarity variables given by equations (11-59) or (11-61) are introduced into the system of partial differential equations (11-56) and the indicated operations are performed, a new set of partial differential equations are obtained in the dependent variables $g_1, g_2, \ldots, g_n$. In the new system the independent variables $\eta_2, \eta_3, \ldots, \eta_m$ are $(m-1)$ in number, which is one less than that for the original system (11-56). This procedure may be repeated to achieve further reduction in the number of independent variables until a system of ordinary differential equations are obtained.

The advantage of this method is that it is simple to apply and there is no guessing. On the other hand, the transformations are developed with no concern about the transformation of the boundary and initial conditions for the problem. It is only after the similarity transformations are established that the transformation of the boundary and initial conditions are examined. To achieve the transformation of the boundary and initial conditions, they should be such that some coalesce under the similarity transformation. Usually the similarity in the independent variable that extends from zero to infinity is more suitable for the transformation of the boundary and initial conditions.

We now illustrate the application of this method in the reduction of the partial differential equations of heat conduction into ordinary differential equations.

Example 11-4.   Consider the heat-conduction equation given in the form

$$\frac{1}{r^{m-1}} \frac{\partial}{\partial r}\left[r^{m-1} k(T) \frac{\partial T}{\partial r} \right] = \rho C_p \frac{\partial T}{\partial t} \qquad\qquad (11\text{-}62a)$$

where $m = 1, 2$, and 3 for slab, cylinder, and sphere, respectively, $\rho C_p =$ constant, and $k(T)$ depends on temperature in the form

$$k(T) = k_0 \left(\frac{T}{T_0} \right)^n \qquad\qquad (11\text{-}62b)$$

Here, k_0 is the thermal conductivity at a reference temperature T_0 and n is a constant. We will now transform this equation into an ordinary differential equation by the application of one-parameter group transformation.

Solution.   We write equation (11-62) in the form

$$\frac{1}{r^{m-1}}\frac{\partial}{\partial r}\left(r^{m-1}U^n\frac{\partial U}{\partial r}\right)=\frac{\partial U}{\partial \tau}\tag{11-63a}$$

where

$$U=\frac{T}{T_0},\qquad \tau=\alpha_0 t=\frac{k_0}{\rho C_p}t\tag{11-63b}$$

The one-parameter group transformation is taken as

$$\bar{r}=a^b r,\qquad \bar{\tau}=a^d\tau,\qquad \text{and}\qquad \bar{U}=a^e U\tag{11-64}$$

Introducing equation (11-64) into equation (11-63a) we obtain

$$a^{2b-(n+1)e}\cdot\frac{1}{\bar{r}^{m-1}}\frac{\partial}{\partial \bar{r}}\left(\bar{r}^{m-1}\bar{U}^n\frac{\partial \bar{U}}{\partial \bar{r}}\right)=a^{d-e}\frac{\partial \bar{U}}{\partial \bar{\tau}}\tag{11-65}$$

The differential equation (11-63a) remains absolutely invariant under this transformation if

$$2b-(n+1)e=d-e\qquad \text{or}\qquad 2b-ne=d\tag{11-66}$$

To transform equation (11-63a) one may seek similarity either in the τ or the r variable. To illustrate the procedure we examine similarity for each of these cases separately.

1.   *Similarity in τ.*   Since the variable τ is to be eliminated, both sides of equation (11-66) are divided by the exponent d

$$2\left(\frac{b}{d}\right)-n\left(\frac{e}{d}\right)=1\tag{11-67}$$

For convenience we define $b/d\equiv A$; then

$$\frac{e}{d}=\frac{2A-1}{n}\tag{11-68}$$

where A is an arbitrary constant. The similarity variables η and $g(\eta)$ are determined according to equations (11-59) as

$$\eta=\frac{r}{\tau^{b/d}}=\frac{r}{\tau^A}\qquad \text{and}\qquad g(\eta)=\frac{U}{\tau^{e/d}}=\frac{U}{\tau^{(2A-1)/n}}\tag{11-69}$$

When the similarity variables (11-69) are introduced into equation (11-63a), the following ordinary differential equation is obtained

$$\frac{d}{d\eta}\left(\eta^{m-1}g^n\frac{dg}{d\eta}\right)=\frac{2A-1}{n}\eta^{m-1}g-A\eta^m\frac{dg}{d\eta}\tag{11-70}$$

For the right-hand side of equation (11-70) to be of the form

$$RHS \equiv -\frac{d}{d\eta}(\beta\eta^m g) = -Bmn^{m-1}g - B\eta^m\frac{dg}{d\eta} \qquad (11\text{-}71)$$

we choose

$$-Bm = \frac{2A-1}{n} \quad \text{and} \quad B = A$$

Then

$$B = A = \frac{1}{2+mn} \qquad (11\text{-}72)$$

and equation (11-70) becomes

$$\frac{d}{d\eta}\left(\eta^{m-1}g^n\frac{dg}{d\eta}\right) + \frac{1}{2+mn}\frac{d}{d\eta}(\eta^m g) = 0 \qquad (11\text{-}73)$$

Thus we transformed the partial differential equation (11-63a) into an ordinary differential equation (11-73) by seeking similarity in the variable τ. The similarity variables (11-69) that achieved this transformation, when A is given by equation (11-72), become

$$\eta = r\tau^{-1/(2+mn)} \quad \text{and} \quad g(\eta) = U(r,\tau)\tau^{m/(2+mn)} \qquad (11\text{-}74)$$

We note that for the special case of $A = \frac{1}{2}$ the similarity variables (11-69) reduce to

$$\eta = r/\sqrt{\tau} \quad \text{and} \quad g(\eta) = U(r,\tau) \qquad (11\text{-}75)$$

which are the Boltzmann transformation given by equation (11-44).

2. *Similarity in r.* Since the r variable is to be eliminated, we divide both sides of equation (11-66) by the exponent b

$$2 - n\frac{e}{b} = \frac{d}{b} \qquad (11\text{-}76)$$

For convenience we define $d/b \equiv A$, then

$$\frac{e}{b} = \frac{2-A}{n} \qquad (11\text{-}77)$$

The similarity variables η and $g(\eta)$ are determined according to equation (11-59) as

$$\eta = \frac{\tau}{r^{d/b}} = \frac{\tau}{r^A} \quad \text{and} \quad g(\eta) = \frac{U}{r^{e/b}} = \frac{U}{r^{(2-A)/n}} \qquad (11\text{-}78)$$

When the similarity variables (11-78) are introduced into equation (11-63a) and the value of the arbitrary constant A is chosen as $A = 2$, the following ordinary differential equation is obtained

$$\frac{d}{d\eta}\left(\eta^2 g^n \frac{dg}{d\eta}\right) - \frac{1}{2}\eta g^n \frac{dg}{d\eta} - \frac{2(m-1)\eta + 1}{4}\frac{dg}{d\eta} = 0 \qquad (11\text{-}79)$$

and the corresponding similarity variables (11-78) for $A = 2$ becomes

$$\eta = \tau/r^2 \qquad \text{and} \qquad g(\eta) = U(r, \tau) \qquad (11\text{-}80)$$

Example 11-5.   Consider the following nonlinear heat-conduction problem

$$\frac{\partial}{\partial x}\left(U^n \frac{\partial U}{\partial x}\right) = \frac{\partial U}{\partial \tau} \qquad 0 < x < \infty, \ \tau > 0 \qquad (11\text{-}81a)$$

$$U = f(\tau) \qquad\qquad x = 0, \ \tau > 0 \qquad (11\text{-}81b)$$

$$U = 0 \qquad\qquad x \to \infty, \ \tau > 0 \qquad (11\text{-}81c)$$

$$U = 0 \qquad\qquad \tau = 0, \ x \geq 0 \qquad (11\text{-}81d)$$

The differential equation can be transformed into an ordinary differential equation as discussed in Example 11-4. Examine, under what conditions the boundary and initial conditions for this problem can be transformed for similarity in the variable τ.

Solution.   Equation (11-81a) is a special case of (11-63a) for $m = 1$. If similarity is sought in the variable τ, the resulting similarity variables are immediately obtained from equation (11-74) by setting $m = 1$ and replacing r by x. We find

$$\eta = x\tau^{-1/(2+n)} \qquad \text{and} \qquad g(\eta) = U(x, \tau)\tau^{1/(2+n)} \qquad (11\text{-}82)$$

Under the transformation (11-82), equation (11-81a) is transformed to

$$\frac{d}{d\eta}\left(g^m \frac{dg}{d\eta}\right) + \frac{1}{2+n}\frac{d}{d\eta}(\eta g) = 0, \qquad \eta > 0 \qquad (11\text{-}83)$$

which is also obtainable from equation (11-73) for $m = 1$. The boundary and initial conditions 11-81b, c, and d are, respectively, transformed into

$$g(\eta) = f(\tau) \cdot \tau^{1/(2+n)} \qquad \eta = 0 \text{ (i.e., } x = 0) \qquad (11\text{-}84a)$$

$$g(\eta) = 0 \qquad\qquad \eta = \infty \text{ (i.e., } x \to \infty) \qquad (11\text{-}84b)$$

$$g(\eta) = 0 \qquad\qquad \eta = \infty \text{ (i.e., } \tau = 0) \qquad (11\text{-}84c)$$

We note that the boundary condition (11-81c) and the initial condition (11-81d) of the original problem are coalesced into a single condition

$g(\eta) = 0$ for $\eta = \infty$. However, the boundary condition (11-84a) is not suitable, because it should be independent of τ; this requirement is satisfied if the function $f(\tau)$ is chosen in the form

$$f(\tau) = \tau^{-1/(2+n)} \tag{11-85}$$

With this choice of $f(\tau)$, the boundary conditions (11-84) reduce to

$$g(\eta) = 1 \qquad \eta = 0 \tag{11-86a}$$

$$g(\eta) = 0 \qquad \eta = \infty \tag{11-86b}$$

Thus, under the similarity transformation (11-82) the nonlinear heat-conduction problem (11-81) is reduced to the solution of a nonlinear ordinary differential equation (11-83) subject to the boundary conditions (11-86) with $f(\tau)$ as given by equation (11-85).

Example 11-6. Consider the following nonlinear heat-conduction equation

$$\frac{\partial}{\partial x}\left(k\frac{\partial T}{\partial x}\right) + \frac{\partial}{\partial y}\left(k\frac{\partial T}{\partial y}\right) = \rho C_p \frac{\partial T}{\partial t} \tag{11-87a}$$

where

$$k = k_0\left(\frac{T}{T_0}\right)^s, \qquad C_p = C_{p0}\left(\frac{T}{T_0}\right)^p, \qquad \rho = \text{constant} \tag{11-87b}$$

where k_0 and C_{p0} are the thermal conductivity and the specific heat at a reference temperature T_0, the exponents s and p are constants, and $s \neq -1$. Examine the similarity transformation of this equation with respect to the time variable.

Solution. Equation (11-87) can be written in the form

$$\frac{\partial}{\partial x}\left(U^n\frac{\partial U}{\partial x}\right) + \frac{\partial}{\partial y}\left(U^n\frac{\partial U}{\partial y}\right) = \frac{\partial U}{\partial \tau} \tag{11-88a}$$

where

$$U = \left(\frac{T}{T_0}\right)^{p+1} \quad \text{or} \quad U^{1/(p+1)} = \frac{T}{T_0}, \qquad \tau = \frac{k_0}{\rho C_{p0}}t, \qquad \frac{s-p}{p+1} = n \tag{11-88b}$$

and normally the case $n > 0$ is of physical interest. To obtain equation (11-88a) we made use of the relations

$$T^p\frac{\partial T}{\partial t} = \frac{1}{p+1}\frac{\partial T^{p+1}}{\partial t}, \qquad T^p\frac{\partial T}{\partial x} = \frac{1}{p+1}\frac{\partial T^{p+1}}{\partial x}, \qquad \text{etc.} \tag{11-89}$$

We now transform equation (11-88a) by seeking similarity in τ, namely, we remove from this equation the independent variable τ. The one-parameter group transformation is chosen as

$$\bar{x} = a^{c_1}x, \qquad \bar{y} = a^{c_2}y, \qquad \bar{\tau} = a^{c_3}\tau, \qquad \text{and} \qquad \bar{U} = a^{c_4}U \qquad (11\text{-}90)$$

When this transformation is introduced into equation (11-88a) we obtain

$$a^{2c_1-(n+1)c_4}\frac{\partial}{\partial \bar{x}}\left(\bar{U}^n\frac{\partial \bar{U}}{\partial \bar{x}}\right) + a^{2c_2-(n+1)c_4}\frac{\partial}{\partial \bar{y}}\left(\bar{U}^n\frac{\partial \bar{U}}{\partial \bar{y}}\right) = a^{c_3-c_4}\frac{\partial \bar{U}}{\partial \tau} \qquad (11\text{-}91)$$

The differential equation (11-88) remains absolutely invariant under this transformation if

$$2c_1 - (n+1)c_4 = 2c_2 - (n+1)c_4 = c_3 - c_4 \qquad (11\text{-}92a)$$

or

$$2c_1 - nc_4 = 2c_2 - nc_4 = c_3 \qquad (11\text{-}92b)$$

As we seek similarity in τ, we divide both sides of equation (11-92b) by c_3, for $c_3 \neq 0$, and obtain

$$2\frac{c_1}{c_3} - n\frac{c_4}{c_3} = 2\frac{c_2}{c_3} - n\frac{c_4}{c_3} = 1 \qquad (11\text{-}93a)$$

For convenience we define

$$\frac{c_1}{c_3} = \frac{c_2}{c_3} \equiv A \qquad (11\text{-}93b)$$

Then, (11-93a) yields

$$\frac{c_4}{c_3} = \frac{2A-1}{n} \qquad (11\text{-}93c)$$

where A is an arbitrary constant.

The similarity variables η_1, η_2, and $g(\eta_1, \eta_2)$ are determined according to equation (11-59) as

$$\eta_1 = \frac{x}{\tau^{c_1/c_3}} = \frac{x}{\tau^A}, \qquad \eta_2 = \frac{y}{\tau^{c_2/c_3}} = \frac{y}{\tau^A} \qquad (11\text{-}94a)$$

and

$$g(\eta_1, \eta_2) = \frac{U}{\tau^{c_4/c_3}} = \frac{U}{\tau^{(2A-1)/n}} \qquad (11\text{-}94b)$$

Substituting the similarity variables (11-94) into the differential equation

(11-88), we obtain

$$\frac{\partial}{\partial \eta_1}\left(g^n \frac{\partial g}{\partial \eta_1}\right) + \frac{\partial}{\partial \eta_2}\left(g^n \frac{\partial g}{\partial \eta_2}\right) + A\left(\eta_1 \frac{\partial g}{\partial \eta_1} + \eta_2 \frac{\partial g}{\partial \eta_2}\right) - \frac{2A-1}{n} = g = 0$$

$$(11\text{-}95)$$

This equation can be put into the symmetric form if the constant A is chosen as

$$A = \frac{1}{2n+2} \qquad (11\text{-}96)$$

Then equation (11-95) becomes

$$\frac{\partial}{\partial \eta_1}\left(\frac{\partial g^{n+1}}{\partial \eta_1} + \tfrac{1}{2}\eta_1 g\right) + \frac{\partial}{\partial \eta_2}\left(\frac{\partial g^{n+1}}{\partial \eta_2} + \tfrac{1}{2}\eta_2 g\right) = 0 \qquad (11\text{-}97)$$

where $g \equiv g(\eta_1, \eta_2)$. When the constant A is given by equation (11-96), the similarity transformations (11-94) take the form

$$\eta_1 = x\tau^{-1/(2n+2)}, \qquad \eta_2 = y\tau^{-1/(2n+2)}, \qquad \text{and} \qquad g = U\tau^{2/(2n+2)} \qquad (11\text{-}98)$$

Equation (11-97) is now a partial differential equation in the two independent variables. A further application of the similarity transformation can reduce equation (11-97) into an ordinary differential equation.

Equation (11-97) requires four boundary conditions whereas the original differential equation (11-88) requires five conditions; this implies that two of the original conditions should coalesce into one condition. We have not considered the boundary and initial conditions for the above problem; the transformation of the boundary and initial conditions under the transformation (11-98) may or may not be possible.

11-5 TRANSFORMATION INTO INTEGRAL EQUATION

The differential equation of heat conduction with temperature-dependent thermal conductivity can be transformed into an equation with constant thermal conductivity but with a temperature-dependent heat-generation term [10]. The resulting equation can then be transformed into an integral equation that can be solved by the method of successive approximation with a suitable numerical scheme if appropriate boundary conditions are prescribed. The heat-conduction problem subject to a nonlinear boundary condition can also be transformed into an integral equation that can be solved by the method of successive approximations. In this section we present a brief discussion of the transformation of the nonlinear heat-conduction problems into integral equations.

Temperature-Dependent Thermal Conductivity

Consider the heat-conduction equation given in the form

$$\nabla \cdot [k(T)\nabla T] = \rho C_p \frac{\partial T(\mathbf{r}, t)}{\partial t} \quad \text{in region } R \quad (11\text{-}99)$$

where $\rho C_p = $ constant and $k(T)$ is given in the form

$$k(T) = k_0[1 + \beta\phi(T)] \quad (11\text{-}100)$$

Here k_0 is thermal conductivity at a reference temperature T_0, β is a constant, and $\phi(T)$ is a specified function of temperature. Introducing (11-100) into (11-99), we obtain

$$\nabla^2 T + \frac{\beta}{k_0} g(T) = \frac{1}{\alpha_0} \frac{\partial T}{\partial t} \quad \text{in } R, \ t > 0 \quad (11\text{-}101a)$$

where

$$\alpha_0 \equiv \frac{k_0}{\rho C_p} \quad \text{and} \quad g(T) \equiv k_0 \nabla \cdot [\phi(T)\nabla T] \quad (11\text{-}101b)$$

In equation (11-101a) the term $g(T)$ is equivalent to a temperature-dependent heat-generation term.

We now examine the solution of equation (11-101a) subject to the following boundary and initial conditions

$$T(\mathbf{r}, t) = f(\mathbf{r}) \quad \text{on boundary } S \text{ of } R, \ t > 0 \quad (11\text{-}102a)$$

$$T(\mathbf{r}, t) = F(\mathbf{r}) \quad \text{for } t = 0, \text{ in } R \quad (11\text{-}102b)$$

where $f(\mathbf{r})$ and $F(\mathbf{r})$ specified boundary and initial condition functions, respectively.

Let, the function $T_0(\mathbf{r}, t)$ be the solution of the following linear heat-conduction problem in the same region R.

$$\nabla^2 T_0(\mathbf{r}, t) = \frac{1}{\alpha_0} \frac{\partial T_0(\mathbf{r}, t)}{\partial t} \quad \text{in } R, \ t > 0 \quad (11\text{-}103a)$$

$$T_0(\mathbf{r}, t) = f(\mathbf{r}) \quad \text{on boundary } S \text{ of } R, \ t > 0 \quad (11\text{-}103b)$$

$$T_0(\mathbf{r}, t) = F(\mathbf{r}) \quad \text{for } t = 0, \text{ in } R \quad (11\text{-}103c)$$

and $G(\mathbf{r}, t | \mathbf{r}', \tau)$ be the Green's function appropriate for the solution of the problem defined by equations (11-103). Suppose an initial guess is available for the generation term $g^{(0)}(\mathbf{r}, t)$. Then, by setting $g(T) \equiv g^{(0)}(\mathbf{r}, t)$, the solution of equation (11-101) subject to the boundary and initial conditions (11-102) gives the first approximation for the temperature $T^{(1)}(\mathbf{r}, t)$ as

$$T^{(1)}(\mathbf{r}, t) = T_0(\mathbf{r}, t) + \beta \frac{\alpha_0}{k_0} \int_{\tau=0}^{t} d\tau \int_R G(\mathbf{r}, t | \mathbf{r}', \tau) g^{(0)}(\mathbf{r}', \tau) d\mathbf{r}' \quad (11\text{-}104)$$

Equation (11-104) can be evaluated numerically and the first approximation for $T^{(1)}(\mathbf{r}, t)$ determined in this manner is used to compute $g^{(1)}(\mathbf{r}, t)$, which is then used in equation (11-104) to obtain a second approximation for the temperature $T^{(2)}(\mathbf{r}, t)$. The procedure is repeated until the solution converges sufficiently. A limitation for the usefulness of this method is, generally, the convergence of the solution; also a large amount of computation time may be required to perform such calculations.

Nonlinear Boundary Conditions

The heat-conduction problems with nonlinear boundary conditions can be transformed into a nonlinear integral equation, which can then be solved by the method of successive approximations.

To illustrate the procedure we consider the following heat-conduction problem subject to a nonlinear boundary condition (see Example 9-3)

$$\frac{\partial^2 T}{\partial x^2} = \frac{1}{\alpha} \frac{\partial T(x, t)}{\partial t} \qquad \text{in } x > 0, \ t > 0 \qquad (11\text{-}105\text{a})$$

$$-k \frac{\partial T}{\partial x} = f(t) - \phi(T_s) \qquad \text{at } x = 0, \ t > 0 \qquad (11\text{-}105\text{b})$$

$$T = 0 \qquad \text{for } t = 0, \ \text{in } x \geq 0 \qquad (11\text{-}105\text{c})$$

where $\phi(T_s)$ is a function of the surface temperature T_s at $x = 0$, $f(t)$ is specified, and α is constant.

We now consider the following linear problem for the same region $x > 0$:

$$\frac{\partial^2 \theta}{\partial x^2} = \frac{1}{\alpha} \frac{\partial \theta(x, t)}{\partial t} \qquad \text{in } x > 0, \ t > 0 \qquad (11\text{-}106\text{a})$$

$$-k \frac{\partial \theta}{\partial x} = f^*(t) \qquad \text{at } x = 0, \ t > 0 \qquad (11\text{-}106\text{b})$$

$$\theta = 0 \qquad \text{for } t = 0, \ x \geq 0 \qquad (11\text{-}106\text{c})$$

where $f^*(t)$ is a specified function. The solution of this linear problem is given as (see Note 3)

$$\theta(x, t) = \frac{\alpha^{1/2}}{k\pi^{1/2}} \int_{\tau=0}^{t} \frac{f^*(t)}{(t - \tau)^{1/2}} \exp\left(-\frac{x^2}{4\alpha(t - \tau)}\right) d\tau \qquad (11\text{-}107)$$

Now, assuming a guess is made for the surface temperature T_s, the function $\phi(T_s)$ appearing in the boundary condition (11-105b) is considered known. Then, the solution of the problem (11-105) is written, analogous to equation (11-107), as

$$T(x,t) = \frac{\alpha^{1/2}}{k\pi^{1/2}} \int_{\tau=0}^{t} \frac{f(t) - \phi(T_s)}{(t-\tau)^{1/2}} \exp\left(-\frac{x^2}{4\alpha(t-\tau)}\right) d\tau \qquad (11\text{-}108)$$

when this equation is evaluated at $x = 0$, where $T(0,t) \equiv T_s$, we obtain

$$T_s(t) = \frac{\alpha^{1/2}}{k\pi^{1/2}} \int_{\tau=0}^{t} \frac{f(t) - \phi[T_s(t)]}{(t-\tau)^{1/2}} d\tau \qquad (11\text{-}109)$$

which is a Volterra type integral equation for the surface temperature $T_s(t)$. Volterra equations may be solved by a number of analytic or numerical methods [59–62]. In this particular equation the kernel $(t-\tau)^{-1/2}$ becomes singular at the upper limit and the function $\phi[T_s]$ is nonlinear; but, the kernel singularity can be removed [20]. The method of successive approximations can be used to solve equation (11-109). In this method an initial guess is made for $T_s(t)$, which is substituted into $\phi(T_s)$ and the integration on the right-hand side of equation (11-109) is carried out to obtain a first approximation for the surface temperature $T_s^{(1)}(t)$. This first approximation is then used to obtain a second approximation, and the procedure is continued until the solution converges sufficiently. If a sufficiently good initial guess is made for $T_s(t)$, the convergence is fast. Furthermore, if the function $[f(t) - \phi(T_s)]$ is a monotone function (either increasing or decreasing) the successive approximations lie alternately above and below the exact solution for $T_s(t)$, and the convergence becomes fast.

Example 11-7. A semi-infinite medium $x \geq 0$ is initially at zero temperature. For times $t > 0$, the boundary surface $x = 0$ is subjected to heating according to the fourth power radiation law from an environment at constant temperature T_∞. Express the solution of this problem in the form of an integral equation for the surface temperature $T_s(t)$.

Solution. The mathematical formulation of this problem is given as

$$\frac{\partial^2 T}{\partial x^2} = \frac{1}{\alpha}\frac{\partial T(x,t)}{\partial t} \qquad \text{in } x > 0,\ t > 0 \qquad (11\text{-}110a)$$

$$-k\frac{\partial T}{\partial x} = \varepsilon\sigma(T_\infty^4 - T_s^4) \qquad \text{at } x = 0,\ t > 0 \qquad (11\text{-}110b)$$

$$T = 0 \qquad \text{for } t = 0,\ x > 0 \qquad (11\text{-}110c)$$

where ε is the emissivity of the surface and σ is the Stefan-Boltzmann constant. This problem is similar to that defined above by equations (11-105) if we set

$$f(t) \equiv \varepsilon\sigma T_\infty^4 = \text{constant}, \qquad \phi(T_s) \equiv \varepsilon\sigma T_s^4 \qquad (11\text{-}111)$$

Then, the solution given by equation (11-109) becomes

$$T_s(t) = \frac{\varepsilon\sigma\alpha^{1/2}}{k\pi^{1/2}} \int_{\tau=0}^{t} \frac{T_\infty^4 - T_s^4(t)}{(t-\tau)^{1/2}} d\tau \qquad (11\text{-}112)$$

After removing the kernel singularity by introducing new variables, this equation has been solved [20] numerically by the method of successive approximations. The initial guess $T_s^{(0)}(t)$ needed to start the calculations is taken as the solution of the problem (11-110) in which the nonlinear boundary condition (11-110b) is replaced by the following linearized form

$$-k\frac{\partial T}{\partial x} = 4\varepsilon\sigma T^3(T_\infty - T_s) \qquad (11\text{-}110b^*)$$

The convergence was fast; that is, two or three iterations were sufficient.

REFERENCES

1. H. S. Carslaw and J. C. Jaeger, *Operational Methods in Applied Mathematics*, Oxford University Press, London, 1941.
2. H. S. Carslaw and J. E. Jaeger, *Conduction of Heat in Solids*, 2nd ed., Oxford University Press, London, 1959.
3. W. E. Ames, ed., *Nonlinear Problems of Engineering*, Academic Press, New York, 1964.
4. W. F. Ames, *Nonlinear Partial Differential Equations in Engineering*, Academic Press, New York, 1965.
5. A. V. Luikov, *Analytical Heat Diffusion Theory*, Academic Press, New York, 1968.
6. M. N. Özışık, *Boundary Value Problems of Heat Conduction*, International Textbook Co., Scranton, Pa., 1968.
7. J. Crank, *The Mathematics of Diffusion*, 2nd ed., Clarendon Press, London, 1975.
8. L. Boltzmann, *Ann. Physik* **53**, 959, 1894.
9. G. Kirchhoff, *Vorlesungen über die Theorie der Warme*, Barth, Leipzig, 1894.
10. M. R. Hopkins, *Proc. Phys. Soc.* **50**, 703, 1938.
11. M. L. Storm, *J. Appl. Phys.* **22**, 940–951, 1951.
12. Y. B. Zel'dovic and A. S. Kompaneec, On the Theory of Propagation of Heat with Conductivity Depending upon the Temperature, *Sbornik posvyascennyi semidesyatiletiyu academika A. F. Ioffe*, Izdat. Akad. Nauk SSR, Moscow, 1950, p. 61.
13. J. C. Jaeger, *Proc. Camb. Phil. Soc.* **20**, 634–641, 1950.
14. C. J. Wagner, *J. Chem. Phys.* **18**, 1227–1230. 1950.
15. C. Wagner, *Trans. J. Metal* **4**, 91, 1952.
16. R. H. Stokes, *Trans. Faraday Soc.* **48**, 887–892, 1952.
17. H. Fujita, *Text. Res. J.* **22**, 757–760, 823–827, 1952.

18. Kwang-Tzu Yang, *Trans. ASME J. Appl. Mech.* **79**, 146–147, 1958.

19. R. E. Pattle, *Quart. J. Mech. Appl. Math.* **12**, 407, 1959.

20. P. L. Chambre, *J. Appl. Phys.* **30**, 1683–1688, 1959.

21. R. H. Boyer, *J. Math. Phys.* **40**, 41, 1960.

22. J. R. Philip, *Aust. J. Phys.* **13**, 1–12, 1960.

23. M. H. Cobble, *Int. J. Nonlinear Mech.* **2**, 417–426, 1967.

24. N. N. Kochina, *Sov. Phys.-Dokl.* **13**, 305–307, 1968.

25. D. F. Hays and H. N. Curd, *Int. J. Heat Mass Transfer* **11**, 285–295, 1968.

26. J. R. Philip, *Adv. Hydrosci.* **5**, 215, 1969.

27. N. G. Yampol'skiy and A. M. Ayzen, *Heat Transfer—Sov. Res.* **2**, 114–118, 1970.

28. R. R. Gilpin, *Phys. Fluids* **15**, 1529–1531, 1972.

29. B. Vujanović, *Int. J. Heat Mass Transfer* **16**, 1111–1117, 1973.

30. J. R. Philip, *Aust. J. Phys.* **26**, 513–519, 1973.

31. J. R. Philip and J. H. Knight, *Soil. Sci* **117**, 1–13, 1974.

32. J. H. Knight and J. R. Philip, *J. Eng. Math.* **8**, 219–227, 1974.

33. B. Vujanović and B. Bačlič, *Int. J. Heat Mass Transfer* **19**, 721–730, 1976.

34. M. Suzuki, S. Matsumoto, and S. Maeda, *Int. J. Heat Mass Transfer* **20**, 883–889, 1977.

35. T. R. Goodman, in *Advances in Heat Transfer*, T. Irvine and J. Hartnett, eds., Academic Press, New York, 1964.

36. T. R. Goodman, *J. Aerospace Sci.* **26**, 187–188, 1959.

37. M. A. Biot, *J. Aerospace Sci.* **26**, 367–381, 1959.

38. J. C. Y. Koh, *J. Aerospace Sci.* **28**, 989–990, 1961.

39. W. Zyszkowski, *J. Heat Transfer* **91c**, 77–82, 1969.

40. Dj. Djukic and B. Vujanović, *Z. Angew. Math. Mech.* **51**, 611–616, 1971.

41. B. Vujanović and A. M. Strauss, *AIAA J.* **9**, 327–330, 1971.

42. B. Krajewski, *Archwm. Mech. Stosow.* **5**, 20, 1968.

43. B. Krajewski, *Int. J. Heat Mass Transfer* **18**, 495–502, 1975.

44. V. V. Salomatov, *Heat Transfer—Sov. Res.* **4**, 41–49, 1972.

45. A. Aziz and J. Y. Benzies, *Int. J. Heat Mass Transfer* **19**, 217–276, 1976.

46. T. Geis, Ähnliche Grenzschichten an Rotationskorper, Festschrift "50 Jahre Grenzschichtforschung." Verlag F. Vieweg, Braunschweig, 1955.

47. W. Mangler, *ZAMM* **23**, 243, 1943.

48. C. B. Cohen and F. Reshotko, Similar Solutions for the Compressible Laminar Boundary Layer, with Heat Transfer and Pressure Gradient, NACA TN3325, 1955.

49. A. G. Hansen, *Trans. ASME* **80**, 1553, 1958.

50. A. G. Hansen, *Similarity Analysis of Boundary Value Problems in Engineering*, Prentice-Hall, Inc., Englewood Cliffs, N.J., 1964.

51. D. E. Abbott and S. J. Kline, Simple Methods for Classification and Construction of Similarity Solutions of Partial Differential Equations, Rept. MD-6, Dept. of Mech. Eng., Stanford University, Stanford, California. AFOSR-TN-60-1163.

52. A. D. Michal, *Proc. Natl. Acad. Sci.* **37**, 623, 1952.

53. G. Birkhoff, *Hydrodynamics*, Princeton Univ. Press., 1960.

54. A. J. A. Morgan, *Quart. J. Math.* (Oxford) **3**, 250–259, 1952.

55. A. J. A. Morgan, *Trans. ASME* **80**, 1559, 1958.

56. W. F. Ames, *Ind. Eng. Chem. Fundamentals* **4**, 72–76, 1965.

57. R. Manohar, Some Similarity Solutions of Partial Differential Equations of Boundary Layer, Univ. of Visconsin, MRC Report # 375, Jan. 1963.

58. M. J. Moran and R. A. Gaggioli, *AIAA J.* **6**, 2014–2016, 1968.

59. F. G. Tricomi, *Integral Equations*, Academic Press, New York, 1957.

60. L. Fox, *Numerical Solution of Ordinary and Partial Differential Equations*, Addison-Wesley, Reading, Mass., 1962, Chapter 2.

61. C. Wagner, *J. Math. Phys.* **32**, 289–301, 1952–3.

62. A. K. Azziz, *Not. AMS* **11**, Abstr. 64T-114, 1964.

PROBLEMS

11-1   A slab in $0 \le x \le L$ is initially at a uniform temperature T_i. For times $t > 0$, the boundary surface at $x = 0$ is kept insulated, the boundary at $x = L$ is kept at zero temperature and there is heat generation at a constant rate of g_0 W/m³ (or Btu/hr ft³). The thermal conductivity depends on temperature in the form

$$k(T) = k_0(1 + \beta T)$$

Assuming that the thermal diffusivity α remains constant, obtain an expression for the temperature distribution in the slab for times $t > 0$.

11-2   Determine the steady-state temperature distribution in a two-dimensional square region, $0 \le x \le a, 0 \le y \le a$, for which the thermal conductivity varies with temperature in the form

$$k(T) = k_0(1 + \beta T)$$

and subject to the following boundary conditions: $T = 0$ at $x = 0$; $T = 0$ at $x = a$; $T = 0$ at $y = 0$; and $T = \sin(\pi x/a)$ at $y = a$.

11-3   Consider the following nonlinear heat-conduction equation

$$\frac{1}{r^{m-1}} \frac{\partial}{\partial r}\left(r^{m-1} k \frac{\partial T}{\partial r}\right) = \rho C_p \frac{\partial T}{\partial r}$$

where $m = 1, 2, 3$ for the rectangular, cylindrical, and spherical coordinate system, respectively. The thermal conductivity and specific heat depend on temperature in the form

$$k = k_0\left(\frac{T}{T_0}\right)^s, \qquad C_p = C_{p0}\left(\frac{T}{T_0}\right)^p$$

where k_0, C_{p0} are the thermal conductivity and specific heat at a reference temperature T_0, the exponents s and p are constants, and the density ρ is constant.

1.   Show that, the above heat-conduction equation can be written in the form

$$\frac{1}{r^{m-1}} \frac{\partial}{\partial r}\left(r^{m-1} U^n \frac{\partial U}{\partial r}\right) = \frac{\partial U}{\partial \tau}$$

where

$$U = \left(\frac{T}{T_0}\right)^{p+1} \quad \text{or} \quad U^{1/(p+1)} = \frac{T}{T_0}, \quad \tau = \frac{k_0}{\rho C_{po}}t, \quad \frac{s-p}{p+1} = n$$

2. Eliminate the independent variable τ by the similarity transformation.

11-4 Transform the heat-conduction problem considered in Example 11-5 into an ordinary differential equation by seeking similarity in the x variable.

11-5 Consider the following heat-conduction problem

$$\frac{\partial^2 T}{\partial x^2} = \frac{1}{\alpha}\frac{\partial T}{\partial t} \qquad \text{in } x > 0, \ t > 0$$

$$T = T_0 \qquad \text{at } x = 0, \ t > 0$$

$$T = 0 \qquad \text{as } x \to \infty, \ t > 0$$

$$T = 0 \qquad \text{for } t = 0, \ x \geq 0$$

where α is constant. By the application of one-parameter group theory, show that the similarity variables for this problem may be taken in the form

$$F(\eta) = T(x, y), \qquad \eta = \frac{x}{t^{1/2}}$$

and under this transformation the above heat-conduction problem is reduced to the following ordinary differential equation

$$\frac{d^2 F}{d\eta^2} + \frac{1}{2\alpha}\eta\frac{dF}{d\eta} = 0 \qquad \text{in } \eta > 0$$

$$F = T_0 \qquad \text{at } \eta = 0$$

$$F = 0 \qquad \text{at } \eta \to \infty$$

Solve this problem and compare the solution with that of Problem 2-4 of Chapter 2.

11-6 Consider the following heat-conduction problem subject to a nonlinear boundary condition at $x = 0$:

$$\frac{\partial^2 T}{\partial x^2} = \frac{1}{\alpha}\frac{\partial T(x,t)}{\partial t} \qquad \text{in } x > 0, \ t > 0$$

$$-k\frac{\partial T}{\partial x} = c(T - T_\infty)^n \qquad \text{at } x = 0, \ t > 0$$

$$T = T_i \qquad \text{for } t = 0, \ x \geq 0$$

where α, c, n, and k are constants. Transform this problem into an integral equation for the surface temperature $T_s(t)$.

NOTES

1. Details of the transformation of equation (11-27b) into (11-29a): From equation (11-28a)

$$\frac{\partial X}{\partial x} = \alpha^{-1/2} \tag{1}$$

The term $\partial U/\partial x$ is expressed as

$$\frac{\partial U}{\partial x} = \frac{\partial U^*(x,t)}{\partial X} \cdot \frac{\partial X}{\partial x} = \frac{\partial U^*}{\partial X} \alpha^{-1/2} \tag{2}$$

and the left-hand side of equation (11-27b) is evaluated as

$$\alpha^{1/2} \frac{\partial}{\partial x}\left(\alpha^{1/2} \frac{\partial U}{\partial x} \right) = \alpha^{1/2} \frac{\partial}{\partial X}\left[\alpha^{1/2} \frac{\partial U^*}{\partial X} \alpha^{-1/2} \right] \frac{\partial X}{\partial x} = \frac{\partial^2 U^*}{\partial X^2} \tag{3}$$

then, equation (11-27b) takes the form

$$\frac{\partial^2 U^*}{\partial X^2} = \frac{\partial U}{\partial t} \tag{4}$$

The right-hand side of equation (4) is now expressed in terms of U^* as

$$
\begin{aligned}
\frac{\partial U}{\partial t} &= \frac{\partial U^*}{\partial X} \cdot \frac{\partial X}{\partial t} + \frac{\partial U^*}{\partial t} \\
&= \frac{\partial U^*}{\partial X}\left[\int_0^x \frac{\partial \alpha^{-1/2}}{\partial t} dx \right] + \frac{\partial U^*}{\partial t}
\end{aligned}
\tag{5}
$$

where

$$\frac{\partial \alpha^{-1/2}}{\partial t} = \left(\frac{d\alpha^{-1/2}}{dU} \right)\frac{\partial U}{\partial t} = \frac{d\alpha^{-1/2}}{dU}\frac{\partial^2 U^*}{\partial X^2} \tag{6}$$

since $\partial U/\partial t$ is given by equation (4). Equation (6) is introduced into equation (5)

$$\frac{\partial U}{\partial t} = \frac{\partial U^*}{\partial X}\left\{ \int_0^x \left[\frac{d\alpha^{-1/2}}{dU}\frac{\partial^2 U^*}{\partial X^2} \cdot \alpha^{1/2} dX \right] \right\} + \frac{\partial U^*}{\partial t} \tag{7}$$

since $dx = \alpha^{1/2} dX$.

Equation (7) is written in the alternative form as

$$\frac{\partial U}{\partial t} = \frac{\partial U^*}{\partial X} \left\{ \int_0^X \left[\frac{d}{dU}(\ln \alpha^{-1/2}) \right] \frac{\partial^2 U^*}{\partial X^2} dX \right\} + \frac{\partial U^*}{\partial t} \tag{8}$$

since

$$\frac{1}{v} \frac{dv}{dx} = \frac{d}{dx}(\ln v)$$

Introducing equation (8) into (4) we obtain

$$\frac{\partial^2 U^*}{\partial X^2} = \frac{\partial U^*}{\partial t} + \frac{\partial U^*}{\partial X} \left\{ \int_0^X \left[\frac{d}{dU}(\ln \alpha^{-1/2}) \right] \frac{\partial^2 U^*}{\partial X^2} dX \right\} \tag{9}$$

which is the same as equation (11-29a)

2. Details of the transformation of equation (11-33) into (11-35): From the transformation (11-34) we have

$$\frac{dU^*}{dW} = -\frac{1}{AW} \tag{1}$$

Consider equation (11-33)

$$\frac{\partial^2 U^*}{\partial X^2} = \frac{\partial U^*}{\partial t} + A\left(\frac{\partial U^*}{\partial X} \right)^2 + Af(t)\frac{\partial U^*}{\partial X} \tag{2}$$

various terms in this expression are expressed in terms of W as follows:

$$\frac{\partial U^*}{\partial X} = \frac{\partial U^*}{\partial W} \cdot \frac{\partial W}{\partial X} = -\frac{1}{AW}\frac{\partial W}{\partial X} \tag{3a}$$

$$\frac{\partial^2 U^*}{\partial X^2} = \frac{\partial}{\partial X}\left(\frac{\partial U^*}{\partial X} \right) = -\frac{1}{A}\frac{\partial}{\partial X}\left(\frac{1}{W}\frac{\partial W}{\partial X} \right) = -\frac{1}{A}\left[\frac{1}{W}\frac{\partial^2 W}{\partial X^2} - \frac{1}{W^2}\left(\frac{\partial W}{\partial X} \right)^2 \right] \tag{3b}$$

$$\frac{\partial U^*}{\partial t} = \frac{\partial U^*}{\partial W} \cdot \frac{\partial W}{\partial t} = -\frac{1}{AW}\frac{\partial W}{\partial t} \tag{3c}$$

Introducing equations (3) into (2) we obtain

$$\frac{\partial^2 W}{\partial X^2} = \frac{\partial W}{\partial t} + Af(t)\frac{\partial U^*}{\partial X} \tag{4}$$

which is the same as equation (11-35).

3. Consider the problem

$$\frac{\partial^2 \psi}{\partial x^2} = \frac{1}{\alpha}\frac{\partial \psi}{\partial t} \qquad \text{in } x > 0, \ t > 0 \tag{1a}$$

$$-k \frac{\partial \psi}{\partial x} = f_0 = \text{constant} \qquad \text{at } x = 0, \ t > 0 \qquad (1b)$$

$$\psi = 0 \qquad\qquad\qquad t = 0, \ x \geq 0 \qquad (1c)$$

The solution of this problem is given as

$$\psi(x, t) = \frac{f_0}{k} \int_{x=0}^{\infty} \text{erfc}\left(\frac{x}{\sqrt{4\alpha t}}\right) dx \qquad (2)$$

In the above problem if the boundary condition (1b) is replaced by $-k(\partial\psi/\partial x) = f(t)$, then the corresponding solution, by Duhamel's theorem given by equation (5-8) becomes

$$\psi(x, t) = \frac{1}{k} \int_{\tau=0}^{t} f(\tau) \cdot \frac{\partial}{\partial t}\left[\int_{x=0}^{\infty} \text{erfc}\left(\frac{x}{\sqrt{4\alpha t}}\right) dx \right] d\tau \qquad (3)$$

This result simplifies to

$$\psi(x, t) = \frac{\alpha^{1/2}}{k\pi^{1/2}} \int_{\tau=0}^{t} f(\tau) \frac{\exp\left[-x^2/4\alpha(t-\tau)\right]}{(t-\tau)^{1/2}} d\tau \qquad (4)$$

which is the expression given by equation (11-107).

CHAPTER 12

Numerical
METHODS OF SOLUTION

In the previous chapter we discussed analytic methods for solving the boundary-value problems of heat conduction. Numerical methods are useful for handling problems involving nonlinearities, complex geometries, complicated boundary conditions or a system of coupled partial differential equations. A commonly used numerical scheme for the solution of partial differential equations is the *finite-difference* method, which is described in several references [1–21]. The *Monte Carlo* method [22–27], which derives its name from the fact that it is based on probability sampling techniques, and the *finite-element* method [28–35] which has its origin in the field of solid mechanics and structural analysis, have also been applied to the solution of heat-conduction problems. The primary advantages of the finite-element method over the finite-difference method are that the irregular boundaries can be handled easily and the size of the finite elements can be varied readily over the region. On the other hand the finite-difference representation of partial differential equations is a more straightforward matter than the finite-element representation. In the limited space available here we consider only the finite-difference methods and discuss their use in the solution of boundary-value problems of heat conduction. To achieve this objective, finite-difference representation of partial derivatives at a given point and the errors associated with such approximation are discussed, and the applications of the finite difference methods to the solution of heat-conduction problems are illustrated.

12-1 FINITE DIFFERENCE APPROXIMATION OF DERIVATIVES THROUGH TAYLOR'S SERIES

Numerical calculations such as addition, subtraction, multiplication, and division are readily performed by a digital computer at a very fast speed.

Therefore, the first step in the numerical solution of heat-conduction problems by a digital computer is the transformation of the partial differential equation of heat conduction into a form such that the differentiation can be performed by numerical calculations. The derivative of a function at a given point can be represented by *finite-difference approximation* using a Taylor series expansion of the function about that point. Let $f(x)$ be a function that can be expanded in a Taylor series. Then a Taylor series expansion of the functions $f(x + h)$ and $f(x - h)$ about x as illustrated in Fig. 12-1 is given as

$$f(x + h) = f(x) + hf'(x) + \frac{h^2}{2!}f''(x) + \frac{h^3}{3!}f'''(x)t \ldots \qquad (12\text{-}1a)$$

$$f(x - h) = f(x) - hf'(x) + \frac{h^2}{2!}f''(x) - \frac{h^3}{3!}f'''(x)t \ldots \qquad (12\text{-}1b)$$

where primes denote derivatives with respect to x. The first- and second-order derivatives $f'(x)$ and $f''(x)$ can be represented in the finite difference form in many different ways by utilizing Taylor series expansions given by equations (12-1) as now described.

First Derivatives

To obtain expressions for the finite-difference form of the first-order derivative $f'(x)$, equations (12-1a) and (12-1b) are solved for $f'(x)$. We, respectively, obtain

$$f'(x) = \frac{f(x + h) - f(x)}{h} - \frac{h}{2}f''(x) - \frac{h^2}{6}f'''(x) \ldots \qquad (12\text{-}2)$$

$$f'(x) = \frac{f(x) - f(x - h)}{2} + \frac{h}{2}f''(x) + \frac{h^2}{6}f'''(x) + \ldots \qquad (12\text{-}3)$$

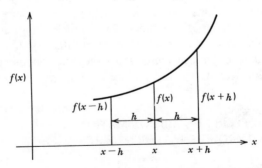

Fig. 12-1   Nomenclature for a Taylor series representation.

Subtracting equations (12-1a) and (12-1b) and solving for $f'(x)$ we obtain

$$f'(x) = \frac{f(x+h)-f(x-h)}{2h} - \frac{h^2}{6}f'''(x) - \dots \qquad (12\text{-}4)$$

From equations (12-2) to (12-4) the following approximations can be written respectively for the first derivative of a function $f(x)$ about the point x.

$$f'(x) = \frac{f(x+h)-f(x)}{h} + 0(h) \qquad \text{forward difference} \qquad (12\text{-}5)$$

$$f'(x) = \frac{f(x)-f(x-h)}{h} + 0(h) \qquad \text{backward difference} \qquad (12\text{-}6)$$

$$f'(x) = \frac{f(x+h)-f(x-h)}{2h} + 0(h^2) \qquad \text{central difference} \qquad (12\text{-}7)$$

Here the notation $0(h)$ is used to show that the error involved is of the order of h; similarly $0(h^2)$ is for the error of the order of h^2.

If we now introduce the notation

$$x = ih, \qquad x+h = (i+1)h, \qquad x-h = (i-1)h, \qquad \text{etc.} \qquad (12\text{-}8a)$$

$$f(x)=f_i, \qquad f(x+h)=f_{i+1}, \qquad f(x-h)=f_{i-1}, \qquad \text{etc.} \qquad (12\text{-}8b)$$

as illustrated in Fig. 12-2, then the finite difference representation of the first derivative of function $f(x)$ about x, given by equations (12-5) to (12-7), are written, respectively, as

$$f_i' = \frac{f_{i+1}-f_i}{h} + 0(h) \qquad \text{forward difference} \qquad (12\text{-}9)$$

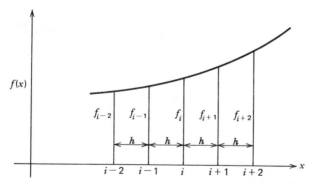

Fig. 12-2 Nomenclature for finite difference representation of $f(x)$.

$$f_i' = \frac{f_i - f_{i-1}}{h} + 0(h) \qquad \text{backward difference} \qquad (12\text{-}10)$$

$$f_i' = \frac{f_{i+1} - f_{i-1}}{2h} + 0(h^2) \quad \text{central difference} \qquad (12\text{-}11)$$

where

$$f_i' \equiv \left.\frac{df}{dx}\right|_i$$

We note that forward and backward differences are accurate to the order (h) whereas the central-difference expression is accurate to the order (h^2). More accurate expressions can be obtained for the forward and backward difference representation of the first-order derivative as will be discussed later in this section.

Second Derivatives

We now proceed to the finite-difference representation of the second derivative $f''(x)$ of a function $f(x)$ about the point x. To obtain such results we consider a Taylor series expansion of functions $f(x + 2h)$ and $f(x - 2h)$ about x as

$$f(x + 2h) = f(x) + 2hf'(x) + 2h^2 f''(x) + \tfrac{4}{3}h^3 f'''(x) + \ldots \quad (12\text{-}12a)$$

$$f(x - 2h) = f(x) - 2hf'(x) + 2h^2 f''(x) - \tfrac{4}{3}h^3 f'''(x) + \ldots \quad (12\text{-}12b)$$

Eliminating $f'(x)$ between equations (12-1a) and (12-12a) we obtain

$$f''(x) = \frac{f(x) + f(x + 2h) - 2f(x + h)}{h^2} - hf'''(x) \qquad (12\text{-}13)$$

similarly, eliminating $f'(x)$ between equations (12-1b) and (12-12b) we find

$$f''(x) = \frac{f(x - 2h) + f(x) - 2f(x - h)}{h^2} + hf'''(x) \qquad (12\text{-}14)$$

Eliminating $f'(x)$ between equations (12-1a) and (12-1b) we obtain

$$f''(x) = \frac{f(x - h) + f(x + h) - 2f(x)}{h^2} - \tfrac{1}{12}h^2 f''''(x) \qquad (12\text{-}15)$$

Using the subscript notation defined by equations (12-8), various forms of the finite-difference representation of the second-order derivative $f''(x)$ about the point x given by equations (12-13) to (12-15) are written, respectively, as

$$f_i'' = \frac{f_i - 2f_{i+1} + f_{i+2}}{h^2} + 0(h) \qquad \text{forward difference} \qquad (12\text{-}16)$$

$$f_i'' = \frac{f_{i-2} - 2f_{i-1} + f_i}{h^2} + 0(h) \qquad \text{backward difference} \qquad (12\text{-}17)$$

$$f_i'' = \frac{f_{i-1} - 2f_i + f_{i+1}}{h^2} + 0(h^2) \qquad \text{central difference} \qquad (12\text{-}18)$$

where

$$f_i'' \equiv \frac{d^2 f(x)}{dx^2}\bigg|_i$$

We note that the central-difference representation is accurate to $0(h^2)$ whereas the forward and backward differences to $0(h)$.

More Accurate Finite-Difference Representations

The forward and backward finite-difference representations given above are accurate to $0(h)$. More accurate expressions can be obtained as now described. Suppose $f'(x)$ is to be represented in forward differences to $0(h^2)$. Equation (12-13) is introduced into equation (12-2) and $f''(x)$ is eliminated. We obtain

$$f'(x) = \frac{-3f(x) + 4f(x+h) - f(x+2h)}{2h} + \tfrac{1}{3}h^2 f'''(x) \qquad (12\text{-}19)$$

which is written more compactly in the form

$$f_i' = \frac{-3f_i + 4f_{i+1} - f_{i+2}}{2h} + 0(h^2) \qquad \text{forward difference} \qquad (12\text{-}20)$$

similarly introducing equation (12-14) into equation (12-3) to eliminate $f''(x)$, we find

$$f_i' = \frac{f_{i-2} - 4f_{i-1} + 3f_i}{2h} + 0(h^2) \qquad \text{backward difference} \qquad (12\text{-}21)$$

The above procedure can be extended to obtain more accurate expressions for the first and second derivatives. Such expressions are presented in reference [36] for various order derivatives. We present below a summary of the finite-difference representation of the first- and second-order derivatives of a function $f(x)$ at a node i illustrated in Fig. 12-2. In the following summary h denotes the spacing between the nodes $i, i+1, i+2, \ldots$; f_i,

$f_{i+1}, \ldots$ denotes the value of the function $f(x)$ at the nodes $i, i+1, \ldots$, respectively, and the notations FD, BD, and CD are used to denote, respectively, the forward, backward, and central differences.

Summary of First-Order Derivatives

Two-point formulas:

$$f_i' = \frac{1}{h}(f_{i+1} - f_i) + 0(h) \qquad \text{FD} \qquad (12\text{-}22a)$$

$$f_i' = \frac{1}{h}(f_i - f_{i-1}) + 0(h) \qquad \text{BD} \qquad (12\text{-}22b)$$

Three-point formulas:

$$f_i' = \frac{1}{2h}(-3f_i + 4f_{i+1} - f_{i+2}) + 0(h^2) \qquad \text{FD} \qquad (12\text{-}23a)$$

$$f_i' = \frac{1}{2h}(f_{i-2} - 4f_{i-1} + 3f_i) + 0(h^2) \qquad \text{BD} \qquad (12\text{-}23b)$$

$$f_i' = \frac{1}{2h}(f_{i+1} - f_{i-1}) + 0(h^2) \qquad \text{CD} \qquad (12\text{-}23c)$$

Summary of Second-Order Derivatives

$$f_i'' = \frac{1}{h^2}(2f_i - 5f_{i+1} + 4f_{i+2} - f_{i+3}) + 0(h^2) \qquad \text{FD} \qquad (12\text{-}24a)$$

$$f_i'' = \frac{1}{h^2}(-f_{i-3} + 4f_{i-2} - 5f_{i-1} + 2f_i) + 0(h^2) \qquad \text{BD} \qquad (12\text{-}24b)$$

$$f_i'' = \frac{1}{h^2}(f_{i-1} - 2f_i + f_{i+1}) + 0(h^2) \qquad \text{CD} \qquad (12\text{-}24c)$$

Example 12-1. The following numerical representation of $f(x)$ is given at equally spaced intervals $\Delta x \equiv h = 1$.

x	0	1	2	3	4	5
$f(x)$	15	18	12	10	1	-6

Using finite differences, determine $f_0' \equiv f'(x = 0), f_5' \equiv f'(x = 5)$ and $f_0'' \equiv f''(x = 0)$ accurate to the order h^2.

Solution. The first-order derivatives accurate to $0(h)^2$ are given by equations (12-23a) and (12-23b). The forward difference formulae (12-23a) is used to determine f'_0 because no points are available in the backward direction and the backward difference formulae (12-23b) is used to determine f'_5 because no points are available in the forward direction. Hence we have

$$f'_0 = \tfrac{1}{2}(-3f_0 + 4f_1 - f_2) = \tfrac{1}{2}(-45 + 72 - 12) = 7.5 \qquad 0(1)^2$$

$$f'_5 = \tfrac{1}{2}(f_3 - 4f_4 + 3f_5) = \tfrac{1}{2}(10 - 4 - 18) = -6 \qquad 0(1)^2$$

Formulae (12-24a) are used to determine f''_0 ; we find

$$f''_0 = \tfrac{1}{2}(2f_0 - 5f_1 + 4f_2 - f_3) = \tfrac{1}{2}(30 - 90 + 48 - 10) = -11 \quad 0(1)^2.$$

12-2 FINITE-DIFFERENCE REPRESENTATION OF STEADY-STATE HEAT-CONDUCTION PROBLEMS

Consider the two-dimensional steady-state heat-conduction equation with heat generation given in the form

$$\frac{\partial^2 T}{\partial x^2} + \frac{\partial^2 T}{\partial y^2} + \frac{1}{k}g(x, y) = 0 \qquad \text{in region } R \qquad (12\text{-}25)$$

subject to a set of boundary conditions. Here we consider only the finite-difference representation of the differential equation over the region. A finite-difference net of rectangular mesh of size $(\Delta x, \Delta y)$ is constructed over the region as illustrated in Fig. 12-3. Let the coordinates (x, y) of a point P

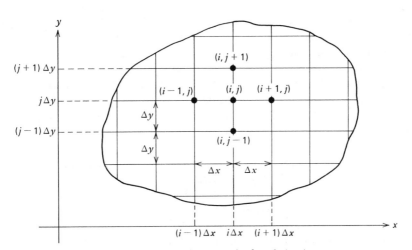

Fig. 12-3 Rectangular network of mesh Δx, Δy.

at a node be represented as

$$x = i\Delta x \qquad \text{and} \qquad y = j\Delta y \qquad (12\text{-}26)$$

where i and j are integers. The temperature $T(x, y)$ and the heat generation $g(x, y)$ at the point P is denoted by

$$T(x, y)|_P = T(i\Delta x, j\Delta y) \equiv T_{i,j} \qquad (12\text{-}27a)$$

$$g(x, y)|_P = g(i\Delta x, j\Delta y) \equiv g_{i,j} \qquad (12\text{-}27b)$$

The finite difference form of the second derivatives of $T(x, y)$ with respect to x and y at the point P are represented by the central-difference formula given by equation (12-24) as

$$\left.\frac{\partial^2 T}{\partial x^2}\right|_P = \left.\frac{\partial^2 T}{\partial x^2}\right|_{i,j} = \frac{T_{i-1,j} - 2T_{i,j} + T_{i+1,j}}{(\Delta x)^2} \qquad (11\text{-}28a)$$

$$\left.\frac{\partial^2 T}{\partial y^2}\right|_P = \left.\frac{\partial^2 T}{\partial y^2}\right|_{i,j} = \frac{T_{i,j-1} - 2T_{i,j} + T_{i,j+1}}{(\Delta y)^2} \qquad (11\text{-}28b)$$

Introducing equations (12-27b) and (12-28) into equation (12-25), we obtain the finite-difference form of equation (12-25) as

$$\frac{T_{i-1,j} - 2T_{i,j} + T_{i+1,j}}{(\Delta x)^2} + \frac{T_{i,j-1} - 2T_{i,j} + T_{i,j+1}}{(\Delta y)^2} + \frac{1}{k}g_{i,j} = 0 \quad (12\text{-}29)$$

If we assume a square mesh $\Delta x = \Delta y = l$, equation (12-29) simplifies to

$$(T_{i-1,j} + T_{i+1,j} + T_{i,j-1} + T_{i,j+1} - 4T_{i,j}) + \frac{l^2}{k}g_{i,j} = 0 \qquad (12\text{-}30)$$

We note that, in this equation, the terms inside the paranthesis are the sum of the temperatures at the four nodes surrounding the node (i, j) and subtracted from them four times the temperature $T_{i,j}$ at the node (i, j).

We now examine the finite-difference representation of the above heat-conduction equation (12-25) at a node (i, j), which is located on a boundary subjected to convection or kept insulated.

Node (i, j) on a Convection Boundary

Figure (12-4a) illustrates a node (i, j) located on a boundary surface satisfying the convection boundary condition defined as

$$k\frac{\partial T}{\partial x} + hT = hT_\infty \qquad \text{at} \qquad x = il \qquad (12\text{-}31)$$

We now imagine that at the boundary surface $x = il$, the heat conducting region is extended by a distance l so that there is an imaginary mode

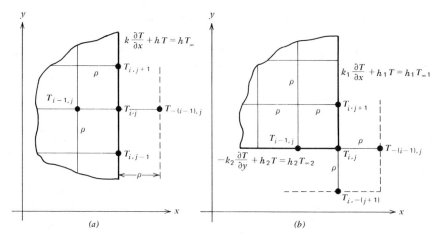

Fig. 12-4 (a) Node i, j on a convection boundary. (b) Node i, j at the intersection of two convection boundaries.

$[-(i-1), j]$ at a temperature $T_{-(i-1),j}$ as illustrated in Fig. 12-4a. Then, the finite difference form of the heat-conduction equation (12-25) at the node (i, j) is written as

$$(T_{i-1,j} + T_{-(i-1),j} + T_{i,j-1} + T_{i,j+1} - 4T_{i,j}) + \frac{l^2}{k}g_{i,j} = 0 \quad (12\text{-}32)$$

The finite-difference form of the boundary condition (11-31), using the central difference formula (12-23c) becomes

$$k\frac{T_{-(i-1),j} - T_{i-1,j}}{2l} + hT_{i,j} = hT_{\infty} \quad (11\text{-}33)$$

Eliminating $T_{-(i-1),j}$ between equations (12-32) and (12-33) we obtain

$$\left[2T_{i-1,j} + T_{i,j-1} + T_{i,j+1} - \left(4 + \frac{2lh}{k}\right)T_{i,j}\right] + \left(\frac{2lh}{k}T_{\infty} + \frac{l^2}{k}g_{i,j}\right) = 0 \quad (12\text{-}34)$$

Equation (12-34) is the desired finite-difference form of the heat-conduction equation (12-25) at the node (i, j) located on the convective boundary shown in Fig. 12-4a.

If the boundary shown in this figure was insulated, the corresponding finite-difference form of equation (12-25) on the node (i, j) is immediately obtainable from equation (12-34) merely by setting $h = 0$. That is

$$(2T_{i-1,j} + T_{i,j-1} + T_{i,j+1} - 4T_{i,j}) + \frac{l^2}{k}g_{i,j} = 0 \quad (12\text{-}35)$$

Node (i, j) at the Intersection of Two Convection Boundaries

We now consider a node (i, j) located at the intersection of two convection boundaries as illustrated in Fig. 12-4b, satisfying the boundary conditions

$$k \frac{\partial T}{\partial x} + h_1 T = h_1 T_{\infty 1} \qquad \text{at } x = il \qquad (12\text{-}36\text{a})$$

$$-k \frac{\partial T}{\partial y} + h_2 T = h_2 T_{\infty 2} \qquad \text{at } y = jl \qquad (12\text{-}36\text{b})$$

We now imagine that at the boundary surfaces $x = il$ and $y = jl$ the heat-conducting region is extended by a distance l. As a result we consider the existence of two imaginary nodes $[-(i-1), j]$ and $[i, -(j+1)]$ at temperatures $T_{-(i-1),j}$ and $T_{i,-(j+1)}$ respectively as illustrated in Fig. 12-4b. Then, the finite-difference form of the heat-conduction equation (12-25) at the node (i, j) is written as

$$[T_{i-1,j} + T_{-(i-1),j} + T_{i,j+1} + T_{i,-(j+1)} - 4T_{i,j}] + \frac{l^2}{k} g_{i,j} = 0 \quad (12\text{-}37)$$

The finite difference form of the boundary conditions (12-36), using the central difference formula (12-23c) becomes

$$k \frac{T_{-(i-1),j} - T_{i-1,j}}{2l} + h_1 T_{i,j} = h_1 T_{\infty 1} \qquad (12\text{-}38\text{a})$$

$$-k \frac{T_{i,j+1} - T_{i,-(j+1)}}{2l} + h_2 T_{i,j} = h_2 T_{\infty 2} \qquad (12\text{-}38\text{b})$$

Now $T_{-(i-1),j}$ and $T_{i,-(j+1)}$ are solved from equations (12-38a) and (12-38b), respectively, and introduced into equation (11-37). We obtain

$$\left[2T_{i-1,j} + 2T_{i,j+1} - \left(4 + \frac{2lh_1}{k} + \frac{2lh_2}{k} \right) T_{i,j} \right]$$

$$+ \left(\frac{2lh_1}{k} T_{\infty 1} + \frac{2lh_2}{k} T_{\infty 2} + \frac{l^2}{k} g_{i,j} \right) = 0 \qquad (12\text{-}39)$$

Equation (11-39) is the desired finite-difference form of the heat-conduction equation (12-25) at the node (i, j) which is situated at the intersection of two convection boundary conditions. Clearly, several special cases are obtainable from equation (12-39). For example, if the boundaries at $x = il$ and $y = jl$ are both insulated, the finite-difference form of the heat-conduction equation (12-25) at the node (i, j) is immediately obtainable from equation (12-39) by setting $h_1 = h_2 = 0$. We find

$$(2T_{i-1,j} + 2T_{i,j+1} - 4T_{i,j}) + \frac{l^2}{k} g_{i,j} = 0 \qquad (12\text{-}40)$$

Example 12-2. Consider a square region $0 \le x \le a, 0 \le y \le a$ as illustrated in Fig. 12-5. The boundary at $x = 0$ is kept insulated, boundaries at $x = a$ and $y = 0$ dissipates heat by convection into an environment at temperature T_∞ with a heat-transfer coefficient h and the boundary at $y = a$ is kept at a prescribed temperature. A finite difference net with square mesh is drawn over this region as illustrated in Fig. 12-5. Write the finite-difference form of the steady-state heat-conduction equation

$$\frac{\partial^2 T}{\partial x^2} + \frac{\partial^2 T}{\partial y^2} + \frac{1}{k} g = 0$$

where g is constant, for each of the 12 nodes at which the temperatures $T_k, k = 1$ to 12, are to be determined.

Solution. A very coarse network is drawn over the region because the

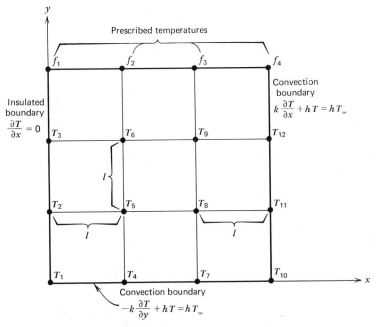

Fig. 12-5 Boundary condition and network for Example 12-1.

problem is intended for illustration only. In practice much finer network is constructed over the region. The temperatures f_1, f_2, f_3, and f_4 at the four nodes on the boundary $y = a$ are considered known. Let the mesh lengths be $\Delta x = \Delta y = l$. Twelve equations needed to determine the twelve unknown temperatures $T_k, k = 1$ to 12, are obtained by utilizing the finite-difference expressions (12-32), (12-34), and (12-39) by making appropriate changes in the notation. We summarize below the resulting twelve equations

Node Number	Finite-Difference Equation
1	$2T_2 + 2T_4 - 4T_1 + \dfrac{gl^2}{k} = 0$
2	$T_1 + T_3 + 2T_5 - 4T_2 + \dfrac{gl^2}{k} = 0$
3	$T_2 + f_1 + 2T_6 - 4T_3 + \dfrac{gl^2}{k} = 0$
4	$T_1 + T_7 + 2T_5 - \left(4 + \dfrac{2lh}{k}\right)T_4 + \left(\dfrac{2lh}{k}T_\infty + \dfrac{gl^2}{k}\right) = 0$
5	$T_2 + T_8 + T_4 + T_6 - 4T_5 + \dfrac{gl^2}{k} = 0$
6	$T_3 + T_9 + T_5 + f_2 - 4T_6 + \dfrac{gl^2}{k} = 0$
7	$T_4 + T_{10} + 2T_8 - \left(4 + \dfrac{2lh}{k}\right)T_7 + \left(\dfrac{2lh}{k}T_\infty + \dfrac{gl^2}{k}\right) = 0$
8	$T_5 + T_{11} + T_7 + T_9 - 4T_8 + \dfrac{gl^2}{k} = 0$
9	$T_6 + T_{12} + T_8 + f_3 - 4T_9 + \dfrac{gl^2}{k} = 0$
10	$2T_7 + 2T_{11} - \left(4 + \dfrac{4lh}{k}\right)T_{10} + \left(\dfrac{4lh}{k}T_\infty + \dfrac{gl^2}{k}\right) = 0$
11	$2T_8 + T_{10} + T_{12} - \left(4 + \dfrac{2lh}{k}\right)T_{11} + \left(\dfrac{2lh}{k}T_\infty + \dfrac{gl^2}{k}\right) = 0$
12	$2T_9 + T_{11} + f_4 - \left(4 + \dfrac{2lh}{k}\right)T_{12} + \left(\dfrac{2lh}{k}T_\infty + \dfrac{gl^2}{k}\right) = 0$

These equations can be written in the matrix form as shown in equation (12-41):

$$
\begin{bmatrix}
-4 & 2 & 0 & 2 & 0 & 0 & 0 & 0 & 0 & 0 & 0 & 0 \\
1 & -4 & 1 & 0 & 2 & 0 & 0 & 0 & 0 & 0 & 0 & 0 \\
0 & 1 & -(4+2H) & 0 & 0 & 2 & 0 & 0 & 0 & 0 & 0 & 0 \\
1 & 0 & 0 & -4 & 2 & 0 & 2 & 0 & 0 & 0 & 0 & 0 \\
0 & 1 & 0 & 1 & -4 & 1 & 0 & 2 & 0 & 0 & 0 & 0 \\
0 & 0 & 1 & 0 & 1 & -(4+2H) & 0 & 0 & 2 & 0 & 0 & 0 \\
0 & 0 & 0 & 1 & 0 & 0 & -4 & 2 & 0 & 1 & 0 & 0 \\
0 & 0 & 0 & 0 & 1 & 0 & 1 & -4 & 1 & 0 & 1 & 0 \\
0 & 0 & 0 & 0 & 0 & 1 & 0 & 1 & -(4+2H) & 0 & 0 & 1 \\
0 & 0 & 0 & 0 & 0 & 0 & 1 & 0 & 0 & -(4+4H) & 2 & 0 \\
0 & 0 & 0 & 0 & 0 & 0 & 0 & 1 & 0 & 2 & -(4+2H) & 1 \\
0 & 0 & 0 & 0 & 0 & 0 & 0 & 0 & 2 & 0 & 1 & -(4+2H)
\end{bmatrix}
\begin{bmatrix}
T_1 \\ T_2 \\ T_3 \\ T_4 \\ T_5 \\ T_6 \\ T_7 \\ T_8 \\ T_9 \\ T_{10} \\ T_{11} \\ T_{12}
\end{bmatrix}
=
\begin{bmatrix}
-G \\
-G \\
-G - f_1 \\
-G - 2HT_\infty \\
-G \\
-G - f_2 \\
-G - 2HT_\infty \\
-G \\
-G - f_3 \\
-G - 4HT_\infty \\
-G - 2HT_\infty \\
-G - 2HT_\infty
\end{bmatrix}
\tag{12-41}
$$

where we have defined

$$
G \equiv \frac{gl^2}{k} \qquad \text{and} \qquad H \equiv \frac{2hl}{k}
$$

483

Thus, the solution of the partial differential equation is reduced to the solution of a set of simultaneous algebraic equations for the unknown temperatures at the nodes of the network constructed over the region. In this example, we have only twelve equations because a coarse network is considered. In actual applications finer network is used and hundreds of equations are to be solved. We note that the matrix in equation (12-41) is banded, namely, the nonzero elements are in a band on either side of the main diagonal. These equations can readily be solved with a digital computer using standard computer subroutines prepared for such purposes. In the following section we present a brief discussion of the methods of solution of simultaneous algebraic equations.

12-3 METHOD OF SOLVING SIMULTANEOUS LINEAR ALGEBRAIC EQUATIONS

Simultaneous algebraic equations can be considered in two groups: The coefficient matrix is *dense* (few zero elements) and the coefficient matrix is *sparce* (many zero elements).

The two commonly used methods of solving simultaneous algebraic equations include the *direct method* that makes use of the *Gause elimination* or *Gauss-Jordan elimination* procedure, and the *iterative method* that makes use of the *Gauss-Siedel* iteration procedure to solve the equations. These methods are now decribed briefly.

Direct Method

Direct methods are well suited for solving large sets of equations having banded coefficients. The method is efficient and straightforward, and standard computer codes employing this technique are available for solving sets of simultaneous algebraic equations. To illustrate the procedure, we consider a set of equations having a tridiagonal coefficient matrix as given by equation (12-42).

$$
\begin{bmatrix}
a_1 & b_1 & 0 & & 0 & 0 & 0 \\
a_2 & b_2 & c_2 & & & & 0 \\
0 & b_3 & c_3 & & & & 0 \\
0 & 0 & c_4 & & & & \vdots \\
\hline
\vdots & & & U_{n-3} & & 0 \\
\vdots & & & U_{n-2} & V_{n-2} & 0 \\
0 & & & U_{n-1} & V_{n-1} & W_{n-1} \\
0 & 0 & 0 & --- & 0 & V_n & W_n
\end{bmatrix}
\begin{bmatrix}
T_1 \\ T_2 \\ T_3 \\ \vdots \\ \vdots \\ \vdots \\ T_{n-1} \\ T_n
\end{bmatrix}
=
\begin{bmatrix}
A_1 \\ A_2 \\ A_3 \\ \vdots \\ \vdots \\ \vdots \\ A_{n-1} \\ A_n
\end{bmatrix}
\tag{12-42}
$$

The Gaussian elimination can be applied to solve these equations as now described. A suitable multiple of the top equation of the system (12-42) is subtracted from the second to eliminate the nonzero element a_2 of the second equation. A suitable multiple of the second equation is subtracted from the third to eliminate the nonzero element b_3 of the third equation. The procedure is repeated until the coefficient matrix is transformed into upper bidiagonal form as illustrated in equations (12-43). In this system, the last equation gives T_n. Knowing T_n, the temperature T_{n-1} is determined from the $(n-1)$th equation, and the calculations are carried out until T_1 is determined from the first equation.

$$
\begin{bmatrix}
a_1^* & b_1^* & 0 & --- & 0 & 0 & 0 \\
0 & b_2^* & c_2^* & & & & 0 \\
0 & 0 & c_3^* & & \cdot & & 0 \\
\hline
\vdots & & & & & & \\
\vdots & & & U_{n-1}^* & & 0 & \\
\vdots & & & U_{n-2}^* & V_{n-2}^* & 0 & \\
0 & & & 0 & V_{n-1}^* & W_{n-1}^* & \\
0 & 0 & 0 & --- & 0 & 0 & W_n^*
\end{bmatrix}
\begin{bmatrix}
T_1 \\ T_2 \\ T_3 \\ \vdots \\ \vdots \\ \vdots \\ T_{n-1} \\ T_n
\end{bmatrix}
=
\begin{bmatrix}
A_1^* \\ A_2^* \\ A_3^* \\ \vdots \\ \vdots \\ \vdots \\ A_{n-1}^* \\ A_n^*
\end{bmatrix}
\qquad (12\text{-}43)
$$

In the foregoing example, the number of operations needed for the solution of n equations having a tridiagonal coefficient matrix is of the order of $0(n)$. If the bandwidth increases, both the number of operations and the storage locations needed increase. Therefore, the direct elimination method is suitable for solving large sets of equations if the coefficient matrix is banded. The reader should consult references [10] and [11] for the handling of sparse systems of equations and reference [14] for a complete guide on elimination methods and the procedures for their implementation.

Iterative Method

When large sets of equations with sparse (not banded) coefficient matrices are to be solved and if the computer storage is critical, it is desirable to use a method that does not require large storage space. An iterative method is suitable for such purposes. In this method a first approximation is used to calculate a second approximation, which is then used to calculate a third approximation, and so on; the iteration is terminated when desired convergence criterion is satisfied. A discussion of various iterative methods is given in several references [6, 8, 9, 16, 17]. The most frequently used iterative method is the Gauss-Siedel iteration. One difficulty with the Gauss-Siedel method is that its convergence is relatively slow. The convergence is improved with the method called *successive overrelaxation*, first originated in references

[37] and [38] and discussed in greater detail in various references [9, 16, 17, 39,]. The reader should consult such references for the detailed discussion of this method of solution of linear equations.

In solving the linear differential equations with finite differences, in general, it is a good strategy to start with a coarse net. Such results can then be used with some extrapolation to construct the initial guess for the finer mesh constructed over the region and with the iterative method of solution.

12-4 ERRORS INVOLVED IN NUMERICAL SOLUTIONS

In numerical solution of heat-conduction problems with the method of finite differences, the partial differential equation is approximated with finite-difference expressions at each nodal point, and as a result the solution of the differential equation is transformed to the solution of a set of algebraic equations. We have seen in Section 12-4 that whenever a derivative is approximated by finite differences using a Taylor series expansion an error is involved. Such an error is called the *truncation error* or the *discretization error*; the order of magnitude of the error involved is illustrated in equations (12-22) to (12-24) for the first- and second-order derivatives. These errors are committed because a continuous operator such as the first- or the second-order derivative is replaced by finite-difference approximation. In addition, numerical calculations are carried out only to a finite number of *decimal places* or *significant figures*; as a result at each step in the calculations some error is introduced due to this rounding-off process, called the *round-off error*.

Clearly, if the finite-difference approximation is made by using formulas having truncation errors of high order, the truncation error at each step is minimum. Also, by decreasing the step size, the truncation error is reduced for each step; however, a limit also is reached at which further reduction in step size increases the total number of calculations and as a result the round-off errors may become dominant.

Ideally, if it were possible to carry out the finite-difference calculations with extremely small steps and to perform the calculations to an infinite number of decimal places, the resulting solution would be exact. However, due to the cumulative effects of the rounding off and the discretization errors the solutions obtained by the finite-differences method is expected to deviate from the exact result; therefore, the solution computed is the *numerical solution* but not the *exact result*. It is very difficult to determine the cumulative departure of the numerical solution from the exact result due to the cumulative effects of such errors. Comparison of numerical solutions with exact analytic solutions reveals that for most cases the results are very close indeed. After some experience with different methods and different step sizes, a suitable combination can be chosen for the numerical solution of a given problem. Therefore an *overall error analysis* is a very important part of a numerical method of solution.

In addition to the error analysis, it is important to know how these errors affect the calculations in the following steps. If the errors tend to accumulate rapidly they will give rise to instability of the solution. Thus, the problems of *stability* and *convergence* of the solution, which are generally interrelated, are important for numerical analysis. By the *convergence* it is meant that as the step size $l \to 0$, the finite difference solution of the differential equation tends to the exact solution at each location considered. The *stability* of finite difference equations has been discussed in detail is several references [1, 5, 6, 8, 9, 10, 39], but its precise definition is rather difficult. To illustrate the physical significance of the concept of stability, let T be the exact solution and T^* be the numerical solution of a given heat-conduction problem. The quantity $(T^* - T)$ is the departure of the numerical solution from the exact solution resulting from the errors introduced at the mesh points. Let the errors introduced at each mesh point be less than δ. Then the finite difference scheme is called *stable* if the maximum value of $(T^* - T)$ tends to zero as δ tends to zero and does not increase exponentially with the number of calculations. The subject of stability of finite difference solutions is also discussed in the following section.

12-5 FINITE-DIFFERENCE REPRESENTATION OF TIME-DEPENDENT HEAT-CONDUCTION EQUATION

The stability consideration plays an important role in the finite-difference solution of time-dependent heat-conduction problems. There are several schemes available to express the time-dependent heat-conduction equation in finite difference form. For example, 13 different schemes, ranging from the so-called *explicit form* to the *fully implicit form*, for finite differencing of the one-dimensional time-dependent heat-conduction equation is listed in reference [5]. Each of these differencing schemes has its advantages and limitations. We now discuss some of them with particular emphasis to the finite-difference approximation of the one-dimensional time-dependent heat-conduction equation in the rectangular coordinate system.

Explicit Method

We consider the one dimensional, time-dependent heat-conduction equation for a finite region $0 \le x \le L$ given as

$$\frac{\partial T}{\partial t} = \alpha \frac{\partial^2 T}{\partial x^2} \quad \text{in} \quad 0 < x < L, \; t > 0 \tag{12-44}$$

The region of interest in the space domain is bounded, i.e., $0 \le x \le L$, and in the time domain extends from $t = 0$ to infinity. We construct a finite difference net in the x domain with constant mesh size Δx as illustrated in Fig. 12-6. In the time domain, let, the step size be Δt. Then, the space and time coordinates x and t are denoted by

$$x = j\Delta x \quad j = 0, 1, 2, \ldots, N \quad \text{with } L = N\Delta x \tag{12-45a}$$

$$t = n\Delta t \quad n = 0, 1, 2, 3 \ldots \tag{12-45b}$$

and the temperature $T(x, t)$ is represented by

$$T(x, t) = T(j\Delta x, n\Delta t) \equiv T_j^n \tag{12-46}$$

Using this notation, the finite-difference representation of $\partial^2 T / \partial x^2$ at the node (j) (i.e., $x = j\Delta x$) and for the nth time step (i.e., $t = n\Delta t$) is written with the *central-difference formula* (12-24c) *as*

$$\left. \frac{\partial^2 T}{\partial x^2} \right|_{j,n} = \frac{T_{j-1}^n - 2T_j^n + T_{j+1}^n}{(\Delta x)^2} + 0(\Delta x)^2 \tag{12-47a}$$

The first derivative with respect to the time variable, $\partial T / \partial t$, is represented in the finite difference form at the nth time step using the *forward-difference*

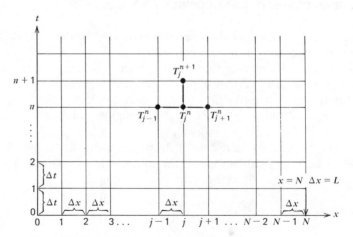

Fig. 12-6 The subdivision of (x, t) domain into intervals $(\Delta x, \Delta t)$.

formula (12-9) as

$$\frac{\partial T}{\partial t}\bigg|_{j,n} = \frac{T_j^{n+1} - T_j^n}{\Delta t} + 0(\Delta t) \tag{12-47b}$$

Introducing equations (12-47) into (12-44), the finite-difference representation of the heat-conduction equation (12-44) becomes

$$\frac{T_j^{n+1} - T_j^n}{\Delta t} = \alpha \frac{T_{j-1}^n - 2T_j^n + T_{j+1}^n}{(\Delta x)^2} \tag{12-48}$$

with a truncation error of $0(\Delta t) + 0(\Delta x)^2$. Solving equation (12-48) for T_j^{n+1} we obtain

$$T_j^{n+1} = rT_{j-1}^n + (1 - 2r)T_j^n + rT_{j+1}^n \quad j = 1, 2, 3, \ldots, N - 1 \quad n = 0, 1, 2 \ldots \tag{12-49}$$

where

$$r = \frac{\alpha \Delta t}{(\Delta x)^2} \tag{12-50}$$

The finite-difference representation given by equation (12-49) is called the *explicit* form because the unknown temperature T_j^{n+1} at the time step $(n + 1)$ can be directly determined from the knowledge of temperatures T_{j-1}^n, T_j^n, and T_{j+1}^n at the previous time (n) step according to equation (12-49).

The explicit form of finite-difference representation given by equation (12-49) provides a relatively straightforward expression for the determination of the unknowns $T_j^{n+1}, j = 1, 2, \ldots, N - 1$, at the time step $(n + 1)$, from the knowledge of T_j^n, at the previous time step n. The only disadvantage of this method is that once α and the step size Δx are fixed, there is a maximum permissible step size Δt, which should not be exceeded by instability considerations. For example, when the boundary conditions at $x = 0$ and $x = L$ are both of the first kind (i.e., specified temperatures), the restriction imposed on the parameter r defined by equation (11-50) is [9, p. 93].

$$0 < r \equiv \frac{\alpha \Delta t}{(\Delta x)^2} \leq \frac{1}{2} \tag{12-51}$$

That is, for given values of α and Δx, if the time step Δt exceeds the limit imposed on by the above criteria, the numerical calculations become unstable resulting from the amplification of errors. Figure 12-7 illustrates what happens to the numerical calculations when the above stability criteria is violated. In this figure, the numerical calculations performed with a time step satisfying the condition $r = \frac{5}{11} < \frac{1}{2}$ is in good agreement with the exact solution; whereas the numerical solution of the same problem with slightly

$T(x, t)$

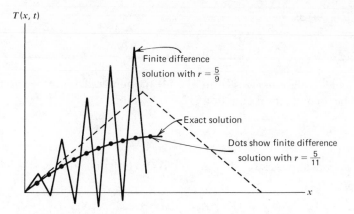

Fig. 12-7   Effects of parameter $r = \alpha \Delta t/(\Delta x)^2$ on the stability of finite-difference solution of the one-dimensional time-dependent heat-conduction equation.

larger time step which violates the above stability criteria, i.e., $r = \frac{5}{9} > \frac{1}{2}$, results in an unstable solution.

Stability of Solution. There are two different methods of investigating the stability, that is, the growth of errors, of the solution of finite-difference equations. In one of these methods the finite-difference representation of the problem, including the differential equation and the boundary conditions, is represented in the matrix form and the eigenvalues of the associated matrix is examined for the propagation of the errors [8, Chapter 18; 9, Chapter 3]. In the other method, called the Fourier series approach, only the stability of the differential equation is investigated for the propagation of error as t increases [9, 40]. The latter approach is simpler, but does not accommodate the effects of boundary conditions.

To illustrate the concept of stability, we discuss the Fourier series method, which is also called the von Neumann method, of determination of the stability criteria for the explicit finite difference form given above by equation (12-48).

In this approach, the initial errors at the grid points are assumed expressible in terms of a finite Fourier series as

$$E(x) = \sum_{k=0}^{k} A_k e^{i\beta_k(j\Delta x)} \qquad \text{for } t = 0, \ j = 0, 1, \dots, N \qquad (12\text{-}52a)$$

where $E(x)$ is the error and $i = \sqrt{-1}$. The analysis is then concerned with the examination of the propagation of the error as time increases. The difference equations being linear, we need to consider only the propagation of the error due to a single term, say, $e^{i\beta(j\Delta x)}$; since the coefficient A_k is constant, it is neglected. Then, we assume that the error due to this single term at any time $t = n\Delta t$ is given by

$$E_{j,n} = e^{\gamma(n\Delta t)} \cdot e^{i\beta(j\Delta x)} \equiv \xi^n \cdot e^{i\beta(j\Delta x)} \tag{12-52b}$$

where γ, in general, is complex, and $\xi \equiv e^{\gamma\Delta t}$. We also note that for $t = 0$, the error (12-52b) reduces to the initial error. Clearly, the initial error $e^{i\beta x}$ will not increase as time increases if

$$|\xi| \leq 1 \tag{12-53}$$

for all $\gamma \equiv \gamma(\beta)$.

To determine the stability criteria for the explicit finite-difference equation (12-48), we introduce equation (12-52b) into equation (12-48) because the error $E_{j,n}$ satisfies the same equation. We obtain

$$e^{i\beta(j\Delta x)}(\xi^{n+1} - \xi^n) = \frac{\alpha\Delta t}{(\Delta x)^2} e^{i\beta(j\Delta x)} \cdot \xi^n(e^{-i\beta\Delta x} - 2 + e^{i\beta\Delta x}) \tag{12-54a}$$

or

$$\xi - 1 = \frac{2\alpha\Delta t}{(\Delta x)^2}\left(\frac{e^{i\beta\Delta x} + e^{-i\beta\Delta x}}{2} - 1\right) \tag{12-54b}$$

$$\xi = 1 - \frac{2\alpha\Delta t}{(\Delta x)^2}(1 - \cos\beta\Delta x) = 1 - \frac{2\alpha\Delta t}{(\Delta x)^2}\cdot 2\sin^2\frac{\beta\Delta x}{2} \tag{12-54c}$$

Here the quantity ξ is called the *amplification factor*. That is, the initial errors will not be amplified and the finite difference calculations will be *stable* if $|\xi| \leq 1$ for all values of $\beta\Delta x$. For the relation given by equation (12-54c), this condition is satisfied if

$$\frac{2\alpha\Delta t}{(\Delta x)^2} \leq 1 \qquad \text{or} \qquad r \equiv \frac{\alpha\Delta t}{(\Delta x)^2} \leq \frac{1}{2} \tag{12-55}$$

which is the stability criteria for the *stable* solution of the explicit finite-difference equation (12-48) or (12-49).

The Fourier series or von Neumann method discussed above does not accommodate the effects of the boundary conditions on the stability analysis; this limitation should be recognized.

Implicit Method

The explicit method discussed above is simple computationally, but very small time step should be used because of stability considerations. Therefore, prohibitively a large number of time steps may be required if solutions are to be performed over a large period of time. It is for this reason, other finite difference forms that are less restrictive to the size of time step Δt are developed. One such scheme is the fully *implicit method*. We illustrate this method by considering the finite-difference representation of the heat conduction equation (12-44). The partial derivative $\partial^2 T/\partial x^2$ is represented in finite differences at the node j, for the $(n+1)$th time step using the central difference formula (12-44c), whereas the time derivative $\partial T/\partial t$ is represented in the finite-difference form at the $(n+1)$th time step using the backward difference expression. Then, the finite difference form of equation (12-44) becomes

$$\frac{T_j^{n+1} - T_j^n}{\Delta t} = \alpha \frac{T_{j+1}^{n+1} - 2T_j^{n+1} + T_{j+1}^{n+1}}{(\Delta x)^2} \tag{12-56}$$

This is called an *implicit form* of finite-difference representation, because to determine the unknowns $T_j^{n+1}, j = 1, 2, \ldots, N-1$, at the $(n+1)$th time step, a set of simultaneous algebraic equations are to be solved. The advantage of the implicit method is that it is stable for all sizes of time step Δt, thus there is no size restriction on Δt. Only size restriction on Δt is due to the consideration of the truncation error.

Stability of Solution. The Fourier series method discussed above is now applied to illustrate that the finite-difference equation (12-56) is stable for all values of $r = \alpha \Delta t/(\Delta x)^2$. To prove this result, the error function (12-52b) is introduced into equation (12-56). We obtain

$$\xi^{n+1} - \xi^n = \frac{2\alpha\Delta t}{(\Delta x)^2} \xi \left(\frac{e^{i\beta\Delta x} + e^{-i\beta\Delta x}}{2} - 1 \right) \tag{12-57a}$$

$$\xi - 1 = 2r \cdot \xi(\cos \beta\Delta x - 1) = -4r\xi \sin^2 \frac{\beta\Delta x}{2} \tag{12-57b}$$

where $r \equiv \alpha\Delta t/(\Delta x)^2$. Solving for ξ we obtain

$$\xi = \left(1 + 4r \sin^2 \frac{\beta\Delta x}{2} \right)^{-1} \tag{12-57c}$$

For stability we need $|\xi| \leq 1$; this condition is valid for all positive values of r in equation (12-57c). Therefore, the implicit form of finite-difference representation of heat-conduction equation (12-44) is stable for all positive values of r.

The truncation errors for both explicit and implicit forms of finite difference representations of the heat-conduction equation is of the order $(\Delta x)^2$ for $\partial^2 T/\partial x^2$ and of the order Δt for $\partial T/\partial t$. But the actual accumulated error in both methods need not be the same. Depending on the nature of the problem, one of the methods may be preferred to the other.

Crank-Nicolson Method

Crank and Nicolson [2] suggested a modified implicit method. To illustrate this method we represent the heat-conduction equation (12-44) in finite differences with this approach. The partial derivative with respect to the space variable, $\partial^2 T/\partial x^2$, is represented in finite differences by taking the arithmetic average of the right-hand sides of the explicit form (12-48) and the implicit form (12-56). Then, the finite-difference representation of the heat-conduction equation (12-44) using the Crank-Nicolson method becomes

$$\frac{T_j^{n+1} - T_j^n}{\Delta t} = \frac{\alpha}{2}\left[\frac{T_{j-1}^{n+1} - 2T_j^{n+1} + T_{j+1}^{n+1}}{(\Delta x)^2} + \frac{T_{j-1}^n - 2T_j^n + T_{j+1}^n}{(\Delta x)^2} \right] \quad (12\text{-}58)$$

The advantage of this method is that for given values of the space and time steps Δx and Δt, the resulting solution involves less truncation error due to Δt than the explicit and the implicit forms discussed above. On the other hand the Crank-Nicolson form involves additional computation. If there are N internal mesh points over the region this method involves the solution of N simultaneous algebraic equations for each time step. It is stable [9, p. 65; 5] for all values of $r = \alpha\Delta t/(\Delta x)^2$ and the truncation error is of the order of $(\Delta t)^2 + (\Delta x)^2$.

To provide a better insight to the physical significance of Crank-Nicolson representation, we write equation (12-58) in a more general form by taking a weighted average of the two terms in the bracket

$$\frac{T_j^{n+1} - T_j^n}{\Delta t} = \alpha\left[\eta\frac{T_{j-1}^{n+1} - 2T_j^{n+1} + T_{j+1}^{n+1}}{(\Delta x)^2} + (1-\eta)\frac{T_{j-1}^n - 2T_j^n + T_{j+1}^n}{(\Delta x)^2} \right]$$

$$(12\text{-}59)$$

where $0 \le \eta \le 1$ is called the *degree of implicitness*. Clearly, equation (12-59) reduces to the explicit form given by equation (12-48) for $\eta = 0$, to the implicit form given by equation (12-56) for $\eta = 1$ and to the Crank-Nicolson form (12-58) for $\eta = \frac{1}{2}$. Equation (12-59) is stable for all $r = \alpha\Delta t/\Delta x^2$ for $\eta \ge \frac{1}{2}$. For $0 \le \eta < \frac{1}{2}$ we must have $\alpha\Delta t/(\Delta x)^2 \le 1/2(1 - 2\eta)$ for stable solution.

Alternating-Direction Implicit Method

The implicit methods discussed above are advantageous to use because of the superior stability properties. On the other hand, the computational problems become enormous when they are applied to the solution of time-dependent heat-conduction problems involving two or three space dimensions, because a large number of simultaneous equations are to be solved at each time step. For example, for a three-dimensional problem with N interior nodal points in each direction there are a total of N^3 nodes, hence $N^3 \times N^3$ matrix equations must be solved for each time increment. The procedure becomes impractical if N exceeds, say, approximately 10.

The *alternating-direction implicit* (A.D.I.) method introduced by Peaceman and Rachford [4], provides an efficient method for solving problems involving large number of nodes. To illustrate the procedure we consider the following two-dimensional, time-dependent heat-conduction equation

$$\frac{\partial^2 T}{\partial x^2} + \frac{\partial^2 T}{\partial y^2} = \frac{1}{\alpha}\frac{\partial T}{\partial t} \quad \text{in region } R \quad (12\text{-}60)$$

We construct a rectangular network of mesh size $\Delta x, \Delta y$ over the region and consider time steps of size Δt. Then, the coordinates x, y, and t are denoted by

$$x = i\Delta x, \qquad y = j\Delta y, \qquad \text{and} \qquad t = n\Delta t \quad (12\text{-}61a)$$

and the temperature $T(x, y, t)$ at the location (x, y), at time t is represented by

$$T(x, y, t) = T(i\Delta x, j\Delta y, n\Delta t) \equiv T_{i,j}^n \quad (12\text{-}61b)$$

where i, j, and n are integers.

To represent the space derivatives in finite differences, the central difference formula is used with an *implicit* and *explicit* difference approximation alternatively for $\partial^2 T/\partial x^2$ and $\partial^2 T/\partial y^2$. For example, if $\partial^2 T/\partial x^2$ is represented in the implicit form in terms of the unknown values of $T_{i,j}^{n+1}$ from the $(n+1)$th time level, the derivative $\partial^2 T/\partial y^2$ is represented by an *explicit* approximation. That is, the finite difference form of various derivatives in terms of the unknown values of temperature for the $(n+1)$th time level becomes

$$\frac{\partial T}{\partial t} = \frac{T_{i,j}^{n+1} - T_{i,j}^n}{\Delta t} \quad (12\text{-}62a)$$

$$\frac{\partial^2 T}{\partial x^2} = \frac{T_{i-1,j}^{n+1} - 2T_{i,j}^{n+1} + T_{i+1,j}^{n+1}}{(\Delta x)^2} \quad (12\text{-}62b)$$

$$\frac{\partial^2 T}{\partial y^2} = \frac{T_{i,j-1}^n - 2T_{i,j}^n + T_{i,j+1}^n}{(\Delta y)^2} \quad (12\text{-}62c)$$

Then, the finite-difference form of equation (12-60), to proceed the solution from the (n)th step to the $(n+1)$th step, becomes

$$\frac{1}{\alpha}\frac{T_{i,j}^{n+1} - T_{i,j}^n}{\Delta t} = \frac{T_{i-1,j}^{n+1} - 2T_{i,j}^{n+1} + T_{i+1,j}^{n+1}}{(\Delta x)^2} + \frac{T_{i,j-1}^n - 2T_{i,j}^n + T_{i,j+1}^n}{(\Delta y)^2} \quad (12\text{-}63a)$$

The finite difference form of equation (12-60), to proceed the solution from the $(n+1)$th step to the $(n+2)$th step, is written using an *explicit* form for

$\partial^2 T/\partial x^2$ and implicit form for $\partial^2 T/\partial y^2$ as

$$\frac{1}{\alpha} \frac{T_{i,j}^{n+2} - T_{i,j}^{n+1}}{\Delta t} = \frac{T_{i-1,j}^{n+1} - 2T_{i,j}^{n+1} + T_{i+1,j}^{n+1}}{(\Delta x)^2} + \frac{T_{i,j-1}^{n+2} - 2T_{i,j}^{n+2} + T_{i,j+1}^{n+2}}{(\Delta y)^2}$$

$$(12\text{-}63\text{b})$$

The procedure is repeated alternately in the subsequent time steps.

The advantage of the A.D.I. method over the Crank-Nicolson implicit method results from the fact that it reduces the number of equations to be solved simultaneously for each time step. Consider for example a two-dimensional, time-dependent problem with N internal nodes along the $0x$ axis and N nodes along the $0y$ axis. The A.D.I. method requires the solution of N simultaneous equations N times for each time step, whereas the Crank-Nicolson method requires the solution of N^2 equations at once. Clearly, the former is much easier computationally than the latter.

The solution of two-dimensional, time-dependent heat-conduction problems with the A.D.I. method shows that it is stable for all values of time step Δt [4]. The method has also been used to solve two-dimensional plane (x, y) and axially symmetric (r, z) steady-state heat-conduction problems [41]. However, for the solution of three-dimensional problems it appears to be unstable for certain values of Δt [13, 42]. The reader should consult references [4], [6], [9], and [43–45] for further discussion of this method.

Other Methods

The *alternating direction explicit* (A.D.E.) method, the principles of which was proposed in reference [46] and then expanded [47], provides an efficient approach for the solution of multidimensional, time-dependent heat-conduction problems. A comparison of this method by the A.D.I. method for the solution of two-dimensional problems shows that the former is superior over the latter by a possible saving in computer time [47]. For two-dimensional problems, an examination of the mathematical models for A.D.I. and A.D.E. methods indicates that they should be of comparable accuracies. For the three-dimensional problems the A.D.E. method appears to have a marked advantage in computation time [13].

Other forms of the A.D.I. method include the Douglas-Rachford implicit scheme [48], its modification by Brian [49], and the alternative form given by D'Yakonov [50]. Barakat and Clark [51] describe an explicit scheme that is unconditionally stable for the solution of time-dependent, multidimensional heat-conduction equation. The method possesses the advantages of the implicit scheme with no severe limitations on the size of time step Δt and the simplicity of the explicit scheme. To solve the two-dimensional, time-dependent heat-conduction equation (12-60) subject to a specified boundary and initial conditions with this scheme, the temperature $T_{j,k}^{n+1}$ at any time level $(n + 1)$ is taken as the arithmetic average of two functions $U_{j,k}^{n+1}$ and $V_{j,k}^{n+1}$ as

$$T_{j,k}^{n+1} = \tfrac{1}{2}(U_{j,k}^{n+1} + V_{j,k}^{n+1}) \tag{12-64a}$$

It is assumed that $U_{j,k}^{n+1}$ and $V_{j,k}^{n+1}$ functions satisfy the same boundary and initial conditions as the temperature $T_{j,k}^{n+1}$, and the finite difference expressions for these two auxiliary functions are given as

$$\frac{U_{j,k}^{n+1} - U_{j,k}^n}{\Delta t} = \frac{U_{j+1,k}^n - U_{j,k}^n - U_{j,k}^{n+1} + U_{j-1,k}^{n+1}}{(\Delta x)^2}$$

$$+ \frac{U_{j,k+1}^n - U_{j,k}^n - U_{j,k}^{n+1} + U_{j,k-1}^{n+1}}{(\Delta x)^2} \tag{12-64b}$$

and a similar expression for the $V_{j,k}$ function with superscripts n and $(n + 1)$ being interchanged on the right-hand side of the above equation. To show that the finite-difference expression given by equations (12-64) is always stable, we consider an error term given in the form

$$E_{j,k,n} = e^{\gamma(n\Delta t)} \cdot e^{i(\beta_1 j\Delta x + \beta_2 k\Delta y)} \equiv \zeta^n e^{i(\beta_1 j\Delta x + \beta_2 k\Delta y)}$$

where $\zeta \equiv e^{\gamma\Delta t}$ and γ, in general, is complex. Substituting this error term into equation (12-64b) because the error satisfies the same equation, we obtain, after rearranging, the following expression for ζ

$$\frac{\zeta^{n+1}}{\zeta^n} = \zeta = \frac{1 - \dfrac{\Delta t}{(\Delta x)^2}(1 - e^{i\beta_1\Delta x}) - \dfrac{\Delta t}{(\Delta y)^2}(1 - e^{i\beta_2\Delta y})}{1 + \dfrac{\Delta t}{(\Delta x)^2}(1 - e^{-i\beta_1\Delta x}) - \dfrac{\Delta t}{(\Delta y)^2}(1 - e^{-i\beta_2\Delta y})} \tag{12-65}$$

The original error will not amplify with time if $|\zeta| \leq 1$. Clearly, equation (12-65) satisfies this criteria for all value of Δt, Δx, and Δy. Hence, the above finite-difference scheme is unconditionally stable.

12-6 APPLICATIONS OF FINITE-DIFFERENCE METHODS TO TIME-DEPENDENT HEAT-CONDUCTION PROBLEMS

In the previous sections we discussed various methods of finite-difference representation of time-dependent heat-conduction equation. In this section we illustrate with examples the finite-difference representation of one-dimensional, time-dependent heat-conduction problems with different methods.

Example 12-3. Consider the following one-dimensional, time-dependent heat conduction problem for a slab $0 \leq x \leq L$ subject to the boundary conditions of the third kind at both boundaries

$$\alpha \frac{\partial^2 T}{\partial x^2} = \frac{\partial T}{\partial t} \qquad \text{in } 0 < x < L, \; t > 0 \qquad (12\text{-}66a)$$

$$-k_1 \frac{\partial T}{\partial x} + h_1 T = f_1 \qquad \text{at } x = 0, \; t > 0 \qquad (12\text{-}66b)$$

$$k_2 \frac{\partial T}{\partial x} + h_2 T = f_2 \qquad \text{at } x = L, \; t > 0 \qquad (12\text{-}66c)$$

$$T = F(x) \qquad \text{for } t = 0, \text{ in } 0 \leq x \leq L \qquad (12\text{-}66d)$$

Using the *explicit* method for the finite differencing of the differential equation, simple *forward* and simple *backward* differences for the boundary conditions at $x = 0$ and $x = L$, respectively, write the finite-difference representation of this heat-conduction problem.

Solution. The (x, t) domain is divided into interval $\Delta x, \Delta t$ as illustrated in Fig. 12.6. Then

$$x = j\Delta x \qquad j = 0, 1, 2, \ldots, N \qquad \text{with } L = N\Delta x$$

$$t = n\Delta t \qquad n = 0, 1, 2, \ldots$$

and the temperature $T(x, t)$ is represented by

$$T(x, t) = T(j\Delta x, n\Delta t) \equiv T_j^n \qquad (12\text{-}67)$$

Using *forward* difference for the boundary condition at $x = 0$ and *backward* difference for the one at $x = L$ we have

$$-k_1 \frac{T_1^{n+1} - T_0^{n+1}}{\Delta x} + h_1 T_0^{n+1} = f_1 \qquad n = 0, 1, 2, \ldots; \; j = 0 \quad (12\text{-}68a)$$

$$k_2 \frac{T_N^{n+1} - T_{N-1}^{n+1}}{\Delta x} + h_2 T_N^{n+1} = f_2 \qquad n = 0, 1, 2, \ldots; \; j = N \quad (12\text{-}68b)$$

Solving equation (12-68a) for T_0^{n+1} and (12-68b) for T_N^{n+1} we obtain

$$T_0^{n+1} = \frac{1}{1 + (h_1 \Delta x / k_1)} \left[T_1^{n+1} + \frac{f_1 \cdot \Delta x}{k_1} \right] \qquad n = 0, 1, 2, 3, \ldots; \; j = 0 \quad (12\text{-}69a)$$

$$T_N^{n+1} = \frac{1}{1 + (h_2 \Delta x / k_2)} \left[T_{N-1}^{n+1} + \frac{f_2 \cdot \Delta x}{k_2} \right] \qquad n = 0, 1, 2, 3, \ldots; \; j = N \quad (12\text{-}69b)$$

with truncation error of the order of (Δx). The finite-difference representation of the heat-conduction equation (12-66a) in the *explicit* form is given, according to equation (12-49), as

$$T_j^{n+1} = rT_{j-1}^n + (1 - 2r)T_j^n + rT_{j+1}^n, \qquad j = 1, 2, \ldots; N - 1, \qquad n = 0, 1, 2, \ldots$$
$$(12\text{-}70)$$

where $r = \alpha \Delta t/(\Delta x)^2$, with a truncation error of the order of $(\Delta t) + (\Delta x)^2$. Equations (12-70) includes on the right-hand side T_0^n for $j = 1$ and T_N^n for $j = N - 1$. The temperatures T_0^n and T_N^n are obtained from equations (12-69a) and (12-69b) respectively if the superscript $(n + 1)$ is replaced by (n); T_0^n and T_N^n obtained in this manner are introduced into equations (12-70) for $j = 1$ and $N - 1$. We now summarize equations (12-70) together with equations (12-69).

$$T_0^{n+1} = \frac{1}{\beta_1}(T_1^{n+1} + \gamma_1) \qquad\qquad \text{at } j = 0 \qquad\qquad (12\text{-}71)$$

$$T_1^{n+1} = \left(1 - 2r + \frac{r}{\beta_1}\right)T_1^n + rT_2^n + \frac{r\gamma_1}{\beta_1} \qquad \text{at } j = 1 \qquad (12\text{-}72a)$$

$$T_j^{n+1} = rT_{j-1}^n + (1 - 2r)T_j^n + rT_{j+1}^n \qquad \text{at } j = 2, 3, \ldots, N - 2 \quad (12\text{-}72b)$$

$$T_{N-1}^{n+1} = rT_{N-2}^n + \left(1 - 2r + \frac{r}{\beta_2}\right)T_{N-1}^n + \frac{r\gamma_2}{\beta_2} \quad \text{at } j = N - 1 \qquad (12\text{-}72c)$$

$$T_N^{n+1} = \frac{1}{\beta_2}(T_{N-1}^{n+1} + \gamma_2) \qquad\qquad \text{at } j = N \qquad\qquad (12\text{-}73)$$

where $n = 0, 1, 2, \ldots$ and

$$\beta_i = 1 + \frac{h_i \Delta x}{k_i}, \qquad \gamma_i \equiv \frac{f_i \Delta x}{k_i}, \qquad i = 1 \text{ or } 2$$

Finally the initial conditions (12-66d) is written as

$$T_j^0 = F(j\Delta x) \equiv F_j, \qquad j = 0, 1, 2, \ldots, N \qquad (12\text{-}74)$$

Equations (12-71) to (12-74) give the complete finite-difference representation of the heat-conduction problem (12-66). The procedure for solving these equations is as follows.

Equations (12-72) provide $(N - 1)$ algebraic equations for the $(N - 1)$ unknown nodal point temperatures $T_1^{n+1}, T_2^{n+1}, \ldots, T_{N-1}^{n+1}$. These equations are uncoupled because an explicit scheme is used; therefore each equation is calculated individually. The calculation is started with $n = 0$ and temperature $T_1^1, T_2^1, T_3^1, \ldots, T_{N-1}^1$ are determined from equations (12-72) since the temperatures on the right-hand side of these equations are now the initial temperatures that are known by equation (12-74). Knowing $T_1^1, T_2^1, \ldots, T_{N-1}^1$, the temperatures $T_1^2, T_2^2, \ldots, T_{N-1}^2$ at the end of the second time step are calculated from equations (12-72) by setting $n = 1$. The procedure is repeated to calculate temperatures at the following time steps.

The boundary surface temperatures T_0^{n+1} and T_N^{n+1} are calculated from equations (12-71) and (12-73), respectively, since the temperatures T_1^{n+1} and T_{N+1}^{n+1} are known from the solution of equations (12-72).

In the foregoing calculations once α and Δx are fixed, the size of the time step Δt is limited by the following stability criteria

$$0 < r \equiv \frac{\alpha \Delta t}{(\Delta x)^2} \leq \frac{1}{2} \tag{12-75}$$

In this example, the truncation error associated with the finite differencing of the boundary conditions using the simple forward and backward differences is of the order of (Δx). This error can be reduced to $0(\Delta x)^2$ if the central-difference approximation is used for the boundary conditions as illustrated in the following example.

Example 12-4. Write the finite-difference representation of the heat-conduction problem (12-66) using the explicit method for the differential equation and the central-differences for the boundary conditions.

Solution. As in the previous example, the (x, t) domain is divided into intervals $\Delta x, \Delta t$ such that

$$x = j\Delta x \qquad j = 0, 1, 2, \ldots, N \qquad \text{with } L = N\Delta x$$

$$t = n\Delta t \qquad n = 0, 1, 2, \ldots$$

and we consider fictitious nodal points $j = -1$ and $j = N + 1$ outside the region as illustrated in Fig. 12-8.

The finite-difference representation of the boundary conditions (12-66b)

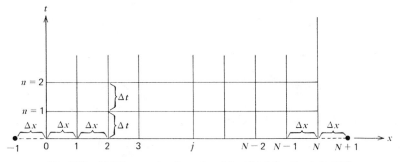

Fig. 12-8 Fictitious nodes $J = -1$ and $j = N + 1$ for Example 12-3.

and (12-66c) using the central-differences is given as [see equation (12-11)]

$$-k_1 \frac{T_1^n - T_{-1}^n}{2\Delta x} + h_1 T_0^n = f_1 \tag{12-76a}$$

$$k_2 \frac{T_{N+1}^n - T_{N-1}^n}{2\Delta x} + h_2 T_N^n = f_2 \tag{12-76b}$$

with a truncation error of the order $(\Delta x)^2$. Solving equation (12-76a) for T_{-1}^n and (12-76b) for T_{N+1}^n we obtain

$$T_{-1}^n = T_1^n + \frac{2\Delta x}{k_1}(f_1 - h_1 T_0^n) \tag{12-77a}$$

$$T_{N+1}^n = T_{N-1}^n + \frac{2\Delta x}{k_2}(f_2 - h_2 T_N^n) \tag{12-77b}$$

The finite-difference representation of heat-conduction equation (12-66a) in the *explicit* form is given, according to equation (12-49), as

$$T_j^{n+1} = r T_{j-1}^n + (1 - 2r)T_j^n + r T_{j+1}^n \qquad \begin{array}{l} j = 0, 1, 2, \ldots, N \\ n = 0, 1, 2, 3, \ldots \end{array} \tag{12-78}$$

where

$$r = \frac{\alpha \Delta t}{(\Delta x)^2}$$

with a truncation error of the order of $(\Delta t) + (\Delta x)^2$. Equations (12-78) include on the right-hand side the fictitious temperatures T_{-1}^n for $j = 0$ and T_{N+1}^n for $j = N$. These quantities are obtained from equations (12-77) and introduced into equations (12-78) for $j = 0$ and $j = N$. We summarize below the resulting equations (12-78).

$$T_0^{n+1} = (1 - 2r\beta_1)T_0^n + 2r T_1^n + 2r\gamma_1, \qquad j = 0 \tag{12-79a}$$

$$T_j^{n+1} = r T_{j-1}^n + (1 - 2r)T_j^n + r T_{j+1}^n, \qquad j = 1, 2, \ldots, N-1 \tag{12-79b}$$

$$T_N^{n+1} = 2r T_{N-1}^n + (1 - 2r\beta_2)T_N^n + 2r\gamma_2 \qquad j = N \tag{12-79c}$$

for $n = 0, 1, 2, 3, \ldots$, and where we defined

$$\beta_i \equiv 1 + \frac{h_i \Delta x}{k_i}, \qquad \gamma_i \equiv \frac{f_i \Delta x}{k_i}, \qquad i = 1 \text{ or } 2$$

Finally, the initial condition (12-66d) is written as

$$T_j^0 = F(j\Delta x) \equiv F_j, \qquad j = 0, 1, 2, \ldots, N \tag{12-80}$$

Equations (12-79) provide $(N + 1)$ algebraic equations for the determination of $(N + 1)$ nodal point temperatures $T_0^{n+1}, T_1^{n+1}, \ldots, T_N^{n+1}$. These equations are uncoupled because an explicit scheme is used. Each equation can be calculated individually. The calculations are started with $n = 0$ and the temperatures $T_0^1, T_1^1, T_2^1, \ldots, T_N^1$ are evaluated because the initial temperatures $T_0^0, T_1^0, \ldots, T_N^0$ on the right-hand side of equations (12-79) are available by equation (12-80). Knowing $T_0^1, T_1^1, \ldots, T_N^1$ the temperatures $T_0^2, T_1^2, \ldots, T_N^2$ at the end of the second time step are evaluated by setting $n = 1$ in equations (12-79). The procedure is repeated to calculate temperatures at the subsequent time steps.

Once α and Δx are fixed, the permissible size of the time step Δt is restricted by the stability criteria. In this case the solution is stable if [9, p. 69]

$$r \le \min\left(\frac{1}{1 + \beta_1} \text{ or } \frac{1}{1 + \beta_2}\right) \tag{12-81}$$

where $r \equiv \alpha \Delta t/(\Delta x)^2$ and β_1 and β_2 are as defined above. In this example the truncation error associated with the finite difference representation of the heat-conduction equation is of the order of $(\Delta t) + (\Delta x)^2$. This error can be reduced if Crank-Nicolson method is used as illustrated in the following example.

Example 12-5. Write the finite-difference representation of the heat-conduction problem (12-66) using the *Crank-Nicolson* method for the differential equation (12-66a) and the central-differences for the boundary conditions.

Solution. The (x, t) domain is divided into intervals $\Delta x, \Delta t$ such that

$$x = j\Delta x \qquad j = 0, 1, 2, \ldots, N \qquad \text{with } L = N\Delta x$$

$$t = n\Delta t \qquad n = 0, 1, 2, \ldots$$

and we consider fictitious nodal points $j = -1$ and $j = N + 1$ outside the region as illustrated in Fig. 12-8. The differential equation (12-66a) is represented in finite differences using the Crank-Nicolson method, according to equation (12-58), as

$$\frac{T_j^{n+1} - T_j^n}{\Delta t} = \frac{\alpha}{2}\left[\frac{T_{j-1}^{n+1} - 2T_j^{n+1} + T_{j+1}^{n+1}}{(\Delta x)^2} + \frac{T_{j-1}^n - 2T_j^n + T_{j+1}^n}{(\Delta x)^2}\right],$$

$$j = 0, 1, 2, \ldots, N \tag{12-82}$$

with a truncation error of the order of $(\Delta t)^2 + (\Delta x)^2$. This equation is rearranged in the form

$$-rT_{j-1}^{n+1} + (2 + 2r)T_j^{n+1} - rT_{j+1}^{n+1} = rT_{j-1}^n + (2 - 2r)T_j^n + rT_{j+1}^n \tag{12-83}$$

where $r \equiv \alpha \Delta t/(\Delta x)^2$ and $j = 0, 1, 2, \ldots, N$. The finite-difference form of the boundary conditions (12-66b) and (12-66c) using the central differences is obtained immediately from equation (12-77a) and (12-77b), respectively, as

$$T_{-1}^n = T_1^n + \frac{2\Delta x}{k_1}(f_1 - h_1 T_0^n) \tag{12-84b}$$

$$T_{N+1}^n = T_{N-1}^n + \frac{2\Delta x}{k_2}(f_2 - h_2 T_N^n) \tag{12-84b}$$

with a truncation error of the order of $(\Delta x)^2$. The initial condition (12-66d) is written as

$$T_j^0 = F(j\Delta x) \equiv F_j, \qquad j = 0, 1, 2, \ldots, N \tag{12-85}$$

Equations (12-83) to (12-85) give the complete finite-difference representation of the heat-conduction problem (12-66) with the Crank-Nicolson method. We note that equations (12-83) include the fictitious temperatures T_{-1}^n, T_{-1}^{n+1} for $j = 0$ and T_{N+1}^n, T_{N+1}^{n+1} for $j = N$. These quantities are obtained from equations (12-84) and introduced into equations (12-83). Then, the equations (12-83) take the form

$$(2 + 2r\beta_1)T_0^{n+1} - 2rT_1^{n+1} = (2 - 2r\beta_1)T_0^n + 2rT_1^n + 4r\gamma_1, \quad \text{for } j = 0 \tag{12-86a}$$

$$-rT_{j-1}^{n+1} + (2 + 2r)T_j^{n+1} - rT_{j+1}^{n+1} = rT_{j-1}^n + (2 - 2r)T_j^n + rT_j^n$$
$$\text{for } j = 1, 2, \ldots, N - 1 \tag{12-86b}$$

$$-2rT_{N-1}^{n+1} + (2 + 2r\beta_2)T_N^{n+1} = 2rT_{N-1}^n + (2 - 2r\beta_2)T_N^n + 4r\gamma_2,$$
$$\text{for } j = N \tag{12-86c}$$

where

$$\beta_i \equiv 1 + \frac{h_i\Delta x}{k_i}, \qquad \gamma_i \equiv \frac{f_i\Delta x}{k_i}, \qquad i = 1 \text{ or } 2 \qquad \text{and} \qquad n = 0, 1, 2, 3, \ldots$$

Equations (12-86) are written in the matrix form as

$$
\begin{bmatrix}
(2+2r\beta_1) & -2r & 0 & 0 \cdots & 0 & 0 & 0 \\
-r & (2+2r) & -r & 0 \cdots & 0 & 0 & 0 \\
0 & -r & (2+2r) & -r \cdots & 0 & 0 & 0 \\
\vdots & & & & & & \vdots \\
0 & 0 & 0 & 0 \cdots -r & (2+2r) & -r \\
0 & 0 & 0 & 0 \cdots & 0 & -2r & (2+2r\beta_2)
\end{bmatrix}
\begin{bmatrix}
T_0^{n+1} \\
T_1^{n+1} \\
T_2^{n+1} \\
\vdots \\
T_{N-1}^{n+1} \\
T_N^{n+1}
\end{bmatrix}
$$

$$
=
\begin{bmatrix}
(2-2r\beta_1) & 2r & 0 & 0 \cdots 0 \cdots & 0 & 0 \\
r & (2-2r) & r & 0 & 0 & 0 & 0 \\
0 & r & (2-2r) & r & 0 & 0 & 0 \\
\vdots & & & & & & \vdots \\
0 & 0 & 0 & 0 \cdots r & (2-2r) & r \\
0 & 0 & 0 & 0 \cdots 0 & 2r & (2-2r\beta_2)
\end{bmatrix}
\begin{bmatrix}
T_0^n \\
T_1^n \\
T_2^n \\
\vdots \\
T_{N-1}^n \\
T_N^n
\end{bmatrix}
+
\begin{bmatrix}
4r\gamma_1 \\
0 \\
0 \\
\vdots \\
0 \\
4r\gamma_2
\end{bmatrix}
$$

$$\tag{12-87}$$

Equations (12-86) or (12-87) are $(N + 1)$ simultaneous algebraic equations for the $(N + 1)$ unknown temperatures $T_0^{n+1}, \ldots, T_N^{n+1}$ at the time level $(n + 1)$ in terms of the $(N + 1)$ known temperatures $T_0^n, \ldots, T_N^n$ of the previous time level n. Clearly, in the Crank-Nicolson method, $(N + 1)$ algebraic equations are to be solved simultaneously for each time step Δt. The calculations are started with $n = 0$. The system (12-87) becomes $(N + 1)$ simultaneous equations for the unknown temperatures $T_0^1, \ldots, T_N^1$ in terms of the known initial temperatures $T_0^0, \ldots, T_N^0$. Once $T_0^1, \ldots, T_N^1$ are known, we set $n = 1$ and the temperature $T_0^2, \ldots, T_N^2$ are evaluated. Knowing $T_0^2, \ldots, T_N^2$, we set $n = 2$ to evaluate $T_0^3, \ldots, T_N^3$. The procedure is repeated to calculate the temperatures for the subsequent time levels.

12-7 FINITE DIFFERENCE IN CYLINDRICAL AND SPHERICAL COORDINATE SYSTEMS

In this section we present a discussion of the finite-difference representation of the heat-conduction equation in the cylindrical and spherical coordinate systems. The basic approach is essentially similar to the one discussed in connection with finite differencing in the rectangular coordinate system.

Cylindrical Coordinate System

We consider the two-dimensional steady-state heat-conduction equation in the form

$$\frac{\partial^2 T}{\partial r^2} + \frac{1}{r}\frac{\partial T}{\partial r} + \frac{1}{r^2}\frac{\partial^2 T}{\partial \phi^2} + \frac{1}{k}g(r, \phi) = 0 \qquad \text{in region } R \qquad (12\text{-}88)$$

We interlace the region with a cylindrical (r, ϕ) network as shown in Fig. 12-9, and represent the coordinates (r, ϕ) of a point P at a node by

$$r = i\Delta r \qquad \text{and} \qquad \phi = j\Delta\phi \qquad (12\text{-}89a)$$

where i and j are integers. Then, the temperature $T(r, \phi)$ and the generation rate $g(r, \phi)$ at a point P are denoted by

$$T(r, \phi)\big|_P = T(i\Delta r, j\Delta\phi) \equiv T_{i,j} \qquad (12\text{-}89b)$$

$$g(r, \phi)\big|_P = g(i\Delta r, j\Delta\phi) \equiv g_{i,j} \qquad (12\text{-}89c)$$

For nonzero values of r, the finite-difference forms of various partial derivatives in equation (12-88) are readily determined by a Taylor series expansion as discussed in Section 12-1. Then, the finite-difference expressions for the derivatives $\partial^2 T/\partial r^2$ and $\partial^2 T/\partial \phi^2$ in central differences are

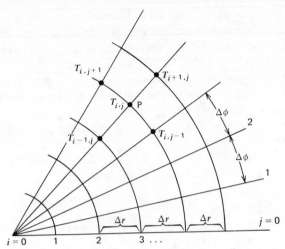

Fig. 12-9 An (r, ϕ) network in the cylindrical coordinate system.

immediately obtained from equation (12-18) as

$$\left.\frac{\partial^2 T}{\partial r^2}\right|_P = \left.\frac{\partial^2 T}{\partial r^2}\right|_{i,j} = \frac{T_{i-1,j} - 2T_{i,j} + T_{i+1,j}}{(\Delta r)^2} + 0(\Delta r)^2 \qquad (12\text{-}90a)$$

$$\left.\frac{\partial^2 T}{\partial \phi^2}\right|_P = \left.\frac{\partial^2 T}{\partial \phi^2}\right|_{i,j} = \frac{T_{i,j-1} - 2T_{i,j} + T_{i,j+1}}{(\Delta \phi)^2} + 0(\Delta \phi)^2 \qquad (12\text{-}90b)$$

Also using the central differences, $\partial T/\partial r$ is given, according to equation (12-11), as

$$\left.\frac{\partial T}{\partial r}\right|_P = \left.\frac{\partial T}{\partial r}\right|_{i,j} = \frac{T_{i+1,j} - T_{i-1,j}}{2\Delta r} + 0(\Delta r)^2 \qquad (12\text{-}90c)$$

Introducing equations (12-90) into equation (12-18) and setting $r = i\Delta r$ and $g(r, \phi)|_{i,j} = g_{i,j}$, we obtain

$$\frac{T_{i-1,j} - 2T_{i,j} + T_{i,j+1}}{(\Delta r)^2} + \frac{1}{i\Delta r} \cdot \frac{T_{i+1,j} - T_{i-1,j}}{2\Delta r}$$

$$+ \frac{1}{i^2(\Delta r)^2}(T_{i,j-1} - 2T_{i,j} + T_{i,j+1}) + \frac{1}{k}g_{i,j} = 0 \qquad (12\text{-}91)$$

After rearranging we find

$$\frac{1}{(\Delta r)^2}\left[\left(1 - \frac{1}{2i}\right)T_{i-1,j} - 2T_{i,j} + \left(1 + \frac{1}{2i}\right)T_{i+1,j}\right]$$

$$+ \frac{1}{i^2(\Delta r\Delta\phi)^2}(T_{i,j-1} - 2T_{i,j} + T_{i,j+1}) + \frac{1}{k}g_{i,j} = 0 \qquad (12\text{-}92)$$

where i, j are integers. Equation (12-92) is the finite-difference form of the heat-conduction equation (12-88) for nonzero values of r.

At the origin, $r = 0$, difficulty arises, because equation (12-88) appears to have singularities. To deal with this situation, the Laplacian operator in the cylindrical coordinate system is replaced by its Cartesian equivalent so that equation (12-88) takes the form

$$\frac{\partial^2 T}{\partial x^2} + \frac{\partial^2 T}{\partial y^2} + \frac{1}{k}g = 0 \qquad \text{as} \quad r \to 0 \qquad (12\text{-}93a)$$

We construct a circle of radius Δr, center at $r = 0$. Let T_0 be the temperature at $r = 0$ and T_1, T_2, T_3, T_4 be the temperatures at the four nodes this circle intersects the x and y axes. Then the finite difference form of this equation about $r = 0$ becomes

$$\frac{T_1 + T_2 + T_3 + T_4 - 4T_0}{(\Delta r)^2} + \frac{1}{k}g_0 = 0 \qquad (12\text{-}93b)$$

with a truncation error of the order of $(\Delta r)^2$. The rotation of the $0x$ and $0y$ axes about $r = 0$ also leads to a similar difference equation. If we now denote $\bar{T}_1$ as the arithmetic mean of the temperatures around the circle of radius Δr_1 then equation (12-93b) becomes

$$4\frac{\bar{T}_1 - T_0}{(\Delta r)^2} + \frac{1}{k}g_0 = 0 \qquad \text{at} \qquad r = 0 \qquad (12\text{-}94)$$

where $\bar{T}_1$ is the arithmetic mean of the values of $T_{1,j}$ around the circle of radius Δr with center at $r = 0$, T_0 is the value of temperature at $r = 0$. Equation (12-94) is the finite difference form of the heat-conduction equation (12-88) at $r = 0$.

The extension of the above finite-difference procedure to the three-dimensional (r, ϕ, z) heat-conduction equation in the cylindrical coordinates is straightforward.

If the above two-dimensional heat-conduction problem possesses cylindrical symmetry, equation (12-88) reduces to

$$\frac{d^2 T}{dr^2} + \frac{1}{r}\frac{dT}{dr} + \frac{1}{k}g(r) = 0 \qquad (12\text{-}95a)$$

The finite difference form of this equation, for nonzero values of r, is immediately obtainable from equation (12-92) as

$$\frac{1}{(\Delta r)^2}\left[\left(1 - \frac{1}{2i}\right)T_{i-1} - 2T_i + \left(1 + \frac{1}{2i}\right)T_{i+1}\right] + \frac{1}{k}g_i = 0 \qquad (12\text{-}95b)$$

where $r = i\Delta r$, $T(r) = T(i\Delta r) \equiv T_i$ and i is positive integer.

At the center, $r = 0$, we have

$$\lim_{r \to 0} \left(\frac{1}{r} \frac{dT}{dr} \right) = \frac{d^2 T}{dr^2}$$

by L'Hospital's rule. Then, equation (12-95a) takes the form

$$2 \frac{d^2 T}{dr^2} + \frac{1}{k} g = 0 \qquad \text{at} \qquad r = 0 \qquad (12\text{-}95c)$$

and its finite difference form becomes

$$4 \frac{T_1 - T_0}{(\Delta r)^2} + \frac{1}{k} g_0 = 0 \qquad \text{at} \qquad i = 0 \qquad (12\text{-}95d)$$

Example 12-6. Write the finite-difference representation of the heat-conduction equation

$$\frac{\partial^2 T}{\partial r^2} + \frac{1}{r} \frac{\partial T}{\partial r} + \frac{\partial^2 T}{\partial z^2} + \frac{1}{k} g(r, z) = 0 \qquad (12\text{-}96)$$

Also consider the situation at the origin, $r = 0$.

Solution. We construct a finite-difference net of rectangular mesh $(\Delta r, \Delta z)$ in the (r, z) domain over the region. Then the coordinates (r, z) are represented by

$$r = i\Delta r, \qquad z = k\Delta z$$

where $i, k = $ integers and the temperature $T(r, z)$ at a node (i, k) is denoted by

$$T(r, z) = T(i\Delta r, k\Delta z) \equiv T_{i,k}$$

Various derivatives in equation (12-96) at a node (i, k) are represented in the finite-difference form using the *central* difference formula as

$$\left. \frac{\partial^2 T}{\partial r^2} \right|_{i,k} = \frac{T_{i-1,k} - 2T_{i,k} + T_{i+1,k}}{(\Delta r)^2} + 0(\Delta r)^2 \qquad (12\text{-}97a)$$

$$\left. \frac{\partial^2 T}{\partial z^2} \right|_{i,k} = \frac{T_{i,k-1} - 2T_{i,k} + T_{i,k+1}}{(\Delta z)^2} + 0(\Delta z)^2 \qquad (12\text{-}97b)$$

$$\left. \frac{\partial T}{\partial r} \right|_{i,k} = \frac{T_{i+1,k} - T_{i-1,k}}{2\Delta r} + 0(\Delta r)^2 \qquad (12\text{-}97c)$$

Introducing equations (12-97) into equation (12-96) we obtain

$$\frac{1}{(\Delta r)^2}\left[\left(1-\frac{1}{2i}\right)T_{i-1,k} - 2T_{i,k} + \left(1+\frac{1}{2i}\right)T_{i+1,k}\right]$$
$$+\frac{1}{(\Delta z)^2}(T_{i,k-1} - 2T_{i,k} + T_{i,k+1}) + \frac{1}{k}g_{i,k} = 0 \qquad (12\text{-}98)$$

which is the finite-difference form of the heat-conduction equation (12-96) at the node (i,k) for nonzero values of r.

For $r=0$, we have

$$\lim_{r\to 0}\left(\frac{1}{r}\frac{\partial T}{\partial r}\right) = \frac{\partial^2 T}{\partial r^2} \qquad (12\text{-}99)$$

Then the heat-conduction equation (12-96) at the location $r=0$ takes the form

$$2\frac{\partial^2 T}{\partial r^2} + \frac{\partial^2 T}{\partial z^2} + \frac{1}{k}g(r,z) = 0 \qquad \text{at} \qquad r = 0 \qquad (12\text{-}100)$$

and its finite-difference form at the node $(0,k)$ becomes

$$4\frac{T_{1,k} - T_{0,k}}{(\Delta r)^2} + \frac{T_{0,k-1} - 2T_{0,k} + T_{0,k+1}}{(\Delta z)^2} + g_{0,k} = 0 \qquad (12\text{-}101)$$

Node (i,j) at the Intersection of a Convection and an Insulated Boundary

We now consider the finite-difference representation of the heat-conduction equation

$$\frac{\partial^2 T}{\partial r^2} + \frac{1}{r}\frac{\partial T}{\partial r} + \frac{1}{r^2}\frac{\partial^2 T}{\partial \phi^2} + \frac{1}{k}g(r,\phi) = 0 \qquad (12\text{-}102)$$

for a node (i,j), which is located at the intersection of a convection boundary and an insulated boundary as illustrated in Fig. 12-10. In this figure the region is interlaced with an (r,ϕ) network of mesh size $(\Delta r, \Delta\phi)$, such that the coordinates (r,ϕ) of a node are given by

$$r = i\Delta r \qquad \text{and} \qquad \phi = j\Delta\phi$$

and the temperature $T(r,\phi)$ is denoted by $T_{i,j}$. The two boundary conditions at the surfaces intersecting at the node (i,j) are given as

$$k_1\frac{\partial T}{\partial r} + h_1 T = h_1 T_\infty \qquad \text{at } r = i\Delta r \qquad (12\text{-}103a)$$

$$\frac{\partial T}{\partial \phi} = 0 \qquad \text{at } \phi = j\Delta\phi \qquad (12\text{-}103b)$$

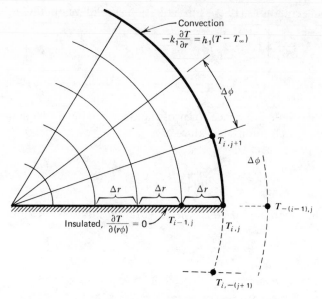

Fig. 12-10 Node (i, j) at the intersection of a convection and an insulated boundaries in the cylindrical coordinate system.

We now imagine that there are two additional fictitious nodes surrounding the node (i, j) at distances Δr and $\Delta \phi$ at temperatures $T_{-(i-1),j}$ and $T_{i,-(j+1)}$, respectively, as illustrated in Fig. 12-10. The finite-difference form of the heat-conduction equation (12-102) at the node (i, j) in terms of temperatures at this node and its neighboring four nodes is immediately written according to equation (12-92) as

$$\frac{1}{(\Delta r)^2}\left[\left(1 - \frac{1}{2i}\right)T_{i-1,j} - 2T_{i,j} + \left(1 + \frac{1}{2i}\right)T_{-(i-1),j}\right]$$

$$+ \frac{1}{i^2(\Delta r\Delta\phi)^2}(T_{i,-(j+1)} - 2T_{i,j} + T_{i,(j+1)}) + \frac{1}{k}g_{i,j} = 0 \qquad (12\text{-}104)$$

This equation contains fictitious temperatures $T_{-(i-1),j}$ and $T_{i,-(j+1)}$, which can be eliminated by means of the boundary conditions as now described.

The finite-difference form of the boundary condition (12-103a) gives

$$k_1 \frac{T_{-(i-1),j} - T_{(i-1),j}}{2\Delta r} + h_1 T_{i,j} = h_1 T_\infty$$

or

$$T_{-(i-1),j} = T_{(i-1),j} - \frac{2h_1\Delta r}{k_1}T_{i,j} + \frac{2h_1\Delta r}{k_1}T_\infty \qquad (12\text{-}105a)$$

and the boundary condition (12-103b) yields

$$\frac{T_{i,(j+1)} - T_{i,-(j+1)}}{2\Delta\phi} = 0 \quad \text{or} \quad T_{i,-(j+1)} = T_{i,(j+1)} \quad (12\text{-}105\text{b})$$

Introducing equations (12-105) into equation (12-104) to eliminate the fictitious temperatures $T_{-(i-1),j}$ and $T_{i,-(j+1)}$, we obtain the finite-difference form of the heat-conduction equation (12-102) as

$$\frac{2}{(\Delta r)^2}[T_{(i-1),j} - T_{i,j}] + \frac{2h_1}{k_1 \Delta r}\left(1 + \frac{1}{2i}\right)(T_\infty - T_{i,j})$$

$$+ \frac{2}{i^2(\Delta r \Delta\phi)^2}[T_{i,(j+1)} - T_{i,j}] + \frac{1}{k}g_{i,j} = 0 \quad (12\text{-}106)$$

Clearly, the nodes located at the boundary surfaces subjected to different types of boundary conditions can be handled in a similar manner.

Spherical Coordinate System

The partial derivatives with respect to the space variable appearing in the heat-conduction equation in the spherical coordinate system are represented in finite difference by a procedure similar to those described above for the cylindrical coordinates. If the problem involves (r, ϕ, θ) variables, a three-dimensional network of mesh size $(\Delta r, \Delta\phi, \Delta\theta)$ is considered and each partial derivative is represented in finite differences.

For the simplest case of steady-state heat-conduction involving r variable only, we consider the heat-conduction equation as

$$\frac{d^2 T(r)}{dr^2} + \frac{2}{r}\frac{dT(r)}{dr} + \frac{1}{k}g(r) = 0 \quad (12\text{-}107)$$

A network of mesh size Δr is constructed over the region and the temperature $T(r)$ is represented by $T(r) = T(i\Delta r) = T_i$, where (i) is integer. The finite-difference form of the derivatives $\partial^2 T/\partial r^2$ and $\partial T/\partial r$ are immediately obtainable from equations (12-90a) and (12-90c), respectively, with appropriate change in the notation. Then, the finite-difference form of equation (12-107), for $r \neq 0$, becomes

$$\frac{1}{(\Delta r)^2}\left[\left(1 - \frac{1}{i}\right)T_{i-1} - 2T_i + \left(1 + \frac{1}{i}\right)T_{i+1}\right] + \frac{1}{k}g_i = 0, \quad i = 1, 2, 3, \dots$$

$$(12\text{-}108)$$

We now consider the situation when the node (i) is at the origin, $r = 0$, where

$$\lim_{r \to 0} \left(\frac{2}{r} \frac{dT}{dr} \right) = 2 \frac{d^2 T}{dr^2} \tag{12-109}$$

Then the heat-conduction equation (12-107) takes the form

$$3 \frac{d^2 T}{dr^2} + \frac{1}{k} g(r) = 0 \qquad \text{at } r = 0 \tag{12-110a}$$

and its finite-difference form is taken as

$$6 \frac{T_1 - T_0}{(\Delta r)^2} + \frac{1}{k} g_0 = 0 \qquad \text{at } r = 0 \tag{12-110b}$$

where T_0 is the temperature at the origin $(r = 0)$ and T_1 is the temperature at a distance Δr away from the origin.

In the case of a three-dimensional heat-conduction equation in the spherical coordinate system we have

$$\nabla^2 T(r, \theta, \phi) + \frac{1}{k} g(r, \theta, \phi) = 0 \tag{12-111a}$$

where ∇^2 is the three-dimensional Laplacian operator in the spherical coordinate system. The finite-difference representation of this equation using a network of mesh size $(\Delta r, \Delta \phi, \Delta \theta)$ is straightforward. However a difficulty may arise for $r = 0$. In this case, the spherical Laplacian operator ∇^2 at $r = 0$ is replaced by its Cartesian equivalent and the heat-conduction equation takes the form

$$\frac{\partial^2 T}{\partial x^2} + \frac{\partial^2 T}{\partial y^2} + \frac{\partial^2 T}{\partial z^2} + \frac{1}{k} g = 0 \qquad \text{as } r \to 0 \tag{12-111b}$$

We construct a circle of radius Δr, center at $r = 0$. Let T_0 be the temperature at $r = 0$, at $T_i, i = 1$ to 6 be the temperatures at the six nodes this circle intersects the x, y, and z axes. Then, the finite-difference form of this equation at $r = 0$ becomes

$$\frac{\sum_{i=1}^{8} T_i - 6 T_0}{(\Delta r)^2} + \frac{1}{k} g_0 = 0 \qquad \text{at } r = 0 \tag{12-111c}$$

which can be approximated by

$$6 \frac{\bar{T}_1 - T_0}{(\Delta r)^2} + \frac{1}{k} g_0 = 0 \qquad \text{at } r = 0 \tag{12-111d}$$

where $\bar{T}_1$ is the arithmetic mean values of temperatures around the sphere of radius Δr with center at $r = 0$ and T_0 is the value of temperature at $r = 0$.

12-8 VARIABLE THERMAL PROPERTIES

In many engineering problems the thermal properties of the material vary with temperature. If the temperature differences are large or thermal properties vary with temperature rapidly, the temperature dependence must be included in the equation. In the rectangular coordinate system, for example, the heat-conduction equation takes the form

$$\frac{\partial}{\partial x}\left(k\frac{\partial T}{\partial x}\right) + \frac{\partial}{\partial y}\left(k\frac{\partial T}{\partial y}\right) + \frac{\partial}{\partial z}\left(k\frac{\partial T}{\partial z}\right) + g = \rho C_p \frac{\partial T}{\partial t} \qquad (12\text{-}112)$$

To solve this problem with finite-differences, the region is interlaced with a network of mesh size $(\Delta x, \Delta y, \Delta z)$ such that

$$i = i\Delta x, \qquad y = j\Delta y, \qquad z = k\Delta z$$

where i, j, and k are positive integers and the time domain is divided into small steps Δt such that

$$t = n\Delta t$$

Then the temperature at any location (x, y, z) at any time (t) is represented by

$$T(x, y, z, t) = T(i\Delta x, j\Delta y, k\Delta z, n\Delta t) = T_{i,j,k}^n \qquad (12\text{-}113)$$

If, for example, an *implicit* scheme is used, the finite-difference representation of equation (12-112) is given as

$$(\rho c)_{i,j,k} \frac{T_{i,j,k}^{n+1} - T_{i,j,k}^n}{\Delta t}$$

$$= \frac{k_{i-1/2,j,k}\left[T_{i-1,j,k}^{n+1} - T_{i,j,k}^{n+1}\right] - k_{i+1/2,j,k}\left[T_{i,j,k}^{n+1} - T_{i+1,j,k}^{n+1}\right]}{(\Delta x)^2}$$

$$+ \frac{k_{i,j-1/2,k}\left[T_{i,j-1,k}^{n+1} - T_{i,j,k}^{n+1}\right] - k_{i,j+1/2,k}\left[T_{i,j,k}^{n+1} - T_{i,j+1,k}^{n+1}\right]}{(\Delta y)^2}$$

$$+ \frac{k_{i,j,k-1/2}\left[T_{i,j,k-1}^{n+1} - T_{i,j,k}^{n+1}\right] - k_{i,j,k+1/2}\left[T_{i,j,k}^{n+1} - T_{i,j,k+1}^{n+1}\right]}{(\Delta z)^2} + g_{i,j,k}^{n+1/2}$$

$$(12\text{-}114)$$

Here, the subscript $(i - \frac{1}{2})$ for the thermal conductivity denotes a mean value between the nodes $(i - 1)$ and (i); similarly $(i + \frac{1}{2})$ refers to a mean value between the nodes (i) and $(i + 1)$, and so forth. The superscript $(n + \frac{1}{2})$ for the generation term denotes that $g_{i,j,k}$ is evaluated at a time $[n\Delta t + (\Delta t/2)]$ in order to get an average value of heat generation at a time step Δt.

Equation (12-14) can be written more compactly if both sides are multiplied by $(\Delta x, \Delta y, \Delta z)$ and a subscript p is used to denote a node whose coordinates are (i, j, k).

$$C_p \frac{T_p^{n+1} - T_p^n}{\Delta t} = G_p^{n+(1/2)} + \sum_m K_{pm}(T_m^{n+1} - T_p^{n+1}) \qquad (12\text{-}115)$$

where $p = $ nodal point (i, j, k)

$m = $ nodes neighbouring to the node p

$C_p = \rho c \Delta x \Delta y \Delta z = $ heat capacity of the cell at the node p

$G_p = g_p \Delta x \Delta y \Delta z$

$K_{pm} = \dfrac{A_{pm} k_{pm}}{l_{pm}} = $ mean conductance of the heat flow path pm

$A_{pm} = $ interface area between the cells p and m

$l_{pm} = $ distance between the nodes p and m

$k_{pm} = $ thermal conductivity of the material in the path l_{pm}

The convection boundary condition, the contact resistance and even the radiation from the surface can be accounted for in the formula (12-115) by proper interpretation of K_{pm} as described below.

If the surface A_s of the cell p is subjected to *convection* with a heat transfer coefficient h_s, K_{pm} is defined as

$$\frac{1}{K_{pm}} = \frac{1}{h_s A_s} + \frac{1}{K_{ps}} \qquad (12\text{-}116a)$$

where K_{ps} is the conductance of the heat flow path between the node p and surface A_s.

If there is a *contact resistance* between the cells p and m across the contacting surface A_s, K_{pm} is evaluated as

$$\frac{1}{K_{pm}} = \frac{1}{K_{ps}} + \frac{1}{A_s h_c} + \frac{1}{K_{sm}} \qquad (12\text{-}116b)$$

where h_c is the contact conductance, K_{ps} and K_{sm} are the conductances of the paths from the node p to surface A_s and from surface A_s to the node m.

The steady-state formula is obtainable from equation (12-115) by setting $T_p^{n+1} = T_p^n$ on the left-hand side.

The system defined by equations (12-115) provides N simultaneous algebraic equations for the determination of N unknown temperatures T^{n+1} for each time step Δt if there are $p = 1, 2, \dots, N$ nodes in the region. An iterative method of solution of this system by extrapolated Liebman method has been discussed in reference [52].

Numerous computer codes have been developed for the solution of two- and three-dimensional, steady, and time-dependent heat-conduction problems. For example, a generalized explicit form transient-heat-transfer computer program titled NATA (Numerical Analysis for Thermal Applications) is reported in reference [53]. A generalized heat-conduction code to solve steady and transient three-dimensional heat-conduction problems with variable thermal properties and allowing up to 950 nodes is presented in reference [54]. A two-dimensional steady-state program to solve plane and axially symmetric problems allowing up to 5000 points is given in reference [41]. A heat-conduction code to solve two- and three-dimensional problems, utilizing an implicit scheme, and allowing up to 1200 mesh points is discussed in reference [52]. A two-dimensional, time-dependent heat-conduction computer code is given in reference [55]. A two-dimensional, nonsteady heat-conduction code for heterogeneous, anisotropic solids, using the explicit method is discussed in reference [56]. A three-time level implicit scheme for the numerical solution of multidimensional heat-conduction equation with variable properties has been presented in reference [57].

12-9 CURVED BOUNDARIES

When a region has a curved boundary, it is possible that the curved boundary intersects the finite-difference network at points that are not the mesh nodes. Then the finite-difference formulae derived in the previous sections are not applicable to represent the second derivatives at a node near the boundary. Therefore, the purpose of this section is to illustrate the procedure for the finite-difference representation of second-order derivative at a node near a curved boundary. For this purpose we consider the heat-conduction equation given as

$$\frac{\partial^2 T}{\partial x^2} + \frac{\partial^2 T}{\partial y^2} = 0 \quad \text{in region } R \qquad (12\text{-}117)$$

and assume that the boundaries of the region are subjected to *prescribed temperature* boundary condition. Suppose a $(\Delta x, \Delta y)$ network is constructed over the region, and we wish to write the finite difference form of this equation at the nodes (N, j) and (N, M) as illustrated in Figs. 12-11a and b, respectively. The procedure for this finite-differencing is as now described.

Boundary Intersects One String

Figure 12-11a shows a situation in which only one of the strings from the node (N, j) is intersected by the curved boundary. Let T_B be the prescribed temperature of the boundary at the point B where the boundary intersects

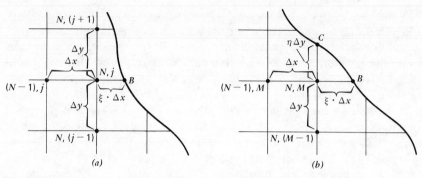

Fig. 12-11 (a) One string intersected by the curved boundary; (b) Two strings intersected by the curved boundary.

the string. The distance $(\xi\Delta x)$ between the nodes (N,j) and B, where $\xi \leq 1$, is less than the mesh size Δx. By a Taylor series expansion in powers of $(\xi\Delta x)$ and $(-\Delta x)$ we, respectively, obtain

$$T_B = T_{N,j} + (\xi\Delta x)\frac{\partial T}{\partial x}\bigg|_{N,j} + \frac{(\xi\Delta x)^2}{2!}\frac{\partial^2 T}{\partial x^2}\bigg|_{N,j} + 0(\Delta x)^3 \quad (12\text{-}118a)$$

$$T_{N-1,j} = T_{N,j} - \Delta x \cdot \frac{\partial T}{\partial x}\bigg|_{N,j} + \frac{(\Delta x)^2}{2!}\frac{\partial^2 T}{\partial x^2}\bigg|_{N,j} + 0(\Delta x)^3 \quad (12\text{-}118b)$$

Eliminating $[\partial T/\partial x]_{N,j}$ between these two relations, we obtain

$$\frac{\partial^2 T}{\partial x^2}\bigg|_{N,j} = \frac{2}{(\Delta x)^2}\left[\frac{T_B}{\xi(1+\xi)} + \frac{T_{N-1,j}}{1+\xi} - \frac{T_{N,j}}{\xi}\right] \quad (12\text{-}119)$$

The finite-difference representation of $[\partial^2 T/\partial y^2]_{N,j}$ using the central differences is obtainable from equation (11-28b) as

$$\frac{\partial^2 T}{\partial y^2}\bigg|_{N,j} = \frac{T_{N,j-1} - 2T_{N,j} + T_{N,j+1}}{(\Delta y)^2} \quad (12\text{-}120)$$

Substituting equations (12-119) and (12-120) into equation (12-117) we obtain

$$\left[\frac{\partial^2 T}{\partial x^2} + \frac{\partial^2 T}{\partial y^2}\right]_{N,j} = \frac{2}{(\Delta x)^2}\left[\frac{T_B}{\xi(1+\xi)} + \frac{T_{N-1,j}}{1+\xi} - \frac{T_{N,j}}{\xi}\right]$$
$$+ \frac{1}{(\Delta y)^2}[T_{N,j-1} - 2T_{N,j} + T_{N,j+1}] = 0, \quad 0 \leq \xi \leq 1 \quad (12\text{-}121)$$

which is the finite-difference form of the heat-conduction equation (12-117) at the node (N,j) next to a curved boundary as illustrated in Fig. 12-11a. We note that for $\xi = 1$ equation (12-121) reduces to the standard form discussed previously.

If $\partial^2 T/\partial x^2$ is eliminated between equations (12-118a, b) we obtain the finite-difference representation of $\partial T/\partial x$ at the node (N, j) as

$$\frac{\partial T}{\partial x}\bigg|_{N,j} = \frac{1}{\Delta x}\left[\frac{T_B}{\xi(1+\xi)} - \frac{\xi}{1+\xi}T_{N-1,j} - \frac{1-\xi}{\xi}T_{N,j}\right] \quad (12\text{-}122)$$

with an error of the order of $(\Delta x)^2$.

Boundary Intersects Two Strings

Figure 12-11b illustrates a situation in which two of the strings from the node (N, M) is intersected by the curved boundary. Let T_B and T_C be the prescribed temperatures at points B and C, respectively on the boundary, $(\xi\Delta x)$ be the distance between the points (N, M) and B, and $(\eta\Delta y)$ be the distance between the points (N, M) and C, and $\xi, \eta < 1$. By a Taylor series expansion in powers of $(\xi\Delta x)$ and $(\eta\Delta y)$ we, respectively, obtain

$$T_B = T_{N,M} + (\xi\Delta x)\frac{\partial T}{\partial x}\bigg|_{N,M} + \frac{(\xi\Delta x)^2}{2!}\frac{\partial^2 T}{\partial x^2}\bigg|_{N,M} + 0(\Delta x)^3 \quad (12\text{-}123a)$$

$$T_C = T_{N,M} + (\eta\Delta y)\frac{\partial T}{\partial x}\bigg|_{N,M} + \frac{(\eta\Delta y)^2}{2!}\frac{\partial^2 T}{\partial y^2}\bigg|_{N,M} + 0(\Delta y)^3 \quad (12\text{-}123b)$$

where $0 \le \xi \le 1$ and $0 \le \eta \le 1$. Also, by a Taylor series expansion in powers of $(-\Delta x)$ and $(-\Delta y)$ we have

$$T_{N-1,M} = T_{N,M} - \Delta x\frac{\partial T}{\partial x}\bigg|_{N,M} + \frac{(\Delta x)^2}{2!}\frac{\partial^2 T}{\partial x^2}\bigg|_{N,M} + 0(\Delta x)^3 \quad (12\text{-}124a)$$

$$T_{N,M-1} = T_{N,M} - \Delta y\frac{\partial T}{\partial y}\bigg|_{N,M} + \frac{(\Delta y)^2}{2!}\frac{\partial^2 T}{\partial y^2}\bigg|_{N,M} + 0(\Delta y)^3 \quad (12\text{-}124b)$$

Eliminating $\dfrac{\partial T}{\partial x}\bigg|_{M,N}$ and $\dfrac{\partial T}{\partial y}\bigg|_{M,N}$ among equations (12-123) and (12-124) we obtain the finite-difference representation for $\partial^2 T/\partial x^2$ and $\partial^2 T/\partial y^2$ at the node (N, M). Then, the finite-difference form of the heat-conduction equation (12-117) at the node (N, M) becomes

$$\left[\frac{\partial^2 T}{\partial x^2} + \frac{\partial^2 T}{\partial y^2}\right]_{N,M} = \frac{2}{(\Delta x)^2}\left[\frac{T_B}{\xi(1+\xi)} + \frac{T_{N-1,M}}{1+\xi} - \frac{T_{N,M}}{\xi}\right]$$

$$+ \frac{2}{(\Delta y)^2}\left[\frac{T_C}{\eta(1+\eta)} + \frac{T_{N,M-1}}{1+\eta} - \frac{T_{N,M}}{\eta}\right] = 0, \quad 0 \le \xi, \eta \le 1$$

$$(12\text{-}125)$$

For a square network, $\Delta x = \Delta y = h$, equation (12-125) reduces to

$$\left[\frac{\partial^2 T}{\partial x^2} + \frac{\partial^2 T}{\partial y^2}\right]_{N,M} = \frac{2}{h^2}\left[\frac{T_B}{\xi(1+\xi)} + \frac{T_C}{\eta(1+\eta)} + \frac{T_{N-1,M}}{1+\xi}\right.$$

$$\left. + \frac{T_{N,M-1}}{1+\eta} - \left(\frac{1}{\xi}+\frac{1}{\eta}\right)T_{N,M}\right] = 0, \qquad (12\text{-}126)$$

with an error of the order of h.

The finite-difference representation of $\partial T/\partial y$ at the node (N, M) is obtainable from equations (12-123b) and (12-124b) by eliminating $\partial^2 T/\partial y^2$. We find

$$\left.\frac{\partial T}{\partial y}\right|_{N,M} = \frac{1}{\Delta y}\left[\frac{T_C}{\eta(1+\eta)} - \frac{\eta}{1+\eta}T_{N,M-1} - \frac{1-\eta}{\eta}T_{N,M}\right] \qquad (12\text{-}127)$$

with an error of the order of $(\Delta y)^2$.

REFERENCES

1. R. V. Southwell, *Relaxation Methods in Engineering Science*, Oxford University Press, London, 1940.

2. J. Crank and P. Nicolson, *Proc. Camb. Phil. Soc.* **43**, 50–67, 1947.

3. G. G. O'Brien, M. A. Hyman, and S. Kaplan, *J. Math. Phys.* **29**, 223–251, 1951.

4. D. W. Peaceman and H. H. Rachford, *J. Soc. Indust. Appl. Math*, **3**, 28–41, 1955.

5. R. D. Richtmeyer and K. W. Morton, *Difference Methods for Initial Value Problems*, 2nd ed., Interscience Publishers, Inc., New York, 1965.

6. G. E. Forsythe and W. R. Wasov, *Finite Difference Methods for Partial Differential Equations*, John Wiley, New York, 1960.

7. G. M. Dusinberre, *Heat Transfer Calculations by Finite Differences*, International Textbook Company, Scranton, Pa., 1961.

8. L. Fox, *Numerical Solution of Ordinary and Partial Differential Equations*, Addison-Wesley Publishing Company, Inc., Reading, Mass., 1962.

9. G. D. Smith, *Numerical Solution of Partial Differential Equations with Exercises and Worked Solutions*, Oxford University Press, London, 1965.

10. J. K. Reid, ed., *Large Sparse Sets of Linear Equations*, Academic Press, New York, 1971.

11. D. J. Rose and R. A. Willoughby, eds., *Sparce Matrices and Their Applications*, Plenum Press, New York, 1972.

12. B. K. Larkin, *Chem. Eng. Prg. Sym. Ser.* **61**, 59, 1965.

13. S. R. Allada and D. Quon, *Heat Transfer Los Angeles, Chemical Engineering Progress Symposium Series* **62**, No. 64, 151–156, 1966.

14. J. H. Wilkinson and C. Reinsch, *Handbook for Automatic Computation, Vol. 2: Linear Algebra*, Springer-Verlag, New York, 1971.

15. G. J. Trezek and J. G. Witwer, *J. Heat Transfer* **94c**, 321–323, 1972.

16. G. Dahlquist and A. Björck, *Numerical Methods*, N. Anderson, trans., Prentice-Hall, Inc., Englewood Cliffs, New Jersey, 1974.

17. R. W. Hornbeck, *Numerical Methods*, Quantum Publishers, Inc., New York, 1975.

18. A. K. Aziz, ed., *Numerical Solutions of Boundary Value Problems for Ordinary Differential Equations*, Academic Press, Inc., New York, 1975.

19. G. E. Scneider, A. B. Strong, and M. M. Yavanovich, A Physical Approach to the Finite Difference Solution of the Conduction Equation in Orthogonal Curvilinear Coordinates, ASME paper No. 75-WA/HT-94, 1975.

20. N. D'Souza, Numerical Solution of One-Dimensional Inverse Transient Heat Conduction by Finite-Difference Method, ASME paper No. 75-WA/HT-81, 1975.

21. M. L. James, G. M. Smith, and J. C. Wolford, *Applied Numerical Methods for Digital Computation*, IEP-Dun-Donnelley Publisher, New York, 1977.

22. J. M. Hammersley and D. C. Handscomb, *Monte Carlo Method*, Methuen and Co., Ltd., London, 1964.

23. L. W. Ehrlich, *J. Assoc. Comp. Mach.* **6**, 204–218, 1959.

24. N. P. Buslenko, D. I. Golenko, Y. A. Shreider, I. M. Sobol' and V. G. Sragovich, *Monte Carlo Method*, by G. J. Tee, transl. Pergamon Press, New York, 1966, pp. 35–47.

25. A Haji-Sheikh and E. M. Sparrow, The Solution of Heat Conduction Problems by Probability Methods, ASME Paper No. 66-WA/HT-1.

26. A. Haji-Sheikh, Application of Monte Carlo Methods to Thermal Conduction Problems, Ph.D. Thesis, Mechanical Engineering, University of Minnesota, Minneapolis, Minn., December 1965.

27. J. H. Curtis, Sampling Methods Applied to Differential and Difference Equations, *Proceedings of IBM Seminar on Scientific Computation*, November 1949; International Business Machines Corporation, New York (1950), pp. 87–109.

28. R. E. Nickel and E. Wilson, *Nucl. Eng. Des.* **4**, 276–286, 1966.

29. G. A. Ramirez and J. T. Oden, Finite-Element Technique Applied to Heat Conduction in Solids with Temperature Dependent Thermal Conductivity, ASME paper No. 69-WA/HT-34, 1969.

30. A. F. Emery and W. W. Carson, Evaluation of Use of the Finite Element Method in Computation of Temperature, ASME paper No. 69-WA/HT-38, 1969.

31. E. F. Rybicki and A. T. Hopper, Higher Order Finite Element Method for Transient Temperature Analysis of Inhomogeneous Problems, ASME paper No. 69-WA/HT-33, 1969.

32. O. C. Zienkiewicz and I. K. Cheung, *The Finite Element Method in Engineering Science*, McGraw-Hill Book Company, New York, 1971.

33. O. Ural, *Finite Element Method: Basic Concepts and Applications*, International Textbook Company, Scranton, Pa., 1973.

34. H. C. Martin and G. F. Carey, *Introduction to Finite-Element Analysis*, McGraw-Hill Book Co., New York, 1973.

35. K. H. Huebner, *Finite Element Method for Engineers*, John Wiley & Sons, Inc., New York, 1975.

36. I. S. Berezin and N. P. Zhidkov, *Computing Methods*, Vol. 1, Addison-Wesley Publishing Co., Inc., Reading, Mass., 1965, pp. 210–215.

37. S. P. Frankel, *Math. Tables Aids Comput.* **4**, 65–75, 1950.

38. D. M. Young, *Trans. Am. Math. Soc.* **76**, 92–111, 1954.

39. W. F. Ames, *Nonlinear Partial Differential Equations in Engineering*, Academic Press, New York, 1965, Chapter 7.

40. G. G. O'Brian, M. A. Hyman, and S. Kaplan, *J. Math. Phys.* **29**, 223–251, 1951.

41. R. B. Smith and J. Spainer, *Hot-1: A Two-Dimensional Steady-State Heat Conduction Program for the Philco-2000*, WAPD-TM-465, July 1964, Bettis Atomic Power Laboratory, West Mifflin, Pa.

42. J. Douglas, Jr., in *Advances in Computers*, F. L. Alt., ed., Vol. 2, Academic Press, New York, 1961, p. 1.

43. R. S. Varga, *Matrix Iterative Analysis*, Prentice-Hall, Englewood Cliffs, N.J., 1962.

44. J. R. Westlake, *A Handbook of Numerical Matrix Inversion and Solution of Linear Equations*, John Wiley & Sons, New York, 1968.

45. A. R. Mitchell, *Computational Methods in Partial Differential Equations*, John Wiley & Sons Ltd., London, 1976.

46. V. K. Saul'ev, *Dokl. Akad. Nauk SSSR* **115** (6), 1077, 1957; **117** (1), 36, 1957.

47. B. K. Larkin, *Math. Comp.* **18** (86), 196, 1964.

48. J. Douglas and H. H. Rachford, *Trans. Am. Math. Soc.* **82**, 421–439, 1956.

49. P. L. T. Brian, *AIChEJ.* **7**, 367–370, 1961.

50. Y. G. D'Yakonov, *Z. Vycisl. Mati. Mat. Fiz.* **3**, 385–388, 1963.

51. H. Z. Barakat and J. A. Clark, *J. Heat Transfer* **88c**, 421–427, 1966.

52. R. F. Thomas and M. D. J. MacRoberts, *RATH Thermal Analysis Program*, LA-3264-MS, UC-32 Mathematics and Computers, Los Alamos Scientific Laboratory, Los Alamos, New Mexico, 1965.

53. K. W. Lallier and B. R. Pagnani, *A Three Dimensional Heat Transfer Computer Program for Aerospace Applications*, IBM No. 63-825-862-A, I.B.M. Federal Systems Division, Oswego, N.Y.

54. T. B. Fowler and E. R. Volk, *Generalized Heat Conduction Code for the IBM-704 Computer*, ORNL-2734, Oak Ridge National Laboratory, Oak Ridge, Tennessee, 1959.

55. J. A. McClure, *A Two-Dimensional, Time-Dependent Heat Conduction Program*, IDO-17227, Phillips Petroleum Co., Idaho Operations Office, Idaho, 1967.

56. J. A. Fillo, J. Powell, and R. Benenati, A Nonsteady Heat Conduction Code with Radiation Boundary Conditions, ASME paper No. 75-WA/HT-91, 1975.

57. C. Bonacina and G. Comini, *Int. J. Heat Mass Transfer* **16**, 581–589, 1973.

PROBLEMS

12-1 Using a Taylor's series expansion show that a forward difference representation of df/dx, which is accurate to the order of $O(h^3)$ is given in subscript notation as

$$f_i' = \frac{2f_{i+3} - 9f_{i+2} + 18f_{i+1} - 11f_i}{6h} + O(h^3)$$

12-2 Consider the function $f(x) = 2e^x$. Using a mesh size $\Delta x \equiv h = 0.1$ determine $f'(x)$ at $x = 2$ with the *forward* formulae (12-22a) accurate to $O(h)$ and the *central* difference formula accurate to $O(h)^2$ and compare the results with the exact value.

12-3 Write the finite-difference form of the heat-conduction equation

$$\frac{\partial^2 T}{\partial x^2} + \frac{\partial^2 T}{\partial y^2} + \frac{1}{k} g(x, y) = 0$$

for the twelve nodes, $i = 1, 2, \ldots, 12$, subject to the boundary conditions shown in the accompanying figure. Here, the temperatures f_1, f_2, and f_3 are prescribed.

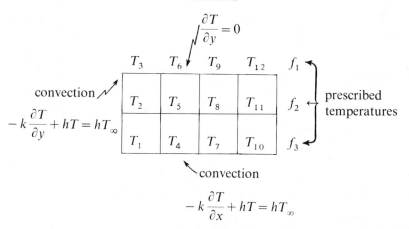

insulated

$$\left. \frac{\partial T}{\partial y} \right| = 0$$

T_3 T_6 T_9 T_{12} f_1

convection

$$-k\frac{\partial T}{\partial y} + hT = hT_\infty$$

T_2 T_5 T_8 T_{11} f_2 prescribed temperatures

T_1 T_4 T_7 T_{10} f_3

convection

$$-k\frac{\partial T}{\partial x} + hT = hT_\infty$$

12-4 Solve the following set of algebraic equations by the Gauss elimination method.

$$T_1 + 3T_2 + T_3 = 10$$
$$2T_1 - 2T_2 + 3T_3 + T_4 = 11$$
$$+ 4T_2 - 2T_3 - T_4 = -2$$
$$+ 4T_3 + 2T_4 = 20$$

12-5 Solve the following steady-state heat-conduction equation by finite differences using mesh sizes $\Delta x = \Delta y = 0.25$ and 0.1; compare the center temperature with the exact solution.

$$\frac{\partial^2 T}{\partial x^2} + \frac{\partial^2 T}{\partial y^2} = 0 \qquad \text{in } 0 < x < 1, \ 0 < y < 1$$

$$T = 0 \qquad \text{at } x = 0, \ x = 1$$

$$\frac{\partial T}{\partial y} = 0 \qquad \text{at } y = 0$$

$$T = \sin \pi x \qquad \text{at } y = 1$$

12-6 Consider the two-dimensional, time-dependent heat-conduction equation given in the form

$$\frac{\partial^2 T}{\partial x^2} + \frac{\partial^2 T}{\partial y^2} = \frac{1}{\alpha} \frac{\partial T}{\partial t}$$

Let the temperature $T(x, y, t)$ be represented by

$$T(x, y, t) = T(j\Delta x, k\Delta y, n\Delta t) \equiv T_{j,k}^n$$

Write the finite-difference representation of this heat-conduction equation for an internal node (j, k) using (1) an explicit method, (2) an implicit method, and (3) the Crank-Nicolson method.

12-7 By assuming that an error term can be represented in the form

$$E_{j,k,n} = e^{\gamma t} \cdot e^{i(\beta_1 x + \beta_2 y)}$$

where $t = n\Delta t$, $x = j\Delta x$, $y = k\Delta y$, show that in the Problem 12-6, the explicit finite-difference representation is stable if

$$\alpha\Delta t \left(\frac{1}{(\Delta x)^2} + \frac{1}{(\Delta y)^2} \right) \leq \frac{1}{2}$$

12-8 Consider the following heat-conduction problem for a solid cylinder

$$\frac{\partial^2 T}{\partial r^2} + \frac{1}{r}\frac{\partial T}{\partial r} + \frac{1}{k}g(r) = \frac{1}{\alpha}\frac{\partial T}{\partial t} \qquad \text{in } 0 \leq r < b, \ t > 0$$

$$T = 0 \qquad\qquad\qquad \text{at } r = b, \ t > 0$$

$$T = F(r) \qquad\qquad\quad \text{in } 0 \leq r \leq b, \ t = 0$$

Let the temperature $T(r, t)$ be represented by

$$T(r, t) = T(j\Delta r, n\Delta t) \equiv T_j^n$$

with $j = 0$ representing $r = 0$ and $j = N$ representing $r = b$. Write the finite-difference representation of this heat-conduction problem using (1) the explicit method and (2) the implicit method.

12-9 Repeat the Problem 12-8 for a solid sphere of radius $r = b$.

12-10 Consider the heat-conduction equation in the cylindrical coordinates gives as

$$\frac{\partial^2 T}{\partial r^2} + \frac{1}{r}\frac{\partial T}{\partial r} + \frac{1}{r^2}\frac{\partial^2 T}{\partial \phi^2} + \frac{1}{k}g(r, \phi) = \frac{1}{\alpha}\frac{\partial T}{\partial t}$$

and let the temperature $T(r, \phi, t)$ be represented by

$$T(r, \phi, t) = T(i\Delta r, j\Delta\phi, n\Delta t) \equiv T_{i,j}^n$$

Write the finite difference form of this heat-conduction equation for a node (i, j) using (1) the explicit scheme and (2) the implicit scheme.

12-11 Consider the heat-conduction equation given as

$$\frac{\partial^2 T}{\partial r^2} + \frac{1}{r}\frac{\partial T}{\partial r} + \frac{\partial^2 T}{\partial z^2} + \frac{1}{k}g(r, z) = \frac{1}{\alpha}\frac{\partial T}{\partial t}$$

where $T(r, z, t)$ is represented by

$$T(r, z, t) = T(i\Delta r, k\Delta z, n\Delta t) \equiv T_{i,k}^n$$

Write the finite difference form of this heat conduction equation for a node (i, k) using the Crank-Nicolson method.

12-12 Consider the following heat-conduction equation

$$\frac{\partial}{\partial x}\left(k \frac{\partial T}{\partial x}\right) + g(x, t) = \rho C_p \frac{\partial T}{\partial t}$$

where $T(x, t)$ is represented by

$$T(x, t) = T(j\Delta x, n\Delta r) \equiv T_j^n$$

Write the finite difference form of this heat-conduction equation for a node (j) using (1) the explicit method and (2) the implicit method.

12-13 Consider the finite-difference form of the heat-conduction equation $\partial^2 T / \partial x^2 = (1/\alpha)(\partial T / \partial t)$ given in the form [see equation (12-59)]

$$\frac{T_j^{n+1} - T_j^n}{\Delta t} = \alpha \left[\eta \, \frac{T_{j-1}^{n+1} - 2T_j^{n+1} + T_{j+1}^{n+1}}{(\Delta x)^2} + (1 - \eta)\frac{T_{j-1}^n - 2T_j^n + T_{j+1}^n}{(\Delta x)^2} \right]$$

Using the Fourier Series method show that for $\frac{1}{2} \leq \eta \leq 1$ the solution is unconditionally stable and for $0 \leq \eta \leq \frac{1}{2}$ it is stable if

$$r = \frac{\alpha \Delta t}{(\Delta x)^2} \leq \frac{1}{2(1 - 2\eta)}.$$

12-14 Consider the following, one-dimensional heat-conduction problem in the dimensionless form

$$\frac{\partial^2 T}{\partial x^2} = \frac{\partial T}{\partial t} \qquad \text{in } 0 < x < 1, \ t > 0$$

$$T = 0 \qquad \text{at } x = 0, \ x = 1 \text{ for } t < 0$$

$$T = \sin \pi x \qquad \text{for } t = 0, \text{ in } 0 \leq x \leq 1$$

Solve this problem with finite differences using an explicit scheme by taking $\Delta x = 0.1$ and $r = \Delta t/(\Delta x)^2 = 0.1$. Compare the results with the exact solution at time $t = 0.01$ at the locations $x = 0.1$ and 0.2.

12-15 Solve the Problem 12-14 using the Crank-Nicolson method.

CHAPTER 13

INTEGRAL-TRANSFORM TECHNIQUE

The solution of partial differential equations of heat conduction by the classical method of separation of variables is not always convenient when the equation and the boundary conditions involve nonhomogeneities. It is for this reason that we considered the Green's function approach for the solution of linear, nonhomogeneous boundary-value problems of heat conduction. The *integral transform technique* provides a systematic, efficient, and straightforward approach for the solution of both homogeneous and nonhomogeneous, steady and time-dependent boundary-value problems of heat conduction. In this method the second partial derivatives with respect to the space variables are generally removed from the partial differential equation of heat conduction by the application of the integral transformation. For example, in time-dependent problems, the partial derivatives with respect to the space variables are removed and the partial differential equation is reduced to a first-order ordinary differential equation in the time variable for the transform of the temperature. The ordinary differential equation is solved subject to the transformed initial condition, and the result is inverted successively to obtain the solution for the temperature. The inversion process is straightforward, because the inversion formulas are available at the onset of the problem. The procedure is also applicable to the solution of steady-state heat-conduction problems involving more than one space variable. In such cases the partial differential equation of heat conduction is reduced to an ordinary differential equation in one of the space variables. The resulting ordinary differential equation for the transformed temperature is solved, and the solution is inverted to obtain the temperature distribution.

The integral transform technique derives its basis from the classical method of separation of variables. That is, the integral transform pairs needed for the solution of a given problem are developed by considering the representation of an arbitrary function in terms of the eigenfunctions of the corresponding eigenvalue problem. Therefore, the eigenfunctions, eigenvalues, and the normalization integrals developed in Chapters 2 to 4 for the solution of homogeneous problems will be utilized for the construction of the integral transform pairs.

The fundamental theory of the integral-transform technique is given in several texts [1-3] and a summary of various transform pairs and transform tables are presented in various references [4-8]. The literature on the use of the integral-transform technique for the solution of heat-conduction problems is evergrowing. The reader should consult references [9-23] for the general solution of three-dimensional problems of finite regions. Its applications for the solution of specific heat-conduction problems in the rectangular [24, 25], cylindrical [26-29], and spherical [30] coordinate systems are also given. Some useful convolution properties of integral transforms are discussed in references [31-34].

In this chapter a general method of analysis of three-dimensional, time-dependent heat-conduction problems of finite region by the integral transform technique is presented first. Its applications for the solution of problems of finite, semi-infinite, and infinite regions in the rectangular, cylindrical, and spherical coordinate systems are then presented systematically.

13-1 THE USE OF INTEGRAL TRANSFORM IN THE SOLUTION OF HEAT-CONDUCTION PROBLEMS IN FINITE REGIONS

In this section we present the use of the integral-transform technique in the solution of three-dimensional, time-dependent, nonhomogeneous boundary-value problems of heat conduction with constant coefficients in finite regions. We consider the following heat-conduction problem

$$\nabla^2 T(\mathbf{r}, t) + \frac{1}{k} g(\mathbf{r}, t) = \frac{1}{\alpha} \frac{\partial T(\mathbf{r}, t)}{\partial t} \qquad \text{in region } R, \ t > 0 \qquad (13\text{-}1a)$$

$$k_i \frac{\partial T(\mathbf{r}_i, t)}{\partial n_i} + h_i T(\mathbf{r}_i, t) = f_i(\mathbf{r}_i, t) \qquad \text{on boundary } S_i, \ t > 0 \qquad (13\text{-}1b)$$

$$T(\mathbf{r}, t) = F(\mathbf{r}) \qquad \text{for } t = 0, \text{ in region } R \qquad (13\text{-}1c)$$

where, $i = 1, 2, \ldots, s$ and s is the number of continuous boundary surfaces of the region R(i.e., $s = 1$ for a semi-infinite medium, $s = 2$ for a slab, $s = 4$ for a rectangular region, etc.); $\partial/\partial n_i$ denotes the normal derivative at the boundary surface S_i in the *outward* direction; h_i and k_i are the boundary-condition coefficients at the boundary surface S_i; k is the thermal conductivity; α is the thermal diffusivity; $f_i(\mathbf{r}_i, t)$ is a specified boundary condition function;

$F(\mathbf{r})$ is a specified initial condition function; and $g(\mathbf{r}, t)$ is the heat-generation term.

The basic steps in the solution of this problem by the integral-transform technique can be summarized as

1. Appropriate integral transform pair is developed.
2. By the application of integral transformation, the partial derivatives with respect to the space variables are removed from the heat-conduction equation, thus reducing it to an ordinary differential equation for the transform of temperature.
3. The resulting ordinary differential equation is solved subject to the transformed initial condition. When the transform of the temperature is inverted by the inversion formula the desired solution is obtained. The procedure is now described in detail.

1. Development of Integral-Transform Pair

The integral transform pair needed for the solution of the above heat-conduction problem can be developed by considering the following eigenvalue problem

$$\nabla^2 \psi(\mathbf{r}) + \lambda^2 \psi(\mathbf{r}) = 0 \qquad \text{in region } R \qquad (13\text{-}2a)$$

$$k_i \frac{\partial \psi(\mathbf{r}_i)}{\partial n_i} + h_i \psi(\mathbf{r}_i) = 0 \qquad \text{on boundary } S_i \qquad (13\text{-}2b)$$

$i = 1, 2, \ldots, s$, and $k_i, h_i, \partial/\partial n_i$ are as defined previously. We note that this eigenvalue problem is obtainable by the separation of the homogeneous version of the heat-conduction problem (13-1).

The eigenfunctions $\psi(\lambda_m, \mathbf{r})$ of this eigenvalue problem satisfy the following orthogonality condition (see Note 1 for a proof of this orthogonality relation)

$$\int_R \psi(\lambda_m, \mathbf{r}) \psi(\lambda_n, \mathbf{r}) \, dv = \begin{cases} 0 & \text{for } m \neq n \\ N(\lambda_m) & \text{for } m = n \end{cases} \qquad (13\text{-}3a)$$

where the *normalization integral* $N(\lambda_m)$ is defined as

$$N(\lambda_m) = \int_R [\psi(\lambda_m, \mathbf{r})]^2 \, dv \qquad (13\text{-}3b)$$

We now consider the representation of a function $T(\mathbf{r}, t)$, defined in the finite region R, in terms of the eigenfunctions $\psi(\lambda_m, \mathbf{r})$ in the form

$$T(\mathbf{r}, t) = \sum_{m=1}^{\infty} C_m(t) \psi(\lambda_m, \mathbf{r}) \qquad \text{in } R \qquad (13\text{-}4)$$

where the summation is taken over all discrete spectrum of eigenvalues λ_m.

To determine the unknown coefficients we operate on both sides of equation (13-4) by the operator

$$\int_R \psi(\lambda_n, \mathbf{r}) \, dv$$

[that is, multiply by $\psi(\lambda_n, \mathbf{r})$ and integrate over the region R] then utilize the orthogonality relation (13-3) to obtain

$$C_m(t) = \frac{1}{N(\lambda_m)} \int_R \psi(\lambda_m, \mathbf{r}) T(\mathbf{r}, t) \, dv \qquad (13\text{-}5)$$

This expression is introduced into equation (13-4) and the resulting representation is split up into two parts to define the *integral-transform pair* in the space variable $\mathbf{r}$ for the function $T(\mathbf{r}, t)$ as

$$\text{Inversion formula:} \qquad T(\mathbf{r}, t) = \sum_m \frac{\psi(\lambda_m, \mathbf{r})}{N(\lambda_m)} \bar{T}(\lambda_m, t) \qquad (13\text{-}6\text{a})$$

$$\text{Integral transform:} \qquad \bar{T}(\lambda_m, t) = \int_R \psi(\lambda_m, \mathbf{r}') T(\mathbf{r}', t) \, dv' \qquad (13\text{-}6\text{b})$$

where $\bar{T}(\lambda_m, t)$ is called the integral transform of the function $T(\mathbf{r}, t)$ with respect to the space variable $\mathbf{r}$. It is to be noted that in the above formal representation, the summation is actually a triple, a double, or a single summation; and the integral is a volume, a surface, or a line integral for the three-, two-, or one-dimensional regions, respectively. Similarly, the eigenfunctions $\psi(\lambda_m, \mathbf{r})$ and the normalization integral $N(\lambda_m)$ are composed of the products of one-dimensional eigenfunctions and normalization integrals, respectively. Furthermore, the analysis being formal, we did not use the Sturm-Liouville weighting function (i.e., 1 for the rectangular, r for the cylindrical coordinates, etc.) in these expressions. These matters will be illustrated with examples later in this chapter.

2. Integral Transform of Heat Conduction Problem

Having established the appropriate integral-transform pair as given above, the next step in the analysis is the removal of the partial derivatives with respect to the space variables from the differential equation (13-1a) by the application of the integral transform (13-6b). That is, both sides of equation (13-1a) is multiplied by $\psi_m(\mathbf{r})$ and integrated over the region R

$$\int_R \psi_m(\mathbf{r}) \nabla^2 T(\mathbf{r}, t) \, dv + \frac{1}{k} \int_R \psi_m(\mathbf{r}) g(\mathbf{r}, t) \, dv = \frac{1}{\alpha} \frac{\partial}{\partial t} \int_R \psi_m(\mathbf{r}) T(\mathbf{r}, t) \, dv \qquad (13\text{-}7)$$

where $\psi_m(\mathbf{r}) \equiv \psi(\lambda_m, \mathbf{r})$. By utilizing the definition of the integral transform

(13-6b), this expression is written as

$$\int_R \psi_m(\mathbf{r})\nabla^2 T(\mathbf{r},t)\,dv + \frac{1}{k}\bar{g}(\lambda_m,t) = \frac{1}{\alpha}\frac{d\bar{T}(\lambda_m,t)}{dt} \tag{13-8}$$

where $\bar{g}(\lambda_m,t)$ and $\bar{T}(\lambda_m,t)$ are the integral transforms of the function $g(\mathbf{r},t)$ and $T(\mathbf{r},t)$, respectively, defined as

$$\bar{g}(\lambda_m,t) = \int_R \psi_m(\mathbf{r})g(\mathbf{r},t)\,dv \tag{13-9a}$$

$$\bar{T}(\lambda_m,t) = \int_R \psi_m(\mathbf{r})T(\mathbf{r},t)\,dv \tag{13-9b}$$

The integral on the left-hand side of equation (13-8) can be evaluated by making use of the Green's theorem expressed as [see Note 2 in Chapter 6]

$$\int_R \psi_m(\mathbf{r})\nabla^2 T(\mathbf{r},t)\,dv = \int_R T\nabla^2\psi_m(\mathbf{r})\,dv + \sum_{i=1}^{s}\int_{S_i}\left(\psi_m\frac{\partial T}{\partial n_i} - T\frac{\partial\psi_m}{\partial n_i}\right)ds_i' \tag{13-10}$$

where $i = 1, 2, \ldots, s$ and s is the number of continuous boundary surfaces of the region R. Various terms on the right-hand side of equation (13-10) are evaluated as now described.

The integral $\int_R T\nabla^2\psi_m\,dv$ is evaluated by writing equation (13-2a) for the eigenfunction $\psi_m(\mathbf{r})$, multiplying both sides by $T(\mathbf{r},t)$, integrating over the region R and utilizing the definition of the integral transform. We find

$$\int_R T\nabla^2\psi_m\,dv = -\lambda_m^2\int_R T\psi_m\,dv = -\lambda_m^2\bar{T}(\lambda_m,t) \tag{13-11a}$$

The surface integral in equation (13-10) is evaluated by making use of the boundary conditions (13-1b) and (13-2b). That is, equation (13-1b) is multiplied by $\psi_m(\mathbf{r})$, equation (13-2b) is multiplied by $T(\mathbf{r},t)$ and the results are subtracted; we obtain

$$\psi_m\frac{\partial T}{\partial n_i} - T\frac{\partial\psi_m}{\partial n_i} = \frac{\psi_m(\mathbf{r}_i)}{k_i}f_i(\mathbf{r}_i,t) \tag{13-11b}$$

Equations (13-11) are introduced into equation (13-10)

$$\int_R \psi_m(\mathbf{r})\nabla^2 T(\mathbf{r},t)\,dv = -\lambda_m^2\bar{T}_m(t) + \sum_{i=1}^{s}\int_{S_i}\frac{\psi_m(\mathbf{r}_i')}{k_i}f_i(\mathbf{r}_i',t)\,ds_i' \tag{13-12}$$

Substituting equation (13-12) into (13-8) we obtain

$$\frac{d\bar{T}(\lambda_m,t)}{dt} + \alpha\lambda_m^2\bar{T}(\lambda_m,t) = A(\lambda_m,t) \qquad \text{for } t > 0 \tag{13-13a}$$

where

$$A(\lambda_m,t) \equiv \frac{\alpha}{k}\bar{g}(\lambda_m,t) + \alpha\sum_{i=1}^{s}\int_{S_i}\frac{\psi_m(\mathbf{r}_i')}{k_i}f_i(\mathbf{r}',t)\,ds_i' \tag{13-13b}$$

Thus by the application of the integral-transform technique, we removed from the heat-conduction equation (13-1a) all the partial derivatives with respect to the space variables and reduced it to a first-order ordinary differential equation (13-13a) for the integral transform $\bar{T}(\lambda_m, t)$ of the temperature. In the process of integral transformation, we utilized the boundary conditions (13-1b); therefore the boundary conditions for the problem are incorporated in this result.

The integral transform of the initial condition (13-1c) becomes

$$\bar{T}(\lambda_m, t) = \int_R \psi_m(\mathbf{r}) F(\mathbf{r}) \, dv \equiv \bar{F}(\lambda_m) \qquad \text{for } t = 0 \qquad (13\text{-}13c)$$

3. Solution for Transform and Inversion

The solution of equation (13-13a) subject to the initial condition (13-13c) gives the transform $\bar{T}(\lambda_m, t)$ of temperature as

$$\bar{T}(\lambda_m, t) = e^{-\alpha \lambda_m^2 t} \left[\bar{F}(\lambda_m) + \int_0^t e^{\alpha \lambda_m^2 t'} A(\lambda_m, t') \, dt' \right] \qquad (13\text{-}14)$$

Introducing this integral transform into the inversion formula (13-6a), we obtain the solution of the boundary-value problem of heat conduction, equations (13-1), in the form

$$T(\mathbf{r}, t) = \sum_{m=1}^{\infty} \frac{1}{N(\lambda_m)} e^{-\alpha \lambda_m^2 t} \psi_m(\mathbf{r}) \left[\bar{F}(\lambda_m) + \int_0^t e^{\alpha \lambda_m^2 t'} A(\lambda_m, t') \, dt' \right] \qquad (13\text{-}15a)$$

where

$$A(\lambda_m, t') \equiv \frac{\alpha}{k} \bar{g}(\lambda_m, t') + \alpha \sum_{i=1}^{s} \int_{S_i} \frac{\psi_m(\mathbf{r}_i')}{k_i} f_i(\mathbf{r}', t') \, ds_i' \qquad (13\text{-}15b)$$

$$\bar{F}(\lambda_m) \equiv \int_R \psi_m(\mathbf{r}') F(\mathbf{r}') \, dv' \qquad (13\text{-}15c)$$

$$\bar{g}(\lambda_m, t') \equiv \int_R \psi_m(\mathbf{r}') g(\mathbf{r}', t') \, dv' \qquad (13\text{-}15d)$$

$$N(\lambda_m) \equiv \int_R [\psi_m(\mathbf{r}')]^2 \, dv' \qquad (13\text{-}15e)$$

and the summation is taken over all eigenvalues.

The foregoing solution is derived formally for a boundary condition of the third kind for all boundaries. If some of the boundaries are of the second kind and some of the third kind, the general form of the solution still remains unchanged. However, some modification is needed in the term $A(\lambda_m, t')$ if the problem involves boundary condition of the first kind. Suppose the boundary condition for the surface $i = 1$ is of the first kind; this implies that the boundary-condition coefficient k_1 should be set equal to zero. This situation causes difficulty in the interpretation of the term $A(\lambda_m, t')$ given by equation (13-15b), because k_1 appears in the denominator. This difficulty can be alleviated by making the following change in equation (13-15b): When $k_1 = 0$, replace

$$\frac{\psi_m(\mathbf{r}'_1)}{k_1}$$

by

$$-\frac{1}{h_1}\frac{\partial\psi_m(\mathbf{r}'_1)}{\partial n_1} \tag{13-15f}$$

The validity of this replacement becomes apparent if we rearrange the boundary condition (13-2b) of the eigenvalue problem for $i = 1$, in the form

$$\frac{\psi_m(\mathbf{r}_1)}{k_1} = -\frac{1}{h_1}\frac{\partial\psi_m(\mathbf{r}_1)}{\partial n_1}$$

on boundary S_1.

Finally, when all boundary conditions are of the second kind, the interpretation of the general solution (13-15) requires special consideration. The reason for this, $\lambda_0 = 0$ is also an eigenvalue corresponding to the eigenfunction $\psi_0 = \text{constant} \neq 0$, for this particular case. This matter will be illustrated later in this section.

Since the foregoing analysis is formal, we did not include explicitly the Sturm-Liouville weighting function (i.e., 1 for the rectangular coordinates, r for the cylindrical coordinates, etc.) in the results. When the problem involves a Sturm-Liouville weighting function, it appears under the integral sign in the definition of the integral transform and the normalization integral as it will now be illustrated for the one-dimensional finite region.

One-Dimensional Finite Region

We now consider the one-dimensional version of the heat-conduction problem (13-1) in the space variable x_1 (i.e., x, y, z, r, etc.) for a finite region R_1. Let $\psi(\beta_m, x_1)$ be the eigenfunctions, $N(\beta_m)$ be the normalization integral, β_m the eigenvalues, and $w(x_1)$ the Sturm-Liouville weighting function of the one-dimensional version of the eigenvalues problem (13-2). As it was discussed in Note 1 of Chapter 2, the eigenfunctions $\psi(\beta_m, x_1)$ are orthogonal with respect to the weighting function $w(x_1)$; that is

$$\int_{R_1} w(x_1)\psi(\beta_m, x_1)\psi(\beta_n, x_1)\,dx_1 = \begin{cases} 0 & \text{for } \lambda_m \neq \lambda_n \\ N(\beta_m) & \text{for } \lambda_m = \lambda_n \end{cases} \tag{13-16a}$$

where

$$N(\beta_m) \equiv \int_{R_1} w(x_1)[\psi(\beta_m, x_1)]^2 \, dx_1 \qquad (13\text{-}16b)$$

Suppose we wish to represent a function $T(x_1, t)$, defined in the finite interval R_1, in terms of the eigenfunctions $\psi(\beta_m, x_1)$. Such a representation is immediately obtained by utilizing the above orthogonality condition and the result is written as

$$T(x_1, t) = \sum_{m=1}^{\infty} \frac{\psi(\beta_m, x_1)}{N(\beta_m)} \int_{R_1} w(x_1')\psi(\beta_m, x_1')T(x_1', t) \, dx_1', \qquad \text{in region } R_1$$

$$(13\text{-}16c)$$

The desired integral transform pair is constructed by splitting up this representation into two parts as

Inversion formula : $\qquad T(x_1, t) = \sum_{m=1}^{\infty} \frac{\psi(\beta_m, x_1)}{N(\beta_m)} \bar{T}(\beta_m, t) \qquad (13\text{-}17a)$

Integral transform : $\qquad \bar{T}(\beta_m, t) = \int_{R_1} w(x_1')\psi(\beta_m, x_1')T(x_1', t) \, dx_1' \quad (13\text{-}17b)$

The solution of the one-dimensional version of the heat-conduction problem (13-1) is obtained from the general solution (13-15) as

$$T(x_1, t) = \sum_{m=1}^{\infty} \frac{\psi(\beta_m, x_1)}{N(\beta_m)} e^{-\alpha\beta_m^2 t} \left[\bar{F}(\beta_m) + \int_0^t e^{\alpha\beta_m^2 t'} A(\beta_m, t') \, dt' \right] \qquad (13\text{-}18a)$$

where

$$A(\beta_m, t') = \frac{\alpha}{k}\bar{g}(\beta_m, t') + \alpha\left\{ \left[w(x_1')\frac{\psi(\beta_m, x_1')}{k_1} \right]_{S_1} f_1(t') \right.$$
$$\left. + \left[w(x_1')\frac{\psi(\beta_m, x_1')}{k_2} \right]_{S_2} f_2(t') \right\} \qquad (13\text{-}18b)$$

$$\bar{F}(\beta_m) = \int_{R_1} w(x_1')\psi(\beta_m, x_1')F(x_1') \, dx_1' \qquad (13\text{-}18c)$$

$$\bar{g}(\beta_m, t') = \int_{R_1} w(x_1')\psi(\beta_m, x_1')g(x_1', t) \, dx_1' \qquad (13\text{-}18d)$$

$$N(\beta_m) = \int_{R_1} w(x_1')[\psi(\beta_m, x_1')]^2 \, dx_1' \qquad (13\text{-}18e)$$

We note that, for the two-point boundary-value problem considered here the term $A(\beta_m, t')$ defined by equation (13-18b), contains the function $[w(x_1')\psi(\beta_m, x_1')/k_i]_{S_i}$, $i = 1$ or 2, evaluated at the two boundary points of the region R_1, instead of the function being integrated over the boundary surface as in the case of equation (13-15b) for the multidimensional problem.

If the boundary condition is of the first kind at any of the boundaries, the following adjustment should be made in equation (13-18b): when $k_i = 0$ replace

$$\frac{\psi(\beta_m, x_1')}{k_i}$$

by

$$-\frac{1}{h_i}\frac{\partial\psi(\beta_m, x_1')}{\partial n_i} \tag{13-19}$$

where $i = 1$ or 2, and $\partial/\partial n_i$ denotes derivative along the outward drawn normal to the boundary surface.

Boundary Condition of the Second Kind for All Boundaries

When the boundary conditions are all of the second kind, that is all h_i's are zero in the heat-conduction problem (13-1) for a finite region, then the eigenvalue problem (13-2) takes the form

$$\nabla^2\psi(\mathbf{r}) + \lambda^2\psi(\mathbf{r}) = 0 \qquad \text{in region } R \tag{13-20a}$$

$$\frac{\partial\psi(\mathbf{r}_i)}{\partial n_i} = 0 \qquad \text{on all boundaries } S_i \tag{13-20b}$$

For this particular case, $\lambda_0 = 0$ is also an eigenvalue corresponding to the eigenfunction $\psi_0 = \text{constant} \neq 0$. The validity of this statement can be verified by integrating equation (13-20a) over the region R, applying Green's theorem to change the volume integral to the surface integral and then utilizing the boundary conditions (13-20b). We obtain

$$\lambda^2 \int_R \psi(\mathbf{r})\,dv = -\int_R \nabla^2\psi(\mathbf{r})\,dv = -\sum_{i=1}^{s}\int_{S_i}\frac{\partial\psi}{\partial n_i}\,ds_i = 0 \tag{13-21}$$

Clearly, $\lambda_0 = 0$ is also an eigenvalue corresponding to the eigenfunction $\psi_0 = \text{constant} \neq 0$. Without loss of generality, when applying this condition to the general solution (13-15), we can set $\psi_0 = 1$; because ψ_0 will cancel out when it is introduced into the solution (13-15) for the eigenvalue $\lambda_0 = 0$. Then, the general solution (13-15) for the case of all boundary conditions are of the second kind [i.e., $\partial T/\partial n_i = (1/k_i)f_i(\mathbf{r}, t)$] on all S_i, takes the form

$$T(\mathbf{r}, t) = \frac{1}{N_0}\left[\bar{F}(\lambda_0) + \int_0^t A(\lambda_0, t')\,dt'\right]$$

$$+ \sum_{m=1}^{\infty}\frac{1}{N_m}e^{-\alpha\lambda_m^2 t}\psi(\lambda_m, \mathbf{r})\left[\bar{F}(\lambda_m) + \int_0^t e^{\alpha\lambda_m^2 t'}A(\lambda_m, t')\,dt'\right] \tag{13-22}$$

where

$$N_0 = \int_R dv' \tag{13-23a}$$

$$\bar{F}(\lambda_0) = \int_R F(\mathbf{r}') \, dv' \tag{13-23b}$$

$$A(\lambda_0, t') = \frac{\alpha}{k} \int_R g(\mathbf{r}', t') \, dv' + \alpha \sum_{i=1}^{s} \int_{S_i} \frac{f_i(\mathbf{r}', t')}{k_i} \, ds_i' \tag{13-23c}$$

and the function $A(\lambda_m, t')$, $\bar{F}(\lambda_m)$, and N_m are as defined by equations (13-15b), (13-15c), and (13-15e), respectively.

The average value of the temperature over the region R is defined as

$$T_{av}(t) = \frac{\int_R T(\mathbf{r}, t) \, dv}{\int_V dv} \tag{13-24a}$$

and the solution (13-22) is introduced into this expression. If we take into account the relations obtained from equation (13-21) as

$$\int_R \psi(\lambda_m, \mathbf{r}) \, dv = 0 \qquad \text{for } \lambda_m \neq 0 \tag{13-24b}$$

$$\int_R \psi(\lambda_0) \, dv = \int_R dv \qquad \text{since } \psi_0 = 1 \text{ for } \lambda_0 = 0 \tag{13-24c}$$

then equation (13-24a) gives

$$T_{av}(t) = \frac{\left[\bar{F}(\lambda_0) + \int_0^t A(\lambda_0, t') \, dt' \right]}{\int_R dv} \tag{13-25a}$$

This result implies that the first term in the solution (13-22) corresponding to the eigenvalue $\lambda_0 = 0$ is the average value of $T(\mathbf{r}, t)$ over the finite region R. For the special case of no heat generation and all insulated boundaries (i.e., $\partial T/\partial n_i = 0$), the quantity $A(\lambda_0, t')$ vanishes and equation (13-25a) reduces to

$$T_{av}(t) = \frac{\int_R F(\mathbf{r}') \, dv}{\int_R dv} \tag{13-25b}$$

Clearly, the expressions given by equations (13-25) are the generalization of the special cases considered in Examples 2-2 and 3-2 of problems with insulated boundaries.

13-2 ALTERNATIVE FORM OF GENERAL SOLUTION
FOR FINITE REGIONS

The general solutions given by equations (13-15) and (13-22) of the boundary-value problem of heat conduction are exact solutions; but they are not in convenient form for computation purposes especially when the boundary conditions are nonhomogeneous. The reason for this is that the series is not uniformly convergent at the boundary due to the Gibbs phenomena [35]; hence difficulty arises in the computation of temperature at the boundary. This matter was also discussed in Chapters 5 and 6 in connection with the solution of nonhomogeneous problems by Duhamel's method and Green's function approach. We recall that, for such cases, an alternative form of the solution was obtained by integrating the terms corresponding to the term $A(\lambda_m, t')$ by parts. A similar approach is now applied to equation (13-15) to obtain an alternative form.

We write the solution (13-15) in the form

$$T(\mathbf{r}, t) = \sum_{m=1}^{\infty} \frac{1}{N_m} e^{-\alpha\lambda_m^2 t} \psi_m(\mathbf{r}) [\bar{F}(\lambda_m) + J_m] \tag{13-26a}$$

where

$$J_m = \int_0^t e^{\alpha\lambda_m^2 t'} A(\lambda_m, t') \, dt' \tag{13-26b}$$

$$A(\lambda_m, t') = \frac{\alpha}{k} \bar{g}(\lambda_m, t') + \alpha \sum_{i=1}^s \int_{S_i} \frac{\psi_m(\mathbf{r}_i')}{k_i} f_i(\mathbf{r}_i', t') \, ds_i' \tag{13-26c}$$

and other quantities as defined by equations (13-15).

To obtain an alternative form of this solution we integrate the term J_m by parts as

$$J_m = \left[A(\lambda_m, t') \frac{e^{\alpha\lambda_m^2 t'}}{\alpha\lambda_m^2} \right]_0^t - \frac{1}{\alpha\lambda_m^2} \int_0^t e^{\alpha\lambda_m^2 t'} dA(\lambda_m, t')$$

$$= \frac{1}{\alpha\lambda_m^2} \left\{ [A(\lambda_m, t)e^{\alpha\lambda_m^2 t} - A(\lambda_m, 0)] - \int_0^t e^{\alpha\lambda_m^2 t'} dA(\lambda_m, t') \right\} \tag{13-27a}$$

The terms $A(\lambda_m, 0)$ and $dA(\lambda_m, t')$ are determined from equation (13-26c) as

$$A(\lambda_m, 0) = \frac{\alpha}{k} \bar{g}(\lambda_m, 0) + \alpha \sum_{i=1}^s \int_{S_i} \frac{\psi_m(\mathbf{r}_i')}{k_i} f_i(\mathbf{r}_i', 0) \, ds_i' \tag{13-27b}$$

$$dA(\lambda_m, t') = \frac{\alpha}{k} d\bar{g}(\lambda_m, t') + \alpha \sum_{i=1}^s \int_{S_i} \frac{\psi_m(\mathbf{r}_i')}{k_i} df_i(\mathbf{r}_i', t') \, ds_i' \tag{13-27c}$$

Equations (13-27) are introduced into equation (13-26a) together with the explicit form of $A(\lambda_m, t')$ given by equation (13-26c). After replacing the subscript i by j, the result is arranged as

$$T(\mathbf{r}, t) = \sum_{j=0}^{s} T_{0j}(\mathbf{r}, t) + T_h(\mathbf{r}, t) - \sum_{j=0}^{s} T_j(\mathbf{r}, t) \qquad (13\text{-}28a)$$

Here the three distinct groups of simpler solutions $T_{0j}(\mathbf{r}, t)$, $T_h(\mathbf{r}, t)$ and $T_j(\mathbf{r}, t)$ are defined as

$$T_{0j}(\mathbf{r}, t) = \sum_{m=1}^{\infty} \frac{\psi_m(\mathbf{r})}{N_m} \bar{T}_{0j}(\lambda_m, t) \qquad (13\text{-}28b)$$

where

$$\bar{T}_{0j}(\lambda_m, t) = \delta_{0j} \frac{\bar{g}(\lambda_m, t)}{k\lambda_m^2} + \delta_{ij} \frac{1}{\lambda_m^2} \int_{S_i} \frac{\psi_m(\mathbf{r}_i')}{k_i} f_i(\mathbf{r}', t) ds_i'$$

$$\bar{g}(\lambda_m, t) = \int_R \psi_m(\mathbf{r}) g(\mathbf{r}, t) dv$$

$$\delta_{ij} = \begin{cases} 1 & \text{for } i = j \\ 0 & \text{for } i \neq j \end{cases}$$

$$i = 1, 2, \dots, s \qquad \text{and} \qquad j = 0, 1, 2, \dots, s$$

$$T_j(\mathbf{r}, t) = \sum_{m=1}^{\infty} \frac{\psi_m(\mathbf{r})}{N_m} e^{-\alpha\lambda_m^2 t} \int_{t'=0}^{t} e^{\alpha\lambda_m^2 t'} \dot{\bar{T}}_{0j}(\lambda_m, t') dt', \qquad j = 0, 1, 2, \dots, s. \quad (13\text{-}28c)$$

and

$$T_h(\mathbf{r}, t) = \sum_{m=1}^{\infty} \frac{\psi_m(\mathbf{r})}{N_m} e^{-\alpha\lambda_m^2 t} \left[\bar{F}(\lambda_m) - \sum_{j=0}^{s} \bar{T}_{0j}(\lambda_m, 0) \right] \qquad (13\text{-}28d)$$

here the function $\dot{\bar{T}}_{0j}(\lambda_m, t)$ denotes the derivative of $\bar{T}_{0j}(\lambda_m, t)$ with respect to t'. The physical significance of these three simpler solutions defined by the functions $T_{0j}(\mathbf{r}, t)$, $T_h(\mathbf{r}, t)$, and $T_j(\mathbf{r}, t)$ are as follows.

The functions $T_{0j}(\mathbf{r}, t)$ are the solutions of the following quasi-steady-state problem

$$\nabla^2 T_{0j}(\mathbf{r}, t) + \delta_{0j} \frac{g(\mathbf{r}, t)}{k} = 0 \qquad \text{in region } R \qquad (13\text{-}29a)$$

$$k_i \frac{\partial T_{0j}}{\partial n_i} + h_i T_{0j}(\mathbf{r}, t) = \delta_{ij} f_i(\mathbf{r}_i, t) \qquad \text{on boundary } S_i \qquad (13\text{-}29b)$$

$$i = 1, 2, \dots, s \qquad \text{and} \qquad j = 0, 1, 2, \dots, s$$

In this pseudoproblem, the time variable enters merely as a parameter because no time derivative is involved. The function $T_{00}(\mathbf{r}, t)$ corresponds to the solution of the problem with the heat-generation term, but all boundary conditions are homogeneous. The functions $T_{01}(\mathbf{r}, t)$, $T_{02}(\mathbf{r}, t)$, ... for $j = 1, 2, \ldots$, respectively, corresponds to the solution of Problem (13-29) with no heat generation, but for each case only one of the boundary conditions, $i = j$, being nonhomogeneous. For one-dimensional problems, the functions T_{0j} are immediately obtainable by direct integration of equations (13-29); that is there is no need for integral transform technique to solve equations (13-29) for the one-dimensional case.

The function $T_h(\mathbf{r}, t)$ is the solution of the following homogeneous problem

$$\nabla^2 T_h(\mathbf{r}, t) = \frac{1}{\alpha} \frac{\partial T_h(\mathbf{r}, t)}{\partial t} \qquad \text{in region } R, \ t > 0 \qquad (13\text{-}30a)$$

$$k_i \frac{\partial T_h}{\partial n_i} + h_i T_h(\mathbf{r}, t) = 0 \qquad \text{on boundary } S_i, \ t > 0 \qquad (13\text{-}30b)$$

$$T_h(\mathbf{r}, t) = F(\mathbf{r}) - \sum_{j=0}^{s} T_{0j}(\mathbf{r}, 0) \qquad \text{for } t = 0, \ \text{in region } R \qquad (13\text{-}30c)$$

We note that this problem is the homogeneous version of the original problem (13-1), except the initial condition is now modified by subtracting from the original initial condition the solutions of problem (13-29) for $t = 0$.

Finally, the function $T_j(\mathbf{r}, t)$ is related to the solution of the following auxiliary homogeneous problem

$$\nabla^2 \theta_j(\mathbf{r}, \tau, t) = \frac{1}{\alpha} \frac{\partial \theta_j(\mathbf{r}, \tau, t)}{\partial t} \qquad \text{in region } R, \ t > 0 \qquad (13\text{-}31a)$$

$$k_i \frac{\partial \theta_j}{\partial n_i} + h_i \theta_j(\mathbf{r}, \tau, t) = 0 \qquad \text{on boundary } S_i, \ t > 0 \qquad (13\text{-}31b)$$

$$\theta_j(\mathbf{r}, \tau, t) = T_{0j}(\mathbf{r}, \tau) \qquad \text{for } t = 0, \ \text{in } R \qquad (13\text{-}31c)$$

$j = 0, 1, 2, \ldots, s$

and the relationship is given as

$$T_j(\mathbf{r}, t) = \int_{\tau=0}^{t} \frac{\partial \theta_j(\mathbf{r}, \tau', t - \tau)}{\partial \tau'} \bigg|_{\tau' = \tau} d\tau \qquad (13\text{-}32)$$

To prove the validity of equation (13-32), we consider the solution of the auxiliary problem defined by equations (13-31) given in the form

$$\theta_j(\mathbf{r}, \tau, t) = \sum_{m=1}^{\infty} \frac{\psi_m(\mathbf{r})}{N_m} e^{-\alpha \lambda_m^2 t} \bar{T}_{0j}(\lambda_m, \tau) \qquad (13\text{-}33)$$

We now construct from this solution the term

$$\left.\frac{\partial \theta_j(\mathbf{r}, \tau', t - \tau)}{\partial \tau'}\right|_{\tau'=\tau} = \sum_{m=1}^{\infty} \frac{\psi_m(\mathbf{r})}{N_m} e^{-\alpha \lambda_m^2 (t-\tau)} \dot{T}_{0j}(\lambda_m, \tau) \qquad (13\text{-}34\text{a})$$

The integration of this expression with respect to τ yields

$$\int_{\tau=0}^{t} \left.\frac{\partial \theta_j(\mathbf{r}, \tau', t - \tau)}{\partial \tau'}\right|_{\tau'=\tau} d\tau = \sum_{m=1}^{\infty} \frac{\psi_m(\mathbf{r})}{N_m} e^{-\alpha \lambda_m^2 t} \int_{\tau=0}^{t} e^{\alpha \lambda_m^2 \tau} \dot{T}_{0j}(\lambda_m, \tau) d\tau \qquad (13\text{-}34\text{b})$$

Clearly, the right-hand side of equation (13-34b) is exactly the same as the definition of the function $T_j(\mathbf{r}, t)$ given by equation (13-28c). Thus we have

$$\int_{\tau=0}^{t} \left.\frac{\partial \theta_j(\mathbf{r}, \tau', t - \tau)}{\partial \tau'}\right|_{\tau'=\tau} d\tau = T_j(\mathbf{r}, t) \qquad (13\text{-}35)$$

which proves the validity of equation (13-32).

Summary of Alternative Solutions

We now summarize the results of the foregoing analysis leading to the alternative form of solution given by equations (13-28a) as

$$T(\mathbf{r}, t) = \sum_{j=0}^{s} T_{0j}(\mathbf{r}, t) + T_h(\mathbf{r}, t) - \sum_{j=0}^{s} T_j(\mathbf{r}, t) \qquad (13\text{-}28\text{a})$$

This equation implies that the solution of the general boundary-value problem of heat conduction (13-1) is composed of the following three different classes of simpler problems:

1. The solutions of the quasi-steady-state problems (13-29) characterized by the functions $T_{0j}(\mathbf{r}, t)$.
2. The solution of the homogeneous heat-conduction problem (13-30) characterized by the function $T_h(\mathbf{r}, t)$. We note that the problem (13-30) is the homogeneous version of the original problem (13-1) except the initial condition now includes the functions $T_{0j}(\mathbf{r}, t)$.
3. The solutions characterized by the functions $T_j(\mathbf{r}, t)$ are related to the solutions $\theta_j(\mathbf{r}, \tau, t)$ of the homogeneous problem (13-31) according to the expression (13-32).

When the heat-generation function $g(\mathbf{r})$ and the boundary-condition functions $f_i(\mathbf{r})$ are *independent of time*, the solutions characterized by the functions $T_j(\mathbf{r}, t)$ vanish, because $\theta_j(\mathbf{r}, \tau, t)$ does not contain τ hence its derivative $\partial \theta_j / \partial \tau$ vanish. For this special case, the alternative solution contains only the functions $T_{0j}(\mathbf{r})$ and $T_h(\mathbf{r}, t)$; this is similar to the results given by equation (2-158) in Chapter 2.

13-3 APPLICATIONS IN THE RECTANGULAR COORDINATE SYSTEM

The general analysis developed in the previous section is now applied for the solution of time-dependent heat-conduction problems in the rectangular coordinate system. The one-dimensional cases are considered first for the finite, semi-infinite, and infinite regions. The multidimensional problems involving any combinations of the finite, semi-infinite, and infinite regions for the $x, y,$ and z directions are then handled by the successive application of the one-dimensional integral transform.

One-Dimensional Problems of Finite Region

We consider the following heat-conduction problem for a slab, $0 \le x \le L$,

$$\frac{\partial^2 T}{\partial x^2} + \frac{1}{k}g(x,t) = \frac{1}{\alpha}\frac{\partial T(x,t)}{\partial t} \qquad \text{in } 0 < x < L, \ t > 0 \qquad (13\text{-}36a)$$

$$-k_1\frac{\partial T}{\partial x} + h_1 T = f_1(t) \qquad \text{at } x = 0, \ t > 0 \qquad (13\text{-}36b)$$

$$k_2\frac{\partial T}{\partial x} + h_2 T = f_2(t) \qquad \text{at } x = L, \ t > 0 \qquad (13\text{-}36c)$$

$$T(x,t) = F(x) \qquad \text{for } t = 0, \ \text{in } 0 \le x \le L \qquad (13\text{-}36d)$$

The eigenvalue problem associated with the solution of this problem is exactly the same as that given by equations (2-32). Clearly, this eigenvalue problem is the one-dimensional version of the general eigenvalue problem (13-2). To construct the desired integral transform pair for the solution of the above heat-conduction problem, we need the representation of an arbitrary function, defined in the interval $0 \le x \le L$, in terms of the eigenfunctions of the eigenvalue problem (2-32). Such a representation has already been given by equation (2-36). Then the integral transform pair for the temperature function $T(x,t)$ with respect to the x variable is readily obtained by considering its representation in the form given by equation (2-36) and then splitting up the representation into two parts. We find

$$\text{Inversion formula:} \qquad T(x,t) = \sum_{m=1}^{\infty} \frac{X(\beta_m, x)}{N(\beta_m)} \bar{T}(\beta_m, t) \qquad (13\text{-}37a)$$

$$\text{Integral transform:} \qquad \bar{T}(\beta_m, t) = \int_{x'=0}^{L} X(\beta_m, x')T(x', t)\,dx' \qquad (13\text{-}37b)$$

where

$$N(\beta_m) \equiv \int_0^L [X(\beta_m, x)]^2\,dx \qquad (13\text{-}37c)$$

and the functions $X(\beta_m, x)$, $N(\beta_m)$, the eigenvalues β_m are obtainable from Table 2-2 for the nine different combinations of boundary conditions at $x = 0$ and $x = L$.

To solve the heat-conduction problem (13-36), we take the integral transform of equation (13-36a) by the application of the transform (13-37b). That is, we multiply both sides of equation (13-36a) by $X(\beta_m, x)$ and integrate over the region $0 \leq x \leq L$. The resulting expressions contains the term

$$\int_0^L X(\beta_m, x) \frac{\partial^2 T}{\partial x^2} \, dx$$

which is evaluated as discussed in Section 13-1 by making use of Green's theorem (or integrating it by parts twice), utilizing the eigenvalue problem (2-32), and the boundary conditions (13-36b) and (13-36c) of the above heat-conduction problem. Then, the integral transform of equation (13-36a) leads to the following ordinary differential equation for the transform $\bar{T}(\beta_m, t)$ of temperature

$$\frac{d\bar{T}(\beta_m, t)}{dt} + \alpha \beta_m^2 \bar{T}(\beta_m, t) = A(\beta_m, t) \qquad \text{for } t > 0 \qquad (13\text{-}38a)$$

$$\bar{T}(\beta_m, t) = \bar{F}(\beta_m) \qquad\qquad \text{for } t = 0 \qquad (13\text{-}38b)$$

where $\bar{F}(\beta_m)$ is the integral transform of the initial condition function $F(x)$ and $A(\beta_m, t)$ is defined below. The solution of equations (13-38) gives the transform of temperature $\bar{T}(\beta_m, t)$; when this result is inverted by the inversion formula (13-37a) the solution of the heat-conduction problem (13-36) becomes

$$T(x, t) = \sum_{m=1}^{\infty} \frac{X(\beta_m, x)}{N(\beta_m)} e^{-\alpha \beta_m^2 t} \left[\bar{F}(\beta_m) + \int_0^t e^{\alpha \beta_m^2 t'} A(\beta_m, t') dt' \right] \quad (13\text{-}39a)$$

where

$$A(\beta_m, t') = \frac{\alpha}{k} \bar{g}(\beta_m, t') + \alpha \left[\frac{X(\beta_m, x)}{k_1} \Big|_{x=0} f_1(t') + \frac{X(\beta_m, x)}{k_2} \Big|_{x=L} f_2(t') \right] \quad (13\text{-}39b)$$

$$\bar{F}(\beta_m) = \int_0^L X(\beta_m, x') F(x') \, dx' \qquad\qquad (13\text{-}39c)$$

$$\bar{g}(\beta_m, t') = \int_0^L X(\beta_m, x') g(x', t') \, dx' \qquad\qquad (13\text{-}39d)$$

$$N(\beta_m) = \int_0^L [X(\beta_m, x')]^2 \, dx' \qquad\qquad (13\text{-}39e)$$

If the boundary conditions at $x = 0$ or $x = L$ or both are of the first kind the following changes should be made in the term $A(\beta_m, t')$ defined by

equation (13-39b):
when $k_1 = 0$ replace

$$\frac{X(\beta_m, x)}{k_1}\bigg|_{x=0}$$

by

$$\frac{1}{h_1} \frac{dX(\beta_m, x)}{dx}\bigg|_{x=0} \tag{13-39f}$$

when $k_2 = 0$ replace

$$\frac{X(\beta_m, x)}{k_2}\bigg|_{x=0}$$

by

$$-\frac{1}{h_2} \frac{dX(\beta_m, x)}{dx}\bigg|_{x=L} \tag{13-39g}$$

We also note that the solution given by equations (13-39) is also immediately obtainable from the general solution (13-18) by setting $\psi(\beta_m, x_1) = X(\beta_m, x)$, $\psi(\beta_m, x_1') = X(\beta_m, x_1')$ and $w(x_1') = 1$.

The eigenfunctions $X(\beta_m, x)$, the normalization integral $N(\beta_m)$ and the eigenvalues β_m appearing in the solution (13-39) are obtainable from Table 2-2, Chapter 2 for the nine different combinations of the boundary conditions.

Alternative Solution. In some cases it is desirable to use the alternative form of the solution (13-39); it is obtainable from equation (13-28a) as

$$T(x, t) = \sum_{j=0}^{2} T_{0j}(x, t) + T_h(x, t) - \sum_{j=0}^{2} T_j(x, t) \tag{13-40}$$

where the functions $T_{0j}(x, t)$ are the solutions of the following quasi-steady-state problem that is obtained from equations (13-29) as

$$\frac{\partial^2 T_{0j}(x, t)}{\partial x^2} + \delta_{0j} \frac{g(x, t)}{k} = 0 \qquad \text{in } 0 < x < L \tag{13-41a}$$

$$-k_1 \frac{\partial T_{0j}}{\partial x} + h_1 T_{0j} = \delta_{1j} f_1(t) \qquad \text{at } x = 0 \tag{13-41b}$$

$$k_2 \frac{\partial T_{0j}}{\partial x} + h_2 T_{0j} = \delta_{2j} f_2(t) \qquad \text{at } x = L \tag{13-41c}$$

$$\delta_{ij} = \begin{cases} 1 & \text{for } i = j \\ 0 & \text{for } i \neq j \end{cases} \qquad \text{and} \qquad i, j = 0, 1, 2$$

The function $T_h(x, t)$ is the solution of the following homogeneous problem, which is obtained from equations (13-30) as

$$\frac{\partial^2 T_h(x,t)}{\partial x^2} = \frac{1}{\alpha}\frac{\partial T_h(x,t)}{\partial t} \qquad \text{in } 0 < x < L, \; t > 0 \qquad (13\text{-}42\text{a})$$

$$-k_1 \frac{\partial T_h}{\partial x} + h_1 T_h = 0 \qquad \text{at } x = 0, \; t > 0 \qquad (13\text{-}42\text{b})$$

$$k_2 \frac{\partial T_h}{\partial x} + h_2 T_h = 0 \qquad \text{at } x = L, \; t > 0 \qquad (13\text{-}42\text{c})$$

$$T_h(x,t) = F(x) - \sum_{j=0}^{2} T_{0j}(x,0) \qquad \text{for } t = 0, \text{ in } 0 \le x \le L \quad (13\text{-}42\text{d})$$

The functions $T_j(x,t)$ are related to the function $\theta_j(x,\tau,t)$ by the following relation [see equation (13-32)]

$$T_j(x,t) = \int_{\tau=0}^{t} \frac{\partial \theta_j(x,\tau',t-\tau)}{\partial \tau'}\Bigg|_{\tau'=\tau} d\tau \qquad (13\text{-}43)$$

where $\theta_j(x,\tau,t)$ is the solution of the following homogeneous problem obtained from equations (13-31) as

$$\frac{\partial^2 \theta_j}{\partial x^2} = \frac{1}{\alpha}\frac{\partial \theta_j(x,\tau,t)}{\partial t} \qquad \text{in } 0 < x < L, \; t > 0 \qquad (13\text{-}44\text{a})$$

$$-k_1 \frac{\partial \theta_j}{\partial x} + h_1 \theta_j = 0 \qquad \text{at } x = 0, \; t > 0 \qquad (13\text{-}44\text{b})$$

$$k_2 \frac{\partial \theta_j}{\partial x} + h_2 \theta_j = 0 \qquad \text{at } x = L, \; t > 0 \qquad (13\text{-}44\text{c})$$

$$\theta_j(x,\tau,t) = T_{0j}(x,\tau) \qquad \text{for } t = 0, \text{ in } 0 \le x \le L \qquad (13\text{-}44\text{d})$$

where $j = 0, 1, 2$. In the following examples we consider some special cases of the one-dimensional problem (13-36).

Example 13-1. Obtain the solution of the following heat-conduction problem for a slab by utilizing the general solutions given previously.

$$\frac{\partial^2 T}{\partial x^2} + \frac{1}{k}g(x,t) = \frac{1}{\alpha}\frac{\partial T(x,t)}{\partial t} \qquad \text{in } 0 < x < L, \; t > 0 \qquad (13\text{-}45\text{a})$$

$$\frac{\partial T}{\partial x} = 0 \qquad \text{at } x = 0, \; t > 0 \qquad (13\text{-}45\text{b})$$

$$T = 0 \qquad \text{at } x = L, \; t > 0 \qquad (13\text{-}45\text{c})$$

$$T = F(x) \qquad \text{for } t = 0, \text{ in } 0 \le x \le L \qquad (13\text{-}45\text{d})$$

Solution. The solution of this problem is immediately obtainable from the solution (13-39) as

$$T(x,t) = \sum_{m=0}^{\infty} \frac{X(\beta_m, x)}{N(\beta_m)} e^{-\alpha\beta_m^2 t} \left[\bar{F}(\beta_m) + \frac{\alpha}{k} \int_0^t e^{\alpha\beta_m^2 t'} \bar{g}(\beta_m, t') dt' \right] \quad (13\text{-}46)$$

where the integral transforms $\bar{F}(\beta_m)$ and $\bar{g}(\beta_m, t')$ are defined by equations (13-39c) and (13-39d), respectively. The eigenfunctions $X(\beta_m, x)$, the normalization integral $N(\beta_m)$ and the expression defining the eigenvalues β_m are obtained from Table 2-2, case 6, as

$$X(\beta_m, x) = \cos \beta_m x, \qquad \frac{1}{N(\beta_m)} = \frac{2}{L}, \qquad \text{and} \qquad \cos \beta_m L = 0 \quad (13\text{-}47)$$

Introducing equations (13-47) into (13-46) we find

$$T(x,t) = \frac{2}{L} \sum_{m=1}^{\infty} e^{-\alpha\beta_m^2 t} \cos \beta_m x \left\{ \int_{x'=0}^{L} F(x') \cos \beta_m x' \, dx' \right.$$
$$\left. + \frac{\alpha}{k} \int_{t'=0}^{t} e^{\alpha\beta_m^2 t'} \int_{x'=0}^{L} g(x',t') \cos \beta_m x' \, dx' \, dt' \right\} \quad (13\text{-}48)$$

where β_m's are the positive roots of $\cos \beta_m L = 0$ or they are given by $\beta_m = (2m-1)\pi/L, m = 1, 2, 3 \ldots$.

Example 13-2. Obtain the solution of the following heat-conduction problem for a slab

$$\frac{\partial^2 T}{\partial x^2} = \frac{1}{\alpha} \frac{\partial T(x,t)}{\partial t} \qquad \text{in } 0 < x < L, \ t > 0 \qquad (13\text{-}49a)$$

$$\frac{\partial T}{\partial x} = 0 \qquad \text{at } x = 0, \ t > 0 \qquad (13\text{-}49b)$$

$$T = f_2(t) \qquad \text{at } x = L, \ t > 0 \qquad (13\text{-}49c)$$

$$T = 0 \qquad \text{for } t = 0, \text{ in } 0 \le x \le L \qquad (13\text{-}49d)$$

Consider the case when the surface temperature is given by $f_2(t) = \gamma t$, where γ is a constant.

Solution. We solve this problem using both the solution (13-39) and its alternative form (13-40).

1. The solution of this problem is immediately obtainable from the solution (13-39) as

$$T(x,t) = -\alpha \sum_{m=1}^{\infty} \frac{X(\beta_m, x)}{N(\beta_m)} e^{-\alpha\beta_m^2 t} \int_{t'=0}^{t} e^{\alpha\beta_m^2 t'} \left[\frac{dX(\beta_m, x)}{dx} \right]_{x=L} f_2(t') dt') \quad (13\text{-}50)$$

where use is made of equation (13-39g) since the boundary condition at $x = L$ is of the first kind. The eigenfunctions $X(\beta_m, x)$, the normalization integral $N(\beta_m)$ and the eigenvalues β_m are the same as those given by equation (13-47). Then the solution (13-50) becomes

$$T(x,t) = \frac{2\alpha}{L} \sum_{m=1}^{\infty} (-1)^{m-1} e^{-\alpha\beta_m^2 t} \beta \cos \beta_m x \int_{t'=0}^{t} e^{\alpha\beta_m^2 t'} f_2(t') \, dt' \quad (13\text{-}51a)$$

since $\beta_m = (2m-1)\pi/L$ and $dX/dx|_{x=L} = -\beta_m \sin \beta_m L = -\beta_m(-1)^{m-1}$. For $f_2(t) = \gamma t$, this result reduces to

$$T(x,t) = \frac{2\alpha\gamma}{L} \sum_{m=1}^{\infty} (-1)^{m-1} e^{-\alpha\beta_m^2 t} \beta_m \cos \beta_m x \int_{t'=0}^{t} t' e^{\alpha\beta_m^2 t'} \, dt' \quad (13\text{-}51b)$$

The integral term is evaluated as

$$\int_{0}^{t} t' e^{\alpha\beta_m^2 t'} \, dt' = e^{\alpha\beta_m^2 t} \left[\frac{t}{\alpha\beta_m^2} - \frac{1}{\alpha^2\beta_m^4} \right] + \frac{1}{\alpha^2\beta_m^4} \quad (13\text{-}52)$$

Then, the solution (13-51b) takes the form

$$T(x,t) = \gamma t \frac{2}{L} \sum_{m=1}^{\infty} (-1)^{m-1} \frac{\cos \beta_m x}{\beta_m} - \frac{\gamma}{\alpha} \frac{2}{L} \sum_{m=1}^{\infty} (-1)^{m-1} \frac{\cos \beta_m x}{\beta_m^3}$$
$$+ \frac{2\gamma}{\alpha L} \sum_{m=1}^{\infty} (-1)^{m-1} e^{-\alpha\beta_m^2 t} \frac{\cos \beta_m x}{\beta_m^3} \quad (13\text{-}53)$$

Closed-form expressions for the two series are given as (see Note 2 for the derivation of these closed form expressions)

$$\frac{2}{L} \sum_{m=1}^{\infty} (-1)^{m-1} \frac{\cos \beta_m x}{\beta_m} = 1 \quad (13\text{-}54a)$$

$$\frac{2}{L} \sum_{m=1}^{\infty} (-1)^{m-1} \frac{\cos \beta_m x}{\beta_m^3} = -\tfrac{1}{2}(x^2 - L^2) \quad (13\text{-}54b)$$

Introducing these results into equation (13-53) the solution becomes

$$T(x,t) = \gamma t + \frac{\gamma}{2\alpha}(x^2 - L^2) + \frac{2\gamma}{\alpha L} \sum_{m=1}^{\infty} (-1)^{m-1} e^{-\alpha\beta_m^2 t} \frac{\cos \beta_m x}{\beta_m^3} \quad (13\text{-}55)$$

2. We now solve the problem (13-49) by utilizing the alternative form of the solution given by equations (13-40). Then we have

$$T(x,t) = T_{02}(x,t) + T_h(x,t) - T_2(x,t) \quad (13\text{-}56)$$

where the function $T_{02}(x,t)$ satisfies the following quasi-steady-state problem

$$\frac{\partial^2 T_{02}}{\partial x^2} = 0 \qquad \text{in } 0 < x < L \quad (13\text{-}57a)$$

$$\frac{\partial T_{02}}{\partial x} = 0 \qquad \text{at } x = 0 \qquad (13\text{-}57\text{b})$$

$$T_{02} = f_2(t) = \gamma t \qquad \text{at } x = L \qquad (13\text{-}57\text{c})$$

the solution of which is

$$T_{02}(x,t) = \gamma t \qquad (13\text{-}58)$$

The function $T_h(x,t)$ satisfies the following homogeneous problem

$$\frac{\partial^2 T_h}{\partial x^2} = \frac{1}{\alpha} \frac{\partial T_h}{\partial t} \qquad \text{in } 0 < x < L, \ t > 0 \qquad (13\text{-}59\text{a})$$

$$\frac{\partial T_h}{\partial x} = 0 \qquad \text{at } x = 0, \ t > 0 \qquad (13\text{-}59\text{b})$$

$$T_h = 0 \qquad \text{at } x = L, \ t > 0 \qquad (13\text{-}59\text{c})$$

$$T_h = -T_{02}(x,0) = 0 \qquad \text{for } t = 0, \text{ in } 0 \le x \le L \qquad (13\text{-}59\text{d})$$

which has a trivial solution; hence

$$T_h(x,t) = 0 \qquad (13\text{-}60)$$

Finally $T_2(x,t)$ is related to the function $\theta_2(x,t)$ by

$$T_2(x,t) = \int_{\tau=0}^{t} \frac{\partial \theta_2(x,\tau',t-\tau)}{\partial \tau'}\bigg|_{\tau'=\tau} d\tau \qquad (13\text{-}61)$$

where $\theta_2(x,\tau,t)$ is the solution of the following homogeneous problem

$$\frac{\partial^2 \theta_2}{\partial x^2} = \frac{1}{\alpha} \frac{\partial \theta_2}{\partial t} \qquad \text{in } 0 < x < L, \ t > 0 \qquad (13\text{-}62\text{a})$$

$$\frac{\partial \theta_2}{\partial x} = 0 \qquad \text{at } x = 0, \ t > 0 \qquad (13\text{-}62\text{b})$$

$$\theta_2 = 0 \qquad \text{at } x = L, \ t > 0 \qquad (13\text{-}62\text{c})$$

$$\theta_2 = T_{02}(x,\tau) = \gamma\tau \qquad \text{for } t = 0, \text{ in } 0 \le x \le L \qquad (13\text{-}62\text{d})$$

When equations (13-62) are solved and $\theta_2(x,\tau,t)$ is introduced into equation (13-61) we obtain

$$T_2(x,t) = \frac{2\gamma}{\alpha L} \sum_{m=1}^{\infty} (-1)^{m-1}(1 - e^{-\alpha\beta_m^2 t}) \frac{\cos \beta_m x}{\beta_m^3} \qquad (13\text{-}63)$$

Introducing equations (13-58), (13-60), and (13-63) into equation (13-56), we find

$$T(x,t) = \gamma t - \frac{\gamma}{\alpha}\frac{2}{L}\sum_{m=1}^{\infty}(-1)^{m-1}\frac{\cos\beta_m x}{\beta_m^3} + \frac{2\gamma}{\alpha L}\sum_{m=1}^{\infty}(-1)^{m-1}e^{-\alpha\beta_m^2 t}\frac{\cos\beta_m x}{\beta_m^3}$$

(13-64)

when the closed-form expression (13-54b) is introduced, the solution (13-64) becomes

$$T(x,t) = \gamma t + \frac{\gamma}{2\alpha}(x^2 - L^2) + \frac{2\gamma}{\alpha L}\sum_{m=1}^{\infty}(-1)^{m-1}e^{-\alpha\beta_m^2 t}\frac{\cos\beta_m x}{\beta_m^3}$$

(13-65)

which is identical to equation (13-55).

One-Dimensional Problems of Semi-Infinite and Infinite Regions

The integral-transform technique developed for the solution of heat-conduction problems of finite regions is now extended for the solution of problems of semi-infinite regions. Only one of the space variables, the x variable, needs to be considered, because the same results are applicable for the solution of problems involving y- or z- variables.

Region $0 \le x \le \infty$. To illustrate the basic concepts, we consider the solution of the following one-dimensional, time-dependent heat-conduction problem for a semi-infinite region

$$\frac{\partial^2 T}{\partial x^2} + \frac{1}{k}g(x,t) = \frac{1}{\alpha}\frac{\partial T(x,t)}{\partial t} \qquad \text{in } 0 < x < \infty, \ t > 0 \qquad (13\text{-}66a)$$

$$-k_1\frac{\partial T}{\partial x} + h_1 T = f_1(t) \qquad \text{at } x = 0, \ t > 0 \qquad (13\text{-}66b)$$

$$T(x,t) = F(x) \qquad \text{for } t = 0, \text{ in } 0 \le x < \infty \qquad (13\text{-}66c)$$

Basic steps in the solution of this problem can be summarized as follows:

1. Develop the appropriate integral transform pair. The integral-transform pair is developed by considering the eigenvalue problem appropriate for the problem (13-66) and then representing the function $T(x,t)$, defined in the interval $0 \le x < \infty$, in terms of the eigenfunctions of this eigenvalue problem and then by splitting up the representation into two parts as the *inversion formula* and the *integral transform*.

2. Remove the partial derivative $\partial^2 T/\partial x^2$ from the differential equation (13-66a) by the application of the integral transform and utilizing the eigenvalue problem and the boundary conditions for the heat-conduction problem.

3. Solve the resulting ordinary differential equation for the transform of temperature subject to the transformed initial condition. Invert the transform of temperature by the inversion formula to obtain the desired solution.

Step (1) is immediately obtainable from the results available in Chapter 2. That is, the eigenvalue problem is given by equations (2-48) and the representation of a function in the region $0 \leq x < \infty$ is given by equation (2-52). Then, the integral-transform pair with respect to the x variable of the function $T(x, t)$ is immediately obtained according to equation (2-52) as

$$\text{Inversion formula:} \quad T(x, t) = \int_{\beta = 0}^{\infty} \frac{X(\beta, x)}{N(\beta)} \bar{T}(\beta, t) \, d\beta \qquad (13\text{-}67a)$$

$$\text{Integral transform:} \quad \bar{T}(\beta, t) = \int_{x' = 0}^{\infty} X(\beta, x') T(x', t) \, dx' \qquad (13\text{-}67b)$$

where the functions $X(\beta, x)$ and $N(\beta)$ are listed in Table 2-3, for three different boundary conditions at $x = 0$. We note that, the eigenvalues β for a semi-infinite medium is continuous, as a result the inversion formula is an integral over β from zero to infinity instead of a summation over the discrete eigenvalues as for the finite region.

Step 2 involves taking the integral transform of equation (13-66a) by the application of the transform (13-67b); that is, we multiply both sides of equation (13-66a) by $X(\beta, x)$ and integrate with respect to x from $x = 0$ to ∞, to obtain

$$\int_{0}^{\infty} X(\beta, x) \frac{\partial^2 T}{\partial x^2} \, dx + \frac{1}{k} \bar{g}(\beta, t) = \frac{1}{\alpha} \frac{d\bar{T}(\beta, t)}{dt}$$

The integral on the left is performed by integrating it by parts twice and utilizing the eigenvalue problem (2-48) and the boundary condition (13-66b) (*see Note 3 for the details of this portion of the analysis*). Then the resulting equation and the transform of the initial condition (13-66c), respectively, become

$$\frac{d\bar{T}(\beta, t)}{dt} + \alpha \beta^2 \bar{T}(\beta, t) = \frac{\alpha}{k} \bar{g}(\beta, t) + \frac{X(\beta, x)}{k_1} \bigg|_{x=0} \cdot f_1(t) \qquad \text{for } t > 0 \quad (13\text{-}68a)$$

$$\bar{T}(\beta, t) = \bar{F}(\beta) \qquad\qquad\qquad\qquad\qquad\qquad \text{for } t = 0 \quad (13\text{-}68b)$$

In step (3), equation (13-68) is solved for $\bar{T}(\beta, t)$ and the result is inverted by the inversion formula (13-67b) to obtain the solution as

$$T(x, t) = \int_{\beta = 0}^{\infty} \frac{X(\beta, x)}{N(\beta)} e^{-\alpha \beta^2 t} \left[\bar{F}(\beta) + \int_{0}^{t} e^{\alpha \beta^2 t'} A(\beta, t') \, dt' \right] \qquad (13\text{-}69a)$$

where

$$A(\beta, t') = \frac{\alpha}{k} \bar{g}(\beta, t') + \alpha \left. \frac{X(\beta, x')}{k_1} \right|_{x'=0} \cdot f_1(t') \qquad (13\text{-}69\text{b})$$

$$\bar{F}(\beta) = \int\limits_0^\infty X(\beta, x') F(x') \, dx' \qquad (13\text{-}69\text{c})$$

$$\bar{g}(\beta, t') = \int\limits_0^\infty X(\beta, x') g(x', t') \, dx' \qquad (13\text{-}69\text{d})$$

If the boundary condition at $x = 0$ is of the first kind (i.e., $k_1 = 0$) the following change should be made in the term $A(\beta, t')$: Replace

$$\left. \frac{X(\beta, x')}{k_1} \right|_{x'=0}$$

by

$$\left. \frac{1}{h_1} \frac{dX(\beta, x')}{dx'} \right|_{x'=0} \qquad (13\text{-}69\text{e})$$

The functions $X(\beta, x)$ and $N(\beta)$ are obtainable from Table 2-3 for three different boundary conditions at $x = 0$.

Region $-\infty < x < \infty$. We now consider the following heat-conduction problem for an infinite medium

$$\frac{\partial^2 T}{\partial x^2} + \frac{1}{k} g(x, t) = \frac{1}{\alpha} \frac{\partial T(x, t)}{\partial t} \qquad \text{in } -\infty < x < \infty, \ t > 0 \quad (13\text{-}70\text{a})$$

$$T(x, t) = F(x) \qquad \text{for } t = 0, \text{ in the region} \qquad (13\text{-}70\text{b})$$

The eigenvalue problem appropriate for the solution of this problem is given by equation (2-64b) and the representation of a function $F^*(x)$, defined in the interval $-\infty < x < \infty$, in terms of the eigenfunctions of this eigenvalue problem is given by equation (2-66d) as

$$F^*(x) = \frac{1}{\pi} \int\limits_{\beta=0}^\infty \int\limits_{x'=-\infty}^\infty F^*(x') \cos \beta(x - x') \, dx' \, d\beta \qquad (13\text{-}71)$$

This representation is expressed in the alternative form as (see Note 4 for the derivation)

$$F^*(x) = \frac{1}{2\pi} \int\limits_{\beta=-\infty}^\infty e^{-i\beta x} \left[\int\limits_{x'=-\infty}^\infty e^{i\beta x} F^*(x') \, dx' \right] d\beta \qquad (13\text{-}72)$$

where $i = \sqrt{-1}$.

This expression is now utilized to define the integral-transform pair for the temperature $T(x, t)$ with respect to the x variable as

Inversion formula: $\qquad T(x,t) = \dfrac{1}{2\pi} \int\limits_{\beta=-\infty}^{\infty} e^{-i\beta x} \bar{T}(\beta, t)\, d\beta \qquad$ (13-73a)

Integral transform: $\qquad \bar{T}(\beta, t) = \int\limits_{-\infty}^{\infty} e^{i\beta x'} T(x', t)\, dx' \qquad$ (13-73b)

Taking the integral transform of the heat-conduction problem (13-70) according to the transform (13-73b), we obtain

$$\frac{d\bar{T}(\beta, t)}{dt} + \alpha\beta^2 \bar{T}(\beta, t) = \frac{\alpha}{k}\bar{g}(\beta, t) \qquad \text{for } t > 0 \qquad (13\text{-}74a)$$

$$\bar{T}(\beta, t) = \bar{F}(\beta) \qquad\qquad\qquad \text{for } t = 0 \qquad (13\text{-}74b)$$

When this equation is solved for $\bar{T}(\beta, t)$ and the result is inverted by the inversion formula (13-73a), we obtain the solution of the heat-conduction problem (13-70) as

$$T(x,t) = \frac{1}{2\pi} \int\limits_{\beta=-\infty}^{\infty} e^{-\alpha\beta^2 t - i\beta x}\left[\bar{F}(\beta) + \frac{\alpha}{k}\int\limits_{t'=0}^{t} e^{\alpha\beta^2 t'}\bar{g}(\beta, t')\, dt' \right]d\beta \;(13\text{-}75a)$$

where

$$\bar{F}(\beta) = \int\limits_{x'=-\infty}^{\infty} e^{i\beta x'} F(x')\, dx' \qquad (13\text{-}75b)$$

$$\bar{g}(\beta, t') = \int\limits_{x'=-\infty}^{\infty} e^{i\beta x'} g(x', t')\, dx' \qquad (13\text{-}75c)$$

The order of integration is changed and the result is rearranged as

$$T(x,t) = \frac{1}{2\pi} \int\limits_{x'=-\infty}^{\infty} F(x')\, dx' \int\limits_{\beta=-\infty}^{\infty} e^{-\alpha\beta^2 t - i\beta(x-x')}\, d\beta$$

$$+ \frac{1}{2\pi}\frac{\alpha}{k}\int\limits_{t'=0}^{t} dt' \int\limits_{x'=-\infty}^{\infty} g(x', t')\, dx' \int\limits_{\beta=-\infty}^{\infty} e^{-\alpha\beta^2(t-t') - i\beta(x-x')}\, d\beta \quad (13\text{-}76)$$

We make use of the following integral

$$\frac{1}{2\pi} \int\limits_{\beta=-\infty}^{\infty} e^{-\alpha\beta^2 t - i\beta x}\, d\beta = \frac{1}{(4\pi\alpha t)^{1/2}} e^{-x^2/4\alpha t} \qquad (13\text{-}77)$$

then the solution (13-76) becomes

$$T(x,t) = \frac{1}{(4\pi\alpha t)^{1/2}} \int\limits_{x'=-\infty}^{\infty} \exp\left[-\frac{(x-x')^2}{4\alpha t} \right] F(x')\, dx'$$

$$+ \frac{\alpha}{k}\int\limits_{t'=0}^{t} \frac{dt'}{[4\pi\alpha(t-t')]^{1/2}} \int\limits_{x'=-\infty}^{\infty} \exp\left[-\frac{(x-x')^2}{4\alpha(t-t')} \right] g(x', t')\, dx' \quad (13\text{-}78)$$

The procedure described above for the solution of one-dimensional heat-conduction problems in semi-infinite and infinite regions is applicable for the solution of multidimensional problems by the successive applications of one dimensional integral transform. This matter will be illustrated with examples later in this section.

We illustrate the application of the above method of solution with a specific example.

Example 13-3. Obtain the solution of the following heat-conduction problem for a semi-infinite region

$$\frac{\partial^2 T}{\partial x^2} + \frac{1}{k} g(x,t) = \frac{1}{\alpha} \frac{\partial T(x,t)}{\partial t} \qquad \text{in } 0 < x < \infty, \ t > 0 \qquad (13\text{-}79a)$$

$$\frac{\partial T}{\partial x} = 0 \qquad \text{at } x = 0, \ t > 0 \qquad (13\text{-}79b)$$

$$T = F(x) \qquad \text{for } t = 0, \ 0 \le x < \infty \qquad (13\text{-}79c)$$

Solution. The solution of this problem is immediately obtainable from equations (13-69a) as

$$T(x,t) = \int_{\beta=0}^{\infty} \frac{X(\beta,x)}{N(\beta)} e^{-\alpha\beta^2 t} \left[\bar{F}(\beta) + \frac{\alpha}{k} \int_{t'=0}^{t} e^{\alpha\beta^2 t'} \bar{g}(\beta,t') \, dt' \right] \qquad (13\text{-}80a)$$

where

$$\bar{F}(\beta) = \int_{x'=0}^{\infty} X(\beta,x') F(x') \, dx' \qquad (13\text{-}80b)$$

$$\bar{g}(\beta,t) = \int_{x'=0}^{\infty} X(\beta,x') g(x',t') \, dx'$$

The functions $X(\beta, x)$ and $N(\beta)$ are determined from case 2, Table 2-3, as

$$X(\beta,x) = \cos \beta x \qquad \text{and} \qquad \frac{1}{N(\beta)} = \frac{2}{\pi} \qquad (13\text{-}81)$$

Introducing equations (13-81) into (13-80) the solution becomes

$$T(x,t) = \frac{2}{\pi} \int_{\beta=0}^{\infty} e^{-\alpha\beta^2 t} \cos \beta x \int_{x'=0}^{\infty} F(x') \cos \beta x' \, dx' \, d\beta$$

$$+ \frac{2\alpha}{\pi k} \int_{\beta=0}^{\infty} e^{-\alpha\beta^2 t} \cos \beta x \int_{t'=0}^{t} e^{\alpha\beta^2 t'} \int_{x'=0}^{\infty} g(x',t') \cos \beta x' \, dx' \, dt' \, d\beta \qquad (13\text{-}82)$$

In this expression the orders of integration can be changed and the integrations with respect to β can be performed by making use of the following relation [i.e., obtained by adding equations (2-57b) and (2-57c)]

$$\frac{2}{\pi} \int_{\beta=0}^{\infty} e^{-\alpha\beta^2 t} \cos \beta x \cos \beta x' \, d\beta$$

$$= \frac{1}{(4\pi\alpha t)^{1/2}} \left[\exp\left(-\frac{(x - x')^2}{4\alpha t} \right) + \exp\left(-\frac{(x + x')^2}{4\alpha t} \right) \right] \quad (13\text{-}83)$$

Then, the solution (13-82) takes the form

$$T(x, t) = \frac{1}{(4\pi\alpha t)^{1/2}} \int_{x'=0}^{\infty} F(x') \left[\exp\left(-\frac{(x - x')^2}{4\alpha t} \right) + \exp\left(-\frac{(x + x')^2}{4\alpha t} \right) \right] dx'$$

$$+ \frac{\alpha}{k} \int_{t'=0}^{t} \frac{dt'}{\left[4\pi\alpha(t - t') \right]^{1/2}} \int_{x'=0}^{\infty} g(x', t')$$

$$\cdot \left[\exp\left(-\frac{(x - x')^2}{4\alpha(t - t')} \right) + \exp\left(-\frac{(x + x')^2}{4\alpha(t - t')} \right) \right] dx' \quad (13\text{-}84)$$

Several special cases are obtainable from this solution depending on the functional forms of the heat-generation term and the initial condition function.

Multidimensional Problems

The solution of multidimensional, time-dependent heat-conduction problems by the integral transform technique is best handled by the successive application of one-dimensional integral transforms to remove from the equation one of the partial derivatives with respect to the space variable in each step. In the rectangular coordinate system the order of the integral transformation with respect to the space variables is immaterial. This matter is now illustrated with examples.

Example 13-4. Obtain the solution $T(x, y, t)$ of the following heat-conduction problem for a semi-infinite rectangular strip, $0 \leq x < \infty, 0 \leq y \leq b$

$$\frac{\partial^2 T}{\partial x^2} + \frac{\partial^2 T}{\partial y^2} + \frac{g(x, y, t)}{k} = \frac{1}{\alpha} \frac{\partial T}{\partial t} \quad \text{in } 0 < x < \infty, \, 0 < y < b, \, t > 0 \quad (13\text{-}85a)$$

$$T = 0 \qquad\qquad\qquad \text{at all boundaries} \qquad (13\text{-}85b)$$

$$T = 0 \qquad\qquad\qquad \text{for } t = 0, \text{ in the region} \qquad (13\text{-}85c)$$

The integral transform pair for $T(x, y, t)$ with respect to the x variable is defined as [see equations (13-67)]

$$\text{Inversion formula:} \quad T(x, y, t) = \int_{\beta=0}^{\infty} \frac{X(\beta, x)}{N(\beta)} \bar{T}(\beta, y, t) \, d\beta \quad (13\text{-}86a)$$

Integral transform: $\bar{T}(\beta, y, t) = \int\limits_{x'=0}^{\infty} X(\beta, x')T(x', y, t)\,dx'$ (13-86b)

and the integral transform pair for $\bar{T}(\beta, y, t)$ with respect to the y variable is defined as [see equation (13-37)]

Inversion formula: $\bar{T}(\beta, y, t) = \sum\limits_{n=1}^{\infty} \frac{Y(\gamma_n, y)}{N(\gamma_n)}\tilde{\bar{T}}(\beta, \gamma_n, t)$ (13-86c)

Integral transform: $\tilde{\bar{T}}(\beta, \gamma_n, t) = \int\limits_{0}^{b} Y(\gamma_n, y')\bar{T}(\beta, y', t)\,dy'$ (13-86d)

where the bar denotes the transform with respect to the x variable and the tilde with respect to the y variable.

We take the integral transform of the problem (13-85) first with respect to the x variable using the transform (13-86b) and then with respect to the y variable using the transform (13-86d) to obtain

$$\frac{d\tilde{\bar{T}}}{dt} + \alpha(\beta^2 + \gamma_n^2)\tilde{\bar{T}}(\beta, \gamma_n, t) = \frac{\alpha}{k}\tilde{\bar{g}}(\beta, \gamma_n, t) \qquad \text{for } t > 0 \qquad (13\text{-}87a)$$

$$\tilde{\bar{T}}(\beta, \gamma_n, t) = 0 \qquad\qquad\qquad \text{for } t = 0 \qquad (13\text{-}87b)$$

Equation (13-87) is solved and succesively inverted by the inversion formulas (13-86c) and (13-86a) to find the solution of the problem (13-85) as

$$T(x, y, t) = \int\limits_{\beta=0}^{\infty} \sum\limits_{n=1}^{\infty} \frac{X(\beta, x)Y(\gamma_n, y)}{N(\beta)N(\gamma_n)}e^{-\alpha(\beta^2 + \gamma_n^2)t}$$
$$\cdot\frac{\alpha}{k}\int\limits_{t'=0}^{t} e^{\alpha(\beta^2 + \gamma_n^2)t'}\tilde{\bar{g}}(\beta, \gamma_n, t')\,dt'\,d\beta \qquad (13\text{-}88a)$$

where the double transform $\tilde{\bar{g}}(\beta, \gamma_n, t)$ is defined as

$$\tilde{\bar{g}}(\beta, \gamma_n, t') = \int\limits_{y'=0}^{b} \int\limits_{x'=0}^{\infty} X(\beta, x')Y(\gamma_n, y')g(x', y', t')\,dx'\,dy' \qquad (13\text{-}88b)$$

The functions $X(\beta, x)$ and $N(\beta)$ are obtained from case 3, Table 2-3, as

$$X(\beta, x) = \sin \beta x, \qquad \frac{1}{N(\beta)} = \frac{2}{\pi} \qquad (13\text{-}89a)$$

and the functions $Y(\gamma_n, y)$ and $N(\gamma_n)$ from case 9, Table 2-2, as

$$Y(\gamma_n, y) = \sin \gamma_n y, \qquad \frac{1}{N(\gamma_n)} = \frac{2}{b} \qquad (13\text{-}89b)$$

and γ_n's are the positive roots of $\sin \gamma_n b = 0$. Introducing the results (13-89) into equation (13-88), the solution becomes

$$
T(x, y, t) = \frac{4\alpha}{\pi b k} \int\limits_{\beta=0}^{\infty} \sum_{n=1}^{\infty} e^{-\alpha(\beta^2 + \gamma_n^2)t} \sin \beta x \sin \gamma_n y
$$

$$
\cdot \int\limits_{t'=0}^{i} e^{\alpha(\beta^2 + \gamma_n^2)t'} \int\limits_{y'=0}^{b} \int\limits_{x'=0}^{\infty} g(x', y', t') \sin \beta x' \sin \gamma_n y' \, dx' \, dy' \, dt' \, d\beta
$$

$$(13\text{-}90)$$

In this solution, the integration with respect to β can be performed by making use of the following result [see equation (2-57d)]

$$
\frac{2}{\pi} \int\limits_{\beta=0}^{\infty} e^{-\alpha\beta^2(t-t')} \sin \beta x \sin \beta x' \, d\beta
$$

$$
= \frac{1}{[4\pi\alpha(t-t')]^{1/2}} \left[\exp\left(-\frac{(x-x')^2}{4\alpha(t-t')} \right) - \exp\left(-\frac{(x+x')^2}{4\alpha(t-t')} \right) \right] \quad (13\text{-}91)
$$

Then, the solution (13-90) takes the form

$$
T(x, y, t) = \frac{2\alpha}{bk} \sum_{n=1}^{\infty} e^{-\alpha\gamma_n^2 t} \sin \gamma_n y \int\limits_{t'=0}^{t} \frac{e^{\alpha\gamma_n^2 t'}}{[4\pi\alpha(t-t')]^{1/2}}
$$

$$
\cdot \int\limits_{y'=0}^{b} \int\limits_{x'=0}^{\infty} g(x', y', t') \sin \gamma_n y'
$$

$$
\cdot \left[\exp\left(-\frac{(x-x')^2}{4\alpha(t-t')} \right) - \exp\left(-\frac{(x+x')^2}{4\alpha(t-t')} \right) \right] dx' \, dy' \, dt' \quad (13\text{-}92)
$$

Example 13-5. Obtain the solution $T(x, y, z, t)$ of the following heat-conduction problem for a rectangular parallelepiped $0 \leq x \leq a, 0 \leq y \leq b, 0 \leq z \leq c$.

$$
\frac{\partial^2 T}{\partial x^2} + \frac{\partial^2 T}{\partial y^2} + \frac{\partial^2 T}{\partial z^2} + \frac{g(x, y, z, t)}{k} = \frac{1}{\alpha} \frac{\partial T}{\partial t} \qquad \begin{array}{l} \text{in } 0 < x < a, \ 0 < y < b, \quad (13\text{-}93a) \\ \quad 0 < z < c, \ t > 0 \end{array}
$$

$$
T = 0 \qquad \text{at all boundaries} \qquad (13\text{-}93b)
$$

$$
T = 0 \qquad \text{for } t = 0, \text{ in the region} \qquad (13\text{-}93c)
$$

Solution. This problem can be solved by the successive application of the one-dimensional integral transform to the $x, y,$ and z variables, solving the resulting ordinary differential equation and then inverting the transform of temperature successively. It is also possible to write the solution immediately from the general solution (13-15) by setting

$$
\psi_m(\mathbf{r}) \rightarrow X(\beta_m, x) \cdot Y(\gamma_n, y) \cdot Z(\eta_p, z)
$$

$$\lambda_m^2 \rightarrow (\beta_m^2 + \gamma_n^2 + \eta_p^2)$$

$$\sum_m \rightarrow \sum_{m=1}^{\infty} \sum_{n=1}^{\infty} \sum_{p=1}^{\infty} \quad \text{and} \quad \int_R dv \rightarrow \int_{x'=0}^{a} \int_{y'=0}^{b} \int_{z'=0}^{c} dx'\,dy'\,dz'$$

We obtain

$$T(x,y,z,t) = \sum_{m=1}^{\infty} \sum_{n=1}^{\infty} \sum_{p=1}^{\infty} \frac{X(\beta_m,x)Y(\gamma_n,y)Z(\eta_p,z)}{N(\beta_m)N(\gamma_n)N(\eta_p)} e^{-\alpha(\beta_m^2+\gamma_n^2+\eta_p^2)t}$$

$$\cdot \frac{\alpha}{k} \int_{t'=0}^{t} e^{\alpha(\beta_m^2+\gamma_n^2+\eta_p^2)t'} \cdot \bar{\bar{g}}(\beta_m,\gamma_n,\eta_p,t')\,dt' \tag{13-94a}$$

where the triple transform is defined as

$$\bar{\bar{g}}(\beta_m,\gamma_n,\eta_p,t') = \int_{x'=0}^{a} \int_{y'=0}^{b} \int_{z'=0}^{c} X(\beta_m,x')Y(\gamma_n,y')Z(\eta_p,z')g(x',y',z',t')\,dx'\,dy'\,dz'$$

$$\tag{13-94b}$$

The eigenfunctions, the normalization integrals and the eigenvalues are obtained from case 9, Table 2-2, as

$$X(\beta_m,x) = \sin\beta_m x, \qquad N(\beta_m) = \frac{a}{2}, \qquad \sin\beta_m a = 0 \tag{13-95a}$$

$$Y(\gamma_n,y) = \sin\gamma_n y, \qquad N(\gamma_n) = \frac{b}{2}, \qquad \sin\gamma_n b = 0 \tag{13-95b}$$

$$Z(\eta_p,z) = \sin\eta_p z, \qquad N(\eta_p) = \frac{c}{2}, \qquad \sin\eta_p c = 0 \tag{13-95c}$$

13-4 APPLICATIONS IN THE CYLINDRICAL COORDINATE SYSTEM

To solve the heat-conduction problems in the cylindrical coordinate system with the integral-transform technique, appropriate integral transform pairs are needed in the r, ϕ, and z variables. The integral transform pairs for the z variable depends on whether the range of z is finite, semi-infinite, or infinite as well as the boundary conditions associated with it. Since these transform pairs are exactly the same as those discussed previously for the rectangular coordinate system, this matter is not considered here any further. Therefore, in this section we develop the integral transform pairs for the r and ϕ variables and illustrate their application to the solution of heat-conduction problems involving (r,t), (r,ϕ,t), (r,z,t), and (r,ϕ,z,t) variables.

One-Dimensional Problems in (r, t) Variables

The one dimensional, time-dependent heat-conduction problems in the r variable may be confined to any one of the regions $0 \leq r \leq b$, $a \leq r \leq b$, $0 \leq r < \infty$, and $a \leq r < \infty$. The integral-transform pair for the solution of the problem for each of these cases is different. Therefore, to develop the appropriate transform pairs and illustrate the methods of solution, we examine the solution of heat-conduction problems for each of these cases separately.

Problems of Region $0 \leq r \leq b$. We consider the following heat-conduction problem for a solid cylinder of radius $r = b$

$$\frac{\partial^2 T}{\partial r^2} + \frac{1}{r}\frac{\partial T}{\partial r} + \frac{g(r,t)}{k} = \frac{1}{\alpha}\frac{\partial T}{\partial t} \qquad \text{in } 0 \leq r < b, \ t > 0 \qquad (13\text{-}96a)$$

$$k_2 \frac{\partial T}{\partial r} + h_2 T = f_2(t) \qquad \text{at } r = b, \ t > 0 \qquad (13\text{-}96b)$$

$$T = F(r) \qquad \text{for } t = 0, \text{ in } 0 \leq r \leq b \qquad (13\text{-}96c)$$

The appropriate eigenvalue problem is given by equations (3-18) for the case $v = 0$ since the problem considered here possesses azimuthal symmetry. The integral-transform pair with respect to the r variable for the function $T(r,t)$ is determined according to the representation (3-22) and setting $v = 0$. We obtain

$$\text{Inversion formula}: \qquad T(r,t) = \sum_{m=1}^{\infty} \frac{R_0(\beta_m, r)}{N(\beta_m)}\bar{T}(\beta_m, t) \qquad (13\text{-}97a)$$

$$\text{Integral transform}: \qquad \bar{T}(\beta_m, t) = \int_{r'=0}^{b} r' R_0(\beta_m, r) T(r', t)\, dr' \qquad (13\text{-}97b)$$

where the functions $R_0(\beta_m, r)$, $N(\beta_m)$ and the eigenvalues β_m are obtainable from Table 3-1 for three different boundary conditions by setting $v = 0$

To solve problem (13-96), we take integral transform of equation (13-96a) according to the transform (13-97b). That is we operate on both sides of equation (13-96a) by the operator $\int_0^b r R_0(\beta_m, r)\, dr$ and obtain

$$\int_0^b r R_0(\beta_m, r)\left[\frac{\partial^2 T}{\partial r^2} + \frac{1}{r}\frac{\partial T}{\partial r}\right] dr + \frac{1}{k}\bar{g}(\beta_m, t) = \frac{1}{\alpha}\frac{d\bar{T}(\beta, t)}{dt} \qquad (13\text{-}98)$$

The integral on the left is evaluated either by integrating it by parts twice or by using the Green's theorem and then utilizing the boundary conditions

(3-18b) for $v = 0$ and (13-96b); we find

$$\int_0^b r R_0(\beta_m, r) \left[\frac{\partial^2 T}{\partial r^2} + \frac{1}{r} \frac{\partial T}{\partial r} \right] dr = -\beta_m^2 \bar{T}(\beta_m, r) + b \frac{R_0(\beta_m, r)}{k_2} \bigg|_{r=b} f_2(t) \quad (13\text{-}99)$$

Introducing this expression into equation (13-98) and taking the integral transform of the initial condition (13-96c) we obtain

$$\frac{d\bar{T}(\beta_m, t)}{dt} + \alpha \beta_m^2 T(\beta_m, t) = \frac{\alpha}{k} \bar{g}(\beta_m, t) + \alpha b \frac{R_0(\beta_m, r)}{k_2} \bigg|_{r=b} f_2(t) \quad (13\text{-}100a)$$

$$\bar{T}(\beta_m, t) = \bar{F}(\beta) \qquad \text{for } t = 0 \qquad (13\text{-}100b)$$

Equation (13-100) is solved for $\bar{T}(\beta_m, t)$ and inverted by the inversion formula (13-97a) to yield the solution of the problem (13-96) as

$$T(r,t) = \sum_{m=1}^{\infty} \frac{R_0(\beta_m, r)}{N(\beta_m)} e^{-\alpha \beta_m^2 t} \left[\bar{F}(\beta_m) + \int_0^t e^{\alpha \beta_m^2 t'} A(\beta_m, t') dt' \right] \qquad (13\text{-}101a)$$

where

$$A(\beta_m, t') = \frac{\alpha}{k} \bar{g}(\beta_m, t') + \alpha b \frac{R_0(\beta_m, r)}{k_2} \bigg|_{r=b} f_2(t') \qquad (13\text{-}101b)$$

$$\bar{F}(\beta_m) = \int_0^b r' R_0(\beta_m, r') F(r') dr' \qquad (13\text{-}101c)$$

$$\bar{g}(\beta_m, t') = \int_0^b r' R_0(\beta_m, r') g(r', t') dr' \qquad (13\text{-}101d)$$

$$N(\beta_m) = \int_0^b r' [R_0(\beta_m, r')]^2 dr' \qquad (13\text{-}101e)$$

Here, $R_0(\beta_m, r)$, $N(\beta_m)$ and β_m are obtained from Table 3-1 by setting $v = 0$. For a boundary condition of the first kind at $r = b$, the following change should be made in equation (13-101b): Replace

$$\frac{R_0(\beta_m, r)}{k_2} \bigg|_{r=b}$$

by

$$-\frac{1}{h_2} \frac{dR_0(\beta_m, r)}{dr} \bigg|_{r=b} \qquad (13\text{-}101f)$$

Problems of Region $a \leq r \leq b$. We now consider the heat-conduction problem for a hollow cylinder $a \le r \le b$ given as

$$\frac{\partial^2 T}{\partial r^2} + \frac{1}{r}\frac{\partial T}{\partial r} + \frac{g(r,t)}{k} = \frac{1}{\alpha}\frac{\partial T}{\partial t} \qquad \text{in } a < r < b, \ t > 0 \qquad (13\text{-}102a)$$

$$-k_1\frac{\partial T}{\partial r} + h_1 T = f_1(t) \qquad \text{at } r = a, \ t > 0 \qquad (13\text{-}102b)$$

$$k_2\frac{\partial T}{\partial r} + h_2 T = f_2(t) \qquad \text{at } r = b, \ t > 0 \qquad (13\text{-}102c)$$

$$T = F(r) \qquad \text{for } t = 0, \ \text{in } a \le r \le b \quad (13\text{-}102d)$$

The eigenvalue problem is given by equations (3-35) for $v = 0$, and the integral-transform pair is obtained according to equation (3-38) by setting $v = 0$. We find

$$\text{Inversion formula}: \qquad T(r,t) = \sum_{m=1}^{\infty} \frac{R_0(\beta_m, r)}{N(\beta_m)} \bar{T}(\beta_m, t) \qquad (13\text{-}103a)$$

$$\text{Integral transform}: \qquad \bar{T}(\beta_m, t) = \int_{r'=a}^{b} r' R_0(\beta_m, r') T(r', t)\, dr' \quad (13\text{-}103b)$$

where the functions $R_0(\beta_m, r)$, $N(\beta_m)$ and the eigenvalues β_m are obtainable from Table 3-2 for the nine combinations of boundary conditions by setting $v = 0$.

We now take the integral transform of the system (13-102) by the application of the transform (13-103b), utilize the eigenvalue problem (3-35) for $v = 0$ as described previously, solve for the transform of temperature, and invert the result by the inversion formula (13-103a) to obtain the solution for the temperature as

$$T(r,t) = \sum_{m=1}^{\infty} \frac{R_0(\beta_m, r)}{N(\beta_m)} e^{-\alpha\beta_m^2 t}\left[\bar{F}(\beta_m) + \int_0^t e^{\alpha\beta_m^2 t'} A(\beta_m, t')\, dt' \right] \qquad (13\text{-}104a)$$

where

$$A(\beta_m, t') = \frac{\alpha}{k}\bar{g}(\beta_m, t') + \alpha\left[a\frac{R_0(\beta_m, r)}{k_1}\bigg|_{r=a} f_1(t') + b\frac{R_0(\beta_m, r)}{k_2}\bigg|_{r=b} f_2(t') \right]$$

$$(13\text{-}104b)$$

$$\bar{F}(\beta_m) = \int_a^b r' R_0(\beta_m, r') F(r')\, dr' \qquad (13\text{-}104c)$$

$$\bar{g}(\beta_m, t') = \int_a^b r' R_0(\beta_m, r') g(r', t')\, dr' \qquad (13\text{-}104d)$$

$$N(\beta_m) = \int_a^b r'[R_0(\beta_m, r')]^2 \, dr' \tag{13-104e}$$

Here, $R_0(\beta_m, r)$, $N(\beta_m)$, and β_m are obtainable from Table 3-2 by setting $v = 0$. For a boundary condition of the first kind the following changes should be made in equation (13-104b). When $k_1 = 0$ replace

$$\left. \frac{R_0(\beta_m, r)}{k_1} \right|_{r=a}$$

by

$$\left. \frac{1}{h_1} \frac{dR_0(\beta_m, r)}{dr} \right|_{r=a} \tag{13-104f}$$

When $k_2 = 0$ replace

$$\left. \frac{R_0(\beta_m, r)}{k_2} \right|_{r=b}$$

by

$$\left. -\frac{1}{h_2} \frac{dR_0(\beta_m, r)}{dr} \right|_{r=b} \tag{13-104g}$$

Problems of Region $0 \leq r < \infty$. We consider the following heat-conduction problem for an infinite region $0 \leq r < \infty$

$$\frac{\partial^2 T}{\partial r^2} + \frac{1}{r}\frac{\partial T}{\partial r} + \frac{g(r,t)}{k} = \frac{1}{\alpha}\frac{\partial T}{\partial t} \qquad \text{in } 0 \leq r < \infty, \ t > 0 \tag{13-105a}$$

$$T = F(r) \qquad \text{for } t = 0, \text{ in } 0 \leq r < \infty \tag{13-105b}$$

The appropriate eigenvalue problem is given by equations (3-48) for $v = 0$, and the integral-transform pair is constructed according to the representation (3-51) for $v = 0$; we obtain

$$\text{Inversion formula}: \quad T(r,t) = \int_{\beta=0}^{\infty} \beta J_0(\beta r) \bar{T}(\beta, t) \, d\beta \tag{13-106a}$$

$$\text{Integral transform}: \quad \bar{T}(\beta, t) = \int_{r'=0}^{\infty} r' J_0(\beta r') T(r', t) \, dr' \tag{13-106b}$$

We take the integral transform of the system (13-105) by the application of the transform (13-106b), utilize the eigenvalue problem (3-48) for $v = 0$ as discussed previously, solve for the transform of the temperature and invert the result by the inversion formula (13-106a). We obtain

$$T(r,t) = \int\limits_{\beta=0}^{\infty} \beta J_0(\beta r) e^{-\alpha\beta^2 t}\left[\bar{F}(\beta) + \frac{\alpha}{k}\int\limits_{t'=0}^{t} e^{\alpha\beta^2 t'}\bar{g}(\beta,t')\,dt' \right]d\beta \qquad (13\text{-}107a)$$

where

$$\bar{F}(\beta) = \int\limits_{r'=0}^{\infty} r' J_0(\beta r')F(r')\,dr' \qquad (13\text{-}107b)$$

$$\bar{g}(\beta,t') = \int\limits_{r'=0}^{\infty} r' J_0(\beta r')g(r',t')\,dr' \qquad (13\text{-}107c)$$

Introducing (13-107b, c) into (13-107a) and changing the order of integrations we find

$$T(r,t) = \int\limits_{r'=0}^{\infty} r'F(r')\left[\int\limits_{\beta=0}^{\infty} e^{-\alpha\beta^2 t}\beta J_0(\beta r)J_0(\beta r')\,d\beta \right]dr'$$

$$+ \frac{\alpha}{k}\int\limits_{r'=0}^{\infty}\int\limits_{t'=0}^{t} r'g(r',t')\left[\int\limits_{\beta=0}^{\infty} e^{-\alpha\beta^2(t-t')}\beta J_0(\beta r)J_0(\beta r')\,d\beta \right]dt'\,dr' \qquad (13\text{-}108)$$

We now consider the following integral [36, p. 395]

$$\int\limits_{\beta=0}^{\infty} e^{-\alpha\beta^2 t}\beta J_\nu(\beta r)J_\nu(\beta r')\,d\beta = \frac{1}{2\alpha t}\exp\left[-\frac{r^2 + r'^2}{2\alpha t} \right]I_\nu\left(\frac{rr'}{2\alpha t} \right) \qquad (13\text{-}109)$$

By setting $\nu = 0$ in equation (13-109) and introducing the resulting expression into equation (13-108) we obtain

$$T(r,t) = \frac{1}{2\alpha t}\int\limits_{r'=0}^{\infty} r'\exp\left[-\frac{r^2 + r'^2}{4\alpha t} \right]F(r')I_0\left(\frac{rr'}{2\alpha t} \right)dr'$$

$$+ \frac{1}{2k}\int\limits_{r'=0}^{\infty}\int\limits_{t'=0}^{t}\frac{r'}{t-t'}\exp\left[-\frac{r^2 + r'^2}{4\alpha(t-t')} \right]g(r',t')I_0\left(\frac{rr'}{2\alpha(t-t')} \right)dt'\,dr'$$

$$(13\text{-}110)$$

Problems of Region $a \le r < \infty$. We now consider the following heat-conduction problem for a semi-infinite region $a \le r < \infty$

$$\frac{\partial^2 T}{\partial r^2} + \frac{1}{r}\frac{\partial T}{\partial r} + \frac{g(r,t)}{k} = \frac{1}{\alpha}\frac{\partial T}{\partial t} \qquad \text{in } a < r < \infty,\ t > 0 \qquad (13\text{-}111a)$$

$$-k_1\frac{\partial T}{\partial r} + h_1 T = f_1(t) \qquad \text{at } r = a,\ t > 0 \qquad (13\text{-}111b)$$

$$T = F(r) \qquad \text{for } t = 0,\ \text{in } a \le r < \infty \qquad (13\text{-}111c)$$

The eigenvalue problem is given by equations (3-52) and the desired integral transform pair is obtained according to the representation (3-53) as

Inversion formula : $\quad T(r,t) = \int\limits_{\beta=0}^{\infty} \dfrac{\beta}{N(\beta)} R_0(\beta,r)\bar{T}(\beta,t)\,d\beta$ (13-112a)

Integral transform : $\quad \bar{T}(\beta,t) = \int\limits_{r'=a}^{\infty} r' R_0(\beta,r')T(r',t)\,dr'$ (13-112b)

where the functions $R_0(\beta,r)$ and $N(\beta)$ are available from Table 3-3 for the three different boundary conditions at $r = a$. The problem is solved by taking integral transform of the system (13-111) according to the transform (13-112b), utilizing the eigenvalue problem (3-52) as discussed previously, solving for the transform of the temperature and inverting the transform by the inversion formula (13-112a). We obtain

$$T(r,t) = \int\limits_{\beta=0}^{\infty} \dfrac{\beta}{N(\beta)} R_0(\beta,r) e^{-\alpha\beta^2 t}\left[\bar{F}(\beta) + \int\limits_{t'=0}^{\infty} e^{\alpha\beta^2 t'} A(\beta,t')\,dt' \right] d\beta \quad (13\text{-}113\text{a})$$

where

$$A(\beta,t') = \dfrac{\alpha}{k}\bar{g}(\beta,t') + \alpha a \left.\dfrac{R_0(\beta,r)}{k_1}\right|_{r=a} f_1(t') \quad (13\text{-}113\text{b})$$

$$\bar{F}(\beta) = \int\limits_{r'=a}^{\infty} r' R_0(\beta,r')F(r')\,dr' \quad (13\text{-}113\text{c})$$

$$\bar{g}(\beta,t') = \int\limits_{r'=a}^{\infty} r' R_0(\beta,r')g(r',t')\,dr' \quad (13\text{-}113\text{d})$$

Two-Dimensional Problems in (r, ϕ, t) Variables

When the partial derivatives with respect to the r and ϕ variables are to be removed from the heat-conduction equation, the order of integral transformation is important. *It should be applied first with respect to the ϕ variable and then to the r variable.* Therefore, we need the integral-transform pair that will remove from the differential equation the partial derivative with respect to the ϕ variable, that is $\partial^2 T/\partial\phi^2$. The ranges of the ϕ variable in the cylindrical coordinate system include $0 \le \phi \le 2\pi$ as in the case of problems of *full cylinder* and $0 \le \phi \le \phi_0$, for $\phi_0 < 2\pi$, as in the case of problems of a *portion of the cylinder*. The Integral transform pairs for each of these two situations are different. Therefore, we first develop the integral-transform pairs with respect to the ϕ variable for these two cases and then present its application in the solution of heat-conduction problems.

Transform Pair for $0 \le \phi \le 2\pi$. In this case since the region in the ϕ variable is a full circle, no boundary conditions are specified in ϕ except the requirement that the function should be cyclic with a period of 2π. The appropriate eigenvalue problem in ϕ is given by equation (3-126a) and the representation of a function in the interval $0 \le \phi \le 2\pi$ in terms of the eigenfunctions of this eigenvalue problem is given by equation (3-131b). Therefore, the integral-transform pair with respect to the ϕ variable for the function $T(r, \phi, t)$ is obtained according to the representation (3-131b). We find

Inversion formula: $\displaystyle T(r, \phi, t) = \frac{1}{\pi} \sum_{v} \bar{T}(r, v, t)$ (13-114a)

Integral transform: $\displaystyle \bar{T}(r, v, t) = \int\limits_{\phi' = 0}^{2\pi} \cos v(\phi - \phi') T(r, \phi', t) \, d\phi'$

(13-114b)

where $v = 0, 1, 2, 3 \ldots$ and replace π by 2π for $v = 0$.

Transform Pair for $0 \le \phi \le \phi_0 (\phi_0 < 2\pi)$. The region being a portion of a circle, boundary conditions are needed at $\phi = 0$ and $\phi = \phi_0$. These boundary conditions may be any combination of the boundary condition of the first, the second, or the third kind. Therefore, the eigenvalue problem, in the general form, is given as

$$\frac{d^2\Phi(\phi)}{d\phi^2} + v^2\Phi(\phi) = 0 \qquad \text{in } 0 < \phi < \phi_0 (< 2\pi) \qquad (13\text{-}115a)$$

$$-k_1 \frac{d\Phi(\phi)}{d\phi} + h_1\Phi(\phi) = 0 \qquad \text{at } \phi = 0 \qquad (13\text{-}115b)$$

$$k_2 \frac{d\Phi(\phi)}{d\phi} + h_2\Phi(\phi) = 0 \qquad \text{at } \phi = \phi_0 \qquad (13\text{-}115c)$$

which is exactly of the same form as that given by equations (2-32) for the one-dimensional finite region $0 \le x \le L$ in the rectangular coordinate system. Therefore, the integral transform pair in the ϕ variable for the function $T(r, \phi, t)$, defined in the interval $0 \le \phi \le \phi_0$, is immediately obtainable from the integral transform pair (13-37) with appropriate change in the notation. We find

Inversion formula: $\displaystyle T(r, \phi, t) = \sum_{v} \frac{\Phi(v, \phi)}{N(v)} \bar{T}(r, v, t)$ (13-116a)

Integral transform: $\displaystyle \bar{T}(r, v, t) = \int\limits_{\phi = 0}^{\phi_0} \Phi(v, \phi') T(r, \phi', t) \, d\phi'$ (13-116b)

where

$$N(v) = \int_0^{\phi_0} [\Phi(v, \phi)]^2 \, d\phi \qquad (13\text{-}116c)$$

Here the functions $\Phi(v, \phi), N(v)$ and the eigenvalues v are obtainable from Table 2-2, by appropriate change in the notation for any one of the nine combinations of boundary conditions at the surfaces $\phi = 0$ and $\phi = \phi_0$.

Having established the integral transform pairs needed for the removal of the differential operator $\partial^2 T / \partial \phi^2$ from the heat-conduction equation, we now proceed to the solution of heat-conduction problems involving (r, ϕ, t) variables.

Problems of Region $0 \le r \le b, 0 \le \phi \le 2\pi$. We consider the following time-dependent heat-conduction problem for a solid cylinder of radius $r = b$, in which temperature varies both r and ϕ variables

$$\frac{\partial^2 T}{\partial r^2} + \frac{1}{r} \frac{\partial T}{\partial r} + \frac{1}{r^2} \frac{\partial^2 T}{\partial \phi^2} + \frac{g(r, \phi, t)}{k} = \frac{1}{\alpha} \frac{\partial T(r, \phi, t)}{\partial t}$$

$$\text{in } 0 \le r < b, \ 0 \le \phi \le 2\pi, \ t > 0 \quad (13\text{-}117a)$$

$$k_2 \frac{\partial T}{\partial r} + h_2 T = f_2(\phi, t) \qquad \text{at } r = b, \ t > 0 \qquad (13\text{-}117b)$$

$$T(r, \phi, t) = F(r, \phi) \qquad \text{for } t = 0, \text{ in the region} \qquad (13\text{-}117c)$$

This problem is now solved by successive application of the integral transforms with respect to the ϕ and r variables

The integral transform pair in the ϕ variable for the function $T(r, \phi, t)$ is given by equation (13-114). Hence we have

Inversion formula: $\qquad T(r, \phi, t) = \frac{1}{\pi} \sum_v \bar{T}(r, v, t) \qquad (13\text{-}118a)$

Integral transform: $\qquad \bar{T}(r, v, t) = \int_{\phi' = 0}^{2\pi} \cos v(\phi - \phi') T(r, \phi', t) \, d\phi'$

$$(13\text{-}118b)$$

where $v = 0, 1, 2, 3 \dots$ and replace π by 2π for $v = 0$. The integral transform of the system (13-117) by the application of the transform (13-118b) yields (see Note 5 for the details)

$$\frac{\partial^2 \bar{T}}{\partial r^2} + \frac{1}{r} \frac{\partial \bar{T}}{\partial r} - \frac{v^2}{r^2} \bar{T} + \frac{\bar{g}(r, v, t)}{k} = \frac{1}{\alpha} \frac{\partial \bar{T}(r, v, t)}{\partial t} \quad \text{in } 0 \le r < b, \ t > 0 \quad (13\text{-}119a)$$

$$k_2 \frac{\partial \bar{T}}{\partial r} + h_2 \bar{T} = \bar{f}_2(v, t) \qquad \text{at } r = b, \ t > 0 \qquad (13\text{-}119b)$$

$$\bar{T}(r, v, t) = \bar{F}(r, v) \qquad \text{for } t = 0, \text{ in } 0 \leq r \leq b$$

$$(13\text{-}119c)$$

where the bar denotes the integral transform with respect to the ϕ variable.

The integral transform pair in the r variable for the function $\bar{T}(r, v, t)$ is obtainable according to the representation (3-22). We find

Inversion formula: $\qquad \bar{T}(r, v, t) = \sum_{m=1}^{\infty} \dfrac{R_v(\beta_m, r)}{N(\beta_m)} \tilde{\bar{T}}(\beta_m, v, t) \quad (13\text{-}120a)$

Integral transform: $\qquad \tilde{\bar{T}}(\beta_m, v, t) = \int_0^b r' R_v(\beta_m, r') \bar{T}(r', v, t) \, dr' \quad (13\text{-}120b)$

Here, the tilde denotes the integral transform with respect to the r variable. $R_v(\beta_m, r)$ and β_m are the eigenfunctions and eigenvalues associated with the eigenvalue problem given by equations (3-18). The functions $R_v(\beta_m, r)$, $N(\beta_m)$ and the eigenvalues β_m are obtainable from Table 3-1 for the three different boundary conditions at $r = b$.

The integral transform of the system (13-119) by the application of the transform (13-120b) yields (seeNote 6 for the details)

$$\frac{d\tilde{\bar{T}}}{dt} + \alpha\beta_m^2 \tilde{\bar{T}}(\beta_m, v, t) = \frac{\alpha}{k}\tilde{\bar{g}}(\beta_m, v, t) + \alpha b \left.\frac{R_v(\beta_m, r)}{k_2}\right|_{r=b} \cdot \bar{f}_2(v, t) \quad (13\text{-}121a)$$

$$\tilde{\bar{T}}(\beta_m, v, t) = \tilde{\bar{F}}(\beta_m, v) \qquad \text{for } t = 0 \qquad (13\text{-}121b)$$

Equation (13-121) is solved for $\tilde{\bar{T}}(\beta_m, v, t)$ and the resulting double transform is successively inverted by the inversion formulas (13-120a) and (13-118a). Then, the solution of the problem (13-117) becomes

$$T(r, \phi, t) = \frac{1}{\pi} \sum_{v} \sum_{m=1}^{\infty} \frac{R_v(\beta_m, r)}{N(\beta_m)} \cdot e^{-\alpha\beta_m^2 t} \cdot \left[\tilde{\bar{F}}(\beta_m, v) + \int_{t'=0}^{t} e^{\alpha\beta_m^2 t'} A(\beta_m, v, t') \, dt' \right]$$

$$(13\text{-}122a)$$

where $v = 0, 1, 2, 3 \ldots$ and replace π by 2π for $v = 0$

$$A(\beta_m, v, t') = \frac{\alpha}{k}\tilde{\bar{g}}(\beta_m, v, t') + \alpha b \left.\frac{R_v(\beta_m, r)}{k_2}\right|_{r=b} \bar{f}_2(v, t) \quad (13\text{-}122b)$$

$$\bar{f}(v, t) = \int_{\phi'=0}^{2\pi} f_2(\phi', t) \cos v(\phi - \phi') \, d\phi' \quad (13\text{-}122c)$$

$$\tilde{\bar{F}}(\beta_m, v) = \int_{r'=0}^{b} \int_{\phi'=0}^{2\pi} r' R_v(\beta_m, r') \cos v(\phi - \phi') F(r', \phi') \, d\phi' \, dr' \quad (13\text{-}122d)$$

$$\tilde{\bar{g}}(\beta_m, v, t) = \int_{r'=0}^{b} \int_{\phi'=0}^{2\pi} R_v(\beta_m, r') \cos v(\phi - \phi') g(r', \phi', t') \, d\phi' \, dr' \quad (13\text{-}122e)$$

and the functions $R_v(\beta_m, r)$, $N(\beta_m)$ and the eigenvalues β_m are obtainable from Table 3-1.

For a boundary condition of the first kind at $r = b$, the following changes should be made in equation (3-122b). When $k_2 = 0$ replace

$$\left. \frac{R_v(\beta_m, r)}{k_2} \right|_{r=b}$$

by

$$-\left. \frac{1}{h_2} \frac{dR_v(\beta_m, r)}{dr} \right|_{r=b} \tag{13-122f}$$

Problems of Region $a \le r \le b, 0 \le \phi \le 2\pi$. The extension of the above analysis for solid cylinder to the solution of time-dependent heat-conduction problem of a hollow cylinder $a \le r \le b$, in which temperature varies with both r and ϕ variables is a straightforward matter. Clearly, the heat-conduction problem (13-117) will involve an additional boundary condition at $r = a$. The definition of the integral-transform pair (13-118) remains the same, but that of (13-120) is modified by changing the lower limit of the integration to $r = a$; then the functions $R_v(\beta_m, r)$, $N(\beta_m)$ and the eigenvalues β_m are to be obtained from Table 3-2. As a result, the solution (3-122) will include an additional term in the definition of $A(\beta_m, v, t')$ for the effects of the boundary condition at $r = a$ and the lower limit of the integrations with respect to r' will be $r' = a$.

Problems of Region $0 \le r \le b, 0 \le \phi \le \phi_0 (< 2\pi)$. We now consider the solution by the integral transform technique of the following time-dependent heat-conduction problem for a portion of a solid cylinder of radius $r = b$, in the region $0 \le \phi \le \phi_0 (< 2\pi)$

$$\frac{\partial^2 T}{\partial r^2} + \frac{1}{r} \frac{\partial T}{\partial r} + \frac{1}{r^2} \frac{\partial^2 T}{\partial \phi^2} + \frac{g(r, \phi, t)}{k} = \frac{1}{\alpha} \frac{\partial T(r, \phi, t)}{\partial t}$$
$$\text{in } 0 \le r < b, \ 0 < \phi < \phi_0, \ t > 0 \tag{13-123a}$$

$$-k_1 \frac{\partial T}{r \partial \phi} + h_1 T = f_1(r, t) \qquad \text{at } \phi = 0, \ t > 0 \tag{13-123b}$$

$$k_2 \frac{\partial T}{r \partial \phi} + h_2 T = f_2(r, t) \qquad \text{at } \phi = \phi_0, \ t > 0 \tag{13-123c}$$

$$k_4 \frac{\partial T}{\partial r} + h_4 T = f_4(\phi, t) \qquad \text{at } r = b, \ t > 0 \tag{13-123d}$$

$$T(r, \phi, t) = F(r, \phi) \qquad \text{for } t = 0, \text{ in the region} \tag{13-123e}$$

Clearly, several special cases are obtainable from this problem. The problem is now solved by the successive application of the integral transformation, first in the ϕ variable, and then in the r variable.

The integral transform pair in the ϕ variable for the function $T(r, \phi, t)$ is obtained from equations (13-116) as

Inversion formula:
$$T(r, \phi, t) = \sum_{v} \frac{\Phi(v, \phi)}{N(v)} \bar{T}(r, v, t)$$ (13-124a)

Integral transform:
$$\bar{T}(r, v, t) = \int_{0}^{\phi_0} \Phi(v, \phi')T(r, \phi', t)\,d\phi'$$ (13-124b)

where the functions $\Phi(v, \phi)$, $N(v)$ and the eigenvalues v are obtainable from Table 2-2 by appropriate change of the notation (i.e., $L \to \phi_0, \beta_m \to v, x \to \phi$). We note that the eigenvalues v for this case are not integers, but are determined according to the transcendental equations given in Table 2-2.

The integral transform of the system (13-123) by the application of the transform (13-124b) yields

$$\frac{\partial^2 \bar{T}}{\partial r^2} + \frac{1}{r}\frac{\partial \bar{T}}{\partial r} - \frac{v^2}{r^2}\bar{T} + \left[\frac{\Phi(v, \phi)}{k_1}\bigg|_{\phi=0} r \cdot f_1(r, t) + \frac{\Phi(v, \phi)}{k_2}\bigg|_{\phi=\phi_0} r \cdot f_2(r, t)\right]$$
$$+ \frac{1}{k}\bar{g}(r, v, t) = \frac{1}{\alpha}\frac{\partial \bar{T}(r, v, t)}{\partial t} \qquad \text{in } 0 \leq r < b, \ t > 0$$ (13-125a)

$$k_4 \frac{\partial \bar{T}}{\partial r} + h_4 \bar{T} = \bar{f}_4(v, t) \qquad\qquad \text{at } r = b, \ t > 0$$ (13-125b)

$$\bar{T}(r, v, t) = \bar{F}(r, v) \qquad\qquad \text{for } t = 0, \text{ in } 0 \leq r \leq b$$ (13-125c)

where the bar denotes the integral transform of the function with respect to the ϕ variable.

The integral-transform pair in the r variable for the function $\bar{T}(r, v, t)$ is immediately obtained from the transform pair (13-120) as

Inversion formula:
$$\bar{T}(r, v, t) = \sum_{m=1}^{\infty} \frac{R_v(\beta_m, r)}{N(\beta_m)} \tilde{\bar{T}}(\beta_m, v, t)$$ (13-126a)

Integral transform:
$$\tilde{\bar{T}}(\beta_m, v, t) = \int_{0}^{b} r' R_v(\beta_m, r')\bar{T}(r', v, t)\,dr'$$ (13-126b)

where the tilde denotes the integral transform with respect to the r variable. The functions $R_v(\beta_m, r)$, $N(\beta_m)$ and the eigenvalues β_m are obtainable from Table 3-1.

The integral transform of the system (13-125) by the application of the transform (13-126b) yields (i.e., the procedure is similar to that described in

Note 6)

$$\frac{d\tilde{\tilde{T}}}{dt} + \alpha\beta_m^2\tilde{\tilde{T}}(\beta_m, v, t) = A(\beta_m, v, t) \quad \text{for } t > 0 \qquad (13\text{-}127a)$$

$$\tilde{\tilde{T}}(\beta_m, v, t) = \tilde{\bar{F}}(\beta_m, v) \qquad \text{for } t = 0 \qquad (13\text{-}127b)$$

where

$$A(\beta_m, v, t) \equiv \frac{\alpha}{k}\tilde{\bar{g}}(\beta_m, v, t) + \alpha\left[\frac{\Phi(v, \phi)}{k_1}\bigg|_{\phi=0} \cdot \tilde{f}_1^*(\beta_m, t) + \frac{\Phi(v, \phi)}{k_2}\bigg|_{\phi=\phi_0} \tilde{f}_2^*(\beta_m, t)\right.$$

$$\left. + b\frac{R_v(\beta_m, r)}{k_4}\bigg|_{r=b} \cdot \bar{f}_4(v, t)\right] \qquad (13\text{-}128a)$$

$$f_i^* \equiv rf_i, \quad i = 1 \text{ or } 2. \qquad (13\text{-}128b)$$

Equation (13-127) is solved for $\tilde{\tilde{T}}(\beta_m, v, t)$, the resulting double transform of the temperature is successively inverted by the inversion formulas (13-126a) and (13-124a). Then, the solution of the problem (13-123) becomes

$$T(r, \phi, t) = \sum_v \sum_{m=1}^{\infty} \frac{\Phi(v, \phi)R_v(\beta_m, r)}{N(v)N(\beta_m)} e^{-\alpha\beta_m^2 t} \cdot \left[\tilde{\bar{F}}(\beta_m, v) + \int_{t'=0}^{t} e^{\alpha\beta_m^2 t'} A(\beta_m, v, t')dt'\right]$$

$$(13\text{-}129)$$

where $A(\beta_m, v, t')$ is defined by equations (13-128) and $\tilde{\bar{F}}, \tilde{\bar{g}}$ are the double transforms, that is,

$$\tilde{\bar{H}}(\beta_m, v) \equiv \int_{r'=0}^{b} \int_{\phi'=0}^{\phi_0} r'R\ (\beta_m, r')\Phi(v, \phi')\bar{H}(r', \phi')d\phi'\ dr', \quad \text{and} \quad H \equiv F \text{ or } g$$

$$(13\text{-}130)$$

The bar denotes the integral transform with respect to the ϕ variable and the tilde the integral transform with respect to the r variable as defined by equations (13-124b) and (13-126b), respectively.

For a boundary condition of the first kind at any of these boundaries, the usual replacements should be made in the definition of $A(\beta_m, v, t)$ given by equation (13-128a).

Problems of Region $a \leq r \leq b, 0 \leq \phi \leq \phi_0(\phi_0 < 2\pi)$. The extension of the above solution to the problem of time-dependent heat-conduction in a hollow cylinder $a \leq r \leq b$, confined to a region $0 \leq \phi \leq \phi_0(< 2\pi)$ is a straightforward matter. The heat-conduction problem (13-123) will include an additional boundary condition at $r = a$. The definition of the integral transform pair (13-124) remains the same, but that of given by equations (13-126) is modified by changing the lower limit of the integration to $r = a$;

then, the function $R_v(\beta_m, r)$, $N(\beta_m)$ and the eigenvalues β_m are obtained from Table 3-2. As a result, the solution will include an additional term in the definition of $A(\beta_m, v, t)$ given by equation (13-128) to account for the effects of the boundary condition at $r = a$.

Problems of Region $0 \leq r < \infty, 0 \leq \phi \leq 2\pi$. We now consider the solution of the following time dependent heat-conduction problem for an infinite medium in which temperature varies with both r and ϕ variables.

$$\frac{\partial^2 T}{\partial r^2} + \frac{1}{r}\frac{\partial T}{\partial r} + \frac{1}{r^2}\frac{\partial^2 T}{\partial \phi^2} + \frac{g(r, \phi, t)}{k} = \frac{1}{\alpha}\frac{\partial T(r, \phi, t)}{\partial t}$$

$$\text{in } 0 \leq r < \infty, \ 0 \leq \phi \leq 2\pi, \ t > 0 \qquad (13\text{-}131\text{a})$$

$$T(r, \phi, t) = F(r, \phi) \qquad \text{for } t = 0, \text{ in the region} \qquad (13\text{-}131\text{b})$$

The integral-transform pair in the ϕ variable for the function $T(r, \phi, t)$ is given by equation (13-114); hence we have

$$\text{Inversion formula:} \qquad T(r, \phi, t) = \frac{1}{\pi}\sum_v \bar{T}(r, v, t) \qquad (13\text{-}132\text{a})$$

$$\text{Integral transform:} \qquad \bar{T}(r, v, t) = \int_{\phi'=0}^{2\pi} \cos v(\phi - \phi')T(r, \phi', t)\, d\phi'$$

$$(13\text{-}132\text{b})$$

where $v = 0, 1, 2, 3 \ldots$ and replace π by 2π for $v = 0$. The integral transform of the system (13-131) by the application of the transform (13-132b) yields

$$\frac{\partial^2 \bar{T}}{\partial r^2} + \frac{1}{r}\frac{\partial \bar{T}}{\partial r} - \frac{v^2}{r^2}\bar{T} + \frac{\bar{g}(r, v, t)}{k} = \frac{1}{\alpha}\frac{\partial \bar{T}(r, v, t)}{\partial t} \qquad \text{in } 0 \leq r < \infty, \ t > 0 \quad (13\text{-}133\text{a})$$

$$\bar{T}(r, v, t) = \bar{F}(r, v) \qquad\qquad \text{for } t = 0, \text{ in } 0 \leq r < \infty$$

$$(13\text{-}133\text{b})$$

where the bar denotes the integral transform with respect to the ϕ variable.

The integral transform pair in the r variable for the function $\bar{T}(r, v, t)$ is constructed according to the representation (3-51). We find

$$\text{Inversion formula:} \qquad \bar{T}(r, v, t) = \int_{\beta=0}^{\infty} \beta J_v(\beta r)\tilde{\bar{T}}(\beta, v, t)\, d\beta \qquad (13\text{-}134\text{a})$$

$$\text{Integral transform:} \qquad \tilde{\bar{T}}(\beta, v, t) = \int_{r'=0}^{\infty} r' J_v(\beta r')\bar{T}(r', v, t)\, dr' \qquad (13\text{-}134\text{b})$$

where tilde denotes the integral transform with respect to the r variable and the eigenvalue problem associated with this transform pair is given by equations (3-48).

The integral transform of the system (13-133) by the application of the transform (13-134b) gives

$$\frac{d\tilde{\bar{T}}}{dt} + \alpha\beta^2 \tilde{\bar{T}}(\beta, v, t) = \frac{\alpha}{k}\tilde{\bar{g}}(\beta, v, t) \qquad \text{for } t > 0 \qquad (13\text{-}135a)$$

$$\tilde{\bar{T}}(\beta, v, t) = \tilde{\bar{F}}(\beta, v) \qquad \text{for } t = 0 \qquad (13\text{-}135b)$$

Equation (13-135) is solved for $\tilde{\bar{T}}(\beta, v, t)$ and the resulting double transform is successively inverted by the inversion formulas (13-134a) and (13-132a). Then the solution of the problem (13-131) becomes

$$T(r, \phi, t) = \frac{1}{\pi}\sum_v \int_{\beta=0}^{\infty} \beta J_v(\beta r) e^{-\alpha\beta^2 t}\left[\tilde{\bar{F}}(\beta, v) + \frac{\alpha}{k}\int_{t'=0}^{t} e^{\alpha\beta^2 t'}\tilde{\bar{g}}(\beta, v, t')\,dt'\right]d\beta$$
$$(13\text{-}136a)$$

where $v = 0, 1, 2, 3 \ldots$ and replace π by 2π for $v = 0$

$$\tilde{\bar{F}}(\beta, v) = \int_{r'=0}^{\infty}\int_{\phi'=0}^{2\pi} r' J_v(\beta r')\cos v(\phi - \phi')F(r', \phi')\,d\phi'\,dr' \quad (13\text{-}136b)$$

$$\tilde{\bar{g}}(\beta, v, t') = \int_{r'=0}^{\infty}\int_{\phi'=0}^{2\pi} r' J_v(\beta r')\cos v(\phi - \phi')g(r', \phi', t')\,d\phi'\,dr' \quad (13\text{-}136c)$$

Introducing equations (13-136b, c) into equation (13-136a) and changing the order of integrations we obtain

$$T(r, \phi, t) = \frac{1}{\pi}\sum_v \int_{r'=0}^{\infty}\int_{\phi'=0}^{2\pi} r'\cos v(\phi - \phi')F(r', \phi')$$
$$\cdot\left[\int_{\beta=0}^{\infty} e^{-\alpha\beta^2 t}\beta J_v(\beta r)J_v(\beta r')\,d\beta\right]d\phi'\,dr'$$
$$+\frac{1}{\pi}\frac{\alpha}{k}\sum_v \int_{r'=0}^{\infty}\int_{\phi'=0}^{2\pi} r'\cos v(\phi - \phi')g(r', \phi, t')$$
$$\cdot\left[\int_{\beta=0}^{\infty} e^{-\alpha\beta^2(t-t')}\beta J_v(\beta r)J_v(\beta r')\,d\beta\right]dt'\,d\phi'\,dr' \qquad (13\text{-}137)$$

The terms inside the bracket can be evaluated by utilizing the expression (13-109). Then the solution (13-137) becomes

$$T(r, \phi, t) = \frac{1}{2\pi\alpha t}\sum_v \int_{\phi'=0}^{2\pi} r'\cos v(\phi - \phi')F(r', \phi')$$
$$\cdot\exp\left[-\frac{r^2 + r'^2}{4\alpha t}\right]I_v\left(\frac{rr'}{2\alpha t}\right)d\phi'\,dr'$$
$$+\frac{1}{2\pi k}\sum_v \int_{r'=0}^{\infty}\int_{\phi'=0}^{2\pi}\int_{t'=0}^{t}\frac{r'}{t - t'}\cos v(\phi - \phi')g(r', \phi', t')$$
$$\cdot\exp\left[-\frac{r^2 + r'^2}{4\alpha(t-t')}\right]I_v\left(\frac{rr'}{2\alpha(t-t')}\right)dt'\,d\phi'\,dr' \qquad (13\text{-}138)$$

where $v = 0, 1, 2, 3 \ldots$ and replace π by 2π for $v = 0$. Several special cases are obtainable from this solution.

Two-Dimensional Problems in (r, z, t) Variables

The solution of time-dependent heat-conduction problems in the (r, z) variables with the integral-transform technique is now a straightforward matter. The integral-transform pairs with respect to the r variable are the same as those developed in this section for the problems having azimuthal symmetry and those with respect to the z variable are the same as those for the rectangular coordinate system. Also, the order of integral transformation with respect to the r and z variables is immaterial. We illustrate this matter with the following example.

Example 13-6. Consider the solution of the following heat-conduction problem for a solid cylinder of radius $r = b$ and height $z = L$

$$\frac{\partial^2 T}{\partial r^2} + \frac{1}{r}\frac{\partial T}{\partial r} + \frac{\partial^2 T}{\partial z^2} + \frac{g(r,z,t)}{k} = \frac{1}{\alpha}\frac{\partial T(r,z,t)}{\partial t} \quad \text{in } 0 \le r < b,\ 0 < z < L,\ t > 0$$

$$(13\text{-}139a)$$

$$T(r,z,t) = 0 \qquad\qquad\qquad\qquad \text{on all boundaries, } t > 0$$

$$(13\text{-}139b)$$

$$T(r,z,t) = F(r,z) \qquad\qquad\qquad \text{for } t = 0, \text{ in the region}$$

$$(13\text{-}139c)$$

Solution. The integral transform pair for the removal of partial derivatives with respect to the r variable in the region $0 \le r \le b$ is the same as that given by equations (13-97). Hence the transform pair with respect to the r variable for the function $T(r,z,t)$ is

Inversion formula: $\qquad T(r,z,t) = \sum_{m=1}^{\infty} \frac{R_0(\beta_m, r)}{N(\beta_m)}\bar{T}(\beta_m, z, t)$ (13-140a)

Integral transform: $\qquad \bar{T}(\beta_m, z, t) = \int_{r'=0}^{b} r' R_0(\beta_m, r') T(r', z, t)$ (13-140b)

where $R_0(\beta_m, r)$, $N(\beta_m)$, and β_m are obtainable from Table 3-1 by setting $v = 0$ and the bar denotes transform with respect to the r variable.

The integral transform of the system (13-139) by the application of the transform (13-140b) yields

$$-\beta_m^2 \bar{T}(\beta_m, z, t) + \frac{\partial^2 \bar{T}}{\partial z^2} + \frac{\bar{g}(\beta_m, z, t)}{k} = \frac{1}{\alpha}\frac{\partial \bar{T}(\beta_m, z, t)}{\partial t}$$

$$\text{in } 0 < z < L,\ t > 0 \qquad\qquad (13\text{-}141a)$$

$$\bar{T}(\beta_m, z, t) = 0 \qquad\qquad \text{at } z = 0, \ z = L \text{ for } t > 0 \qquad\qquad (13\text{-}141\text{b})$$

$$\bar{T}(\beta_m, z, t) = \bar{F}(\beta_m, z) \qquad \text{for } t = 0, \ \text{in } 0 < z < L \qquad\qquad (13\text{-}141\text{c})$$

The integral-transform pair with respect to the z variable in the region $0 \le z \le L$ is obtained from equations (13-37) as

$$\text{Inversion formula:} \qquad \bar{T}(\beta_m, z, t) = \sum_{p=1}^{\infty} \frac{Z(\eta_p, z)}{N(\eta_p)} \tilde{\bar{T}}(\beta_m, \eta_p, t) \quad (13\text{-}142\text{a})$$

$$\text{Integral transform:} \qquad \tilde{\bar{T}}(\beta_m, \eta_p, t) = \int_{z'=0}^{L} Z(\eta_p, z') \bar{T}(\beta_m, z', t) \, dz'$$
$$(13\text{-}142\text{b})$$

where $Z(\eta_p, z)$, $N(\eta_p)$, and η_p are obtainable from Table 2-2, and the tilde denotes the integral transform with respect to the z variable.

The integral transform of the system (13-141) by the application of the transform (13-142b) is

$$\frac{d\tilde{\bar{T}}}{dt} + \alpha(\beta_m^2 + \eta_p^2)\tilde{\bar{T}}(\beta_m, \eta_p, t) = \frac{\alpha}{k}\tilde{\bar{g}}(\beta_m, \eta_p, t) \qquad t > 0 \qquad (13\text{-}143\text{a})$$

$$\tilde{\bar{T}}(\beta_m, \eta_p, t) = \tilde{\bar{F}}(\beta_m, \eta_p) \qquad\qquad\qquad t = 0 \qquad (13\text{-}143\text{b})$$

Equation (13-143) is solved for $\tilde{\bar{T}}(\beta_m, \eta_p, t)$ and the resulting double transform is successively inverted by the inversion formulas (13-142a) and (13-140a). Then the solution of the problem (13-139) becomes

$$T(r, z, t) = \sum_{m=1}^{\infty} \sum_{p=1}^{\infty} \frac{R_0(\beta_m, r)Z(\eta_p, z)}{N(\beta_m)N(\eta_p)} e^{-\alpha(\beta_m^2 + \eta_p^2)t}$$
$$\cdot \left[\tilde{\bar{F}}(\beta_m, \eta_p) + \frac{\alpha}{k} \int_{t'=0}^{t} e^{\alpha(\beta_m^2 + \eta_p^2)t'} \tilde{\bar{g}}(\beta_m, \eta_p, t') \, dt' \right] \qquad (13\text{-}144\text{a})$$

where the double transforms are defined as

$$\tilde{\bar{H}} = \int_{z'=0}^{L} \int_{r'=0}^{b} R_0(\beta_m, r')Z(\eta_p, z')H \, dr' \, dz', \qquad H \equiv F \text{ or } g \quad (13\text{-}144\text{b})$$

From Table 3-1, case 3, for $v = 0$ we have

$$R_0(\beta_m, r) = J_0(\beta_m r), \qquad \frac{1}{N(\beta_m)} = \frac{2}{b^2 J_0'^2(\beta_m b)} = \frac{2}{b^2 J_1^2(\beta_m b)}$$

and β_m's are the roots of $J_0(\beta_m b) = 0$. From Table 2-2, case 9 we have

$$Z(\eta_p, z) = \sin \eta_p z, \qquad \frac{1}{N(\eta_p)} = \frac{2}{L}$$

and η_p's are the roots of $\sin \eta_p L = 0$.

Three-Dimensional Problems in (r, ϕ, z, t) Variables

The solution of heat-conduction problems in (r, ϕ, z, t) variables is readily handled with the integral-transform technique. The basic steps in the analysis are summarized below.

1. The partial derivative with respect to the z variable is removed by the application of transform in the z variable. The appropriate transform pairs are the same as those given for the rectangular coordinate system.

2. The partial derivative with respect to the ϕ variable is removed by the application of transform in the ϕ variable. If the range of ϕ is $0 \leq \phi \leq 2\pi$, the transform pair is given by equations (13-114); if the range of ϕ is $0 \leq \phi \leq \phi_0, (\phi_0 < 2\pi)$, the transform pair is given by equations (13-116).

3. The partial derivatives with respect to the r variable are removed by the application of transform in the r variable. The transform pair to be used depends on the range of the r variable, that is, $0 \leq r \leq b, a \leq r \leq b$, $0 \leq r < \infty$. For example, the transform pair is as given by equations (13-120) for $0 \leq r \leq b$ or given by equations (13-134) for $0 \leq r < \infty$.

4. The resulting ordinary differential equation with respect to the time variable is solved subject to the triple transformed initial condition. The triple transform of temperature obtained in this manner is successively inverted with respect to the r, ϕ, and z variables to obtain the solution for $T(r, \phi, z, t)$.

13-5 APPLICATIONS IN THE SPHERICAL COORDINATE SYSTEM

To solve heat-conduction problems in the spherical coordinate system with the integral-transform technique, appropriate integral-transform pairs are needed in the r, μ, and ϕ variables. In this section we develop such integral-transform pairs and illustrate their application to the solution of heat-conduction problems involving $(r, t), (r, \mu, t)$ and (r, μ, ϕ, t) variables.

One-Dimensional Problems in (r, t) Variables

The time-dependent heat-conduction problems involving only the r variable can be transformed into a one-dimensional, time-dependent heat-conduction problem in the rectangular coordinate system by defining a new variable $U(r, t) = rT(r, t)$ as discussed in Section 4-4. The resulting heat-conduction problem in the rectangular coordinate system is readily solved with the integral-transform technique as described previously. Therefore, the solution of the problems in (r, t) variables is not considered here any further.

Two-Dimensional Problems in (r, μ, t) Variables

The differential equation of heat conduction in the (r, μ, t) variables is in the form

$$\frac{\partial^2 T}{\partial r^2} + \frac{2}{r}\frac{\partial T}{\partial r} + \frac{1}{r^2}\frac{\partial}{\partial \mu}\left[(1 - \mu^2)\frac{\partial T}{\partial \mu}\right] + \frac{g(r, \mu, t)}{k} = \frac{1}{\alpha}\frac{\partial T(r, \mu, t)}{\partial t} \quad (13\text{-}145)$$

By defining a new variable $V(r, \mu, t)$ as

$$V(r, \mu, t) = r^{1/2}T(r, \mu, t) \quad (13\text{-}146)$$

Equation (13-145) is transformed into

$$\frac{\partial^2 V}{\partial r^2} + \frac{1}{r}\frac{\partial V}{\partial r} - \frac{1}{4}\frac{V}{r^2} + \frac{1}{r^2}\frac{\partial}{\partial \mu}\left[(1 - \mu^2)\frac{\partial V}{\partial \mu}\right] + \frac{r^{1/2}g}{k} = \frac{1}{\alpha}\frac{\partial V}{\partial t} \quad (13\text{-}147)$$

where $g \equiv g(r, \mu, t)$ and $V \equiv V(r, \mu, t)$.

The partial derivatives with respect to the space variables can be removed from this equation by the successive application of integral transforms with respect to the μ and r variables. *The order of transformation is important in this case; it is applied first to the μ variable and then to the r variable.* It will soon be apparent that, after the removal of the derivative in the μ variable, the integral-transform pairs needed for the removal of the r variable are exactly the same as those given previously for the cylindrical coordinate system. Then we need to develop the integral transform pairs only with respect to the μ variable for the following three cases: The range of μ variable is $-1 \le \mu \le 1$ as in the case of the *full sphere*; $0 \le \mu \le 1$ as in the case of the *hemisphere*; or $\mu_0 \le \mu \le 1$ as in the case of *a sphere cut out of a cone* $\theta = \theta_0$ as illustrated in Fig. 4-2.

Transform pair for $-1 \le \mu \le 1$. This case corresponds to the full sphere. Therefore, no boundary conditions are specified in the μ variable except the requirement that the function should remain finite at $\mu = \pm 1$. The integral-transform pair in the μ variable for the function $V(r, \mu, t)$ is constructed by considering the representation of this function in a form similar to that given by equation (4-36) and then splitting up the representation into two parts. We find

Inversion formula: $\quad V(r, \mu, t) = \sum_{n=0}^{\infty} \frac{2n+1}{2} P_n(\mu)\bar{V}(r, n, t) \quad (13\text{-}148\text{a})$

Integral transform: $\quad \bar{V}(r, n, t) = \int_{\mu'=-1}^{1} P_n(\mu')V(r, \mu', t)d\mu' \quad (13\text{-}148\text{b})$

where $P_n(\mu)$ is the Legendre polynomial and $n = 0, 1, 2, 3 \ldots$. The differential equation (i.e., the eigenvalue problem) satisfied by the Legendre polynomials is the Legendre's differential equation given by equation 4-18, that is,

$$\frac{d}{d\mu}\left[(1-\mu^2)\frac{dM}{d\mu}\right]+n(n+1)M(\mu)=0 \qquad (13\text{-}149)$$

Transform Pair for $0 \leq \mu \leq 1$. This case corresponds to the hemisphere and requires a boundary condition at the surface $\mu = 0$. The integral-transform pair in the μ variable for the function $V(r,\mu,t)$ is constructed by considering the representation of this function in the interval $0 \leq \mu \leq 1$ in a form similar to that given by equation (4-51) and then splitting up the representation into two parts. We find

$$\text{Inversion formula:} \qquad V(r,\mu,t)=\sum_{n}^{\infty}(2n+1)P_n(\mu)\bar{V}(r,n,t) \qquad (13\text{-}150a)$$

$$\text{Integral transform:} \qquad \bar{V}(r,n,t)=\int_{\mu'=0}^{1}P_n(\mu')V(r,\mu',t)\,d\mu' \qquad (13\text{-}150b)$$

where the values of n depends on the type of the boundary condition at the surface $\mu = 0$ as follows:

$$n=\begin{cases}1,3,5\ldots & \text{for boundary condition of the first kind} \qquad (13\text{-}150c)\\ 0,2,4,6\ldots & \text{for boundary condition of the second kind} \qquad (13\text{-}150d)\end{cases}$$

and $P_n(\mu)$ functions satisfy the Legendre equation (4-18).

Transform Pair for $\mu_0 \leq \mu \leq 1(\mu_0 > -1)$. This case corresponds to a sphere cut out of a cone $\theta = \theta_0$ as illustrated in Fig. 4-2 and requires a boundary condition at the boundary surface $\theta = \theta_0$ or $\mu = \mu_0$ (i.e., at the surface of the cone). The integral-transform pair in the μ variable for the function $V(r,\mu,t)$ defined in the interval $\mu_0 \leq \mu \leq 1$ is constructed by considering the representation of this function in the interval $\mu_0 \leq \mu \leq 1$ in terms of the Legendre functions $P_n(\mu)$ defined by equation (4-22) for which n will admit both noninteger and integer values. Such a representation is made by utilizing the orthogonality property of $P_n(\mu)$ function in the interval $\mu_0 \leq \mu \leq 1$ given by equation (4-54) for $m = 0$. Then, the intergral-transform pair is constructed by splitting up this representation into two parts as the inversion formula and the integral transform as

$$\text{Inversion formula:} \qquad V(r,\mu,t)=\sum_{n}\frac{1}{N(n)}P_n(\mu)\bar{V}(r,n,t) \qquad (13\text{-}151a)$$

$$\text{Integral transform:} \qquad \bar{V}(r,n,t)=\int_{\mu'=\mu_0}^{1}P_n(\mu')V(r,\mu',t)\,d\mu' \qquad (13\text{-}151b)$$

where the normalization integral $N(n)$ is defined as

$$N(n) = \int_{\mu=\mu_0}^{1} [P_n(\mu)]^2 \, d\mu \tag{13-151c}$$

and the admissible values of n depends on the type of boundary condition at $\mu = \mu_0$. We consider the following two cases:

1. The boundary condition at $\mu = \mu_0$ is of the *first kind*; then n's are the roots of

$$P_n(\mu)\big|_{\mu=\mu_0} = 0 \tag{13-151d}$$

2. The boundary condition at $\mu = \mu_0$ is of the second kind; then n's are the roots of

$$\frac{dP(\mu)}{d\mu}\bigg|_{\mu=\mu_0} = 0 \tag{13-151e}$$

Some of the roots of equation (13-151d) are obtainable from Table 4-1 with $m = 0$ for $\mu_0 = 0.7071, 0.8660$, and 0.9659 corresponding to $\theta = \pi/4, \pi/6$, and $\pi/12$, respectively.

We note that the values of n are noninteger except for $\mu_0 = 0(\theta = \pi/2)$ corresponding to the hemisphere considered previously. For the special case of hemisphere, $P_n(\mu)$ are Legendre polynomials because n's are integers and the admissible values of n for the boundary conditions of the first and second kind are as given by equations (13-150c, d).

Having established the integral transform pairs in the μ variable for the function $V(r, \mu, t)$, we now proceed to the application of these transform pairs for the solution of heat-conduction problems in the (r, μ, t) variables.

Problems of Region $0 \le r \le b, -1 \le \mu \le 1$. We consider the solution of the following time-dependent heat-conduction problem for a solid sphere of radius $r = b$

$$\frac{\partial^2 T}{\partial r^2} + \frac{2}{r}\frac{\partial T}{\partial r} + \frac{1}{r^2}\frac{\partial}{\partial\mu}\left[(1-\mu^2)\frac{\partial T}{\partial\mu}\right] + \frac{g(r,\mu,t)}{k} = \frac{1}{\alpha}\frac{\partial T(r,\mu,t)}{\partial t}$$

$$\text{in } 0 \le r < b, \ -1 \le \mu \le 1, \ t > 0 \tag{13-152a}$$

$$T(r,\mu,t) = 0 \qquad \text{at } r = b, \ t > 0 \tag{13-152b}$$

$$T(r,\mu,t) = F(r,\mu) \qquad \text{for } t = 0, \text{ in the region} \tag{13-152c}$$

Here we considered a homogeneous boundary condition of the first kind for simplicity in the analysis; the analysis for boundary condition of the third kind is performed in a similar manner.

A new dependent variable $V(r, \mu, t)$ is defined as

$$V(r, \mu, t) = r^{1/2} T(r, \mu, t) \tag{13-152d}$$

Then, the problem (13-152) is transformed into

$$\frac{\partial^2 V}{\partial r^2} + \frac{1}{r}\frac{\partial V}{\partial r} - \frac{1}{4}\frac{V}{r^2} + \frac{1}{r^2}\frac{\partial}{\partial \mu}\left[(1 - \mu^2)\frac{\partial V}{\partial \mu}\right] + \frac{r^{1/2}g(r, \mu, t)}{k} = \frac{1}{\alpha}\frac{\partial V(r, \mu, t)}{\partial t}$$

$$\text{in } 0 \le r < b, \ -1 \le \mu \le 1, \ t > 0 \tag{13-153a}$$

$$V(r, \mu, t) = 0 \qquad \qquad \text{at } r = b, \ t > 0 \tag{13-153b}$$

$$V(r, \mu, t) = r^{1/2} F(r, \mu) \qquad \text{for } t = 0, \text{ in the region} \tag{13-153c}$$

The integral transform pair with respect to the μ variable for $-1 \le \mu \le 1$ is obtained from equations (13-148) as

$$\text{Inversion formula:} \qquad V(r, \mu, t) = \sum_{n=0}^{\infty} \frac{2n+1}{2} P_n(\mu)\bar{V}(r, n, t) \tag{13-154a}$$

$$\text{Integral transform:} \qquad \bar{V}(r, n, t) = \int_{\mu=-1}^{1} P_n(\mu')V(r, \mu', t)\,d\mu' \tag{13-154b}$$

where $n = 0, 1, 2, 3 \ldots$.

We take the integral transform of the system (13-153) by the application of the transform (13-154b) to obtain (see Note 7 for details)

$$\frac{\partial^2 \bar{V}}{\partial r^2} + \frac{1}{r}\frac{\partial \bar{V}}{\partial r} - \frac{(n+\frac{1}{2})^2}{r^2}\bar{V} + \frac{\bar{g}^*(r, n, t)}{k} = \frac{1}{\alpha}\frac{\partial \bar{V}(r, n, t)}{\partial t} \qquad \text{in } 0 \le r < b, \ t > 0$$

$$\tag{13-155a}$$

$$\bar{V}(r, n, t) = 0 \qquad \qquad \text{at } r = b, \ t > 0$$

$$\tag{13-155b}$$

$$\bar{V}(r, n, t) = \bar{F}^*(r, n) \qquad \qquad \text{for } t = 0, \text{ in } 0 \le r \le b$$

$$\tag{13-155c}$$

where

$$g^*(r, \mu, t) = r^{1/2} g(r, \mu, t), \qquad F^*(r, \mu) = r^{1/2} F(r, \mu) \tag{13-155d}$$

and the bar denotes the integral transform with respect to the μ variable according to the transform (13-154b).

Equation (13-155a) is similar in form to equation (13-125a) in the cylindrical coordinate system. Therefore, the integral-transform pair needed to remove the partial derivatives with respect to the r variable is immediately obtainable from equation (13-120) or (13-126) by setting $v \equiv n + \frac{1}{2}$. We find

Inversion formula; $\bar{V}(r, n, t) = \sum\limits_{p=1}^{\infty} \dfrac{R_{n+1/2}(\lambda_{np}, r)}{N(\lambda_{np})} \tilde{\bar{V}}(\lambda_{np}, n, t)$ (13-156a)

Integral transform: $\tilde{\bar{V}}(\lambda_{np}, n, t) = \int\limits_{0}^{b} r' R_{n+1/2}(\lambda_{np}, r') \bar{V}(r', n, t) dr'$ (13-156b)

where the tilde denotes the integral transform with respect to the r variable. The functions $R_{n+1/2}(\lambda_{np}, r)$, $N(\lambda_{np})$ and the eigenvalues λ_{np} for the boundary condition of the first kind considered in the problem (13-155) are obtainable from Table 3-1, case 3, as

$$R_{n+1/2}(\lambda_{np}, r) = J_{n+1/2}(\lambda_{np} r), \quad \frac{1}{N(\lambda_{np})} = \frac{2}{b^2 [J'_{n+1/2}(\lambda_{np} b)]^2} \quad (13\text{-}156c)$$

and λ_{np}'s are the positive roots of

$$J_{n+1/2}(\lambda_{np} b) = 0 \quad (13\text{-}156d)$$

Taking the integral transform of the system (13-155) by the application of the transform (13-156b) we obtain

$$\frac{d\tilde{\bar{V}}}{dt} + \alpha \lambda_{np}^2 \tilde{\bar{V}}(\lambda_{np}, n, t) = \frac{\alpha}{k} \tilde{\bar{g}}* \qquad \text{for } t > 0 \quad (13\text{-}157a)$$

$$\tilde{\bar{V}}(\lambda_{np}, n, t) = \tilde{\bar{F}}* \qquad \text{for } t = 0 \quad (13\text{-}157b)$$

Equation (13-157) is solved for $\tilde{\bar{V}}(\lambda_{np}, n, t)$, the resulting double transform is inverted successively by the inversion formulas (13-156a) and (13-154a) to obtain $V(r, \mu, t)$. When $V(r, \mu, t)$ is transformed by the expression (13-152d) into $T(r, \mu, t)$, the solution of the problem (13-151) is obtained as

$$T(r, \mu, t) = \sum_{n=0}^{\infty} \sum_{p=1}^{\infty} \frac{(2n+1) r^{-1/2} J_{n+1/2}(\lambda_{np} r) P_n(\mu)}{b^2 [J'_{n+1/2}(\lambda_{np} b)]^2} e^{-\alpha \lambda_{np}^2 t}$$

$$\cdot \left[\tilde{\bar{F}}* + \frac{\alpha}{k} \int_0^t e^{\alpha \lambda_{np}^2 t'} \tilde{\bar{g}}* \, dt' \right] \quad (13\text{-}158a)$$

where

$$\tilde{\bar{F}}* = \int\limits_{r'=0}^{b} \int\limits_{\mu'=-1}^{1} r'^{3/2} J_{n+1/2}(\lambda_{np} r') P_n(\mu') F(r', \mu') \, d\mu' \, dr' \quad (13\text{-}158b)$$

$$\tilde{\bar{g}}* = \int\limits_{r'=0}^{b} \int\limits_{\mu'=-1}^{1} r'^{3/2} J_{n+1/2}(\lambda_{np} r') P_n(\mu') g(r', \mu', t') \, d\mu' \, dt' \quad (13\text{-}158c)$$

where $n = 0, 1, 2 \ldots$ and λ_{np}'s are the roots of equation (13-156d). For the case of no heat generation, this solution reduces to that given by equation (4-88).

Problems of Region $0 \le r \le b, 0 \le \mu \le 1$. We consider the following time-dependent heat-conduction equation for a hemisphere of radius $r = b$;

$$\frac{\partial^2 T}{\partial r^2} + \frac{2}{r}\frac{\partial T}{\partial r} + \frac{1}{r^2}\frac{\partial}{\partial \mu}\left[(1-\mu^2)\frac{\partial T}{\partial \mu}\right] + \frac{g(r,\mu,t)}{k} = \frac{1}{\alpha}\frac{\partial T(r,\mu,t)}{\partial t}$$

$$\text{in } 0 \le r < b,\ 0 \le \mu \le 1,\ t > 0 \tag{13-159a}$$

$$T(r,\mu,t) = 0 \qquad \text{at } r = b,\ \mu = 0,\ \text{for } t > 0 \tag{13-159b}$$

$$T(r,\mu,t) = F(r,\mu) \qquad \text{for } t = 0, \text{ in the region} \tag{13-159c}$$

The basic steps for the solution of this problem are exactly the same as those described above for the solution of problem (13-152). The only difference is that, the range of μ being $0 \le \mu \le 1$, the integral-transform pair with respect to the μ variable is determined according to equations (13-150) as

$$\text{Inversion formula:} \qquad V(r,\mu,t) = \sum_n (2n+1)P_n(\mu)\bar{V}(r,n,t) \tag{13-160a}$$

$$\text{Integral transform:} \qquad \bar{V}(r,n,t) = \int_{\mu'=0}^{1} P_n(\mu')V(r,\mu',t)\,d\mu' \tag{13-160b}$$

where the values of n are $n = 1, 3, 5, \ldots$ (i.e., odd integers) since the boundary condition at $\mu = 0$ is of the first kind.

The integral-transform pair with respect to the r variable is taken the same as that given by equations (13-156). The system (13-159) is transformed from the $T(r,\mu,t)$ variable into the $V(r,\mu,t)$ variable. Then, by the application of the integral transform with respect to the μ and r variables an ordinary differential equation is obtained for the double transform $\bar{\bar{V}}(\lambda_{np}, n,t)$. The resulting ordinary differential equation is solved and the double transform is successively inverted by the inversion formulas (13-156a) and (13-160a) to obtain $V(r,\mu,t)$. When $V(r,\mu,t)$ is transformed by the transformation (13-152d), the solution $T(r,\mu,t)$ of the problem (13-159) is obtained as

$$T(r,\mu,t) = \sum_{n=1,3,5\ldots}^{\infty} \sum_{p=1}^{\infty} \frac{2(2n+1)r^{-1/2}J_{n+1/2}(\lambda_{np}r)P_n(\mu)}{b^2[J'_{n+1/2}(\lambda_{np}b)]^2} e^{-\alpha\lambda_{np}^2 t}$$

$$\cdot \left[\tilde{\bar{F}}^* + \frac{\alpha}{k}\int_0^t e^{\alpha\lambda_{np}^2 t'}\tilde{\bar{g}}^*\,dt'\right] \tag{13-161a}$$

where

$$\tilde{\bar{F}}^* = \int_{r'=0}^{b}\int_{\mu'=0}^{1} r'^{3/2}J_{n+1/2}(\lambda_{np}r')P_n(\mu')F(r',\mu')\,d\mu'\,dr' \tag{13-161b}$$

$$\tilde{\bar{g}}^* = \int_{r'=0}^{b}\int_{\mu'=0}^{1} r'^{3/2}J_{n+1/2}(\lambda_{np}r')P_n(\mu')g(r',\mu',t')\,d\mu'\,dr' \tag{13-161c}$$

and λ_{np}'s are the roots of $J_{n+1/2}(\lambda_{np}b) = 0.$ (13-161d)

We note that for the case of no heat generation, the solution (13-161) reduces to that given by equations (4-98).

Three-Dimensional Problems in (r, μ, ϕ, t) Variables

The differential equation of heat conduction in the (r, μ, ϕ, t) variables is taken in the form

$$\frac{\partial^2 T}{\partial r^2} + \frac{2}{r}\frac{\partial T}{\partial r} + \frac{1}{r^2}\frac{\partial}{\partial \mu}\left[(1-\mu^2)\frac{\partial T}{\partial \mu}\right] + \frac{1}{r^2(1-\mu^2)}\frac{\partial^2 T}{\partial \phi^2} + \frac{g(r,\mu,\phi,t)}{k}$$

$$= \frac{1}{\alpha}\frac{\partial T(r,\mu,\phi,t)}{\partial t}$$ (13-162)

We consider the problem of *full sphere*, hence choose the ranges of μ and ϕ variables as $0 \le \phi \le 2\pi$ and $-1 \le \mu \le 1$. The range of the r variable may be finite or infinite.

Now a new variable $V(r, \mu, \phi, t)$ is defined as

$$V(r,\mu,\phi,t) = r^{1/2}T(r,\mu,\phi,t)$$ (13-163)

Then equation (13-162) is transformed into

$$\frac{\partial^2 V}{\partial r^2} + \frac{1}{r}\frac{\partial V}{\partial r} - \frac{1}{4}\frac{V}{r^2} + \frac{1}{r^2}\frac{\partial}{\partial \mu}\left[(1-\mu^2)\frac{\partial V}{\partial \mu}\right] + \frac{1}{r^2(1-\mu^2)}\frac{\partial^2 V}{\partial \phi^2} + \frac{r^{1/2}g}{k} = \frac{1}{\alpha}\frac{\partial V}{\partial t}$$ (13-164)

where $0 \le \phi \le 2\pi$, $-1 \le \mu \le 1$ and the range of r is finite or infinite.

The partial derivatives with respect to the space variables can be removed from this equation by the application of integral transform with respect to the ϕ, μ, and r variable. For this particular case the order of transformation is important. *That is, the transformation should be applied first with respect to the ϕ variable, then to the μ variable and finally to the r variable.* The procedure is as follows.

Removal of the Derivative in the ϕ Variable. The range of the ϕ variable being in $0 \le \phi \le 2\pi$, the transform pair with respect to the ϕ variable is obtained from equations (13-114) as

Inversion formula: $\qquad V(r,\mu,\phi,t) = \frac{1}{\pi}\sum_{m=0}^{\infty} \bar{V}(r,\mu,m,t)$ (13-165a)

Integral transform: $\qquad \bar{V}(r,\mu,m,t) = \int_{\phi'=0}^{2\pi} \cos m(\phi - \phi')V(r,\mu,\phi',t)d\phi'$ (13-165b)

where $m = 0, 1, 2, 3 \ldots$ and replace π by 2π for $m = 0$ and the eigenvalue problem associated with this transform pair is the same as that given by equations (3-126a).

The integral transform of equation (13-164) by the application of the transform (13-165b) is

$$\frac{\partial^2 \bar{V}}{\partial r^2} + \frac{1}{r}\frac{\partial \bar{V}}{\partial r} - \frac{1}{4}\frac{\bar{V}}{r^2} + \frac{1}{r^2}\left\{ \frac{\partial}{\partial \mu}\left[(1 - \mu^2)\frac{\partial \bar{V}}{\partial \mu} \right] - \frac{m^2}{1 - \mu^2}\bar{V} \right\} + \frac{\bar{g}^*}{k} = \frac{1}{\alpha}\frac{\partial \bar{V}}{\partial t}$$

$$(13\text{-}166)$$

where $g^* \equiv r^{1/2}g(r, \mu, \phi, t)$, $\bar{V} \equiv \bar{V}(r, \mu, m, t)$ and the bar denotes the integral transform with respect to the ϕ variable. Thus, by the application of the transform (13-165b), we removed from the differential equation the partial derivative with respect to the ϕ variable, that is $\partial^2 V/\partial \phi^2$.

The Removal of the Derivative in the μ Variable. In equation (13-166), the differential operator with respect to the μ variable is in the form

$$\frac{\partial}{\partial \mu}\left[(1 - \mu^2)\frac{\partial \bar{V}}{\partial \mu} \right] - \frac{m^2}{1 - \mu^2}\bar{V},$$

and the range of μ is $-1 \le \mu \le 1$. The integral transform pair to remove this differential operator can be constructed by considering the representation of a function, defined in the interval $-1 \le \mu \le 1$, in terms of the eigenfunctions of Legendre's associated differential equation [see equation (4-13c) or (4-24)]

$$\frac{d}{d\mu}\left[(1 - \mu^2)\frac{dM}{d\mu} \right] + \left[n(n + 1) - \frac{m^2}{1 - \mu^2} \right]M = 0 \qquad (13\text{-}167)$$

and then splitting up the representation into two parts. The resulting integral transform pair with respect to the μ variable for the function $\bar{V}(r, \mu, m, t)$ is given as

Inversion formula: $\quad \bar{V}(r, \mu, m, t) = \sum_{m=0}^{n} \frac{P_n^m(\mu)}{N(m, n)} \tilde{\bar{V}}(r, n, m, t)$ (13-168a)

Integral transform: $\quad \tilde{\bar{V}}(r, n, m, t) = \int_{-1}^{1} P_n^m(\mu')\bar{V}(r, \mu', m, t)\,d\mu'$

$$(13\text{-}168b)$$

where

$$\frac{1}{N(m, n)} = \frac{2n + 1}{2}\frac{(n - m)!}{(n + m)!}, \qquad n \ge m \qquad (13\text{-}168c)$$

n and m are integers, $P_n^m(\mu)$ is the associated Legendre function of degree n, order m, of the first kind; and the tilde denotes the integral transform with respect to the μ variable. It is to be noted that, when the integral transform pairs (13-165) and (13-168) are combined, the expansion given by equation (4-43) in Chapter 4 is obtained.

Taking the integral transform of equation (13-166) by the application of the transform (13-168b) and utilizing equation (13-167) we obtain (see Note 8 for details)

$$\frac{\partial^2 \tilde{\tilde{V}}}{\partial r^2} + \frac{1}{r}\frac{\partial \tilde{\tilde{V}}}{\partial r} - \frac{(n+\frac{1}{2})^2}{r^2}\tilde{\tilde{V}} + \frac{\tilde{\tilde{g}}^*}{k} = \frac{1}{\alpha}\frac{\partial \tilde{\tilde{V}}(r,n,m,t)}{\partial t} \tag{13-169}$$

where the tilde denotes the transform with respect to the μ variable.

The Removal of the Derivative in the r-Variable. The differential operator with respect to the r variable can readily be removed from equation (13-169) by the application of an appropriate transform in the r variable developed previously for the solution of problems in the cylindrical coordinate system. The form of the transform pair depends on the range of r, whether it is finite or infinite. We now illustrate the application with an example given below.

Example 13-7. Solve the following time-dependent, three-dimensional heat-conduction problem for a solid sphere of radius $r = b$.

$$\frac{\partial^2 T}{\partial r^2} + \frac{2}{r}\frac{\partial T}{\partial r} + \frac{1}{r^2}\frac{\partial}{\partial \mu}\left[(1-\mu^2)\frac{\partial T}{\partial \mu}\right] + \frac{1}{r^2(1-\mu^2)}\frac{\partial^2 T}{\partial \phi^2} + \frac{g}{k} = \frac{1}{\alpha}\frac{\partial T}{\partial t}$$

$$\text{in } 0 \leq r < b, \ -1 \leq \mu \leq 1, \ 0 \leq \phi \leq 2\pi, \ t > 0 \quad (13\text{-}170a)$$

$$T = 0 \qquad \text{at } r = b, \ t > 0 \tag{13-170b}$$

$$T = F(r,\mu,\phi) \qquad \text{for } t = 0, \text{ in the region} \tag{13-170c}$$

where $g \equiv g(r,\mu,\phi,t)$ and $T \equiv T(r,\mu,\phi,t)$.

Solution. By defining a new dependent variable as

$$V(r,\mu,\phi,t) = r^{1/2}T(r,\mu,\phi,t) \tag{13-171}$$

the system (13-170) is transformed into

$$\frac{\partial^2 V}{\partial r^2} + \frac{1}{r}\frac{\partial V}{\partial r} - \frac{1}{4}\frac{V}{r^2} + \frac{1}{r^2}\frac{\partial}{\partial \mu}\left[(1-\mu^2)\frac{\partial V}{\partial \mu}\right] + \frac{1}{r^2(1-\mu^2)}\frac{\partial^2 V}{\partial \phi^2} + \frac{r^{1/2}g}{k} = \frac{1}{\alpha}\frac{\partial V}{\partial t}$$

$$\text{in } 0 \leq r < b, \ -1 \leq \mu \leq 1, \ 0 \leq \phi \leq 2\pi, \ t > 0$$

$$\tag{13-172a}$$

$$V = 0 \qquad\qquad \text{at } r = b, \ t > 0 \qquad\qquad\qquad (13\text{-}172\text{b})$$

$$V = r^{1/2} F(r, \mu, \phi) \qquad \text{for } t = 0, \text{ in the region} \qquad (13\text{-}172\text{c})$$

The integral transform of this system with respect to the ϕ variable by the application of the transform (13-165b) yields

$$\frac{\partial^2 \bar{V}}{\partial r^2} + \frac{1}{r}\frac{\partial \bar{V}}{\partial r} - \frac{1}{4}\frac{\bar{V}}{r^2} + \frac{1}{r^2}\left\{ \frac{\partial}{\partial \mu}\left[(1 - \mu^2)\frac{\partial \bar{V}}{\partial \mu} \right] - \frac{m^2}{1 - \mu^2}\bar{V} \right\} + \frac{\bar{g}^*}{k} = \frac{1}{\alpha}\frac{\partial \bar{V}}{\partial t}$$

$$\text{in } 0 \le r < b, \ -1 \le \mu \le 1, \ t > 0 \qquad (13\text{-}173\text{a})$$

$$\bar{V} = 0 \qquad\qquad \text{at } r = b, \ t > 0 \qquad\qquad\qquad (13\text{-}173\text{b})$$

$$\bar{V} = \bar{F}^*(r, \mu, m) \qquad \text{for } t = 0, \text{ in } 0 \le r \le b, \ -1 \le \mu \le 1 \qquad (13\text{-}173\text{c})$$

where $g^* \equiv r^{1/2} g(r, \mu, \phi, t)$, $F^* \equiv r^{1/2} F(r, \mu, \phi)$, $\bar{V} \equiv \bar{V}(r, \mu, m, t)$ and the bar denotes the transform with respect to the ϕ variable.

Now, the integral transform of the system (13-173) with respect to the μ variable, by the application of the transform (13-168b) gives

$$\frac{\partial^2 \tilde{\bar{V}}}{\partial r^2} + \frac{1}{r}\frac{\partial \tilde{\bar{V}}}{\partial r} - \frac{(n + \frac{1}{2})^2}{r^2}\tilde{\bar{V}} + \frac{\tilde{\bar{g}}^*}{k} = \frac{1}{\alpha}\frac{\partial \tilde{\bar{V}}}{\partial t} \qquad \text{in } 0 \le r < b, \ t > 0 \qquad (13\text{-}174\text{a})$$

$$\tilde{\bar{V}} = 0 \qquad\qquad\qquad\qquad\qquad\qquad \text{at } r = b, \ t > 0 \qquad (13\text{-}174\text{b})$$

$$\tilde{\bar{V}} = \tilde{\bar{F}}^*(r, n, m) \qquad\qquad\qquad\qquad \text{for } t = 0, \ 0 \le r \le b \qquad (13\text{-}174\text{c})$$

where $\tilde{\bar{V}} \equiv V(r, n, m, t)$ and the tilde denotes transform with respect to the μ variable. This system is now exactly of the same form as that given by equations (13-155). To remove the differential operator with respect to the r variable the appropriate integral transform pair is exactly the same as that given by equations (13-156). Therefore, taking the integral transform of the system (13-174) by the application of the transform (13-156b) we find

$$\frac{d\overset{x}{\tilde{\bar{V}}}}{dt} + \alpha \lambda_{np}^2 \overset{x}{\tilde{\bar{V}}}(\lambda_{np}, n, m, t) = \frac{\alpha}{k}\overset{x}{\tilde{\bar{g}}}^* \qquad \text{for } t > 0 \qquad (13\text{-}175\text{a})$$

$$\overset{x}{\tilde{\bar{V}}} = \overset{x}{\tilde{\bar{F}}}^*(\lambda_{np}, n, m) \qquad\qquad\qquad\qquad \text{for } t = 0 \qquad (13\text{-}175\text{b})$$

where x denotes the integral transform with respect to the r variable. Equation (13-175) is solved for

$$\overset{x}{\tilde{\bar{V}}}(\lambda_{np}, n, m, t),$$

the resulting triple transform is successively inverted by the inversion formulas (13-156a), (13-168a), and (13-165a) to obtain $V(r,\mu,\phi,t)$. When the function $V(r,\mu,\phi,t)$ is transformed by the expression (13-171) we obtain the solution $T(r,\mu,\phi,t)$ of the problem (13-170) as

$$T(r,\mu,\phi,t) = \frac{1}{\pi} \sum_{n=0}^{\infty} \sum_{m=0}^{n} \sum_{p=1}^{\infty} \frac{r^{-1/2} J_{n+1/2}(\lambda_{np}r) P_n^m(\mu)}{N(m,n)N(\lambda_{np})} e^{-\alpha\lambda_{np}^2 t}$$
$$\cdot \left[\bar{\bar{F}} + \frac{\alpha}{k} \int_0^t e^{-\alpha\lambda_{np}^2 t'} \bar{\bar{g}}^* \, dt' \right] \tag{13-176a}$$

and replace π by 2π for $m = 0$. Various quantities are defined as

$$\bar{\bar{F}} = \int_{r'=0}^{b} \int_{\mu'=-1}^{1} \int_{\phi'=0}^{2\pi} r'^{3/2} J_{n+1/2}(\lambda_{np}r') P_n^m(\mu') \cos m(\phi - \phi') F(r',\mu',\phi') d\phi' \, d\mu' \, dr'$$
$$\tag{13-176b}$$

$$\bar{\bar{g}} = \int_{r'=0}^{b} \int_{\mu'=-1}^{1} \int_{\phi'=0}^{2\pi} r'^{3/2} J_{n+1/2}(\lambda_{np}r') P_n^m(\mu') \cos m(\phi - \phi') g(r',\mu',\phi',t') d\phi' \, d\mu' \, dr'$$
$$\tag{13-176c}$$

$$\frac{1}{N(m,n)} = \frac{2n+1}{2} \frac{(n-m)!}{(n+m)!} \tag{13-176d}$$

$$\frac{1}{N(\lambda_{np})} = \frac{2}{b^2 [J'_{n+1/2}(\lambda_{np}b)]^2} \tag{13-176e}$$

and λ_{np}'s are the positive roots of $J_{n+1/2}(\lambda_{np}b) = 0$ (13-176f)

For the case of no heat generation, this solution reduces to that given by equations (4-118).

13-6 APPLICATION IN THE SOLUTION OF STEADY-STATE PROBLEMS

The integral-transform technique is also very effective in the solution of multidimensional, steady-state heat-conduction problems, because, by the successive application of the integral transform, the partial differential equation is reduced to an ordinary differential equation in one of the space variables. The resulting ordinary differential equation is solved for the transform of the temperature, which is then inverted successively to obtain the desired solution. This procedure is now illustrated with examples.

Example 13-8. Solve the following steady-state heat-conduction problem for a rectangular region $0 \le x \le a, 0 \le y \le b$

$$\frac{\partial^2 T}{\partial x^2} + \frac{\partial^2 T}{\partial y^2} = 0 \qquad \text{in } 0 < x < a, \ 0 < y < b \qquad (13\text{-}177a)$$

$$T = 0 \qquad \text{at } x = 0, \ x = a \text{ and } y = b \qquad (13\text{-}177b)$$

$$T = f(x) \qquad \text{at } y = 0 \qquad (13\text{-}177c)$$

Solution. In this example we prefer to take the integral transform with respect to the x variable, because in the resulting ordinary differential equation the boundary condition at $y = b$ becomes a constant, hence its integration is readily performed.

The integral transform pair with respect to the x variable, for $0 \le x \le a$, of function $T(x, y)$ is defined as

Inversion formula: $\qquad T(x, y) = \sum_{m=1}^{\infty} \frac{X(\beta_m, x)}{N(\beta_m)} \bar{T}(\beta_m, y) \qquad (13\text{-}178a)$

Integral transform: $\qquad \bar{T}(\beta_m, y) = \int_{x'=0}^{b} X(\beta_m, x')T(x', y)dx' \qquad (13\text{-}178b)$

where $X(\beta_m, x), N(\beta_m)$, and β_m are obtained from Table 2-2, case 9 as

$$X(\beta_m, x) = \sin \beta_m x, \quad \frac{1}{N(\beta_m)} = \frac{2}{a} \qquad \text{and} \qquad \sin \beta_m a = 0 \quad (13\text{-}178c)$$

The integral transform of the system (13-177) by the application of the transform (13-178b) yields

$$\frac{d^2 \bar{T}}{dy^2} - \beta_m^2 \bar{T}(\beta_m, y) = 0 \qquad \text{in } 0 < y < b \qquad (13\text{-}179a)$$

$$\bar{T} = \bar{f}(\beta_m) \qquad \text{at } y = 0 \qquad (13\text{-}179b)$$

$$\bar{T} = 0 \qquad \text{at } y = b \qquad (13\text{-}179c)$$

The solution of equations (13-179) is

$$\bar{T}(\beta_m, y) = \bar{f}(\beta_m) \frac{\sinh \beta_m(b - y)}{\sinh \beta_m b} \qquad (13\text{-}180)$$

The inversion of this result with the inversion formula (13-178a) gives

$$T(x, y) = \frac{2}{\alpha} \sum_{m=1}^{\infty} \sin \beta_m x \frac{\sinh \beta_m(b - y)}{\sinh \beta_m b} \int_{x'=0}^{a} \sin \beta_m x' f(x')dx' \quad (13\text{-}181a)$$

where $\beta_m = m\pi/a, m = 1, 2, 3 \dots$. $\qquad (13\text{-}181b)$

Example 13-9. Solve the following steady-state heat-conduction problem for a long solid cylinder

$$\frac{\partial^2 T}{\partial r^2} + \frac{1}{r}\frac{\partial T}{\partial r} + \frac{1}{r^2}\frac{\partial^2 T}{\partial \phi^2} = 0 \qquad \text{in } 0 \le r < b,\ 0 \le \phi \le 2\pi \qquad (13\text{-}182\text{a})$$

$$k_2 \frac{\partial T}{\partial r} + h_2 T = f_2(\phi) \qquad\qquad \text{at } r = b \qquad (13\text{-}182\text{b})$$

Solution. The integral-transform pair with respect to the ϕ variable for $0 \le \phi \le 2\pi$ is obtained from equations (13-114) as

Inversion formula: $\qquad T(r,\phi) = \frac{1}{\pi}\sum_{v} \bar{T}(r,v) \qquad\qquad (13\text{-}183\text{a})$

Integral transform: $\qquad \bar{T}(r,v) = \int_{\phi'=0}^{2\pi} \cos v(\phi - \phi')T(r,\phi')\,d\phi' \quad (13\text{-}183\text{b})$

where $v = 0, 1, 2, 3\dots$ and replace π by 2π for $v = 0$. The integral transform of the system (13-182) by the application of the transform (13-183b) yields

$$\frac{d^2 \bar{T}}{dr^2} + \frac{1}{r}\frac{d\bar{T}}{dr} - \frac{v^2}{r^2}\bar{T}(r,v) = 0 \qquad \text{in } 0 \le r < b \qquad (13\text{-}184\text{a})$$

$$k_2 \frac{d\bar{T}}{dr} + h_2 \bar{T} = \bar{f}_2(v) \qquad\qquad \text{at } r = b \qquad (13\text{-}184\text{b})$$

The solution of equations (13-184) is

$$\bar{T}(r,v) = b\left(\frac{r}{b}\right)^v \frac{\bar{f}_2(v)}{k_2 v + h_2 b} \qquad\qquad (13\text{-}185)$$

The inversion of this result by the inversion formula (13-183a) gives the temperature distribution as

$$T(r,\phi) = \frac{1}{\pi}\sum_{v} b\left(\frac{r}{b}\right)^b \frac{\bar{f}_2(v)}{k_2 v + h_2 b} \qquad\qquad (13\text{-}186\text{a})$$

where

$$\bar{f}_2(v) = \int_{\phi'=0}^{2\pi} \cos v(\phi - \phi')f_2(\phi')\,d\phi' \qquad\qquad (13\text{-}186\text{b})$$

$v = 0, 1, 2, 3\dots$ and replace π by 2π for $v = 0$.

Example 13-10. Solve the following steady-state heat-conduction problem for a solid hemisphere of radius $r = b$.

$$\frac{\partial}{\partial r}\left(r^2\frac{\partial T}{\partial r}\right) + \frac{\partial}{\partial \mu}\left[(1-\mu^2)\frac{\partial T}{\partial \mu}\right] = 0 \qquad 0 \leq r < b,\ 0 < \mu \leq 1 \qquad (13\text{-}187\text{a})$$

$$\frac{\partial T}{\partial \mu} = 0 \qquad\qquad\qquad \text{at } \mu = 0 \qquad (13\text{-}187\text{b})$$

$$T(r,\mu) = f(\mu) \qquad\qquad\qquad \text{at } r = b \qquad (13\text{-}187\text{c})$$

Solution. This problem is the same as that considered in Example 4-10. The integral-transform pair with respect to the μ variable for $0 \leq \mu \leq 1$ and the boundary condition of the second kind at $\mu = 0$ is obtained from equations (13-150) as

Inversion formula: $\qquad T(r,\mu) = \sum_n (2n+1)P_n(\mu)\bar{T}(r,n) \qquad (13\text{-}188\text{a})$

Integral transform: $\qquad \bar{T}(r,n) = \int\limits_{\mu'=0}^{1} P_n(\mu')T(r,\mu')\,d\mu' \qquad (13\text{-}188\text{b})$

where $n = 0, 2, 4, 6 \dots$ (even integers). The integral transform of the system (13-187) by the application of the transform (13-188b) yields

$$\frac{d}{dr}\left(r^2\frac{d\bar{T}}{dr}\right) - n(n+1)\bar{T}(r,n) = 0 \qquad 0 \leq r < b \qquad (13\text{-}189\text{a})$$

$$\bar{T}(r,n) = \bar{f}(n) \qquad\qquad\qquad \text{at } r = b \qquad (13\text{-}189\text{b})$$

The solution of equations (13-189) is

$$\bar{T}(r,n) = \left(\frac{r}{b}\right)^n \bar{f}(n) \qquad (13\text{-}190)$$

The inversion of this result by the inversion formula (13-188a) gives the solution for the temperature as

$$T(r,\mu) = \sum_{n=0,2,4\dots}^{\infty} (2n+1)P_n(\mu)\left(\frac{r}{b}\right)^n \int\limits_{\mu'=0}^{1} P_n(\mu')f(\mu')\,d\mu' \qquad (13\text{-}191)$$

REFERENCES

1. Ian N. Sneddon, *Fourier Transforms*, McGraw-Hill Book Co., New York, 1951.

2. Ian N. Sneddon, *The Use of Integral Transforms*, McGraw-Hill Book Co., New York, 1972.

3. E. C. Titchmarsh, *Fourier Integrals*, 2nd ed., Clarendon Press, London, 1948.

4. A. Erdelyi, W. Magnus, F. Oberhettinger, and F. G. Tricomi, *Tables of Integrals Transforms*, McGraw-Hill Book Co., New York, 1954.

5. C. J. Tranter, *Integral Transforms in Mathematical Physics*, John Wiley and Sons, Inc., New York, 1962.

6. V. A. Ditkin and A. P. Prudnikov, *Integral Transforms and Operational Calculus*, Pergamon Press, New York, 1965.

7. M. N. Özışık, Integral Transform in the Solution of Heat-Conduction Equation in the Rectangular coordinate System, ASME Paper 67-WA/HT-46, 1967.

8. M. N. Özışık, *Boundary Value Problems of Heat Conduction*, International Textbook Co., Scranton, Pa., 1968.

9. A. C. Eringen, *Quart. J. Math. Oxford* **5** (2), 120–129, 1954.

10. R. V. Churchill, *Mich. Math. J.* **3**, 85, 1955–1956.

11. A. McD. Mercer, *Quart. J. Math. Oxford*. **14**, 9–15, 1963.

12. N. Y. Ölçer, *Österr. Ing.-Arch* **18**, 104–113, 1964.

13. N. Y. Ölçer, *Int. J. Heat Mass Transfer* **7**, 307–314, 1964.

14. N. Y. Ölçer, *Int. J. Heat Mass Transfer* **8**, 529–556, 1965.

15. N. Y. Ölçer, *J. Math Phys.* **46**, 99–106, 1967.

16. M. D. Mikhailov, *Int. J. Eng. Sci.* **10**, 577–591, 1972.

17. M. D. Mikhailov, *Int. J. Heat Mass Transfer* **16**, 2155–2164, 1973.

18. M. D. Mikhailov, *Int. J. Heat Mass Transfer* **17**, 1475–1478, 1974.

19. M. D. Mikhailov, *Int. J. Eng. Sci* **11**, 235–241, 1973.

20. M. N. Özışık and R. L. Murray, *J. Heat Transfer* **96c**, 48–51, 1974.

21. Y. Yener and M. N. Özışık, On the Solution of Unsteady Heat Conduction in Multi-Region Media with Time Dependent Heat Transfer Coefficient, *Proc. 5th. Int. Heat Trans. Conference*, Cu 2.5, pp. 188–192, Tokyo, Sept. 1974.

22. M. D. Mikhailov, *Int. J. Heat Mass Transfer* **18**, 344–345, 1975.

23. M. D. Mikhailov, *Int. J. Heat Mass Transfer* **20**, 1409–1415, 1977.

24. N. Y. Ölçer, *Int. J. Heat Mass Transfer* **12**, 393–411, 1969.

25. K. Kobayashi, N. Ohtani, and J. Jung, *Nucl. Sci. Eng.* **55**, 320–328, 1974.

26. I. N. Sneddon, *Phil. Mag.* **37**, 17, 1946.

27. G. Cinelli, *Int. J. Engl Sci.* **3**, 539–559, 1965.

28. N. Y. Ölçer, *Brit. J. Appl. Phys.* **18**, 89–105, 1967.

29. N. Y. Ölçer, *Proc. Camb. Phil. Soc.* **64**, 193–202, 1968.

30. N. Y. Ölçer, *J. Heat Transfer* **91c**, 45–50, 1969.

31. A. W. Jacobson, *Quart. Appl. Math.* **7**, 293–302, 1949.

32. C. J. Tranter, *Quart. J. Math. Oxford* **1**, 1–8, 1950.

33. R. V. Churchill and C. L. Dolph, *Proc. Amer. Math. Soc.* **5**, 93, 1954.

34. R. V. Churchill, *J. Math. Phys.* **33**, 165–178, 1954–1955.

35. R. Courant and D. Hilbert, *Methods of Mathematical Physics*, Vol. 1, Interscience Publishers, Inc., New York, 1953, p. 106.

36. G. N. Watson, *A Treatise on the Theory of Bessel Functions*, Cambridge University Press, London, 1966.

PROBLEMS

13-1 Solve the one-dimensional, time-dependent heat-conduction problem for a slab $0 \leq x \leq L$, which is initially at zero temperature and for times $t > 0$ the boundaries at $x = 0$ and $x = L$ are kept at temperatures zero and $f_2(t)$, respectively. Consider the case when the surface temperature is given by $f_2(t) = \gamma t$, where γ is a constant.

13-2 Solve the one-dimensional, time-dependent heat-conduction problem for a slab $0 \leq x \leq L$, which is initially at zero temperature, and for times $t > 0$ heat is generated in the medium at a rate of $g(x, t)$, W/m^3, while the boundary surface at $x = 0$ is kept insulated and the boundary surface at $x = L$ is kept at zero temperature. Consider the case when the heat source is an instantaneous plane heat source of total strength g_{si} Ws/m^2, situated at $x = b$ and release its heat spontaneously at time $t = 0$, that is, $g(x, t) = g_{si}\delta(x - b)\delta(t)$.

13-3 A semi-infinite medium, $0 \leq x < \infty$, is initially at zero temperature. For times $t > 0$ the boundary at $x = 0$ is kept at zero temperature, while heat is generated in the medium at a rate of $g(x, t)$ W/m^3. Obtain an expression for the temperature distribution $T(x, t)$ in the medium. Consider the cases (1) the heat source is a plane-surface heat source of strength $g_s(t)$ W/m^2, which is situated at $x = b$, that is $g(x, t) = g_s(t)\delta(x - b)$, (2) the heat source is a constant heat source, that is, $g(x, t) = g_0 = $ constant W/m^3.

13-4 An infinite medium $-\infty < x < \infty$ is initially at zero temperature. A plane-surface heat source of strength $g_s(t)$ W/m^2, situated at $x = 0$, releases heat continuously for times $t > 0$. Obtain an expression for the temperature distribution $T(x, t)$ in the medium for times $t > 0$ [i.e., $g(x, t) = g_s(t)\delta(x)$].

13-5 A rectangular region $0 \leq x \leq a, 0 \leq y \leq b$ is initially at zero temperature. For times $t > 0$, heat is generated in the medium at a rate of $g(x, y, t)$ W/m^3, while the boundaries are kept at zero temperature. Obtain an expression for the temperature distribution $T(x, y, t)$ in the region. Also consider the special case, when the heat source is an instantaneous line heat source g_{Li} of strength Ws/m, situated at (x_1, y_1) within the region and releases its heat spontaneously at time $t = 0$, that is, $g(x, y, t) = g_{Li}\delta(x - x_1)\delta(y - y_1)\delta(t)$.

13-6 A three-dimensional infinite medium $-\infty < x < \infty, -\infty < y < \infty, -\infty < z < \infty$ is initially at zero temperature. For times $t > 0$ heat is generated in the medium at a rate of $g(x, y, z, t)$ W/m^3. Obtain an expression for the temperature distribution $T(x, y, z, t)$ in the medium. Also consider the special case when the heat source is an instantaneous point heat source of strength g_{pi} Ws, situated at $x = 0, y = 0, z = 0$ and releasing its heat spontaneously at time $t = 0$, that is, $g(x, y, z, t) = g_{pi}\delta(x)\delta(y)\delta(z)\delta(t)$.

13-7 A solid cylinder, $0 \leq r \leq b$, is initially at zero temperature. For times $t > 0$, heat is generated within the region at a rate of $g(r, t)$ W/m^3, while the boundary at $r = b$ is kept at zero temperature. Obtain an expression for the temperature distribution $T(r, t)$ in the cylinder. Consider the special cases (1) the heat is generated at a constant rate g_0 W/m^3, in the region, (2) the heat source is a line heat source of strength $g_L(t)$ W/m, situated along the axis of the cylinder, that is, $g(r, t) = \dfrac{1}{2\pi r} g_L(t)\delta(r)$.

13-8   A long solid cylinder, $0 \leq r \leq b$, is initially at temperature $F(r)$. For times $t > 0$ the boundary at $r = b$ is kept insulated. Obtain an expression for the temperature distribution $T(r, t)$ in the cylinder.

13-9   A long hollow cylinder, $a \leq r \leq b$, is initially at temperature $F(r)$. For times $t > 0$ the boundaries at $r = a$ and $r = b$ are kept insulated. Obtain an expression for the temperature distribution $T(r, t)$ in the region.

13-10   A long hollow cylinder, $a \leq r \leq b$, is initially at zero temperature. For times $t > 0$ heat is generated in the medium at a rate of $g(r, t)$ W/m^3, while the boundaries at $r = a$ and $r = b$ are kept at zero temperature. Obtain an expression for the temperature distribution $T(r, t)$ in the cylinder. Consider the special cases (1) the heat generation rate is constant, that is, $g_0 = $ constant, and (2) the heat source is an instantaneous cylindrical heat source of radius $r = r_1$ (i.e., $a < r_1 < b$) of strength g_{si} Ws/m, per linear length of the cylinder, which is situated inside the cylinder coaxially and releases its heat spontaneously at time $t = 0$, that is, $g(r, t) = \dfrac{1}{2\pi r} g_{si}\delta(r - r_1)\delta(t)$.

13-11   An infinite region, $0 \leq r < \infty$, is initially at zero temperature. For times $t > 0$ heat is generated in the medium at a rate of $g(r, t)$ W/m^3. Obtain an expression for the temperature distribution $T(r, t)$ in the medium for times $t > 0$. Consider the special cases (1) the heat source is of constant strength, that is, $g(r, t) = g_0 = $ constant, (2) the heat source is an instantaneous line-heat source of strength g_{Li} Ws/m, situated along the z axis in the medium and releases its heat spontaneously at time $t = 0$, that is, $g(r, t) = (1/2\pi r)g_{Li}\delta(r)\delta(t)$.

13-12   The region $a \leq r < \infty$ is initially at zero temperature. For times $t > 0$, heat is generated in the medium at a rate of $g(r, t)$ W/m^3, while the boundary surface at $r = a$ is kept at zero temperature. Obtain an expression for the temperature distribution $T(r, t)$ in the medium for times $t > 0$. Consider the special case of constant heat generation in the medium.

13-13   The cylindrical region $0 \leq r \leq b, 0 \leq \phi \leq 2\pi$ is initially at temperature $F(r, \phi)$. For times $t > 0$ the boundary surface at $r = b$ is kept insulated. Obtain an expression for the temperature distribution $T(r, \phi, t)$ in the region for times $t > 0$.

13-14   The cylindrical region $0 \leq r \leq b, 0 \leq \phi \leq 2\pi$ is initially at zero temperature. For times $t > 0$, heat is generated in the medium at a rate of $g(r, \phi, t)$ W/m^3, while the boundary at $r = b$ is kept at zero temperature. Obtain an expression for the temperature distribution $T(r, \phi, t)$ in the region for times $t > 0$.

13-15   The cylindrical region $a \leq r \leq b, 0 \leq \phi \leq 2\pi$ is initially at temperature $F(r, \phi)$. For times $t > 0$, the boundaries at $r = a$ and $r = b$ are kept at zero temperatures. Obtain an expression for the temperature distribution $T(r, \phi, t)$ in the region for times $t > 0$.

13-16   The cylindrical region consisting of a portion of a cylinder,

$0 \le r \le b, 0 \le \phi \le \phi_0$ where $\phi < 2\pi$ is initially at zero temperature. For times $t > 0$ heat is generated in the medium at a rate of $g(r, \phi, t)\,\text{W/m}^3$, while all boundary surfaces are kept at zero temperature. Obtain an expression for the temperature distribution $T(r, \phi, t)$ in the region for times $t > 0$. Also consider the special case of $g(r, \phi, t) = g_0 = \text{constant}$.

13-17 The cylindrical region consisting of a portion of a cylinder, $a \le r \le b, 0 \le \phi \le \phi_0$ where $\phi_0 < 2\pi$ is initially at temperature $F(r, \phi)$. For times $t > 0$ all boundary surfaces are kept at zero temperature. Obtain an expression for the temperature distribution $T(r, \phi, t)$ in the region for times $t > 0$. Also consider the special case of uniform initial temperature distribution, that is, $F(r, \phi) = T_0 = \text{constant}$.

13-18 The cylindrical region $a \le r \le b, 0 \le \phi \le \phi_0$ where $\phi_0 < 2\pi$ is initially at zero temperature. For times $t > 0$ heat is generated in the medium at a rate of $g(r, \phi, t)\,\text{W/m}^3$, while the boundaries are kept at zero temperature. Obtain an expression for the temperature distribution $T(r, \phi, t)$ in the medium for times $t > 0$.

13-19 A cylindrical region $0 \le r \le b, 0 \le z \le L$ is initially at zero temperature. For times $t > 0$ heat is generated in the medium at a rate of $g(r, z, t)\,\text{W/m}^3$, while the boundary surface at $z = 0$ is kept insulated and all the remaining boundaries are kept at zero temperature. Obtain an expression for the temperature distribution $T(r, z, t)$ in the region.

13-20 A cylindrical region $0 \le r \le b, 0 \le z < \infty$ is initially at temperature $F(r, z)$. For times $t > 0$ all the boundary surfaces are kept at zero temperature. Obtain an expression for the temperature distribution $T(r, z, t)$ in the region for times $t > 0$.

13-21 A hemispherical region $0 \le r \le b, 0 \le \mu \le 1$ is initially at temperature $F(r, \mu)$. For times $t > 0$ the boundary surface at $\mu = 0$ is kept insulated and the boundary surface at $r = b$ is kept at zero temperature. Obtain an expression for the temperature distribution $T(r, \mu, t)$ in the sphere for times $t > 0$.

13-22 A hemispherical region $0 \le r \le b, 0 \le \mu \le 1$ is initially at zero temperature. For times $t > 0$ heat is generated in the medium at a rate of $g(r, \mu, t)\,\text{W/m}^3$, while the boundary surface at $\mu = 0$ is kept insulated and the boundary at $r = b$ is kept at zero temperature. Obtain an expression for the temperature distribution $T(r, \mu, t)$ in the region for times $t > 0$.

13-23 A hollow hemispherical region $a \le r \le b, 0 \le \mu \le 1$ is initially at zero temperature. For times $t > 0$ heat is generated in the medium at a rate of $g(r, \mu, t)\,\text{W/m}^3$, while the boundaries are kept at zero temperature. Obtain an expression for the temperature distribution $T(r, \mu, t)$ in the region.

13-24 A solid sphere of radius $r = b$ is initially at temperature $F(r, \mu, \phi)$. For times $t > 0$ the boundary surface at $r = b$ is kept insulated. Obtain an expression for the temperature distribution $T(r, \mu, \phi, t)$ in the sphere for times $t > 0$.

13-25 Solve for the steady-state temperature distribution $T(x, y)$ in a rectangular strip $0 \leq y \leq b, 0 \leq x < \infty$ subject to the boundary conditions $T = f(y)$ at $x = 0$ and $T = 0$ at $y = 0$ and $y = b$.

13-26 Solve for the steady-state temperature distribution $T(r, \mu, \phi)$ in a solid sphere of radius $r = b$ subject to the boundary condition $T = f(\mu, \phi)$ at the boundary surface $r = b$.

NOTES

1. To prove the orthogonality relation given by equations (13-3), equation (13-2a) is written for two different eigenfunctions $\psi_m(\mathbf{r})$ and $\psi_n(\mathbf{r})$, corresponding two different eigenvalues λ_m and λ_n as

$$\nabla^2 \psi_m(\mathbf{r}) + \lambda_m^2 \psi_m(\mathbf{r}) = 0 \qquad \text{in } R \tag{1a}$$

$$\nabla^2 \psi_n(\mathbf{r}) + \lambda_n^2 \psi_n(\mathbf{r}) = 0 \qquad \text{in } R \tag{1b}$$

The first equation is multiplied by $\psi_n(\mathbf{r})$, the second by $\psi_m(\mathbf{r})$, the results are subtracted and integrated over the region R

$$(\lambda_m^2 - \lambda_n^2) \int_R \psi_m(\mathbf{r}) \psi_n(\mathbf{r}) \, dv = \int_R [\psi_m \nabla^2 \psi_n - \psi_n \nabla^2 \psi_m] \, dv \tag{2}$$

The volume integral on the right is changed to surface integral by Green's theorem as discussed in Note 2 at the end of Chapter 6. We find

$$(\lambda_m^2 - \lambda_n^2) \int_R \psi_m(\mathbf{r}) \psi_n(\mathbf{r}) \, dv = \int_S \left(\psi_m \frac{\partial \psi_n}{\partial n} - \psi_n \frac{\partial \psi_m}{\partial n} \right) ds$$

$$= \sum_{i=1}^s \int_{S_i} \left(\psi_m \frac{\partial \psi_n}{\partial n_i} - \psi_n \frac{\partial \psi_m}{\partial n_i} \right) ds_i \tag{3}$$

The boundary condition (13-2b) is written for two different eigenfunctions $\psi_m(\mathbf{r})$ and $\psi_n(\mathbf{r})$

$$k_i \frac{\partial \psi_m}{\partial n_i} + h_i \psi_m = 0 \tag{4a}$$

$$k_i \frac{\partial \psi_n}{\partial n_i} + h_i \psi_n = 0 \tag{4b}$$

The first is multiplied by ψ_n, the second by ψ_n, the results are subtracted

$$\psi_m \frac{\partial \psi_n}{\partial n_i} - \psi_n \frac{\partial \psi_m}{\partial n_i} = 0 \tag{5}$$

when this result is introduced into equation (3) we obtain

$$(\lambda_m^2 - \lambda_n^2) \int_R \psi_m(\mathbf{r})\psi_n(\mathbf{r})\, dv = 0 \tag{6}$$

Thus

$$\int_R \psi_m(\mathbf{r})\psi_n(\mathbf{r})\, dv = 0 \qquad \text{for } m \neq n \tag{7}$$

2. The closed-form expressions given by equations (13-54) can be derived as now described. Consider the problem

$$\frac{\partial^2 \theta}{\partial x^2} = \frac{1}{\alpha}\frac{\partial \theta}{\partial t} \qquad \text{in } 0 < x < L,\ t > 0 \tag{1a}$$

$$\frac{\partial \theta}{\partial x} = 0 \qquad \text{at } x = 0,\ t > 0 \tag{1b}$$

$$\theta = 0 \qquad \text{at } x = L,\ t > 0 \tag{1c}$$

$$\theta = 1 \qquad \text{for } t = 0,\ \text{in } 0 \le x \le L \tag{1d}$$

The solution of this problem is given as

$$\theta(x,t) = \frac{2}{L}\sum_{m=1}^{\infty} e^{-\alpha\beta_m^2 t}\cos\beta_m x \int_0^L 1\cdot\cos\beta_m x'\, dx'$$

$$= \frac{2}{L}\sum_{m=1}^{\infty} e^{-\alpha\beta_m^2 t}\frac{\cos\beta_m x}{\beta_m}(-1)^{m-1} \tag{2}$$

where $\beta_m = (2m-1)\pi/2L$. For $t = 0$ equation (2) should be equal to the initial condition (1d); hence

$$\frac{2}{L}\sum_{m=1}^{\infty}(-1)^{m-1}\frac{\cos\beta_m x}{\beta_m} = 1 \tag{3}$$

which is the result given the equation (13-54a).

We now consider the problem given by equations (1) for an initial condition $(x^2 - L^2)$. The solution becomes

$$\theta(x,t) = \frac{2}{L}\sum_{m=1}^{\infty} e^{-\alpha\beta_m^2 t}\cos\beta_m x \int_0^L (x'^2 - L^2)\cos\beta_m x'\, dx' \tag{4}$$

After performing the integration we obtain

$$\theta(x,t) = -\frac{4}{L}\sum_{m=1}^{\infty} e^{-\alpha\beta_m^2 t}(-1)^{m-1}\frac{\cos\beta_m x}{\beta_m^3} \tag{5}$$

For $t = 0$, we have $\theta(x, t) = x^2 - L^2$; then

$$x^2 - L^2 = -\frac{4}{L} \sum_{m=1}^{\infty} (-1)^{m-1} \frac{\cos \beta_m x}{\beta_m^3} \tag{6}$$

which is the result given by equation (13-54b)

3. The integral transform of equation (13-66a) according to the definition of the integral transform (13-67b) is

$$\int_{x=0}^{\infty} X(\beta, x) \frac{\partial^2 T}{\partial x^2} dx + \frac{1}{k} \bar{g}(\beta, t) = \frac{1}{\alpha} \frac{d\bar{T}(\beta, t)}{dt} \tag{1}$$

The first term on the left is evaluated by integrating it by parts twice.

$$\int_{x=0}^{\infty} X(\beta, x) \frac{\partial^2 T}{\partial x^2} dx = \left[X \frac{\partial T}{\partial x} \right]_0^{\infty} - \int_0^{\infty} \frac{dX}{dx} \frac{\partial T}{\partial x} dx$$

$$= \left[X \frac{\partial T}{\partial x} - T \frac{dX}{dx} \right]_0^{\infty} + \int_0^{\infty} T \frac{d^2 X}{dx^2} dx \tag{2}$$

The term inside the bracket vanishes at the upper limit; it is evaluated at the lower limit by utilizing the boundary conditions (13-66b) and (2-48b); we obtain

$$\left[X \frac{\partial T}{\partial x} - T \frac{dX}{dx} \right]_0^{\infty} = \frac{X(\beta, x)}{k_1} \bigg|_{x=0} \cdot f_1(t) \tag{3}$$

The second term on the right in equation (2) is evaluated by multiplying equation (2-48a) by $T(x, t)$ and utilizing the definition of the integral transform (13-67b). We obtain

$$\int_0^{\infty} T \frac{d^2 X}{dx^2} dx = -\beta^2 \int_0^{\infty} T X \, dx = -\beta^2 \bar{T}(\beta, t) \tag{4}$$

Introducing equations (2) to (4) into (1) we find

$$\frac{d\bar{T}(\beta, t)}{dt} + \alpha \beta^2 \bar{T}(\beta, t) = \frac{\alpha}{k} \bar{g}(\beta, t) + \frac{X(\beta, x)}{k_1} \bigg|_{x=0} f_1(t) \tag{5}$$

which is the result given by equation (13-68a).

4. We consider the representation

$$F^*(x) = \frac{1}{\pi} \int_{\beta=0}^{\infty} \int_{x'=-\infty}^{\infty} F^*(x') \cos \beta(x - x') \, dx' \, d\beta \tag{1}$$

The integral of the cosine term with respect to β is expressed as a complex integral in the form

$$\int_0^L \cos \beta(x' - x) d\beta = \frac{1}{2} \int_{-L}^L \cos \beta(x' - x) d\beta = \frac{1}{2} \int_{-L}^L e^{i\beta(x' - x)} d\beta \qquad (2a)$$

since

$$\int_{-L}^L \sin \beta(x' - x) d\beta = 0 \qquad (2b)$$

Then, in the limit $L \to \infty$, equation (1) can be written as

$$F^*(x) = \frac{1}{2\pi} \int_{-\infty}^\infty e^{-i\beta x} \int_{-\infty}^\infty e^{i\beta x'} F^*(x') dx' d\beta \qquad (3)$$

which is the result given by equation (13-72).

5. The integral transform of equation (13-117a) with respect to the ϕ variable, by the application of the transform (13-118b) is

$$\frac{\partial^2 \bar{T}}{\partial r^2} + \frac{1}{r} \frac{\partial \bar{T}}{\partial r} + \frac{1}{r^2} \int_{\phi=0}^{2\pi} \cos v(\phi - \phi') \frac{\partial^2 T}{\partial \phi^2} d\phi + \frac{\bar{g}}{k} = \frac{1}{\alpha} \frac{\partial \bar{T}}{\partial t} \qquad (1)$$

The integral term is evaluated as follows: Let $\Phi(\phi) \equiv \cos v(\phi - \phi')$. Then, the integral term becomes

$$\int_0^{2\pi} \Phi(\phi) \frac{\partial^2 T}{\partial \phi^2} d\phi = \left[\Phi \frac{\partial T}{\partial \phi} \right]_0^{2\pi} - \int_0^{2\pi} \frac{d\Phi}{d\phi} \frac{\partial T}{\partial \phi} d\phi$$

$$= \left[\Phi \frac{\partial T}{\partial \phi} - T \frac{d\Phi}{d\phi} \right]_0^{2\pi} + \int_0^{2\pi} T \frac{d^2\Phi}{d\phi^2} d\phi$$

$$= \int_0^{2\pi} T \frac{d^2\Phi}{d\phi^2} d\phi \qquad (2)$$

since the terms in the bracket vanish because the functions are cyclic with a period of 2π. To evaluate this integral we consider the eigenvalue problem given as

$$\frac{d^2\Phi(\phi)}{d\phi^2} + v^2 \Phi(\phi) = 0 \qquad \text{in } 0 \le \phi \le 2\pi \qquad (3)$$

The function $\Phi(\phi)$ is cyclic with a period of 2π.

We multiply this equation by T, integrate with respect to ϕ from 0 to 2π and utilize the definition of the integral transform (13-118b) to obtain

$$\int_0^{2\pi} T \frac{d^2\Phi(\phi)}{d\phi^2} d\phi = - v^2 \int_0^{2\pi} \Phi(\phi) T d\phi = - v^2 \bar{T} \qquad (4)$$

Introducing equations (2) and (4) into (1) we find

$$\frac{\partial^2 \bar{T}}{\partial r^2} + \frac{1}{r}\frac{\partial \bar{T}}{\partial r} - \frac{v^2}{r^2}\bar{T} + \frac{\bar{g}}{k} = \frac{1}{\alpha}\frac{\partial \bar{T}}{\partial t} \tag{5}$$

which is the result given by equation (13-119a).

6. The integral transform of equation (13-119a) by the application of the transform (13-120b) is

$$\int_0^b rR_v(\beta_m, r)\left[\frac{\partial^2 \bar{T}}{\partial r^2} + \frac{1}{r}\frac{\partial \bar{T}}{\partial r} - \frac{v^2}{r^2}\bar{T}\right]dr + \frac{\bar{\bar{g}}}{k} = \frac{1}{\alpha}\frac{d\bar{\bar{T}}}{dt} \tag{1}$$

The integral term is evaluated by integrating it by parts twice, utilizing the eigenvalue problem for the R_v function and the boundary conditions as described below.

$$I \equiv \int_0^b rR_v\left[\frac{\partial^2 \bar{T}}{\partial r^2} + \frac{1}{r}\frac{\partial \bar{T}}{\partial r} - \frac{v^2}{r^2}\bar{T}\right]dr$$

$$= \left[r\left(R_v\frac{\partial \bar{T}}{\partial r} - \bar{T}\frac{dR_v}{dr}\right)\right]_0^b + \int_0^b r\left(\frac{d^2 R_v}{dr^2} + \frac{1}{r}\frac{dR_v}{dr} - \frac{v^2}{r^2}R_v\right)\bar{T}\,dr$$

$$= b\left(R_v\frac{\partial \bar{T}}{\partial r} - \bar{T}\frac{dR_v}{\partial r}\right)\bigg|_{r=b} + \int_0^b r\left(\frac{d^2 R_v}{dr^2} + \frac{1}{r}\frac{dR_v}{dr} - \frac{v^2}{r^2}R_v\right)\bar{T}\,dr \tag{2}$$

since the term inside the bracket vanishes at the lower limit. From the eigenvalue problem (i.e., equation (3-18a)] we have

$$\frac{d^2 R_v}{dr^2} + \frac{1}{r}\frac{dR_v}{dr} + \left(\beta_m^2 - \frac{v^2}{r^2}\right)R_v = 0 \qquad \text{in } 0 \le r < b \tag{3}$$

Multiplying equation (3) by $r\bar{T}$, integrating it with respect to r from $r = 0$ to $r = b$, and utilizing the definition of the integral transform (13-120b) we obtain

$$\int_0^b r\left(\frac{d^2 R_v}{dr^2} + \frac{1}{r}\frac{dR_v}{dr} - \frac{v^2}{r^2}R_v\right)\bar{T}\,dr = -\beta_m^2\int_0^b rR_v\bar{T}\,dr = -\beta_m^2\bar{\bar{T}} \tag{4}$$

From the boundary conditions (13-119b) and (3-18b) we have

$$k_2\frac{\partial \bar{T}}{\partial r} + h_2\bar{T} = \bar{f}_2(v,t) \qquad \text{at } r = b \tag{5a}$$

$$k_2\frac{dR_v}{dr} + h_2R_v = 0 \qquad \text{at } r = b \tag{5b}$$

Multiplying (5a) by R_v and (5b) by $\bar{T}$ and subtracting the results we obtain

$$\left[R_v\frac{\partial \bar{T}}{\partial r} - \bar{T}\frac{dR_v}{dr}\right]_{r=b} = b\frac{R_v}{k_2}\bigg|_{r=b}\cdot\bar{f}_2(v,t) \tag{6}$$

Introducing equations (6), (4), and (2) into equation (1) we find

$$-\beta_m^2 \widetilde{\overline{T}}(\beta_m, v, t) + b\left.\frac{R_v(\beta_m, r)}{k_2}\right|_{r=b} \cdot \bar{f}_2(v, t) + \frac{\widetilde{\overline{g}}(\beta_m, v, t)}{k} = \frac{1}{\alpha}\frac{d\widetilde{\overline{T}}}{dt}$$

or

$$\frac{d\widetilde{\overline{T}}(\beta_m, v, t)}{dt} + \alpha\beta_m^2 \widetilde{\overline{T}}(\beta_m, v, t) = \frac{\alpha}{k}\widetilde{\overline{g}}(\beta_m, v, t) + \alpha b\left.\frac{R_v(\beta_m, r)}{k_2}\right|_{r=b} \cdot f_2(v, t) \quad (7)$$

which is the result given by equation (13-121a).

7. When taking the integral transform of the differential equation (13-153a) by the application of the transform (13-154b), we need to consider only the removal of the following differential operator

$$\nabla^2 V \equiv -\frac{V}{4} + \frac{\partial}{\partial\mu}\left[(1 - \mu^2)\frac{\partial V}{\partial\mu}\right] \quad \text{in} -1 \le \mu \le 1 \quad (1)$$

since the integral transform of the remaining terms is straightforward. The integral transform of this operator under the transform (13-154b) is

$$\overline{\nabla^2 V} \equiv -\tfrac{1}{4}\bar{V} + \int_{-1}^{1} P_n(\mu)\frac{\partial}{\partial\mu}\left[(1 - \mu^2)\frac{\partial V}{\partial\mu}\right]d\mu \quad (2)$$

The integration is performed by integrating it by parts twice

$$\overline{\nabla^2 V} \equiv -\tfrac{1}{4}\bar{V} + \left[(1 - \mu^2)\left(P_n\frac{\partial V}{\partial\mu} - V\frac{dP_n}{d\mu}\right)\right]_{-1}^{1} + \int_{-1}^{1} V\frac{d}{d\mu}\left[(1 - \mu^2)\frac{dP_n}{d\mu}\right]d\mu$$

$$(3)$$

The terms inside the bracket vanishes at both limits. The integral terms is evaluated by noting that $P_n(\mu)$ function satisfies the Legendre equation

$$\frac{d}{d\mu}\left[(1 - \mu^2)\frac{dP_n}{d\mu}\right] + n(n + 1)P_n(\mu) = 0 \quad (4)$$

Multiplying this equation by V and integrating from $\mu = -1$ to 1 we find

$$\int_{-1}^{1} V\frac{d}{d\mu}\left[(1 - \mu^2)\frac{dP_n}{d\mu}\right]d\mu = -n(n + 1)\int_{-1}^{1} P_n(\mu)V\,d\mu = -n(n + 1)\bar{V} \quad (5)$$

Introducing Eq. (5) into (3) we obtain

$$\overline{\nabla^2 V} = -\tfrac{1}{4}\bar{V} - n(n + 1)\bar{V} = -(n + \tfrac{1}{2})^2\bar{V} \quad (6)$$

which is the term that appears in equation (13-155a).

8. When taking the integral transform of the equation (13-166) by the application of the transform (13-168b) we need to consider only the removal

of the following differential operator

$$\nabla^2 \bar{V} \equiv -\tfrac{1}{4}\bar{V} + \left\{\frac{\partial}{\partial\mu}\left[(1-\mu^2)\frac{\partial\bar{V}}{\partial\mu} - \frac{m^2\bar{V}}{1-\mu^2}\right]\right\} \qquad \text{in } -1 \le \mu \le 1 \quad (1)$$

The integral transform of this operator under the transform (13-168b) is

$$\widetilde{\nabla^2\bar{V}} \equiv -\tfrac{1}{4}\tilde{\bar{V}} + \int_{-1}^{1} P_n^m \left\{\frac{\partial}{\partial\mu}\left[(1-\mu^2)\frac{\partial\bar{V}}{\partial\mu}\right]\right\}d\mu - \int_{-1}^{1}\frac{m^2}{1-\mu^2}P_n^m\bar{V}\,d\mu \quad (2)$$

The first integral is performed by integrating by parts twice

$$\widetilde{\nabla^2\bar{V}} \equiv -\tfrac{1}{4}\tilde{\bar{V}} + \left[(1-\mu^2)\left(P_n^m\frac{\partial\bar{V}}{\partial\mu} - \bar{V}\frac{dP_n^m}{d\mu}\right)\right]_{-1}^{1}$$
$$+ \int_{-1}^{1}\bar{V}\left\{\frac{\partial}{\partial\mu}\left[(1-\mu^2)\frac{dP_n^m}{d\mu}\right] - \frac{m^2}{1-\mu^2}\bar{V}\right\}d\mu \quad (3)$$

The second term in the bracket vanishes at both limits. The integral term is evaluated by noting that $P_n^m(\mu)$ function satisfies Legendre's associated differential equation (13-167). That is

$$\frac{d}{d\mu}\left[(1-\mu^2)\frac{dP_n^m}{d\mu}\right] + \left[n(n+1) - \frac{m^2}{1-\mu^2}\right]P_n^m = 0 \quad (4)$$

Multiplying this equation by $\bar{V}$ and integrating from $\mu = -1$ to 1, we find

$$\int_{-1}^{1}\bar{V}\left\{\frac{d}{d\mu}\left[(1-\mu^2)\frac{dP_n^m}{d\mu}\right] - \frac{m^2}{1-\mu^2}P_n^m\right\}d\mu = -n(n+1)\int_{-1}^{1}P_n^m\bar{V}\,d\mu$$
$$= -n(n+1)\tilde{\bar{V}} \quad (5)$$

Introducing equation (5) into (3) we obtain

$$\widetilde{\nabla^2\bar{V}} \equiv -\tfrac{1}{4}\tilde{\bar{V}} - n(n+1)\tilde{\bar{V}} = -(n+\tfrac{1}{2})^2\tilde{\bar{V}} \quad (6)$$

which is the term that appears in equation (13-169).

CHAPTER 14

INTEGRAL-TRANSFORM TECHNIQUE FOR COMPOSITE MEDIUM

In Chapter 8 the method of separation of variables was used to solve the homogeneous problems of a one-dimensional composite medium, and Green's function technique was applied to solve the nonhomogeneous problems. The integral-transform technique provides a systematic and straightforward approach for the solution of both homogeneous and non-homogeneous problems. Therefore, this chapter is devoted for the application of the integral-transform technique for the solution of boundary-value problems of heat conduction of composite medium. The reader should consult references [1-11] for the theory and application of this technique for the solution of heat-conduction problems in a composite medium.

14-1 THE USE OF INTEGRAL TRANSFORM IN THE SOLUTION OF HEAT-CONDUCTION PROBLEMS IN FINITE COMPOSITE REGIONS

In this section we present the use of the integral-transform technique for the solution of three-dimensional, time-dependent, nonhomogeneous boundary-value problems of heat conduction with constant coefficients in finite composite regions. We consider a finite region R bounded by a surface S_0 and subdivided into subregions R_i, $i = 1, 2, \ldots, M$ as illustrated in Fig. 14-1. Let k_i and α_i be the thermal conductivity and thermal diffusivity, respectively, for the region R_i, which are assumed to be uniform within the region but different from those for the neighboring regions. Let h_{i0} be the heat-transfer coefficient at the outer surface S_{i0} of the region R_i and h_{ij} be the thermal contact conductance at the interface S_{ij} between the two adjacent subregions R_i and R_j. It is assumed that h_{i0} and h_{ij} are constant for each interface and $h_{ij} = h_{ji}$. We consider the following heat-conduction problem for this

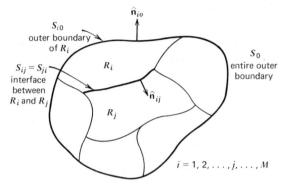

Fig. 14-1 A composite region.

composite medium:

$$\alpha_i \nabla^2 T_i(\mathbf{r}, t) + \frac{\alpha_i}{k_i} g_i(\mathbf{r}, t) = \frac{\partial T_i(\mathbf{r}, t)}{\partial t} \tag{14-1a}$$

in $R_i, i = 1, 2, \ldots, M$ for $t > 0$; subject to the boundary conditions

$$k_i^* \frac{\partial T_i(\mathbf{r}, t)}{\partial n_{i0}} + h_{i0} T_i(\mathbf{r}, t) = f_i(\mathbf{r}, t) \tag{14-1b}$$

at the outer boundary $S_{i0}, t > 0$;

$$-k_i \frac{\partial T_i(\mathbf{r}, t)}{\partial n_{ij}} = h_{ij} [T_i(\mathbf{r}, t) - T_j(\mathbf{r}, t)] = -k_j \frac{\partial T_j(\mathbf{r}, t)}{\partial n_{ij}} \tag{14-1c}$$

at the interface $S_{ij}, i \neq j, t > 0$ and to the initial conditions

$$T_i(\mathbf{r}, t) = F_i(\mathbf{r}) \qquad \text{in } R_i, t = 0, i = 1, 2, \ldots, M \tag{14-1d}$$

In the boundary conditions (14-1b) the quantity with the asterisk, k_i^*, is used in place of k_i to distinguish it as a boundary condition parameter at later stages of the analysis. That is, by setting k_i^* equal to zero the boundary condition of the first kind is obtainable. $\partial/\partial n_{ij}$ denotes the normal derivative at the interface S_{ij} between the subregions R_i and R_j in the sense from R_i to R_j, and $\partial/\partial n_{i0}$ denotes the normal derivative at the outer surface S_{i0} of subregion R_i in the *outward* direction. The quantities $F_i(\mathbf{r}), g_i(\mathbf{r}, t), \alpha_i, k_i, k_i^*, h_{i0}$, and h_{ij} are considered specified.

The basic steps in the solution of this problem by the integral-transform technique is the same as that described in the previous chapter. Namely,

1. The appropriate integral transform pair is developed.
2. By the application of the integral transform, the partial derivatives

with respect to the space variables are removed and the heat-conduction equation is reduced to an ordinary differential equation.

3.   The resulting ordinary differential equation is solved subject to the transformed initial condition. When the transform of temperature is inverted by the inversion formula the desired solution is obtained.

The procedure is as follows.

1.   Development of Integral Transform Pair

The integral-transform pair needed for the solution of the above heat-conduction problem can be developed by considering the following eigenvalue problem.

$$\nabla^2 \psi_i(\mathbf{r}) + \frac{\lambda^2}{\alpha_i} \psi_i(\mathbf{r}) = 0 \qquad \text{in } R_i, i = 1, 2, \ldots, M \quad (14\text{-}2a)$$

$$k_i^* \frac{\partial \psi_i(\mathbf{r})}{\partial n_{i0}} + h_{i0} \psi_i(\mathbf{r}) = 0 \qquad \text{at the outer boundary } S_{i0}$$

$$(14\text{-}2b)$$

$$-k_i \frac{\partial \psi_i(\mathbf{r})}{\partial n_{ij}} = h_{ij}[\psi_i(\mathbf{r}) - \psi_j(\mathbf{r})] = -k_j \frac{\partial \psi_j(\mathbf{r})}{\partial n_{ij}} \qquad \text{at the interface } S_{ij}, i \neq j$$

$$(14\text{-}2c)$$

where $h_{i0}, h_{ij}, k_i^*, \partial/\partial n_{i0}$, and $\partial/\partial n_{ij}$ are defined previously. We note that this eigenvalue problem is obtainable by the separation of the homogeneous version of the heat conduction problem (14-1).

The eigenfunctions $\psi_i(\mathbf{r})$ of this eigenvalue problem satisfy the following orthogonality condition (see Note 1 for a proof of this orthogonality relation)

$$\sum_{i=1}^{M} \frac{k_i}{\alpha_i} \int_{R_i} \psi_i(\lambda_n, \mathbf{r}) \psi_i(\lambda_l, \mathbf{r}) \, dv = \begin{cases} 0 & \text{for } n \neq l \\ N(\lambda_n) & \text{for } n = l \end{cases} \quad (14\text{-}3a)$$

where the normalization integral $N(\lambda_n)$ is defined as

$$N(\lambda_n) = \sum_{j=1}^{M} \frac{k_j}{\alpha_j} \int_{R_j} [\psi_j(\lambda_n, \mathbf{r})]^2 \, dv \qquad (14\text{-}3b)$$

We now consider the representation of a function $T_i(\mathbf{r}, t)$, defined in the region R_i, in terms of the eigenfunctions $\psi_i(\lambda_n, \mathbf{r})$ of the above eigenvalue problem in the form

$$T_i(\mathbf{r}, t) = \sum_{n=1}^{\infty} C_n(t) \psi_i(\lambda_n, \mathbf{r}) \qquad \text{in } R_i, i = 1, 2, \ldots, M \qquad (14\text{-}4)$$

where the summation is taken over all discrete spectrum eigenvalues, λ_n.

The coefficients $C_n(t)$ can be determined by utilizing the above orthogonality relation as now described.

We operate on both sides of equation (14-4) by the operator

$$\frac{k_i}{\alpha_i} \int_{R_i} \psi_i(\lambda_l, \mathbf{r}) \, dv$$

and sum up the resulting expressions from $i = 1$ to M to obtain

$$\sum_{i=1}^{M} \frac{k_i}{\alpha_i} \int_{R_i} \psi_i(\lambda_l, \mathbf{r}) T_i(\mathbf{r}, t) \, dv = \sum_{n=1}^{\infty} C_n(t) \left[\sum_{i=1}^{M} \frac{k_i}{\alpha_i} \int_{R_i} \psi_i(\lambda_n, \mathbf{r}) \psi_i(\lambda_l, \mathbf{r}) \, dv \right] \quad (14\text{-}5)$$

In view of the orthogonality condition (14-3), the term inside the bracket on the right-hand side of equation (14-5) vanishes for $n \neq l$ and becomes equal to $N(\lambda_n)$ for $n = l$. Then the coefficients $C_n(t)$ are determined as

$$C_n(t) = \frac{1}{N(\lambda_n)} \sum_{i=1}^{M} \frac{k_i}{\alpha_i} \int_{R_i} \psi_i(\lambda_n, \mathbf{r}) T_i(\mathbf{r}, t) \, dv \quad (14\text{-}6)$$

Equation (14-6) is introduced into equation (14-4) and the resulting expression is split up into two parts to define the desired integral transform pair for the function $T_i(\mathbf{r}, t)$ as

$$\text{Inversion formula}: \quad T_i(\mathbf{r}, t) = \sum_{n=1}^{\infty} \frac{\psi_i(\lambda_n, \mathbf{r})}{N(\lambda_n)} \bar{T}(\lambda_n, t) \quad (14\text{-}7a)$$

$$\text{Integral transform}: \quad \bar{T}(\lambda_n, t) = \sum_{i=1}^{M} \frac{k_i}{\alpha_i} \int_{R_i} \psi_i(\lambda_n, \mathbf{r}') T_i(\mathbf{r}', t) \, dv' \quad (14\text{-}7b)$$

As in the case of single-region problems, the summation over the eigenvalues is actually a triple, a double, or a single summation; and the integral over the region R_j is a volume, a surface, or a line integral for the three-, two-, or one-dimensional domains, respectively. Similarly, the eigenfunctions $\psi_i(\lambda_n, \mathbf{r})$ and the normalization integral $N(\lambda_n)$ are composed of the products of one-dimensional eigenfunctions and normalization integrals respectively.

2. Integral Transform of Heat Conduction Problem

Having established the appropriate integral transform pair as given above, the next step in the analysis is the removal of the partial derivatives with respect to the space variables from the differential equations (14-1a) by the application of the integral transform (14-7b) as now described.

Both sides of equation (14-1a) are operated on by the operator

$$\frac{k_i}{\alpha_i} \int_{R_i} \psi_i(\lambda_n, \mathbf{r}) \, dv$$

the results are summed up for $i = 1$ to M, and the definition of the integral transform (14-7b) is utilized. We obtain

$$\sum_{i=1}^{M} k_i \int_{R_i} \psi_i(\lambda_n, \mathbf{r}) \nabla^2 T_i(\mathbf{r}, t) \, dv + \sum_{i=1}^{M} \int_{R_i} \psi_i(\lambda_n, \mathbf{r}) g_i(\mathbf{r}, t) \, dv = \frac{d\bar{T}(\lambda_n, t)}{dt} \qquad (14\text{-}8)$$

The first term on the left is evaluated by making use of Green's theorem as [see Equation (13-10) or Note 2 in Chapter 6]

$$\sum_{i=1}^{M} k_i \int_{R_i} \psi_{i,n}(\mathbf{r}) \nabla^2 T_i(\mathbf{r}, t) \, dv = \sum_{i=1}^{M} k_i \int_{R_i} T_i \nabla^2 \psi_{i,n} \, dv$$
$$+ \sum_{i=1}^{M} k_i \int_{S_i} \left(\psi_{i,n} \frac{\partial T_i}{\partial n_i} - T_i \frac{\partial \psi_{i,n}}{\partial n_i} \right) ds_i \qquad (14\text{-}9)$$

To evaluate the first term on the right-hand side of equation (14-9), equation (14-2a) is written for the eigenfunction $\psi_{i,n}$, both sides of the equation are multiplied by $k_i T_i(\mathbf{r}, t)$, integrated over the region R_i, the resulting expressions are summed up for $i = 1$ to M, and the definition of the integral transform (14-7b) is utilized. We find

$$\sum_{i=1}^{M} k_i \int_{R_i} T_i \nabla^2 \psi_{i,n}(\mathbf{r}) \, dv = -\lambda^2 \sum_{i=1}^{M} \frac{k_i}{\alpha_i} \int_{R_i} \psi_{i,n}(\mathbf{r}) T_i(\mathbf{r}, t) \, dv \equiv -\lambda^2 \bar{T}(\lambda_n, t) \quad (14\text{-}10a)$$

The surface integrals on the right-hand side of equation (14-9) consist of integrations over the outer surfaces S_{i0} and integrations over the interfaces S_{ij}. The integrals over the interfaces S_{ij} vanish since the integrals $\int_{S_{ij}}$ and $\int_{S_{ji}}$ are opposite sign; then only contribution is due to the integration over the outer boundary surfaces S_{i0}. The resulting expression becomes (see Note 2 for the details of derivation)

$$\sum_{i=1}^{M} k_i \int_{S_i} \left(\psi_{i,n} \frac{\partial T_i}{\partial n_i} - T_i \frac{\partial \psi_{i,n}}{\partial n_i} \right) dS_i = \sum_{i=1}^{M} k_i \int_{S_{i0}} \frac{\psi_{i,n}(\mathbf{r})}{k_i^*} f_i(\mathbf{r}, t) \, dS_i \qquad (14\text{-}10b)$$

Introducing equations (14-10a, b) into equation (14-9) we obtain

$$\sum_{i=1}^{M} k_i \int_{R_i} \psi_{i,n}(\mathbf{r}) \nabla^2 T_i(\mathbf{r}, t) \, dv = -\lambda^2 \bar{T}(\lambda_n, t) + \sum_{i=1}^{M} k_i \int_{S_{i0}} \frac{\psi_{i,n}(\mathbf{r})}{k_i^*} f_i(\mathbf{r}, t) \, dS_i \quad (14\text{-}11)$$

When equation (14-11) is substituted into equation (14-8) the following ordinary differential equation results for the transform of temperature

$$\frac{d\bar{T}(\lambda_n, t)}{dt} + \lambda_n^2 \bar{T}(\lambda_n, t) = A(\lambda_n, t) \qquad (14\text{-}12a)$$

where

$$A(\lambda_n, t) = \sum_{i=1}^{M} k_i \int_{S_{i0}} \frac{\psi_{i,n}(\mathbf{r})}{k_i^*} f_i(\mathbf{r}, t) \, dS_i + \sum_{i=1}^{M} \int_{R_i} \psi_{i,n}(\mathbf{r}) g_i(\mathbf{r}, t) \, dv \qquad (14\text{-}12b)$$

The initial condition for this equation is obtained by taking the integral transform of the initial condition (14-1d) by the application of the transform (14-7b). That is

$$\bar{T}(\lambda_n, t) = \bar{F}(\lambda_n, t) \qquad \text{for } t = 0 \tag{14-12c}$$

3. Solution for Transform and Inversion

The solution of equation (14-12a) subject to the initial condition (14-12c) gives the transform $\bar{T}(\lambda_n, t)$ of temperature as

$$\bar{T}(\lambda_n, t) = e^{-\lambda_n^2 t}\left[\bar{F}(\lambda_n) + \int_0^t e^{\lambda_n^2 t'} A(\lambda_n, t')\,dt' \right] \tag{14-13}$$

The inversion of this result with the inversion formula (14-7a) gives the temperature distribution $T_i(\mathbf{r}, t)$ in the region R_i as

$$T_i(\mathbf{r}, t) = \sum_{n=1}^{\infty} \frac{1}{N(\lambda_n)} e^{-\lambda_n^2 t} \psi_{i,n}(\mathbf{r}) \left[\bar{F}(\lambda_n) + \int_0^t e^{\lambda_n^2 t'} A(\lambda_n, t')\,dt' \right]$$

$$\text{in } R_i \quad i = 1, 2, \ldots, M \tag{14-14a}$$

where

$$A(\lambda_n, t') = \sum_{j=1}^{M} \int_{R_j} \psi_{j,n}(\mathbf{r}') g_j(\mathbf{r}', t')\,dv' + \sum_{j=1}^{M} k_j \int_{S_{j0}} \frac{\psi_{j,n}(\mathbf{r}')}{k_j^*} f_j(\mathbf{r}', t')\,dS_j' \tag{14-14b}$$

$$\bar{F}(\lambda_n) = \sum_{j=1}^{M} \frac{k_j}{\alpha_j} \int_{R_j} \psi_{j,n}(\mathbf{r}') F_j(\mathbf{r}')\,dv' \tag{14-14c}$$

$$N(\lambda_n) = \sum_{j=1}^{M} \frac{k_j}{\alpha_j} \int_{R_j} [\psi_{j,n}(\mathbf{r})]^2\,dv' \tag{14-14d}$$

The above solution is developed for a boundary condition of the third kind for all outer boundaries. If some of the boundaries are of the third kind and some of the second kind, the general form of the solution given above remains unchanged. However, if some of the boundary conditions are of the first kind, some modification is needed in the term $A(\lambda_m, t')$. Suppose the boundary condition for the surface $j = m$ is of the first kind; then the coefficient k_m^* should be set equal to zero and the following replacement should be made in equation (14-14b): when $k_m^* = 0$ replace

$$\frac{\psi_{m,n}(\mathbf{r})}{k_m^*}$$

by

$$-\frac{1}{h_{m0}} \frac{\partial \psi_{m,n}(\mathbf{r})}{\partial n} \tag{14-14e}$$

The validity of this replacement is apparent from the boundary condition (14-2b).

We note that the solution given above by equation (14-14a) for a composite medium is exactly of the same form as that given by equation (13-15a) for a single-region problem. The only difference is that the integral transform of the function for composite medium involves a summation overall regions $i = 1$ to M. For $M = 1$, that is, a single region, equation (14-14) reduces to the single region solution (13-15) if we replace λ_n^2 by $\alpha \beta_n^2$.

In the foregoing formal analysis we did not include explicitly the Sturm-Liouville weighting function (i.e., 1 for rectangular coordinates, r for cylindrical coordinates, etc.). This matter will be illustrated with examples later in this chapter.

Boundary Condition of the Second Kind For All Boundaries

When the boundary conditions are all of the second kind for all boundaries, that is all h_{i0}'s are zero, $\lambda_0 = 0$ is also an eigenvalue corresponding to the eigenfunction $\psi_{i,0} = $ constant $\neq 0$. As it has already been discussed in the case of a single region, without loss of generality we can set $\psi_{i,0} = 1$. Then, the general solution (14-14) includes an additional term corresponding to the zero eigenvalue and the resulting solution is written as

$$T_i(\mathbf{r}, t) = \frac{1}{N(\lambda_0)} \left[\bar{F}(\lambda_0) + \int_0^t A(\lambda_0, t') dt' \right]$$
$$+ \sum_{n=1}^{\infty} \frac{1}{N(\lambda_n)} e^{-\lambda_n^2 t} \psi_{i,n}(\mathbf{r}) \left[\bar{F}(\lambda_n) + \int_0^t e^{\lambda_n^2 t'} A(\lambda_n, t') dt' \right] \quad (14\text{-}15a)$$

where

$$N(\lambda_0) = \sum_{j=1}^{M} \frac{k_j}{\alpha_j} \int_{R_j} dv' \quad (14\text{-}15b)$$

$$\bar{F}(\lambda_0) = \sum_{j=1}^{M} \frac{k_j}{\alpha_j} \int_{R_j} F_j(\mathbf{r}') dv' \quad (14\text{-}15c)$$

$$A(\lambda_0, t') = \sum_{j=1}^{M} \int_{R_j} g_j(\mathbf{r}, t') dv + \sum_{j=1}^{M} \frac{k_j}{k_j^*} \int_{S_{j0}} f_j(\mathbf{r}, t') dS_j \quad (14\text{-}15d)$$

and the functions $A(\lambda_n, t), \bar{F}(\lambda_n)$, and $N(\lambda_n)$ are as defined by equations (14-14b), (14-14c), and (14-14d), respectively.

As stated previously, in the solutions (14-14) or (14-15), the summation is a triple, a double, or a single summation; the integral over the region is a volume, a surface, or a line integral for the three-, two-, or one-dimensional problems, respectively.

Alternative Form of the General Solution

The general solution (14-14) of the boundary-value problem of heat conduction for a composite medium is an exact solution. But, when the boundary conditions are nonhomogeneous and the temperature is to be computed at the boundaries, the computational difficulties arise because the series is not uniformly convergent at the boundary due to the Gibbs phenomena. An alternative form of the general solution (14-14) can be obtained by integrating it by parts as discussed in the previous chapter. The solution (14-14) for the composite medium being exactly of the same form as the solution (13-15a) for the single region, the integration by parts is performed in exactly the same way as that described in section (13-2), Chapter 13. Then, the general solution (14-14) is split up into three distinct groups of simpler solutions for each region similar to that given by equation (13-28a); but the resulting simpler problems are the composite medium equivalent of the problems defined by equations (13-29) to (13-31).

14-2 ONE-DIMENSIONAL CASE

We now consider, as a special case of the above general problem of heat conduction in a composite medium consisting of M parallel layers of slabs, cylinders, or spheres as illustrated in Fig. 8-1. We assume the one-dimensional problem, contact resistance at the interfaces, and convection from the outer boundaries at $x = x_1$ and $x = x_{M+1}$. Initially each layer is at a specified temperature $T_i(x,0) = F_i(x)$, in $x_i < x < x_{i+1}$, $i = 1, 2, \ldots, M$ and for times $t > 0$ heat is generated in each region at a rate $g_i(x,t)$ W/m^3 (or Btu/hr ft^3). The boundary-value problem of heat conduction is the one-dimensional version of equations (14-1) and given as

$$\alpha_i \frac{1}{x^p} \frac{\partial}{\partial x}\left(x^p \frac{\partial T_i}{\partial x} \right) + \frac{\alpha_i}{k_i} g_i(x,t) = \frac{\partial T_i(x,t)}{\partial t} \quad \text{in } x_i < x < x_{i+1}, \text{ for } t > 0 \quad (14\text{-}16\text{a})$$

$$i = 1, 2, \ldots, M$$

subject to the boundary conditions

$$-k_1^* \frac{\partial T_1}{\partial x} + h_1 T_1(x,t) = f_1(t) \quad \text{at the outer boundary } x = x_1, t > 0 \quad (14\text{-}16\text{b})$$

$$-k_i \frac{\partial T_i}{\partial x} = h_{i+1}[T_i - T_{i+1}] = -k_{i+1} \frac{\partial T_{i+1}}{\partial x} \qquad (14\text{-}16\text{c})$$

at the interface $x = x_{i+1}$, $i = 1, 2, \ldots, M-1$, for $t > 0$

$$k_M^* \frac{\partial T_M}{\partial x} + h_{M+1} T_M(x,t) = f_M(t) \quad \text{at the outer boundary } x = x_{M+1}, \, t > 0$$

(14-16d)

and the initial conditions

$$T_i(x,t) = F_i(x) \quad \text{for } t = 0, \text{ in } x_i < x < x_{i+1}; i = 1, 2, \ldots, M \quad \text{(14-16e)}$$

where

$$p = \begin{cases} 0 & \text{slab} \\ 1 & \text{cylinder} \\ 2 & \text{sphere} \end{cases}$$

The homogeneous version of this problem is identical to the problem given by equations (8-1) to (8-3).

The appropriate eigenvalue problem is given as

$$\frac{1}{x^p} \frac{d}{dx}\left(x^p \frac{d\psi_{i,n}}{dx}\right) + \frac{\beta_n^2}{\alpha_i}\psi_{i,n}(x) = 0 \quad \text{in } x_i < x < x_{i+1}, i = 1, 2, \ldots, M \quad \text{(14-17a)}$$

subject to the boundary conditions

$$-k_1^* \frac{d\psi_{1,n}}{dx} + h_1 \psi_{1,n}(x) = 0 \qquad \text{at the outer boundary } x = x_1 \quad \text{(14-17b)}$$

$$-k_i \frac{d\psi_{i,n}}{dx} = h_{i+1}[\psi_{i,n} - \psi_{i+1,n}] = -k_{i+1} \frac{d\psi_{i+1,n}}{dx} \quad \text{(14-17c)}$$

$$\text{at the interface } x = x_{i+1}, \, i = 1, 2, \ldots, M - 1$$

$$k_M^* \frac{d\psi_{M,n}}{dx} + h_{M+1}\psi_{M,n}(x) = 0 \qquad \text{at the outer boundary } x = x_{M+1} \quad \text{(14-17d)}$$

The eigenfunctions $\psi_{i,n}(x)$ satisfy the following orthogonality condition

$$\sum_{i=1}^{M} \frac{k_i}{\alpha_i} \int_{x_i}^{x_{i+1}} x^p \psi_{i,n}(x)\psi_{i,l}(x)\,dx = \begin{cases} 0 & \text{for } n \neq l \\ N(\beta_n) & \text{for } n = l \end{cases} \quad \text{(14-18a)}$$

where

$$N(\beta_n) = \sum_{j=1}^{M} \frac{k_j}{\alpha_j} \int_{x_j}^{x_{j+1}} x^p [\psi_{j,n}(x)]^2 \, dx \quad \text{(14-18b)}$$

This eigenvalue problem is similar to the one given by equations (8-7) and (8-8); therefore, it can be solved as described in Chapter 8. Once the eigenvalues β_n, eigenfunctions $\psi_{i,n}(x)$ and the normalization integral $N(\beta_n)$ are known, the solution of the heat-conduction problem (14-16) is immediately obtained from the general solution (14-14) as

$$T_i(x,t) = \sum_{n=1}^{\infty} \frac{1}{N(\beta_n)} e^{-\beta_n^2 t} \psi_{i,n}(x) \left[\bar{F}(\beta_n) + \int_0^t e^{\beta_n^2 t'} A(\beta_n, t') \, dt' \right] \quad (14\text{-}19a)$$

$$\text{in } x_i < x < x_{i+1}, \, i = 1, 2, \ldots, M$$

where

$$\bar{F}(\beta_n) = \sum_{j=1}^{M} \frac{k_j}{\alpha_j} \int_{x_j}^{x_{j+1}} x'^p \psi_{j,n}(x') F_j(x') \, dx' \quad (14\text{-}19b)$$

$$A(\beta_n, t') = \sum_{j=1}^{M} \int_{x_j}^{x_{j+1}} x'^p \psi_{jn}(x') g_j(x', t') \, dx' + \left\{ k_1 \left[x'^p \frac{\psi_{1,n}(x')}{k_1^*} \right]_{x'=x_1} f_1(t') \right.$$

$$\left. + k_M \left[x'^p \frac{\psi_{M,n}(x')}{k_M^*} \right]_{x'=x_{m+1}} f_M(t') \right\} \quad (14\text{-}19c)$$

$$N(\beta_n) = \sum_{j=1}^{M} \frac{k_j}{\alpha_j} \int_{x_j}^{x_{j+1}} x'^p [\psi_{j,n}(x')]^2 \, dx' \quad (14\text{-}19d)$$

where $p = 0$, 1, and 2 for slab, cylinder, and sphere, respectively. We note that, for the case of no heat generation and homogeneous boundary conditions the above solution is identical to that given by equations (8-15).

The above solution is derived for boundary conditions of the third kind with both outer boundaries. The boundary condition of the first kind is obtainable at the boundaries $x = x_1$ and/or $x = x_{M+1}$ by setting k_1^* and/or k_M^* equal to zero. For such cases the following changes should be made in the term $A(\beta_n, t')$ given by equation (14-19c): when $k_1^* = 0$ replace

$$\frac{\psi_{1,n}(x')}{k_1^*}$$

by

$$\frac{1}{h_1} \frac{d\psi_{1,n}(x')}{dx'} \quad (14\text{-}19e)$$

when $k_M^* = 0$ replace

$$\frac{\psi_{M,n}(x')}{k_M^*}$$

by

$$-\frac{1}{h_{M+1}} \frac{d\psi_{M,n}(x')}{dx'} \quad (14\text{-}19f)$$

The validity of these results are apparent from equations (14-17b) and (14-17d), respectively.

Use of Green's Functions

The solution given by equations (14-19) can be written in terms of Green's function as

$$
\begin{aligned}
T_i(x,t) = & \sum_{j=1}^{M} \int_{x_j}^{x_{j+1}} x'^p [G_{ij}(x,t|x',t')]_{t'=0} F_j(x')\,dx' \\
& + \int_{t'=0}^{t} \sum_{j=1}^{M} \int_{x_j}^{x_{j+1}} x'^p G_{ij}(x,t|x',t') \left[\frac{\alpha_j}{k_j} g_j(x',t') \right] dx'\,dt' \\
& + \alpha_1 \int_{t'=0}^{t} \left[x'^p \frac{G_{i1}(x,t|x',t')}{k_1^*} \right]_{x'=x_1} f_1(t')\,dt' \\
& + \alpha_M \int_{t'=0}^{t} \left[x'^p \frac{G_{iM}(x,t|x',t')}{k_M^*} \right]_{x'=x_{M+1}} f_M(t')\,dt'
\end{aligned}
\qquad (14\text{-}20a)
$$

where the one-dimensional composite medium Green's function is defined as

$$
G_{ij}(x,t|x',t') = \sum_{n=1}^{\infty} e^{-\beta_n^2(t-t')} \frac{1}{N(\beta_n)} \frac{k_j}{\alpha_j} \psi_{i,n}(x)\psi_{j,n}(x')
\qquad (14\text{-}20b)
$$

The following change should be made in equation (14-20a) for a boundary condition of the first kind at the outer boundaries: when $k_1^* = 0$ replace

$$
\left[\frac{G_{i1}(x,t|x',t')}{k_1^*} \right]_{x'=x_1}
$$

by

$$
\left[\frac{1}{h_1} \frac{\partial G_{i1}(x,t|x',t')}{\partial x'} \right]_{x'=x_1}
\qquad (14\text{-}20c)
$$

when $k_M^* = 0$ replace

$$
\left[\frac{G_{iM}(x,t|x',t')}{k_M^*} \right]_{x'=x_{M+1}}
$$

by

$$
-\left[\frac{1}{h_{M+1}} \frac{\partial G_{iM}(x,t|x',t')}{\partial x'} \right]_{x'=x_{M+1}}
\qquad (14\text{-}20d)
$$

For homogeneous boundary conditions at the outer boundary surfaces, equation (14-20a) reduces to the solution (8-82).

Example 14-1. Solve the following time-dependent heat-conduction problem for a two-region solid cylinder with heat generation in both regions.

$$\frac{\alpha_1}{r}\frac{\partial}{\partial r}\left(r\frac{\partial T_1}{\partial r}\right)+\frac{\alpha_1}{k_1}g_1(r,t)=\frac{\partial T_1(r,t)}{\partial t} \quad \text{in } 0\leq r<a,\ t>0 \quad (14\text{-}21a)$$

$$\frac{\alpha_2}{r}\frac{\partial}{\partial r}\left(r\frac{\partial T_2}{\partial r}\right)+\frac{\alpha_2}{k_2}g_2(r,t)=\frac{\partial T_2(r,t)}{\partial t} \quad \text{in } a<r<b,\ t>0 \quad (14\text{-}21b)$$

subject to the boundary conditions

$$T_1(r,t)=\text{finite} \qquad \text{at } r=0,\ t>0 \qquad (14\text{-}22a)$$

$$T_1(r,t)=T_2(r,t) \qquad \text{at } r=a,\ t>0 \qquad (14\text{-}22b)$$

$$k_1\frac{\partial T_1}{\partial r}=k_2\frac{\partial T_2}{\partial r} \qquad \text{at } r=a,\ t>0 \qquad (14\text{-}22c)$$

$$k_2^*\frac{\partial T_2}{\partial r}+h_2T_2=0 \qquad \text{at } r=b,\ t>0 \qquad (14\text{-}22d)$$

and the initial conditions

$$T_1(r,t)=F_1(r) \qquad \text{for } t=0,\ \text{in } 0<r<a \qquad (14\text{-}23a)$$

$$T_2(r,t)=F_2(r) \qquad \text{for } t=0,\ \text{in } a<r<b \qquad (14\text{-}23b)$$

Solution. The solution of this problem is immediately written according to equation (14-19a) as

$$T_1(r,t)=\sum_{n=1}^{\infty}\frac{e^{-\beta_n^2 t}}{N(\beta_n)}\psi_1(\beta_n,r)\left[\bar{F}(\beta_n)+\int_0^t e^{\beta_n^2 t'}A(\beta_n,t')\,dt'\right] \quad \text{in } 0\leq r<a \quad (14\text{-}24a)$$

$$T_2(r,t)=\sum_{n=1}^{\infty}\frac{e^{-\beta_n^2 t}}{N(\beta_n)}\psi_2(\beta_n,r)\left[\bar{F}(\beta_n)+\int_0^t e^{\beta_n^2 t'}A(\beta_n,t')\,dt'\right] \quad \text{in } a<r<b \quad (14\text{-}24b)$$

where

$$\bar{F}(\beta_n)=\frac{k_1}{\alpha_1}\int_0^a r'\psi_1(\beta_n,r')F_1(r')\,dr'+\frac{k_2}{\alpha_2}\int_a^b r'\psi_2(\beta_n,r')F_2(r')\,dr' \quad (14\text{-}24c)$$

$$A(\beta_n,t')=\int_0^a r'\psi_1(\beta_n,r')g_1(r',t')\,dr'+\int_a^b r'\psi_2(\beta_n,r')g_2(r',t')\,dr' \quad (14\text{-}24d)$$

$$N(\beta_n)=\frac{k_1}{\alpha_1}\int_0^a r'[\psi_1(\beta_n,r')]^2\,dr'+\frac{k_2}{\alpha_2}\int_a^b r'[\psi_2(\beta_n,r')]^2\,dr' \quad (14\text{-}24e)$$

The homogeneous portion of the heat-conduction problem given by equations (14-21) to (14-23) is exactly the same as that considered in Example 8-1.

Therefore the eigenfunctions $\psi_1(\beta_n, r), \psi_2(\beta_n, r)$ and the eigenvalues β_n are exactly the same as those given in Example 8-1; then, the eigenfunctions are obtained from equations (8-38) as

$$\psi_1(\beta_n, r) = J_0\left(\frac{\beta_n}{\sqrt{\alpha_1}} r\right) \tag{14-25a}$$

$$\psi_2(\beta_n, r) = A_{2n} J_0\left(\frac{\beta_n}{\sqrt{\alpha_2}} r\right) + B_{2n} Y_0\left(\frac{\beta_n}{\sqrt{\alpha_2}} r\right) \tag{14-25b}$$

The coefficients A_{2n} and B_{2n} are given by equations (8-43) and the eigenvalues β_n are the roots of the transcendental equation (8-44).

Example 14-2. Solve the following time-dependent heat-conduction problem for a two-layer slab which is in perfect thermal contact and with heat generation in both regions

$$\alpha_1 \frac{\partial^2 T_1}{\partial x^2} + \frac{\alpha_1}{k_1} g_1(x, t) = \frac{\partial T_1(x, t)}{\partial t} \qquad \text{in } 0 < x < a, \ t > 0 \tag{14-26a}$$

$$\alpha_2 \frac{\partial^2 T_2}{\partial x^2} + \frac{\alpha_2}{k_2} g_2(x, t) = \frac{\partial T_2(x, t)}{\partial t} \qquad \text{in } a < x < b, \ t > 0 \tag{14-26b}$$

subject to the boundary conditions

$$T_1(x, t) = 0 \qquad\qquad \text{at } x = 0, \ t > 0 \tag{14-27a}$$

$$T_1(x, t) = T_2(x, t) \qquad \text{at } x = a, \ t > 0 \tag{14-27b}$$

$$k_1 \frac{\partial T_1}{\partial x} = k_2 \frac{\partial T_2}{\partial x} \qquad \text{at } x = a, \ t > 0 \tag{14-27c}$$

$$k_2^* \frac{\partial T_2}{\partial x} + h_3 T_2 = 0 \qquad \text{at } x = b, \ t > 0 \tag{14-27d}$$

and the initial conditions

$$T_1(x, t) = F_1(x) \qquad \text{for } t = 0, \ \text{in } 0 \le x < a \tag{14-28a}$$

$$T_2(x, t) = F_2(x) \qquad \text{for } t = 0, \ \text{in } a < x < b \tag{14-28b}$$

Solution. The solution of this problem is immediately written according to equation (14-19a) as

$$T_1(x, t) = \sum_{n=1}^{\infty} \frac{e^{-\beta_n^2 t}}{N(\beta_n)} \psi_1(\beta_n, x) \left[\bar{F}(\beta_n) + \int_0^t e^{\beta_n^2 t'} A(\beta_n, t') \, dt' \right] \quad \text{in } 0 < x < a \tag{14-29a}$$

$$T_2(x,t) = \sum_{n=1}^{\infty} \frac{e^{-\beta_n^2 t}}{N(\beta_n)} \psi_2(\beta_n, x) \left[\bar{F}(\beta_n) + \int_0^t e^{\beta_n^2 t'} A(\beta_n, t') dt' \right] \quad \text{in } a < x < b \quad (14\text{-}29b)$$

where

$$\bar{F}(\beta_n) = \frac{k_1}{\alpha_1} \int_0^a \psi_1(\beta_n, x') F_1(x') dx' + \frac{k_2}{\alpha_2} \int_a^b \psi_2(\beta_n, x') F_2(x') dx' \quad (14\text{-}29c)$$

$$A(\beta_n, t') = \int_0^a \psi_1(\beta_n, x') g_1(x', t') dx' + \int_a^b \psi_2(\beta_n, x') g_2(x', t') dx' \quad (14\text{-}29d)$$

$$N(\beta_n) = \frac{k_1}{\alpha_1} \int_0^a [\psi_1(\beta_n, x')]^2 dx' + \frac{k_2}{\alpha_2} \int_a^b [\psi_2(\beta_n, x')]^2 dx' \quad (14\text{-}29e)$$

The homogeneous portion of the above heat-conduction problem (14-26) to (14-28) is exactly the same as that considered in Example 8-2. Therefore, the eigenfunctions $\psi_1(\beta_n, x)$, $\psi_2(\beta_n, x)$ and the eigenvalues β_n are exactly the same as those given in Example 8-2; then the eigenfunctions are obtained from equations (8-55) as

$$\psi_1(\beta_n, x) = \sin\left(\frac{\beta_n}{\sqrt{\alpha_1}} x \right) \quad (14\text{-}30a)$$

$$\psi_2(\beta_n, x) = A_{2n} \sin\left(\frac{\beta_n}{\sqrt{\alpha_2}} x \right) + B_{2n} \cos\left(\frac{\beta_n}{\sqrt{\alpha_2}} x \right) \quad (14\text{-}30b)$$

where the coefficients A_{2n} and B_{2n} are given by equations (8-60) and the eigenvalues β_n are the roots of the transcendental equation (8-61).

REFERENCES

1. C. W. Tittle, *J. Appl. Phys.* **36**, 1486–1488, 1965.
2. C. W. Tittle and V. L. Robinson, ASME Paper 65-WA-HT-52, 1965.
3. N. Y. Ölçer, *Ingenieur-Arch.* **36**, 285–293, 1968.
4. N. Y. Ölçer, *Quart. Appl. Math.* **26**, 355–371, 1968.
5. N. Y. Ölçer, *Nucl. Eng. Design* **7**, 97–112, 1968.
6. Kanae Senda, A Family of Integral Transforms and Some Applications to Physical Problems, Technology Reports of the Osaka University, Osaka, Japan, No. 823, **18**, 261–286, 1968.
7. M. H. Cobble, *J. Franklin Inst.* **290** (5), 453–465, 1970.
8. G. P. Mulholland and M. N. Cobble, *Int. J. Heat Mass Transfer* **15**, 147–160, 1972.
9. J. D. Lockwood and G. P. Mulholland, *J. Heat Transfer* **95c**, 487–491, 1973.
10. M. D. Mikhailov, *Int. J. Engng. Sci.* **11**, 235–241, 1973.
11. Y. Yener and M. N. Özışık, On the Solution of Unsteady Heat Conduction in Multi-Region Media with Time Dependent Heat Transfer Coefficient, *Proceedings of the 5th International Heat Transfer Conference*, Cu 2.5, pp. 188–192, Tokyo, Sept. 1974.

PROBLEMS

14-1 A two-layer solid cylinder contains the inner region, $0 \leq r \leq a$, and the outer region, $a \leq r \leq b$, which are in perfect thermal contact. Initially the inner and outer regions are kept at temperatures $F_1(r)$ and $F_2(r)$, respectively. For times $t > 0$, heat is generated at the rates of $g_1(r, t)$ and $g_2(r, t)$ at the inner and outer regions, respectively, while the outer boundary at $r = b$ is kept at zero temperature. Obtain expressions for the temperature distributions $T_1(r, t)$ and $T_2(r, t)$ for the inner and outer regions for times $t > 0$.

14-2 A two-layer slab consists of a first layer $0 \leq x \leq a$ and a second layer $a \leq x \leq b$, which are in perfect thermal contact. Initially the first region is at temperature $F_1(r)$ and the second region at $F_2(r)$. For times $t > 0$, heat is generated in the first region at a rate of $g_1(x, t)$ W/m^3, and in the second region at a rate of $g_2(x, t)$ W/m^3, while the outer surfaces at $x = 0$ and $x = b$ dissipate heat by convection with heat-transfer coefficients h_1 and h_3, respectively, into environments at zero temperature. Obtain expressions for the temperature distributions $T_1(x, t)$ and $T_2(x, t)$ in the regions for times $t > 0$.

14-3 A two-layer hollow sphere consists of the inner layer $a \leq r \leq b$ and the outer layer $b \leq r \leq c$, which are in perfect thermal contact. Initially inner and outer regions are kept at temperatures $F_1(r)$ and $F_2(r)$, respectively. For times $t > 0$, heat is generated in the inner and outer regions at a rate of $g_1(r, t)$ and $g_2(r, t)$ W/m^3, respectively, while the boundaries at $r = a$ and $r = c$ are kept at zero temperature. Obtain expressions for the temperature distributions $T_1(r, t)$ and $T_2(r, t)$ in both regions.

14-4 A two-layer solid cylinder contains the inner region $0 \leq r \leq a$ and the outer region $a \leq r \leq b$. Initially the inner and outer regions are at temperatures $F_1(r)$ and $F_2(r)$, respectively; for times $t > 0$ the boundary at $r = b$ is kept insulated. Obtain an expression for the temperature distribution $T_1(r, t)$ and $T_2(r, t)$ in both regions.

14-5 Repeat Problem (14-2) for the case when the boundary surface at $x = 0$ is kept insulated and the boundary surface at $x = b$ is kept at zero temperature.

14-6 Repeat Problem (14-3) for the case when the boundary surface at $r = a$ is kept insulated and that at $r = c$ is kept at zero temperature.

14-7 Repeat Problem (14-4) for the case when the boundary at $r = b$ dissipates heat by convection into a medium at zero temperature.

NOTES

1. A proof of the orthogonality relation (14-3) is given as follows. Equation (14-2a) is written for two different eigenfunctions $\psi_i(\lambda_n, \mathbf{r}) \equiv \psi_{i,n}(\mathbf{r})$

and $\psi_i(\lambda_p, \mathbf{r}) \equiv \psi_{i,p}(\mathbf{r})$ as

$$\nabla^2 \psi_{i,n}(\mathbf{r}) + \frac{\lambda_n^2}{\alpha_i} \psi_{i,n}(\mathbf{r}) = 0 \qquad \text{in } R_i, \ i = 1, 2, \ldots, M \tag{1}$$

$$\nabla^2 \psi_{i,p}(\mathbf{r}) + \frac{\lambda_p^2}{\alpha_i} \psi_{i,p}(\mathbf{r}) = 0 \qquad \text{in } R_i, \ i = 1, 2, \ldots, M \tag{2}$$

The first equation is multiplied by $\psi_{i,p}(\mathbf{r})$, the second by $\psi_{i,n}(\mathbf{r})$, the results are subtracted and integrated over the region R_i

$$\frac{1}{\alpha_i}(\lambda_n^2 - \lambda_p^2) \int_{R_i} \psi_{i,n}(\mathbf{r})\psi_{i,p}(\mathbf{r}) \, dv = \int_{R_i} [\psi_{i,n}\nabla^2\psi_{i,p} - \psi_{i,p}\nabla^2\psi_{i,n}] \, dv \tag{3}$$

The volume integral on the right is changed to surface integral by Green's theorem, both sides are multiplied by k_i, and the results are summed up for $i = 1, 2, \ldots, M$, (i.e., over all subregions)

$$(\lambda_n^2 - \lambda_p^2) \sum_{i=1}^{M} \frac{k_i}{\alpha_i} \int_{R_i} \psi_{i,n}(\mathbf{r})\psi_{i,p}(\mathbf{r}) \, dv = \sum_{i=1}^{M} k_i \int_{S_i} \left(\psi_{i,n} \frac{\partial\psi_{i,p}}{\partial n_i} - \psi_{i,p} \frac{\partial\psi_{i,n}}{\partial n_i} \right) dS_i \tag{4}$$

The surface integrals on the right-hand side consist of integrations over the outer boundary surfaces S_{i0} and over the interfaces S_{ij}. The surface integrals over the outer surfaces vanish, namely

$$\int_{S_{i0}} k_i^* \left(\psi_{i,n} \frac{\partial\psi_{i,p}}{\partial n_{i0}} - \psi_{i,p} \frac{\partial\psi_{i,n}}{\partial n_{i0}} \right) dS_i = 0 \tag{5}$$

To obtain this result, the boundary condition (14-2b) for the outer surfaces S_{i0} is written for two different eigenfunctions $\psi_{i,p}(\mathbf{r})$ and $\psi_{i,n}(\mathbf{r})$, the first is multiplied by $\psi_{i,n}(\mathbf{r})$, the second by $\psi_{i,p}(\mathbf{r})$, and the results are subtracted

$$k_i^* \left(\psi_{i,n} \frac{\partial\psi_{i,p}}{\partial n_{i0}} - \psi_{i,p} \frac{\partial\psi_{i,n}}{\partial n_{i0}} \right) = h_{i0}(\psi_{i,n}\psi_{i,p} - \psi_{i,p}\psi_{i,n}) = 0 \tag{6}$$

By making use of the interface boundary conditions (14-2c) in a similar manner and noting that the integrals over the interface, $\int_{S_{ij}}$ and $\int_{S_{ji}}$, are of opposite sign hence cancel out when summed up, it is shown that the right-hand side of equation (4) vanishes. Hence we obtain the orthogonality condition as

$$\sum_{i=1}^{M} \frac{k_i}{\alpha_i} \int_{R_i} \psi_{i,n}(\mathbf{r})\psi_{i,p}(\mathbf{r}) \, dr = \begin{cases} 0 & \text{for } n \neq p \\ N(\lambda_n) & \text{for } n = p \end{cases} \tag{7a}$$

where

$$N(\lambda_n) = \sum_{i=1}^{M} \frac{k_i}{\alpha_i} \int_{R_i} [\psi_{i,n}(\mathbf{r})]^2 \, dv \tag{7b}$$

2.   Proof of the equation (14-10b) is as follows: The second term on the right-hand side of equation (14-9) is written as

$$\sum_{i=1}^{M} k_i \int_{S_i} \left(\psi_{i,n} \frac{\partial T_i}{\partial n_i} - T_i \frac{\partial \psi_{i,n}}{\partial n_i} \right) dS_i = \sum_{i=1}^{M} k_i \int_{S_{i0}} \left(\psi_{i,n} \frac{\partial T_i}{\partial n_{i0}} - T_i \frac{\partial \psi_{i,n}}{\partial n_{i0}} \right) dS_i$$

$$+ \sum_{i=1}^{M} k_i (1 - \delta_{ij}) \int_{S_{ij}} \left(\psi_{i,n} \frac{\partial T_i}{\partial n_{ij}} - T_i \frac{\partial \psi_{i,n}}{\partial n_{ij}} \right) dS_i$$

(1)

where

$$\delta_{ij} = \begin{cases} 0 & i \neq j \\ 1 & i = j \end{cases}$$

The first integral on the right-hand side of this equation can be evaluated by utilizing the boundary conditions (14-1b) and (14-2b) for the outer boundary surface. That is, equation (14-1b) is multiplied by $\psi_{i,n}$, equation (14-2b) is multiplied by T_i and the results are subtracted

$$\psi_{i,n} \frac{\partial T_i}{\partial n_{i0}} - T_i \frac{\partial \psi_{i,n}}{\partial n_{i0}} = \frac{\psi_{i,n}}{k_i^*} f_i(\mathbf{r}, t)$$

(2a)

Both sides of this result is multiplied by k_i, integrated over the surface S_{i0} and the results are summed up for $i = 1, 2, \ldots, M$. We obtain

$$\sum_{i=1}^{M} k_i \int_{S_{i0}} \left(\psi_{i,n} \frac{\partial T_i}{\partial n_{i0}} - T_i \frac{\partial \psi_{i,n}}{\partial n_{i0}} \right) dS_i = \sum_{i=1}^{M} k_i \int_{S_{i0}} \frac{\psi_{i,n}}{k_i^*} f_i(\mathbf{r}, t) dS_i$$

(2b)

The integrals over the interfaces S_{ij} in the second term on the right-hand side of equation (1) can be evaluated in a similar manner by making use of the boundary conditions (14-1c) and (14-2c). When the results are summed up for $i = 1, 2, \ldots, M$, no net contribution results from the sum. Therefore, the only contribution is given by equation (2a); hence equation (1) reduces to

$$\sum_{i=1}^{M} k_i \int_{S_i} \left(\psi_{i,n} \frac{\partial T_i}{\partial n_i} - T_i \frac{\partial \psi_{i,n}}{\partial n_i} \right) dS_i = \sum_{i=1}^{M} k_i \int_{S_{i0}} \frac{\psi_{i,n}}{k_i^*} f_i(\mathbf{r}, t) dS_i$$

(3)

which is the result given by equation (14-10b).

CHAPTER 15

HEAT CONDUCTION IN ANISOTROPIC MEDIUM

In the previous chapter we considered heat conduction in solids that are said to be *isotropic*, that is the thermal conductivity does not depend on direction. There are also many natural and man-made materials in which the thermal conductivity varies with direction; they are called *anisotropic* materials. For example crystals, wood, sedimentary rocks, metals that have undergone heavy cold pressing, laminated sheets, cables, heat shielding materials for space vehicles, fiber reinforced structures, and many others are anisotropic materials. In wood, the thermal conductivity is different along the grain, across the grain, and circumferentially. In laminated sheets the thermal conductivity is not the same along and across the laminations. Therefore, heat conduction in anisotropic materials have numerous important applications in various branches of science and engineering. In spite of the importance of this problem only a limited number of work is available on the subject.

Most of the earlier work have been limited to the problems of one-dimensional heat flow in crystal physics [1,2]. As it will be apparent later in this chapter, the differential equation of heat conduction for anisotropic solids involve cross-derivatives of the space variables; therefore, the general analysis of heat conduction in anisotropic solids is complicated. When the cross-derivatives are absent from the heat-conduction equation, as in the case of *orthotropic* solids, the analysis of heat transfer is significantly simplified and has been considered in several references [3–12]. In recent years several works have appeared in the literature on the solution of heat conduction in anisotropic media [13–25]. Experimental work on heat diffusion in anisotropic solids is very limited; the available work [2,5,17] deals with either the one-dimensional situation or the orthotropic materials.

In this chapter we present the differential equation of heat conduction and the boundary conditions for anisotropic solids; discuss the thermal conductivity coefficients in relation to crystal structures; and consider the solution of heat-conduction problems in anisotropic media for the one-dimensional steady-state case, multidimensional orthotropic medium and some specific cases of multidimensional anisotropic medium.

15-1 HEAT FLUX FOR ANISOTROPIC SOLIDS

The heat flux in isotropic solids, as discussed in Chapter 1, obeys the Fourier law, that is,

$$\mathbf{q} = -k\nabla T \tag{15-1}$$

where the thermal conductivity is independent of direction and the heat flux vector $\mathbf{q}$ is normal to the isothermal surface passing through the spacial position considered.

In the case of anisotropic solids the situation is quite different. The component of the heat flux, say, q_1, along $0x_1$, depends in general upon a linear combination of the temperature gradients along the $0x_1, 0x_2$, and $0x_3$ directions. With this consideration, the general expressions for the three components of the heat flux q_1, q_2, and q_3 along the $0x_1, 0x_2$, and $0x_3$ directions in the rectangular coordinate system are given, respectively, as [26]

$$-q_1 = k_{11}\frac{\partial T}{\partial x_1} + k_{12}\frac{\partial T}{\partial x_2} + k_{13}\frac{\partial T}{\partial x_3} \tag{15-2a}$$

$$-q_2 = k_{21}\frac{\partial T}{\partial x_1} + k_{22}\frac{\partial T}{\partial x_2} + k_{23}\frac{\partial T}{\partial x_3} \tag{15-2b}$$

$$-q_3 = k_{31}\frac{\partial T}{\partial x_1} + k_{32}\frac{\partial T}{\partial x_2} + k_{33}\frac{\partial T}{\partial x_3} \tag{15-2c}$$

which can be written more compactly in the form

$$q_i = -\sum_{j=1}^{3} k_{ij}\frac{\partial T}{\partial x_j} \qquad i = 1, 2, 3 \tag{15-3}$$

Therefore, for an anisotropic solid the heat flux vector $\mathbf{q}$ is not necessarily normal to the isothermal surface passing through the point considered. The thermal conductivity of an anisotropic solid involves nine components, k_{ij}, called the *conductivity coefficients*, that are considered to be the components of a second-order tensor $\bar{\bar{k}}$

$$\bar{\bar{k}} \equiv \begin{vmatrix} k_{11} & k_{12} & k_{13} \\ k_{21} & k_{22} & k_{23} \\ k_{31} & k_{32} & k_{33} \end{vmatrix} \tag{15-4a}$$

From Onsagar's [26] principles of thermodynamics of irreversible processes it is shown that when the fluxes (i.e., q_i) and the forces (i.e., $\partial T/\partial x_i$) are related to each other linearly as given by equations (15-2) and the phenomenologic coefficients obey the reciprocity relation. A further discussion of the application of Onsagar's reciprocity relation for the thermal conductivity coefficients associated with heat conduction in anisotropic solids is given by Casimir [27]. Therefore, the conductivity coefficients k_{ij} can be considered to obey the reciprocity relation

$$k_{ij} = k_{ji} \qquad i,j = 1,2,3 \tag{15-4b}$$

Furthermore, as discussed in reference [28], according to irreversible thermodynamics, the coefficients k_{11}, k_{22}, and k_{33} are positive, that is,

$$k_{ii} > 0 \tag{15-4c}$$

and the magnitude of the coefficients k_{ij}, for $i \neq j$, is limited by the requirement

$$k_{ii}k_{jj} - k_{ij}^2 > 0 \qquad \text{for} \qquad i \neq j \tag{15-4d}$$

The expression for the heat flux components, given by equation (15-3) for the rectangular coordinate system, can readily be generalized for the orthogonal curvilinear coordinate system (u_1, u_2, u_3) as

$$q_i = - \sum_{j=1}^{3} \frac{1}{a_j} k_{ij} \frac{\partial T}{\partial u_j} \qquad i = 1,2,3 \tag{15-5}$$

where a_j's are the scale factors discussed in Chapter 1.

For the (x_1, x_2, x_3) *rectangular coordinate* system equation (15-5) reduces to equations (15-2).

For the (r, ϕ, z) *cylindrical coordinate* system we set $u_1 = r, u_2 = \phi, u_3 = z$ and $a_1 = 1, a_2 = r, a_3 = 1$; then equation (15-5) gives

$$- q_r = k_{11} \frac{\partial T}{\partial r} + k_{12} \frac{1}{r} \frac{\partial T}{\partial \phi} + k_{13} \frac{\partial T}{\partial z} \tag{15-6a}$$

$$- q_\phi = k_{21} \frac{\partial T}{\partial r} + k_{22} \frac{1}{r} \frac{\partial T}{\partial \phi} + k_{23} \frac{\partial T}{\partial z} \tag{15-6b}$$

$$- q_z = k_{31} \frac{\partial T}{\partial r} + k_{32} \frac{1}{r} \frac{\partial T}{\partial \phi} + k_{33} \frac{\partial T}{\partial z} \tag{15-6c}$$

For the (r, ϕ, θ) *spherical coordinate* system we set $u_1 = r, u_2 = \phi, u_3 = \theta$ and $a_1 = 1, a_2 = r \sin \theta, a_3 = r$ and obtain

$$- q_r = k_{11} \frac{\partial T}{\partial r} + k_{12} \frac{1}{r \sin \theta} \frac{\partial T}{\partial \phi} + k_{13} \frac{1}{r} \frac{\partial T}{\partial \theta} \tag{15-7a}$$

$$-q_\phi = k_{21}\frac{\partial T}{\partial r} + k_{22}\frac{1}{r\sin\theta}\frac{\partial T}{\partial\phi} + k_{23}\frac{1}{r}\frac{\partial T}{\partial\theta} \tag{15-7b}$$

$$-q_\theta = k_{31}\frac{\partial T}{\partial r} + k_{32}\frac{1}{r\sin\theta}\frac{\partial T}{\partial\phi} + k_{33}\frac{1}{r}\frac{\partial T}{\partial\theta} \tag{15-7c}$$

15-2 HEAT-CONDUCTION EQUATION FOR ANISOTROPIC SOLIDS

The differential equation of heat conduction for an anisotropic solid in the orthogonal curvilinear coordinate system (u_1, u_2, u_3) is given as

$$-\frac{1}{a_1 a_2 a_3}\left[\frac{\partial}{\partial u_1}(a_2 a_3 q_1) + \frac{\partial}{\partial u_2}(a_1 a_3 q_2) + \frac{\partial}{\partial u_3}(a_1 a_2 q_3)\right] + g = \rho C_p \frac{\partial T}{\partial t} \tag{15-8}$$

where q_1, q_2, and q_3 are the three components of the heat flux vector according to equation (15-5), g is the heat-generation term, and the other quantities are as defined previously.

We now present explicit form of the heat-conduction equation (15-8) for the rectangular, cylindrical, and spherical coordinates for the case of constant conductivity coefficients.

Rectangular Coordinate System

For the (x, y, z) rectangular coordinate system we set $u_1 = x, u_2 = y, u_3 = z$, and $a_1 = a_2 = a_3 = 1$; then equation (15-8) with q_i's given by equation (15-5) yields

$$k_{11}\frac{\partial^2 T}{\partial x^2} + k_{22}\frac{\partial^2 T}{\partial y^2} + k_{33}\frac{\partial^2 T}{\partial z^2} + (k_{12} + k_{21})\frac{\partial^2 T}{\partial x\partial y} + (k_{13} + k_{31})\frac{\partial^2 T}{\partial x\partial z}$$

$$+ (k_{23} + k_{32})\frac{\partial^2 T}{\partial y\partial z} + g(x, y, z, t) = \rho C_p \frac{\partial T(x, y, z, t)}{\partial t} \tag{15-9}$$

where $k_{12} = k_{21}, k_{13} = k_{31}$, and $k_{23} = k_{32}$ by the reciprocity relation.

Cylindrical Coordinate System

For the (r, ϕ, z) cylindrical coordinate system we set $u_1 = r, u_2 = \phi, u_3 = z$, and $a_1 = 1, a_2 = r, a_3 = 1$. Then, from equations (15-8) and (15-5) we obtain

$$k_{11}\frac{1}{r}\frac{\partial}{\partial r}\left(r\frac{\partial T}{\partial r}\right) + k_{22}\frac{1}{r^2}\frac{\partial^2 T}{\partial\phi^2} + k_{33}\frac{\partial^2 T}{\partial z^2} + (k_{12} + k_{21})\frac{1}{r}\frac{\partial^2 T}{\partial\phi\partial z}$$

$$+ (k_{13} + k_{31})\frac{\partial^2 T}{\partial r \partial z} + \frac{k_{13}}{r}\frac{\partial T}{\partial z} + (k_{23} + k_{32})\frac{1}{r}\frac{\partial^2 T}{\partial \phi \partial z} + g(r, \phi, z, t)$$

$$= \rho C_p \frac{\partial T(r, \phi, z, t)}{\partial t} \tag{15-10}$$

where $k_{ij} = k_{ji}$.

Spherical Coordinate System

For the (r, ϕ, θ) spherical coordinate system we set $u_1 = r, u_2 = \phi, u_3 = \theta$, and $a_1 = 1, a_2 = r \sin \theta, a_3 = r$; then from equations (15-8) and (15-5) obtain

$$k_{11}\frac{1}{r^2}\frac{\partial}{\partial r}\left(r^2\frac{\partial T}{\partial r}\right) + k_{22}\frac{1}{r^2 \sin^2 \theta}\frac{\partial^2 T}{\partial \phi^2} + k_{33}\frac{1}{r^2 \sin \theta}\frac{\partial}{\partial \theta}\left(\sin \theta \frac{\partial T}{\partial \theta}\right)$$

$$+ \frac{(k_{12} + k_{21})}{r \sin \theta}\frac{\partial^2 T}{\partial r \partial \phi} + k_{12}\frac{1}{r^2 \sin \theta}\frac{\partial T}{\partial \phi} + \frac{(k_{13} + k_{31})}{r}\frac{\partial^2 T}{\partial r \partial \theta} + k_{13}\frac{1}{r^2}\frac{\partial T}{\partial \theta}$$

$$+ (k_{23} + k_{32})\frac{1}{r^2 \sin \theta}\frac{\partial^2 T}{\partial \theta \partial \phi} + g(r, \phi, \theta, t) = \rho C_p \frac{\partial T(r, \phi, \theta, t)}{\partial t} \tag{15-11}$$

where $k_{ij} = k_{ji}$.

15-3 BOUNDARY CONDITIONS

The boundary conditions for the heat-conduction equation for an anisotropic medium may be of the first, second, or third kind. We consider a boundary surface S_i normal to the coordinate axis u_i. The boundary condition of the third kind can be written as

$$\mp \delta_i k_{ref} \cdot \frac{\partial T}{\partial n^*} + h_i T = f_i \qquad \text{on boundary } S_i \tag{15-12}$$

where

$$\frac{\partial T}{\partial n^*} \equiv \sum_{j=1}^{3} \frac{1}{a_j}\frac{k_{ij}}{k_{ref}}\frac{\partial T}{\partial u_j} \tag{15-13}$$

where a_j = scale factor
k_{ref} = a reference conductivity that may be chosen as k_{11}, k_{22}, or k_{33}.
δ_i = zero or unity; that is, by setting $\delta_i = 0$, the boundary condition of the first kind is obtained.
Here $\partial/\partial n^*$ is the derivative as defined by equation (15-13). The choice of *plus* or *minus* sign in equation (15-12) depends on whether the outward drawn normal to the boundary surface S_i is pointing in the *positive* or *negative* u_i direction respectively.

We illustrate the boundary conditions for the anisotropic medium with specific examples given below.

Example 15-1. Write the boundary conditions of the third kind for an anisotropic slab at the boundary surfaces $x = 0$ and $x = L$.

Solution. For the (x, y, z) rectangular coordinate system we write

$$-\left(k_{11}\frac{\partial T}{\partial x} + k_{12}\frac{\partial T}{\partial y} + k_{13}\frac{\partial T}{\partial z} \right) + h_1 T = f_1 \qquad \text{at } x = 0 \quad (15\text{-}14a)$$

$$+\left(k_{11}\frac{\partial T}{\partial x} + k_{12}\frac{\partial T}{\partial y} + k_{13}\frac{\partial T}{\partial z} \right) + h_2 T = f_2 \qquad \text{at } x = L \quad (15\text{-}14b)$$

Equations (15-14) can be written more compactly in the form given by equation (15-12) by setting $k_{\text{ref}} \equiv k_{11}$.

$$-k_{11}\frac{\partial T}{\partial n^*} + h_1 T = f \qquad \text{at } x = 0 \qquad\qquad (15\text{-}14c)$$

$$k_{11}\frac{\partial T}{\partial n^*} + h_2 T = f \qquad \text{at } x = L \qquad\qquad (15\text{-}14d)$$

where

$$\frac{\partial}{\partial n^*} \equiv \frac{\partial}{\partial x} + \varepsilon_{12}\frac{\partial}{\partial y} + \varepsilon_{13}\frac{\partial}{\partial z} \qquad\qquad (15\text{-}14e)$$

$$\varepsilon_{ij} \equiv k_{ij}/k_{11} \qquad\qquad (15\text{-}14f)$$

Example 15-2. Write the boundary conditions of the third kind for an anisotropic hollow cylinder at the boundary surfaces $r = a$ and $r = b$.

Solution. For the (r, ϕ, z) cylindrical coordinate system and take the scale factors as $a_1 = 1, a_2 = r$, and $a_3 = 1$ and write

$$-\left(k_{11}\frac{\partial T}{\partial r} + k_{12}\frac{1}{r}\frac{\partial T}{\partial \phi} + k_{13}\frac{\partial T}{\partial z} \right) + h_1 T = f_1 \qquad \text{at } r = a \quad (15\text{-}15a)$$

$$+\left(k_{11}\frac{\partial T}{\partial r} + k_{12}\frac{1}{r}\frac{\partial T}{\partial \phi} + k_{13}\frac{\partial T}{\partial z} \right) + h_2 T = f_2 \qquad \text{at } r = b \quad (15\text{-}15b)$$

Equations (15-15) can be written more compactly in the form given by equation (15-12) by setting $k_{\text{ref}} \equiv k_{11}$.

$$-k_{11}\frac{\partial T}{\partial n^*} + h_1 T = f_1 \qquad \text{at } r = a \qquad\qquad (15\text{-}15c)$$

$$k_{11} \frac{\partial T}{\partial n*} + h_2 T = f_2 \qquad \text{at } r = b \tag{15-15d}$$

where

$$\frac{\partial}{\partial n*} \equiv \frac{\partial}{\partial r} + \varepsilon_{12} \frac{1}{r} \frac{\partial}{\partial \phi} + \varepsilon_{13} \frac{\partial}{\partial z} \tag{15-15e}$$

$$\varepsilon_{ij} = k_{ij}/k_{11}$$

15-4 THERMAL-RESISTIVITY COEFFICIENTS

In the previous sections we expressed each component of the heat-flux vector as a linear sum of temperature gradients along the $0x_1, 0x_2$, and $0x_3$ axes, that is, equation (15-2). Sometimes it is desirable to express the temperature gradient in a given direction as linear combination of the heat flux components in the $0x_1, 0x_2$, and $0x_3$ directions. To obtain such a relationship in the (x_1, x_2, x_3) rectangular coordinate system we write equations (15-2) in matrix notation as

$$- [k_{ij}] \left[\frac{\partial T}{\partial x_i} \right] = [q_i] \tag{15-16a}$$

or

$$- \left[\frac{\partial T}{\partial x_i} \right] = [k_{ij}]^{-1} [q_i] \tag{15-16b}$$

Let r_{ij} be the elements of the inverse matrix $[k_{ij}]^{-1}$, then equation (15-16b) is written explicitly as

$$- \frac{\partial T}{\partial x_1} = r_{11} q_1 + r_{12} q_2 + r_{13} q_3 \tag{15-17a}$$

$$- \frac{\partial T}{\partial x_2} = r_{21} q_1 + r_{22} q_2 + r_{23} q_3 \tag{15-17b}$$

$$- \frac{\partial T}{\partial x_3} = r_{31} q_1 + r_{32} q_2 + r_{33} q_3 \tag{15-17c}$$

where the coefficients r_{ij} are called the *thermal resistivity coefficients*. The coefficients r_{ij} can be determined in terms of k_{ij} by the matrix inversion procedure. Since $k_{ij} = k_{ji}$, it can be shown that r_{ij}'s given by

$$r_{ij} = (-1)^{i+j} \frac{a_{ij}}{\Delta} \tag{15-18a}$$

where

$$\Delta \equiv \begin{vmatrix} k_{11} & k_{12} & k_{13} \\ k_{21} & k_{22} & k_{23} \\ k_{31} & k_{32} & k_{33} \end{vmatrix} \tag{15-18b}$$

a_{ij} is the cofactor obtained from Δ by omitting the ith row and the jth column. As in the case of thermal conductivity coefficients, k_{ij}, the thermal resistivity coefficients, r_{ij}, obey the reciprocity relation, $r_{ij} = r_{ji}$.

To illustrate the application of equation (15-18), we write below the thermal-resistivity coefficient r_{12}, in terms of the thermal conductivity coefficients as

$$r_{12} = (-1)^3 \frac{\begin{vmatrix} k_{21} & k_{23} \\ k_{31} & k_{33} \end{vmatrix}}{\Delta} = \frac{k_{23}k_{31} - k_{21}k_{33}}{\Delta} \tag{15-19}$$

15-5 TRANSFORMATION OF AXES AND CONDUCTIVITY COEFFICIENTS

We consider the heat flux for an anisotropic medium written in *indicial notation* as

$$q_i = -k_{ij}\frac{\partial T}{\partial x_j} \qquad i, j = 1, 2, 3 \tag{15-20}$$

In this equation, whenever a letter index is repeated twice in the same term, summation with respect to that index is automatically understood (i.e., $j = 1, 2, 3$). Thus equation (15-20) is equivalent to equations (15-2) and it establishes the dependence of the three heat flux components q_i's on the temperature gradients $\partial T/\partial x_j$'s through the conductivity tensor k_{ij}. We note that in equation (15-20) the definition of the axes x_j within the material is chosen arbitrarily except the fact that they are mutually orthogonal; and k_{ij} represents the conductivity coefficients with respect to the rectangular coordinates $0x_j$. Suppose we transform the coordinates from the *old* axes $0x_j$ to a set of *new* axes $0x'_j$ as illustrated in Fig. 15-1. Then the *old* conductivity coefficients k_{ij} will change to a set of *new* conductivity coefficients k'_{ij}. We now examine the determination of the *new* conductivity coefficients k'_{ij} under such coordinate transformation.

Let C_{ij} denote the cosine of the angle between the *new* axes $0x'_i$ and the *old* axes $0x_j$; that is, the first subscript in C_{ij} refers to the *new* axes and the second to the *old*. Thus C_{ij}'s are the direction cosines. For example, C_{23} is the cosine of the angle between the new axis $0x'_2$ and the old axes $0x'_3$,

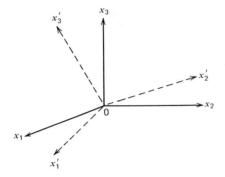

Fig. 15-1   Transformation from the *old* axes $0x_1, 0x_2, 0x_3$ to *new* axes $0x'_1, 0x'_2, 0x'_3$.

etc. Then, the coordinates (x'_1, x'_2, x'_3) of a point P with respect to the *new* coordinates $0x'_1, 0x'_2, 0x'_3$ are given by

$$x'_i = C_{ij}x_j \quad \text{(i.e. new in terms of old)} \tag{15-21}$$

or more explicitly

$$x'_1 = C_{11}x_1 + C_{12}x_2 + C_{13}x_3 \tag{15-22a}$$

$$x'_2 = C_{21}x_1 + C_{22}x_2 + C_{23}x_3 \tag{15-22b}$$

$$x'_3 = C_{31}x_1 + C_{32}x_2 + C_{33}x_3 \tag{15-22c}$$

Conversely, the coordinates (x_1, x_2, x_3) of a point P with respect to the *old* coordinate system $0x_1, 0x_2, 0x_3$ are related to the coordinates of the new $0x'_1, 0x'_2, 0x'_3$ system by

$$x_i = C_{ji}x'_j \quad \text{(i.e., old in terms of new)} \tag{15-23}$$

or more explicitly

$$x_1 = C_{11}x'_1 + C_{21}x'_2 + C_{31}x'_3 \tag{15-24a}$$

$$x_2 = C_{12}x'_1 + C_{22}x'_2 + C_{32}x'_3 \tag{15-24b}$$

$$x_3 = C_{13}x'_1 + C_{23}x'_2 + C_{33}x'_3 \tag{15-24c}$$

Then, the conductivity coefficients k'_{ij} in the *new* coordinates can be expressed in terms of k_{ij} in the *old* coordinates as now described.

Analogous to equation (15-21), q'_i in the *new* coordinates are written in terms of q_m in the *old* as

$$q'_i = C_{im}q_m \tag{15-25a}$$

According to equation (15-20), q_m is given by

$$q_m = -k_{ml}\frac{\partial T}{\partial x_l} \tag{15-25b}$$

Analogous to equation (15-23), $\partial T/\partial x_l$ in the *old* coordinates are written in terms of $\partial T/\partial x_j'$ in the *new* as

$$\frac{\partial T}{\partial x_l} = C_{jl}\frac{\partial T}{\partial x_j'} \tag{15-25c}$$

Equations (15-25) are combined

$$q_i' = C_{im}q_m = -C_{im}k_{ml}\frac{\partial T}{\partial x_l} = -C_{im}k_{ml}C_{jl}\frac{\partial T}{\partial x_j'} \tag{15-26a}$$

and we write this expression as

$$q_i' = -k_{ij}'\frac{\partial T}{\partial x_j'} \tag{15-26b}$$

From equations (15-26), the *new* conductivity coefficients k_{ij}' are determined in terms of the *old* conductivity coefficients k_{ml} as

$$k_{ij}' = C_{im}C_{jl}k_{ml} \tag{15-27}$$

Here, the indices m, l occur in pair, which imply summation for $m, l = 1, 2, 3$; then the right-hand side of equation (15-27) involves nine terms and is written explicitly as

$$\begin{aligned}
k_{ij}' =\ & C_{i1}C_{j1}k_{11} + C_{i1}C_{j2}k_{12} + C_{i1}C_{j3}k_{13} \\
& + C_{i2}C_{j3}k_{23} + C_{i2}C_{j1}k_{21} + C_{i2}C_{j2}k_{22} \\
& + C_{i3}C_{j1}k_{31} + C_{i3}C_{j2}k_{32} + C_{i3}C_{j3}k_{33}
\end{aligned} \tag{15-28}$$

For each pair of (i, j) one can write such an equation.

Conversely, the expression relating the *old* conductivity coefficients k_{ij} to the *new* coefficients k_{ml}' is written as

$$k_{ij} = C_{mi}C_{lj}k_{ml}' \tag{15-29}$$

A comparison of equations (15-27) and (15-29) reveals that the indices for the direction cosines are interchanged.

15-6 GEOMETRICAL INTERPRETATION OF CONDUCTIVITY COEFFICIENTS

In the study of anisotropy it is of interest to examine how a conductivity coefficient k_{jj} varies with the direction in which it is measured. It is instructive to discuss this matter by presenting a geometrical interpretation of the conductivity coefficients.

We consider the equation for a second-degree surface (i.e., a *quadric*) with reference to the rectangular axes $0x_1, 0x_2, 0x_3$, referred to its center as origin

$$s_{ij}x_ix_j = 1 \quad \text{with } s_{ij} = s_{ji} \tag{15-30a}$$

This equation is written in the explicit form as

$$s_{11}x_1^2 + s_{22}x_2^2 + s_{33}x_3^2 + 2s_{12}x_1x_2 + 2s_{13}x_1x_3 + 2s_{23}x_2x_3 = 1 \tag{15-30b}$$

Reader should consult reference [31] for a discussion of the properties of a quadric.

Equation (15-30a) is now transformed from the *old* $0x_1, 0x_2, 0x_3$ coordinate system to the *new* $0x_1', 0x_2', 0x_3'$ coordinate system by utilizing the relation given by equation (15-23), i.e.,

$$x_i = C_{li}x_l' \quad \text{(old in terms of new)} \tag{15-31a}$$

$$x_j = C_{mj}x_m' \quad \text{(old in terms of new)} \tag{15-31b}$$

Then equation (15-30) takes the form

$$s_{ij}C_{li}C_{mj}x_l'x_m' = 1 \tag{15-31}$$

which can be written in the form

$$s_{lm}'x_l'x_m' = 1 \tag{15-32a}$$

where

$$s_{lm}' = C_{li}C_{mj}s_{ij} \tag{15-32b}$$

We now compare the result (15-32) with equation (15-27) for the transformation of conductivity coefficients, that is,

$$k_{ij}' = C_{im}C_{jl}k_{ml} \tag{15-33}$$

The two transformations, i.e., Eqs. (15-32b) and (15-33), are of the identical form so far as the relative positions of the indices are concerned. Therefore, the transformation of the conductivity coefficients is similar to the transformation of the coefficients of a quadric.

The quadric defined by equation (15-30a) has nine coefficients s_{ij} that are considered to be the components of a second-order symmetric tensor in the form

$$\bar{\bar{s}} \equiv \begin{vmatrix} s_{11} & s_{12} & s_{13} \\ s_{21} & s_{22} & s_{23} \\ s_{31} & s_{32} & s_{33} \end{vmatrix} \tag{15-34}$$

where $s_{ij} = s_{ji}$. The coefficient tensor (15-34) is in exactly the same form as the conductivity tensor (15-4a). One property of the quadric defined by equation (15-30) is that, a transformation from the original rectangular coordinate system $0x_1, 0x_2, 0x_3$ to a new rectangular coordinate system $0\xi_1, 0\xi_2, 0\xi_3$ can be found such that equation (15-30b) simplifies to

$$s_1\xi_1^2 + s_2\xi_2^2 + s_3\xi_3^2 = 1 \tag{15-35}$$

Then, the coefficients tensor (15-34) reduces to

$$\begin{vmatrix} s_1 & 0 & 0 \\ 0 & s_2 & 0 \\ 0 & 0 & s_3 \end{vmatrix} \tag{15-36}$$

Here the coefficients s_1, s_2, s_3 are called the *principal coefficients* and the new coordinate axes $0\xi_1, 0\xi_2, 0\xi_3$ are called the *principal axes*. Equation (15-35) represents an *ellipsoid* if s_1, s_2, s_3 are all positive. The quantities $1/\sqrt{s_1}, 1/\sqrt{s_2}$, and $1/\sqrt{s_3}$ are the lengths of the semiaxes of the ellipsoid along the $0\xi_1, 0\xi_2$, and $0\xi_3$ directions, respectively.

We now return to our original problem of variation of conductivity coefficient k'_{jj} along the direction $0x'_j$ in which it is measured. We set in equation (15-28) $i = j$ to obtain

$$k'_{jj} = C_{j1}^2 k_{11} + C_{j2}^2 k_{22} + C_{j3}^2 k_{33} + 2C_{j1}C_{j2}k_{12} + 2C_{j1}C_{j3}k_{13} + 2C_{j2}C_{j3}k_{23} \tag{15-37}$$

For convenience we denote the direction cosines of the direction $0x'_j$ with the coordinate axes $0x_1, 0x_2, 0x_3$ as

$$C_{j1} \equiv l_1, \qquad C_{j2} \equiv l_2, \qquad C_{j3} \equiv l_3$$

Then, equation (15-37) is written as

$$k'_{jj} = k_{11}l_1^2 + k_{22}l_2^2 + k_{33}l_3^2 + 2k_{12}l_1l_2 + 2k_{13}l_1l_3 + 2k_{23}l_2l_3 \tag{15-38}$$

If we define new variables as

$$x_i = \frac{l_i}{\sqrt{k'_{jj}}} \qquad i = 1, 2, 3 \tag{15-39}$$

Equation (15-38) takes the form

$$k_{11}x_1^2 + k_{22}x_2^2 + k_{33}x_3^2 + 2k_{12}x_1x_2 + 2k_{13}x_1x_3 + 2k_{33}x_2x_3 = 1 \tag{15-40}$$

Thus equation (15-40) is exactly the same form as the equation for ellipsoid given by equation (15-30b). Then if we consider a length $1/\sqrt{k'_{jj}}$ measured from the center 0 in the direction $0x_j$ (i.e., direction cosines l_1, l_2, l_3), the locus of the end point of this length

$$x_1 = \frac{l_1}{\sqrt{k'_{jj}}}, \qquad x_2 = \frac{l_2}{\sqrt{k'_{jj}}}, \qquad x_3 = \frac{l_3}{\sqrt{k'_{jj}}} \tag{15-41}$$

is the ellipsoid defined by equation (15-40). This is called the *conductivity ellipsoid*.

Equations (15-38) and (15-40) being quadric, it is possible to transform them from the original axes, $0x_1, 0x_2, 0x_3$, to the principal axes $0\xi_1, 0\xi_2, 0\xi_3$. They respectively are transformed to

$$k_1 l_1^2 + k_2 l_2^2 + k_3 l_3^2 = k'_{jj} \tag{15-42a}$$

$$k_1 \xi_1^2 + k_2 \xi_2^2 + k_3 \xi_3^2 = 1 \tag{15-42b}$$

where k_1, k_2, k_3 are called the *principal conductivities*. When referred to the principal axes, as in equation (15-42), the conductivity tensor simplifies to

$$\begin{vmatrix} k_1 & 0 & 0 \\ 0 & k_2 & 0 \\ 0 & 0 & k_3 \end{vmatrix} \tag{15-43}$$

Figure 10-2 shows a *conductivity ellipsoid* with reference to the principal axes. In this figure, the lengths of the semiaxes along the principal axes $0\xi_1, 0\xi_2$, and $0\xi_3$ represents $1/\sqrt{k_1}, 1/\sqrt{k_2}$, and $1/\sqrt{k_3}$, respectively. When referred to the principal axes, the three components of the heat fluxes given by equations (15-2) reduces to

$$q_1 = -k_1 \frac{\partial T}{\partial \xi_1}, \qquad q_2 = -k_2 \frac{\partial T}{\partial \xi_2}, \qquad q_3 = -k_3 \frac{\partial T}{\partial \xi_3} \tag{15-44}$$

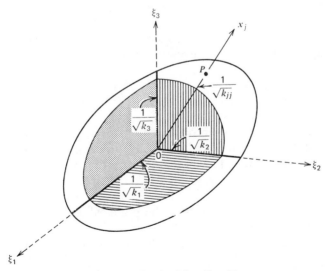

Fig. 15-2   Conductivity ellipsoid.

Determination of Principal Conductivities

The principal conductivities k_1, k_2, k_3 of an anisotropic solid can be determined when the conductivity coefficients k_{ij} referred to a set of rectangular axes $0x_1, 0x_2, 0x_3$ are known. A comparison of the conductivity matrices given by equations (15-4a) and (15-43) reveals that the latter is merely a diagonal form of the former. For any symmetric matrix a change to a diagonal form is always possible [30]. Then the principal conductivities k_1, k_2, k_3 are the eigenvalues of the following secular equation

$$\begin{vmatrix} k_{11} - \lambda & k_{12} & k_{31} \\ k_{21} & k_{22} - \lambda & k_{32} \\ k_{31} & k_{32} & k_{33} - \lambda \end{vmatrix} = 0 \qquad (15\text{-}45)$$

Equation (15-45) is a cubic equation in λ and has three roots. Each of these roots are real numbers because the conductivity coefficients k_{ij} are real numbers (see reference [29], p. 259, for proof) and correspond to the three values of the principal conductivities, i.e., $\lambda_1 = k_1, \lambda_2 = k_2, \lambda_3 = k_3$.

Determination of Directions of Principal Axes

The problem of determining the directions of the three principal axes relative to the original axes $0x_1, 0x_2, 0x_3$ is similar to the problem of determining the proper coordinate transformation associated with the diagonalization of a symmetric, second-order tensor with real coefficients as now described.

Let l_1, l_2, l_3 be the direction cosines of the principal axis $0\xi_1$ with respect to the axes $0x_1, 0x_2, 0x_3$ and $\lambda_1 = k_1$ be the principal conductivity along the direction $0\xi_1$. Then l_1, l_2, l_3 satisfy the relation

$$\begin{vmatrix} k_{11} - \lambda_1 & k_{12} & k_{13} \\ k_{21} & k_{22} - \lambda_1 & k_{23} \\ k_{31} & k_{32} & k_{33} - \lambda_1 \end{vmatrix} \begin{vmatrix} l_1 \\ l_2 \\ l_3 \end{vmatrix} = 0 \qquad (15\text{-}46a)$$

which provides three homogeneous equations for the three unknown l_1, l_2, l_3; only two of these equations are linearly independent. An additional relation is obtained from the requirement that the direction cosines satisfy

$$l_1^2 + l_2^2 + l_3^2 = 1 \qquad (15\text{-}46b)$$

Thus the three direction cosines of the principal axis $0\xi_1$ are determined from equations (15-46).

The procedure is repeated with $\lambda_2 = k_2$ for the determination of m_1, m_2, m_3 of the principal axis $0\xi_2$ and with $\lambda_3 = k_3$ for n_1, n_2, n_3 of the principal axes $0\xi_3$.

15-7 THE SYMMETRY OF CRYSTALS

The thermal conductivity of an anisotropic solid, such as a crystal, is represented, in general, by a second-order tensor that involves nine conductivity coefficients when they are referred to arbitrary axes. However, only six of these coefficients are independent because the conductivity tensor is a symmetric tensor. When the crystal has symmetry and the axes are chosen in the appropriate crystallographic directions, the number of independent components is reduced. In this section we present a brief discussion of symmetry within crystals. The reader should consult references [1], [2], and [31] for a detailed discussion of this subject.

The symmetry elements in crystals can be considered in the following three groups.

The plane symmetry. The crystal can be divided by an imaginary plane into two equal portions each of which is a mirror image of the other.

The n-fold rotation axis symmetry. The crystal appears unchanged when it is rotated about an imaginary axis through $2\pi/n$ degrees where n is a positive integer.

The center symmetry. Every face of the crystal has an identical face at an equal distance on the opposite side of the center. This operation is also known as *inversion.* These symmetry operations, however, are not all independent.

Two hundred thirty crystal forms have been observed; but, on the basis of their symmetry they may be grouped into 32 classes, which may be grouped into the following seven crystal systems [1, 2, 31].

1. *Triclinic.* The system has no symmetry. Examples include $K_2Cr_2O_7$, H_3BO_3, $CuSO_4 \cdot 5H_2O$.

2. *Monoclinic.* The system has a single 2-fold (i.e., diad) rotation axis. That is, the crystal remains unchanged after a rotation of 180° about the axis of symmetry. Examples include Monoclinic sulfur, $CaSO_4 \cdot 2H_2O$, $Na_2SO_4 \cdot 10H_2O$, $Na_2B_4O_7 \cdot 10H_2O$.

3. *Orthorhombic.* The system has three mutually perpendicular 2-fold (i.e., diad) rotation axes. Examples include Rhombic sulfur, KNO_3, K_2SO_4, $BaSO_4$ (Baryte).

4. *Hexagonal.* The system has a single 6-fold (i.e., hexad) rotation axis. Examples include PbI_2, Mg, ZnO (Zincite).

5. *Tetragonal.* The system has a single 4-fold (i.e., tetrad) rotation axis. Examples include TiO_2 (Rutile), $ZrSiO_4$ (Zircon), SnO_2 (cassiterite).

6. *Trigonal.* The system has a single 3-fold (i.e., triad) rotation axis.

7. *Cubic.* The system has four 3-fold (i.e., triad) rotation axis. Examples include NaC1, KC1, diamond.

The thermal conductivity tensors for the above seven crystal systems are summarized below.

Triclinic   Monoclinic

$$\begin{vmatrix} k_{11} & k_{12} & k_{13} \\ k_{21} & k_{22} & k_{23} \\ k_{31} & k_{32} & k_{33} \end{vmatrix} \qquad \begin{vmatrix} k_{11} & k_{12} & 0 \\ k_{21} & k_{22} & 0 \\ 0 & 0 & k_{33} \end{vmatrix} \qquad (15\text{-}47a)$$

Orthorhombic   Hexagonal, Tetragonal, Trigonal

$$\begin{vmatrix} k_{11} & 0 & 0 \\ 0 & k_{22} & 0 \\ 0 & 0 & k_{33} \end{vmatrix} \qquad \begin{vmatrix} k_{11} & k_{12} & 0 \\ -k_{12} & k_{11} & 0 \\ 0 & 0 & k_{33} \end{vmatrix} \qquad (15\text{-}47b)$$

Cubic

$$\begin{vmatrix} k_{11} & 0 & 0 \\ 0 & k_{11} & 0 \\ 0 & 0 & k_{11} \end{vmatrix} \qquad (15\text{-}47c)$$

Here, the symmetry consideration implies that in equation (15-47b) we should have $k_{12} = 0$.

15-8 ONE-DIMENSIONAL STEADY-STATE HEAT CONDUCTION IN ANISOTROPIC SOLIDS

To illustrate the determination of conductivity coefficients for an anisotropic solid by simple heat-flow measurements, we consider below two specific situations: (a) the steady-state heat flow across a thin slab, and (b) the steady-state heat flow along a long rod the lateral surfaces of which are insulated.

Heat Flow Across a Thin Slab (Temperature is a Function of x'_3 Only)

Consider a large, thin, anisotropic plate as illustrated in Fig. 15-3. The two surfaces of the slab perpendicular to the $0x'_3$ axis are maintained at two different temperatures. Since the plate is very large compared to its thickness, the isothermals must run parallel to the surface of the plate, except at the ends. Therefore, the temperature gradient vector ∇T is perpendicular to the plate surface; but, the heat flux vector $\mathbf{q}$ need not to be parallel to ∇T as the

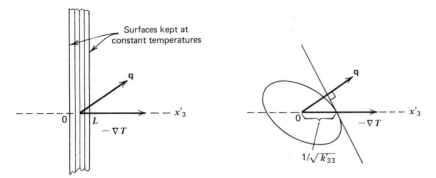

Fig. 15-3 Heat flow across an anisotropic thin slab and the conductivity ellipsoid. (Temperature gradient ∇T is parallel to Ox'_3 axis).

material is anisotropic. This situation is also illustrated in Fig. 15-3. Since the applied temperature gradient is in the Ox'_3 direction, *the temperature is a function of x'_3 only*; as a result the temperature gradients in the Ox'_1 and Ox'_2 directions are zero, that is

$$\frac{dT}{dx'_1} = \frac{dT}{dx'_2} = 0 \tag{15-48}$$

In view of this result, the three components of the heat flux along the Ox'_1, Ox'_2, Ox'_3 directions, as obtained from equations (15-2), simplify to

$$q_1 = -k'_{13}\frac{dT}{dx'_3}, \qquad q_2 = -k'_{23}\frac{dT}{dx'_3}, \qquad q_3 = -k'_{33}\frac{dT}{dx'_3} \tag{15-49}$$

Then, the measured heat flux across the plate is only the component q_3, since the components q_1 and q_2 denote the transverse heat flow. The analysis of the problem now becomes identical to one-dimensional steady heat flow across an isotropic slab. That is, knowing dT/dx'_3 and q_3 from the measurements, the conductivity component k'_{33} is readily determined from the relation

$$q_3 = -k'_{33}\frac{dT}{dx'_3} \tag{15-50}$$

Figure 15-3 also illustrates the relative positions of $\mathbf{q}$ and $-\nabla T$ in the conductivity ellipsoid; the radius of this ellipsoid in the Ox'_3 direction is equal to $1/\sqrt{k'_{33}}$.

A number of measurements should be made in different directions in order to determine the principal conductivity coefficients k_1, k_2, k_3 and the direction cosines of the principal axes. The measured conductivity coefficient k'_{33} is related to the principal conductivities k_1, k_2, k_3 and the direction cosines l_1, l_2, l_3 of the $0x'_3$ axis with the principal axes by equation (15-42a) as

$$k_1 l_1^2 + k_2 l_2^2 + k_3 l_3^2 = k'_{33} \qquad (15\text{-}51)$$

If the $0x'_3$ axis is oriented parallel to the principal conductivity axis $0\xi_3$, then the measured conductivity coefficient k'_{33} is equal to k_3. By making two additional measurements with the material cut perpendicular to the $0\xi_1$ and $0\xi_2$ principal axes, the principal conductivities k_1 and k_2 can be determined.

Heat Flow Along a Thin Rod (Heat Flow is in the Direction of the $0x'_3$ axis)

Consider a thin, long, anisotropic rod with its two ends kept at two different constant temperatures and sides are insulated as illustrated in Fig. 15-4. Since there is no heat loss from the lateral surfaces into the surrounding, the heat flow through the rod must be along the $0x'_3$ direction only. Then we have

$$q_1 = q_2 = 0 \qquad (15\text{-}52)$$

and the heat flux vector $\mathbf{q}$ is along $0x'_3$ axis. When the result in equation (15-52) is introduced into equation (15-17), the three components of the temperature gradient vector ∇T becomes

$$-\frac{dT}{dx'_1} = r'_{13} q_3, \qquad -\frac{dT}{dx'_2} = r'_{23} q_3, \qquad -\frac{dT}{dx'_3} = r'_{33} q_3 \qquad (15\text{-}53)$$

The temperature gradient vector ∇T need not be in the same direction as the heat flux vector $\mathbf{q}$ as illustrated in Fig. 15-4.

We now consider the expression for dT/dx'_3 obtained from equation (15-53) as

$$-\frac{dT}{dx'_3} = r'_{33} q_3 \qquad (15\text{-}54)$$

The result implies that, knowing dT/dx'_3 and q_3 from the measurements, the thermal resistivity coefficient r'_{33} can be determined from equation (15-54).

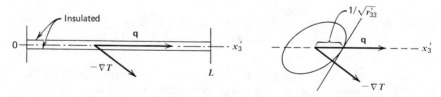

Fig. 15-4 Heat flow along a thin anisotropic rod and the resistivity ellipsoid (Heat flux vector $\mathbf{q}$ is parallel to $0x'_3$ axis).

Figure 15-4 also illustrates the thermal resistivity ellipsoid and the relative positions of $\mathbf{q}$ and $-\nabla T$; the radius of the ellipsoid along the direction $0x_3'$ is equal to $1/\sqrt{r_{33}'}$.

The resistivity coefficient r_{33}' is related to the principal conductivities k_1, k_2, k_3 by

$$r_{33}' = \frac{l_1^2}{k_1} + \frac{l_2^2}{k_2} + \frac{l_3^2}{k_3} \tag{15-55}$$

A number of measurements should be made in different directions to determine the principal conductivities. If $0x_3'$ is oriented parallel to the principal axis $0\xi_3$, the measured resistivity becomes the principal resistivity r_3, which is equal to $1/k_3$.

If $k_1 = k_2$ and $l_3 = \cos\theta$, equation (15-55) reduces to

$$r_{33}' = \frac{1}{k_1} + \left(\frac{1}{k_3} - \frac{1}{k_1}\right)\cos^2\theta \tag{15-56}$$

since

$$l_1^2 + l_2^2 + l_3^2 = 1$$

15-9 ONE-DIMENSIONAL TIME-DEPENDENT
HEAT CONDUCTION IN ANISOTROPIC SOLIDS

We now examine the time-dependent version of the two specific one-dimensional heat-conduction problems considered in the previous section.

Heat Flow Across a Thin Slab

We consider a thin anisotropic plate as illustrated in Fig. 15-3. The slab is initially at a uniform temperature T_0 and for times $t > 0$ the boundaries at $x_3' = 0$ and $x_3' = L$ are kept at uniform temperatures T_1 and T_L, respectively. The mathematical formulation of this heat-conduction problem is given as now described.

Since the applied temperature gradient is in the $0x_3'$ direction only, the transverse temperature gradients vanish, that is

$$\frac{dT}{dx_1'} = \frac{dT}{dx_2'} = 0$$

In view of this result, the differential equation of heat conduction (15-9), for the case of no heat generation, reduces to

$$\frac{\partial^2 T}{\partial x_3'^2} = \frac{1}{\alpha_3} \frac{\partial T(x_3', t)}{\partial t} \qquad \text{in } 0 < x_3' < L, \ t > 0 \qquad (15\text{-}57)$$

where $\alpha_3 \equiv k_{33}'/\rho C_p$. Thus, for heat flow across a very thin slab the one-dimensional time-dependent heat-conduction equation for an anisotropic solid can be approximated by that for an insotropic solid and solved readily subject to appropriate boundary and initial conditions.

The conductivity coefficient k_{33}' is related to the principal conductivities k_1, k_2, k_3 according to equation (15-51).

Heat Flow Along a Thin Rod

We now consider a thin, anisotropic rod as illustrated in Fig. 15-4. Initially the rod is at a uniform temperature T_0; for times $t > 0$ the two ends are kept at two different temperatures, while the lateral surface is kept insulated.

The heat flow is along the direction $0x_3'$ since the lateral surfaces are insulated. Then we have

$$q_1 = q_2 = 0 \qquad (15\text{-}58)$$

and the results given by equation (15-53) holds; we write

$$-\frac{dT}{dx_3'} = r_{33}' q_3 \qquad (15\text{-}59)$$

For the rectangular coordinate system and no heat generation, the heat-conduction equation (15-8) is simplified by the application of equations (15-58) and (15-59); we obtain

$$\frac{1}{r_{33}'} \frac{\partial^2 T}{\partial x_3'} = \rho C_p \frac{\partial T(x_3', t)}{\partial t}$$

or

$$\frac{\partial^2 T}{\partial x_3'} = \frac{1}{\alpha_3} \frac{\partial T(x_3', t)}{\partial t} \qquad \text{in } 0 < x < L, \ t > 0 \qquad (15\text{-}60)$$

where $\alpha_3 \equiv 1/r_{33}' \rho C_p$.

Thus, for the one-dimensional case considered here, the heat-conduction equation for an anisotropic solid is of the same form as that for an isotropic medium.

The resistivity coefficient r_{33}' is related to the principal conductivities according to equation (15-55).

15-10 HEAT CONDUCTION IN AN ORTHOTROPIC MEDIUM

In the case of noncrystalline anisotropic solids, such as wood, the thermal conductivities k_1, k_2, and k_3 are in the mutually perpendicular directions. Then the three components of the heat flux (q_1, q_2, q_3) are given in the (u_1, u_2, u_3) orthogonal curvilinear coordinate system as

$$q_1 = -\frac{k_1}{a_1}\frac{\partial T_1}{\partial u_1}, \qquad q_2 = -\frac{k_2}{a_2}\frac{\partial T_2}{\partial u_2}, \qquad q_3 = -\frac{k_3}{a_3}\frac{\partial T_3}{\partial u_3} \qquad (15\text{-}61)$$

where a_1, a_2, a_3 are the scale factors.

Introducing equation (15-61) into the energy equation (15-8), the heat-conduction equation for an orthotropic solid becomes

$$\frac{1}{a_1 a_2 a_3}\left[\frac{\partial}{\partial u_1}\left(\frac{a_2 a_3}{a_1}k_1\frac{\partial T}{\partial u_1}\right) + \frac{\partial}{\partial u_2}\left(\frac{a_1 a_3}{a_2}k_2\frac{\partial T}{\partial u_2}\right) + \frac{\partial}{\partial u_3}\left(\frac{a_1 a_2}{a_3}k_3\frac{\partial T}{\partial u_3}\right)\right]$$

$$+ g = \rho C_p \frac{\partial T}{\partial t} \qquad (15\text{-}62)$$

Assuming k_1, k_2, k_3 constant, equation (15-62) for the rectangular, cylindrical, and spherical coordinates takes the following form.

Rectangular coordinate system (x, y, z):

$$k_1 \frac{\partial^2 T}{\partial x^2} + k_2 \frac{\partial^2 T}{\partial y^2} + k_3 \frac{\partial^2 T}{\partial z^2} + g = \rho C_p \frac{\partial T}{\partial t} \qquad (15\text{-}63)$$

Cylindrical coordinate system (r, ϕ, z):

$$k_1 \frac{1}{r}\frac{\partial}{\partial r}\left(r \frac{\partial T}{\partial r}\right) + k_2 \frac{1}{r^2}\frac{\partial^2 T}{\partial \phi^2} + k_3 \frac{\partial^2 T}{\partial z^2} + g = \rho C_p \frac{\partial T}{\partial t} \qquad (15\text{-}64)$$

Spherical coordinate system (r, ϕ, θ):

$$k_1 \frac{1}{r^2}\frac{\partial}{\partial r}\left(r^2 \frac{\partial T}{\partial r}\right) + k_2 \frac{1}{r^2 \sin\theta}\frac{\partial^2 T}{\partial \phi^2} + k_3 \frac{1}{r^2 \sin\theta}\frac{\partial}{\partial \theta}\left(\sin\theta \frac{\partial T}{\partial \theta}\right) + g = \rho C_p \frac{\partial T}{\partial t}$$

$$(15\text{-}65)$$

We note that the above equations are equivalent to those of crystalline solids when they are referred to the principal axes, with corresponding principal conductivities k_1, k_2, k_3.

Transformation of Equation

The heat-conduction equation for an orthotropic solid as given above can be transformed to the standard heat-conduction equation for an isotropic solid as now described.

We consider equation (15-63) and define new variables x_1, y_1, z_1 as

$$x_1 = \left(\frac{k}{k_1}\right)^{1/2} x, \qquad y_1 = \left(\frac{k}{k_2}\right)^{1/2} y, \qquad z_1 = \left(\frac{k}{k_3}\right)^{1/2} z \qquad (15\text{-}66)$$

where k is a reference conductivity. Then equation (15-63) is transformed to

$$k\left(\frac{\partial^2 T}{\partial x_1^2} + \frac{\partial^2 T}{\partial y_1^2} + \frac{\partial^2 T}{\partial z_1^2}\right) + g(x_1, y_1, z_1, t) = \rho C_p \frac{\partial T}{\partial t} \qquad (15\text{-}67)$$

which is the same as the standard heat-conduction equation for an isotropic solid. The choice of the reference conductivity k is not, however, arbitrary, even though it appears so from equation (15-67). The reason for this is that a volume element in the original space $dx\,dy\,dz$ transforms, under the transformation (15-66), into

$$\frac{(k_1 k_2 k_3)^{1/2}}{k^{3/2}} dx_1\, dy_1\, dz_1$$

If the quantities ρC_p and the generation term g, defined on the basis of unit volume, should have the same physical significance we should have

$$\frac{(k_1 k_2 k_3)^{1/2}}{k^{3/2}} = 1 \qquad (15\text{-}68)$$

Several other ways of arriving at the result given by equation (15-68) are discussed in reference [8]. Similar transformations are applicable to transform the equation into the standard form for the cylindrical and spherical coordinate systems.

Under the transformation discussed above, the solution of the resulting heat-conduction equation is a straightforward matter, but the transformation of the solution to the original physical space requires additional computations according to the transformation used.

There are also other ways for the handling of problems of this type. We illustrate with examples the solution of heat-conduction problems for orthotropic medium.

Example 15-3. Consider the steady-state heat-conduction problem for an orthotropic rectangular region $0 \le x \le a, 0 \le y \le b$ in which heat is generated at a constant rate of g_0 W/m³. Boundaries at $x = 0$ and $y = 0$ are kept insulated and those at $x = a$ and $y = b$ are dissipating heat by convection into an environment at zero temperature. The orthotropic thermal conductivities in the $0x$ and $0y$ directions are, respectively, k_1 and k_2. Obtain an expression for the steady-state temperature distribution in the region.

Solution. The mathematical formulation of this problem is given as

$$\frac{\partial^2 T}{\partial x^2} + \frac{1}{\varepsilon^2}\frac{\partial^2 T}{\partial y^2} = -\frac{g_0}{k_1} \qquad \text{in } 0 < x < a,\ 0 < y < b \qquad (15\text{-}69a)$$

$$\frac{\partial T}{\partial x} = 0 \qquad\qquad \text{at } x = 0 \qquad\qquad (15\text{-}69b)$$

$$\frac{\partial T}{\partial x} + H_1 T = 0 \qquad\qquad \text{at } x = a \qquad\qquad (15\text{-}69c)$$

$$\frac{\partial T}{\partial y} = 0 \qquad\qquad \text{at } y = 0 \qquad\qquad (15\text{-}69d)$$

$$\frac{\partial T}{\partial y} + H_2 T = 0 \qquad\qquad \text{at } y = b \qquad\qquad (15\text{-}69e)$$

where

$$\varepsilon^2 \equiv \frac{k_1}{k_2}, \qquad H_1 = \frac{h_1}{k_1}, \qquad H_2 = \frac{h_2}{k_2}.$$

We define the integral transform pair with respect to the x variable as

$$\text{Transform}: \qquad \bar{T}(\beta_m, y) = \int_0^a X(\beta_m, x')T(x', y')\,dx' \qquad (15\text{-}70a)$$

$$\text{Inversion}: \qquad T(x, y) = \sum_{m=1}^{\infty} \frac{1}{N(\beta_m)} X(\beta_m, x)\bar{T}(\beta_m, y) \qquad (15\text{-}70b)$$

where $X(\beta_m, x)$, $N(\beta_m)$, and β_m are obtained from Table 2-2, case 4 as

$$X(\beta_m, x) = \cos\beta_m x, \qquad \frac{1}{N(\beta_m)} = 2\,\frac{\beta_m^2 + H_1^2}{a(\beta_m^2 + H_1^2) + H_1} \qquad (15\text{-}70c)$$

and β_m's are the roots of

$$\beta_m \tan\beta_m a = H_1 \qquad\qquad (15\text{-}70d)$$

Taking the integral transform of system (15-69) by the application of the transform (15-70a) we obtain

$$\frac{d^2\bar{T}}{dy^2} - \beta_m^2\varepsilon^2 \bar{T}(\beta_m, y) = -\frac{\varepsilon^2}{k_1}\bar{g}_0 \qquad \text{in } 0 < y < b \qquad (15\text{-}71a)$$

$$\frac{d\bar{T}}{dy} = 0 \qquad\qquad \text{at } y = 0 \qquad\qquad (15\text{-}71b)$$

$$\frac{d\bar{T}}{dy} + H_2\bar{T} = 0 \qquad\qquad \text{at } y = b \qquad\qquad (15\text{-}71c)$$

The solution of the system (15-71) is

$$\bar{T}(\beta_m, y) = \frac{1}{k_1\beta_m^2}\bar{g}_0 - \frac{1}{k_1\beta_m^2}\bar{g}_0 \frac{\cosh \beta_m \varepsilon y}{\frac{\beta_m \varepsilon}{H_2}\sinh \beta_m \varepsilon b + \cosh \beta_m \varepsilon b} \tag{15-72a}$$

where

$$\bar{g} = \int_0^a g_0 \cos \beta_m x \, dx = \frac{\sin \beta_m a}{\beta_m}g_0 \tag{15-72b}$$

The inversion of (15-72) by the inversion formula (15-70b) yields

$$T(x, y) = \frac{g_0}{k_1}\sum_{m=1}^{\infty}\frac{1}{N(\beta_m)}\frac{\cos \beta_m x \sin \beta_m a}{\beta_m^3}$$

$$-\frac{g_0}{k_1}\sum_{m=1}^{\infty}\frac{1}{\beta_m^3 N(\beta_m)}\frac{\cos \beta_m x \sin \beta_m a \cosh \beta_m \varepsilon y}{\frac{\beta_m \varepsilon}{H_2}\sinh \beta_m \varepsilon b + \cosh \beta_m \varepsilon b} \tag{15-73}$$

A closed-form expression for the first summation on the right is determined as (see Note 1)

$$\sum_{m=1}^{\infty}\frac{1}{N(\beta_m)}\frac{\cos \beta_m x \sin \beta_m a}{\beta_m^3} = \frac{a}{H_1} + \frac{1}{2}(a^2 - x^2) \tag{15-74}$$

Then the solution (15-73) takes the form

$$T(x, y) = \frac{g_0 a}{k_1 H_1} + \frac{g_0}{2k_1}(a^2 - x^2) - \frac{2g_0}{k_1}\sum_{m=1}^{\infty}\frac{1}{\beta_m^3}\frac{\beta_m^2 + H_1^2}{a(\beta_m^2 + H_1^2) + H_1}$$

$$\cdot \frac{\cos \beta_m x \sin \beta_m a \cosh \beta_m \varepsilon y}{\frac{\beta_m \varepsilon}{H_2}\sinh \beta_m \varepsilon b + \cosh \beta_m \varepsilon b} \tag{15-75a}$$

where β_m's are the roots of

$$\beta_m \tan \beta_m a = H_1 \tag{15-75b}$$

Example 15-4. Consider the time-dependent heat-conduction problem for an orthotropic rectangular region $0 \le x \le a, 0 \le y \le b$. Initially the region is at a uniform temperature T_0. For times $t > 0$, the boundaries at $x = 0$ and $y = 0$ are kept insulated and those at $x = a$ and $y = b$ are dissipating heat by convection into an environment at zero temperature, while heat is generated in the region at a constant rate of g_0 W/m³. The orthotropic thermal conductivities in the $0x$ and $0y$ directions are, respectively, k_1 and k_2. Obtain an expression for the time-dependent temperature distribution $T(x, y, t)$ in the region for times $t > 0$.

Solution. The mathematical formulation of this problem is given as

$$\frac{\partial^2 T}{\partial x^2} + \frac{1}{\varepsilon^2}\frac{\partial^2 T}{\partial y^2} + \frac{g_0}{k_1} = \frac{1}{\alpha_1}\frac{\partial T}{\partial t} \qquad \text{in } 0 < x < a,\ 0 < y < b,\ t > 0 \qquad (15\text{-}76\text{a})$$

$$\frac{\partial T}{\partial x} = 0 \qquad\qquad\qquad \text{at } x = 0,\ t > 0 \qquad\qquad (15\text{-}76\text{b})$$

$$\frac{\partial T}{\partial x} + H_1 T = 0 \qquad\qquad \text{at } x = a,\ t > 0 \qquad\qquad (15\text{-}76\text{c})$$

$$\frac{\partial T}{\partial y} = 0 \qquad\qquad\qquad \text{at } y = 0,\ t > 0 \qquad\qquad (15\text{-}76\text{d})$$

$$\frac{\partial T}{\partial y} + H_2 T = 0 \qquad\qquad \text{at } y = b,\ t > 0 \qquad\qquad (15\text{-}76\text{e})$$

$$T = T_0 \qquad\qquad\qquad \text{for } t = 0,\ \text{in the region} \qquad (15\text{-}76\text{f})$$

where

$$\varepsilon^2 \equiv \frac{k_1}{k_2}, \qquad H_1 = \frac{h_1}{k_1}, \qquad H_2 = \frac{h_2}{k_2}, \qquad \alpha_1 = \frac{k_1}{\rho C_p}$$

It is convenient to split up this problem into two simpler problems as

$$T(x, y, t) = T_s(x, y) + T_h(x, y, t) \qquad\qquad (15\text{-}77)$$

Where the steady-state temperature $T_s(x, y)$ is the solution of the following problem

$$\frac{\partial^2 T_s}{\partial x^2} + \frac{1}{\varepsilon^2}\frac{\partial^2 T_s}{\partial y^2} + \frac{g_0}{k_1} = 0 \qquad \text{in } 0 < x < a,\ 0 < y < b \qquad (15\text{-}78\text{a})$$

$$\frac{\partial T_s}{\partial x} = 0 \qquad\qquad\qquad \text{at } x = 0 \qquad\qquad\qquad (15\text{-}78\text{b})$$

$$\frac{\partial T_s}{\partial x} + H_1 T_s = 0 \qquad\qquad \text{at } x = a \qquad\qquad\qquad (15\text{-}78\text{c})$$

$$\frac{\partial T_s}{\partial y} = 0 \qquad\qquad\qquad \text{at } y = 0 \qquad\qquad\qquad (15\text{-}78\text{d})$$

$$\frac{\partial T_s}{\partial y} + H_2 T_s = 0 \qquad\qquad \text{at } y = b \qquad\qquad\qquad (15\text{-}78\text{e})$$

and the transient temperature $T_h(x, y, t)$ is the solution of the following homogeneous problem

$$\frac{\partial^2 T_h}{\partial x^2} + \frac{1}{\varepsilon^2}\frac{\partial^2 T_h}{\partial y^2} = \frac{1}{\alpha_1}\frac{\partial T_h}{\partial t} \qquad \text{in } 0 < x < a, \ 0 < y < b, \ t > 0 \qquad (15\text{-}79\text{a})$$

$$\frac{\partial T_h}{\partial x} = 0 \qquad\qquad\qquad \text{at } x = 0, \ t > 0 \qquad\qquad (15\text{-}79\text{b})$$

$$\frac{\partial T_h}{\partial x} + H_1 T_h = 0 \qquad\qquad \text{at } x = a. \ t > 0 \qquad\qquad (15\text{-}79\text{c})$$

$$\frac{\partial T_h}{\partial y} = 0 \qquad\qquad\qquad \text{at } y = 0, \ t > 0 \qquad\qquad (15\text{-}79\text{d})$$

$$\frac{\partial T_h}{\partial y} + H_2 T_h = 0 \qquad\qquad \text{at } y = b, \ t > 0 \qquad\qquad (15\text{-}79\text{e})$$

$$T_h = T_0 - T_s(x, y) \equiv F(x, y) \quad \text{for } t = 0, \ \text{in the region} \qquad (15\text{-}79\text{f})$$

The steady-state problem (15-78) is exactly the same as that considered in Example 15-3; therefore its solution is immediately obtainable from equation (15-75). The homogeneous problem defined by equations (15-79) can readily be solved by the integral-transform technique as now described.

We define the integral-transform pair with respect to the x variable as

$$\text{Transform}: \qquad \bar{T}(\beta_m, y, t) = \int_0^a X(\beta_m, x')T(x', y, t)\,dx' \qquad (15\text{-}80\text{a})$$

$$\text{Inversion}: \qquad T(x, y, t) = \sum_{m=1}^{\infty} \frac{1}{N(\beta_m)} X(\beta_m, x)\bar{T}(\beta_m, y, t) \qquad (15\text{-}80\text{b})$$

where

$$X(\beta_m, x) = \cos\beta_m x, \qquad \frac{1}{N(\beta_m)} = 2\frac{\beta_m^2 + H_1^2}{a(\beta_m^2 + H_1^2) + H_1} \qquad (15\text{-}80\text{c})$$

and β_m's are the roots of

$$\beta_m \tan\beta_m a = H_1 \qquad\qquad\qquad (15\text{-}80\text{d})$$

The integral transform pair with respect to the y variable is defined as

$$\text{Transform}: \qquad \tilde{\bar{T}}(\beta_m, \gamma_n, t) = \int_0^b Y(\gamma_n, y')\bar{T}(\beta_m, y', t)\,dy' \qquad (15\text{-}81\text{a})$$

$$\text{Inversion}: \qquad \bar{T}(\beta_m, y, t) = \sum_{n=1}^{\infty} \frac{Y(\gamma_n, y)}{N(\gamma_n)}\tilde{\bar{T}}(\beta_m, \gamma_n, t) \qquad (15\text{-}81\text{b})$$

where

$$Y(\gamma_n, y) = \cos \gamma_n y, \qquad \frac{1}{N(\gamma_n)} = 2\frac{\gamma_n^2 + H_2^2}{b(\gamma_n^2 + H_2^2) + H_2} \qquad (15\text{-}81\text{c})$$

and γ_n's are the roots of

$$\gamma_n \tan \gamma_n b = H_2 \qquad (15\text{-}81\text{d})$$

The integral transform of the system (15-79) with respect to the x variable by the application of the transform (15-80a) is

$$-\beta_m^2 \bar{T}_h(\beta_m, y, t) + \frac{1}{\varepsilon^2}\frac{\partial^2 \bar{T}_h}{\partial y^2} = \frac{1}{\alpha_1}\frac{\partial \bar{T}}{\partial t} \qquad \text{in } 0 < y < b, \ t > 0 \quad (15\text{-}82\text{a})$$

$$\frac{\partial \bar{T}_h}{\partial y} = 0 \qquad\qquad \text{at } y = 0, \ t > 0 \qquad (15\text{-}82\text{b})$$

$$\frac{\partial \bar{T}_h}{\partial y} + H_2 \bar{T}_h = 0 \qquad\qquad \text{at } y = b, \ t > 0 \qquad (15\text{-}82\text{c})$$

$$\bar{T}_h = \bar{F}(\beta_m, y) \qquad\qquad \text{for } t = 0, \text{ in } 0 \le y \le b \quad (15\text{-}82\text{d})$$

The integral transform of the system (15-82) with respect to the y variable by the application of the transform (15-81a) gives

$$-\beta_m^2 \bar{\bar{T}}_h(\beta_m, \gamma_n, t) - \frac{1}{\varepsilon^2}\gamma_n^2 \bar{\bar{T}}_n = \frac{1}{\alpha_1}\frac{d\bar{\bar{T}}_h}{dt}$$

or

$$\frac{d\bar{\bar{T}}_h}{dt} + \alpha_1 \lambda_{mn}^2 \bar{\bar{T}}_h = 0 \qquad \text{for } t > 0 \qquad (15\text{-}83\text{a})$$

$$\bar{\bar{T}}_h(\beta_m, \gamma_n, t) = \bar{\bar{F}}(\beta_m, \gamma_n) \qquad\qquad (15\text{-}83\text{b})$$

where

$$\lambda_{mn}^2 = \beta_m^2 + \frac{1}{\varepsilon^2}\gamma_n^2 \qquad\qquad (15\text{-}83\text{c})$$

The solution of equation (15-83) is

$$\bar{\bar{T}}_h(\beta_m, \gamma_n, t) = e^{-\alpha_1 \lambda_{mn}^2 t}\bar{\bar{F}}(\beta_m, \gamma_n) \qquad\qquad (15\text{-}84)$$

The inversion of equation (15-84) successively by the inversion formulas (15-81b) and (15-80b) gives the solution for $T_h(x, y, t)$ as

$$T_h(x, y, t) = \sum_{m=1}^{\infty} \sum_{n=1}^{\infty} \frac{e^{-\alpha_1 \lambda_{mn}^2 t}}{N(\beta_m)N(\gamma_n)} \cos \beta_m x \cos \gamma_n y$$

$$\cdot \int_{x'=0}^{a} \int_{y'=0}^{b} \cos \beta_m x' \cos \gamma_n y' F(x', y') \, dx' \, dy' \qquad (15\text{-}85)$$

where $N(\beta_m)$ and $N(\gamma_n)$ are defined by equations (15-80c) and (15-81c), respectively, β_m and γ_n are the roots of the transcendental equations (15-80d) and (18-81d), respectively, and λ_{mn}^2 is defined by equation (15-83c). The function $F(x', y')$ being specified according to equations (15-79f) and (15-75), the integral with respect to the space variables in equation (15-85) can be evaluated analytically or numerically.

15-11 MULTIDIMENSIONAL HEAT CONDUCTION IN AN ANISOTROPIC MEDIUM

The multidimensional heat-conduction equation for the case of general anisotropy, involves cross derivatives, whereas the boundary conditions may contain various partial derivatives with respect to the space variables. As a result, the analytic solution of the multidimensional heat-conduction problem for the general anisotropic case is difficult to obtain, especially for finite regions. However, the solutions can be obtained for special situations semi-infinite or infinite regions as illustrated in the following examples.

Example 15-5. We consider a two-dimensional, time-dependent heat-conduction problem for an anisotropic region $0 \leq x \leq \infty$, $-\infty < y < \infty$ in the rectangular coordinate system. The medium is initially at temperature $F(x, y)$ and for times $t > 0$ the boundary surface at $x = 0$ is kept at zero temperature. Obtain an expression for the temperature distribution $T(x, y, t)$ in the region for times $t > 0$.

Solution. Since no temperature variation is considered in the z direction, we have $\partial T/\partial z = 0$. Then, the heat-conduction equation (15-9) reduces to

$$\frac{\partial^2 T}{\partial x^2} + \varepsilon_{22}\frac{\partial^2 T}{\partial y^2} + 2\varepsilon_{12}\frac{\partial^2 T}{\partial x\partial y} = \frac{1}{\alpha_{11}}\frac{\partial T}{\partial t} \quad \text{in } 0 < x < \infty, \ -\infty < y < \infty, t > 0$$

(15-86a)

with the boundary and initial conditions

$$T = 0 \qquad \text{at } x = 0, \text{ for } t > 0 \tag{15-86b}$$

$$T = F(x, y) \qquad \text{for } t = 0, \text{ in } 0 \leq x < \infty, \ -\infty < y < \infty \tag{15-86c}$$

where we defined

$$\varepsilon_{ij} = \frac{k_{ij}}{k_{11}}, \qquad k_{ij} = k_{ji}, \qquad \text{and} \qquad \alpha_{11} = \frac{k_{11}}{\rho C_p} \tag{15-86d}$$

We note that the differential equation involves one cross derivative and the region in the y direction is infinite in extend. Therefore, the integral transform with respect to the y variable can be applied to remove from this equation the first and second partial derivatives with respect to the y variable.

The integral transform pair with respect to the y variable is defined as [see equation (13-73)].

$$\text{Inversion}: \qquad T(x, y, t) = \frac{1}{2\pi} \int_{-\infty}^{\infty} e^{-i\gamma y} \bar{T}(x, \gamma, t) \, d\gamma \qquad (15\text{-}87\text{a})$$

$$\text{Transform}: \qquad \bar{T}(x, \gamma, t) = \int_{y'=-\infty}^{\infty} e^{i\gamma y'} T(x, y', t) \, dy' \qquad (15\text{-}87\text{b})$$

where the bar denotes the integral transform with respect to the y variable.

The integral transform of the system (15-86) by the application of the transform (15-87b) yields (see Note 2 for the transform of the second and the first derivatives with respect to the y variable)

$$\frac{\partial^2 \bar{T}}{\partial x^2} - \gamma^2 \varepsilon_{22} \bar{T} - 2i\gamma\varepsilon_{12} \frac{\partial \bar{T}}{\partial x} = \frac{1}{\alpha_{11}} \frac{\partial \bar{T}}{\partial t} \qquad \text{in } 0 < x < \infty, \ t > 0 \qquad (15\text{-}88\text{a})$$

$$\bar{T} = 0 \qquad\qquad \text{at } x = 0, \ t > 0 \qquad (15\text{-}88\text{b})$$

$$\bar{T} = \bar{F}(x, \gamma) \qquad\qquad \text{for } t = 0, \text{ in } 0 \leq x < \infty \qquad (15\text{-}88\text{c})$$

where $\bar{T} \equiv \bar{T}(x, \gamma, t)$. The partial derivative $\partial \bar{T}/\partial x$ can be removed from this equation by defining a new variable $\bar{w}(x, \gamma, t)$ as

$$\bar{T}(x, \gamma, t) = \bar{w}(x, \gamma, t) e^{i\gamma\varepsilon_{12}x} \qquad (15\text{-}89)$$

Then, the system (15-88) is transformed to

$$\frac{\partial^2 \bar{w}}{\partial x^2} - \gamma^2 (\varepsilon_{22} - \varepsilon_{12}^2) \bar{w} = \frac{1}{\alpha_{11}} \frac{\partial \bar{w}}{\partial t} \qquad \text{in } 0 < x < \infty, \ t > 0 \qquad (15\text{-}90\text{a})$$

$$\bar{w} = 0 \qquad\qquad \text{at } x = 0, \ t > 0 \qquad (15\text{-}90\text{b})$$

$$\bar{w} = e^{-i\gamma\varepsilon_{12}x} \bar{F}(x, \gamma) \qquad\qquad \text{for } t = 0, \text{ in } 0 \leq x < \infty \qquad (15\text{-}90\text{c})$$

To remove the partial derivative with respect to the x variable from this system, the integral transform pair with respect to the x variable for the region $0 < x < \infty$ is defined as [see equations (13-67) and Table 2-3, case 3, in chapter 2]

$$\text{Inversion}: \qquad \bar{w}(x, \gamma, t) = \frac{2}{\pi} \int_{\beta=0}^{\infty} \sin \beta x \, \tilde{\bar{w}}(\beta, \gamma, t) \, d\beta \qquad (15\text{-}91\text{a})$$

$$\text{Transform}: \qquad \tilde{\bar{w}}(\beta, \gamma, t) = \int_{x'=0}^{\infty} \sin \beta x' \, \bar{w}(x', \gamma, t) \, dx' \qquad (15\text{-}91\text{b})$$

where the tilde denotes the transform with respect to the x variable.

The integral transform of the system (15-90) by the application of the transform (15-91b) gives

$$\frac{d\tilde{\bar{w}}}{dt} + \alpha_{11}\lambda^2\tilde{\bar{w}}(\beta,\gamma,t) = 0 \qquad \text{for } t > 0 \qquad (15\text{-}92a)$$

$$\tilde{\bar{w}} = \tilde{\bar{H}}(\beta,\gamma) \qquad \text{for } t = 0 \qquad (15\text{-}92b)$$

where $\lambda^2 \equiv \beta^2 + \gamma^2(\varepsilon_{22} - \varepsilon_{12}^2)$ $\hspace{3cm}$ (15-93a)

$$\varepsilon_{22} - \varepsilon_{12}^2 > 0 \qquad \text{according to equation (15-4d)} \qquad (15\text{-}93b)$$

$$\tilde{\bar{H}}(\beta,\gamma) = \int\limits_{x'=0}^{\infty} e^{-i\gamma\varepsilon_{12}x'}\bar{F}(x',\gamma)\sin\beta x'\,dx' \qquad (15\text{-}93c)$$

$$\bar{F}(x',\gamma) = \int\limits_{y'=-\infty}^{\infty} e^{i\gamma y'}F(x',y')\,dy' \qquad (15\text{-}93d)$$

The solution of equation (15-92) is

$$\tilde{\bar{w}}(\beta,\gamma,t) = \tilde{\bar{H}}(\beta,\gamma)e^{-\alpha_{11}\lambda^2 t} \qquad (15\text{-}94)$$

The inversion of equation (15-94) by the inversion formula (15-91a) and then the application of equation (15-89) yields

$$\bar{T}(x,\gamma,t) = \frac{2}{\pi}\int\limits_{\beta=0}^{\infty} \sin\beta x\,\tilde{\bar{H}}(\beta,\gamma)e^{-\alpha_{11}\lambda^2 t + i\gamma\varepsilon_{12}x}\,d\beta \qquad (15\text{-}95)$$

This result is inverted by the inversion formula (15-87a), the explicit form of $\tilde{\bar{H}}(\beta,\gamma)$ is introduced and the order of integrations are rearranged

$$T(x,y,t) = \int\limits_{x'=0}^{\infty}\int\limits_{y'=-\infty}^{\infty} F(x',y')\cdot\left[\frac{1}{2\pi}\int\limits_{\gamma=-\infty}^{\infty} e^{-\alpha_{11}(\varepsilon_{22}-\varepsilon_{12}^2)\gamma^2 t - i\gamma[(y-y')-\varepsilon_{12}(x-x')]}\,d\gamma\right]$$

$$\cdot\left[\frac{2}{\pi}\int\limits_{\beta=0}^{\infty} e^{-\alpha_{11}\beta^2 t}\sin\beta x\sin\beta x'\,d\beta\right]dy'\,dx' \qquad (15\text{-}96)$$

In this result the integrals with respect to the variables γ and β can be evaluated by making use of the integrals given by equations (13-77) and (13-91), respectively; that is

$$\frac{1}{2\pi}\int\limits_{\gamma=-\infty}^{\infty} e^{-\gamma^2 At - i\gamma z}\,d\gamma = \frac{1}{(4\pi At)^{1/2}}e^{-z^2/4At} \qquad (15\text{-}97a)$$

$$\frac{2}{\pi}\int\limits_{\beta=0}^{\infty} e^{-\beta^2\alpha t}\sin\beta x\sin\beta x'\,d\beta$$

$$= \frac{1}{(4\pi\alpha t)^{1/2}}\left[\exp\left(-\frac{(x-x')^2}{4\alpha t}\right) - \exp\left(-\frac{(x+x')^2}{4\alpha t}\right)\right] \qquad (15\text{-}97b)$$

Then, the solution (15-96) takes the form

$$T(x, y, t) = \frac{1}{[4\pi\alpha_{11}(\varepsilon_{22} - \varepsilon_{12}^2)t]^{1/2}[4\pi\alpha_{11}t]^{1/2}} \int\limits_{x'=0}^{\infty} \int\limits_{y'=-\infty}^{\infty} F(x', y')$$
$$\cdot \exp\left(-\frac{[(y-y')^2 - \varepsilon_{12}(x-x')^2]^2}{4\pi\alpha_{11}(\varepsilon_{22} - \varepsilon_{12}^2)t}\right)$$
$$\cdot \left[\exp\left(-\frac{(x-x')^2}{4\alpha_{11}t}\right) - \exp\left(-\frac{(x+x')^2}{4\alpha_{11}t}\right)\right] dy' \, dx' \quad (15\text{-}98)$$

Example 15-6. An anisotropic medium $0 \le x < \infty$, $-\infty < y < \infty$ is initially at zero temperature. For times $t > 0$, heat is generated in the medium at a rate of $g(x, y, t)$ W/m^3 while the boundary surface at $x = 0$ is kept at zero temperature. Obtain an expression for the temperature distribution $T(x, y, t)$ in the region for times $t > 0$.

Solution. The mathematical formulation of the heat-conduction problem is given as

$$\frac{\partial^2 T}{\partial x^2} + \varepsilon_{22}\frac{\partial^2 T}{\partial y^2} + 2\varepsilon_{12}\frac{\partial^2 T}{\partial x \partial y} + \frac{1}{k_{11}}g(x, y, t) = \frac{1}{\alpha_{11}}\frac{\partial T}{\partial t}$$

$$\text{in } 0 < x < \infty, \ -\infty < y < \infty, \ t > 0 \quad (15\text{-}99a)$$

$$T = 0 \quad \text{at } x = 0, \ t > 0 \quad (15\text{-}99b)$$

$$T = 0 \quad \text{for } t = 0, \text{ in } 0 \le x < \infty, \ -\infty < y < \infty \quad (15\text{-}99c)$$

where we defined

$$\varepsilon_{ij} = \frac{k_{ij}}{k_{11}}, \quad k_{ij} = k_{ji}, \quad \text{and} \quad \alpha_{11} = \frac{k_{11}}{\rho C_p} \quad (15\text{-}99d)$$

This problem is similar to that considered in Example 15-5, except for the heat generation and the zero initial condition. Therefore, the integral transform pairs defined in the previous example are applicable for the solution of this problem.

The integral transform of the system (15-99) by the application of the transform (15-87b) gives

$$\frac{\partial^2 \bar{T}}{\partial x^2} - \gamma^2\varepsilon_{22}\bar{T} - 2i\gamma\varepsilon_{12}\frac{\partial \bar{T}}{\partial x} + \frac{1}{k_{11}}\bar{g}(x, \gamma, t) = \frac{1}{\alpha_{11}}\frac{\partial \bar{T}}{\partial t}$$

$$\text{in } 0 < x < \infty, \ t > 0 \quad (15\text{-}100a)$$

$$\bar{T} = 0 \quad \text{at } x = 0, \ t > 0 \quad (35\text{-}100b)$$

$$\bar{T} = 0 \quad \text{for } t = 0, \text{ in } 0 \le x < \infty \quad (15\text{-}100c)$$

where $\bar{T} \equiv \bar{T}(x, \gamma, t)$.

The partial derivative $\partial \bar{T}/\partial x$ can be removed from equation (15-100a) by the application of the transform (15-89). Then the system (15-100) is transformed to

$$\frac{\partial^2 \bar{w}}{\partial x^2} - \gamma^2(\varepsilon_{22} - \varepsilon_{12}^2)\bar{w} + \frac{1}{k_{11}}e^{-i\gamma\varepsilon_{12}x}\bar{g}(x, \gamma, t) = \frac{1}{\alpha_{11}}\frac{\partial \bar{w}}{\partial t}$$

$$\text{in } 0 < x < \infty, \ t > 0 \qquad (15\text{-}101a)$$

$$\bar{w} = 0 \qquad \text{at } x = 0, \ t > 0 \qquad (15\text{-}101b)$$

$$\bar{w} = 0 \qquad \text{for } t = 0, \ \text{in } 0 \le x < \infty \qquad (15\text{-}101c)$$

The partial derivative with respect to the x variable is removed from equation (15-101a) by the application of the transform (15-91b). Then, the system (15-101) is reduced to the following ordinary differential equation

$$\frac{d\tilde{\bar{w}}}{\partial t} + \alpha_{11}\lambda^2 \tilde{\bar{w}}(\beta, \gamma, t) = \frac{\alpha_{11}}{k_{11}}\tilde{\bar{G}}(\beta, \gamma, t) \qquad \text{for } t > 0 \qquad (15\text{-}102a)$$

$$\tilde{\bar{w}}(\beta, \gamma, t) = 0 \qquad \text{for } t = 0 \qquad (15\text{-}102b)$$

where

$$\lambda^2 \equiv \beta^2 + \gamma^2(\varepsilon_{22} - \varepsilon_{12}^2) \qquad (15\text{-}103a)$$

$$\varepsilon_{22} - \varepsilon_{12}^2 > 0 \qquad (15\text{-}103b)$$

$$\tilde{\bar{G}}(\beta, \gamma, t) = \int_{x'=0}^{\infty} e^{-i\gamma\varepsilon_{12}x'}\bar{g}(x', \gamma, t)\sin \beta x' \, dx' \qquad (15\text{-}103c)$$

$$\bar{g}(x', \gamma, t) = \int_{y'=-\infty}^{\infty} e^{i\gamma y'}g(x', y', t)\,dy' \qquad (15\text{-}103d)$$

The solution of equations (15-102) is

$$\tilde{\bar{w}}(\beta, \gamma, t) = e^{-\alpha_{11}\lambda^2 t}\int_0^t \frac{\alpha_{11}}{k_{11}}\tilde{\bar{G}}(\beta, \gamma, t)e^{\alpha_{11}\lambda^2 t'}\,dt' \qquad (15\text{-}104)$$

The inversion of this result by the inversion formula (15-91a) and then the application of equation (15-89) yields

$$T(x, \gamma, t) = \frac{2}{\pi}\int_{\beta=0}^{\infty}\int_{t'=0}^{t}\frac{\alpha_{11}}{k_{11}}\sin \beta x \tilde{\bar{G}}(\beta, \gamma, t)e^{-\alpha_{11}\lambda^2(t-t')+i\gamma\varepsilon_{12}x}\,dt'\,d\beta \qquad (15\text{-}105)$$

This result is inverted by the inversion formula (15-87a), the explicit form of $\tilde{\bar{G}}(\beta, \gamma, t)$ defined by equation (15-103) is introduced and the order of the integrations are rearranged

$$T(x, y, t) = \int_{x'=0}^{\infty} \int_{y'=-\infty}^{\infty} \int_{t'=0}^{t} g(x', y', t')$$

$$\cdot \left\{ \frac{1}{2\pi} \int_{\gamma=-\infty}^{\infty} e^{-\alpha_{11}(\varepsilon_{22} - \varepsilon_{12}^2)\gamma^2(t-t') - i\gamma[(y-y') - \varepsilon_{12}(x-x')]} d\gamma \right\}$$

$$\cdot \left\{ \frac{2}{\pi} \int_{\beta=0}^{\infty} e^{-\alpha_{11}\beta^2(t-t')} \sin \beta x \sin \beta x' \, d\beta \right\} dt' \, dy' \, dx' \qquad (15\text{-}106)$$

The integrals with respect to the variables γ and β can be evaluated by making use of the integrals (15-97a) and (15-97b); then the solution (15-106) takes the form

$$T(x, y, t) = \frac{1}{[4\pi\alpha_{11}(\varepsilon_{22} - \varepsilon_{12}^2)(t-t')]^{1/2}[4\pi\alpha_{11}(t-t')]^{1/2}}$$

$$\cdot \int_{x'=0}^{\infty} \int_{y'=-\infty}^{\infty} \int_{t'=0}^{t} g(x', y', t') \cdot \exp\left(-\frac{[(y-y') - \varepsilon_{12}(x-x')]^2}{4\pi\alpha_{11}(\alpha_{22} - \varepsilon_{12}^2)(t-t')} \right)$$

$$\cdot \left[\exp\left(-\frac{(x-x')^2}{\alpha_{11}(t-t')} \right) - \exp\left(-\frac{(x+x')^2}{4\alpha_{11}(t-t')} \right) \right] dt' \, dy' \, dx' \quad (15\text{-}107)$$

Example 15-7. An anisotropic cylindrical region $0 \le r \le h$, $-\infty < z < \infty$ is initially at temperature $F(r, z)$. For times $t > 0$ the boundary surface at $r = b$ is kept at zero temperature. Obtain an expression for the temperature distribution $T(r, z, t)$ in the cylinder for times $t > 0$.

Solution. Since there is no azimuthal variation of temperature, we have $\partial T/\partial \phi = 0$. Then the heat-conduction equation (15-10) becomes

$$\frac{1}{r}\frac{\partial}{\partial r}\left(r\frac{\partial T}{\partial r} \right) + \varepsilon_{33}\frac{\partial^2 T}{\partial z^2} + 2\varepsilon_{13}\frac{\partial^2 T}{\partial r \partial z} + \varepsilon_{13}\frac{1}{r}\frac{\partial T}{\partial z} = \frac{1}{\alpha_{11}}\frac{\partial T}{\partial t}$$

$$\text{in } 0 \le r < b, \ -\infty < z < \infty, \ t > 0 \qquad (15\text{-}108a)$$

with the boundary and initial conditions

$$T = 0 \qquad \text{at } t = b, \ t > 0 \qquad (15\text{-}108b)$$

$$T = F(r, z) \qquad \text{for } t = 0, \text{ in } 0 \le r < b, \ -\infty < z < \infty \qquad (15\text{-}108c)$$

where we defined

$$\varepsilon_{ij} = \frac{k_{ij}}{k_{11}}, \qquad k_{ij} = k_{ji}, \qquad \text{and} \qquad \alpha_{11} = \frac{k_{11}}{\rho C_p} \qquad (15\text{-}108d)$$

This problem is now solved by the application of integral-transform technique as now described.

The integral-transform pair with respect to the z variable for $-\infty < z < \infty$ is defined as

$$\text{Inversion}: \quad T(r,z,t) = \frac{1}{2\pi} \int_{-\infty}^{\infty} e^{-i\gamma z} \bar{T}(r,\gamma,t)\, d\gamma \qquad (15\text{-}109a)$$

$$\text{Transform}: \quad \bar{T}(r,\gamma,t) = \int_{z'=-\infty}^{\infty} e^{i\gamma z'} T(r,z',t)\, dz' \qquad (15\text{-}109b)$$

The integral transform of the system (15-108) by the application of the transform (15-109b) yields

$$\frac{\partial^2 \bar{T}}{\partial r^2} + \frac{1}{r}\frac{\partial \bar{T}}{\partial r} - \gamma^2 \varepsilon_{33}\bar{T} - 2i\gamma\varepsilon_{13}\frac{\partial \bar{T}}{\partial r} - i\gamma\frac{\varepsilon_{13}}{r}\bar{T} = \frac{1}{\alpha_{11}}\frac{\partial \bar{T}}{\partial t}$$

or

$$\frac{\partial^2 \bar{T}}{\partial r^2} + \left(\frac{1}{r} - 2i\gamma\varepsilon_{13}\right)\frac{\partial \bar{T}}{\partial r} - \left(\frac{i\gamma\varepsilon_{13}}{r} + \gamma^2\varepsilon_{33}\right)\bar{T} = \frac{1}{\alpha_{11}}\frac{\partial \bar{T}}{\partial t}$$

$$\text{in } 0 \le r < b, \ t > 0 \qquad (15\text{-}110a)$$

$$\bar{T} = 0 \qquad\qquad \text{at } r = b, \ t > 0 \qquad (15\text{-}110b)$$

$$\bar{T} = \bar{F}(r,\gamma) \qquad \text{for } t = 0, \ \text{in } 0 \le r < b \qquad (15\text{-}110c)$$

where $\bar{T} \equiv \bar{T}(r,\gamma,t)$.

A new variable $\bar{w}(r,\gamma,t)$ is defined as

$$\bar{T}(r,\gamma,t) = \bar{w}(r,\gamma,t)\cdot e^{i\gamma\varepsilon_{13}r} \qquad (15\text{-}111)$$

Then the system (15-110) is transformed to

$$\frac{\partial^2 \bar{w}}{\partial r^2} + \frac{1}{r}\frac{\partial \bar{w}}{\partial r} - (\varepsilon_{33} - \varepsilon_{13}^2)\gamma^2\bar{w} = \frac{1}{\alpha_{11}}\frac{\partial \bar{w}}{\partial t} \qquad \text{in } 0 \le r < b, \ t > 0 \qquad (15\text{-}112a)$$

$$\bar{w} = 0 \qquad\qquad\qquad\qquad\qquad \text{at } r = b, \ t > 0 \qquad (15\text{-}112b)$$

$$\bar{w} = e^{-i\gamma\varepsilon_{13}r}\bar{F}(r,\gamma) \qquad\qquad \text{for } t = 0, \ \text{in } 0 \le r \le b \qquad (15\text{-}112c)$$

To remove the partial derivative with respect to the r variable, the integral-transform pair is defined as [see equations (13-97) and Table 3-1, case 3]

$$\text{Inversion}: \quad \bar{w}(r,\gamma,t) = \sum_{m=1}^{\infty} \frac{1}{N(\beta_m)} J_0(\beta_m r)\tilde{\bar{w}}(\beta_m,\gamma,t) \qquad (15\text{-}113a)$$

$$\text{Transform}: \quad \tilde{\bar{w}}(\beta_m,\gamma,t) = \int_{r'=0}^{b} r' J_0(\beta_m r')\bar{w}(r',\gamma,t)\, dr' \qquad (35\text{-}113b)$$

where

$$\frac{1}{N(\beta_m)} = \frac{2}{b^2} \frac{1}{J_0'^2(\beta_m b)} = \frac{2}{b^2 J_1^2(\beta_m b)} \tag{15-113c}$$

and β_m's are the roots of

$$J_0(\beta_m b) = 0 \tag{15-113d}$$

The integral transform of the system (15-112) by the application of the transform (15-113b) is

$$\frac{d\tilde{w}}{dt} + \alpha_{11}\lambda^2 \tilde{w}(\beta_m, \gamma, t) = 0 \qquad \text{for } t > 0 \tag{15-114a}$$

$$\tilde{w}(\beta_m, \gamma, t) = \tilde{H}(\beta_m, \gamma) \qquad \text{for } t = 0 \tag{15-114b}$$

where

$$\lambda^2 \equiv \beta_m^2 + \gamma^2(\varepsilon_{33} - \varepsilon_{13}^2) \tag{15-115a}$$

$$\varepsilon_{33} - \varepsilon_{13}^2 > 0 \tag{15-115b}$$

$$\tilde{H}(\beta_m, \gamma) = \int_{r'=0}^{b} r' J_0(\beta_m, r') e^{-i\gamma\varepsilon_{13}r'} \bar{F}(r', \gamma) dr' \tag{15-115c}$$

$$\bar{F}(r', \gamma) = \int_{z'=-\infty}^{\infty} e^{i\gamma z'} F(r', z') dz' \tag{15-115d}$$

The solution of equation (15-114) is

$$\tilde{w}(\beta_m, \gamma, t) = e^{-\alpha_{11}\lambda^2 t} \tilde{H}(\beta_m, \gamma) \tag{15-116}$$

The inversion of (15-116) by the inversion formula (15-113a) gives

$$\bar{w}(r, \gamma, t) = \sum_{m=1}^{\infty} \frac{1}{N(\beta_m)} J_0(\beta_m r) e^{-\alpha_{11}\lambda^2 t} \tilde{H}(\beta_m, \gamma) \tag{15-117}$$

This result is introduced into equation (15-111) to obtain

$$\bar{T}(r, \gamma, t) = \sum_{m=1}^{\infty} \frac{1}{N(\beta_m)} J_0(\beta_m r) \cdot e^{-\alpha_{11}\lambda^2 t + i\gamma\varepsilon_{13}r} \tilde{H}(\beta_m, \gamma) \tag{15-118}$$

The inversion of equation (15-118) by the inversion formula (15-109a) gives

$$T(r, z, t) = \frac{1}{2\pi} \sum_{m=1}^{\infty} \int_{\gamma=-\infty}^{\infty} \frac{1}{N(\beta_m)} \cdot J_0(\beta_m r) \tilde{H}(\beta_m, \gamma) e^{-\alpha_{11}\lambda^2 t - i\gamma(z - \varepsilon_{13}r)} d\gamma \tag{15-119}$$

where

$$\lambda^2 \equiv \beta_m^2 + \gamma^2(\varepsilon_{33} - \varepsilon_{13}^2)$$

$\tilde{\tilde{H}}(\beta_m, \gamma)$ defined by equations (15-115) is introduced into equation (15-119) and the order of integrations are rearranged.

$$T(r,z,t) = \sum_{m=1}^{\infty} e^{-\alpha_{11}\beta_m^2 t} \frac{1}{N(\beta_m)} J_0(\beta_m, r) \int_{z'=-\infty}^{\infty} \int_{r'=0}^{b} r' J_0(\beta_m r') F(r', z') \, dr' \, dz'$$

$$\cdot \left\{ \frac{1}{2\pi} \int_{\gamma=-\infty}^{\infty} e^{-\gamma^2 \alpha_{11}(\varepsilon_{33} - \varepsilon_{13})t - i\gamma[(z-z') + \varepsilon_{13}(r'-r)]} \, d\gamma \right\} \tag{15-120}$$

The integral with respect to γ can be evaluated according to equation (15-97a). Then, the solution becomes

$$T(r,z,t) = \frac{1}{\sqrt{4\pi\alpha_{11}(\varepsilon_{33} - \varepsilon_{13}^2)t}} \sum_{m=1}^{\infty} e^{-\alpha_{11}\beta_m^2 t} \cdot \frac{1}{N(\beta_m)} J_0(\beta_m r)$$

$$\cdot \int_{z'=-\infty}^{\infty} \int_{r'=0}^{b} r' J_0(\beta_m r') \cdot F(r', z')$$

$$\cdot \exp\left\{ -\frac{[(z-z') + \varepsilon_{13}(r'-r)]^2}{4\alpha_{11}(\varepsilon_{33} - \varepsilon_{13}^2)t} \right\} dr' \, dz' \tag{15-121}$$

where $N(\beta_m)$ is given by equation (15-113c) and β_m's are the roots of equation (15-113d).

REFERENCES

1. W. A. Wooster, *A Textbook in Crystal Physics*, Cambridge University Press, London, 1938.

2. J. F. Nye, *Physical Properties of Crystals*, Clarendon Press, London, 1957.

3. H. S. Carslaw and J. C. Jeager, *Conduction of Heat in Solids*, Clarendon Press, London, 1959.

4. M. N. Özisik, *Boundary Value Problems of Heat Conduction*, International Textbook, Scranton, Pa., 1968.

5. W. H. Giedt and D. R. Hornbaker, *ARS J.* **32**, 1902–1909, 1962.

6. K. J. Touryan, *AIAA J.* **2**, 124–126, 1964.

7. B. Venkatraman, S. A. Patel, and F. V. Pohle, *J. Aerospace Sci.* **29**, 628–629, 1962.

8. B. T. Chao, *Appl. Sci. Res.* **A12**, 134–138, 1963.

9. H. F. Cooper, Joulean Heating of an Infinite Rectangular Red with Orthotropic Thermal Properties, ASME Paper No. 66-WA/HT-14, 1966.

10. H. F. Cooper, Transient and Steady State Temperature Distribution in Foil Wound Solenoids and Other Electric Apparatus of Rectangular Cross-Section, 1965 *IEEE International Convention Record*, Part 10, March 1965, pp. 67–75.

11. N. Vutz and S. W. Angrist, Thermal Contact Resistance of Anisotropic Materials, ASME Paper 69-HT-47, 1969.

12. R. C. Pfahl, *Int. J. Heat Mass Transfer* **18**, 191–204, 1975.

13. B. F. Blackwell, *An Introduction to Heat Conduction in an Anisotropic Medium*, SC-RR-69-542, Oct. 1969, Sandia Lab., Albuquerque, New Mexico.

14. Y. P. Chang, C. S. Kang, and D. J. Chen, *Int. J. Heat Mass Transfer* **16**, 1905–1918, 1973.

15. J. Padovan, *J. Heat Transfer* **96c**, 428–431, 1974.

16. J. Padovan, *AIAA J.* **10**, 60–64, 1972.

17. K. Katayama, Transient Heat Conduction in Anisotropic Solids, *Proceedings of the 5th International Heat Transfer Conference*, Cu 1.4, pp. 137–141, Tokyo, Sept. 3974.

18. M. H. Cobble, *Int. J. Heat Mass Transfer* **17**, 379–380, 1974.

19. G. P. Mulholland and B. P. Gupta, *J. Heat Transfer* **99c**, 135–137, 1977.

20. Y. P. Chang and C. H. Tsou, *J. Heat Transfer* **99c**, 132–134, 1977.

21. Y. P. Chang and C. H. Tsou, *J. Heat Transfer* **99c**, 41–47, 1977.

22. Y. P. Chang, *Int. J. Heat Mass Transfer* **20**, 1019–1025, 1977.

23. M. N. Özışık and S. M. Shouman, Transient Heat Conduction in an Anisotropic Medium in Cylindrical Coordinates, *J. Franklin Institute* (to be published).

24. J. Padovan, *J. Heat Transfer* **96c**, 313–318, 1974.

25. G. P. Mulholland, Diffusion Through Laminated Orthotropic Cylinders, *Proceedings of the 5th International Heat Transfer Conference*, Cu 4.3, pp. 250–254, Tokyo, 1974.

26. L. Onsagar, *Phys Rev.* **37**, 405–426, 1931; **38**, 2265–2279, 1931.

27. H. B. G. Casimir, *Rev. Mod. Phys.* **17**, 343–350, 1945.

28. I. Prigogine, *Thermodynamics of Irreversible Processes*, Wiley-Interscience, New York, 1961.

29. L. P. Eisenhart, *Coordinate Geometry*, Dover Publications, Inc., New York, 1962.

30. A. R. Amir-Moe'z and A. L. Fass, *Elements of Linear Spaces*, Pergamon Press, New York, 1962.

31. S. H. Maron and C. F. Prutton, *Principles of Physical Chemistry*, McMillan Co., New York, 1958.

PROBLEMS

15-1 Write the expressions for the three components of the heat flux, q_i, $i = 1, 2, 3$, for an anisotropic medium in the following orthogonal coordinate systems: (1) prolate spheroid; (2) oblate spheroid.

15-2 Write the time-dependent heat-conduction equation for an anisotropic medium with constant conductivity coefficients for the following cases:

1. In the cylindrical coordinate system when temperature is a function of r, ϕ variables.

2. In the spherical coordinate system when temperature is a function of r, ϕ variables.

15-3 Write the boundary conditions of the third kind for an anisotropic solid at the following boundary surfaces.

1. At the boundary surfaces $z = 0, z = L$, and $r = b$ of a solid cylinder of radius b, height L.

2. At the surface $r = b$ of a solid sphere.

15-4 Write the thermal resistivity coefficients r_{11}, r_{13}, and r_{23} in terms of the thermal conductivity coefficients k_{ij}.

15-5   Let C_{ij} be the direction cosines between the *new* axes $0x_i'$ and the *old* axes $0x_j$. Write the conductivity coefficients k_{12}' and k_{11}' referred to the new coordinate system in terms of the conductivity coefficients k_{ij} referred to the old coordinate system.

15-6   Consider steady-state heat-conduction in an orthotropic solid cylinder $0 \le r \le b, 0 \le z \le L$ in which heat is generated at a uniform rate of g_0 W/m³ while the boundaries are kept at zero temperature. The thermal conductivity coefficients in the r and z directions are k_1 and k_2, respectively. Obtain an expression for the steady-state temperature distribution $T(r, z)$ in the cylinder.

15-7   Consider an orthotropic region $0 \le x < \infty, 0 \le y < \infty$, which is initially at temperature $F(x, y)$ and for times $t > 0$ the boundaries at $x = 0$ and $y = 0$ are kept at zero temperature. The thermal conductivity coefficients for the x and y directions are k_1 and k_2, respectively. Obtain an expression for the temperature distribution $T(x, y, t)$ in the medium for times $t > 0$.

15-8   An orthotropic solid cylinder $0 \le r \le b, 0 \le x \le L$ is initially at temperature $F(r, z)$. For times $t > 0$ the boundaries are kept at zero temperature. The thermal conductivity coefficients for the r and z directions are k_1 and k_2, respectively. Obtain an expression for the temperature distribution $T(r, z, t)$ in the solid for times $t > 0$.

15-9   Heat is generated at a constant rate of g_0 W/m³ in an orthotropic hemisphere of radius $r = b$ while the boundaries are kept at zero temperature. The thermal conductivities for the r and μ (i.e., $\mu = \cos^{-1} \theta$) directions are k_1 and k_2, respectively. Obtain an expression for the steady-state temperature distribution $T(r, \mu)$ in the hemisphere.

15-10   Consider time-dependent, two-dimensional heat-conduction problem for an anisotropic medium $0 \le x < \infty, -\infty < y < \infty$ which is initially at temperature $F(x, y)$ and for times $t > 0$ the boundary surface at $x = 0$ is kept insulated. Obtain an expression for the temperature distribution $T(x, y, t)$ in the medium for times $t > 0$.

15-11   Consider time-dependent, two-dimensional heat-conduction problem for an anisotropic region $0 \le x < \infty, -\infty < y < \infty$ which is initially at zero temperature. For times $t > 0$, heat is generated in the medium at a rate of $g(x, y, t)$ W/m³, while the boundary at $x = 0$ is kept insulated. Obtain an expression for the temperature distribution $T(x, y, t)$ in the medium for times $t > 0$.

15-12   Consider time-dependent, two-dimensional heat conduction in an anisotropic hollow cylinder $a \le r \le b, -\infty < z < \infty$, which is initially at temperature $F(r, z)$. For times $t > 0$, the boundaries at $r = a$ and $r = b$ are kept at zero temperature. Obtain an expression for the temperature distribution $T(r, z, t)$ in the medium for times $t > 0$.

NOTES

1. The closed-form expression given by equation (15-74) is determined as now described. We consider the following heat-conduction problem

$$\frac{d^2 T}{dx^2} + \frac{g_0}{k} = 0 \qquad \text{in } 0 < x < a \tag{1a}$$

$$\frac{dT}{dx} = 0 \qquad \text{at } x = 0 \tag{1b}$$

$$\frac{dT}{dx} + H_1 T = 0 \qquad \text{at } x = a \tag{1c}$$

This problem is solved both by direct integration and using the integral transform technique as given below.

(1) When it is solved by direct integration we obtain

$$T = \frac{g_0 a}{k_1 H_1} + \frac{g_0}{2k_1}(a^2 - x^2) \tag{2}$$

(2) To solve the system, equation (1), by the integral transform technique, we take its transform by the application of transform (15-70a) and obtain

$$\bar{T} = \frac{1}{k_1 \beta^2} \bar{g}_0 \tag{3a}$$

where

$$\bar{g}_0 = \int_0^a g_0 \cos \beta_m x \, dx = \frac{\sin \beta_m a}{\beta_m} g_0 \tag{3b}$$

Introducing the transform (3) into the inversion formula (15-70b), we obtain the solution as

$$T = \frac{g_0}{k_1} \sum_{n=0}^{\infty} \frac{1}{N(\beta_m)} \cdot \frac{\cos \beta_m x \sin \beta_m a}{\beta_m^3} \tag{4}$$

Since equations (2) and (4) are the solution of the same problem, by equating them we obtain

$$\sum_{n=0}^{\infty} \frac{1}{N(\beta_m)} \frac{\cos \beta_m x \sin \beta_m a}{\beta_m^3} = \frac{a}{H_1} + \frac{1}{2}(a^2 - x^2) \tag{5}$$

which is the result given by equation (15-74).

2. The integral transform of $\partial^2 T / \partial y^2$ by the application of the transform

(15-87b) is determined as

$$\int_{-\infty}^{\infty} e^{i\gamma y} \frac{\partial^2 T}{\partial y^2} dy = \left[\frac{\partial T}{\partial y} e^{i\gamma y} - i\gamma T e^{i\gamma y} \right]_{y=-\infty}^{\infty} - \gamma^2 \int_{-\infty}^{\infty} e^{i\gamma y} T \, dy$$

$$= -\gamma^2 \int_{-\infty}^{\infty} e^{i\gamma y} T \, dy = -\gamma^2 \bar{T} \tag{1}$$

To obtain this result we integrated by parts twice, assumed that T and $\partial T/\partial y$ both vanish as $y \rightarrow \pm \infty$ and utilized the definition of the transform (15-87b).

The integral transform of $\partial^2 T/\partial x \partial y$ is determined as

$$\int_{-\infty}^{\infty} e^{i\gamma y} \frac{\partial^2 T}{\partial x \partial y} dy = \left[\frac{\partial T}{\partial x} e^{i\gamma y} \right]_{-\infty}^{\infty} - i\gamma \frac{\partial}{\partial x} \int_{-\infty}^{\infty} e^{i\gamma y} T \, dy$$

$$= -i\gamma \frac{\partial}{\partial x} \int_{-\infty}^{\infty} e^{i\gamma y} T \, dy = -i\gamma \frac{\partial \bar{T}}{\partial x} \tag{2}$$

where we assumed that $\partial T/\partial x$ vanish at $y \rightarrow \pm \infty$.

APPENDICES

ROOTS OF TRANSCENDENTAL EQUATIONS

First six roots β_n of $\beta \tan \beta = c$

c	β_1	β_2	β_3	β_4	β_5	β_6
0	0	3.1416	6.2832	9.4248	12.5664	15.7080
0.001	0.0316	3.1419	6.2833	9.4249	12.5665	15.7080
0.002	0.0447	3.1422	6.2835	9.4250	12.5665	15.7081
0.004	0.0632	3.1429	6.2838	9.4252	12.5667	15.7082
0.006	0.0774	3.1435	6.2841	9.4254	12,5668	15.7083
0.008	0.0893	3.1441	6.2845	9.4256	12.5670	15.7085
0.01	0.0998	3.1448	6.2848	9.4258	12.5672	15.7086
0.02	0.1410	3.1479	6.2864	9.4269	12.5680	15.7092
0.04	0.1987	3.1543	6.2895	9.4290	12.5696	15.7105
0.06	0.2425	3.1606	6.2927	9.4311	12.5711	15.7118
0.08	0.2791	3.1668	6.2959	9.4333	12.5727	15.7131
0.1	0.3111	3.1731	6.2991	9.4354	12.5743	15.7143
0.2	0.4328	3.2039	6.3148	9.4459	12.5823	15.7207
0.3	0.5218	3.2341	6.3305	9.4565	12.5902	15.7270
0.4	0.5932	3.2636	6.3461	9.4670	12.5981	15.7334
0.5	0.6533	3.2923	6.3616	9.4775	12.6060	15.7397
0.6	0.7051	3.3204	6.3770	9.4879	12.6139	15.7460
0.7	0.7506	3.3477	6.3923	9.4983	12.6218	15.7524
0.8	0.7910	3.3744	6.4074	9.5087	12.2696	15.7587
0.9	0.8274	3.4003	6.4224	9.5190	12.6375	15.7650
1.0	0.8603	3.4256	6.4373	9.5293	12.6453	15.7713
1.5	0.9882	3.5422	6.5097	9.5801	12.6841	15.8026
2.0	1.0769	3.6436	6.5783	9.6296	12.7223	15.8336
3.0	1.1925	3.8088	6.7040	9.7240	12.7966	15.8945
4.0	1.2646	3.9352	6.8140	9.8119	12.8678	15.9536

(Continued)

c	β_1	β_2	β_3	β_4	β_5	β_6
5.0	1.3138	4.0336	6.9096	9.8928	12.9352	16.0107
6.0	1.3496	4.1116	6.9924	9.9667	12.9988	16.0654
7.0	1.3766	4.1746	7.0640	10.0339	13.0584	16.1177
8.0	1.3978	4.2264	7.1263	10.0949	13.1141	16.1675
9.0	1.4149	4.2694	7.1806	10.1502	13.1660	16,2147
10.0	1.4289	4.3058	7.2281	10.2003	13.2142	16.2594
15.0	1.4729	4.4255	7.3959	10.3898	13.4078	16.4474
20.0	1.4961	4.4915	7.4954	10.5117	13.5420	16.5864
30.0	1.5202	4.5615	7.6057	10.6543	13.7085	16.7691
40.0	1.5325	4.5979	7.6647	10.7334	13.8048	16.8794
50.0	1.5400	4.6202	7.7012	10.7832	13.8666	16.9519
60.0	1.5451	4.6353	7.7259	10.8172	13.9094	17.0026
80.0	1.5514	4.6543	7.7573	10.8606	13.9644	17.0686
100.0	1.5552	4.6658	7.7764	10.8871	13.9981	17.1093
∞	1.5708	4.7124	7.8540	10.9956	14.1372	17.2788

Roots are all real if $c > 0$.

First six roots β_n of $\beta \cot \beta = -c$

c	β_1	β_2	β_3	β_4	β_5	β_6
-1.0	0	4.4934	7.7253	10.9041	14.0662	17.2208
-0.995	0.1224	4.4945	7.7259	10.9046	14.0666	17.2210
-0.99	0.1730	4.4956	7.7265	10.9050	14.0669	17.2213
-0.98	0.2445	4.4979	7.7278	10.9060	14.0676	17.2219
-0.97	0.2991	4.5001	7.7291	10.9069	14.0683	17.2225
-0.96	0.3450	4.5023	7.7304	10.9078	14.0690	17.2231
-0.95	0.3854	4.5045	7.7317	10.9087	14.0697	17.2237
-0.94	0.4217	4.5068	7.7330	10.9096	14.0705	17.2242
-0.93	0.4551	4.5090	7.7343	10.9105	14.0712	17.2248
-0.92	0.4860	4.5112	7.7356	10.9115	14.0719	17.2254
-0.91	0.5150	4.5134	7.7369	10.9124	14.0726	17.2260
-0.90	0.5423	4.5157	7.7382	10.9133	14.0733	17.2266
-0.85	0.6609	4.5268	7.7447	10.9179	14.0769	17.2295
-0.8	0.7593	4.5379	7.7511	10.9225	14.0804	17.2324
-0.7	0.9208	4.5601	7.7641	10.9316	14.0875	17.2382
-0.6	1.0528	4.5822	7.7770	10.9408	14.0946	17.2440
-0.5	1.1656	4.6042	7.7899	10.9499	14.1017	17.2498
-0.4	1.2644	4.6261	7.8028	10.9591	14.1088	17.2556
-0.3	1.3525	4.6479	7.8156	10.9682	14.1159	17.2614
-0.2	1.4320	4.6696	7.8284	10.9774	14.1230	17.2672

(Continued)

c	β_1	β_2	β_3	β_4	β_5	β_6
-0.1	1.5044	4.6911	7.8412	10.9865	14.1301	17.2730
0	1.5708	4.7124	7.8540	10.9956	14.1372	17.2788
0.1	1.6320	4.7335	7.8667	11.0047	14.1443	17.2845
0.2	1.6887	4.7544	7.8794	11.0137	14.1513	17.2903
0.3	1.7414	4.7751	7.8920	11.0228	14.1584	17.2961
0.4	1.7906	4.7956	7.9046	11.0318	14.1654	17.3019
0.5	1.8366	4.8158	7.9171	11.0409	14.1724	17.3076
0.6	1.8798	4.8358	7.9295	11.0498	14.1795	17.3134
0.7	1.9203	4.8556	7.9419	11.0588	14.1865	17.3192
0.8	1.9586	4.8751	7.9542	11.0677	14.1935	17.3249
0.9	1.9947	4.8943	7.9665	11.0767	14.2005	17.3306
1.0	2.0288	4.9132	7.9787	11.0856	14.2075	17.3364
1.5	2.1746	5.0037	8.0385	11.1296	14.2421	17.3649
2.0	2.2889	5.0870	8.0962	11.1727	14.2764	17.3932
3.0	2.4557	5.2329	8.2045	11.2560	14.3434	17.4490
4.0	2.5704	5.3540	8.3029	11.3349	14.4080	17.5034
5.0	2.6537	5.4544	8.3914	11.4086	14.4699	17.5562
6.0	2.7165	5.5378	8.4703	11.4773	14.5288	17.6072
7.0	2.7654	5.6078	8.5406	11.5408	14.5847	17.6562
8.0	2.8044	5.6669	8.6031	11.5994	14.6374	17.7032
9.0	2.8363	5.7172	8.6587	11.6532	14.6870	17.7481
10.0	2.8628	5.7606	8.7083	11.7027	14.7335	17.7908
15.0	2.9476	5.9080	8.8898	11.8959	14.9251	17.9742
20.0	2.9930	5.9921	9.0019	12.0250	15.0625	18.1136
30.0	3.0406	6.0831	9.1294	12.1807	15.2380	18.3018
40.0	3.0651	6.1311	9.1987	12.2688	15.3417	18.4180
50.0	3.0801	6.1606	9.2420	12.3247	15.4090	18.4953
60.0	3.0901	6.1805	9.2715	12.3632	15.4559	18.5497
80.0	3.1028	6.2058	9.3089	12.4124	15.5164	18.6209
100.0	3.1105	6.2211	9.3317	12.4426	15.5537	18.6650
∞	3.1416	6.2832	9.4248	12.5664	15.7080	18.8496

Roots are all real if $c > -1$.

ERROR FUNCTIONS

Numerical Values of Error Function $\mathrm{erf}\, z = \dfrac{2}{\sqrt{\pi}} \int_0^z e^{-\xi^2} d\xi$

z	$\mathrm{erf}\, z$	z	$\mathrm{erf}\, z$	z	$\mathrm{erf}\, z$	z	$\mathrm{erf}\, z$	z	$\mathrm{erf}\, z$
0.00	0.00000	0.50	0.52049	1.00	0.84270	1.50	0.96610	2.00	0.99532
0.01	0.01128	0.51	0.52924	1.01	0.84681	1.51	0.96727	2.20	0.99814
0.02	0.02256	0.52	0.53789	1.02	0.85083	1.52	0.96841	2.40	0.99931
0.03	0.03384	0.53	0.54646	1.03	0.85478	1.53	0.96951	2.60	0.99976
0.04	0.04511	0.54	0.55493	1.04	0.85864	1.54	0.97058	2.80	0.99992
0.05	0.05637	0.55	0.56332	1.05	0.86243	1.55	0.97162	3.00	0.99998
0.06	0.06762	0.56	0.57161	1.06	0.86614	1.56	0.97262		
0.07	0.07885	0.57	0.57981	1.07	0.86977	1.57	0.97360		
0.08	0.09007	0.58	0.58792	1.08	0.87332	1.58	0.97454		
0.09	0.10128	0.59	0.59593	1.09	0.87680	1.59	0.97546		
0.10	0.11246	0.60	0.60385	1.10	0.88020	1.60	0.97634		
0.11	0.12362	0.61	0.61168	1.11	0.88353	1.61	0.97720		
0.12	0.13475	0.62	0.61941	1.12	0.88678	1.62	0.97803		
0.13	0.14586	0.63	0.62704	1.13	0.88997	1.63	0.97884		
0.14	0.15694	0.64	0.63458	1.14	0.89308	1.64	0.97962		
0.15	0.16799	0.65	0.64202	1.15	0.89612	1.65	0.98037		
0.16	0.17901	0.66	0.64937	1.16	0.89909	1.66	0.98110		
0.17	0.18999	0.67	0.65662	1.17	0.90200	1.67	0.98181		
0.18	0.20093	0.68	0.66378	1.18	0.90483	1.68	0.98249		
0.19	0.21183	0.69	0.67084	1.19	0.90760	1.69	0.98315		
0.20	0.22270	0.70	0.67780	1.20	0.91031	1.70	0.98379		
0.21	0.23352	0.71	0.68466	1.21	0.91295	1.71	0.98440		
0.22	0.24429	0.72	0.69143	1.22	0.91553	1.72	0.98500		
0.23	0.25502	0.73	0.69810	1.23	0.91805	1.73	0.98557		
0.24	0.26570	0.74	0.70467	1.24	0.92050	1.74	0.98613		

(Continued)

z	erf z	z	erf z	z	erf z	z	erf z	z	erf z
0.25	0.27632	0.75	0.71115	1.25	0.92290	1.75	0.98667		
0.26	0.28689	0.76	0.71753	1.26	0.92523	1.76	0.98719		
0.27	0.29741	0.77	0.72382	1.27	0.92751	1.77	0.98769		
0.28	0.30788	0.78	0.73001	1.28	0.92973	1.78	0.98817		
0.29	0.31828	0.79	0.73610	1.29	0.93189	1.79	0.98864		
0.30	0.32862	0.80	0.74210	1.30	0.93400	1.80	0.98909		
0.31	0.33890	0.81	0.74800	1.31	0.93606	1.81	0.98952		
0.32	0.34912	0.82	0.75381	1.32	0.93806	1.82	0.98994		
0.33	0.35927	0.83	0.75952	1.33	0.94001	1.83	0.99034		
0.34	0.36936	0.84	0.76514	1.34	0.94191	1.84	0.99073		
0.35	0.37938	0.85	0.77066	1.35	0.94376	1.85	0.99111		
0.36	0.38932	0.86	0.77610	1.36	0.94556	1.86	0.99147		
0.37	0.39920	0.87	0.78143	1.37	0.94731	1.87	0.99182		
0.38	0.40900	0.88	0.78668	1.38	0.94901	1.88	0.99215		
0.39	0.41873	0.89	0.79184	1.39	0.95067	1.89	0.99247		
0.40	0.42839	0.90	0.79690	1.40	0.95228	1.90	0.99279		
0.41	0.43796	0.91	0.80188	1.41	0.95385	1.91	0.99308		
0.42	0.44746	0.92	0.80676	1.42	0.95537	1.92	0.99337		
0.43	0.45688	0.93	0.81156	1.43	0.95685	1.93	0.99365		
0.44	0.46622	0.94	0.81627	1.44	0.95829	1.94	0.99392		
0.45	0.47548	0.95	0.82089	1.45	0.95969	1.95	0.99417		
0.46	0.48465	0.96	0.82542	1.46	0.96105	1.96	0.99442		
0.47	0.49374	0.97	0.82987	1.47	0.96237	1.97	0.99466		
0.48	0.50274	0.94	0.83423	1.48	0.96365	1.98	0.99489		
0.49	0.51166	0.99	0.83850	1.49	0.96489	1.99	0.99511		

The error function of argument x is defined as

$$\text{erf}(x) = \frac{2}{\sqrt{\pi}} \int_0^x e^{-\eta^2} \, d\eta \tag{1}$$

and we have

$$\text{erf}(\infty) = 1 \qquad \text{and} \qquad \text{erf}(-x) = -\text{erf}\,x \tag{2}$$

The complimentary error function, erfc(x), is defined as

$$\text{erfc}(x) = 1 - \text{erf}(x) = \frac{2}{\sqrt{\pi}} \int_x^\infty e^{-\eta^2} \, d\eta \tag{3}$$

The derivatives of error function are given as

$$\frac{d}{dx}\operatorname{erf}(x) = \frac{2}{\sqrt{\pi}}e^{-x^2}, \qquad \frac{d^2}{dx^2}\operatorname{erf}(x) = -\frac{4}{\sqrt{\pi}}xe^{-x^2}, \text{ etc.} \qquad (4)$$

The repeated integrals of error function are defined as

$$i^n\operatorname{erfc}(x) = \int_x^\infty i^{n-1}\operatorname{erfc}\eta\,d\eta, \qquad n = 0, 1, 2\dots \qquad (5a)$$

with

$$i^{-1}\operatorname{erfc}(x) = \frac{2}{\sqrt{\pi}}e^{-x^2}, \qquad i^0\operatorname{erfc} x = \operatorname{erfc} x \qquad (5b)$$

Then we have

$$i\operatorname{erfc} x = \frac{1}{\sqrt{\pi}}e^{-x^2} - x\operatorname{erfc} x \qquad (6)$$

$$i^2\operatorname{erfc} x = \tfrac{1}{4}\left[(1 + 2x^2)\operatorname{erfc} x - \frac{2}{\sqrt{\pi}}xe^{-x^2}\right] \qquad (7)$$

series expansion for error function is given as

$$\operatorname{erf}(x) = \frac{2}{\sqrt{\pi}}\sum_{n=0}^{\infty}(-1)^n\frac{x^{2n+1}}{n!(2n+1)} \qquad (8)$$

For large values of x, its asymptotic expansion is

$$\operatorname{erfc}(x) = 1 - \operatorname{erf}(x) \cong \frac{e^{-x^2}}{\sqrt{\pi}x}\left[1 + \sum_{n=1}^{\infty}(-1)^n\frac{1.3\dots(2n-1)}{(2x^2)^n}\right] \qquad (9)$$

The error function, its derivatives, and integrals have been tabulated $[1, 2]$.

REFERENCES

1. M. Abramowitz and I. A. Stegun, *Handbook of Mathematical Functions*, National Bureau of Standards, Applied Mathematic Series 55, U.S. Government Printing Office, Washington, D.C., 1964.
2. E. Jahnke and F. Emde, *Tables of Functions*, 2nd. ed., Dover Publications, New York, 1945.

APPENDIX III

$\mathbf{B}$ESSEL FUNCTIONS

The differential equation

$$\frac{d^2R}{dz^2} + \frac{1}{z}\frac{dR}{dz} + \left(1 - \frac{v^2}{z^2}\right)R = 0 \tag{1}$$

is called Bessels's differential equation of order v. Two linearly independent solutions of this equation for all values of v are $J_v(z)$, the Bessel function of the first kind of order v and $Y_v(z)$, the Bessel function of the second kind of order v. Thus, the general solution of equation (1) is written as [1, 2, 3]

$$R(z) = c_1 J_v(z) + c_2 Y_v(z) \tag{2}$$

The Bessel function $J_v(z)$ in series form is defined as

$$J_v(z) = (\tfrac{1}{2}z)^v \sum_{k=0}^{\infty} (-1)^k \frac{(\tfrac{1}{2}z)^{2k}}{k!\Gamma(v+k+1)} \tag{3}$$

where $\Gamma(x)$ is the gamma function.

The differential equation

$$\frac{d^2R}{dz^2} + \frac{1}{z}\frac{dz}{dz} - \left(1 + \frac{v^2}{z^2}\right)R = 0 \tag{4}$$

is called Bessel's modified differential equation of order v. Two linearly independent solutions of this equation for all values of v are $I_v(z)$, the modified Bessel function of the first kind of order v and $K_v(z)$, the modified Bessel function of the second kind of order v. Thus, the general solution of equation (4) is written as

$$R(z) = c_1 I_v(z) + c_2 K_v(z) \tag{5}$$

$I_v(z)$ and $K_v(z)$ are real and positive when $v > -1$ and $z > 0$. The Bessel function $I_v(z)$ in series form is given by

$$I_v(z) = (\tfrac{1}{2}z)^v \sum_{k=0}^{\infty} \frac{(\tfrac{1}{2}z)^{2k}}{k!\Gamma(v+k+1)} \tag{6}$$

659

When v *is not zero or not a positive integer*, the general solutions (2) and (5) can be taken, respectively, in the form

$$R(z) = c_1 J_v(z) + c_2 J_{-v}(z) \tag{7a}$$

$$R(z) = c_1 I_v(z) + c_2 I_{-v}(z) \tag{7b}$$

When $v = n$ is a positive integer, the solutions $J_n(z)$ and $J_{-n}(z)$ are not independent; they are related by

$$J_n(z) = (-1)^n J_{-n}(z) \quad \text{and} \quad J_{-n}(z) = J_n(-z)(n = \text{integer}) \tag{8}$$

similarly, when $v = n$ is a positive integer, the solutions $I_n(z)$ and $I_{-n}(z)$ are not independent.

We summarize various form of solutions of equation (1) as [2]

$$R(z) = c_1 J_v(z) + c_2 Y_v(z) \qquad \text{always} \tag{9a}$$

$$R(z) = c_1 J_v(z) + c_2 J_{-v}(z) \qquad v \text{ is not zero or a positive integer} \tag{9b}$$

and the solutions of equation (4) as [2]

$$R(z) = c_1 I_v(z) + c_2 K_v(z) \qquad \text{always} \tag{10a}$$

$$R(z) = c_1 I_v(z) + c_2 I_{-v}(z) \qquad v \text{ is not zero or positive integer} \tag{10b}$$

GENERALIZED BESSEL EQUATION

Sometimes a given differential equation, after suitable transformation of the independent variable, yields a solution that is a linear combination of Bessel functions. A convenient way of finding out whether a given differential equation possesses a solution in terms of Bessel functions is to compare it with the *generalized Bessel equation* developed by Douglas [4, p. 210]

$$\frac{d^2 R}{dx^2} + \left[\frac{1 - 2m}{x} - 2\alpha \right] \cdot \frac{dR}{dx} + \left[p^2 a^2 x^{2p-2} + \alpha^2 + \frac{\alpha(2m-1)}{x} \right.$$
$$\left. + \frac{m^2 - p^2 v^2}{x^2} \right] R = 0 \tag{11a}$$

and the corresponding solution of which is

$$R = x^m \cdot e^{ax} [c_1 J_v(ax^p) + c_2 Y_v(ax^p)] \tag{11b}$$

where c_1 and c_2 are arbitrary constants.

For example, by comparing the differential equation

$$\frac{d^2 R}{dx^2} + \frac{1}{x} \frac{dR}{dx} - \frac{\beta}{x} R = 0 \tag{12}$$

with the above generalized Bessel equation we find

$$\alpha = 0, \qquad m = 0, \qquad p = \tfrac{1}{2}, \qquad p^2 v^2 = -\beta, \qquad a = 2i\sqrt{\beta}, \qquad v = 0$$

Hence, the solution of differential equation (12) is in the form

$$R = c_1 J_0(2i\sqrt{\beta}x) + c_2 Y_0(2i\sqrt{\beta}x) \tag{13a}$$

or

$$R = c_1 I_0(2\sqrt{\beta}x) + c_2 K_0(2\sqrt{\beta}x) \tag{13b}$$

which involves Bessel functions.

LIMITING FORM FOR SMALL Z

For small values of $z(z \to 0)$, the retention of the leading terms in the series results in the following approximations for the values of Bessel functions [5, p. 360]

$$J_v(z) \cong (\tfrac{1}{2}z)^v \frac{1}{\Gamma(v+1)} \qquad v \neq -1, -2, -3 \ldots \tag{14a}$$

$$Y_v(z) \cong -\frac{1}{\pi}\left(\frac{2}{z}\right)^v \Gamma(v) \qquad v \neq 0 \text{ and } Y_0(z) \cong \frac{2}{\pi}\ln z \tag{14b}$$

$$I_z(z) \cong (\tfrac{1}{2}z)^v \frac{1}{\Gamma(v+1)} \qquad v \neq -1, -2, -3 \ldots \tag{15a}$$

$$K_v(z) \cong \tfrac{1}{2}\left(\frac{2}{z}\right)^v \Gamma(v) \qquad v \neq 0 \text{ and } K_0(z) \cong -\ln z \tag{15b}$$

LIMITING FORM FOR LARGE Z

For large values of $z(z \to \infty)$ the values of Bessel functions can be approximated as [5, p. 364 and 377]

$$J_v(z) \cong \sqrt{\frac{2}{\pi z}} \cdot \cos\left(z - \frac{\pi}{4} - \frac{v\pi}{2}\right) \tag{16a}$$

$$Y_v(z) \cong \sqrt{\frac{2}{\pi z}} \cdot \sin\left(z - \frac{\pi}{4} - \frac{v\pi}{v}\right) \tag{16b}$$

$$I_v(z) \cong \frac{e^z}{\sqrt{2\pi z}} \qquad \text{and} \qquad K_v(z) \cong \sqrt{\frac{\pi}{2z}} \cdot e^{-z} \tag{16c}$$

DERIVATIVES OF BESSEL FUNCTIONS [3, pp. 161–163]

$$\frac{d}{dz}\left[z^{v}W_{v}(\beta z)\right] = \begin{cases} \beta z^{v}W_{v-1}(\beta z) & \text{for } W \equiv J, Y, I \quad (17a) \\ -\beta z^{v}W_{v-1}(\beta z) & \text{for } W \equiv K \quad (17b) \end{cases}$$

$$\frac{d}{dz}\left[z^{-v}W_{v}(\beta z)\right] = \begin{cases} -\beta z^{-v}W_{v+1}(\beta z) & \text{for } W \equiv J, Y, K \quad (18a) \\ \beta z^{-v}W_{v+1}(\beta z) & \text{for } W \equiv I \quad (18b) \end{cases}$$

For example by setting $v = 0$, we obtain

$$\frac{d}{dz}\left[W_{0}(\beta z)\right] = \begin{cases} -\beta W_{1}(\beta z) & \text{for } W \equiv J, Y, K \quad (19a) \\ \beta W_{1}(\beta z) & \text{for } W = I \quad (19b) \end{cases}$$

INTEGRATION OF BESSEL FUNCTIONS

$$\int z^{v}W_{v-1}(\beta z)\,dz = \frac{1}{\beta}z^{v}W_{v}(\beta z) \qquad \text{for } W \equiv J, Y, I \tag{20}$$

$$\int \frac{1}{z^{v}}W_{v+1}(\beta z)\,dz = -\frac{1}{\beta z^{v}}W_{v}(\beta z) \quad \text{for } W \equiv J, Y, K \tag{21}$$

For example by setting $v = 1$ in Eq. (20)

$$\int z W_{0}(\beta z)\,dz = \frac{1}{\beta}z W_{1}(\beta z) \qquad \text{for } W \equiv J, Y, I \tag{22}$$

Infinite integrals involving Bessel functions are [1, pp. 394–395]

$$\int_{0}^{\infty} e^{-pz^{2}}z^{v+1}J_{v}(az)\,dz = \frac{a^{v}}{(2p)^{v+1}}e^{-a^{2}/4p} \tag{23}$$

$$\int_{0}^{\infty} e^{-pz^{2}}z J_{v}(az)J_{v}(bz)\,dz = \frac{1}{2p}e^{-(a^{2}+b^{2})/4p}I_{v}\left(\frac{ab}{2p}\right) \tag{24}$$

RECURRENCE RELATIONS

The recurrence formulae for the Bessel functions are given as [1, pp. 45 and 66; 5, p. 361]

$$W_{v-1}(z) + W_{v+1}(z) = \frac{2v}{z}W_{v}(z) \tag{25a}$$

$$W_{v-1}(z) - W_{v+1}(z) = 2W_{v}'(z) \tag{25b}$$

$$W_{v-1}(z) - \frac{v}{z} W_v(z) = W_v(z) \tag{25c}$$

$$- W_{v+1}(z) + \frac{v}{z} W_v(z) = W_v'(z) \tag{25d}$$

where $W = J$ or Y or any linear combination of these functions, the coefficients in which are independent of z and v.

A sytematic tabulation of various integrals involving Bessel functions are given in Refs. [6 and 7].

In Tables III-1 we present the numerical values of $J_n(z)$, $Y_n(z)$, $I_n(z)$, and $K_n(z)$ functions for $n = 0$ and 1 [2, pp. 215–221] and in Table III-2 we present the first ten roots of $J_n(z)$ function for $n = 0, 1, 2, 3, 5$.

Finally, in Tables III-3 and III-4 we present the roots of $\beta J_1(\beta) - cJ_0(\beta) = 0$ and $J_0(\beta)Y_0(c\beta) - Y_0(\beta)J_0(c\beta) = 0$, respectively [8, p. 493; 5, p. 414–415].

Table III-1 Numerical Values of Bessel Functions

$$J_0(z)$$

z	0	0.1	0.2	0.3	0.4	0.5	0.6	0.7	0.8	0.9
0	1.0000	0.9975	0.9900	0.9776	0.9604	0.9385	0.9120	0.8812	0.8463	0.8075
1	0.7652	0.7196	0.6711	0.6201	0.5669	0.5118	0.4554	0.3980	0.3400	0.2818
2	0.2239	0.1666	0.1104	0.0555	0.0025	−0.0484	−0.0968	−0.1424	−0.1850	−0.2243
3	−0.2601	−0.2921	−0.3202	−0.3443	−0.3643	−0.3801	−0.3918	−0.3992	−0.4026	−0.4018
4	−0.3971	−0.3887	−0.3766	−0.3610	−0.3423	−0.3205	−0.2961	−0.2693	−0.2404	−0.2097
5	−0.1776	−0.1443	−0.1103	−0.0758	−0.0412	−0.0068	+0.0270	+0.0599	0.0917	0.1220
6	0.1506	0.1773	0.2017	0.2238	0.2433	0.2601	0.2740	0.2851	0.2931	0.2981
7	0.3001	0.2991	0.2951	0.2882	0.2786	0.2663	0.2516	0.2346	0.2154	0.1944
8	0.1717	0.1475	0.1222	0.0960	0.0692	0.0419	0.0146	−0.0125	−0.0392	−0.0653
9	−0.0903	−0.1142	−0.1367	−0.1577	−0.1768	−0.1939	−0.2090	−0.2218	−0.2323	−0.2403
10	−0.2459	−0.2490	−0.2496	−0.2477	−0.2434	−0.2366	−0.2276	−0.2164	−0.2032	−0.1881
11	−0.1712	−0.1528	−0.1330	−0.1121	−0.0902	−0.0677	−0.0446	−0.0213	+0.0020	0.0250
12	0.0477	0.0697	0.0908	0.1108	0.1296	0.1469	0.1626	0.1766	0.1887	0.1988
13	0.2069	0.2129	0.2167	0.2183	0.2177	0.2150	0.2101	0.2032	0.1943	0.1836
14	0.1711	0.1570	0.1414	0.1245	0.1065	0.0875	0.0679	0.0476	0.0271	0.0064
15	−0.0142	−0.0346	−0.0544	−0.0736	−0.0919	−0.1092	−0.1253	−0.1401	−0.1533	−0.1650

When $z > 15.9$,

$$J_0(z) \simeq \sqrt{\left(\frac{2}{\pi z}\right)} \left\{ \sin\left(z + \tfrac{1}{4}\pi\right) + \frac{1}{8z} \sin\left(z - \tfrac{1}{4}\pi\right) \right\}$$

$$\simeq \frac{0.7979}{\sqrt{z}} \left\{ \sin(57.296z + 45)^\circ + \frac{1}{8z} \sin(57.296z - 45)^\circ \right\}.$$

$$J_1(z)$$

z	0	0.1	0.2	0.3	0.4	0.5	0.6	0.7	0.8	0.9
0	0.0000	0.0499	0.0995	0.1483	0.1960	0.2423	0.2867	0.3290	0.3688	0.4059
1	0.4401	0.4709	0.4983	0.5220	0.5419	0.5579	0.5699	0.5778	0.5815	0.5812
2	0.5767	0.5683	0.5560	0.5399	0.5202	0.4971	0.4708	0.4416	0.4097	0.3754
3	0.3391	0.3009	0.2613	0.2207	0.1792	0.1374	0.0955	0.0538	0.0128	-0.0272
4	-0.0660	-0.1033	-0.1386	-0.1719	-0.2028	-0.2311	-0.2566	-0.2791	-0.2985	-0.3147
5	-0.3276	-0.3371	-0.3432	-0.3460	-0.3453	-0.3414	-0.3343	-0.3241	-0.3110	-0.2951
6	-0.2767	-0.2559	-0.2329	-0.2081	-0.1816	-0.1538	-0.1250	-0.0953	-0.0652	-0.0349
7	-0.0047	+0.0252	0.0543	0.0826	0.1096	0.1352	0.1592	0.1813	0.2014	0.2192
8	0.2346	0.2476	0.2580	0.2657	0.2708	0.2731	0.2728	0.2697	0.2641	0.2559
9	0.2453	0.2324	0.2174	0.2004	0.1816	0.1613	0.1395	0.1166	0.0928	0.0684
10	0.0435	0.0184	-0.0066	-0.0313	-0.0555	-0.0789	-0.1012	-0.1224	-0.1422	-0.1603
11	-0.1768	-0.1913	-0.2039	-0.2143	-0.2225	-0.2284	-0.2320	-0.2333	-0.2323	-0.2290
12	-0.2234	-0.2157	-0.2060	-0.1943	-0.1807	-0.1655	-0.1487	-0.1307	-0.1114	-0.0912
13	-0.0703	-0.0489	-0.0271	-0.0052	+0.0166	0.0380	0.0590	0.0791	0.0984	0.1165
14	0.1334	0.1488	0.1626	0.1747	0.1850	0.1934	0.1999	0.2043	0.2066	0.2069
15	0.2051	0.2013	0.1955	0.1879	0.1784	0.1672	0.1544	0.1402	0.1247	0.1080

When $z > 15.9$,

$$J_1(z) \simeq \sqrt{\left(\frac{2}{\pi z}\right)} \left\{ \sin(z - \tfrac{1}{4}\pi) + \frac{3}{8z}\sin(z + \tfrac{1}{4}\pi) \right\}$$

$$\simeq \frac{0.7979}{\sqrt{z}} \left\{ \sin(57.296z - 45)° + \frac{3}{8z}\sin(57.296z + 45)° \right\}.$$

Table III-1 (*Continued*)

$Y_0(z)$

z	0	0.1	0.2	0.3	0.4	0.5	0.6	0.7	0.8	0.9
0	$-\infty$	-1.5342	-1.0811	-0.8073	-0.6060	-0.4445	-0.3085	-0.1907	-0.0868	$+0.0056$
1	0.0883	0.1622	0.2281	0.2865	.3379	0.3824	0.4204	0.4520	0.4774	0.4968
2	0.5104	0.5183	0.5208	0.5181	0.5104	0.4981	0.4813	0.4605	0.4359	0.4079
3	0.3769	0.3431	0.3071	0.2691	0.2296	0.1890	0.1477	0.1061	0.0645	0.0234
4	-0.0169	-0.0561	-0.0938	-0.1296	-0.1633	-0.1947	-0.2235	-0.2494	-0.2723	-0.2921
5	-0.3085	-0.3216	-0.3313	-0.3374	-0.3402	-0.3395	-0.3354	-0.3282	-0.3177	-0.3044
6	-0.2882	-0.2694	-0.2483	-0.2251	-0.1999	-0.1732	-0.1452	-0.1162	-0.0864	-0.0563
7	-0.0259	$+0.0042$	0.0339	0.0628	0.0907	0.1173	0.1424	0.1658	0.1872	0.2065
8	0.2235	0.2381	0.2501	0.2595	0.2662	0.2702	0.2715	0.2700	0.2659	0.2592
9	0.2499	0.2383	0.2245	0.2086	0.1907	0.1712	0.1502	0.1279	0.1045	0.0804
10	0.0557	0.0307	0.0056	-0.0193	-0.0437	-0.0675	-0.0904	-0.1122	-0.1326	-0.1516
11	-0.1688	-0.1843	-0.1977	-0.2091	-0.2183	-0.2252	-0.2299	-0.2322	-0.2322	-0.2298
12	-0.2252	-0.2184	-0.2095	-0.1986	-0.1858	-0.1712	-0.1551	-0.1375	-0.1187	-0.0989
13	-0.0782	-0.0569	-0.0352	-0.0134	$+0.0085$	$+0.0301$	$+0.0512$	0.0717	0.0913	0.1099
14	0.1272	0.1431	0.1575	0.1703	0.1812	0.1903	0.1974	0.2025	0.2056	0.2065
15	0.2055	0.2023	0.1972	0.1902	0.1813	0.1706	0.1584	0.1446	0.1295	0.1132

When $z > 15.9$,

$$Y_0(z) \simeq \sqrt{\left(\frac{2}{\pi z}\right)}\left\{\sin\left(z - \tfrac{1}{4}\pi\right) - \frac{1}{8z}\sin\left(z + \tfrac{1}{4}\pi\right)\right\}$$
$$\simeq \frac{0.7979}{\sqrt{z}}\left\{\sin(57.296z - 45)° - \frac{1}{8z}\sin(57.296z + 45)°\right\}.$$

$Y_1(z)$

z	0	0.1	0.2	0.3	0.4	0.5	0.6	0.7	0.8	0.9
0	$-\infty$	-6.4590	-3.3238	-2.2931	-1.7809	-1.4715	-1.2604	-1.1032	-0.9781	-0.8731
1	-0.7812	-0.6981	-0.6211	-0.5485	-0.4791	-0.4123	-0.3476	-0.2847	-0.2237	-0.1644
2	-0.1070	-0.0517	+0.0015	+0.0523	0.1005	0.1459	0.1884	0.2276	0.2635	0.2959
3	0.3247	0.3496	0.3707	0.3879	0.4010	0.4102	0.4154	0.4167	0.4141	0.4078
4	0.3979	0.3846	0.3680	0.3484	0.3260	0.3010	0.2737	0.2445	0.2136	0.1812
5	0.1479	0.1137	0.0792	0.0445	0.0101	-0.0238	-0.0568	-0.0887	-0.1192	-0.1481
6	-0.1750	-0.1998	-0.2223	-0.2422	-0.2596	-0.2741	-0.2857	-0.2945	-0.3002	-0.3029
7	-0.3027	-0.2995	-0.2934	-0.2846	-0.2731	-0.2591	-0.2428	-0.2243	-0.2039	-0.1817
8	-0.1581	-0.1331	-0.1072	-0.0806	-0.0535	-0.0262	+0.0011	+0.0280	0.0544	0.0799
9	+0.1043	0.1275	0.1491	0.1691	0.1871	0.2032	0.2171	0.2287	0.2379	0.2447
10	0.2490	0.2508	0.2502	0.2471	0.2416	0.2337	0.2236	0.2114	0.1973	0.1813
11	0.1637	0.1446	0.1243	0.1029	0.0807	0.0579	0.0348	0.0114	-0.0118	-0.0347
12	-0.0571	-0.0787	-0.0994	-0.1189	-0.1371	-0.1538	-0.1689	-0.1821	-0.1935	-0.2028
13	-0.2101	-0.2152	-0.2182	-0.2190	-0.2176	-0.2140	-0.2084	-0.2007	-0.1912	-0.1798
14	-0.1666	-0.1520	-0.1359	-0.1186	-0.1003	-0.0810	-0.0612	-0.0408	-0.0202	+0.0005
15	0.0211	0.0413	0.0609	0.0799	0.0979	0.1148	0.1305	0.1447	0.1575	0.1686

When $z > 15.9$,

$$Y_1(z) \simeq \sqrt{\left(\frac{2}{\pi z}\right)} \left\{ \sin\left(z - \tfrac{3}{4}\pi\right) + \frac{3}{8z} \sin\left(z - \tfrac{1}{4}\pi\right) \right\}$$
$$\simeq \frac{0.7979}{\sqrt{z}} \left\{ \sin(57.296z - 135)° + \frac{3}{8z} \sin(57.296z - 45)° \right\}.$$

Table III-1 (*Continued*)

$$I_0(z)$$

	z	0	0.1	0.2	0.3	0.4	0.5	0.6	0.7	0.8	0.9
	0	1.0000	1.0025	1.0100	1.0226	1.0404	1.0635	1.0920	1.1263	1.1665	1.2130
	1	1.2661	1.3262	1.3937	1.4693	1.5534	1.6467	1.7500	1.8640	1.9896	2.1277
	2	2.2796	2.4463	2.6291	2.8296	3.0493	3.2898	3.5533	3.8417	4.1573	4.5027
	3	4.8808	5.2945	5.7472	6.2426	6.7848	7.3782	8.0277	8.7386	9.5169	10.369
$10 \times$	4	1.1302	1.2324	1.3442	1.4668	1.6010	1.7481	1.9093	2.0858	2.2794	2.4915
$10 \times$	5	2.7240	2.9789	3.2584	3.5648	3.9009	4.2695	4.6738	5.1173	5.6038	6.1377
$10 \times$	6	6.7234	7.3663	8.0718	8.8462	9.6962	10.629	11.654	12.779	14.014	15.370
$10^2 \times$	7	1.6859	1.8495	2.0292	2.2266	2.4434	2.6816	2.9433	3.2309	3.5468	3.8941
$10^2 \times$	8	4.2756	4.6950	5.1559	5.6626	6.2194	6.8316	7.5046	8.2445	9.0580	9.9524
$10^3 \times$	9	1.0936	1.2017	1.3207	1.4514	1.5953	1.7535	1.9275	2.1189	2.3294	2.5610

When $z \geq 10$, $I_0(z) \simeq \dfrac{0.3989 e^z}{z^{1/2}} \left\{ 1 + \dfrac{1}{8z} + \dfrac{9}{128z^2} + \dfrac{75}{1024z^3} \right\}.$

$K_0(z)$

z	0	0.1	0.2	0.3	0.4	0.5	0.6	0.7	0.8	0.9
0	∞	2.4271	1.7527	1.3725	1.1145	0.9244	0.7775	0.6605	0.5653	0.4867
1	0.4210	0.3656	0.3185	0.2782	0.2437	0.2138	0.1880	0.1655	0.1459	0.1288
$10^{-1}\times$ 2	1.1389	1.0078	0.8926	0.7914	0.7022	0.6235	0.5540	0.4926	0.4382	0.3901
$10^{-1}\times$ 3	0.3474	0.3095	0.2759	0.2461	0.2196	0.1960	0.1750	0.1563	0.1397	0.1248
$10^{-2}\times$ 4	1.1160	0.9980	0.8927	0.7988	0.7149	0.6400	0.5730	0.5132	0.4597	0.4119
$10^{-2}\times$ 5	0.3691	0.3308	0.2966	0.2659	0.2385	0.2139	0.1918	0.1721	0.1544	0.1386
$10^{-3}\times$ 6	1.2440	1.1167	1.0025	0.9001	0.8083	0.7259	0.6520	0.5857	0.5262	0.4728
$10^{-3}\times$ 7	0.4248	0.3817	0.3431	0.3084	0.2772	0.2492	0.2240	0.2014	0.1811	0.1629
$10^{-4}\times$ 8	1.4647	1.3173	1.1849	1.0658	0.9588	0.8626	0.7761	0.6983	0.6283	0.5654
$10^{-4}\times$ 9	0.5088	0.4579	0.4121	0.3710	0.3339	0.3006	0.2706	0.2436	0.2193	0.1975

When $z \geq 10$, $K_0(z) \simeq \dfrac{1.2533 e^{-z}}{z^{1/2}} \left\{ 1 - \dfrac{1}{8z} + \dfrac{9}{128z^2} - \dfrac{75}{1024z^3} \right\}$.

Table III-1 (*Continued*)

$$I_1(z)$$

z	0	0.1	0.2	0.3	0.4	0.5	0.6	0.7	0.8	0.9
0	0	0.0501	0.1005	0.1517	0.2040	0.2579	0.3137	0.3719	0.4329	0.4971
1	0.5652	0.6375	0.7147	0.7973	0.8861	0.9817	1.0848	1.1963	1.3172	1.4482
2	1.5906	1.7455	1.9141	2.0978	2.2981	2.5167	2.7554	3.0161	3.3011	3.6126
3	3.9534	4.3262	4.7343	5.1810	5.6701	6.2058	6.7927	7.4357	8.1404	8.9128
4 $10 \times$	0.97595	1.0688	1.1706	1.2822	1.4046	1.5389	1.6863	1.8479	2.0253	2.2199
5 $10 \times$	2.4336	2.6680	2.9254	3.2080	3.5182	3.8588	4.2328	4.6436	5.0946	5.5900
6 $10 \times$	6.1342	6.7319	7.3886	8.1100	8.9026	9.7735	10.730	11.782	12.938	14.208
7 $10^2 \times$	1.5604	1.7138	1.8825	2.0679	2.2717	2.4958	2.7422	3.0131	3.3110	3.6385
8 $10^2 \times$	3.9987	4.3948	4.8305	5.3096	5.8366	6.4162	7.0538	7.7551	8.5266	9.3754
9 $10^3 \times$	1.0309	1.1336	1.2467	1.3710	1.5079	1.6585	1.8241	2.0065	2.2071	2.4280

When $z \geq 10$, $I_1(z) \simeq \dfrac{0.3989 e^z}{z^{1/2}} \left\{ 1 - \dfrac{3}{8z} - \dfrac{15}{128z^2} - \dfrac{105}{1024z^3} \right\}.$

$$K_1(z)$$

z	0	0.1	0.2	0.3	0.4	0.5	0.6	0.7	0.8	0.9
0	∞	9.8538	4.7760	3.0560	2.1844	1.6564	1.3028	1.0503	0.8618	0.7165
1	0.6019	0.5098	0.4346	0.3725	0.3208	0.2774	0.2406	0.2094	0.1826	0.1597
2	$10^{-1}\times$ 1.3987	1.2275	1.0790	0.9498	0.8372	0.7389	0.6528	0.5774	0.5111	0.4529
3	$10^{-1}\times$ 0.4016	0.3563	0.3164	0.2812	0.2500	0.2224	0.1979	0.1763	0.1571	0.1400
4	$10^{-2}\times$ 1.2484	1.1136	0.9938	0.8872	0.7923	0.7078	0.6325	0.5654	0.5055	0.4521
5	$10^{-2}\times$ 0.4045	0.3619	0.3239	0.2900	0.2597	0.2326	0.2083	0.1866	0.1673	0.1499
6	$10^{-3}\times$ 1.3439	1.2050	1.0805	0.9691	0.8693	0.7799	0.6998	0.6280	0.5636	0.5059
7	$10^{-3}\times$ 0.4542	0.4078	0.3662	0.3288	0.2953	0.2653	0.2383	0.2141	0.1924	0.1729
8	$10^{-4}\times$ 1.5537	1.3964	1.2552	1.1283	1.0143	0.9120	0.8200	0.7374	0.6631	0.5964
9	$10^{-4}\times$ 0.5364	0.4825	0.4340	0.3904	0.3512	0.3160	0.2843	0.2559	0.2302	0.2072

When $z \geq 10$, $K_1(z) \simeq \dfrac{1.2533 e^{-z}}{z^{1/2}} \left\{ 1 + \dfrac{3}{8z} - \dfrac{15}{128z^2} + \dfrac{105}{1024z^3} \right\}.$

Table III-2 First Ten Roots of $J_n(z) = 0$; $n = 0, 1, 2, 3, 4, 5$

First Ten Roots of $J_n(z) = 0$; $n = 0, 1, 2, 3, 4, 5$

	J_0	J_1	J_2	J_3	J_4	J_5
1	2.4048	3.8317	5.1356	6.3802	7.5883	8.7715
2	5.5201	7.0156	8.4172	9.7610	11.0647	12.3386
3	8.6537	10.1735	11.6198	13.0152	14.3725	15.7002
4	11.7915	13.3237	14.7960	16.2235	17.6160	18.9801
5	14.9309	16.4706	17.9598	19.4094	20.8269	22.2178
6	18.0711	19.6159	21.1170	22.5827	24.0190	25.4303
7	21.2116	22.7601	24.2701	25.7482	27.1991	28.6266
8	24.3525	25.9037	27.4206	28.9084	30.3710	31.8117
9	27.4935	29.0468	30.5692	32.0649	33.5371	34.9888
10	30.6346	32.1897	33.7165	35.2187	36.6990	38.1599

Table III-3 First Six Roots of $\beta J_1(\beta) - cJ_0(\beta) = 0$

First Six Roots β_n of $\beta J_1(\beta) - cJ_0(\beta) = 0$

c	β_1	β_2	β_3	β_4	β_5	β_6
0	0	3.8317	7.0156	10.1735	13.3237	16.4706
0.01	0.1412	3.8343	7.0170	10.1745	13.3244	16.4712
0.02	0.1995	3.8369	7.0184	10.1754	13.3252	16.4718
0.04	0.2814	3.8421	7.0213	10.1774	13.3267	16.4731
0.06	0.3438	3.8473	7.0241	10.1794	13.3282	16.4743
0.08	0.3960	3.8525	7.0270	10.1813	13.3297	16.4755
0.1	0.4417	3.8577	7.0298	10.1833	13.3312	16.4767
0.15	0.5376	3.8706	7.0369	10.1882	13.3349	16.4797
0.2	0.6170	3.8835	7.0440	10.1931	13.3387	16.4828
0.3	0.7465	3.9091	7.0582	10.2029	13.3462	16.4888
0.4	0.8516	3.9344	7.0723	10.2127	13.3537	16.4949
0.5	0.9408	3.9594	7.0864	10.2225	13.3611	16.5010
0.6	1.0184	3.9841	7.1004	10.2322	13.3686	16.5070
0.7	1.0873	4.0085	7.1143	10.2419	13.3761	16.5131
0.8	1.1490	4.0325	7.1282	10.2516	13.3835	16.5191
0.9	1.2048	4.0562	7.1421	10.2613	13.3910	16.5251
1.0	1.2558	4.0795	7.1558	10.2710	13.3984	16.5312
1.5	1.4569	4.1902	7.2233	10.3188	13.4353	16.5612
2.0	1.5994	4.2910	7.2884	10.3658	13.4719	16.5910
3.0	1.7887	4.4634	7.4103	10.4566	13.5434	16.6499
4.0	1.9081	4.6018	7.5201	10.5423	13.6125	16.7073
5.0	1.9898	4.7131	7.6177	10.6223	13.6786	16.7630
6.0	2.0490	4.8033	7.7039	10.6964	13.7414	16.8168
7.0	2.0937	4.8772	7.7797	10.7646	13.8008	16.8684
8.0	2.1286	4.9384	7.8464	10.8271	13.8566	16.9179
9.0	2.1566	4.9897	7.9051	10.8842	13.9090	16.9650
10.0	2.1795	5.0332	7.9569	10.9363	13.9580	17.0099
15.0	2.2509	5.1773	8.1422	11.1367	14.1576	17.2008
20.0	2.2880	5.2568	8.2534	11.2677	14.2983	17.3442
30.0	2.3261	5.3410	8.3771	11.4221	14.4748	17.5348
40.0	2.3455	5.3846	8.4432	11.5081	14.5774	17.6508
50.0	2.3572	5.4112	8.4840	11.5621	14.6433	17.7272
60.0	2.3651	5.4291	8.5116	11.5990	14.6889	17.7807
80.0	2.3750	5.4516	8.5466	11.6461	14.7475	17.8502
100.0	2.3809	5.4652	8.5678	11.6747	14.7834	17.8931
∞	2.4048	5.5201	8.6537	11.7915	14.9309	18.0711

From Carslaw and Jaeger [2].

Table III-4 First Five Roots of $J_0(\beta)Y_0(c\beta) - Y_0(\beta)J_0(c\beta) = 0$

c	β_1	β_2	β_3	β_4	β_5
1.2	15.7014	31.4126	47.1217	62.8302	78.5385
1.5	6.2702	12.5598	18.8451	25.1294	31.4133
2.0	3.1230	6.2734	9.4182	12.5614	15.7040
2.5	2.0732	4.1773	6.2754	8.3717	10.4672
3.0	1.5485	3.1291	4.7038	6.2767	7.8487
3.5	1.2339	2.5002	3.7608	5.0196	6.2776
4.0	1.0244	2.0809	3.1322	4.1816	5.2301

REFERENCES

1. G. N. Watson, *A Treatise on the Theory of Bessel Functions*, 2nd ed., Cambridge at the University Press, London, 1966.

2. N. W. McLachlan, *Bessel Functions for Engineers*, 2nd. ed., Oxford at the Clarendon Press, London, 1961.

3. F. B. Hildebrand, *Advanced Calculus for Engineers* Prentice-Hall, Inc., Englewood Cliffs, N.J., 1949.

4. T. K. Sherwood and C. E. Reed, *Applied Mathematics in Chemical Engineering*, McGraw-Hill Book Co., New York, 1939.

5. M. Abramowitz and I. A. Stegun, *Handbook of Mathematical Functions*, National Bureau of Standards, Applied Mathematic Series 55, U.S. Government Printing Office, Washington, D.C., 20402, 1964.

6. I. S. Gradshteyn and I. M. Ryzhik, *Table of Integrals, Series, and Products*, Trans. from the Russian and edited by Alan Jeffrey. Academic Press, New York, 1965.

7. Y. L. Luke, *Integrals of Bessel Functions*, McGraw-Hill Book Company, New York, 1962.

8. H. S. Carslaw and J. C. Jaeger, *Conduction of Heat in Solids*, Oxford at the Clarendon Press, London, 1959.

NUMERICAL VALUES OF LEGENDRE POLYNOMIALS OF THE FIRST KIND

x	$P_1(x)$	$P_2(x)$	$P_3(x)$	$P_4(x)$	$P_5(x)$	$P_6(x)$	$P_7(x)$
0.00	0.0000	−.5000	0.0000	0.3750	0.0000	−.3125	0.0000
.01	.0100	−.4998	−.0150	.3746	.0187	−.3118	−.0219
.02	.0200	−.4994	−.0300	.3735	.0374	−.3099	−.0436
.03	.0300	−.4986	−.0449	.3716	.0560	−.3066	−.0651
.04	.0400	−.4976	−.0598	.3690	.0744	−.3021	−.0862
.05	.0500	−.4962	−.0747	.3657	.0927	−.2962	−.1069
.06	.0600	−.4946	−.0895	.3616	.1106	−.2891	−.1270
.07	.0700	−.4926	−.1041	.3567	.1283	−.2808	−.1464
.08	.0800	−.4904	−.1187	.3512	.1455	−.2713	−.1651
.09	.0900	−.4878	−.1332	.3449	.1624	−.2606	−.1828
.10	.1000	−.4850	−.1475	.3379	.1788	−.2488	−.1995
.11	.1100	−.4818	−.1617	.3303	.1947	−.2360	−.2151
.12	.1200	−.4784	−.1757	.3219	.2101	−.2220	−.2295
.13	.1300	−.4746	−.1895	.3129	.2248	−.2071	−.2427
.14	.1400	−.4706	−.2031	.3032	.2389	−.1913	−.2545
.15	.1500	−.4662	−.2166	.2928	.2523	−.1746	−.2649
.16	.1600	−.4616	−.2298	.2819	.2650	−.1572	−.2738
.17	.1700	−.4566	−.2427	.2703	.2769	−.1389	−.2812
.18	.1800	−.4514	−.2554	.2581	.2880	−.1201	−.2870
.19	.1900	−.4458	−.2679	.2453	.2982	−.1006	−.2911
.20	.2000	−.4400	−.2800	.2320	.3075	−.0806	−.2935
.21	.2100	−.4338	−.2918	.2181	.3159	−.0601	−.2943
.22	.2200	−.4274	−.3034	.2037	.3234	−.0394	−.2933

(Continued)

x	$P_1(x)$	$P_2(x)$	$P_3(x)$	$P_4(x)$	$P_5(x)$	$P_6(x)$	$P_7(x)$
.23	.2300	− .4206	− .3146	.1889	.3299	− .0183	− .2906
.24	.2400	− .4136	− .3254	.1735	.3353	.0029	− .2861
.25	.2500	− .4062	− .3359	.1577	.3397	.0243	− .2799
.27	.2600	− .3986	− .3461	.1415	.3431	.0456	− .2720
.27	.2700	− .3906	− .3558	.1249	.3453	.0669	− .2625
.28	.2800	− .3824	− .3651	.1079	.3465	.0879	− .2512
.29	.2900	− .3738	− .3740	.0906	.3465	.1087	− .2384
.30	.3000	− .3650	− .3825	.0729	.3454	.1292	− .2241
.31	.3100	− .3558	− .3905	.0550	.3431	.1492	− .2082
.32	.3200	− .3464	− .3981	.0369	.3397	.1686	− .1910
.33	.3300	− .3366	− .4052	.0185	.3351	.1873	− .1724
.34	.3400	− .3266	− .4117	− .0000	.3294	.2053	− .1527
.35	.3500	− .3162	− .4178	− .0187	.3225	.2225	− .1318
.36	.3600	− .3056	− .4234	− .0375	.3144	.2388	− .1098
.37	.3700	− .2946	− .4284	− .0564	.3051	.2540	− .0870
.38	.3800	− .2834	− .4328	− .0753	.2948	.2681	− .0635
.39	.3900	− .2718	− .4367	− .0942	.2833	.2810	− .0393
.40	.4000	− .2600	− .4400	− .1130	.2706	.2926	− .0146
.41	.4100	− .2478	− .4427	− .1317	.2569	.3029	.0104
.42	.4200	− .2354	− .4448	− .1504	.2421	.3118	.0356
.43	.4300	− .2226	− .4462	− .1688	.2263	.3191	.0608
.44	.4400	− .2096	− .4470	− .1870	.2095	.3249	.0859
.45	.4500	− .1962	− .4472	− .2050	.1917	.3290	.1106
.46	.4600	− .1826	− .4467	− .2226	.1730	.3314	.1348
.47	.4700	− .1686	− .4454	− .2399	.1534	.3321	.1584
.48	.4800	− .1544	− .4435	− .2568	.1330	.3310	.1811
.49	.4900	− .1398	− .4409	− .2732	.1118	.3280	.2027
.50	.5000	− .1250	− .4375	− .2891	.0898	.3232	.2231
.51	.5100	− .1098	− .4334	− .3044	.0673	.3166	.2422
.52	.5200	− .0944	− .4285	− .3191	.0441	.3080	.2596
.53	.5300	− .0786	− .4228	− .3332	.0204	.2975	.2753
.54	.5400	− .0626	− .4163	− .3465	− .0037	.2851	.2891
.55	.5500	− .0462	− .4091	− .3590	− .0282	.2708	.3007
.56	.5600	− .0296	− .4010	− .3707	− .0529	.2546	.3102
.57	.5700	− .0126	− .3920	− .3815	− .0779	.2366	.3172
.58	.5800	.0046	− .3822	− .3914	− .1028	.2168	.3217
.59	.5900	.0222	− .3716	− .4002	− .1278	.1953	.3235
.60	.6000	.0400	− .3600	− .4080	− .1526	.1721	.3226
.61	.6100	.0582	− .3475	− .4146	− .1772	.1473	.3188
.62	.6200	.0766	− .3342	− .4200	− .2014	.1211	.3121

(*Continued*)

x	$P_1(x)$	$P_2(x)$	$P_3(x)$	$P_4(x)$	$P_5(x)$	$P_6(x)$	$P_7(x)$
.63	.6300	.0954	− .3199	− .4242	− .2251	.0935	.3023
.64	.6400	.1144	− .3046	− .4270	− .2482	.0646	.2895
.65	.6500	.1338	− .2884	− .4284	− .2705	.0347	.2737
.66	.6600	.1534	− .2713	− .4284	− .2919	.0038	.2548
.67	.6700	.1734	− .2531	− .4268	− .3122	− .0278	.2329
.68	.6800	.1936	− .2339	− .4236	− .3313	− .0601	.2081
.69	.6900	.2142	− .2137	− .4187	− .3490	− .0926	.1805
.70	.7000	.2350	− .1925	− .4121	− .3652	− .1253	.1502
.71	.7100	.2562	− .1702	− .4036	− .3796	− .1578	.1173
.72	.7200	.2776	− .1469	− .3933	− .3922	− .1899	.0822
.73	.7300	.2994	− .1225	− .3810	− .4026	− .2214	.0450
.74	.7400	.3214	− .0969	− .3666	− .4107	− .2518	.0061
.75	.7500	.3438	− .0703	− .3501	− .4164	− .2808	− .0342
.76	.7600	.3664	− .0426	− .3314	− .4193	− .3081	− .0754
.77	.7700	.3894	− .0137	− .3104	− .4193	− .3333	− .1171
.78	.7800	.4126	.0164	− .2871	− .4162	− .3559	− .1588
.79	.7900	.4362	.0476	− .2613	− .4097	− .3756	− .1999
.80	.8000	.4600	.0800	− .2330	− .3995	− .3918	− .2397
.81	.8100	.4842	.1136	− .2021	− .3855	− .4041	− .2774
.82	.8200	.5086	.1484	− .1685	− .3674	− .4119	− .3124
.83	.8300	.5334	.1845	− .1321	− .3449	− .4147	− .3437
.84	.8400	.5584	.2218	− .0928	− .3177	− .4120	− .3703
.85	.8500	.5838	.2603	− .0506	− .2857	− .4030	− .3913
.86	.8600	.6094	.3001	− .0053	− .2484	− .3872	− .4055
.87	.8700	.6354	.3413	.0431	− .2056	− .3638	− .4116
.88	.8800	.6616	.3837	.0947	− .1570	− .3322	− .4083
.89	.8900	.6882	.4274	.1496	− .1023	− .2916	− .3942
.90	.9000	.7150	.4725	.2079	− .0411	− .2412	− .3678
.91	.9100	.7422	.5189	.2698	.0268	− .1802	− .3274
.92	.9200	.7696	.5667	.3352	.1017	− .1077	− .2713
.93	.9300	.7974	.6159	.4044	.1842	− .0229	− .1975
.94	.9400	.8254	.6665	.4773	.2744	.0751	− .1040
.95	.9500	.8538	.7184	.5541	.3727	.1875	.0112
.96	.9600	.8824	.7718	.6349	.4796	.3151	.1506
.97	.9700	.9114	.8267	.7198	.5954	.4590	.3165
.98	.9800	.9406	.8830	.8089	.7204	.6204	.5115
.99	.9900	.9702	.9407	.9022	.8552	.8003	.7384
1.00	1.0000	1.0000	1.0000	1.0000	1.0000	1.0000	1.0000

From W. E. Byerly, *Fourier Series and Spherical, Cylindrical, and Ellipsoidal Harmonics*, Dover Publications, Inc., New York, 1959, pp. 280–281.

INDEX

Abbot, D. E., 465
Abramowitz, M., 138, 187, 434, 658, 674
Agrawal, H. C., 432
Allen, D. N. G., 433
Alternating-direction method, 493
  explicit, 494
  implicit, 494
Altman, M., 391
Ames, W. F., 392, 464, 465, 517
Amplification factor, 491
Analytic function, 264, 292
Angrist, S. W., 646
Anisotropic medium, 611
  boundary conditions, 615
  conductivity coefficients, 618
    geometrical interpretation of, 620
  conductivity ellipsoid, 623
  heat conduction equation for, 614, 615
  heat flux, 612, 613
  multi-dimensional heat flow in, a semi-
    infinite medium, 638, 641
    a solid cylinder, 643
  one-dimensional heat flow in, a thin rod,
    628, 630
    a thin slab, 626, 629
  orthotropic medium, heat conduction
    equation, 631
    heat flow in a rectangle, 632, 634
    transformation of heat conduction
      equation, 632
  symmetry of crystals, 625
  thermal conductivity tensor, 612
  thermal resistivity coefficients, 618
Approximate analytical methods, 20, 335
  Galerkin method, 372

integral method, 335
moment method, 356
partial integration, 380
Ritz method, 367
Arfken, G., 21
Arpaci, V. S., 21, 76, 290, 329, 392
Atthey, R. D., 433
Aziz, A. K., 465, 517

Backward difference, 473, 474, 475, 476
Bačlič, B., 465
Baer functions, 30
Bailey, J. A., 433
Baker, B. S., 329
Bankoff, S. B., 434
Barakat, H. Z., 495, 518
Barnes, E. W., 187
Bartels, R. C., 206, 290
Bateman, H., 187
Baxter, D. C., 433
Beach, H. L., 329
Bellman, R., 77
Benenati, R., 518
Bengston, H. H., 391
Benzies, J. Y., 465
Berezin, I. S., 517
Bernoulli, 18
Bessel functions, 85, 87
  asymptotic expressions for, 293, 661
  derivatives of, 661
  first and second kind, 85
  graphical representation, 85, 87
  integrations of, 662
  modified, 87
  numerical values of, I_0, I_1, 668, 670

J_0, J_1, 664, 665
K_0, K_1, 669, 671
Y_0, Y_1, 666, 667
orthogonality relations, 89, 93
recurrence relations, 661
roots of transcendental equation, 672
Bessel's differential equation, 85
generalized, 660
modified, 87
Bholanath, Pal, 187
Biot, M. A., 392, 398, 432, 465
Biot number, 15
Birkhoff, G., 465
Björck, A., 516
Blackwell, B. F., 646
Branch cut, 269, 292
Branch point, 269, 292
Brian, P. L. T., 495, 518
Boger, D. V., 433
Boggs, P. T., 434
Boley, B. A., 398, 432, 433, 434
Boltzmann, L., 464
Boltzmann transformation, 448
Bonacina, C., 433, 518
Bonilla, C. F., 433
Boundary conditions, 12
  for anisotropic medium, 615
  for isotropic medium, 12, 13
    first kind, 13
    second kind, 13
    third kind, 13
  for moving interface, 398, 401, 402
  nonlinear, 15, 462
Boyers, R. H., 465
Budhia, H., 432
Bulavin, P. E., 328
Burniston, E. E., 77
Buslenko, N. P., 517
Byerly, W. E., 187, 677

Carey, G. F., 517
Carslaw, H. S., 21, 76, 138, 187, 206, 240,
    290, 329, 432, 464, 473, 474, 646
Carson, W. W., 517
Casimir, H. B. G., 627, 647
Castello, F. A., 391
Central differences, 473, 474, 475, 476
Chambre, P. L., 465
Chang, Y. P., 647
Chao, B. T., 646

Chase, C. A., 329
Chen, D. J., 647
Cheung, I. K., 517
Cho, S., 392, 432, 433
Chuang, Y. K., 432
Churchill, R. V., 21, 76, 206, 290, 583
Churchill, S. W., 433
Cinelli, G., 138, 583
Clapeyron, B. P., 397, 432
Clark, J. A., 495, 518
Cobble, M. H., 329, 465, 607, 647
Cohen, C. B., 465
Collatz, L., 392
Comini, G., 433, 518
Composite medium, 294
  eigenfunctions, 300
  Green's function, 317
  heat flow in, slab-semi-infinite layer, 325
    two semi-infinite layers, 323
    two slabs, 307, 314, 322, 606
    two solid cylinders, 303, 319, 605
  orthogonal expansion, 295
  transcendental equation, 301
Conductivity coefficients, 612
  geometrical interpretation of, 620
  principal coefficients, 623
Conductivity ellipsoid, 623
Convolution, generalized, 198, 256
Cooper, H. F., 646
Courant, R., 240, 583
Cramer's rule, 302
Crandall, S. H., 392
Crank, J., 187, 329, 433, 464, 516
Crank-Nicolson method, 493, 495
Curd, H. N., 392, 465
Curtis, J. H., 517
Curvilinear coordinate system, 9
  differential area, length, volume, 10, 11
  oblate spheroidal, 23
  prolate spheroidal, 23
Cylindrical coordinate system, problems in
    r, t variables, hollow cylinder, 104,
    105, 230, 553
  infinite medium, 106, 555
  semi-infinite medium, 108, 109, 556
  solid cylinder, 101, 102, 103, 136, 137,
    204, 205, 226, 280, 289, 552
  problems in r, z, t variables, hollow cylin-
    der, 110
  semi-infinite medium, 112

problems in r, ϕ, t variables, hollow cylinder, 119
portion of a cylinder, 120
solid cylinder, 116, 118
problems in r, ϕ, z, t variables, portion of a hollow cylinder, 125
solid cylinder, 123, 556
steady-state problems in r, z variables, 129, 132, 133, 134
steady-state problems in r, ϕ variables, 131, 581
two-layer cylinder in r, t variables, 303, 319

Dahlquist, G., 516
d'Alembert, 18
Daughaday, H., 432
Davila, I. R., 433
Degree of implicitness, 493
Dettman, J. W., 21, 76, 240
Dicker, D., 393
Dimensionless parameters, 15
Dirac delta function, 425, 428
Direct method, 484, 485
Discretization error, 486
Ditkin, V. A., 583
Djukic, D., 392, 465
Dolph, C. L., 583
Dolton, T. A., 391
Domoto, G. A., 432
Douglas, 660
Douglas, J., 433, 518
Drezewiecki, T., 433
D'souza, N., 517
Duhamel's theorem, 194
applications to heat flow in, a semi-infinite medium, 199
a slab, 201
a solid cylinder, 204, 205
proof of, 197
special cases of, 195, 196
Dusinberre, G. M., 433, 516
Dwight, H. B., 77, 290
D'Yakanov, Y. G., 518

Ehrlich, L. W., 517
Eigenfunctions, 27
Eigenfunction tabulation in, cylindrical coordinates for, hollow cylinder, 96, 97

semi-infinite region, 100
solid cylinder, 92
rectangular coordinates for, semi-infinite region, 41
slab, 35
Eigenvalue problem, 27
Eigenvalues, 27
Electrical network analog, 398
Emde, F., 658
Emery, A. F., 517
Energy integral equation, 336
for phase-change problem, 417, 422
Eraslan, A. H., 393
Erdelyi, A., 76, 290, 583
Erdoğan, F., 393
Eringen, A. C., 583
Error function, 43
properties of, 658
tabulation of, 656, 657
Euler-Lagrange equation, 361, 364, 365
Euler's constant, 262
Explicit method, 487
Exponential integral function, 413
definition, 438
tabulation of, 437
Extrapolated Liebman method, 512
Eyres, N. R., 433

Fasano, A., 433
Faulstich, A. J., 393
Ferrer's associated functions, 152
Feshbach, H., 21, 76, 240, 392
Fillo, J. A., 518
Finite difference approximation, of first derivative, 472, 473, 476
second derivative, 474, 475, 476
steady-state heat conduction equation, 477, 481
time-dependent heat conduction equation, using alternating direction implicit method, 494
Crank-Nicolson method, 493, 501
Douglas-Rachford implicit method, 495
explicit method, 487, 499
implicit method, 491
Finite difference method, convergence, 487
stability, 487, 490, 491
stability criteria, 499

Finite difference representation of heat
  conduction equation, at curved
  boundaries, 513
  in cylindrical coordinates, 503
  in spherical coordinates, 509
  with variable thermal property, 511
Finite element, 471
Finlayson, B. A., 392, 393
Fomin, S. V., 392
Forsythe, A. R., 392
Forsythe, G. E., 516
Forward difference, 473, 475, 476
Fourier, J. B., 1, 21
Fourier equation, 6
Fourier law, 2
Fourier number, 15
Fowler, T. B., 518
Fox, L., 465, 516
Frankel, S. P., 517
Free parameter method, 452
Friedman, M. B., 393
Frost, W., 393
Fujita, H., 450, 464
Functional, 358

Gaggioli, R. A., 465
Galerkin, G. B., 392
Galerkin method, 20, 372
  application of, 378, 379, 387, 388
  boundary conditions, 375, 376
Gallie, T. M., 433
Gamma functions, 153, 248
Gauss elimination, 484
Gauss-Jordan elimination, 484
Gauss-Siedel, 484, 485
Geiger, G. E., 391, 392, 432
Geis, T., 465
Gelfand, I. M., 392
Generalized Bessel equation, 660
Gidaspow, D., 329
Giedt, W. H., 646
Gilpin, R. R., 434, 465
Goldstein, S., 139, 290
Golenko, D. I., 517
Goodman, T. R., 329, 336, 391, 398, 432,
  465
Gradshteyn, I. S., 674
Grange, B. W., 434
Green's function, 209, 398
  definition, 210

determination, 216, 218
product of, 239
reciprocity relation, 211
Green's function applications to problems of,
  composite media, 319
one-dimensional, single region hollow
  cylinder, 230
  hollow sphere, 232
  infinite medium, 219
  slab, 221
  solid cylinder, 226
  solid sphere, 235, 237
  three-dimensional region, 210, 224
  224
Griffin, O. M., 392
Group theory, 452
Güceri, S., 433
Gupta, B. P., 647
Gupta, R. S., 433
Gurtin, M. E., 392
Güzelsu, A. N., 433

Haji-Sheikh, A., 517
Hammersley, J. M., 517
Handscomb, D. C., 517
Hansen, A. G., 465
Hartree, D. R., 433
Hatcher, J. D., 392, 432
Hays, D. F., 392, 465
Heat, 1
Heat-balance integral, 336
Heat conduction equation for, anisotropic
  medium in, curvilinear coordinates,
  614
  cylindrical coordinates, 614
  rectangular coordinates, 614
  spherical coordinates, 615
isotropic medium in, curvilinear coordinates, 10
  cylindrical coordinates, 7
  rectangular coordinates, 7
  spherical coordinates, 8
Heat flux for, anisotropic medium in, curvilinear coordinates, 613
  cylindrical coordinates, 613
  rectangular coordinates, 612
  spherical coordinates, 613
isotropic medium in, curvilinear coordinates, 10
  rectangular coordinates, 2

Helmholtz equation, 30
  separation of, 30, 31
Hilbert, D., 240, 583
Hildebrand, F. B., 434, 674
Ho, C. Y., 21
Hobson, E. W., 187
Hodgkins, W. R., 434
Homogeneous problems, 17
  definition, 17
  separation in, cylindrical coordinates, 83
    rectangular coordinates, 30
    spherical coordinates, 144
Hopkins, M. R., 464
Hopper, A. T., 517
Hornbaker, D. R., 646
Hornbeck, R. W., 517
Huebner, K. H., 517
Hwang, C. L., 432
Hyman, M. A., 516, 517
Hypergeometric function, 189
Hypergeometric series, 151, 190

Ingham, J., 433
Integral method, 335, 398, 439
Integral method, applications to cylindrical
    symmetry, 342
  nonlinear problems, 347
  nonuniform initial condition, 355
  phase-change problems, 352, 416
  problems with heat generation, 345
  region exterior to cylindrical hole, 342
  semi-infinite medium, 337, 345, 348
  slab, 352
  spherical symmetry, 342
  variable property, 350
Integral transform technique, 18, 522
  applications to composite medium, two-
      layer cylinder, 605
    two-layer slab, 606
  single region, cylindrical coordinates,
      problems in r, t variables, 552
    problems in r, ϕ, t variables, 557
    problems in r, z, t variables, 566
    problems in r, ϕ, z, t variables, 568
  rectangular coordinates, one-dimension-
      al infinite region, 545
    one-dimensional semi-infinite region,
      543, 547
    rectangular parallelepiped, 550
    rectangular strip, 548

slab, 536, 539, 540
  spherical coordinates, problems in r, t
      variables, 568
    problems in r, μ, t variables, 569
    problems in r, μ, ϕ, t variables, 575
    steady state problems 579
    hemisphere, r, μ, variables, 581
    rectangle, 580
    solid cylinder, r, ϕ variables, 581
  finite composite medium, 594
  finite single medium, 523
Irving, J., 290
Iterative method, 484, 485

Jackson, R., 433
Jacobson, A. W., 583
Jaeger, J. C., 21, 76, 138, 187, 206, 240,
    290, 329, 432, 464, 646, 673, 674
James, M. L., 76, 517
Janke, E., 658
Jarjant, R. J., 433
Jiji, L. M., 432, 433
Jolley, H. S., 206
Jung, J., 583

Kabayashi, K., 583
Kang, C. S., 647
Kantorovich, L. V., 392
Kaplan, S., 517
Kaplan, W., 290
Kascheev, V. M., 328
Katayama, K., 647
Kirchhoff, G., 464
Kirchhoff transformation, 440
Kline, S. J., 465
Knight, C. A., 434
Knight, J. H., 465
Kochina, N. N., 465
Koh, J. C. Y., 465
Kompaneec, A. S., 464
Krajewski, B., 392, 465
Kreith, F., 432, 433
Kryloff, N., 392

Lallier, K. W., 518
Lamé functions, 30
Lamé, G., 397, 432
Landahl, H. O., 391
Landis, F., 391, 433
Laplace equation, 6

Laplace transform, 246
  definition, 246
  integration of, 257
  inversion by contour integration, 263
  inversion formula, 247, 258
  properties, 248
  tables of, 259-262
Laplace transform applications to semi-
      infinite medium, 274, 276, 323, 325
  slab, 277, 285, 286
  small and large times, 283, 285, 286, 287,
      289
  sphere, 287
Laplace transform of change of scale, 250
  convolution, 254, 256
  delta function, 254
  derivative, 249, 256
  generalized convolution, 256
  integral, 250
Lardner, T. J., 345, 391, 392, 432
Larkin, B. K., 518
Larkin, S. R., 516
Laura, P. A., 393
Lazaridis, L., 433
Lebedev, N. N., 434
Lederman, J. M., 432
Lee, Y. F., 432
Legendre functions, 144
  associated, 148, 151
  generalized, 153
Legendre polynomials, 149, 150
  graphical representation, 150
  numerical values, 675, 676, 677
  orthogonality, 154, 158, 160
Legendre's differential equation, 146
  associated, 145, 151
Liebman, G., 433
Lightfoot, N. M. H., 398, 423, 432
Liley, P. E., 21
Linear algebraic equations, solution, 484
Linearization, 439, 443
Liouville, J., 79
Liquidus temperature, 431
Lockwood, J. D., 329, 607
Luikov, A. V., 21, 76, 137, 187, 290, 329,
      464
Luke, Y. L., 674
Lyons, D. W., 392, 432

MacRoberts, M. D. J., 518

MacRobert, T. M., 187
Maeda, S., 465
Magnus, W., 76, 187, 583
Mangler, W., 465
Manohar, R., 465
Martin, H. C., 517
Masters, J. I., 139
Mathieu functions, 30
Matsumoto, S., 465
McClure, J. A., 518
McLachlan, N. W., 138, 290, 393, 674
Mercer, A. McD., 583
Merk, H. J., 336, 391
Meyer, G. H., 433
Michal, A. D., 465
Mikhailov, M. D., 329, 434, 583, 607
Mikhlin, S. G., 392
Mitchell, A. R., 518
Mody, K., 392, 432
Moment method, 355, 356
Monoclinic, 625
Monte Carlo method, 20, 471
Moon, P., 21, 76, 138
Moore, C. J., 329
Moran, M. J., 77, 465
Morgan, A. J. A., 465
Morse, M. P., 21, 76, 240, 392
Morton, K. W., 516
Moving boundary, 397
Moving heat source method, 398, 423
Muehlbauer, J. C., 392, 432, 434
Mulholland, G. P., 329, 607, 647
Mullineaux, N., 290
Murphy's expression, 151
Murray, R. L., 433, 583
Murray, W. D., 433

Neumann, 410
Neumann method, 490
Newton-Raphson method, 37
Newton's law of cooling, 14
n-fold rotation axis of symmetry, 625
Nickel, R. E., 517
Nonhomogeneous problems, 17
Nonlinear problems, 439
  applications, 442, 446, 449, 463
  linearization, 443
  nonlinear boundary conditions, 462
  temperature dependent k(T), 461
  transformation of dependent variable, 440

transformation of independent variable, 448
Norm, 28
Normalization integral, 28, 524, 596
Numerical methods, 20, 471
Numerical solution, 486
Nye, J. E., 646

Oberhettinger, F., 76, 187, 583
O'Brien, G. G., 516, 517
Ockendon, J. R., 434
Oden, J. T., 517
Ohtani, N., 583
Ölçer, N. Y., 329, 583, 607
Olson, D. R., 433
Onsagar, L., 613, 647
Orthorhombic, 625
Orthotropic, 611, 631
Otis, D. R., 433
Outward drawn normal unit vector, 5
Özisik, 21, 76, 187, 240, 329, 391, 392, 432, 433, 434, 464, 583, 607, 646, 647

Padovan, J., 329, 647
Pagnani, B. R., 518
Patel, P. D., 434
Patel, S. A., 646
Paterson, S., 413, 415, 434
Pattle, R. E., 465
Peaceman, W. D., 494, 516
Peck, R. E., 329
Pedroso, R. I., 432
Persson, B., 392
Persson, L., 391
Perturbation method, 398, 439
Pfahl, R. C., 646
Phahle, R. D., 433
Phase change, 397
    approximate solutions for, melting of a
        half-space, 416
        solidification of a slab, 419
    exact solutions for, melting of a half-space, 409
        solidification of a cylinder, 412
        solidification of a half-space, 406, 410, 424
    over a temperature range, 430
Philip, J. R., 465
Pohle, F. B., 391, 345

Pohle, F. V., 646
Pohlhausen, 398
Poles, 265, 292
Pootes, G., 391, 432
Powell, J., 518
Powell, R. W., 3, 21
Prasad, A., 432
Prigogine, I., 647
Primicerio, M., 433
Principal axes, 624
Principal conductivity, 623, 624
Product solution in, cylindrical coordinates, 127
    rectangular coordinates, 54, 56
Prudnikov, A. P., 583

Quon, D., 516
Rachford, H. H., 494, 516
Rafalski, P., 392
Ramirez, G. A., 517
Rathjen, K. A., 432, 433
Rayleigh-Ritz method, 20
Rectangular coordinate system, composite
        medium problems for, slab and semi-
        infinite medium, 326
    two semi-infinite medium, 324
    two slabs, 307, 314, 322, 606
    single region problems for, infinite medium,
        43, 219
    rectangle, 47, 56
    rectangular parallelepiped, 49, 224, 550
    semi-infinite, two dimensional, 51, 56, 548
    semi-infinite medium, 39, 41, 199, 274, 276, 547
    steady state problems for, rectangle, 58, 67, 580
    semi-infinite strip, 61, 62, 64
Reed, C. E., 674
Regula falsi, 37
Reid, J. K., 516
Reinsch, C., 516
Representation of an arbitrary function in,
        cylindrical coordinates, 88
    hollow cylinder ($a < r < b$), 91, 93
    infinite medium ($0 < r < \infty$), 98
    semi-infinite medium ($a < r < \infty$), 98
    solid cylinder ($0 < r < b$), 88, 89
    rectangular coordinates, infinite medium
        ($-\infty < x < \infty$), 44

semi-infinite medium $(0 < x < \infty)$, 40
slab $(0 < x < L)$, 34
spherical coordinates, full sphere
  $(-1 \leq \mu \leq 1)$, 154
  hemisphere $(0 \leq \mu \leq 1)$, 157
  potion of a sphere $(\mu_0 \leq \mu \leq 1)$, 159
Reshotko, F., 465
Residue theorem, 264
Reynolds, W. C., 391
Richardson, P. D., 392
Richtmeyer, R. D., 516
Riley, D. S., 432
Ritz, W., 392
Ritz method, 358, 367
Rodrigues, O., 187
Rodrigues' formula, 149
Romie, F. E., 433
Rose, D. J., 516
Round off error, 486
Rubenstein, L. T., 398, 432
Rybicki, E. F., 517
Ryzhik, I. M., 674

Sackett, G. G., 433
Salomatov, V. V., 465
Sareen, S. S., 329
Saul'ev, V. K., 518
Scale factors, 10
  curvilinear coordinates, 10
  cylindrical coordinates, 11
  spherical coordinates, 12
Schechter, R. S., 392
Schlichting, H., 391
Schneider, G. E., 517
Schneider, P. J., 21, 391
Scriven, L. E., 392, 393
Seider, W. D., 433
Selby, S. M., 434
Senda, K., 329, 607
Separation of heat conduction equation in,
  cylindrical coordinates, 83
  rectangular coordinates, 30
  spherical coordinates, 144
Separation of variables, 25
Severn, R. T., 433
Shamsunder, N., 433
Sherwood, T. K., 674
Shih, Y. P., 432
Shouman, S. M., 647
Shreider, Y. A., 517

Siewert, C. E., 77
Sikarshie, D. L., 432
Similarity transformation, 452
Similarity variables, 452
Smith, F. T., 432
Smith, G. D., 516
Smith, G. M., 76, 290, 517
Smith, R. B., 517
Sneddon, I. N., 21, 138, 187, 206, 240, 290,
  582, 583
Snyder, L. J., 393
Sobol, I. M., 517
Solidus temperature, 430
Solomon, A. D., 434
Southwell, R. V., 516
Spainer, J., 517
Sparrow, E. M., 433, 517
Spencer, D. E., 21, 76, 138
Spherical coordinate system, problems in
    r, t variables for, hollow sphere, 164,
      166, 167, 232
    solid sphere, 162, 163, 185, 235, 237,
      287
  problems in r, μ, t variables for, hemi-
      sphere, 170, 173, 574
    solid sphere, 168, 571
  problems in r, μ, ϕ, t variables for, portion
      of a sphere, 178
    solid sphere, 176, 177
  steady-state problems for, hemisphere, 183
    solid sphere, 182, 581, 582
Spiggs, T. W., 393
Splitting up heat conduction problem,
      cylindrical coordinates, 136, 137
  rectangular coordinates, 69
  spherical coordinates, 185
Springer, G. S., 433
Sragovich, V. G., 517
Stability of numerical solution, 487, 490,
  492
Steady-state problems with heat generation
      in, cylindrical coordinates, 133, 134
  rectangular coordinates, 66, 67
Steady-state problems without heat genera-
      tion in, cylindrical coordinates, 129,
      131, 132
  rectangular coordinates, 57, 58, 61, 62
  spherical coordinates, 182, 183
Stefan, J., 397, 406, 432
Stefan number, 406

Stegun, I. A., 187, 434, 658, 674
Step function, 252
Stevenson, W. H., 434
Stewart, W. E., 393
Stokes, R. H., 464
Storm, M. L., 444, 464
Straus, A. M., 392, 465
Strupczewski, A. L., 433
Sturm, J. C. F., 79
Sturm-Liouville problem, 28, 79, 80
Successive approximations, 450
Successive overrelaxation, 485
Sunderland, J. E., 392, 432, 433, 434
Suzuki, M., 465
Szekely, J., 432, 433

Tao, L. C., 433
Temperature, 1
Temperature gradient, 10
Themelis, M. J., 433
Thermal conductivity, 2
  of materials, 4
  of metals at low temperature, 3
Thermal diffusivity, 6
Thermal layer, 336
Thermal resistivity coefficients, 617
Thomas, L. T., 433
Thomas, R. F., 518
Thorsen, R., 391
Tien, R. H., 391, 392, 432
Titchmarsh, E. C., 76, 77, 138, 139, 290, 582
Tittle, C. W., 328, 607
Touryan, K. J., 646
Transcendental equations, 34
  roots of, 653, 654, 655, 673, 674
Transformation of axes, 618
Tranter, C. J., 21, 583
Trezek, G. J., 516
Trial function, 359
Triclinic, 625
Tricomi, F. G., 76, 465, 583
Truncation error, 486
Tsou, C. H., 647

Ural, O., 517

Uzzel, J. C., 434

Varga, R. S., 518
Variable eigenvalue, 398
Variational form of heat conduction
  equation, 363, 365, 367
Variational formulation, 398
Variational principles, 358
Variation operator, 360
Venkatraman, B., 646
Vest, C. M., 392
Viskanta, R., 434
Vodicka, V., 328
Volk, E. R., 518
Volterra integral equation, 463
Von Kármán, 398
Vujanović, B., 392, 465
Vutz, N., 646

Wagner, C. J., 464, 465
Wagstaff, J. B., 433
Wasan, D., 329
Wasov, W. R., 516
Watson, G. N., 138, 187, 583, 674
Weber functions, 30
Weimbaum, S., 432
Weinstock, R., 392
Westlake, J. R., 518
Westwater, J. E., 433
Whittaker, E. T., 138, 187
Wilkinson, J. H., 516
Willoughby, R. A., 516
Wilson, D. G., 434
Wilson, E., 517
Witwer, J. G., 516
Wolford, J. C., 76, 517
Wooster, W. A., 646

Yagoda, H. P., 432
Yampol'skiy, N. G., 465
Yang, K. T., 391, 465
Yener, Y., 329, 433, 583, 607
Young, D. M., 517

Zel'dovic, Y. B., 464
Zhidkov, N. P., 517
Zienkiewicz, O. C., 517
Zyskowski, W., 392, 432, 465